Eliz
17 B

⊚Harden's

London Baby Guide

IN ASSOCIATION WITH

NATURAL
MINERAL WATER

by Kate Calvert

Text © Kate Calvert, 2004
Listings © Kate Calvert and Harden's Limited, 2004

Kate Calvert has asserted her right under the Copyright, Designs and
Patents Act 1988 to be identified as Author of this work.

Editor: Peter Harden
Production Manager: Elizabeth Warman
Production Assistant: Jordan Holcomb
Research and editorial assistants: Sarah Ashpole, Margaret Carlstrom

Harden's Limited
14 Buckingham Street
London WC2N 6DF

Our thanks to Caroline Clark for providing the original inspiration
for this book.

ISBN 1-873721-57-9

British Library Cataloguing-in-Publication data: a catalogue record for
this book is available from the British Library.

Printed and bound in Italy by Printer Trento

CONTENTS

SPA'S UNIQUE PROPERTIES

SPA is delighted to be sponsoring Harden's London Baby Guide because we believe that SPA Reine still natural mineral water is uniquely suited to both pregnant and feeding mothers, babies and young children because of its very low mineral and salt content.

This means that it delivers the essential functions of water very effectively while having a clean neutral taste. Produced in the town of Spa in the Belgian Ardennes, the water emanates from the iron-rich 'Pouhons', and this, with the unique natural filter of the 'Fagnes' (a peaty soil), creates the high purity of SPA waters. The town of Spa is famous for water, and to this day hosts the Thermes de Spa – a renowned centre for water-based therapy.

Many people are turning to bottled water for the first time – and more specifically natural mineral water – as a better tasting and completely natural alternative to tap water and a healthier alternative to soft drinks and other beverages. EU and UK legislation does not permit the use of chemical or disinfectant treatment of natural mineral water, which makes waters such as SPA an important element in a natural healthy diet for all the family.

WATER: GOLDEN RULES FOR MOTHERS AND BABIES

1. Proper hydration is important for pregnant mothers, with symptoms of tiredness, headaches and indigestion often indicating dehydration. Water also helps keep kidneys functioning, eliminates waste, regulates body temperature, cushions joints, and carries oxygen in the blood and nutrients to the cells.

2. For breast-feeding mothers, drinking is vital to ensure a good supply of milk. The average breast-feeding mother should consume a minimum of 1.8 litres a day. This is equivalent to eight glasses. Ensure you have enough water by drinking a glass of water when you wake up, one with each meal/snack and one when you go to bed – and always have a glass of water handy for yourself during baby's feeding time.

3. For babies and young children, drinking enough fluid is essential to health and wellbeing as approximately 75% of a new born baby's body weight is water. **NB. From birth to six months, babies should drink only breast milk or formula milk**.

4. Never serve sparkling water to babies and, until mixed feeding is introduced at the age of five/six months, juices should be avoided. However, after six months, still water may be used to dilute fruit juices, to make them suitable for babies, and water is ideal to serve when a drink is needed instead of milk – for example in hot weather – when babies and young children can become dehydrated.

5. Always boil any water used to make up infant formula feed or to serve as a drink to infants aged six months or under.

BOTTLED OR TAP WATER
FOR FORMULA FEEDS?

SPA wishes to underline the Department of Health's recommendation that mothers should breast-feed if at all possible for the first four months of a baby's life and, ideally, throughout the first year. However, the following information is provided for mothers who, for whatever reason, want or are advised by their health professional to introduce formula milk.

The UK Government's advice on the type of water to use in making up infant feed is in the process of being changed. Under the new regulations, parents are to be advised that bottled waters such as SPA – whose contents comply with certain guidelines – may be served to babies of any age as and when appropriate. Appropriate bottled waters, including natural mineral waters, will shortly be allowed to be labelled as 'suitable for infant feed'.

However in much of Continental Europe, still natural mineral water has been recommended for the preparation of infant feeds for the last twenty years. SPA Reine is endorsed by the Belgian Royal Academy of Medicine and Gynaecologists as being suitable for both pregnant and nursing mothers, babies and young children.

Nonetheless there are certain rules which apply to water being used for infant formula.

• Only use waters with a low mineral content for babies, and we suggest filtering mains water.

• Look for bottled waters labelled as 'suitable for infant feed'.

• All water being given to infants aged 6 months and under should first be boiled and immediately cooled before serving.

SOME TIPS FOR OLDER BABIES AND TODDLERS

- You don't have to boil water for healthy babies and toddlers over six months.

- Never let a child suck on or sip fruit juices for prolonged periods. According to the Department of Health, if fruit juices are to be given, they should be kept to mealtimes only, be dispensed from a cup, be well-diluted and only served after the age of six months.

- Milk and water are the best fluids to serve young children according to the British Dental Association.

- Natural mineral waters, like SPA Reine, carry a 'typical analysis' on their labels indicating their mineral and salt content. Spa Reine's uniquely low mineral salt content makes it ideal for serving to young children.

HOW BOTTLED WATERS DIFFER

Not all bottled waters are the same. Some are 'natural' waters whilst others are 'processed'.

Natural Mineral Water – must be a 'natural' water taken from a protected underground source – and could be described as being 'designed by nature' especially for drinking. Only natural mineral waters are guaranteed to be naturally wholesome with nothing added, except in some cases carbon dioxide to make them sparkle. By UK law, nothing may be done to natural mineral waters which alters their natural characteristics so you and your family can drink them just as nature intended. You also have the reassurance that with natural mineral waters – and SPA Reine in particular – you know exactly what you are drinking – time after time.

Spring Water – also a groundwater but, confusingly, these may be 'natural' or 'processed' waters under current UK law. However, across much of Europe, spring waters must by law be untreated and these European regulations were implemented in the UK in December 2003.

Other Bottled Drinking Water – almost always 'processed' waters including other bottled drinking or 'table' waters, and purified or distilled water.

Mains Water – processed water which must contain a number of cleansing agents and other chemicals to ensure it is safe to drink from the tap.

REMEMBER

A still natural mineral water, such as SPA Reine, which is uniquely low in minerals, is ideal when it comes to maintaining or restoring the delicate balance of water in a mother and her baby's bodies during pregnancy. SPA still water from the Reine source has a natural purity, which makes it a perfect choice for growing babies, young children and their parents.

source
of purity

HOW TO USE

Listings and cross-referencing

Many of the organisations listed in the guide appear in a number of chapters. To avoid duplication, most listings appear only with a telephone number and website. Complete contact information including a full postal address can be found in *5.02 Index of Organisations* at the back of the guide.

A few chapters have listings where there is little overlap with other areas of the guide. These stand-alone listings include all contact details and are not included in *5.02 Index of organisations*. Listings in this category include: *Antenatal Classes*; *Postnatal (Classes)*; *Birth Equipment (Hire Companies)*; *Baby & toddler activities*; *Feeding (Organic Food Suppliers)*; *Portraits*; and *Baby-friendly restaurants*.

For the shops and suppliers detailed in section 3 (the consumer guide), full contact details are given in chapter *3.14 Shopping Directory*.

Reading

Books are referred to throughout the book as follows:

Title – Author's name ('Subtitle'; Publisher; Date of publication; Price; ISBN) – Brief critique of book.

One or two good out-of-print titles are included on the basis that they are particularly useful, and may be found in libraries, or via second-hand book dealers on the internet.

Websites

Although most organisations and firms now have some kind of presence on the net, quite a number have sites that are still in preparation. It has been our practice to include the latter on the basis that they are expected to be up and running within the lifetime of this guide.

Prices

Prices quoted in the guide were all checked in 2003/4. Most figures have been rounded to the nearest pound, and some large numbers have been rounded to the nearest five pounds.

Symbols

📫 Mail order supplier.

Q Second-hand supplier.

★ Recommended book

INTRODUCTION

Despite all being members of the human race, few of us realise what is actually involved in joining it. Once pregnant the question becomes rather more pressing, but an estimated 70% of pregnant mothers do not get the information they want from the people in charge of their antenatal care.

Though no book can answer all your questions, this one aims to provide the nitty-gritty information you need to make the transition into parenthood easier. Getting a birth 'right' does appear to have long-term benefits. Greater satisfaction with the event apparently leads to greater confidence as a parent, and, according to at least one birth specialist, a better long term future for your baby.

Many women feel vulnerable when they are pregnant, especially if there is anything at all unusual about the pregnancy. For the sake of simplicity we have tended to address a fictional norm in the main body of the book. At the same time a point has been made of including sources of more information in case they are required.

To the extent that we hope it is helpful, we have indicated some pointers on generally accepted thinking, current issues and beliefs, for example about the physical aspects of childcare. However, recommendations change with monotonous regularity so should by no means be regarded as commandments.

Like most people who have had a baby, the author has developed ideas of how things should be done. Those ideas are, as in all cases, more a result of the character of the baby concerned and her mother's prejudices than any hard-and-fast rules. There are no hard-and-fast rules to bringing up children. If when writing this book personal beliefs have surfaced from time to time – despite our best efforts to keep them out – I apologise for this. In mitigation I can add that the information and advice given has come from expert sources and checked to the best of our abilities.

Once you know your options, probably the best way to decide the best approach for you is to rely on your own intuition. If that doesn't feel right use logic. The main thing is to feel in charge of what is going on. It gives you a better chance of feeling happy, and if you feel happy your baby is more likely to be happy as well.

Where medical issues are concerned, if in doubt do not hesitate to ask questions, and remember that the standard answer almost always refers lugubriously to the wellbeing of your baby – a sure way of getting most mothers to do as they are told.

A last thought: it takes a little while to realise it, but children are only on loan to their parents. Tiny babies move on swiftly to being small people of ever-growing independence. That means it's worth enjoying them as much as you can while they are around you. We hope this book will help with that.

NOTES FOR USERS

It has not been possible for me to check personally on the quality of all the services listed in this book. Inclusion in itself is not an endorsement.

Over the four years this book has been in preparation it has become clear that there are baby fashions, not just in clothes or equipment, but also in the issues and concerns considered important by parents. As much as possible, we have tried to relegate "fashionable" issues to their appropriate long-term degree of importance in the overall scheme of becoming a parent.

Throughout the text, I have generally tried to avoid using either a masculine or feminine pronoun to describe babies and children. Where it has been necessary, I have used the pronoun 'she' in preference to 'it', as the infant most closely associated with the testing and researching for this guide is a girl.

ACKNOWLEDGEMENTS

Thanks in particular to Alice Charlwood, Rachna and Aman Kanwar, Maud Giles, Sabi Grant-Yavuz and Rosemary and Francis Kinghorn who gave their precious time to the end of improving the text.

Kate Calvert

Kate Calvert
March 2004

Preparing for birth

CHAPTER 1.01

WHERE TO HAVE THE BABY

1. **Know your choices**
2. **Your lead professional**
3. **Hospital births – NHS**
4. **Hospital births – Private**
5. **Home births – NHS**
6. **Home births – Private**
7. **Hospital performance tables – NHS & Private**

I. KNOW YOUR CHOICES

Introduction

Maternity is one of the UK's most publicly debated areas of medical care. Headlines tend to be negative, sometimes with reason. In January 2004 figures showed that the number of NHS midwives hit an all-time low. This on-going shortage of midwives in many NHS hospitals (especially in London and the south-east) makes a total mockery of a much-trumpeted 1993 target: that by 1998 three quarters of women would be looked after at birth by a midwife known to them through their antenatal care.

Financial pressures on hospitals are also having an effect, with expectations in many NHS hospitals of birth within 12 hours, and three women per bed every 24 hours in the birth unit. Both factors help explain the boom in births at some private hospitals and growing demand for the services offered by birth doulas and independent midwives.

It remains to be seen whether government initiatives to make hospital wards more family-friendly and to enhance the role of midwives will actually have an effect. Currently two out of three British maternity units are reportedly understaffed, the worst cases being in London. Promises include an extra 2,000 midwives by the year 2006 with the resurrected aim of providing all mothers with one-to-one care.

Militating against better service for mothers though are the plans for hospital maternity units to be merged, with one super-unit replaced as many as three of the current ones. This will make access more difficult, but could be offset by the introduction of local birthing centres for low risk mothers. The Birth Centre in Edgware is an example of this potential model.

In 2003, The National Service Framework (NFS) – designed to focus attention on specific areas of the NHS – looked at services for children pre-birth, at birth, post-birth and neo-nate. Recommendations are expected in the course of 2004 for implementation thereafter.

Another hot topic is medical intervention during birth and the increasing rate of Caesarean sections (discussed in chapter *4.03 Medical issues at birth*). While medical progress has made birth increasingly safe for those with evident difficulties, debate rages over the most appropriate way to care for the majority of mothers, for whom pregnancy/the run-up to labour is largely problem-free.

Many birth experts – including many doctors – are concerned by the high (and growing) Caesarean rate and the cause of the problems is thought by some health campaigners to be chronic shortages of midwives along with a lack of intensive care beds for babies.

The overall picture is far from bleak, however. Having a baby at the start of the twenty-first century is immeasurably safer than it was at the start of the twentieth.

Moreover, by debating the justification for the 'medicalisation' of birth, organisations such as the National Childbirth Trust (NCT) and the Association for Improvement in Maternity Care Services (AIMS) have helped make care in pregnancy become considerably more woman-centred. Home birth is emerging once again as an option for mothers, and there is an improved recognition of a woman's psychological needs in birth.

Finally, changes to the NHS as a result of the government's abolition of the Conservative's 'internal market' has led to greater choice for mothers of which hospital she gives birth in.

Taken together, the result is that mothers possibly now have the safest, widest choice in history of how and where to have their child. That is not to say that there is no room for improvement however, nor that all options are perfect. As the NCT noted in its 1999 report The More Things Change "…maternity care varied widely from one district to another and often varied within communities and within hospitals."

Your birthing venue – make an informed choice

Most women still don't know their NHS options when it comes to choosing where to have a baby. In a 1997 survey for the Audit Commission, only 30% of those questioned thought there was any choice of hospital, and less than 20% thought that a home birth was a possibility.

Similarly, few pregnant women know all the possibilities afforded by private healthcare. The private market is quite fragmented, and information about the various routes available can be difficult to track down.

Some women are very happy to leave it to their GP to book them into a local hospital and are perfectly satisfied with the results.

Not every GP or midwife is sufficiently well informed to offer real guidance in this area, though, and, like all individuals, some have prejudices which may push you one way or another. Anecdotal evidence suggests that some GPs, for example, do not mention the option of home birth or birth in a midwife-led scheme, or dismiss them because they don't approve of them. Not all GPs see it as their place to discuss the differences in ethos of different local hospitals where intervention rates may differ perceptibly.

The happier you are that you understand your choice – even if it is just to accept your GP's initial recommendation – the more likely it is that everything will go right. Fear and a feeling of events being outside your control play a genuine role in making labour difficult.

If anything is worrying you about your care, it is a good idea to try to sort it out well in advance, even if that means changing your mind in the

Maternity Services at The Portland Hospital

London's largest private Maternity Unit providing tailored care throughout pregnancy for your individual needs

- Choice of Consultant or Midwife Led Care
- Choice of all birthing options including natural birth, water birth, epidural with your first contraction or Caesarean section as required
- Opportunity to see your baby's face in high detail in the womb with 3D ultrasound
- Antenatal child preparation advice classes
- Antenatal exercise classes including Yoga and Pilates

- Massage for pregnancy, Bowen Therapy and physiotherapy for back pain
- One midwife to one patient during labour
- Qualified nursery nurses to look after your baby should you need a rest

- Emergency obstetric theatre, adult high dependency unit, neonatal intensive care and baby special care units, supported by specialists on-site 24-7
- Private en-suite rooms including 3 double bedded rooms
- Modern cuisine designed with women in mind
- Paediatric services available for your child up to 16 years of age

For more information call 020 7390 8269 or email info@portland.hcahealthcare.co.uk

www.theportlandhospital.com

The Portland Hospital
for Women and Children

middle of pregnancy. You are perfectly entitled to do so right up until the baby's birth.

USEFUL CONTACTS

The Active Birth Centre, ☎ (020) 7281 6760
⌂ www.activebirthcentre.com
The centre's four-week course: 'preparing for labour and birth' includes discussions of a number of the different options available at different types of birth venue, including home births, the use of water in birth and why you might prefer one hospital over another. / *HOURS shop Mon-Fri 9.30am-6.30pm (Fri 4pm), Sat 10am-4pm.*

Association for Improvement in Maternity Services (AIMS), ☎ (0870) 765 1433 *⌂ www.aims.org.uk*
This campaigning group is an excellent source of advice and encouragement for mothers and mothers-to-be. / *HOURS Mon-Fri 9.30am-5pm; PUBLICATIONS Wide range of leaflets (from £1.50), including: Home and water births; Choices in Childbirth Pack (£7.50); The Journal (quarterly magazine, £3 – free with £15 membership) includes relevant research & personal accounts; send SAE for publications list.*

Association of Radical Midwives, ☎ (0121) 444 2257
⌂ www.midwifery.org.uk
Support for those experiencing difficulty with care in the NHS, and particularly information on how to attain sympathetic and personalised midwifery care. (The term 'radical', incidentally, refers to returning to the roots of the issue, not to being non-conformist.) / *HOURS Mon-Fri 9am-5pm; PUBLICATIONS Leaflets (send SAE): What is a midwife?; Choices in childbirth. Quarterly newsletter (£2 – free with £22 membership).*

Birth Choice UK, *⌂ www.BirthChoiceUK.com*
A free public information website designed to help women choose where to have their baby.

The Midwives Information & Resource Service (MIDIRS), ☎ (0800) 581009 *⌂ www.midirs.org*
An organisation primarily focused on providing information for health professionals and midwives. It publishes a number of 'informed choice' leaflets, which are available direct. / *HOURS Mon-Fri 9am-5pm.*

National Childbirth Trust (NCT), ☎ Enquiry line (0870) 444 8707
⌂ www.nctpregnancyandbabycare.co.uk; www.nctparentsconnect.co.uk
Produces leaflets on the subject of choosing your birth venue. / *HOURS Mon-Thurs 9am-5pm, Fri 9am-4pm; or answerphone.*

Royal College of Midwives (RCM), ☎ (020) 7312 3535
⌂ www.rcm.org.uk
The governing body for midwives runs an information line for the public about their Informed Choice in Maternity Care Initiative. The associated range of leaflets should be available from your midwife or doctor. / *HOURS Mon-Fri 9am-5pm; PUBLICATIONS Leaflets: Support in Labour; Fetal Heart Rate Monitoring in Labour; Ultrasound Scans in Early Pregnancy; Alcohol and Pregnancy; Where will you have your baby?; Positions in Labour and Delivery; Blood Tests – Looking for Problems.*

Key factors in choosing where to have the baby

Read the points below in conjunction with the table overleaf for a brief overview. For a full discussion of each choice, see the section indicated in the table.

VENUES

More than 90% of women in London still give birth in an NHS hospital. However, the demand for home and private births is increasing. Home births are, if you move fast, available on the NHS as well as privately.

Within the private hospital sector, most births take place in fully independent hospitals, though there is the possibility of taking advantage of the backup facilities of a private unit attached to an NHS hospital. Each of the fully private hospitals and birth units have their own distinct selling points.

STYLE OF CARE (CHOICE OF LEAD PROFESSIONAL)

Your lead professional is simply that: the person who takes the lead with managing your care up to and during the birth. Your care may be midwife-led, consultant-led, or, more rarely, GP-led.

On the NHS, you once theoretically had the right to be involved in the choice of lead professional (including requesting that a consultant lead your care). In practice, though, consultant time has always largely been restricted to women with complications.

This modus operandi has, since October 2003, had the blessing of the National Institute for Clinical Excellence (NICE), whose new guidelines for antenatal care states that in uncomplicated pregnancies, care should be midwife- or GP-led. (The basis for this advice, is evidence that routinely involving obstetricians leads to no better outcome than involving them as dictated by need.)

With many NHS hospital deliveries, your lead professional antenatally and at birth will be whichever midwife is on duty at the time (though, if you fall into the right catchment area, or opt for a home birth, there is more chance that the same midwife or team of midwives will handle all your care throughout). If at any stage you are assessed as being at risk of complications, a consultant and his or her team will be called in. Otherwise, it may be that you don't see a doctor at any stage, particularly for a second or subsequent birth.

With a private birth, you can choose your carers (unless you are reliant on private medical insurance which dictates certain routes). Those opting for private care have traditionally done so in order to have the consultant of their choice. In recent years, however, the increased emphasis on natural childbirth has also raised the demand for midwife-led private care, with an obstetrician only brought in if events call for emergency backup.

SUITABILITY FOR HIGHER-RISK MOTHERS

From an early stage in your pregnancy, antenatal tests (see chapter *1.03 Tests*) will be used to assess your health and any possible difficulties.

As a sweeping simplification, pregnant women can be split into two groups – low risk and high risk. In the latter group, potential difficulties are often identified well before labour, often in early pregnancy.

Mothers at higher risk of problems are placed under more intensive obstetric supervision and are recommended to go for safer birth options. This may mean that a private hospital may be less suitable (and even a private room as this can leave the mother without the continuous supervision offered in a ward).

Concerns have arisen about the safety of private hospitals for birth. In January 2002, the Laura Touche inquest involving a death at The Portland put this issue into the spotlight. and in December 2002 there was an inquest into another mother who died at the hospital. (In the latter an open verdict was returned while in the former there was a finding of negligence against an individual midwife). A new body, the NCSC (see listings) has been created to regulate private units.

Home births are usually discouraged in cases with potential problems (though for more on this see Home Births below). In addition, because first-time mothers have an 'un-tried pelvis', they tend automatically to be classed as higher risk, simply because they are an unknown quantity, and many doctors don't like home births for a first baby.

Given the vast medical resources and emergency backup of large NHS hospitals – particularly those which are referral units for difficult cases –

THE OPTIONS FOR – AND KEY FACTORS IN DECIDING – WHERE TO HAVE YOUR BABY

Options for type of birth ————————————— *Factors to consider* —————————————

	VENUE	STYLE OF CARE	SEE SECTION	SUITABILITY FOR HIGHER RISK BIRTHS	CONTINUITY OF CARE	COMFORT LEVEL
NHS	Hospital	Midwife-led under consultant supervision	3 & 7	●●●●●	●●●	●●
	Amenity bed in NHS Hospital	Midwife-led under consultant supervision	3, 4 & 7	●●●●●	●●●	●●●
	Home	Midwife-led with emergency consultant back-up in hospital	5	●	●●●●	●●●●
PRIVATE	Private birth at NHS Hospital	Typically consultant-led (some midwife-led)	3, 4 & 7	●●●●●	●●●●	●●●●
	Private hospital	Consultant-led	4 & 7	●●●	●●●●●	●●●●
		Midwife-led	4 & 7	●●●	●●●●●	●●●●●
	Home	Midwife-led with emergency consultant back-up in hospital	6	●	●●●●	●●●●

● poor; ●● reasonable; ●●● good; ●●●● very good; ●●●●● excellent.   ●●● variable: black shading indicating lowest expectations, grey highest (so this example indicates reasonable to good)

many doctors would recommend them over fully private institutions for difficult cases.

By the same token, it is argued that if you do want a home birth you will get the full back-up of the NHS if you do so with an NHS community team who usually attend a large number of deliveries so are very experienced.

If a serious emergency arises at a stand-alone private hospital or with a private midwife, a transfer to an NHS hospital is likely. For all the bleak reputation of the NHS, it has the kind of facilities even the most sophisticated private units cannot afford to run.

CONTINUITY OF CARE

Study after study has shown that women's experience of birth is transformed by being attended and supported by carers who they have met before and who know them. In concrete terms this means an easier birth, less need of pain relief and – as acknowledged by an influential 2001 audit of maternity practice – a reduced risk of a Caesarean section.

One of the great advantages of going private is that you can choose the style of care that you want (be it consultant-led, or midwife-led) and that, whichever route you choose, continuity is much more likely. In addition, the simple fact that you are paying does shift the balance in the relationship between the mother and her carers, who are more likely to take into account her opinions and wishes.

Different NHS hospitals succeed to different degrees in this area, and the tables (pages 50–56) give some guidance on this.

COMFORT AND CONVIENCE LEVEL

The standards of cooking, cleanliness, comfort of the rooms and overall atmosphere in private hospitals bear no comparison with some of the more dated NHS maternity units (though deficiencies tend to be concentrated on the postnatal wards rather in the labour units themselves). Another advantage of private care is a tradition of much greater access for partners, who may generally stay overnight with the mother and newborn.

Another advantage of a private birth is greater flexibility in the scheduling of checks and tests (and greater likelihood of prompt service at the appointed time).

A half-way-house, if you are in a position to supplement the cost of the birth to a limited extent, is the hire of an amenity or private room at an NHS hospital. In most respects you still get the NHS experience, but – if you succeed in obtaining a room – you can rest afterwards, if not in luxury, in greater privacy and quiet. (See Private wards at NHS hospitals under Hospital Births – Private, below)

2. YOUR LEAD PROFESSIONAL

Midwives

WHO ARE THEY?

Nurses who undertake further specialised training in the care of women and babies during uncomplicated pregnancy and labour, through to providing postnatal care.

Private independent midwives and NHS community midwives need to be able to operate under less supervision than hospital midwives, and are usually much more highly trained. However, as the NHS moves away from doctor-focused care, midwives generally are being expected to show greater autonomy: for example in offering ultrasound scans, administering drugs, and looking after specific problems like pregnancy diabetes. This generally higher standard of midwifery is eroding some of the distinctions between in-house and community midwives.

All normal antenatal checks and hospital antenatal classes are conducted by midwives. A midwife will usually attend the mother throughout labour and deliver the baby. However, if there are unexpected difficulties – for example 'failure to progress', or the need for a forceps or ventouse delivery – the midwife must refer to a doctor.

While some hospital and clinic-based midwives are notably well informed, not all fully understand the reasoning behind procedures or advice. Even if you are attending regular antenatal classes with discussion sessions at your hospital, you may not be satisfied by the answers your receive to all your questions and may need to research further. (For a starting point see chapter *4.03 Medical Issues at Birth*.)

Hospital midwives tend to be more inclined to medically managed births than community midwives. In London, however, the distinction is less clear, as many community midwives are still attached to a hospital and may work in both areas.

The titles:

> **Senior nursing officer:** (at one time known as matron).
> **Nursing officer:** (once known as sister); a senior midwife will be of nursing officer level.
> **Staff midwife.**

STYLE OF CARE
Because the vast majority of midwives are women – some with their own children – mothers often feel comfortable with their approach to birth and derive great encouragement from the emotional support they offer.

Midwives tend to be in sympathy with the idea of offering the mother choice and control. As such their style tends to suit women who don't want to treat birth as a medical event. In contrast, most midwives' relative lack of obstetric training means that more medically-minded women have a tendency to feel less comfortable in their hands without supervision by a doctor.

Obstetricians

WHO ARE THEY?
Doctors with specialist training in maternity care, expert above all in the care of women with complicated pregnancies.

Obstetricians act as advisers on actual and suspected abnormalities, are responsible for the care of women with obstetric emergencies, and practice foetal medicine. For some people, the term is almost synonymous with that of consultant obstetrician – the most senior such doctors who oversee NHS maternity units and who manage most private births.

In NHS maternity units, consultants' schedules are extremely stretched, and they have relatively little time for individual cases. If your pregnancy deviates from the norm, you will be given an appointment to see a consultant in clinic. The consultant will – in discussion with you – decide on the best plan of action to take, and thereafter this policy may largely be put into effect by juniors (registrars and senior house officers), who lead care on the unit on a day-to-day basis.

Private consultants are similarly very busy. Though they tend to be less detached than on an NHS unit, they tend to direct much of the antenatal care from afar, and are rarely present in person throughout the entire birth.

The titles

Consultant: the most senior doctors, with overall medical responsibility for the maternity unit.

Senior registrar and registrar: qualified doctors specialising in obstetrics; the people who perform most of the Caesareans and instrumental deliveries on a unit.

Senior house officer (houseman or SHO): a junior doctor training in obstetrics (which could mean anything from one day to three years' experience in the speciality), or a GP trainee doing a six-month stint.

Student doctor.

STYLE OF CARE

If your attitude to birth is, "the more obstetric backup the better", and if you are able to afford your own private obstetrician, then consultations will be part of the natural course of your pregnancy.

In all other situations, however, the involvement of a doctor usually results from some kind of problem. By its nature, therefore, the doctor-mother relationship tends to be a more vexed one than that between midwife and mother.

As in all branches of medicine, doctors in obstetrics have something of a reputation for arrogance, and an alleged tendency to make decisions for – rather than in discussion with – women in their care. Questioning a consultant or doctor working in the NHS about their judgements can be made more intimidating by the gaggle of juniors habitually in attendance – you may be outnumbered at an appointment 8:1.

Where problems arise, some people question whether doctors resort too readily to medical intervention rather than adopting a wait-and-see attitude. It has been suggested that, as a doctor's training and experience largely relates to problem cases, this may lead to a tendency to diagnose them in borderline ones. Another factor is widely thought to be a fear by doctors of the growing tide of litigation – complaints tend to be that no action was taken, rather than the wrong action.

As in all areas of medicine, male doctors predominate, and female consultants are often in high demand. Don't just try to plump for a female doctor on the basis of her sex, though: they are not always the best bet if you are looking for a sympathetic approach.

GP (General practitioner)

A local doctor is involved at some stage in around 98% of all UK births, although this is generally limited to an initial visit, or as part of antenatal care shared with midwives. (Your GP may also offer some postnatal care and support.)

If he or she has had extra training in obstetrics, your GP can become your lead professional, though less than 6% of UK births are managed this way (mostly in rural areas). You can find a qualified GP by consulting the local obstetric list, which should be available from your local health authority or local public library. Standards for inclusion on the list vary between authorities – not all require any recent training. Alternatively private or hospital midwives should be able to recommend someone suitable.

The qualification DRCOG means that a GP has a diploma in obstetrics and gynaecology from the Royal College of Obstetricians & Gynaecologists. You are entitled to visit a GP with such experience for the duration of your pregnancy, while remaining registered with your own GP for all other care.

HOW TO CHANGE GP

You can change GP by applying to your GP of choice. A phone call should be enough to find out if they have room on their list. Details of local GPs are available from NHS Direct, including on the web site. A new medical card should be issued by the Primary Care Trust, which will also automatically transfer your records. There is no requirement to give a reason for the change.

USEFUL CONTACTS

NHS Direct, ☎ *(0845) 4647* ⌘ *www.nhsdirect.nhs.uk*
Can provide a list of local GPs.

3. HOSPITAL BIRTHS – NHS

The process

FIRST STEP: GP OR ANTENATAL CLINIC

With the improved reliability of over-the-counter pregnancy tests, many women nowadays find out that they are pregnant within the walls of their own home.

For 75% of women, the next step is a visit to a GP or health centre. It comes as a surprise to some women that – if they have done a test at home (and particularly with second or subsequent pregnancies, even if they haven't) – many GPs don't bother with an 'official' test as well. The purpose of this initial visit has nowadays largely become to discuss where you might give birth and the practicalities of your antenatal care.

Practically all women who do not see a GP head straight for a hospital antenatal clinic. As a pregnant woman, you do not technically need a GP's referral to a hospital (as you might do with a medical condition), though some maternity units do habitually require one.

If you go for this latter option, you might like to consider the information on possible hospitals first (see Section 7, Hospital performance tables – NHS & Private).

If you choose your hospital independently, it would certainly be courteous to involve your GP, or at least to inform him or her that you have chosen to go direct.

WHAT YOU SHOULD BE TOLD

When it comes to choosing between hospitals, most people are fairly hazy about how the system actually operates. If you do not already have a specific venue in mind and might wish to consider options other than your GP's recommendations, the system is discussed immediately below under *Your choice of hospital.*

If you independently research a shortlist, you may wish to consider visiting the respective hospitals: many run regular tours of their maternity unit to help prospective parents get a feel for the establishment concerned.

As well as suggested hospitals, you should also be informed that home birth is an option, and – if this is something you wish to consider further – be advised on how to go about organising this in your area. It is not unknown to receive incomplete information about this and details of other sources are given below in the home birth section.

YOUR CHOICE OF HOSPITAL

As a result of changes to the NHS since Labour came to power, pregnant women now have a much wider choice of hospitals than they did under the previous administration.

With the abolition of the NHS 'internal market', the decision over where you can give birth has effectively shifted from the health authority to the hospital. If you can persuade a hospital to take you, funding is available for you to give birth anywhere in the country.

Already popular maternity units – some of which are over-subscribed – have had to evolve their own criteria governing which women they are able to care for, and which must be sent elsewhere. Some such units prioritise applications on the basis of geographical proximity. Some insist on a GP referral (even though one is not actually required for your birth to be funded).

Otherwise, in the absence of some reason why it would be impractical or clinically unsafe for you to use a given institution – the presumption should be that the hospital can take you. The system under which you can get such treatments appears to have been named by an organisation blind to ridicule. It's called OATS (Out of Area Treatments).

BOOKING YOURSELF INTO A HOSPITAL

There are obvious advantages to choosing an institution near where you live – it is convenient for antenatal visits and avoids worry about getting to the hospital in time (although first labours in particular usually offer ample time for travel). Choosing a local hospital also means you are more likely to receive continuity of antenatal and birth care.

On the other hand, a few hospitals offer particular care or facilities (such as availability of amenity rooms) or simply enjoy a particularly good reputation. This may attract you to a hospital which is less close to home.

Once you have chosen a hospital, you can contact the maternity clinic at that hospital to arrange your first appointment. This is often referred to as a 'booking visit'.

At this first visit it is common for the midwives to take a fairly comprehensive medical history, and arrange for a wide variety of antenatal tests. The results of some tests have important consequences, and it is wise to read up on them in advance (see chapter *1.03 Tests*.)

At some hospitals it may be that you see a consultant, registrar or SHO on this initial visit. In other hospitals – in the absence of any potential complications – all of your care may be conducted by midwives.

Though theory does not always coincide with practice, you should be assigned a 'named midwife'. The idea behind this is that there is someone on the team of midwives who you can ask for by name, should you have questions or need help. For some women this system works fantastically well. Others barely meet this person.

In most hospitals you will also be given possession of your medical notes. These detail the results of your antenatal tests and factors relating to the management of the birth (including your wishes on the matter in the form of a birth plan).

YOUR ANTENATAL CARE

Historically it has only been possible to talk in generalities about antenatal care, with many variations in its provision across institutions.

New October 2003 guidelines for NHS providers for the first time set a schedule of what antenatal appointments a woman with a normal pregnancy should receive and what checks should take place when (see chapter *1.03 Tests*).

How this NHS programme of care is actually provided, however, will necessarily remain somewhat variable depending on who your lead carers are and where they are based. For example, your care may be midwife-led or GP-led (the latter operating more in rural areas); midwives may be hospital-based, or operate shared care (see below); or – as is usually the case with home births say – your care may be supervised by midwives entirely in the community.

The trend was supposedly for interim care to be carried out in the community and by midwives operating in teams. This was with the aim of both increasing the likelihood that you would have met (during the course of your antenatal care) the midwives assisting you at the birth, and increasing the amount of antenatal care delivered in the convenience of a woman's home or local antenatal clinic, rather than in hospital. Budgetary constraints mean this is an option many hospitals are cutting back on.

It remains the case that, except for the fortunate minority who live in the right catchment area for full community midwifery services, the objective of greater continuity of care remains just that: an objective.

Shared care involves appointments with your GP's surgery and a local health centre as well as at the hospital. This may be more convenient, particularly in terms of location. However, because liaison is not a strength of the system you may end up with more appointments than necessary (a situation the guidelines referred to above aim at remedying) and spend a lot of time telling the person you are seeing what the last one had said or done. You may well also have to chase for test results, find it difficult to get hold of people who do admit involvement, and find yourself referred to other parts of the system who are irritated that others didn't provide the right paperwork.

On the other hand, if all your care is hospital-based you may spend hours waiting for every appointment. Here as elsewhere the vogue for assigning hospital midwifes to named 'teams' can raise illusory hopes among pregnant women of knowing their carers, where in reality this is not common. Many women will be lucky to have met the midwife caring for them in labour and – should the labour over-run the end of that midwife's shift – will then have to get used to someone else entirely new. Recent research in a Portsmouth Hospital tracked the labours of 20 women. They spent a collective 123 hours in labour in which time they were attended by 108 different midwives and doctors.

MIDWIFE JARGON

There is no need to know any of the following terms, but you may find them useful in deciphering what people are talking to you about.

Caseload midwifery: see team midwifery.

Community midwifery: midwives providing antenatal care in the pregnant woman's home, or at local antenatal clinics, and undertaking care at home births.

Domino: stands for DOMicillary IN and Out). A very loose term, originally used to describe births where the mother decided at the onset of labour whether to remain at home for her birth looked after by her midwife, or to go into hospital with the midwife to deliver the baby and then return home shortly after the birth. Now sometimes used to refer to other community midwifery schemes.

Hospital care: antenatal care handled by the hospital's antenatal clinic.

Integrated care: care handled by midwives, usually in teams, who work both in hospital antenatal clinics and in the community.

One-2-One: a much lauded, innovative, community midwifery scheme, pioneered in W3 and W12 by Queen Charlotte's Hospital.

Shared care: combined care from your GP and/or community midwife team as well as a hospital antenatal clinic.

Team midwifery: a system whereby antenatal care and labour are handled in teams, so increasing the likelihood that a woman will have met the midwife handling the delivery during her antenatal care.

If you would like to join a community midwife scheme you need to arrange it as soon as possible as they are usually booked up well in advance. To do this, either ask your GP or ring (or write to) the Supervisor of Midwives for the area (usually based at the local hospital). Sometimes, even though your delivery is booked at one hospital, your antenatal care will be handled by midwives from a completely different hospital.

Unfortunately, Domino and similar midwifery services are generally the first to be suspended if there is a shortage of funds or staff. A 1996 audit of Domino births for Kings Healthcare, for example, found community midwives attended only about 60% of planned Domino births as the community midwives' caseload makes it difficult for them to be available for all such births.

IF YOU WANT TO SEE A CONSULTANT

As noted above, access to consultants within the NHS is largely limited to those who are facing complications of one sort or another.

If you do suspect a potential problem, your GP, other mothers, and midwives may be able to offer information on the style of care adopted by particular consultants on a unit. Note, however, that busy schedules mean you may not always see the actual consultant that you requested (nor even the one to whom you were originally referred).

If you want to see a female consultant you can request this at all hospitals, but as they are rarer than male consultants you may have difficulty succeeding.

4. HOSPITAL BIRTHS – PRIVATE

(For an overview of private options, see the table on page 34, Options for a private birth in hospital – including details of NHS amenity rooms.)

Of the 100,000 or so births that take place annually in London, 3,500–4,000 are paid for privately.

The capital has three fully private birth units: The Portland (by far the largest); the Hospital of St John & St Elizabeth; and a small private midwife-led unit in Tooting called The Birth Centre, which specialises in active birth.

In addition, about one in three of London's 30 or so NHS maternity hospitals has a private wing or rooms. Of these, the Lindo Wing at St Mary's is the largest, and the only unit to have its own obstetric operating theatres. With practically all other NHS hospitals, private births take place on the standard NHS maternity unit, with a transfer to the private wing for postnatal care.

Antenatal, birth and postnatal tests and care, plus a hospital stay, can reach a total of around £10,000 (see below for details). However mixing and matching, for example, a privately-managed labour with NHS antenatal tests and care can reduce that figure considerably. The Portland is one institution which has started to quote a separate rate on this basis.

In April 2002 a new health watchdog, the National Care Standards Commission (NCSC) was set up to regulate private hospitals, along with care homes and cosmetic surgery clinics. Under this new system of regulation, hospitals such as the Portland and St John and St Elizabeth are now inspected every six months.

Which comes first: the professional or the venue?

As with all private medicine, there are no hard and fast rules as to which you should choose first: the expert who will handle your care, or the institution where that care will be carried out.

You may have been recommended, and wish to use, a certain obstetrician or independent midwife. In such a case, your choice of institution will be largely decided by where they habitually practice.

On the other hand, if you have a particular hospital or birth centre in mind, the institution in question will refer you to a professional who regularly practices there.

Details of the costs of going private via either route are given below.

Choosing your professional first

As in all areas of medicine, without a personal recommendation it is hard to know how good any given professional is. Some people simply select someone who treats royalty and celebrities. Alternatives include asking for a referral from your GP, or recommendations from other mothers or private antenatal teachers.

For most women organising a private birth, choosing a professional means choosing a consultant. However, you may also wish to consider the increasingly popular alternative of a midwife-led birth in hospital.

Information relating to choosing a midwife to lead your care is set out in Section 6, Home births – Private.

Caveats when choosing a private consultant:

➢ Many consultants do not attend the entire labour and midwives look after you for the initial part.

➢ You may be at increased risk of an induced labour, because of your consultant's tight schedules. Watch out for weekends, bank holidays and holiday seasons.

➢ Check that your consultant is not planning a holiday when the baby is due. If so, you might like to ask for at least one appointment with whoever will be covering for him or her.

➢ It is worth bearing in mind the temptation – conscious or unconscious – for the doctor to carry out more interventions because each one involves a further payment.

➢ A further such temptation, in the patient's financial interest, is to declare an emergency when one does not really exist. Medical insurance policies will usually pay for all accommodation and medical costs if, for example, an emergency Caesarean is performed. Natural spontaneous birth is not normally covered.

Antenatal tests and other care will be carried out at an institution with which your chosen lead professional maintains close ties.

USEFUL CONTACTS
Royal College of Obstetricians & Gynaecologists,
☎ *Admin (020) 7772 6200, Bookshop (020) 7772 6275* ⌂ *www.rcog.org.uk*
Note that although the college does provide some information for pregnant women (primarily on the subject of looking after themselves), it does not recommend consultants, believing that your GP is the appropriate person to do so. / *HOURS Mon-Fri 9am-5pm; PUBLICATIONS Leaflets (£1.50 each) including Birth at Home.*

Costs when choosing by professional

Distinct areas of care are commonly charged for and invoiced individually.

CONSULTANT'S FEES
Consultant's fees for antenatal care and delivery are likely to be around £3,000 to £4,000, though details are sometimes negotiable.

Note that while some consultants charge a 'flat fee' covering all consultations in pregnancy, others charge per visit.

In the event that a Caesarean section is required, your consultant will often make an extra charge for the services of an assistant.

MIDWIFE'S FEES
Unless you are organising a private hospital birth led by a midwife, the cost of midwifery services relating to the birth will be included in the hospital fees (see below).

If you do opt for a birth led by a midwife, in home or in hospital, expect to pay a fee of £2,000–£3,000. (For more information on independent midwives, see below in Section 6, Home births – Private).

If you go down the independent midwife route, you generally won't need to pay consultants' fees, as you can rely on NHS care in the case of some medical necessity.

ANAESTHETISTS' FEES
An anaesthetist will need to be on-hand in case you require pain-relief, the fee for which is usually about £170. Expect this fee to be much more in the event that you require an epidural – about £485, slightly more for a caesarean.

PAEDIATRICIANS' FEES
A paediatrician usually examines the newborn shortly after birth. Allow a little over £200.

If your child needs intensive neonatal care, and this is provided privately, then additional charges for this can be substantial.

HOSPITAL FEES
The precise details of what is offered vary from hospital to hospital. There is generally a fee for handling a delivery that includes the cost of a night or 24 hours in hospital, and then a per-night or per-24-hour charge thereafter.

For example, the Lindo Wing at St Mary's Hospital charges approximately £1,500 for delivery and the first night stay and in the region of £650 per day thereafter.

At the Portland Hospital, a normal delivery is £2202 (which includes three nights stay) and then there is a charge of £857 per night thereafter.

Most NHS hospitals charge something under £1,000 for a normal delivery, with a typical room rate of £300–£400 per day. One or two offer extremely good value, all-inclusive rates that include two nights' stay for a normal birth (and five for a Caesarean delivery).

If you deliver via Caesarean section, there is usually an additional hospital charge, and one or two units charge a higher nightly rate to cover the additional nursing the procedure entails.

If you are having a private midwife-led birth in an NHS hospital, there is generally no charge for using it.

TESTS

Various tests are given routinely in pregnancy, and others will be given depending upon the age or condition of the mother. A complicated pregnancy, where a heavy level of testing and/or monitoring is required, can result in a requirement for quite considerable additional expenditure. A typical pregnancy would require spending £700–£1,1400 on testing (for a test-by-test breakdown of prices, see chapter *1.03 Tests*).

With a private birth at an NHS hospital, if you are happy with the normal NHS service, it may be that you can get all your antenatal testing non-privately.

INSURANCE COVER

Private health cover for a normal, uncomplicated pregnancy is included only in one or two of the most expensive policies, and then may require that the woman has subscribed to the policy for a number of years. The coverage of the majority of private health schemes is restricted to complications. This includes the need for emergency Caesarean deliveries. Urban legend suggests that this factor partially explains the relatively high rate of Caesarean sections for private deliveries.

Policies usually cover babies (and children too, up to a specified age), but it would be wise to check this in advance and to secure confirmation in writing.

Your options if you choose by venue

If you do not have a particular professional in mind you can choose an establishment in which you would like to organise your birth who can refer you to a suitable professional.

STAND-ALONE PRIVATE UNITS

The differing styles of the biggest private units:

The Portland Hospital: by far and away the largest private maternity hospital in London, owned and run by HCA Inc (formerly Hospital Corporation of America) which has around 200 hospitals including two in Switzerland and six in London. Although the hospital has recently introduced a midwife-led scheme, deliveries are still predominantly consultant-led. Each consultant operates his own practice and midwives work as obstetric nurses. According to figures published in 2003, 45% of deliveries were Caesarean – most of them elective; almost 90% of women having an epidural. There is a NICU suitable for babies from 28 weeks gestation. In 2003 the Evening Standard reported on a draft report from the NCSC (which now regulates the Portland, see listings) that had criticised the hospital. The final April report identified six areas of concern. These were disputed by the hospital, and following a May re-inspection it was found to comply fully. Problems appear to have arisen from the fact that the consultant-led ethos of the unit left diminished scope for midwives to exercise their skills and accordingly the hospital attracted a high proportion of agency staff. However, anecdotal evidence suggests that the hospital is now addressing these problems and monitoring and nursing care standards have improved. The midwife-led birth package already accounts for about 5% of deliveries. There are five classes of bedroom, including at the top end suites with living rooms, though the majority are much smaller.

St John & St Elizabeth: St John's Wood hospital which is a charitable foundation where profits from all departments are used to help fund the Hospital's hospice (50% funded by the Department of Health), which is free to all users on a GP referral. The Birth Unit is run by a consultant obstetrician dedicated to encouraging active birth, who has made the hospital a leading centre for water birth. Along with facilities like a birthing pool in each delivery suite, rooms offer double beds where parents are encouraged to spend time with the new arrival. A midwife-led package is strongly featured (the option used by the majority of women) and intervention rates are low. The hospital projects that in a couple of years the number of births it handles will have tripled since 2000. The hospital has an independent risk management committee chaired by an independent outsider and has been auditing birth outcomes since before the practice was introduced in the NHS. As a low risk centre without a specialised baby care unit, the birth unit does not undertake care in the case of known problems, and does not deliver twins because of the potential need for paediatric back-up.

The Birth Centre: a small centre run by birth campaigner Caroline Flint Midwifery Services that's near to St George's Hospital Tooting. As you would expect, the combination of ethos and highly trained midwives leads to a low intervention rate but the proximity to the hospital means that back-up is available if required.

The Lindo Wing, St Mary's Hospital: where the Queen gave birth to all of her children – the largest private unit attached to an NHS hospital; the only private NHS facility with its own dedicated obstetric operating theatre (though emergency Caesareans after 6pm happen in the NHS part of the hospital); and one of only two private NHS units to have its own labour rooms. Deliveries are almost exclusively consultant-led. The consultants block-book the rooms up to 10 months in advance so you need to move particularly fast if you want to give birth here.

PRIVATE WARDS AT NHS HOSPITALS

Many mothers value the resources and emergency backup of NHS hospitals, while retaining the control and comfort available in the private sector.

The largest NHS units:

The Lindo Wing, St Mary's Hospital: see above.

Sir Stanley Clayton Ward, Queen Charlotte's: approximately the same size as the Lindo Wing (approximately 300 births per annum). Delivery is in the same labour rooms and theatres as the NHS unit, with ante- and postnatal care in the private ward.

Nuffield House, Guy's Hospital: a little smaller than the two options above (230 births per annum). The only NHS unit currently offering a midwife-led package. Delivery is in the same labour rooms and theatres as the NHS unit, with ante- and postnatal care in the private ward.

Chelsea & Westminster Hospital: a private maternity unit opened Spring 2002. The expected throughput at the unit is likely to make it one of the more popular private NHS maternity facilities. It will, like The Lindo Wing, have its own private labour rooms, but share the operating theatre of the main unit.

OPTIONS FOR A PRIVATE BIRTH IN HOSPITAL (INCLUDING DETAILS OF NHS AMENITY ROOMS)

If not stated by the hospital, prices assume fees as follows – consultant £2,500, anaesthetist (assumes epidural) £300, paediatrician £150. Private antenatal testing is not generally included. Caesarean delivery price is for an elective procedure – emergency Caesareans are generally somewhat cheaper.

PRIVATE HOSPITALS	Amenity rooms	Amenity beds price (£)	Name of private ward	Telephone no.	Normal birth	Caesarean birth	Midwife-led birth	Daily room rate
St John & St Elizabeth	n/a	n/a	n/a	n/a	£1100	£2240	£4800, 3 nts	£740
St Mary's (Lindo Wing)	n/a	n/a	Lindo Wing	n/a	£1500	£5412	n/a	£650
The Birth Centre	n/a	n/a	Private	(020) 7498 2322	£3500–£4600	£3500–£4600	£3500–£4600	all included
The Portland	n/a	n/a	Private	-	£2202, 3 nts	£2878, 3 nts	£3202–£5000, 2 nts	£857

NHS HOSPITALS	Amenity rooms	Amenity beds price (£)	Name of private ward	Telephone no.	Normal birth	Caesarean birth	Midwife-led birth	Daily room rate
Barnet General	n/a	n/a	n/a	n/a	n/a	n/a	n/a	n/a
Central Middlesex	-	-	-	-	-	-	-	-
Chase Farm	6	£120	-	Hd of midwifery	£1800	£2500	£1800	£375
Chelsea & Westminster	6	£630	Kensington Wing	(020) 8746 8616	£1575	£2365	£1400	£630
Ealing	7	£40	no	n/a	n/a	n/a	n/a	n/a
Edgware Birth Centre	n/a	n/a	no	n/a	-	-	-	-
Elizabeth Garrett And'n	4	£150	no	n/a	n/a	n/a	n/a	n/a
Farnborough	11	£100	no	n/a	n/a	n/a	n/a	n/a
Guy's & St Thomas'	6	£550	Landsell Suite	(020) 7922 8025	£1325	£1745	£3000–£4650 (ant'l; 4 nts)	£550

Homerton	7	£140, 2 nts	no	n/a	n/a	n/a	n/a	n/a
King George	4	£51	Juniper Ward	n/a	£1780, 2 day stay	£3760, 5 day stay	n/a	£365
King's College	n/a	n/a	no	n/a	n/a	n/a	n/a	n/a
Kingston	n/a	£55	n/a	n/a	n/a	n/a	n/a	n/a
Lewisham	5	£45	no	no	n/a	n/a	n/a	n/a
Mayday University	12	£45	no	n/a	n/a	n/a	n/a	n/a
Newham General	n/a	n/a	no	n/a	n/a	n/a	n/a	n/a
North Middlesex	4	£50	no	n/a	n/a	n/a	n/a	n/a
Northwick Park	9	£75	no	n/a	n/a	n/a	n/a	n/a
Queen Charlotte's	8	£324	Sir Stanley Clayton Ward	(020) 8383 3569	£877	£1308	coming soon	£324
Queen Elizabeth	9	£35	no	n/a	n/a	n/a	n/a	n/a
Queen Mary's	10	£27	no	n/a	n/a	£3500	n/a	£196
Royal Free	5	£155-185	no	n/a	£1800	£1800	n/a	£401
Royal London	n/a	n/a	no	n/a	n/a	n/a	n/a	n/a
St George's	4	£33	no	n/a	n/a	n/a	n/a	n/a
St Helier	n/a	n/a	no	n/a	n/a	n/a	n/a	n/a
St Mary's	n/a	n/a	Lindo Wing	(020) 7886 1624	n/a	n/a	no	n/a
West Middlesex								
Whipps Cross	5	£95	no	n/a	n/a	£2000	no	n/a
Whittington	7	£85	no	n/a	n/a	n/a	n/a	n/a

Other options for private NHS births are detailed in the table on pages 34–35.

Private births in NHS hospitals:

➤ May be organised, via a consultant or independent midwife, in much the same manner as they would organise a private birth for you in a private hospital.

➤ May be organised by contacting one of the NHS units with facilities for private births, and asking for a referral to a consultant. This is less likely to be successful as consultants often block book beds for their patients as much as nine or 10 months in advance . You would therefore need to be happy with one of these consultants – who still has free slots – to take advantage of this.

➤ May come about when a mother in the course of her antenatal care on the NHS arranges to be delivered privately by one of the consultants working in the unit.

It is worth remembering that most NHS hospitals now have a Private Patients Manager (responsible for organising all private treatments). If luxurious wards are not the main concern, it may, in the right circumstances, be possible to organise a private birth at hospitals not listed in the table.

If having your own consultant or access to private antenatal care is not a prime concern, it is also worth considering private recuperation, rather than a fully private birth. This is just like a normal NHS birth, but with rather more comfortable accommodation after the birth. This can be achieved at quite a basic level if an amenity room is available, or for much more comfort by having a room booked on a private ward (the rates for both options are given in the table on pages 34–35).

AMENITY BEDS

A number of NHS hospitals have rooms on wards that are primarily for use in an emergency, but which, subject to their not being occupied, may be hired privately.

Whenever you ask for an amenity room (and you can do so once you have booked yourself in at a given hospital), you will only know if it is actually available after the birth.

By hiring an amenity room you have a normal NHS birth, but gain more privacy and quiet for postnatal recuperation.

Whether or not an NHS hospital has such rooms is shown in the table on pages 34–35.Not all are en suite, and if there is a choice the price we have quoted is the cheaper option. En suite rooms, if available, are typically about £30 more.

Costs when choosing by venue

CONSULTANT-LED OPTIONS

It is not common to see an all-in price quoted for a consultant-led birth. The usual system remains – even when the hospital suggests a particular doctor to a woman – that the hospital quotes its charges, but that the consultant's fees are a matter between mother and consultant.

Some of the NHS hospitals are unusual, in that they offer an all-in rate including accommodation. So, for example, it is assumed that you will need a five-day stay for a Caesarean section, and this is included in the price.

MIDWIFE-LED OPTIONS

All the fully private hospitals now offer such options: St John & St Elizabeth Hospital (£4,800), the Birth Centre in Tooting (£3,500) and even now The Portland (£5,000, £4,200 for second-time mothers). Different packages include different amounts of time in the unit and – in particular – antenatal testing. A full care package at The Birth Centre in Tooting costs £4,600. This includes all antenatal testing, postnatal care and an overnight stay in the Birth Centre if you deliver there. By contrast, The Portland offer a package for £3,200 if you get referred to them having already had all your antenatal testing on the NHS.

Nuffield House at Guy's hospital has been unusual among NHS hospitals in offering a midwife-led package (for £3,600). Again, this price assumes normal NHS antenatal care and testing. Midwife-led options are now also in operation at the Chelsea & Westminster, Chase Farm and (coming soon) Queen Charlotte's – though in some cases the price quoted is just for the use of the hospital and assumes a separate fee to an independent midwife (see Home births – Private).

USEFUL CONTACTS

National Care Standards Commission (NCSC), ☎ *Helpline (0191) 233 3556, HQ (0191) 233 3600 ⌁ www.carestandards.org.uk*
An independent public body with responsibility for the registration and inspection of private care services in the UK. Registration is mandatory for all private establishments, which includes (amongst other things) private doctors, hospitals and clinics and the latest inspection reports on any such provider are available via the website, or your local office (there are 71 across the country). (From April 2004 the commission will be split into the Commission for Healthcare Improvement, and the Commission for Social Care Inspection. Hospitals will come under the first.) / *HOURS Mon-Fri 8.30am-5.30pm.*

5. HOME BIRTHS – NHS

Until the early '60s, about one-third of births were at home. In subsequent decades, however, in part due to vigorous campaigning by the medical profession, such deliveries became almost unknown.

Until 1992 government policy had become set against home births. In that year, the pendulum started to swing back, when the House of Commons Health Select Committee concluded that "the policy of encouraging all women to give birth in hospitals cannot be justified on the grounds of safety". The current government has offered further support for home births.

The report concluded that women with normal pregnancies should be offered the choice of home births. By the end of the decade, the home birth rate had reached approximately 2%.

The advantages cited for home birth reflect what some see as the 'over-medicalisation' of birth in recent years, particularly in hospitals. Supporters of home birth highlight the benefits for the mother of giving birth in the privacy and comfort of her own home, supported by carers known to her. In Holland, one in three women still give birth at home (though for various reasons this high proportion is being eroded).

Benefits cited by home birth supporters:

Environment: home birth offers much greater privacy than a birth in hospital – an experience some find embarrassing. Even compared with a luxurious private hospital (and especially compared with a birth in an NHS hospital), your home may be a considerably more comfortable and agreeable place to be. After the birth you may be more able to rest – in

hospital crying babies and hospital noise and routines can mean disturbance and little chance to sleep and recover. (If you already have children
and don't have help to look after them, this last point may not apply.)

Continuity of care: even on the NHS, the system supporting home
births is such that, bar exceptional circumstances, you are likely to know
the midwife attending your labour.

Control: it is easier to be sure that your approach to labour will be
respected at home than in hospital. You can wear what you like, move
around as you like, eat and drink when you want. In hospital you may
feel under observation and judged.

Health: according to one piece of research, around one mother in five
contracts an infection in hospital – a rate approximately five times higher
than at home.

Partner participation: fathers are more likely to feel they have a real
role to play in a home birth.

Other children: if you have other children, you may like the fact that
– apart from during the actual birth – you can keep some kind of eye on
them. Afterwards they have an opportunity of meeting their sibling in a
familiar environment.

Reduced disruption: a home birth is believed by some observers to
result in a reduced likelihood of baby blues because there is no change of
environment for the mother to cope with.

Safety of home vs hospital

The relative safety of home and hospital births remains an area debated by
obstetricians and home birth campaigners.

What is not really in dispute any more (officially at any rate) is that
– especially for births for 'low-risk' mothers – home births are safe enough.

The areas of dispute centre on: how do you define a low risk woman;
and which is actually safer – home or hospital.

As regards the former, the 'grey area' for women who should not
consider a home birth is set out below.

As regards the latter, home birth campaigners claim that home is actually safer than hospital for low-risk women. Most doctors assert the
opposite.

The public debate in recent years seems to have focused more on the
issue of risks to the mother, rather than to the baby. Exchanges of letters
in *The Times* and the *British Medical Journal* aired the issues some years
back. A spokesman for the Royal College of Obstetricians and
Gynaecologists accepted the good results achieved by expert midwives
at home, but asserted that these results are flattered by the fact that only
women with relatively low-risk pregnancies are permitted home births,
whereas hospital figures include practically all the tough cases.

The letter cited the government's national Confidential Enquiry
Surveying Stillbirths and Neonatal Deaths in England, Wales and Northern
Ireland. In 1997 this survey calculated for the first time the neonatal death
rate for 'low-risk' births in hospital. The result was one in 1,561 over a
three-year period – a lower rate of risk than the one in 500 for home births
of a good independent midwifery practice.

In a riposte to this letter, Dr Gavin Young – a GP supportive of those
wanting to give birth at home – rejected the presumption that all women
who choose home birth are low risk, as some women who choose home
over hospital do so against professional advice, and some women reject
advice when complications arise. Therefore, according to his argument, the

risk for home births where low-risk births are concerned is actually lower than one in 500.

Whatever the validity of these counter-arguments, even many of those who believe hospital is actually the safer option accept that the risk involved in a home delivery for a 'normal' birth is small. The spokesman for the Royal College of Obstetricians and Gynaecologists concluded in the letter referred to above: "Although hospital birth is, on current evidence, three times safer than home birth, both risks are low and home birth should be available to women who choose it."

Dr Young believes that the key issue is not to make calculations as to which of two low levels of risk is the lower, but to try to ensure that it is only women who fit the medical criteria who should be offered the option of home birth.

Contra-indications for a home birth include:
➤ High blood pressure.
➤ Twins (particularly with an NHS midwife as few have experience of delivering multiple births).
➤ A breech baby (again few NHS midwives have experience delivering these as most are delivered by Caesarean section).
➤ Diabetes.
➤ A blood disorder.
➤ HIV or hepatitis B.
➤ Some other serious medical conditions.
➤ Ante-partum haemorrhage in this pregnancy.
➤ Post-partum haemorrhage in a previous labour.
➤ A previous birth by Caesarean (having a scar on your womb means it may not contract completely effectively in labour).
➤ Proven growth retardation of the baby
➤ If the mother is extremely young.
➤ If the mother has used illegal drugs.

Greyer areas include:
➤ A first baby – because the mother's ability to give birth is an unknown quantity, but also because first-time mothers are often less confident and more tense. Being an older mother (aged over 35) or a small mother (usually defined as under 5' 1") would be compounding factors.
➤ A previous delivery by forceps.
➤ An extremely obese mother.
➤ An overdue baby (a hospital birth allows more effective monitoring).

Reasons you might prefer to be in hospital:

Safety: if you encounter serious complications no-one disputes that you are safer in hospital, and you might feel safer and more relaxed (especially in a first birth) with backup close at hand.

Fear of the unknown: birth in hospital is the established procedure in the UK.

Lack of support at home: if your home environment is difficult or there will be no-one to help you, hospital may be a more attractive proposition.

Protected space: the post-birth visiting hours of a hospital may protect you against too many visitors all at once, or other such pressures.

Lack of support for a home birth: especially given the ambivalent attitude of many doctors to home birth, people can worry – particularly parents and in-laws – some of whom may make their misgivings known, sometimes with startling violence of feeling.

READING

Home Birth – Nicky Wesson (A comprehensive guide to planning childbirth at home; Vermilion Arrow; 1996; £8.99; 0-091812-51-8) – *A practical handbook with stories of women who chose home birth; it can now be difficult to find a copy.*

Home Birth (NCT; £2.50) – *A booklet including information about the options, including pain relief. Also available for 50p is a Home Birth Information Sheet.* / NCT Maternity Sales (0870) 112 1120, www.nctms.co.uk.

[Video] **Home Birth - Your Choice** (NCT Outreach; 1992; £18) / ACE Graphics, (01959 524622) – www.acegraphics.com.au.

Home Birth Handbook – Marianne Monaco & Viki Junor (Souvenir; 1984; £4.95; 0-285626-20-5) – *Pros and cons; dos and don'ts.* / 47 Valence Road, Lewes, Sussex or Manor House, Thelnetham, nr Diss, Norfolk IP22 1JZ.

Homebirth and Other Alternatives to Hospital – Sheila Kitzinger (Dorling Kindersley; 1995; £9.99; 0-751301-65-5) – *By one of the main figures in the movement to re-introduce home birth into the UK.*

Safer Childbirth – Marjorie Tew (A critical history of maternity care; Free Association Books; 1998; £17.95; 1853434264) – *A detailed report for those who are very interested.*

Spritual Midwifery – Ina May Gaskin (Book Publishing Co; 1985; £14.99; 0913990639) – *More inspirational than practical – accounts of home births in the US in the '70s.* / NCT Maternity Sales, (0870) 112 1120;www.nctms.co.uk.

Where to be Born? – Rona Campbell & Alison Macfarlane (National Perinatal Epidemiology Unit; 1995; £7; 095124051X) / NCT Maternity Sales, (0870) 112 1120; www.nctms.co.uk.

CONTACTS

Association for Improvement in Maternity Services (AIMS), ☎ (0870) 765 1433 ⬧ www.aims.org.uk

The organisation's website includes much useful information, including a sample letter to use if you have been told that your health authority cannot or will not supply a midwife to attend your planned home birth. / HOURS Mon-Fri 9.30am-5pm.

homebirth, ⬧ www.homebirth.org.uk

Very useful website run by Angela Horn, the home birth co-ordinator of the NCT as an 'informed lay person'; a good in-depth source of information and numerous links for those considering such a delivery, and an online chat group.

Independent Midwives Association, ☎ (01483) 821104 Answer phone ⬧ www.independentmidwives.org.uk

The 90 or so independent midwives in the country (of which about 20 are located in London) are listed by area on the organisation's website.

International Home Birth Movement, ☎ (01865) 300266 ⬧ www.sheilakitzinger.com

A rather informally run organisation (allied to Sheila Kitzinger) which provides support to those who want a home birth, helping mothers-to-be to think through the pros and cons, to explore the various options, and to help them attain a home birth if that is what they want.

Nursing & Midwifery Council, ☎ (020) 7637 7181 ⬧ www.nmc-uk.org

Previously known as the United Kingdom Central Council – the governing body regulating midwives, nurses and health visitors can supply the codes of practice applying to these carers and can verify the qualifications of any carer under its domain; one section of the council deals with home birth, so this could a useful body to consult for background information if you are considering a home birth.

CLASSES

Lesley Pavincich, ☎ (020) 8677 5776

Lesley runs home birth workshops through the Lambeth & Southwark branch of the NCT, at Soup Dragon in Lordship Lane. The three-hour workshops take up a Sunday afternoon, and are run once every two months. Partners are welcome – £10 per person. Concessions available. To book a place, contact Lesley directly or through NCT HQ.

The process

In view of the relative rarity of home births and because the system for such a birth on the NHS relies on the popular community midwifery service, a home birth is best organised well in advance.

DO YOU HAVE A SUPPORTIVE GP?

A sympathetic doctor is a boon if you wish to organise a home birth, but many GPs (and, indeed consultants and some midwives) continue to harbour misgivings about the desirability of such deliveries.

In 1995 the Royal College of General Practitioners told GPs that striking a woman off their register because she requests a home birth is indefensible. (It is also worth noting that you cannot be struck off without your consent once you have registered for antenatal care.)

Subsequent directives from the College impose a duty on your GP to inform you fully of your options for a home delivery – though anecdotal reports suggest that many continue not to do so.

If you want to change your GP, see the GP section in Section 2, Your lead professional, for an explanation of how you can do so.

If you don't want to run the risk of antagonising your GP whom you suspect to be anti-home birth, you could approach a local GP who you know to be sympathetic and ask for cover until after the birth when you would return to your own GP. Local midwives can sometimes offer details of GPs willing to do this.

It is not necessary to have a doctor present for a home birth. Should the midwife need to consult a doctor she can, at her own discretion, call out a GP on the obstetrics list for emergency backup, or speak to an obstetrician at the hospital. Should you insist on a home birth against your doctor's advice, midwives still have a duty to continue to give care.

Advice from the home birth movement includes arranging to see your GP occasionally during pregnancy even if midwives are providing your main care. This ensures that your GP will receive a payment for your care (not the case otherwise).

GOING DIRECT TO THE MIDWIVES

If you want to go direct to a midwife, the easiest way to contact one is through the midwifery department of a local hospital, though some require a referral from a GP first. The head of midwifery is the ideal person to get in touch with, requesting a booking appointment for a home delivery. A letter will ensure that your request is on file but you can also phone first. Once this is organised, it is the midwife's job to find a GP who will cover you for home birth.

You will probably continue to see the same midwife team throughout pregnancy and for the birth, and if you have difficulties with the person allocated to you, then you would be well advised to ring the midwifery supervisor/director sooner rather than later and ask if someone else could look after you. Don't feel awkward or guilty if you need to do this. The midwife should be aware that it is part of her job to deal with situations such as this tactfully, and with no personal recriminations.

ANTENATAL CARE

The general scheme of antenatal care for an NHS home birth is practically the same as that for an NHS hospital birth. Because the care is provided by community members of a given hospital's midwife team, there is a greater likelihood that the care will take place at your home, and/or locally (either at your GP's or a local antenatal clinic) rather than in the hospital.

With a private home birth, there is likely to be greater scope for you to organise antenatal appointments at your convenience, subject to the schedule of your midwife.

THE BIRTH

Midwives attending home births carry gas and air, oxygen and resuscitation equipment, plus respiratory stimulants and drugs to counter heavy bleeding. TENS machines and birthing pools (usually but not always to be hired privately) can offer further pain relief.

Community midwives are qualified to carry out episiotomies and stitch tears. Generally two midwives attend births, though in some areas only one does.

If complications occur you may be advised to transfer to hospital, even in an advanced stage of labour.

AFTER THE BIRTH

After a home birth, unlike one in hospital, the baby will not be seen by a paediatrician, but by the midwife and by your GP, who will check the baby either at your home (probably the next day), or in the surgery (at a later date). If need be, you might then be referred on to a paediatrician.

Potential problems

The opposition you might face in planning a home birth can be demoralising when you may already be feeling quite vulnerable and suggestible.

It certainly helps if your partner is on your side. If your partner is not keen, one of the contact groups (see above) should be able to put him in touch with other fathers who have experienced a home birth. This may be able to provide him with the reassurance he needs to get comfortable with the idea. NCT contacts or active birth teachers should also be a fund of further information and help to affirm your choice.

You might like to contact one or more of the groups listed before broaching the subject with your carers. Most consultants are probably at least as negative about home birth as GPs, and members of both groups have been known to resort to intimidating tactics to dissuade women from their chosen course (as occasionally have midwives). Your doctor or consultant might ask you to sign a waiver absolving him or her of all responsibility should anything go wrong. These are legally questionable, and if you do sign anything you should insert the name of the person who is insisting you do so, and why you are signing.

Catchment areas for home births are sometimes considerably reduced compared to the full area theoretically offered. This is usually because of staff/funds shortages. Reasons given to reduce pressures on the service include restricting eligible mothers for example by age and to second and subsequent births.

Finally, if you have any complaint about your medical treatment during pregnancy, the birth, or subsequently, you would be doing all mothers a service if you wrote to those responsible about it, (see How to make a complaint about your care, in chapter *4.03 Medical issues at birth*). Some health managers are making a concerted effort to improve their maternity services and to listen more to what women want, so there is a better than usual chance that your thoughts and recommendations will be listened to.

6. HOME BIRTHS – PRIVATE

(Much of the preceding section relating to home births on the NHS is relevant to a private birth, particularly the Safety of home vs hospital.)

The process

CHOOSING AN INDEPENDENT MIDWIFE

Renewed interest in births at home, lack of continuity of care on the NHS, and increasing interest in midwife-led births in hospital is creating something of a 'come back' for independent midwives.

A few years ago, independent midwives seemed to risk becoming something of an endangered species with the withdrawal of professional insurance cover by the Royal College of Midwives and the prohibitively high cost – then about £16,000 – of securing it independently.

Today. even that independent cover is no longer available and all independent midwives now work uninsured. It's worth remembering, though, that the cover never protected against something bad happening per se, but against the midwife being negligent. Many women feel this is sufficiently unlikely – especially as they get to pick the carer concerned (unlike on the NHS) – to take that risk. For many practices theproblem has now become too little work rather than too much.

There are around 20-30 independent midwives in London, working either alone or as part of a practice. Some midwives work for more than one practice. The geographical area covered by a practice varies according to the number of bookings they currently have (and where they are) and whether all the midwives are available for the relevant period.

In addition, there is the Albany Group Practice, with self-employed midwives, but attached to King's College Hospital and obeying its rules in return for indemnity insurance cover. Their caseload is higher than most midwife practices at 36 births per midwife a year, but their intervention rates are more in line with independent midwife averages and much lower than in most hospitals, even though 63% of the births are in hospital.

The big strength of private midwives is that they are very positive about the whole birth experience, and immensely reassuring to mothers who are feeling somewhat at sea.

Early booking is advisable, to get plenty of time to talk through plans for the birth. The only circumstances in which an independent midwife might judge a location unsuitable for a home birth is where there might be a risk of physical danger to mother, baby or midwife. Otherwise they are highly flexible.

You will be able to shop around to find someone whose approach to birth matches what you are looking for. Independent midwives are particularly good at discussing birth options and how to achieve what you want, with both you and your partner. They are generally in favour of active birth and accept complementary therapies. Some have training in the latter, and others will be able to recommend specialist practitioners.

ANTENATAL CARE

Throughout your pregnancy, birth and postnatal care, you usually see only one midwife who works with another for backup, or both members of a two-woman team.

There is a greater element of control for the mother with an independent midwife than with NHS midwives, as those who practice privately usually recognise that they are in effect an employee of the mother. Discussion on all issues is the norm.

In general, independent midwives offer greater convenience with flexible antenatal visit times, often carried out at home or at work. They also offer a greater chance of discussing various birth options.

BACKUP

Should a referral to a consultant prove necessary, an independent midwife can make an appropriate choice, based on a given consultant's known approach. The midwife might accompany the mother or simply discuss the case with the consultant informally. A referral would be made in the case that a hospital birth was considered wise and the midwife would still attend the mother at the birth as an advocate and supporter.

AFTER THE BIRTH

The midwives will leave when they feel the mother is ready – perhaps after three hours – but are generally on 24-hour call and will carry out all postnatal visits.

USEFUL CONTACTS

Independent Midwives Association, ☎ *(01483) 821104 Answer phone* ⌕ *www.independentmidwives.org.uk*
The 90 or so independent midwives in the country (of which about 20 are located in London) are listed by area on the organisation's website.

Price guide:
➤ Fees for independent midwives are generally something over £2,000 and often closer to £3,000 in London. Payments are sometimes made in instalments.
➤ Antenatal tests are done either at a hospital, through the mother's GP, or privately (for which there would be an extra charge, unless a full care package has been arranged). Blood test samples might be taken by the midwives and sent to the local hospital for analysis. Scans are usually done at a local hospital. (For details of costs of tests see Section 4, Hospital Births – Private.)
➤ Should your birth be problematic, the midwives will be able to refer you to a consultant, either within the NHS system or privately.
➤ All midwifery equipment is supplied but midwives may ask the mother to provide such items as plastic sheeting.

The performance of private midwives:

Caseload: depending on their own independent circumstances, attitude to the care they wish to provide mothers and where they live, independent midwives take on very varied caseloads. Some independent midwives might only deliver half a dozen women per year, whereas others might deliver up to 30; in either case, this is a lower level than a midwife in most NHS hospitals.

Pain relief: water births are often arranged – in fact some independent midwives do more births in water than not in water. In addition to pools, pain relief including gas and air and TENS are offered, plus epidurals in hospital. There is usually an effort to avoid pethidine, though women who want it may be asked to get a prescription for it from their GP. However, the focus of the midwives tends to be on psychological support ("kind words and encouragement" to quote one) and help with breathing techniques, water births and massage.

Breast-feeding: is generally encouraged, with a 90%–100% success rate.

Active birth: less than 1% of mothers give birth in bed or on their back.

Policies on duration of different stages of labour: none.

Induction: rare – most midwives will wait up to 42 weeks before discussing this.

Third stage: except for emergency hospital referrals, this is practically always 'physiological', unless there is excessive bleeding.

7. HOSPITAL PERFORMANCE TABLES – NHS & PRIVATE

National data

National figures given below and in Table C are taken from *NHS Maternity Statistics, England: 2001-02* (published by the Department of Health (DOH) in May 2003).

Hospital data

Information was gathered directly from the hospitals by questionnaire. Units were asked to supply data for the year ended December 2002, or the best equivalent.

We do not include in the questionnaire the following issues:

Policy on issues such as time allowed for labour, induction and various forms of intervention/active birth: anecdotal evidence suggests it is common for a hospital to have in place policies which are ignored or unknown by a number of the medical staff. Alternatively they may simply be interpreted differently. What will affect your care therefore is not the institution's choice in the matter, but that of the people caring you on the day. How this situation changes with the increasing number of national NICE – National Institute for Clinical Excellent – guidelines (which it is soon planned to extend to care in labour) remains to be seen.

Special Care Baby Units (SCBUs) or neonatal Intensive care units (NICUs): one in 10 babies born in the UK will require some kind of special care and 3% require intensive care. If you have any reason to believe that this might apply to your baby – whether because of a previous miscarriage or a condition developing during pregnancy – try to pick a hospital with appropriate facilities. However, note that staff shortages mean these sometimes these units do not run at full capacity.

Cleanliness: it is reported that since 2000 there has been a rise in maternal deaths from postnatal infection. Hospitals generally contract out their cleaning and standards vary widely. The government's Clean Hospitals programme may help with this but one critic argues that only one of the programme's 19 criteria is directly linked to hygiene.

Health and safety: government figures uncovered in 2003 indicated that one in 10 hospital wards and patient areas do not comply with regulations, largely because hospitals say they don't have the resources to carry out the required work. Watch out for example for wards with extra beds crammed on to them.

DISCLAIMER

The publishers and author of this guide have collected the following data to give mothers: i) a general guide and some context for statistics relating to birth; and ii) a starting point for discussion with carers about issues relating to their birth that are important to them.

The figures have not been prepared with the rigour that would be required in, say, a medical journal. If a point is of particular importance to you, you should double check the data with the hospital(s) concerned.

The tables are divided into four sections:
A. Overview information
B. Midwifery services
C. Obstetric interventions
D. Water births

Notes regarding tables

All percentages over 10% have been rounded to the nearest unit, all those below 10% to the nearest 0.1%.

Meaning of abbreviations:
—	No answer given, or no information available
n/a	Not applicable
del	on delivery
≈	Approximately
c/s	Caesarean section
m/w	Midwife
p/a	Per annum
t/d	To date

TABLE A. OVERVIEW INFORMATION

Referral unit: indicates whether the hospital is a centre of excellence in obstetrics, and hence has difficult cases referred to it by other hospitals. Intervention rates are generally higher in such units.

Teaching hospital: people sometimes take comfort that they are being looked after in a teaching hospital. Actually, a more significant indicator in judging the level of expertise at a particular institution is whether it is a referral unit (see above).

Home births: the proportion of births handled at home by community midwives based at the hospital.

Postnatal review: indicates whether or not there is a formal process by which someone from the hospital 'debriefs' mothers about the birth and asks for their input about how the woman feels her care was handled.

Breast-feeding: the proportion of mothers breast-feeding on discharge; in some cases hospitals supplied us with the figure for those feeding on delivery (marked del); in others the hospital gave us two figures – the total solely breast-feeding and (shown in brackets) the total breast-feeding in combination with bottle-feeding.

TABLE B. MIDWIFERY SERVICES

Births per midwife per annum: a ratio showing how many mothers an average midwife on the unit will deliver in a year. The higher the number, the greater the caseload each midwife on the unit has to cope with. The lowest figure in the survey of 1:19 (cf 1998 1:22) was again reported at the private St John & Elizabeth, a hospital which places great weight on personal attention. This compares with similar low figures at some NHS referral units. The highest figure in the survey was 1:50 (cf 1998 1:43) at Kingston (who inform us they are just completing a major recruiting drive.)

'Named'/known midwife: an indication of how much continuity of care each hospital aims to provide. As first enshrined by the Patient's

Charter, a woman is supposed to have a 'named' midwife, i.e. someone charged directly with looking after her. The 1992 *Changing Childbirth* report set all NHS hospitals the target that by 1997, 75% of births would be handled by the woman's 'named' midwife. As the figures show, performance varies widely on this score, with much room for general improvement.

Midwife-managed births: the proportion of births in which recourse to a consultant was unnecessary.

Care in community: a measure of how many women received their antenatal care at local health centres and in their own homes, rather than in hospital.

Community midwifery area: this is the area in which you must live in order to be eligible for community-based, rather than hospital-based antenatal care. This is defined by the individual hospitals.

TABLE C. OBSTETRIC INTERVENTIONS

(For further information about these medical procedures, see 4.03 Medical issues at birth.)

Crude ranking of the figures supplied by the hospitals does not produce a fair comparison of their performance. This is primarily due to various factors which can increase interventions: notably whether or not a hospital is a referral unit (and therefore deals with a higher than average proportion of difficult cases); and average maternal age, older women being more likely to have a Caesarean delivery. (An unusual ethnic mix can also skew the figures, but – this being London – every hospital in the survey answered "yes" to that question). There is also the problem that different hospitals sometimes use different definitions for these procedures in presenting their statistics.

Whether a hospital is a referral unit and the average maternal age are covered in the first two columns of the table as yes/no answers. Where the answer to first question is 'yes', or the average age is high one would expect the level of interventions at a given hospital to be higher than average. (With the latter, an average age was not always available, and in some cases the hospitals indicated the age range into which the majority of their mothers fell).

The last edition of this guide used statistics from 1998, and these are shown in brackets for comparison purposes.

Caesarean section – emergency: the proportion of women where the decision to perform a Caesarean section was taken in the latter stages of pregnancy or during labour. The range of 10%–20% (cf 1998 10%–17%) in the NHS hospitals in our survey compares with a national average of 12% reported in the DOH report.

Caesarean section – elective: the proportion of women who choose a Caesarean section as their preferred method of delivery. Different hospitals have different policies about whether to make such a choice available to women on non-clinical grounds. The range in NHS hospitals of 7%–14% (cf 1998 4%–13%) in our survey compares with an average of 10% reported by the DOH figures. The fully private institutions diverge to extremes – from the very low 3% at The Birth Centre, to 29% at The Portland.

Caesarean section – total: at the NHS hospitals, the range of 19%–31% (cf 1998 15%–27%) in our survey of compares with an average of 22% in the DOH report.

Episiotomies: at the NHS hospitals, the range reported in our survey of 7.5%–28% (cf 1998 8%–35%) compares with a national average of 13%.

This procedure is virtually unknown at the midwife-driven Birth Centre (0.05%) and the Edgware Birth Unit (2%).

Forceps all the NHS hospitals reported a low rate of 1.8%–3.5% (cf 1998 0.5%–7%) which compares with the national average reported by the DOH of 7%. The Portland reported a rate higher than the NHS hospitals, but lower than the national average at 5.2%

Ventouse: the range reported in our survey of 3.7%–16% (cf 1998 4%–12%) compares with a national average reported by the DOH of 4%.

Induction: the range of 5.5%–38% (cf 1998 6%–28%) compares with a national average reported by the DOH of 21%.

Epidural: this procedure seems more common in London than nationally: the range reported was 10%–63%, but most hospitals exceeded the 33% which is the national average.

Mobile epidural available: indicates the availability of this more convenient form of epidural.

TABLE D. WATER BIRTHS

The figures for the usage of birthing pools vary widely from institution to institution, though it is striking how common water births are becoming in the more midwife-driven private units (and the low intervention rates that they achieve). The independent midwives who largely attend home births also comment on the very large proportion of births they assist with in water). It used to be the case in some hospitals that they would only "allow" use of pools for pain relief during labour (rather than for the actual delivery), but this seems now to be relatively rare.

Can deliver in water: in nearly all instances this is available: "p/r" indicates use mainly for pain relief.

Frequency of use: there is a stark different between the NHS hospital maternity units (other than Guys and the Homerton around 2%, practically all the remainder under 1%), and the NHS midwife-led Edgware Birth Centre (66%), and the private Birth Centre in Tooting (52%), and The Hospital of St John & St Elilzabeth (23%).

TABLE A. OVERVIEW INFORMATION

For issues relating to this table, see page 46.

NHS HOSPITALS	Address	Telephone no.	Unit built	Referral unit	Teaching unit	Births annually	Delivery rooms	Total maternity beds	Home births (%)	post-natal review (%)	Breast-feeding (%)	Notes
Barnet General	Wellhouse Lane, Barnet, EN5 3OJ	(020) 8216 5218	1997	yes	yes	3286	9	32	.01%	no		79%	increase midwife led care
Central Middlesex	Acton Lane, NW10 7NS	(020) 8453 2327	1950	-	-	-	-	-	-	-	-	re-opens with birth centre in summer 2004
Chase Farm	The Ridgeway, Enfield, EN2 8JL	(020) 8366 6600	1970s	yes	yes	3000	9	41	1%	no	-	-
Chelsea & Westminster	369 Fulham Rd, SW10 9NH	(020) 8846 7903	1993	yes	yes	4084	12	77	1%	if complex	96%	expansion in progress
Ealing	Uxbridge Rd, Southall, UB1 3HW	(020) 8967 5000	1988	no	no	2611	11	38	0.5%	no	50%	-
Edgware Birth Centre	Burnt Oak Broadway, Edgware, HA8 0AD	(020) 8732 6777	—	no	no	455	5	5	0	yes	85%	new building June 2004, 3 pools, 6 'suites'
Elizabeth Garrett And'n	Huntley St, WC1E 6DH	(020) 7387 9300	—	yes	yes	2950	14	14	<1%	yes	75%	-
Farnborough	Farnborough Common, Orpington, BR6 8ND	(01689) 863560	2003	yes	yes	2700	10	47	-	no	67%	-
Guy's & St Thomas'	Lambeth Palace Rd, SE1 7EH	(020) 7922 8012	2001	yes	yes	5000	28	92	n/a	if complex	67% (77%)	increasing community care
Homerton	Homerton Row, E9 6SR	(020) 8510 7177	1986	yes	yes	4275	11	64	1.5%	no	-	-
King George	Barley Lane, Goodmayes, IG3 8YB	(020) 8983 8000	1993	no	-	4320	10	58	0.6%	no	-	-
King's College	Denmark Hill, SE5 9RS	(020) 7346 3246	2002	yes	yes	3863	12	50	8%	no	86%	-
Kingston	Galsworthy Rd, Kingston, KT2 7QB	(020) 8546 7711	1995	yes	no	4700	10	59	1.3%	no	72-80%	-
Lewisham	Lewisham High St, SE13 6LH	(020) 8333 3000	1996	yes	yes	3300	10	52	3%	on request	59%	-
Mayday University	London Rd, Thornton Heath, CR7 7YE	(020) 8401 3000	1900/70s	yes	yes	4200	11	71	2%	no	68%	-

Hospital	Address	Phone	Year									home birth team
Newham General	Glen Rd, E13 8SL	(020) 7476 4000	1983	no	yes	4300	14	44	-	no	-	
North Middlesex	Sterling Way, N18 1QX	(020) 8887 2000	1970	no	yes	3000	11	32	1.9%	if complex	76%	bigger maternity day unit; more midwife led care
Northwick Park	Watford Rd, Harrow, HA1 3UJ	(020) 8864 3232	1971	no	yes	3598	10	53	0.6%	no	>64%	-
Queen Charlotte's	150 Du Cane Rd, W12 0HS	(020) 8383 1111	2000	yes	yes	5318	19	79	7.6%	yes	75%-80%	-
Queen Elizabeth	Stadium Road, Woolwich, SE18 4QH	(020) 8836 5055	2001	yes	yes	3220	11	48	3.4%	no	55%	-
Queen Mary's	Frognal Avenue, Sidcup, DA14 6LT	(020) 8302 2678	1971	yes	yes	3140	12	53	1%	yes	54%	-
Royal Free	Pond St, NW3 2QG	(020) 7794 0500	2003	yes	yes	3000	8	-	1%	-	-	-
Royal London	Whitechapel Rd, E1 1BB	(020) 7377 7431	1960s	yes	yes	3750	9	57	1.6%	no	40% (70%)	-
St George's	Blackshaw Rd, SW17 0QT	(020) 8672 1255	1981	yes	yes	3710	14	60	1.5%	if op. del	69% (79%)	-
St Helier	Wrythe Lane, Carshalton, SM5 1AA	(020) 8296 2863	1982	yes	yes	2600	10	58	2%	no	70%	-
St Mary's	Praed St, W2 1NY	(020) 7886 6666	—	yes	yes	2900	8	56	1%	if complex	85%	new building
West Middlesex	Twickenham Rd, Isleworth, TW7 6AF	(020) 8565 5008	1960	no	no	2840	-	-	-	-	-	-
Whipps Cross	Whipps Cross Rd, E11 1NR	(020) 8535 6861	1973	no	yes	3998	10	67	1%	no	54% del	midwife-led unit
Whittington	Highgate Hill, N19 5NW	(020) 7288 5249	1800s	no	yes	3200	7	49	3%	no	72%	new building planned, more midwife-led care

PRIVATE HOSPITALS

Hospital	Address	Phone	Year									
St John & St Elizabeth	60 Grove End Rd, NW8 9NH	(020) 7286 5126	1992	no	no	485	3	12	-	no	96%	expanding to enable 750 deliveries p.a.
St Mary's (Lindo Wing)	Praed St, W2 1NY	(020) 7725 1913	1937	yes	yes	850	6	17	0	no	75%	plan drop-in antenatal clinic
The Birth Centre	37 Coverton Rd, SW17 0QW	(020) 8767 8294	1994	-	-	173	3	3	45%	yes	97%	expansion planned
The Portland	209 Gt Portland St, W1N 6AH	(020) 7580 4400	1983	yes	no	2038	5	37	n/a	no	-	

TABLE B. MIDWIFERY SERVICES

For issues relating to this table, see page 46.

NHS HOSPITALS	M/ws:Mother's	Named (known) m/w	M/w-managed births	Care in community m/w	No. of m/w teams	No. of community m/w teams	No. of which community teams run m/w per team	Community area
Barnet General	30	38%	38%	60%	5	6	6	NW9, HA8, WD6, NW7, EN5
Central Middlesex	-	-	-	-	-	-	-	-
Chase Farm	-	-	65%	75%	5	5	6	EN1, EN2, EN3, N13, N11, N21, N14, N9
Chelsea & Westminster	35	50%	50%	51%	7	7	6	SW1, SW3, SW5, SW7, SW10, W8; parts of SW6, SW18, SW14, SW15
Ealing	29	n/a	n/a	75%	7	7	6	W5, W7, W13, UB1, UB2, UB5, UB6; parts of W3 NW10
Edgware Birth Centre	29	70%	100%	29%	8	8	1-5	Northwest London
Elizabeth Garrett And'n	50	65%	46%	70%	4	3	6	NW1, NW5, EC1, N7; part of EC2
Farnborough	-	-	-	-	-	-	-	-
Guy's & St Thomas'	30	n/a	n/a	90%	17	16	6	-
Homerton	40	-	65%	45%	11	-	9	Hackney & City of London
King George	40	>10%	-	60-70%	-	-	-	IG1-5, RM9, RM10; parts of IG7, RM8
King's College	30	32.8%	60%	20%	9	-	5	Southwark & parts of Lambeth & Lewisham
Kingston	37	-	-	80%	-	-	-	KT10, KT9, KT6, KT7, KT8, KT2, TW10, TW11, SW13, SW14, TW9
Lewisham	35	-	65%	85%	4	4	7-8	SE12, SE13, BR1, SE26, SE23, SE3, SE4, SE6
Mayday University	-	-	68%	70%	-	-	-	Croydon

Hospital								
Newham General	-	-	80%	60%	4	4	6	E6, E13, E7, E12, E15
North Middlesex	35	20%	10%	80%	5	5	6	N18, N17, N22, N9, N15
Northwick Park	44	-	60%	most	-	-	6	Brent & Harrow
Queen Charlotte's	37	-	-	50%	4	-	6	W4, W6, W12, SW6; most of W3, W14; parts of W5, W10, W11, NW10
Queen Elizabeth	33	-	67%	-	8	-	8	-
Queen Mary's	-	13%	58%	80%	3	3	6.5	SE2, SE28, SE9, DA5-8, DA1, DA14-15, DA17-18
Royal Free	-	-	-	-	-	-	-	-
Royal London	-	-	70%	80-90%	7	7	8	E1, E2, E3, E14
St George's	29	13%	38%	66%	7	7	6	SW11, SW12, SW16, SW17, SW18, SW19, CR4
St Helier	34	-	65%	60-70%	3	3	6	-
St Mary's	35	-	60%	71%	8	4	5	W2, W11, W9, W10, NW8; part of W1
West Middlesex	-	-	-	-	-	-	-	-
Whipps Cross	35	-	66%	60%	-	-	-	-
Whittington	-	18%	58%	80%	10	2	7	N1, N4, N5, N6, N7, N8, N10, N15, N19, N22, EC1; part of N16

PRIVATE HOSPITALS

Hospital								
St John & St Elizabeth	19	-	70%	0%	n/a	n/a	n/a	n/a
St Mary's (Lindo Wing)	-	n/a	n/a	0%	n/a	n/a	n/a	n/a
The Birth Centre	35	100%	100%	98%	-	-	-	-
The Portland	n/a	n/a	2.9%	n/a	n/a	n/a	n/a	n/

TABLE C. OBSTETRIC INTERVENTIONS

For issues relating to this table, see page 47.

NHS HOSPITALS	Referral unit	Avg maternal age	c/s – emergency	c/s – elective	c/s – total	Total episiotomies	Total instrumental deliveries	Forceps deliveries	Ventouse deliveries	Tears	Inductions	Epidural	Mobile epi available?
National average	n/a	n/a	12%	10%	22%	13%	11%	7%	4%	—	21%	—	—
Barnet General	yes	30+	12%	11%	23%	14%	9%	2%	7%	39%	15%	36%	yes
Central Middlesex	-	-	-	-	-	-	-	-	-	-	-	-	-
Chase Farm	yes	-	14%	11%	25%	16%	10%	2.7%	7.2%	-	20%	38%	-
Chelsea & Westminster	yes	34	16%	-	28%	-	-	-	-	-	31%	40%	yes
Ealing	no	29.8	16%	9.4%	26%	15%	8.6%	2%	6.6%	20%	18%	59%	no
Edgware Birth Centre	no	31-35	5.4%	0%	5.4%	≈2%	5.6%	1.8%	3.9%	65%	n/a	n/a	n/a
Elizabeth Garrett And'n	yes	33	15%	14%	30%	-	12%	2.9%	8.6%	31%	12%	43.8	yes
Farnborough	yes	-	18%	11%	29%	28%	14%	2.6%	12%	34%	38%	34%	no
Guy's & St Thomas'	yes	26-35	20%	7.3%	27%	7.5%	12%	2.8%	9.6%	40%	15%	38%	no
Homerton	yes	32	17%	8.3%	25%	8.7%	8%	3%	5%	33%	15%	26%	no
King George	no	-	12%	8.3%	20%	12%	9.5%	2.6%	6.9%	26%	17%	30%	no
King's College	yes	29.5	17%	9.6%	26%	11%	11%	2.2%	8.3%	30%	11%	50%	no
Kingston	yes	32	15%	10%	24%	18%	14%	3%	10%	-	20%	58%	yes
Lewisham	yes	-	17%	10%	27%	12%	7.7%	-	-	22%	5.5%	-	no
Mayday University	yes	-	11%	10%	21%	15%	10%	1.5%	9%	≈20%	≈25%	25%	n

Newham General	no	25	10%	10%	20%	-	-	-	-	-	20%	-	no
North Middlesex	no	35	12%	7%	19%	16%	7%	3%	4%	30%	20%	10%	no
Northwick Park	no	-	18%	10%	28%	16%	11%	3%	8%	30%	15%	29%	yes
Queen Charlotte's	yes	31.2	17%	14%	31%	14%	12%	2.4%	9%	28%	21%	63%	yes
Queen Elizabeth	yes	28.7	14%	7.9%	22%	9.9%	8.1%	1.9%	6.3%	32%	15%	35%	yes
Queen Mary's	yes	30	16%	12%	28%	15%	12%	2%	10%	31%	19%	43%	no
Royal Free	yes	-	16%	12%	26%	-	10%	2.2%	7.8%	-	13%	44%	yes
Royal London	yes	20-29	14%	6.1%	20%	-	9.8%	3.5%	6.3%	-	17%	25%	yes
St George's	yes	30	14%	8.5%	22%	11%	14%	2.6%	12%	39%	16%	27%	yes
St Helier	yes	-	14%	6.6%	20%	16%	18%	2.7%	16%	-	15%	34%	yes
St Mary's	yes	-	16%	11%	26%	13%	11%	3%	8%	34%	14%	36%	yes
West Middlesex	no	-	-	-	22%	-	12%	3%	9%	-	-	-	-
Whipps Cross	no	-	16%	12%	28%	14%	6%	2.2%	3.7%	26%	17%	19%	yes
Whittington	no	25-34	15%	7%	22%	15%	12%	3.2%	8.9%	53%	20%	21%	yes

PRIVATE HOSPITALS

St John & St Elizabeth	no	32-42	11%	10%	21%	7%	6%	3%	3%	55%	18%	47%	yes
St Mary's (Lindo Wing)	yes	25-45	8%	25%	33%	28%	15%	2.8%	12%	23%	28%	-	yes
The Birth Centre	-	36	9%	3%	12%	0.05%	7%	1%	6%	10%	0%	8%	yes
The Portland	yes	30+	16%	29%	46%	n/a	12%	5.2%	7%	-	-	53%	yes

TABLE D. WATER BIRTHS

For issues relating to this table, see page 48.

NHS HOSPITALS	No. of pools	First installed	Can hire independently?	Can deliver in water?	Frequency of use
Barnet General	0	-	-	-	-
Central Middlesex	-	-	-	-	-
Chase Farm	2	1997	n/a	yes	0.5%
Chelsea & Westminster	2	1993	-	yes	0.7%
Ealing	1	1995	yes	yes	0.3%
Edgware Birth Centre	3	1997	no	yes	66%
Elizabeth Garrett And'n	1	1998	-	yes	0.8%
Farnborough	1	2003	no	yes	-
Guy's & St Thomas'	2	2002	-	yes	0.2%
Homerton	3	1992	yes	yes	2.5%
King George	1	1995	no	p/r	minimal
King's College	2	2002	no	yes	≈1.5%
Kingston	0	-	-	-	n/a
Lewisham	1	2003	yes	yes	small, growing
Mayday University	1	1997	no	yes	≈0.1%
Newham General	1	1994	no	-	-
North Middlesex	2	1995	yes	yes	0.7%
Northwick Park	1	1998	n/a	yes	-
Queen Charlotte's	2	2000	-	yes	0.7%
Queen Elizabeth	1	2001	h/bs	yes	0.6%
Queen Mary's	1	2004	yes	yes	0.4%
Royal Free	1	2003	no	yes	-
Royal London	1	2003	no	yes	-
St George's	2	2002	h/bs	yes	1%
St Helier	1	1992	no	yes	0.2%
St Mary's	1	2002	-	yes	1%
West Middlesex	-	-	-	-	-
Whipps Cross	0	-	-	-	-
Whittington	2	1996	h/bs	yes	0.9%

PRIVATE HOSPITALS

	No. of pools	First installed	Can hire independently?	Can deliver in water?	Frequency of use
St John & St Elizabeth	2	1991	-	yes	23%
St Mary's (Lindo Wing)	n/a	n/a	n/a	n/a	n/a
The Birth Centre	3	1994	yes	yes	52%
The Portland	1		yes	yes	0.5%

CHAPTER 1.02

LOOKING AFTER YOURSELF

1. **Introduction**
2. **Common problems**
3. **Diet**
4. **Clean living**
5. **Potential hazards**
6. **Illness**
7. **Travelling when pregnant**

I. INTRODUCTION

In any pregnancy, and especially with a first baby, it's hard to know quite what to expect when so many changes are happening to your body. You may experience all kinds of minor ailments or simply feel perfectly normal – and sometimes even better than normal.

At the same time the slightest twinge can seem to have some sinister significance. A good pregnancy book can therefore be invaluable, helping check out any symptoms, and suggesting possible remedies. (For suggested specific titles, see chapter *4.05 Finding out more*.)

Reading can also be a useful form of gentle mental preparation for the birth and life thereafter. Practically all of the general pregnancy texts are packed with information and tips. It is rare, though, that one source – however good – will have all the answers an individual mother seems to need.

IF YOU WANT TO PSYCHE YOURSELF UP

Meditations and Positive Thoughts for Pregnancy & Birth – Gilli Moorhawk (Piatkus; 1994; £7.99; 0749913959) – *Ideas for New Agers: positive affirmation for each trimester, the birth and thereafter.*

My Pregnancy Journal – Charlotte King and Debi Treloar with Gill Thorn (Ryland, Peters & Small; 2003; £14.99; 1-84172-435-1) – *Eight tabbed sections, with introductory thoughts and tips (and lots of space for entering your own), plus space to record medical details, and a pocket for storing souvenirs and papers.*
/ *www.rylandpeters.com.*

LISTENING TO YOUR BABY

For many expectant parents it's a thrill listening to their baby's heartbeat and it might help you psyche yourself up. It used to be that the experience was reserved for trips to the antenatal clinic, but consumer models for sale or rent are increasingly available.

Baby Echos (& Rad Pad)
Alison Brazendale, 349 Hungerford Road, Crewe Cheshire CW1 5EZ ☎ (01270) 255 201 ✆ www.babyechos.co.uk
The BebeSounds Prenatal Gift Set (£48 including P&P) allows parents and siblings to listen in to the baby with a foetal monitor on the abdomen. The pack includes a recording cable to connect to a tape recorder or CD. A microphone is also provided to help parents talk, read and sing to the baby more directly, offering extra prenatal stimulation. / *SEE ALSO 2.03 Baby health; 3.02 Baby equipment; 3.03 Nursery decor.*

Baby Pulse
Ultrasound Technologies, Lodge Way, Portskewett, Caldicot South Wales NP26 5PS
☎ *(01291) 425 425* ⏱ *www.babypulse.com*
A consumer product from manufacturers of foetal dopplers (heartbeat monitors) for
hospitals and medical use. The portable foetal Doppler is a simpler, lightweight unit
for non-medical use. The baby can be detected as early as 8 weeks. The product is
available to buy (about £140 all in) or you can rent at £29.38 per month (minimum
two months), plus £6.50 delivery, plus £2.94 per container of gel.

Thames Medical Ltd
16, Brook Barn Way, Goring by Sea, Worthing West Sussex BN12 4DW ☎ *(01903)*
522 911 ⏱ *www.thamesmedical.com*
The manufacturers of the Baby Pulse (see also) make a range of professional foetal
dopplers (for monitoring heart beats) including one specifically designed to be usable
in waterbirths. Mostly they supply hospitals and midwives, but they will sell direct.

2. COMMON PROBLEMS

Side effects of pregnancy may – *but by no means necessarily will* – include
nausea (morning sickness), depression, backache, varicose veins,
headaches, indigestion, constipation, haemorrhoids (piles) or rectal bleeding, vaginal infection (including thrush), vaginal discharge, cystitis, oedema
(puffiness caused by water retention), sore breasts, sleeplessness, dizziness and fainting (especially when hot), nosebleeds (or a blocked nose),
bleeding gums, changes in skin colour, finger pains, leg cramps, trem-
bling legs, changes to your eyes (which can make contact lenses
uncomfortable), high blood pressure and more. On top of all that you
may find yourself on a roller coaster of emotions.

Many of these problems are just due to the temporary changes that
occur during pregnancy. Others may be an indication of something more
problematic, and require medical attention. Consult your doctor if any
of the symptoms listed above is particularly persistent, or increasingly
painful – for example, severe oedema (swelling) of the extremities or face,
or painful varicose veins. If you notice vaginal spotting (or changes to
vaginal discharge) call your doctor or midwife for a check-up.

FREE TREATMENTS
All NHS prescriptions are free during pregnancy and for 12 months after
the birth (see chapter *1.05 Rights*). You should check that anything prescribed to you or bought over the counter is safe in pregnancy, as doctors
and pharmacists sometimes forget to bear this issue in mind.

You are also allowed free dental treatment. (You must tell the dentist that you are pregnant so that you are not given an x-ray.)

USEFUL CONTACTS
Piles Advisory Bureau (PAB)
☎ *Helpline (020) 7617 0818* ⏱ *www.pilesadvice.co.uk*
Information funded by the manufacturers of the Anusol treatment – check out the
website or send of for a leaflet on how to prevent and treat piles during pregnancy.

READING
Caring for Your Pelvic Floor (NCT; 2002; £2.50) – *One of a series of NCT brochures,
each of approximately 20 pages. / NCT Maternity Sales (0870) 112 1120; www.nctms.co.uk.*

Avoid stress
Throughout pregnancy get plenty of sleep. If, after the birth, your child
does not sleep for significant periods at night you will need resources to
draw on.

If you decide to move house – and an estimated 40% of couples do
so during pregnancy or within six weeks of the birth – the earlier you can

manage this the better. The same goes for any building work you do on existing property.

You may also be planning to give up work – another potential stress factor. The more you can avoid combining different pressures the better. Severe stress can affect your health. Research published in 2003 confirmed that discontent at work is more likely to lead to premature birth, inter-fere with the baby's nutrition before birth; and lead to a child prone to prolonged crying.

Physical stress in pregnancy:

First trimester: upper back problems can occur in part because of rapid increase in breast size.

Second trimester: the pelvic ligaments relax, and the ribs and diaphragm become stretched, which may cause aching in the lower back, sacroiliac pain, rib discomfort and heartburn.

Third trimester: postural change can cause coccyx discomfort, pubic pain, hip restriction, sciatica, constipation, headaches, fluid retention, and carpel tunnel syndrome (a type of Repetitive Strain Injury).

Nausea (morning sickness)

Some 65%–90% of pregnant women in the UK suffer from nausea and vomiting in the first seven to 12 weeks of pregnancy with 9% experienc-ing continuing symptoms thereafter.

Commonly called 'morning' sickness, the nausea may appear at any or all times of the day. This should ease by the end of the third month, although certain smells or foods may still affect women right through pregnancy (and a few women find that nausea lasts for the full nine months).

Interestingly nausea is apparently rare in the Third World and a study of 500 women in Toronto reported in 2003 that often the cause is psy-chological rather than physical with a very weak correlation between women's perception of the problem and their actual symptoms.

Conventional medicine has little to offer by way of relief, but com-plementary treatments for nausea include reflexology, homeopathy, acupuncture and nutritional programmes. Mild herbal remedies, such as ginger in various forms, and acupressure wristbands (such as those designed for seasickness) were found effective in studies in Belfast and Italy (see chapter *4.02 Complementary medicine & Health practitioners*). Rest (especially in the mornings, before rising), smaller and more frequent meals, and snacks approximately every two hours can help – especially plain, high carbohydrate foods like crackers, or more nutritionally use-fully, something like bananas.

If you are unable to keep any foods or fluids down, you may become dehydrated, and should consult your doctor or midwife. Hyperemesis gravidum – excessive nausea and vomiting in pregnancy, which can lead to malnourishment and dehydration – is thought to occur in about three in 1000 pregnancies. The condition can be treated – Patrick Holford of the Institute of Optimum Nutrition believes that by ensuring sufficient intake of B6, B12, folic acid, iron and zinc, even the worst cases can be alleviated.

USEFUL CONTACTS

Blooming Awful, ☎ *(07020) 969728, Helpline (07050) 655094*
🖰 *www.hyperemesis.org.uk*
A UK volunteer-run organisation for sufferers of hyperemesis gravidum (Hg).
Self-help information, details on prescription drugs offered to HG sufferers and
a helpline is provided.

Daval, ☎ *(01264) 364474* 🖰 *www.travelwell.co.uk*
Stocks a tape ('TravelWell') developed at curing motion sickness when travelling,
but which it is also claimed eases morning sickness; costs £10; part of the 'Daval
programme' – a "revolutionary discovery". / HOURS *Mon-Fri 9.30am-5.30pm.*

Morning Well, ☎ *Spain +34 965 406 112, or NCT Maternity Sales (0870) 112
1120, Life Long Products (0800) 458 1771* 🖰 *www.MorningWell.co.uk*
Sold through NCT Maternity Sales and other outlets, an audio programme of
a single cassette of music, frequencies and pulses reported to cure pregnancy nausea
with a 90% success rate in NHS trials and at the Andover Birth centre, reducing or
clearing symptoms within two days. The theory is that the sounds draw the attention
of the vestibular system away from its balancing and acoustic duties. Once focused
on the programme it cannot then send the signals that cause morning sickness
between the brain and the gut. It can apparently be used while going about your
normal activities.

READING

Morning Sickness – Nicky Wesson (Vermilion; 1997; £6.99; 009181538X) – *Facts, case
histories and possible causes: simple remedies, dietary suggestions, medical treatments
and alternative therapies.*

Protecting Your Baby-to-Be – Margie Profet (Preventing birth defects in the first
three months of pregnancy; Time Warner; 1997; £7.99; 0-7515-1848-4) – *By
a biologist, a guide arguing that pregnancy sickness actually has a role, defending the
embryo from toxins which could cause birth defects. The book advises on foods which
may harm, and those which may help.*

Depression

(For sources of help in combating depression, see chapter 2.01 Postnatal).

Though more usually identified as a problem postnatally, some sources
estimate that as many as two fifths of postnatal depression sufferers may
also be depressed during pregnancy.

It can come as a shock to find that this state of being pregnant – often
something that's been longed for and planned for – can create such feelings. It's actually very common.

If you feel that this describes how you feel, consider seeking help
sooner rather than later. This is not only for your own sake – some experts
believe that a depressed mother can affect her child's development.

Back problems

The mother's posture changes as the baby grows. The extra weight of
the baby throwing the centre of gravity forward, the increasing curvature of the lower spine, the stretching of the abdominal muscles (which
usually help maintain posture) and the softening of the ligaments all make
back problems more likely. Around half – by some estimates as many as
85% – of pregnant women experience back problems at some stage.
Getting on for one third of women still complain of backache three
months after birth.

Corsets are not generally considered a good idea. To work they have
to be tight and that is likely to affect the baby. Lying down, often suggested to help with back problems, is not recommended in pregnancy
because of the way the weight of the baby may affect major blood vessels.

A pelvic tilting exercise can help (see chapter *1.04 Antenatal classes*), as can the knowledge that backache is often caused by weak stomach muscles: simply pulling your stomach in when standing can alleviate pain.

If you are still having problems, consider a visit to a physiotherapist, an Alexander Technique teacher, or an osteopath or cranial osteopath (see chapter *4.02 Complementary medicine & Health practitioners*). All of the above, or a fitness or yoga teacher can also give you advice on less painful positions for sitting, getting up from a lying position and getting out of a car. Back in Action (see listings) offers an hour-long session in ways to move and sit which will place the least strain on the body frame.

PREVENTION IS BETTER THAN CURE

To help prevent back problems in the first place, an upright or even for-ward-leaning posture in the mother is important, when sitting as well as standing. Such a posture also tends to encourage the baby to settle into the easiest position for birth.

Leaning back, on the other hand, tends to encourage a baby to lie back-to-back with the mother's spine. This 'posterior' position often leads to a prolonged and more painful labour. To avoid the temptation of slouching on the sofa when watching television you could, for example, invest in a couple of large cushions or a beanbag, and train yourself to sit leaning forwards over them.

Further advice includes: avoid sitting with your legs crossed; avoid twisting movements; lie on your side in bed; if you lie on your back, place pillows beneath your knees to keep them bent; and if you are standing for any length of time, keep your bottom tucked in to reduce the curvature of the lower spine, and to prevent the weight of the baby being thrown on to your abdominal wall.

You might like to consider investing in a good, hard bed. Alternatively, move your mattress onto the floor, or put a board under the mattress. If you work at a desk you might also like to consider buying a serious orthopaedic chair (see listings).

USEFUL CONTACTS

(For information on osteopaths, cranial osteopaths and Alexander Technique teachers, see chapter 4.02 Complementary medicine & Health practitioners.)

Association of Chartered Physiotherapists in Women's Health, ☎ *(020) 7242 1941* ⌂ *www.acpwh.org.uk*

Useful publications which can be ordered via website. / PUBLICATIONS *bi-annual journal – back issues with articles on preganancy-related issues can be purchased.*

BackCare (The National Organisation for Healthy Backs),
☎ *(020) 8977 5474* ⌂ *www.backcare.org.uk*

Charitable organisation (formerly known as the National Back Pain Association) with back pain prevention information for mothers and babies. / PUBLICATIONS *Back Care, Pregnancy & Children, £2; Basic Back Care, £2; Active Back Care, £4.95; Back to Bed, £2; Back in the Office, £2.*

Grobag, ☎ *(01548) 854 444* ⌂ *www.grobag.com*

Stockists of the Theraline Maternity and Nursing pillow, a V-shaped pillow suitable for support in pregnancy, and also a maternity support belt. / HOURS *Mon-Fri 9am-7pm, Sat 10am-1pm.*

Organisation of Chartered Physiotherapists in Private Practice (OCPPP), ☎ *(01327) 354441* ⌂ *www.physiofirst.org.uk*

An 'occupational group' of the Chartered Society of Physiotherapists, which exists – amongst other things – to set standards for its members and to promote them to the public. The website has a 'Find a physio' database of their members which can be searched by location and speciality.

USEFUL PRODUCTS

CENTRAL

Back 2 ⌂
28 Wigmore St W1H 9DF ☎ (0800) 374604, (020) 7935 0351 ⌁ www.back2.co.uk
Specialist retailers with a range of useful equipment for preventing back problems;
cushions to support your belly while you sleep; seat wedges to help your posture;
the Balans range of kneeling chairs which help you adopt an open, upright posture –
making breathing easier and opening the hips to make more space for a growing
belly; and reclining chairs – recommended for putting your feet up if you are
suffering from swollen feet and legs. / HOURS *Mon-Fri 9am-5.30pm, Sat 10am-6pm, Sun noon-
5pm; SEE ALSO 2.02 Feeding; 3.02 Baby equipment.*

Back in Action
11 Whitcomb St WC2H 7HA ☎ (020) 7930 8309 ⌁ www.backinaction.co.uk
The stores sell office chairs which help pregnant women sit more naturally and avoid
stretching ligaments in the spine. Relaxation chairs suitable before and after the birth,
and for nursing, are also stocked. / HOURS *Mon-Fri 9.30am-5pm; SEE ALSO 3.02 Baby equipment.*

The Back Shop ⌂
14 New Cavendish St W1G 8UW ☎ (020) 7935 9120 ⌁ www.thebackshop.co.uk
Sells back supports (some with a carrying handle for portability) for use in standard
seats to encourage an upright posture. Prices start at £16.50 up to £60+. Also
stockists of Balans chairs. / HOURS *Mon-Fri 10am-5.30pm, Sat 10.30am-5pm; SEE ALSO 3.02 Baby
equipment.*

WEST

The Back Store ⌂
330 King St W6 0RR ☎ (020) 8741 5022 ⌁ www.thebackstore.co.uk
Stockists of a supportive belt, recommended by some obstetric physiotherapists,
which is made of canvas with rigid cotton web straps and an elastic panel to go under
the belly. The idea is to support the sacroiliac joint at the base of the spine. Also
stocks lumbar support cushions. / HOURS *Mon-Fri 9am-5pm, Sat 10am-4pm; SEE ALSO 3.02 Baby
equipment; 3.03 Nursery decor.*

OUTSIDE LONDON

Bettacare ⌂
*Bettacare House, 9-10 Faygate Business Centre, Faygate West Sussex RH12 4DN
☎ (01293) 851896 ⌁ www.bettacare.co.uk*
This nursery equipment company produces a wedge-shaped 'comfy sleep cushion'
for pregnant women, designed to take the weight off the stomach and relieve
backache in bed. / HOURS *Mon-Fri 8.30am-5pm; SEE ALSO 3.02 Baby equipment.*

Bellybra
A product (distributed in the UK by Grobag, see Useful Contacts opposite) looking
something like a Lycra vest for pregnancy, and designed to alleviate backache and
pelvis pain with a one-way stretch back panel to gently pull the wearer's shoulders
back, while a two-inch elastic bellyband lifts weight from the pelvis.

Varicose veins
Pregnant women are susceptible to the swelling of veins, especially in the
legs which is caused by a combination of increased blood supply and the
relaxation of veins caused by hormonal changes.

Walking helps with the problem because the pumping of the muscles keeps the blood circulating. Standing has the opposite effect, so should
be avoided for more than a few minutes at a time.

Tips for alleviating varicose veins:
➢ Support stockings (see chapter *3.01 Maternity wear*).
➢ Aquanatal classes (see chapter *1.04 Antenatal classes*), which offer exer-
cise, as well as the beneficial effect of the water pressure on your body.
➢ Resting with your feet above your head (bearing in mind the points
on posture above).

➤ Aromatherapy, but as prevention rather than cure – so start early (see chapter *4.02 Complementary medicine & Health practitioners*).

➤ Avoid – as much as possible – sitting in the ordinary way (on a chair with your feet a lot lower than your hips). Sit on the floor, with your back well supported, so your feet and hips are on the same level and loosen your ankles by drawing circles with your toes (also improving blood circulation).

Teeth and gums

Bleeding gums in particular can be a problem in pregnancy, necessitating greater care than usual. Free NHS dental treatment is available because of this. A water jet (stocked in bigger chemists) is particularly useful for keeping the gum line clean.

3. DIET

(For information about nutritionists, see chapter 4.02 Complementary medicine & Health practitioners.)

A growing number of studies indicate that eating well in pregnancy promotes the baby's health – not just in childhood, but throughout life. Low birthweight babies are statistically more likely to suffer problems such as diabetes and cardiovascular disease. Extra heavy babies are also at greater risk of certain problem conditions.

A reasonable diet is also important for your own health: as your digestive system gives the baby first option on all nutrients: your body will only get the leftovers. You don't need to consume much more food than usual in pregnancy (an estimated 500 extra calories per day, with probably no more than 6g more protein). What is important is to eat well.

It appears there are vast differences in individual requirements for nutrients. Few GPs receive training in nutrition, and if this subject is important to you, you may wish to seek expert help (see Nutrition in chapter *4.02 Complementary medicine & Health practitioners*).

OBESITY

If you suffer from being seriously overweight, then you need to take more care of yourself throughout pregnancy and the postnatal period than someone of slighter build. This is due to the slight risk of a potentially fatal thromboembolism.

A key recommendation of the December 2001 report from The Confidential Enquiries into Maternal Deaths in the United Kingdom was that antenatal carers pay more attention to this risk. Those with a body mass index (BMI), of over 30 kg/m² are of particular concern.

If this sounds like it might apply to you, then you should ask for advice from your carers, and keep as active as possible.

HYPERACTIVITY

(For further information on hyperactivity, see chapter 2.03 Baby health.)

The Hyperactive Children's Support Group reports that 70% of hyperactive children are hyperactive before birth (kicking violently in the womb, for example). The root cause of the condition may be an allergy to some of the foods the mother eats during pregnancy. Some experts suspect that residual pesticides in food may also be a contributory factor.

USEFUL CONTACTS

Department of Health, ☎ (0800) 555777 🖰 www.doh.gov.uk

Free brochures (allow two to four weeks for delivery) – available from many antenatal clinics. / PUBLICATIONS *Women and Health – free, Weaning your Baby, Feeding your child from 1-3 years; also many on breast feeding.*

The Food Commission, ☎ (020) 7837 2250 🖰 www.foodcomm.org.uk; www.parentsjury.org.uk

Although unable to handle personal queries, The Food Commission can provide general information on food safety. Those interested can subscribe to their quarterly magazine which provides plenty of warnings against undue faith in mass produced food. / HOURS Mon-Fri 9.30am-5.30pm; PUBLICATIONS *The Food Magazine (1 year subscription, £22).*

The Food Standards Agency, ☎ (0845) 606 0667

🖰 www.foodstandards.gov.uk/
The government agency responsible for monitoring food safety and standards produces a number of publications of potential interest in pregnancy, including Inherent Natural Toxicants in Our Food (which highlights potential hazards such as uncooked kidney beans, mouldy dough and green potatoes)paper no. 51, £14.99 and Healthy Eating. / HOURS Helpline 9am-5pm.

Health Development Agency, ☎ (0870) 121 4194

🖰 www.hda-online.org.uk
Formerly called the Health Education Authority, this agency runs health education campaigns on behalf of the government. It produces a large range (66-page catalogue) of books and leaflets. Many of the latter are free from GPs and antenatal clinics, but there is a small charge (often under £1, although up to 30 are free) if ordered direct; see the website for details. All first-time mothers are entitled to a free copy of The New Pregnancy Book and (after the birth) The New Birth to Five Book, published by the HEA; ask your midwife if you do not receive them. / PUBLICATIONS *Numerous leaflets ad publications concerning pregnancy, children, breast feeding etc.*

Penrhos Court, ☎ (01544) 230720 🖰 www.greencuisine.org

An attractive hotel in Herefordshire specialising in organic food and offering courses on cooking and nutrition in pregnancy (and for babies); the courses do not cover any meat cooking; also individual training; partner participation encouraged; also yoga and if there are babies as well, baby massage; two days with full board £200.

Primal Health Research Centre, ☎ (020) 7485 0095

🖰 www.birthworks.org/primalhealth
Founded by water birth specialist Dr Michel Odent, the centre co-ordinates research into the development of the foetus and related implications for adult life. For example, there is a range of illnesses and conditions which appear to have a connection with drugs taken during labour. Membership (£12 a year) includes a newsletter.

Sainsbury's/Wellbeing Eating for Pregnancy Helpline,

☎ (0845) 130 3646 🖰 www.shef.ac.uk/pregnancy-nutrition
With its database on Nutritional Interventions in Pregnancy, the helpline (run by Wellbeing – the charitable arm of the Royal College of Gynaecologists and Obstetricians) has access to the latest research on food safety relating to factors such as toxoplasmosis, alcohol, herbal teas, eggs, folic acid, fish and shellfish, and can give advice on all aspects of nutrition, diet and food safety pre-conception and during pregnancy. / HOURS 10am-4pm; PUBLICATIONS *Healthy Eating Before, During and After Pregnancy.*

The Vegan Society, ☎ (01424) 427393 🖰 www.vegansociety.com

The society can advise on a vegan diet during pregnancy and thereafter, for both mother and baby. / PUBLICATIONS *'A Practical Guide to Veganism During Pregnancy & Throughout Childhood', £1.50; 'Pregnancy, Children & the Vegan Diet' by Dr Michael Kalper, £7.95.*

The Vegetarian Society, ☎ (0161) 928 0793 🖰 www.vegsoc.org

An information officer can help with advice on vegetarian diets when pregnant.

Wellbeing, ☎ (020) 7262 5337 🖰 www.wellbeing.org.uk

The charitable arm of the Royal College of Obstetricians and Gynaecologists primarily provides a sponsored helpline for pregnant women (the Sainsbury's/Wellbeing Eating for Pregnancy Helpline – see above). The organisation itself does not run any form of helpline, but does offer a few interesting fact sheets. / HOURS helpline 9.30am-4pm.

Dietary pointers

As with all dietary advice, pointers for pregnancy seem to change every year, and to include wildly contradictory exhortations.

The basic aim is to avoid anything which could poison the baby or trigger a miscarriage – either because of the nature of the ingredients or because food has a tendency to go off.

The standard advice about good diet obviously applies – that you should eat a variety of foods, preferably wholesome and fresh, high on fruit and vegetables (five portions a day, each portion a fistful as measured by the eater or 80g, equivalent to a medium apple or three tablespoons of peas), plus complex carbohydrates (bread, pasta, potatoes, rice) and cutting down on highly processed and sugary foods, which contain fewer nutrients.

If you read enough on the subject, it can seem as though practically all foods are to be avoided. For the record (while noting the need for the use of common sense), the following are current areas of concern and common advice:

Alcohol: The Royal College of Obstetricians and Gynaecologists does not particularly encourage complete abstinence, but advises a limit of one glass of wine or equivalent per day, see also Section 4, Clean living, below.

Poultry and meat: should be cooked thoroughly until the juices run clear. Raw meat or fish should be avoided entirely – raw meat may carry toxoplasma, for example (see chapter *1.03 Tests*). According to government estimates, one in three chickens carries salmonella and a report in 2001 found one in two contaminated with campylobacter – a cause of food poisoning. Avoid cross-contamination between cooked and raw meats.

Liver: should be avoided as it is high in vitamin A, which can be toxic in large quantities. Also, a concern is raised by European studies (see Joanna Blythman's *The Food We Eat*, in chapter *2.02 Feeding*) that eating liver is three times more likely to pass on residues of drugs than eating muscle meat, as it is the part of the body which breaks down toxins.

Soft, ripened and blue veined cheeses: should be avoided because of the danger of listeria. Unpasteurised goat's cheese also carries the risk of toxoplasma.

Unpasteurised dairy products: raw milk (from cows, sheep or goats) may contain bacteria and other harmful organisms.

Food poisoning: eat cooked food within 48 hours; avoid all except the freshest deli foods; avoid all pâtés – including fish and vegetable ones – unless shrink-wrapped and marked pasteurised; avoid cooked chilled chicken; heat pre-prepared meals thoroughly; avoid shellfish unless thoroughly cooked. Even pre-washed salad and vending-whipped ice cream are thought to carry the risk of listeria.

Nuts: it is best to avoid them if there is any nut allergy in the family. A Department of Health 1998 report on Toxicity of Chemicals in Food advises pregnant and breast-feeding women to avoid peanuts (and products containing peanuts) if they, their partner or children have other allergic conditions such as asthma, eczema and hay fever. The aim is to reduce the likelihood of the child developing an allergy.

Egg dishes: in recent years, advice has been that eggs should be cooked right through because of the danger of salmonella, and to avoid dishes with raw eggs like mayonnaise and mousses. However, according to the British Egg Information Service, the Lion Quality scheme introduced in 1998 means that most UK eggs are from hens vaccinated against salmonella, virtually eliminating it from UK eggs.

Caffeine: is considered acceptable in limited quantities, but best avoided if only because it aggravates a bladder already under pressure. As a diuretic it may also wash calcium as well as fluid out of the body and can interfere with iron absorption. Five to eight cups of coffee a day has been associated with heart rhythm irregularities in newborns, and in the BMJ it was reported that four to seven cups a day increases the chance of stillbirth. On the other hand, up to three cups a day was apparently associated with a lower risk of stillbirth, compared to drinking no coffee at all. Three cups of fresh or instant coffee are calculated as equivalent to six cups of cocoa, hot chocolate or medium strength tea, or 9 cups of cola. Tentative links have been made between caffeine consumption and cot death but nothing conclusive has been established. Another reason for avoiding caffeine, particularly near the date of birth, is the belief that it can make the baby hyperactive. Tea and coffee can also stimulate acid production so avoid them before sleeping if you are suffering from heartburn.

Oily fish: A Danish study published in 2002 indicated that consumption of fish in early pregnancy may help combat premature birth. The Omega 3 and Omega 6 fatty acids found in oily fish in particular (mackerel, herring, salmon etc) are important for a baby's development both before and after birth (and – if part of the mother's diet – are found in breast milk). Supplements may sometimes be suggested as an alternative particularly in view of the point below.

Large oily fish: those like swordfish, shark and marlin should be avoided because, although good for you, it has been discovered that they contain worrying levels of mercury – an extremely toxic element which can damage an unborn baby's brain and nervous system (though some research questions whether the mercury is actually absorbed by the foetus). In 2003 the Food Standards Agency advised avoiding these three fish entirely in pregnancy, and eating no more than one tuna steak, or two tins of tuna once a week.

Water and naturally high-fibre foods: are recommended to help avoid constipation that can occur as pregnancy hormones relax muscles, including those of the intestine. However, high added-fibre (as found in certain breakfast cereals) is not recommended as it can leach desirable nutrients.

Citrus fruit: is considered desirable for vitamin C

Certain herbal formulations and aromatherapy treatments: herbalists advise against the use of various herbs during pregnancy, usually due to risk of miscarriage. Note that the quantities typically found in normal food dishes are not of concern, but their concentrated use is. Substances on the 'hitlist' include quinine (found in tonic water), sage, thyme, rosemary, saffron and rhubarb.

Additives: some additives are believed to be related to problems in pregnancy. E154 for example (used to stain kippers), is thought to be related to genetic mutations. Others, including E924, E925, E926 and E927, are believed to reduce the amount of vitamin E (an antioxidant thought to guard against congenital defects) available to the body. Avoidance of nitrates (E251, E252), used to cure meats, is also recommended by some (if only because of a link with cancer). The pink dye used to colour some farmed salmon is a vitamin A derivative (see comments under Liver), so also best avoided.

Aluminium: a metal linked with neural degeneration. Some experts, including Foresight, recommend not cooking in aluminium pans or using foil, and avoiding powdered milk and fruit juice in cartons lined with aluminium foil. Additives to avoid because of aluminium include E556, E173 and E554. Antacids without aluminium can be taken if required to treat indigestion.

Man-made fats (e.g. processed oils and margarine): Michel Odent, the well known childbirth consultant, suggests that one of the reasons for the low rate of medical intervention in Japan may be to do with diet – particularly the low levels of synthetic fats. He believes they act as blocking agents in certain processes that regulate a natural birth.

Salt: because of the greater volume of blood in your system you may need more salt than usual. However, if your blood pressure rises you may be advised to cut down.

READING

Eat Right 4 Your Baby – Dr Peter J D'Adamo with Catherine Whitney (The individualized guide to fertility and maximum health during pregnancy, nursing and your baby's first year; Michael Joseph/Penguin; 2003; £17.99; 0718146271) – *D'Adamo, an American naturopath, has had success with this slightly controversial book, which advocates different diets, depending on the eater's blood type. The concept is extended to cover the requirements a mother's requirements both before and after the birth, as well as to the baby's. / www.penguin.co.uk.*

Eating for Two – Amanda Grant (The complete guide to a healthy diet before, during and after pregnancy; Mitchell Beazley; 2001; £10.99; 1840004282) – *Nutrients you need: how much, why and where you find them, plus foods to avoid. Includes 40 recipes.*

The Farmer and the Obstetrician – Michel Odent (Free Association Books; 2002; £13.95; 1853435651) – *A collation of evidence from the Primal Health Research databank about the effect of chemicals such as PCBs, dioxins, non-ionic detergents and the like on the health of children. Odent argues that exposure to pollution in the womb has consequences which may last for generations.*

Food for Life – Maternity Alliance (A woman's guide to food and diet before, during and after pregnancy; Health Development Agency; 1996; £2.99; 0946741255) / The Maternity Alliance.

Good Food for Mums – Sara Lewis (Recipes and advice for pre-conception, pregnancy and new mums, in association with Practical Parenting; Hamlyn; 2003; £14.99; 0600604160) – *A guide explaining why you need certain foods and nutrients in pregnancy and when breastfeeding.It helps you work out a healthy eating plan and includes some easy-to-prepare recipes. / www.hamlyn.co.uk.*

Health Defence – Dr Paul Clayton (How you can combine the most protective nutrients from the world's healthiest diets to slow ageing and achieve optimum health.; Accelerated Learning Systems; £12.99) – *Originally intended as a text on pharmaco-nutrition (the science behind nutritional recommendations) for use in courses attended by GPs – its straightforward English has allowed it to find a wider audience. It includes material on brain development in infants and the make up of a healthy pregnancy. Purchasers receive a free 'cook book' showing how to mix and match foods to achieve specific health benefits, and suggestions of web-sites providing additional information. / (Freepost Aylesbury HP22 4BR £1 p&p).*

Healthy Eating for Pregnancy – Wendy Doyle (Teach Yourself; 1996; £5.99; 0340679123) – *A senior research dietician at the Institute of Brain Chemistry and Human Nutrition, gives sensible tips and useful checklists for a healthy diet with information on food safety, and general health checks. Also, how to assess your diet, change your eating habits, and improve your lifestyle.*

Healthy Eating for Pregnancy – Amanda Grant (Mitchell Beazley; 2003; £10.99; 1840007397) – *Includes more than 60 quick, easy and delicious breakfast, lunch supper and snack recipes, structured to provide the nutrients needed during pregnancy.*

Healthy Parents, Healthy Baby – Maryon Stewart (Headline; 1995; £10.99; 0-747278-41-5) – *By one of the UK's leading experts on women's nutrition. / www.thinknatural.com.*

The Oliver family book – Jules Oliver (Penguin; 2004) – *It may be impossible to miss this work, untitled as we go to press, by Jamie Oliver's missus. It is to cover pregnancy and motherhood, with particular emphasis on diet in pregnancy, with recipes for mother and child by the chef.*

Planning for a Healthy Baby – Belinda Barnes (Vermilion; 1994; £8.99; 0091790298) – *Guidelines from the Association for Preconceptual Care (Foresight).*

Practical Parenting - Healthy Pregnancy – Gill Thorn (A practical guide to diet, exercise and relaxation; Hamlyn; 2003; £5.99; 060060666X) – *Advice on what to eat, how to avoid excess weight gain, giving up bad habits, gentle exercises and positions for birth. / www.hamlyn.co.uk.*

Protecting Your Baby-To-Be – Margie Profet (Time Warner; 1997; £7.99; 0751518484) – *Award-winning US biologist covers the first three months of pregnancy: for example, how nausea may play a role in shielding the embryo from potentially harmful toxins.*

Safe Foods – Hannah Hulme Hunter & Rosemary Dodds (What to eat and drink in pregnancy; NCT/Thorsons Books; 1998; £5.99 (order 0870 900 2050); 0-722536-07-0) – *A guide to food and supplements for pre-conception, during pregnancy and while breast-feeding, including how to deal with ailments such as morning sickness and heartburn.*

Weight Management and Fitness Through Childbirth – Theresa Francis-Cheung (Hodder Help Yourself; 2001; £6.99; 0-340-75693-4) – *The book you need if you fear becoming a mummy blob. It contains lots of detailed information about how much weight you need to gain, food guidelines, and weight loss after birth. The good news is that for the six months after birth a woman's body is physiologically designed to lose any weight gained: this is much easier if you do not gain more than the recommended amount in pregnancy. / www.help-yourself.co.uk.*

While you are Pregnant – Food Standards Agency (How to avoid infection from food and from contact with animals; Food Standards Agency; 1996; free) – *A useful booklet with advice on the possible sources of infection during pregnancy. / Food Standards Agency (0845) 606 0667.*

Dietary supplements

Too many supplements – even of vitamins like D as well as the more toxic vitamin A – can harm a foetus. Indeed, in 2003 The Food Standards Agency published a report with warnings about over-supplementation. However, some specialists feel that many of the warnings were unduly cautious and out of step with research in the field.

Vitamin and mineral levels in our food have – apparently – more than halved over the last 60 years. If so, supplementation is probably useful for everyone and particularly in pregnancy.

Note that not all supplements are of equal quality. Current thinking is that supplements should be 'food state' – i.e. as close as possible to their condition in food – or they will not be properly absorbed. Chelation, for example, is a system of binding a substance to something else, say an amino acid, to make it more easily absorbed by the body. Nutritionists have their own favourites, but, in general, expert advice is to avoid own-brand and low-priced products. (For more information and details of nutritionists, see Nutrition in chapter *4.02 Complementary medicine & Health practitioners*).

Some products may cause nausea, in which case you should seek an alternative. You may wish to discuss any supplements you take – including how you combine them – with a nutritionist, or one of your antenatal carers.

SUPPLEMENTS TO COMBAT ANAEMIA

About a fifth of mothers become iron deficient in pregnancy, and many pregnant women take iron supplements to help avoid the condition.

Where the mother is concerned, anaemia is thought to lead to less efficient and more painful contractions during labour, and greater vulnerability to infection after the birth. For the baby, the lower levels of oxygen in the mother's blood that the condition causes are thought to result in slow growth and, perhaps, premature labour.

Anaemia can be difficult to diagnose – the symptoms are those of pregnancy in general: dizziness; tiredness; shortness of breath or a sore tongue. The diagnostic blood test can be open to interpretation.

Though a widespread practice, the advisability of taking iron supplements in the absence of any firm indication that you are anaemic is questioned by some commentators. They believe that the iron used by the baby is often comparable to the amount that the mother lost previously during menstruation – at least for the first part of pregnancy. Later in pregnancy, it seems that the mother's body compensates and is better able to absorb iron.

Artificially raising iron levels may have side effects of diarrhoea, or more often constipation (black stools as the body excretes iron rather than absorbs it) and nausea.

Ask a practitioner you trust what they recommend and beware of taking iron supplements in the first three months of pregnancy. Foods with high iron contents are listed below.

Commonly used supplements:

Folic acid: if taken before conceiving (ideally from when you stop using contraception) and for the first 12 weeks of pregnancy, folic acid is widely believed to help avoid spina bifida and other neural tube defects (NTDs) in the baby. More recent research in Sweden also indicated that women with higher levels of folate were less likely to miscarry.

Iron: see Anaemia above. Iron is available either over the counter or from your GP, who may also prescribe Floradix (see below). Rather than take supplements you might like to eat foods which are high in iron, for example, red meat, wheat germ, watercress, parsley, dark green vegetables, dried apricots and nuts. Bran, tea and coffee are believed to inhibit iron absorption. Floradix, available in liquid or tablet form, is sometimes recommended as it contains iron along with yeast, vitamins and herb extracts from vegetable sources. However, it is not recommended for sufferers of thrush and candida, who might like to try Spirulina (powdered seaweed – not particularly palatable) or chelated iron. Alternatively Spatone Iron+ is fortified drinking water which may be more palatable, and is reputed to allow excess iron to be easily excreted.

Calcium: is considered useful not just for the baby's healthy growth but also to prevent osteoporosis and possibly also pre-eclampsia. Although milk and dairy products are often recommended, calcium is also found in canned fish with bones, sesame seeds, molasses, dried figs, spring greens, kale, broccoli, dried beans, almonds and peanuts. Complementary practitioners, though, are dubious about absorption of calcium from the standard recommended foods, particularly dairy products. Instead they may recommend a herbal product.

Zinc: Emeritus Professor of Chemistry, Derek Bryce Smith, has made a particular study of nutrition and foetal development. His findings indicate that zinc is of great importance to the development of a healthy baby, while the famous obstetrician Michel Odent notes that its absence is related to the development of schizophrenia and non-insulin-dependent diabetes. It is generally believed to be best to take zinc separately from folic acid, and iron supplements in particular, as these interfere with zinc's absorption. Some people argue precisely the opposite.

Multi-vitamins and minerals: can help with specific pregnancy problems, such as cramps and nausea, but you should consult a specialist practitioner rather than adopting a scattergun approach, or at least take only a product specifically designed for use antenatally as this will ensure useful levels of elements like folic acid and absence of anything potentially dangerous like high levels of vitamin A. Look particularly for vitamin C, as research in the US indicated that it reduces the risk of premature birth, and it is also considered helpful in preventing hemorrhage in the baby and bleeding gums in the mother. As Vitamin C cannot be stored it needs to be taken daily. Low iodine levels have been implicated in cot death.

Essential Fatty Acids: increasingly understood to be vital for healthy development of the foetus.

USEFUL CONTACTS

Association for Spina Bifida & Hydrocephalus (ASBAH),
☎ *(020) 8441 9967, (020) 8449 0475* ⌁ *www.asbah.org*
/ HOURS *Mon-Fri 9am-5pm;* PUBLICATIONS *Information on vitamin supplementation to prevent these conditions.*

Foresight, The Association for the Promotion of Pre-Conceptual Care, ☎ *(01483) 427839* ⌁ *www.foresight-preconception.org.uk*
Charity aiming to combat a variety of conditions through promotion of better nutrition. It operates a comprehensive preconception programme (including hair mineral analysis and use of dietary supplements) which can be followed from conception to the conclusion of breast-feeding and which it believes can improve parental wellbeing and hence reduce incidences of infertility, miscarriage, premature birth and malformation. Written enquiries preferred. / PUBLICATIONS *Information on the testing and their book – SAE with 34p stamp; variety of books, leaflets and a video.*

Water

Drinking plenty of liquid will help your body eliminate waste effectively. This appears to be the case regardless of whether or not you have oedema (which is variously estimated to affect from one half to four fifths of pregnant women).

You can avoid possible toxins in tap water systems by drinking filtered water. However, filters may not remove dissolved solids, such as aluminium, lead, cadmium, iron, arsenic and nitrates. If used, a filter should be changed regularly to prevent bacteria building up inside the filter.

Bottled water can be a good solution, but you should choose your brand with care as there are differing types. Those labelled 'Table' water, for example, may have been processed in a similar manner to tap water. The best bets are generally those labelled Natural Mineral Water or Spring Water. Distilled water is quite a fashionable option, though the complete absence of minerals is not *per se* a good thing.

USEFUL CONTACTS

Culligan International (UK) Ltd, ☎ *(01484) 512537*
Water treatment specialists who produce various water filters, many of which can be installed under sinks. The company claims to offer improved filtration – removing pesticides, bacteria and aluminium. Call for your nearest stockist.

The Freshwater Company, ☎ *(08457) 023998*
⌁ *www.freshwateruk.com*
Supplier of both spring water and distilled water (available in both office coolers and ceramic pots for use in homes) which makes weekly deliveries in London. Both Chilternhurst spring water or distilled water (the trend in California, apparently) comes in 12 or 19 litre containers at £4/£6. Containers are recycled. / HOURS *24hr answerphone.*

Thames Water Utilities, ☎ *(0845) 920 0800* ⌁ *www.thameswater.com*
The company can provide a free water quality report for your local area – a March report covers the previous year, a September report covers the first six months of the year. It will also provides a free check for the quantity of lead in the water at properties built before 1970 which may have a lead connection pipe – the EC limit is 50ppm. (However, the company points out that as London is a hard water area, lead is unlikely to dissolve from the pipe into the water, because calcium deposited on the inner surface of the pipe creates an impermeable barrier).

The Wholistic Research Company, ☎ *(01438) 833100*
⌁ *www.wholisticresearch.com*
Stockists of – among other products – water distillers (more expensive than filters). / HOURS *Mon-Fri 9am-5pm.*

4. CLEAN LIVING

Alcohol

Many experts recommend giving up all but a minimum of alcohol in pregnancy. The Royal College of Obstetricians and Gynaecologists notes that there is "no conclusive evidence" of adverse effects on the foetus with consumption of up to 15 units of alcohol per week, but actually advises a limit of one unit per day (a unit is equivalent to a small glass of wine, or half a pint of beer). Binge drinking, even just once, is considered particularly harmful.

Some sources – particularly American ones, but including a few in the UK – reckon that all consumption should be avoided. One Washington study suggested that vulnerability to alcohol is greater in certain non-Caucasian ethnic groups.

Smoking

If you have not already done so, now is the time to give up smoking. It stops nutrients from getting to the baby, increases the risk both of miscarriage and of stillbirth or perinatal death by around 30%, and doubles the likelihood of a premature or low-birthweight baby.

Babies of smokers are considered four times more likely to suffer cot death than those of non-smokers and in total the NHS estimates that around 400 babies a year die because their mothers smoked during pregnancy. There may also be long-term effects on the child's learning skills.

Smoking usually makes pregnancy symptoms like nausea more unpleasant and longer lasting.

If you both smoke and drink to excess, some sources consider that your baby is five times more likely to be growth retarded.

Drugs – recreational and otherwise

Recreational drugs are almost universally advised against in pregnancy. Medical drugs are more of a grey area with different practitioners taking different standpoints. Naturally no drugs are tested on pregnant women unless specific to pregnancy, so knowledge of side-effects is limited. An example of potential side effects is research published in 2002, based on statistics from the 1990s, which indicated that taking antibiotics in pregnancy might be linked to asthma in children. However, if you have a chronic condition, doing without drugs entirely just may not be possible – for more information see the list of suggested reading.

It is advisable to avoid new medicines when pregnant and your GP should be aware that you are pregnant before issuing a repeat prescription. Skin creams with steroids are not advised, and neither are barbiturates, DES, ganglion-blocking agents, iodides and iodine, methotrexate, monoamine oxidase inhibitors, tetracyclines, oral hypoglycaemic agents and oral progestogens; similarly, live vaccines of rubella, smallpox, measles, polio and yellow fever. Aspirin is best avoided in the first three months.

READING

Alcohol & pregnancy (Midwives Information & Resource Service (MIDIRS); free) – *One of a series of leaflets available to download from the website.* / www.midirs.org.

Drugs in Conception, Pregnancy and Childbirth – Judy Priest & Kathy Attawell (HarperCollins; 1998; £9.99; 0722535945)

Miscarriage – Margaret Leroy (Macdonald Optima in co-operation with the Miscarriage Association; 1988; £5.99; 0-356128-88-1) – *Although potentially a worrying book, it is one of the best sources of information on hazards in pregnancy (with excellent sections on teratogens, and the effects of infections). Now out of print – you may be able to find a copy in the library or via Amazon's 'zShop' service for out of print titles.*

SUPPORT GROUPS

Alcohol Concern, ☎ (020) 7928 7377, Info Line 020 7922 8667
🖰 www.alcoholconcern.org.uk
Information service, with details of helplines. / HOURS *Mon-Fri 1pm-5pm Information Line;* PUBLICATIONS *'A Women's Guide to Alcohol' plus a factsheet on drinking during pregnancy, send SAE.*

Alcoholics Anonymous (AA), ☎ (01904) 644026, Helpline (0845) 767 7555 🖰 www.alcoholics-anonymous.org.uk
Anonymous self-help groups whose members help each other stay off alcohol through a total abstinence programme and shared experience. The only requirement for membership, which is free, is a desire to stop drinking. Each group is autonomous and self-supporting – call for details of your nearest meetings. / HOURS *Mon-Fri 9am-5pm (Fri 4.30pm);* PUBLICATIONS *Leaflets on the AA and giving up alcohol (send SAE).*

The Angel Drug Services, ☎ (020) 7833 9899, (0800) 169 2679
🖰 www.angeldrug.org.uk
Drop-in help centre in Islington for drug users, offering assessments.

Drinkline, ☎ (0800) 917 8282
Information and advice line for people with drink problems, their friends and partners. For a pregnant woman, they can inform of the dangers of drinking and could recommend a suitable agency for help. Outside normal hours there is a 24-hour dial-and-listen service. Languages spoken on their language line (you will be connected when you call the general number) – which also operates a dial-and-listen service out-of-hours – include Hindi, Urdu, Gujerati, and Punjabi. / HOURS *Tues-Thurs 9am-11pm, Weekends Fri 9am-Mon 11pm.*

Eating Disorders Association, ☎ Helpline (0845) 6341414, Under 18s Helpline (0845) 6347650, Admin (01603) 619090 🖰 www.edauk.com
For sufferers of bulimia and anorexia nervosa – a national charity which puts you in touch with local groups, and advises on help available in your area. Membership £25. / HOURS *Mon-Fri 8.30am-8.30pm, Sat 1pm-4pm, under 18s Mon-Fri 4pm-6.30pm, Sat 1pm-4.30pm;* PUBLICATIONS *Members' newsletter; free publications for non-members.*

Families Anonymous, ☎ (020) 7498 4680, Helpline (0845) 1200 660
🖰 www.famanon.org.uk
Non profit-making self-help organisation for the families and friends of drug users; provides access to relevant literature. / HOURS *office hours Mon-Fri 1pm-4pm;* PUBLICATIONS *Various publications, some available for free others up to £2.50 +15% P&P, available online.*

London Drug & Alcohol Network, ☎ (020) 7704 0004, Drinkline 0800 917 8282, 🖰 www.ldan.org.uk
Hold a list of 'projects' and can refer people to support and/or professional help in their local area. An online map is available through which you can find help in your local area.

Narcotics Anonymous, ☎ Helpline (020) 7730 0009, Office (020) 7251 4007 🖰 www.ukna.org
Helpline run by recovering addicts offering support in coming off and staying off drugs. Local meetings are free and anonymous, some with crèche facilities. Call the office to purchase a list. Details of London meetings on website or call helpline for info. / HOURS *Helpline Mon-Sun 10am-10pm.*

National Drugs Helpline (aka "Talk to Frank"),
☎ (0800) 776600 🖰 www.talktofrank.com
Confidential information 24-hours, with information on local sources of help. Some advice and counselling and if requested referral to one-to-one counselling or detox. Translators available in 120 languages. / PUBLICATIONS *Various leaflets.*

The Promis Counselling Centre, ☎ (020) 7581 8222, Crisis line (0800) 374318 🖰 www.promis.co.uk
A private centre (though it does take NHS referrals) based in South Kensington which can help with addictions of all kinds; also a recovery centre based in Kent. / HOURS *crisis line open 24hrs.*

Quit, ☎ *Smokers Quitline (0800) 002200, (020) 7487 3000* ⌁ *www.quit.org.uk*
Giving up smoking will help your baby, however late you leave it in pregnancy. This
organisation offers advice (for both parents) on how to give up; details of local
support services and a free QUIT pack for helpline, on which trained counsellors
advise and encourage. There is also a Helpline: 0800 169 9169. / PUBLICATIONS *Various
publications available, call for details.*

Release, ☎ *(020) 7729 5255* ⌁ *www.release.org.uk*
A national helpline organisation that provides advice on both prescribed and illicit
drugs. It has experience of advising those who are concerned about the possible
effects of drugs taken before they discovered that they are pregnant. / HOURS *Mon-Fri
10am-6pm.*

Specialist Smoking Cessation Service, ☎ *(01524) 845 145*
A free service for pregnant women and their partners.

5. POTENTIAL HAZARDS

In 2002 the Birth Defects Foundation reported an increase of birth defects
in the UK of up to 50% in the previous five years. While the causes of this
are unclear, it highlights the importance of avoiding as many potential
triggers as possible.

Toxins

There is strong scientific evidence that toxins encountered by the mother
prior to birth are likely to result in problems for an unborn child. Lead,
for example – which can leach into your water supply from old pipes – is
heavily implicated in increased miscarriage, congenital problems, prematurity, learning disabilities, hyperactivity and lower-than-average mental
skills. Pollution inhaled from diesel engines is linked to reduced head
growth in unborn children, kidney damage, and restricted sexual development. Exposure to PCBs before birth have been found to be associated
with lower IQ scores at the age of 11.

To date, there has been little research into the effect of agricultural
chemicals on a developing foetus, but there is a belief among some medics
that chemicals in food may be implicated in miscarriage. There is, however, no proof of this. One well-publicised concern is the residual level
of organophosphates in carrots. Although peeling, topping and tailing the
carrots may help, some of the chemicals used are believed to penetrate
the whole vegetable. Many expectant women and mothers prefer to buy
organic food as a result of such concerns (for suppliers, see chapter *2.02
Feeding*).

More recently there has been concern about mercury in fish (see
above) as mercury can cause cognitive and motor defects in the baby.

There has also be concern about drifting chemicals from crop spraying,
particularly organophosphates.

Some household products include strong chemicals and should certainly be used sparingly, and ideally not by you when pregnant. These
include: aerosols, solvents, pesticides and certain disinfectants (anything
with toxicity warnings), as well as products like oven cleaners or any substance with powerful fumes.

Even the chemicals in hair perms and dyes are considered best avoided
by a growing number of experts, particularly following revelations that
manufacturers did not always carry out complete safety tests on many
ingredients. Others give them the OK, but point out that you should tell
your haidresser that you are pregnant, because your abnormal hormone
levels may affect both how well the perm holds and any colouring. It may
be that vegetable-based colours are safer than chemical ones.

There is even growing concern about a wide range of chemicals found in bodycare products, including shampoo. For more details see chapter 3.09 *Lotions & Potions*.

Paints can also be a source of toxins. Latex paints are believed to contain unsafe levels of mercury for example, while older paints may contain lead. For safe options, see chapter *3.03 Nursery decor*. It is recommended that pregnant women stay well out of the way when paint is being removed because of the possibility of lead in old paint as well as the toxicity of chemical strippers.

The Wolrd Wildlife Fund together with the Women's Institute and Co-operative Bank launched a campaign in 2003 to increase awareness of chemicals in everyday life. It points out that flame retardants (poly brominated diphenyl ethers) have known links to hormonal and behavioural problems and apparently innocent activities like picking up dry cleaning similarly expose us to chemicals that have been similarly implicated.

The Department of Health has ruled that as a precaution, amalgam tooth fillings should not be disturbed in pregnancy, unless a filling is needed urgently – another reason why it is important to inform your dentist if you are pregnant.

Other less well defined concerns are over chlorine at high levels in swimming pools.

USEFUL CONTACTS

Biolab Medical Unit, ☎ *(020) 7636 5959/5905* ⌂ *www.biolab.co.uk*
With a GP or doctor referral only, you can get your body toxin levels checked using hair mineral analysis, £29. / HOURS *Mon-Fri 9am-5.30pm.*

Foresight, The Association for the Promotion of Pre-Conceptual Care, ☎ *(01483) 427839* ⌂ *www.foresight-preconception.org.uk*
Provide information on protecting against toxins with dietary supplements.

X-rays

X-rays particularly between 8 and 15 weeks after conception are believed to involve a risk of damage to the foetus's brain.

Radiation from VDUs, etc

(For more information on hazards at work see chapter 1.05 Rights.)
Along with concerns surrounding the emission of electromagnetic radiation from microwave ovens, mobile phones, electric blankets (a Yale study) and even fluorescent lighting, the effect of computer screens (VDUs) on pregnant women has been flagged by some people as a potentially serious health issue.

Under the Management Health & Safety Regulations, employers are under a duty to assess the risks to employees' health and safety. An amendment in 1994 means that a special assessment should be made of a pregnant woman's working environment. To date, studies of the potential hazard from VDUs have produced conflicting and inconclusive results. It has been suggested that the stress of computer work or poor posture when typing is where the dangers actually lie. The National Radiological Protection Board "does not consider such levels [of electromagnetic radiation generated by display screen equipment] to pose a significant risk to health."

If the radiation is a danger, it is more intense behind rather than in front of a terminal.

Display Screen Equipment Regulations, published by the Health & Safety Commission, suggests that after an hour's work you might take a five minute break. If you feel this is insufficient you could ask for a transfer to a job with no or less VDU work.

USEFUL CONTACTS

Coghill Research Laboratories, ☎ *(01495) 752 122*
🖰 *www.cogreslab.co.uk*
The 'Mouse' produced by this firm measures electric and magnetic fields from VDUs as well as from other electrical equipment and sources.

Electromagnetic Hazard & Therapy Advice Line, ☎ *Premium rate advice line (0906) 4010237 £1.50 per minute* 🖰 *www.em-hazard-therapy.com*
An organisation (linked with the director of Powerwatch, see also) that runs an advice line and produces quarterly reports on electromagnetic hazards (£27 per year); hires out field monitors (£30 per week) and RS meters (£35 per week). / HOURS *Mon-Fri 9am-5pm*.

Perspective Scientific, ☎ *(020) 7486 6837* 🖰 *www.perspective.co.uk*
Manufacturers of hand-held monitors which measure some forms of electromagnetic and ionising radiation, including the microwave emissions from, for example, mobile phones. Prices start at £125.

Powerwatch, ☎ *Premium rate advice line (0906) 4010237, Credit card payments for publications call (01353) 778814* 🖰 *www.powerwatch.org.uk*
A briefing organisation looking at the issues of electronic radiation, largely from AC electricity supplies, and the health effects sometimes associated, such as cot death, ME and leukaemia. Monitoring equipment is available for hire or sale. / PUBLICATIONS *Range of publications – SAE for list or see website.*

Baths & saunas

Ordinary baths are fine, but very hot baths, saunas and jacuzzis are not advised.

USEFUL CONTACTS

Ecozone, ☎ *(020) 8777 3121* 🖰 *www.ecozone.co.uk*
An online vendor of a selection of environmentally friendly cleaning products, low on hazardous chemicals.

Friends of the Earth, ☎ *Information service (0808) 800 1111, HQ (020) 7490 1555* 🖰 *www.foe.co.uk/safer_chemicals*
Campaigns of the prominent lobbyists include raising awareness of the risks posed by chemicals in everyday items from pesticides in fruit & veg to phthalates in plastics, cosmetics and toys. / PUBLICATIONS *Free parents' guide to Chemicals in the Home, produced in conjunction with the NCT.*

Health & Safety Executive, ☎ *Infoline (08701) 545500, Publications (01787) 881165* 🖰 *www.hse.gov.uk*
The organisation exists to advise employers of their responsibilities to their workforce under the law. They will provide pregnant women with information as to how the law stands, but not advice. / PUBLICATIONS *New and expectant mothers at work – a guide for employers (£9.50 + VAT); Infections in the work place for new and expectant mothers (£10.50); A guide for new & expectant mothers who work (free).*

London Hazards Centre, ☎ *(020) 7794 5999* 🖰 *www.lhc.org.uk*
Independent charity partially funded by association of London government to provide advice, information and training – mainly on occupational health and work hazards, but with some information relating to hazards in home and environmental hazards in the community. / HOURS *helpline 10am-noon & 2pm-5pm (except Wed); 24hr answerphone;* PUBLICATIONS *20 factsheets, some specifically relating to reproductive health and workplace safety, including one on VDUs.*

Pesticide Action Network UK (PEX Action on Pesticide Exposure), ☎ *(020) 7274 8895, (020) 7274 6611* 🖰 *www.pan-uk.org*
A non-profit action group working to eliminate the hazards of pesticides and promote sustainable alternatives with regular coverage of issues relating to pregnancy and babies in the organisation's journal. / PUBLICATIONS *Publishes Pesticide News covers pesticide problems and alternatives in the UK, European and worldwide (https://secure.virtuality.net/panukcom/subs.htm) £20 a year with three free issues for new subscribers. Also free on-line pesticide information update service.*

Royal College of Obstetricians & Gynaecologists, ☎ *Admin*
(020) 7772 6200, Bookshop (020) 7772 6275 ✆ *www.rcog.org.uk*
The college provides a list of publications (available from the bookshop) and
information on the latest research related to problems during pregnancy and birth. It
also maintains a charitable arm (Wellbeing – see also), which is a further source of
information. / HOURS *Mon-Fri 9am-5pm;* PUBLICATIONS *Publications include: Alcohol Consumption in
Pregnancy; Working with VDUs in Pregnancy; Birth at Home; Bleeding after Childbirth; Travel in
Pregnancy; HIV Screening in Pregnancy (£1.50 each) Contact Bookshop directly.*

21st Century Health, ☎ *(020) 7935 5440* ✆ *www.21stcenturyhealth.co.uk*
Suppliers of hair, skin and bodycare products, household products and natural
remedies without harsh chemicals. Produces a Clean House Clean Planet Kit with
recipes for safer cleaning products.

READING

The Environment Handbook (What Doctors Don't Tell You; £6.35) – *Concerns
regarding food, drink, computer terminals, power lines, and mobile phones: their links to
specific ailments including infertility, and steps to reduce risks.* / WDDTY (020) 8944 9555,
www.wddty.co.uk.

Having Faith – Sandra Steingraber (An ecologist's journey to motherhood; Perseus
Publishing; 2002; 1903985145) – *By a biologist, ecologist and mother, the title
describes how environmental contamination is threatening pregnancy, as evidenced by
the levels of toxins found in breast milk and growing rates of abnormalities in newborns.*
/ *www.theperseuspress.com or NCT Maternity Sales (0870) 112 1120 www.nctms.co.uk.*

Your Healthy House (WDDTY; 2000; £8.70) – *Details of the "11 most deadly
ingredients in toiletries and how to avoid them", plus information on cleaning products,
pesticides, carpets, paints and more.* / WDDTY, Satellite House, 2 Salisbury Road, London
SW10 4EZ (0800) 146 054.

6. ILLNESS

How any condition that may afflict you during pregnancy will affect your
baby is a natural cause for concern, while at the same time pregnancy
itself makes you more prone to certain conditions.

Seeking good advice is always a sensible course, yet does not necessarily involve bothering your GP. The organisations listed below provide
general health-related information.

USEFUL CONTACTS

NHS Direct, ☎ *(0845) 4647* ✆ *www.nhsdirect.nhs.uk*
The NHS information service which replaces the NHS Health Information Service.
Advice is available over the phone, and so in straightforward cases is a diagnosis,
though referral is often made to your GP all the same. Your call is automatically
directed to one of 28 regional offices appropriate to your area (London has three).
The exact scope of services vary from area to area, but most can offer details of local
NHS services (where to find a dentist, doctor, specialist centre) and some – North
Thames for example – will research specific conditions for you in their library.

**Women's Health & Reproduction Rights Information
Centre (WHRRIC)**, ☎ *(0845) 125 5254* ✆ *www.womenshealthlondon.org.uk*
The centre specialises in gynaecological and sexual health problems and can put you
in touch with relevant self-help groups. Its health enquiry line is a suitable place to
talk through any choices your GP doesn't have time to discuss. Membership brings
a quarterly newsletter, together with access to their library. / HOURS *Mon-Fri 9.30am-
1.30pm;* PUBLICATIONS *Call the centre for information on relevant leaflets.*

General conditions which are particularly serious in pregnancy:

Toxoplasmosis: an infection caused by a parasite which can cause miscarriage, stillbirth and damage to the brain and other organs of a baby –
30%-40% of infected mothers pass it to their baby. It can be caught from
eating raw or undercooked meat (e.g. Parma ham), or raw and unwashed
fruit and vegetables, and unpasteurised dairy products; also from contact
with cat litter and newborn lambs. Avoidance tactics include increased
hygiene precautions when preparing food, washing all fruit and vegeta-

bles, and wearing gloves when gardening or dealing with cat litter (the parasite can remain active in soil for 18 months).

Rubella (German Measles): can harm the baby, especially if caught in the first three months of pregnancy. However, an estimated six out of seven mothers are immune to rubella, through vaccination or because they had it as children.

Mumps: to some extent associated with abnormalities, and best avoided.

Chicken pox: if you have already had chicken pox, there is thought to be no risk to your baby if you are exposed to it during your pregnancy. However, if you had not had chicken pox before, there is a risk to your baby if you are exposed to it before you are 20 weeks pregnant, or within two weeks either side of the birth

Chlamydia psittaci: this bacteria, which can cause miscarriage, can be picked up from sheep – especially newborn lambs. Clothing and shoes worn on farms should be cleaned thoroughly.

CMV (cytomegalovirus): most people are immune to this virus (which can produce flu-like symptoms), but if it is contracted at any time during pregnancy it can cause the baby serious difficulties. Strict personal hygiene, especially around children and babies, is the only way to avoid this.

USEFUL CONTACTS

Congenital CMV (Cytomegalovirus) Association,
☎ *(01743) 850055*
This support group produces a leaflet on CMV.

Pet Health Council, ⌂ *www.pethealthcouncil.co.uk*
Offers a leaflet on toxoplasmosis. Website has a list of leaflets and factsheets which can be downloaded. / *HOURS 24hr helpline.*

Sense, The National Deafblind & Rubella Association,
☎ *(020) 7272 7774* ⌂ *www.sense.org.uk*
The organisation's leaflet on rubella (which can cause severe problems in children if contracted from the mother while she is pregnant) can be downloaded from the website.

Tommy's, ☎ *(08707) 707070, Infoline (0870) 777 3060*
⌂ *www.tommys-campaign.org*
Advice and information to anyone concerned about toxoplasmosis. / *PUBLICATIONS Factsheets include: Toxoplasmosis and Your Pet Cat – simple measures to avoid any risk of catching the disease; For Women with a Current Toxoplasma Infection During Pregnancy; After Your Baby is Born (SAE for free copies).*

Conditions associated with pregnancy

(For information regarding pre-eclampsia, see chapter 1.03 Tests.)
There are a number of medical conditions associated with pregnancy for which support is available from the organisations listed below.

USEFUL CONTACTS

The British Liver Trust, ☎ *(01473) 276326* ⌂ *www.britishlivertrust.org.uk*
Information and factsheets; in particular, for those who develop obstetric choleostasis, a liver condition that occurs in pregnancy (see also Obstetric Choleostasis Support Group). / *PUBLICATIONS Booklet on OC, its diagnosis, treatment and consequences for future pregnancies – on website or send SAE.*

Cystitis Information Bureau, ⌂ *www.cystitis.org*
Sponsored by the manufacturers of Cystopurin, an informative and user-friendly website. / *PUBLICATIONS A Guide to the Prevention and Treatment of Cystitis, free.*

National Osteoporosis Society, ☎ *Helpline (0845) 450 0230, General enquiries (01761) 471771* ⌂ *www.nos.org.uk*
Osteoporosis (a condition in which bones become porous and thus fragile, so prone to breaking) occasionally occurs in the latter stages of pregnancy or in the months after the birth, generally to the spine or hip, though there is no clear understanding of the causes; a relatively rare condition, it often goes unrecognised and is 70% more

common in first than second or third pregnancies; the national charity runs a helpline staffed by trained medical personnel who can advise for example on possible diagnostic tests, and there is a network of regional support groups. / HOURS Helpline Mon-Fri 9am-5pm; PUBLICATIONS Free booklets and leaflets. Call helpline for 'Osteoperosis & Pregnancy'.

NCT/Symphysis Pubis Disfunction, ☎ (0870) 770 3236
🖰 www.spd-uk.org
Previously a stand-alone website and support group, now run by the NCT. The website offers information for women suffering pelvic disorders resulting from the softening of ligaments that occurs during pregnancy. Diastasis (separation) of the symphysis (joining) of the pelvis – resulting in peripartum pelvic pain (PPPP) – occurs when the connecting ligaments are over-stretched or break; the condition is commonly referred to as SPD – symphysis pubis dysfunction. / PUBLICATIONS Information booklet is downloadable from website or send large SAE with 60p postage and a cheque for £20.

Obstetric Cholestasis Support Group, ☎ (0121) 353 0699
This liver condition can, at its worst, lead to a still birth. The main symptom is a generalised itching (especially of the arms, hands, legs and feet) in the third trimester of pregnancy; other signs can be jaundice, pale stools and dark urine. The organisation aims to provide guidance on its correct treatment through the publication of leaflets, and occasionally may put women in touch with each other to share experiences.

Help with other medical conditions

Pregnancy can be hard enough for someone in the peak of fitness, never mind someone with a serious ailment. If you suffer from a serious medical condition, explore at an early stage what form of back-up may be available to you.

USEFUL CONTACTS

Action for ME, ☎ (01749) 67099 🖰 www.afme.org.uk
Also called Chronic Fatigue, the organisation estimates affects 150,000 in the UK, two thirds of them women. They run local support groups for members (minimum £15 per annum). / HOURS Mon-Fri 9.30am-5pm; PUBLICATIONS Factsheets and information pack on parenting with ME – SAE.

Arthritis Care, ☎ (020) 7380 6500, Helpline (0808) 800 4050
🖰 www.arthritiscare.org.uk
The UK's largest voluntary organisation for people with arthritis, holds a limited amount of information on pregnancy and childcare for sufferers. / HOURS Mon-Fri 8.30am-5.30pm, Free helpline Mon-Fri 12pm-4pm.

British Epilepsy Association, ☎ (0808) 800 5050
🖰 www.epilepsy.org.uk
The association offers general information on adult or child epilepsy (an estimated one in 200 births in the UK is to a sufferer, though the condition is rarely inherited). The organisation offers access to information, not least through its network of local support groups. Membership of £15 (or £10 for unwaged) secures a quarterly magazine and personal accident insurance cover. / HOURS Mon-Thu 9am-4.30pm, Fri 9am-4pm; PUBLICATIONS epilepsy and children, 50p; women and epilepsy, 25p; various other factsheets – send SAE for printed material; videos (including relating to caring for kids) for sale.

Cancer BACUP, ☎ Helpline (0808) 800 1234, (020) 7739 2280, Switchboard (020) 7696 2003 🖰 www.cancerbacup.org.uk
Cancer counselling line staffed by specialist nurses, which can also provide access to face-to-face counselling. / HOURS Switchboard Mon-Fri 9am-5.30pm, Helpline Mon-Fri 9am-7pm; PUBLICATIONS Leaflets: Understanding Radiotherapy; Understanding Chemotherapy (both include sections on fertility and pregnancy, free from Publications order line).

Diabetes UK, ☎ (020) 7424 1000, Careline (0845) 120 2960
🖰 www.diabetes.org.uk
The organisation (formerly known as the British Diabetic Association) provides a confidential advice careline for all sufferers of the disease; and publishes a selection of material relevant to pregnancy and care for children with diabetes. Staff can help with the care of diabetes, including monitoring blood glucose levels and advice on a healthy diet. / HOURS Mon-Fri 9am-5pm; PUBLICATIONS Pregnancy magazine (£3). Balance, general diabetic bi-monthly magazine. Pregnancy & Diabetes: The Complete Handbook (covers eating well and has detailed information about planning for the birth and labour, availabe from bookshops and not the organisation).

Lupus UK, ☎ *(01708) 731251* ⏴ *www.lupusuk.com*

This organisation fund research into Lupus which is an auto-immune disease which can be hard to diagnose (arthritis is a common symptom). There is no cure at present and 90% of sufferers are women, usually in child-bearing years – an estimated one in 1,000 is affected. Membership is £8 and offers contacts with a regional support group, and a newsletter. / PUBLICATIONS *List of books and leaflets on website.*

ME Association, ☎ *(0871) 222 7824* ⏴ *www.meassociation.org.uk*

The organisation provides specialist information and advice and referrals to self-help groups. / HOURS *365 days: 10am-12pm, 2pm-4pm, 7pm-9pm;* PUBLICATIONS *assorted literature, including copies of articles covering pregnancy and ME with pointers on labour.*

Medic Alert Foundation, ☎ *(0800) 581420, (020) 7833 3034* ⏴ *www.medicalert.org.uk*

Providers of an internationally-recognised emergency identification system (started in 1956) using symbols on bracelets or pendants for people with hidden health problems. In the event of an emergency, a 24-hour helpline provides paramedics with a complete medical history. You might like one to wear when you're pregnant, even if there is no need at other times. Membership £30, plus £10 annually. Bracelets start from: steel £20; 9ct gold £129. Necklaces: steel £20; 9ct gold £169; silver disk £35; 9ct gold disk £85. Also have specially designed range for children with nylon sports watch strap and Velcro fastening, decorated with footballs, flowers etc.

7. TRAVELLING WHEN PREGNANT

Travel during pregnancy is usually easiest during the second trimester (months 4–6) of your pregnancy. By this time, the nausea of the first trimester has usually passed as has the period of greatest risk of miscarriage, but your bulge should not yet have grown so big that journeying is especially uncomfortable.

Travelling presents few inherent dangers to mother or unborn child (see below). The most significant hazard is probably that your baby will arrive prematurely while you are in transit. It should be emphasised, though, that it is not thought possible to trigger miscarriage or premature birth simply by travel. A premature birth while travelling is just an unlucky coincidence.

Your choice of destination takes on somewhat greater significance, as does the need to consider medical backup at the other end. The main risks are of any dangers associated with the area, or – should you encounter any complications – the absence of suitable medical support.

Issues relating to journeys

KEEP MOVING

Remaining static during travel is not encouraged, especially in pregnancy. Circulation of the blood is slowed by pressure from the seating and the weight of the foetus. There is some chance of blood clots forming in the deep veins of the legs (deep vein thrombosis, DVT, or so-called Economy Class Syndrome) when circulation is poor. These clots can travel to the heart or lungs with fatal results. However, to put this into context there are an estimated 100 deaths a year worldwide and the risk on a long-haul journey is put at one in 12,000, though some commentators put the figure higher.

Recommended ways of boosting your circulation include wriggling your toes, stretching, tensing your legs and taking a stroll if possible every hour or two. Also helpful can be exercise (such as a walk) before travel, avoiding your calves making prolonged contact with your seat, avoiding tea and coffee on the flight, drinking plenty of water, doing in-flight exercises and wearing support stockings.

If you have a family history of thrombosis (e.g. stroke or heart attack) you might like to ask your doctor if you could be tested for genetic susceptibility. Consider also breaking long journeys.

Note that, apparently, DVT may not make itself felt until up to two weeks after the journey.

TRAVEL BY AIR

If your carers have expressed any doubts over the baby's growth, some consultants recommend avoiding flying altogether.

Flying is also not recommended if you are very anaemic or if you have sickle cell anaemia. You should also check about the safety of flying if you have any history of deep vein thrombosis (see above)

If none of the above apply, the standard request from airlines is that you provide a medical certificate if you will be more than 28 weeks pregnant on your return flight. Such a certificate is available from your GP or antenatal carer and should indicate EDD and level of fitness.

Carriers may refuse to carry women who are more than 32 weeks pregnant and are almost certain not to carry women over 36 weeks pregnant. Details may vary not just from airline to airline (charter airlines tend to be stricter) but also from route to route. Even if you will fall short of the specified cut-off dates, if you have a significant bump it is probably wise to procure a certificate regardless. Reasons cited for these restrictions are generally medical: that cabin pressure causes fluid retention (creating extra pressure on the abdomen) and that flying can increase blood pressure. Cynics query whether of equal concern to airlines is the vast cost of re-routing in the event of a premature birth.

Another concern for pregnant women is the increased exposure to radiation when flying, which at normal cruising altitudes is more than 100 times that at ground level (the equivalent to a single chest X-ray on a return trip from London to New York). This is one reason why pregnant women are advised to avoid unnecessary long distance flights, especially during early pregnancy.

You may be offered priority boarding if seats are not reserved, but it is worth requesting this up-front, rather than waiting for someone to offer it to you. An aisle seat can make it much easier to get up for the recommended walkabout. Place the seatbelt under, not across, your bump.

Wear loose, comfortable clothing and shoes you can slip on and off easily, as your feet may swell.

TRAVEL BY CAR

Legislation insists that even pregnant women must 'belt-up' when travelling by car. However, a car seat belt placed across the abdomen can be dangerous in the event of an accident, so keep the shoulder strap high above your bump, and place the lap belt across your thighs.

Experts advise not undertaking any drive longer than three hours in the last three months, especially if you are driving yourself.

USEFUL CONTACTS

Halfords, ☎ *(08457) 626625* ⌂ *www.halfords.com*
Stockists of a seat belt adjuster for pregnant women (£25), comprising a seat with a central strap that pulls the lap belt down below the bump, minimising the likelihood of injury to the baby in the event of an accident.

Unsuitable destinations

High altitude regions are unsuitable for both mother and unborn child at any stage of pregnancy because of the low levels of oxygen.

Because high fever and dehydration caused by diarrhoea have been implicated in miscarriage, some practitioners feel that it is wise to restrict travel during pregnancy to countries with a developed medical system. At the risk of stating the obvious, the simplest precaution is to avoid destinations where you are more at risk of infections that cause these symptoms.

Countries requiring vaccinations are not a good idea either, as immunisation is not generally recommended during pregnancy, especially those involving a live virus (for example oral polio, measles, rubella and yellow fever), or one likely to cause a high fever (diphtheria and typhoid). The BCG vaccination against TB may affect the foetus and is therefore not given during pregnancy.

The World Health Organisation (WHO) has advised in particular against pregnant women and small children visiting areas where cholera and malaria are endemic. If you are pregnant when you contract the plasmodium malariae strain, for example, it will be passed on to your child. Moreover, there are doubts about taking anti-malarial drugs in pregnancy. There is also evidence, incidentally, that mosquitos are more attracted to pregnant women. Hepatitis A is reported more likely to be severe if contracted during pregnancy.

If you wish to visit a destination where a vaccination is either mandatory or advisable (not the same thing) you should discuss the matter with your GP – ideally at least two months before departure – or contact the experts (see listings).

If you visit a country where there are mosquitoes, note that repellents containing DEET are not recommended for use during pregnancy (see also Health issues in chapter *2.05 Travel*).

USEFUL CONTACTS

Medical Advisory Service for Travellers Abroad (MASTA),
☎ *Helpline (0906) 8224100, General (0113) 238 7501* ✆ *www.masta.org*
Founded in 1984 by the London School of Hygiene and Tropical Medicine, MASTA run a telephone advice line, which covers 250 countries, and can supply a written personalised travel health brief. The website is a further source of information, including advice for pregnant women.

Mobilis Heathcare Group, ☎ *(0161) 678 0233*
✆ *www.mobilishealthcare.com*
A group until recently known as Procare Medisport – suppliers of Veinguard Inflight Socks in four sizes, intended to reduce the risk of DVT.

READING

Health Information for Overseas Travel – Department of Health (Stationery Office; 2000; £7.95 + p&p £2.50; 0113223293) – *Advice and information on a country by country basis. Your GP's practice should have a copy that you can refer to. / The Stationery Office – (020) 7873 0011.*

Leaflet T6, Health Advice for Travellers (Department of Health; Free) – *The leaflet covers health risks around the world, planning ahead and getting treatment. At the back is form E111, a certificate which once stamped and signed by a UK post office, entitles you to free or reduced cost emergency medical treatment in the European Economic Area. It contains a list of the EEA countries, as well as the 40+ Reciprocal Agreement Countries; it emphasises that in Canada, USA, India, the Far East, Africa and Latin America there are no health care agreements with the UK. / Post Offices and the Department of Health, Publications Unit, PO Box 410, Wetherby LS23 7LN – (01937) 840250 or (0800) 555777 (allow at least 4 weeks).*

Travellers' Health – ed Dr Richard Dawood (How to stay healthy abroad; OUP; 2002; £12.50; 0-192622-47-6) – *An incredibly thorough sourcebook covering individual diseases and hazards, infectious diseases by area, and including travel when pregnant. Useful if venturing into the wilds, otherwise perhaps unnecessarily depressing.*

Precautionary steps

Depending on how things are going, and what stage of pregnancy you have reached, you might like to take a copy of your antenatal notes with you. It is definitely wise to keep a record of any medication you are taking. Pack these items in your hand luggage in case your bags go astray.

As standards of local hospital facilities can vary enormously overseas, it can be reassuring to research before your departure what facilities are available in the areas you plan to visit. One precaution is to obtain the name of a recommended local obstetrician. Your hotel, local agent or the tourist office would be the starting points for this. It can also be useful to obtain the local numbers for the British Embassy or Consulate, just in case you need them in an emergency. This is especially true if you are going anywhere at all remote.

The Department of Health's T5 leaflet (see below) details health risks around the world, suggests how to plan ahead, and has advice regarding getting treatment at your destination. It includes lists of countries which have healthcare agreements with the UK, and at the back has form E111 – a certificate which (once stamped and signed at a UK post office) entitles you to urgent medical treatment in the European Economic Area. (In some of these countries it is sufficient merely to show a British passport.)

Even where healthcare is offered, however, it may not cover everything and you may have to pay for some services at the time and then claim back the cost. In some places it may also be difficult to find a doctor willing to treat under the scheme.

To obtain medical treatment away from home in the UK, either go directly to casualty or ask to be registered as a temporary resident with a local GP. Details of any treatment should be sent to your antenatal carers. The local health authority should be able to help if you have a problem.

Insurance

Check for restrictions on the policy. Some policies, for example, do not provide cover for any condition relating to pregnancy. Similarly it may be a requirement that there should not be any pre-existing or hereditary problem related to the pregnancy. Check the small print of annual policies – you may have difficulty claiming for cancellation due to pregnancy.

Claims for problems which occurred on a trip taken against the advice of a doctor may well prove unsuccessful. Matters may be different if you had already booked before the doctor advised against travelling.

Look for policies which offer:
➢ An English language phone service.
➢ Repatriation if necessary.
➢ Extra accommodation and travel expenses for anyone who has to stay on to help.
➢ Direct and immediate payment of bills. A policy that expects you to pay first and reclaim later is inconvenient.

INSURANCE COMPANIES
Coversure, ☎ *(01706) 625559*
Agents for Fortis insurance: cover to 32 weeks on date of return.

Europ Assistance, ☎ *(0870) 737 5720* ✆ *www.europ-assistance.co.uk*
Cover to 32 weeks on date of return.

Medicover Travel Insurance, ☎ *(0870) 735 3600*

⏻ www.medi-cover.co.uk

Specialist travel insurance policies offering cover for pre-existing medical conditions from allergies and asthma through to cancers and heart conditions. (The only time they cannot insure is if the person wishing to be insured is not expected to live more than four months after the date of return.) Premiums are higher than average but vary according to destination, period of holiday, age (infants are eligible) and medical conditions. They also offer an option for carers, which covers costs if you need to return home to look after a sick relative.

Post Office Counters Insurance, ☎ *(0800) 169 9999, General enquiries (08457) 223344* ⏻ www.postoffice.co.uk

Cover to 32 weeks on date of return.

Thomas Cook, ☎ *(01733) 417100*

Cover to 32 weeks on date of return.

Whiteley Insurance, ☎ *(01422) 348411*

Cover to 32 weeks on date of return.

General travel tips

All the usual advice about health when travelling apply with particular force when pregnant. In particular, only eat very freshly cooked food and avoid dubious supplies of water. If you think there could be problems finding healthy food, consider taking some supplies with you, plus vitamins or other supplements recommended by an experienced practitioner Drink plenty at all times to avoid dehydration and associated constipation (this can be a particular problem when flying). Whenever you travel, take plenty of snacks and drinks in case you find yourself stranded at any stage.

Comfortable clothes and support tights may be a good idea if you plan a significant amount of sightseeing. Cooler, looser clothing than you would normally take is also a good idea – women often feel hotter during pregnancy, and wearing hot, tight clothing can encourage thrush.

If you are dubious about the hygiene of food preparation, you could consider eating vegetarian food which is generally safer, and may have to be made up for you. (Note: this strategy is less effective in areas where the water used for rinsing vegetables risks being tainted. In such places, look for peeled and skinned vegetables – even in salads – rather than those that are washed.)

As some organisms like Toxocara could enter your bloodstream through open cuts or blisters on your feet, it is generally considered wise to wear shoes or sandals all the time.

Should you get sick, be careful about any drugs you are prescribed and in particular avoid tetracycline antibiotics. Similarly travel sickness medication should only be taken after consultation with your antenatal carer or GP.

CHAPTER 1.03

TESTS

1. **Introduction**
2. **Maternal tests**
3. **Foetal screening tests**
4. **Foetal diagnostic tests**
5. **Tests after birth**
6. **Extra & private tests**

I. INTRODUCTION

Along with tests to monitor the mother's wellbeing in pregnancy, scans to determine the age of the foetus and screening tests to assess the risks of foetal abnormality have become part of the routine care offered at hospital antenatal clinics.

What form these should take was standardised for the first time in October 2003. Under guidelines published by the National Institute for Clinical Excellence (NICE), there is now an official timetable and check-list of tests that all pregnant women cared for by the NHS should receive (see table overleaf). Under these guidelines, in uncomplicated pregnancies a first-time mother would expect ten antenatal checks, and a second-time mother seven.

The tests that most new parents tend to focus on most are the screening tests, conducted early in pregnancy, which indicate the risk of a particular child being born with -- in particular – Down's syndrome and also conditions such as spina bifida. These tests increasingly utilise ultrasound scans to supplement (and in some instances to replace) the blood tests that have long fulfilled this purpose.

Surveys show that only about one third of pregnant women realise the potentially serious implications of such tests. To combat this, some hospitals make a point of arranging a specific appointment to underline their importance, and to encourage parents to focus on how they might react to a poor result. However, it is also not unknown for such tests to be offered casually on the initial booking visit to a hospital: i.e. before it has occurred to many parents to think through and discuss the implications of going ahead.

Given the serious implications of the tests, they are worth considering at the earliest opportunity (see Is testing right for you? below). If any test is likely to produce a 'result' on the spot (as for example with an ultrasound scan) it is a good idea to take someone with you for moral support.

In most cases, foetal testing offers reassurance. No more than 2%–3% of all babies are 'problem cases'. (Approximately 1% have moderate abnormalities, which can be corrected. About 2% suffer from more severe difficulties.) Even if there is a potential problem many parents feel they would rather know in advance of the birth, so they can be prepared.

It is also very important to realise that these routine 'screening' tests indicate only an above-average *probability* of a problem, not a definitive diagnosis. The majority of women with abnormal screening results in fact go on to have normal babies, because screening tests still produce high rates of 'false positives'.

Because of this low level of accuracy, in the event of an abnormal result a 'diagnostic' test will probably be recommended. These offer a much higher degree of certainty, but unfortunately this greater accuracy is normally 'bought' at the expense of some risk to the foetus – another factor which needs weighing. In addition even a good result to a diagnostic test does not rule out any possibility of a problem. Of the estimated one in 200 babies born with an intellectual disability for example, only 40% are likely to be revealed by chromosomal testing, and even then it isn't possible to run tests for all of the 5,000-odd recognised, single-gene defects.

Because tests are expensive few hospitals offer a full range. If you particularly want a specific one you can request it, and if you are considered to have a good reason you may be able to obtain it on the NHS.

If you feel you definitely want a specific test, it would be wise to discuss this with your antenatal carers at least four weeks in advance of the earliest normal date for it to be performed, in order to allow time to organise it by one route or another. There is also always the option of having a test privately (see the listings below).

Time is of the essence with many tests, as there is only a limited window of opportunity in which they can be carried out. Also the earlier you can secure a result, the earlier you can make any decisions based on it.

This is an area of medicine in which techniques are being refined all the time, and in which there are notable differences between hospitals. It is worth enquiring exactly what tests are offered and being alive to the potential to sign up to new procedures. Take the timings outlined below as indications only as they are changing all the time. For example, amniocentesis results that a couple of years ago took a couple of weeks, may now take just a couple of days.

The types of test

Tests in pregnancy fall into three categories:

Maternal tests: comparatively simple tests on the mother – blood-pressure, weight, blood tests – to assess the mother's wellbeing. Tests at an initial visit establish a baseline reading of what is "normal" for any particular woman. Subsequent results throughout the pregnancy measure the degree of change from this norm and may then affect advice as to how the mother should look after herself, or as to how the birth should be managed. Tests in this category do not consider the baby directly, though some are aimed at assessing the baby's growth.

Foetal screening tests: a combination of ultrasound scans and tests on the mother's blood, which look for a variety of problems – particularly Down's syndrome (and other chromosomal abnormalities) and neural tube defects (NTDs) such as spina bifida. These tests do not give a definite yes/no result, but indicate the likelihood of certain problems. Anyone with an abnormal result may be recommended to undergo a diagnostic test to help resolve this uncertainty.

Foetal diagnostic tests: not universally offered – tests in this category are only used where the foetus has a higher than average risk of abnormality, either because the mother is over a certain age, or because foetal screenings tests indicate a possible problem. These tests (such as amniocentesis) are known as 'invasive' tests. Results offer a much higher degree of certainty than screening tests, but the procedures can harm the foetus.

READING

The Antenatal Testing Book – Vivienne Parry & Anne-Marie Sapstead (The complete guide to testing in pregnancy; Pan; 1993; £6.99; 0330328522)

Antenatal Tests – Mary Nolan (NCT/Thorsons Books; 1998; £5.99 (0870 900 2050); 0-722536-04-6)

Is My Baby Alright? – Christine Gosden, Kypros Nicolaides & Vanessa Whitting (A guide for expectant parents; OUP; 1994; £7.99; 0192624822) – *An excellent handbook on the subject of antenatal testing by top experts in this field (a pointers system helps the layman understand the most important issues). It covers: the pros and cons of testing; how reproduction works; and the causes of abnormalities. Perhaps not ideally read when pregnant. / NCT Maternity Sales, (0870) 112 1120; www.nctms.co.uk.*

The Tentative Pregnancy – Barbara Katz Rothman (Amniocentesis and the sexual politics of motherhood; Rivers Oram Press; 1994; £8.99; 0044409125) – *A New York sociologist gives an overview of the role of testing in pregnancy; includes a sensible practical section at the end.*

Which Tests for My Unborn Baby? – Lachlan de Crespigny with Rhonda Dredge (Ultrasound and other prenatal tests; OUP Australia and New Zealand; 1997; £6.99; 0195539540) – *A guide which aims to arm you with the information you need to know to make informed decisions about prenatal tests, illustrated by accounts from people who have used the various procedures.*

Is testing right for you?

Though widely regarded as routine, and though few women decide not to be tested, it is worth bearing in mind that all antenatal tests, including blood tests, are optional – you may decline any or all of them. Simply being tested makes some people unnecessarily anxious. Being told that there is a 'positive' result for a particular problem causes many more people understandable heartache, even though, as noted above, initial results carry a fair degree of uncertainty.

Where you stand on the question of termination is the heart of this issue. Ideally both parents should discuss the subject thoroughly and well in advance, as this is an area where disagreement can put great strain on a relationship.

If a test does identify a specific problem, it may well not indicate how severe the problem might be. And yet the range of potential outcomes is enormous.

Some conditions such as neural tube defects (NTDs – spina bifida or anencephaly) may be so severe that either you will miscarry anyway, or the baby will be most unlikely to live long after birth. In such an eventuality, you need to decide if you feel termination would make sense.

Some women decide that they would rather keep their baby, whatever abnormalities are discovered. You will need to think beforehand whether you would find termination or leaving nature to take its course the easier decision to live with. If definitely the latter, blissful ignorance (i.e. opting out of pregnancy screening tests) may be your best strategy.

If you do think that you would want to terminate the pregnancy if anything were found to be wrong, the sooner you get the tests done the better. Earlier terminations are physically easier to deal with. Late terminations bear similarities to full-scale labour, and may even result in the mother going on to produce milk.

What if there is a potential problem?

(For further information regarding serious congenital conditions see chapter 4.06 Support groups.)

After any problematic result, whatever position you have reached in advance, it is still generally thought advisable to reconsider the situation – a matter best discussed away from the hospital.

It is important to get help. First, you should consider counselling. Some hospitals offer specialist counselling to help you to come to terms with the problem – potential or otherwise. (Note, though, that surveys show that many parents who have had this experience feel let down in this regard by their hospital.)

Second, you should make sure that you have clear information about the exact nature of the potential problem: how severely it might affect the child, and what may be available in the way of special care. Some of the specialist units listed below in Section 6, Extra & private tests, may be able to provide advice on interpreting test results.

USEFUL CONTACTS

Antenatal Results & Choices (ARC), ☎ (020) 7631 0280, Helpline (020) 7631 0285 ⌂ www.arc-uk.org
(The organisation was founded as Support Around Termination for Fetal Abnormality (SATFA) in 1988 and renamed as ARC in 1998.) A national charitable organisation and helpline which provides free information and support for parents who have undergone antenatal testing. In the event that the baby has a diagnosed abnormality, they can help explain the medical terminology used by the doctors, provide emotional support and point parents in the direction of further help and information. Supported by an advisory body whose members include Professor Kypros Nicolaides and advisors from the Royal Colleges of Midwifery and Nursing. / PUBLICATIONS *Newsletter for members; literature for parents, families and professionals.*

Birth Defects Foundation, ☎ (01543) 468888, Here to Help Nurse Service (08700) 70 70 20 ⌂ www.birthdefects.co.uk
According to the organisation, as many as one in 16 babies born in the UK may have some form of birth defect. The charity advises parents of children with birth defects, expectant parents who wish to reduce the risks of birth defects, and those who are themselves affected by a birth defect. The 'Here to Help Service' offers access to experienced nurses with relevant information, plus back up support from a Scientific and Medical Panel. / HOURS Mon-Fri 9.30am-6pm; PUBLICATIONS *'What Next?' – a booklet for parents who are either awaiting the outcome of medical tests or who have recently received a diagnosis; booklet on Noonan Syndrome; both can be downloaded from the web.*

Life (London office), ☎ Hotline (0800) 849 4545, London Office (020) 7240 1275 ⌂ www.lifeuk.org
Pregnancy counselling from a pro-Life organisation, which aims to offer mothers the opportunity to explore their feelings with a non-directional counsellor or skilled helper who will also discuss the options available. Also offers post-abortion counselling.

2. MATERNAL TESTS

Maternal tests are best done as soon as possible after conception so that any changes brought about in the mother by the pregnancy can be clearly seen and any necessary treatment can be started early. This is particularly important if you have any permanent medical problem, such as diabetes.

At your antenatal booking visit, you will be asked about your personal medical history, including past pregnancies, and may be asked for details about your own and your partner's family's medical history. You are likely to be asked to discuss your lifestyle, social situation and support network. Some hospitals send questionnaires on medical history to be completed in advance.

You should tell your carers if you or your partner have or have had herpes, as this can affect a newborn baby and special treatment may be required. You should also inform your carers if you come into contact with rubella (German measles) or chicken pox and haven't had either of them before (or if you haven't been vaccinated against rubella).

Standard tests

Some of the following tests are carried out by most antenatal clinics:

Foot size: an indicator of the size of the mother's pelvis.

Blood pressure: checked regularly throughout pregnancy to ensure pre-eclampsia is not developing (see below).

Urine test: for sugar, protein, ketones and blood, and to look for infections such as cystitis. An estimated 3–8% of pregnant women have a bacterial infection of the urine without symptoms, and of those, up to 45% will develop cystitis or bladder or kidney infections in the absence of treatment. Sudden rises in sugar or protein in the urine could indicate glucose intolerance (a symptom of diabetes) or pre-eclampsia. However, to put this in context, an estimated half of all pregnant women are found to have some sugar in their urine at some stage in pregnancy. (You can check for sugar and protein yourself with tests available at most pharmacies.)

Weight: sudden changes in weight can signal a complication; and significant obesity is a risk factor for thromboembolism. There appears to be little correlation between maternal weight gain and the baby's growth.

Abdomen may be felt: to check the growth of the uterus (considered by some a more effective way of assessing the baby's growth and age than ultrasound) and the baby's position.

Vaginal (internal) examination: may be suggested to check the progression of the pregnancy, or occasionally to assess pelvic proportions. This test is becoming much less common and can be refused, for instance if it is to be carried out by a male doctor and there is no nurse who can be present.

Baby's heartbeat: checked with either a stethoscope, which the mother can also use, an ear trumpet (a Pinard), or a sonic aid (known as Doppler), which detects the blood flow in the umbilical cord.

Blood group & rhesus antibody screening: knowing your blood group (also called blood type) will help if you need a transfusion in an emergency. This is especially important for women who are rhesus negative (around one in eight). Rhesus positive babies are born to rhesus negative mothers in around one in 11 pregnancies in the UK. The baby may become jaundiced and anaemic, and occasionally brain damaged if the mother develops antibodies to the baby's blood type during the pregnancy. Rhesus negative mothers will, at 28 and 34 weeks, be offered an anti-D immunoglobulin injection (artificial antibodies) to destroy any of the baby's blood which might have entered their circulation, to help prevent rhesus immunisation (and also to prevent problems with further pregnancies of rhesus positive babies). If you have an amniocentesis the anti-D would be given immediately after this. The injection is repeated within 72 hours of the birth (or a miscarriage) if the baby's blood (taken from the placenta or umbilical cord) is rhesus positive.

Heamoglobin: this test checks for anaemia (iron deficiency), and is usually conducted early in pregnancy, and at 28–32 weeks. The principal day-to-day symptom is tiredness. Anaemia can interfere with the blood clotting which is required after birth, and anaemic mothers are more likely to go into premature labour. Anaemia also makes you prone to infection and can mean you don't have sufficient energy for a long labour. After birth, anaemia can cause reduced supplies of breast milk. (See also Diet, in chapter *1.02 Looking after yourself.*)

Hepatitis B: if a carrier, the disease may be passed to the baby unless special care is taken. This may affect the method of delivery chosen.

Rubella ('German measles'): checks reveal whether the mother has immunity so that she can be offered immunisation after the birth to cover her for future pregnancies. Even if she has immunity, it is still considered advisable to stay away from known cases of rubella during the critical period when it can cause miscarriage, stillbirth or physical handicaps. The risk in the first month of pregnancy is calculated at about 50%, in the second month 20% and 7–8% in the third or fourth months.

USEFUL CONTACTS
Sense, The National Deafblind & Rubella Association,
☎ *(020) 7272 7774* ⌁ *www.sense.org.uk*
The organisation's leaflet on rubella (which can cause severe problems in children if contracted from the mother while she is pregnant) can be downloaded from the website.

Less common tests:

Listeria, salmonella or tuberculosis: if there is any reason to suspect that you are a carrier, a test will be carried out.

Glucose test: (not offered by many health authorities) usually given at 28 weeks to reveal whether the mother is developing diabetes (which can be caused temporarily by pregnancy).

HIV and other sexually transmitted diseases: HIV is increasingly routinely tested for, and if there is any reason to suspect that you may have any other sexually transmitted disease, it is important to test for that also. A positive result may affect the way in which the baby is delivered – for example, with an HIV positive mother, a Caesarean delivery may prevent infection spreading to the baby.

USEFUL CONTACTS
Herpes Virus Association (HVA), ☎ *Helpline (020) 7609 9061*
⌁ *www.herpes.org.uk*
Information and advice for those affected by herpes (or shingles). Membership (£25 per annum) includes free leaflets (one of which relates to pregnancy) and quarterly journals. / PUBLICATIONS *Free information pack (send SAE).*

National Sexual Healthline, ☎ *(0800) 567123*
(Formerly known as the National Aids Healthline) – confidential information available 24-hours regarding all issues surrounding sexual health, plus referral to relevant women's groups. / PUBLICATIONS *Various leaflets.*

Testing for pre-eclampsia

All pregnancies are monitored for pre-eclampsia – a combination of high blood pressure (hypertension) in pregnancy, fluid retention (oedema), and more than a trace reading of certain proteins in the urine. This condition can become a problem from 20 weeks, right up to the last few weeks of labour, and including immediately after delivery. In the rare number of serious cases which develop into full-blown eclampsia the condition can be very damaging to both mother and baby and, in a tiny number of cases can lead to death.

A diastolic blood pressure (the 'bottom' number quoted at a blood pressure reading) of over 90, or more than 30 higher than your reading at the beginning of pregnancy is considered worrying. (Note, however, that a slight increase in blood pressure in the first three months of pregnancy, followed by a fall and then a rise in the last three months is normal.) The main confirming 'danger sign' that doctors look for is protein in the urine.

Midwives in clinics are taught to send women with high blood pressure straight to hospital and midwives in hospital are taught to try and prevent women with high blood pressure from discharging themselves. This means that you may just walk in for a regular antenatal check one day, and be told it would be irresponsible both to yourself and to your baby not to cancel all your plans/job/commitments – and to stay in bed, in hospital. This can be a surprising and debilitating experience.

Estimates of the number of pregnancies affected vary from 5–10% – around double these figures for first pregnancies.

Pre-eclampsia is one of the most poorly understood, yet relatively common conditions in medicine. (A position has been reserved outside one American hospital for over 100 years for the statue of the doctor who finally understands pre-eclampsia – the plinth remains bare.)

A report published in 2001 may help. Its study of 1.9 million pregnancies indicated a strong seasonal pattern to the condition, with peaks in November and December. Possible important factors, therefore, may be weather or seasonal diet. A report in Ireland in 2002 noted that women who work during pregnancy are almost five times more likely to suffer the condition.

The condition may (in some cases very rapidly) lead to full-blown eclampsia – indicated by severe headaches, flashing lights, nausea, vomiting and abdominal pain, with convulsions. It is this rapidity of the onset of the condition that makes doctors so concerned.

The problem with pre-eclampsia is the significant number of 'grey area' women who develop high blood pressure but little in the way of protein in the urine. Obstetricians tend to be very medically 'defensive' in how they treat such women. Not only are women with high blood pressure generally confined to hospital bed-rest, but they are also likely to be put under significant pressure to be induced sooner rather than later (with all the entailing subsequent risks of intervention). Pre-eclampsia is considered by some hospitals to be a good reason for a Caesarean.

It is generally accepted that – in the absence of protein in the urine – high blood pressure at the end of pregnancy does not predict a worse outcome for either mother or baby. Despite this, given that your condition could theoretically change at any time, consultants basically want you off their books so they can stop worrying about you. This makes some women feel that the system is taking a sledgehammer to crack a nut.

Some consultants would counter that eclampsia is one of the few remaining significant causes of mortality at birth, and that in their judgement it is better to accept the increased risk that you have an intervention than run the smallest chance of you dying or harm coming to your child.

Given the limited amount which even the experts know in this area, and the conflicting opinions which are held about the risks, there can be scope for wide disagreement about the 'right' course of action in a given case. You do, however, have every right to be consulted about the balance of risks in your case, and the action that should be taken.

You may be able to lower high blood pressure with yoga, acupuncture or homeopathy. Meditation and deep breathing may reduce high blood pressure by up to 10mm.

How accurately does testing predict pre-eclampsia and eclampsia?

➤ Of cases discovered, around 30% are only recognised during labour (which, because the condition affects the functioning of the placenta, may be triggered prematurely).

➤ Although the condition is known to be more common in certain circumstances (for example: mothers with diabetes or kidney disease;

older women; migraine-sufferers) monitoring seldom takes this into
account.

➤ Your blood pressure will tend to rise if you have been rushing or are
feeling under pressure at the test, a condition known as 'white coat
hypertension', both of which can give misleading results at antenatal
checks.

Once diagnosed, how should it be treated?

➤ Diet is thought to affect pre-eclampsia, but advice (as ever) is contradictory, suggesting either low or high amounts of salt plus either
controlled weight gain or high protein intake.

➤ A wide range of drugs may be offered, but it is unclear whether these
are helpful and there is the possibility of creating other problems, particularly for the baby.

➤ The results of research at Oxford University on 10,000 women internationally, published In 2002 in the Lancet, show that injecting
magnesium salts (Epsom salts) into the bloodstream of a sufferer of
pre-eclampsia can reduce the risk by nearly 60%.

How clear is the link between pre-eclampsia and eclampsia?

➤ Some commentators claim only around one in 2,000 cases of pre-
eclampsia turn into full-blown eclampsia.

➤ Alternatively, APEC suggests the figure is one in 50 (and one in 25 in
first pregnancies).

USEFUL CONTACTS
Action on Pre-Eclampsia (APEC), ☎ Helpline (020) 8427 4217,
Admin (020) 8863 3277 ✆ www.apec.org.uk
Offers details of experts to whom you can apply for an NHS referral, information
packs, a befriending service, local groups and a newsletter. Some find the material
a touch alarmist. / HOURS Helpline: Mon-Fri 10am-1pm; PUBLICATIONS Leaflets include: Why Blood
Pressure is Checked in Pregnancy; Signs and Symptoms of Pre-eclampsia (send SAE).

Pre-eclamptic Toxaemia Society (PETS), ☎ (01286) 882685,
(01702) 202088
A 20-year-old organisation offering support and information for women with
pre-eclampsia, including a quarterly newsletter. Send SAE with enquiry.

3. FOETAL SCREENING TESTS

There are two main types of foetal screening tests: serum screening tests
and ultrasound scans. The increasing refinement in the use of ultrasound
means that though serum screening remains quite a widely used test, its
relative importance is dwindling. One of the big advantages of ultrasound
is that it can offer an equivalently reliable result earlier in pregnancy allowing a decision over termination at a less advanced stage.

The majority of London hospitals now offer ultrasound screening,
fewer and fewer offer serum screening and some use a combination of
the two methods.

Be it by ultrasound or by serum screening, mothers whose test indicates a high risk of a problem will in most cases be recommended to have
a diagnostic test, usually amniocentesis.

Ultrasound scans

Ultrasound scans use high frequency sound, inaudible to the human ear.
A computer uses the pattern made by the sound-waves as they bounce
off the uterus, ovaries, baby, placenta and amniotic fluid to produce an
image of the foetus. Low-resolution scans can only provide basic infor-

mation. High-resolution scans can detect chromosomal markers and problems like spina bifida and cleft palates, as well as details of all major organs and limbs.

The increasingly universal nuchal translucency test (NT) is rapidly replacing the use of serum-screening tests for assessing Down's syndrome. NT used in combination with a blood test – 'the combined test' – is widely thought to be the most accurate test currently available and to carry a relatively small incidence of false positives, and it is able to provide a much earlier result than serum screening (though its accuracy is actually at its best if used at a similar time). Even without the combined test, the scan alone is thought to be pretty accurate.

Some hospitals will print out an image of the baby from the machine, usually for a small fee. Depending on the machine used, this picture may fade, and so if you want to keep it you may need to make a durable copy.

It is usually possible to tell the sex of the child from a scan but not if the genitals are hidden. If visible, this knowledge is useful in the case of inherited sex-related disorders such as haemophilia. However, where not medically relevant, some hospitals have a policy of not revealing the sex even if asked, usually to prevent sex-determined terminations.

In addition to the information they can offer, scans are often a good way for partners to start feeling involved in the pregnancy.

A typical testing program would typically include some, but not all, of the following tests:

Early pregnancy assessment scan: at four, or more usually six to 10 weeks, especially used for women who have a previous history of miscarriage or assisted conception, pelvic pain or bleeding in early pregnancy. This confirms the viability and growth of the baby (a heartbeat is usually visible six weeks after the last period). If there is bleeding, the scan identifies the source of the blood loss and can exclude the possibility of an ectopic pregnancy in the Fallopian tubes.

Early pregnancy dating scan: with timing similar to the above, a less invasive procedure to date the pregnancy.

Nuchal translucency scan (Nuchal fold test): a high resolution ultrasound scan typically performed at 10–13 weeks can be used to measure a number of physical markers which may indicate a chromosomal disorder. The fluid-filled space at the back of the foetus's neck, where the neural tube is forming, is seen on ultrasound scans as dark lines. Thickening of these lines indicates the possibility of chromosomal abnormality. Other signs are: the distance between the forming brain and top of the skull; measurements of the heart, kidneys and spine which differ from the average; and wider–than-normal spaces between fingertips and between toes. These measurements, assessed in combination with the mother's age and the foetal heart rate indicate the likelihood of chromosomal disorders like Down's. NFT, carried out by an experienced practitioner, is thought to be 80-85% accurate at 11 weeks. For greatest accuracy a sample of the mother's blood is taken and analysed in combination with results from the scan. In this case results may differ considerably from the provisional result from the scan alone. For greatest accuracy the combined test is carried out slightly later than is often the case: i.e. in the second trimester, rather than the first.

Foetal anomaly scan: may be carried out at 11–13 weeks (see also nuchal fold test) or at 18–23 weeks – exact dates depend on both the hospital and the mother's circumstances. Each part of the anatomy is checked with particular attention to brain, face, spine, heart, stomach, bowel, kidneys and limbs.

Foetal wellbeing scan: may be carried out at any time from 24–42 weeks, but more usually around 32–36 weeks. Both the baby's anatomy (for example to see that there is no heart defect) and the baby's growth are checked. The blood flowing through the umbilical cord is identified by colour Doppler to assess the baby's nutrition during the last weeks of pregnancy. The amniotic fluid is measured and placenta location checked, along with the baby's position. This can be useful if the placenta is low-lying (see placenta praevia in chapter *4.07 Glossary of medical & specialist terms*).

CONCERNS OVER ULTRASOUND

Concerns have been raised in some quarters over whether repeated and, in particular, prolonged exposure to ultrasound can harm the developing foetus. In the US, the American College of Obstetricians and Gynaecologists has recommended ultrasound only be used in pregnancy for specific diagnosis in individual cases, rather than routinely.

Results from a late 2001 study appeared to confirm a pre-existing observation: that babies who have been the subject of ultrasound scans have a greater than average likelihood of being left-handed. Despite the survey's evidence that the scans can sometimes alter brain development, no specific harmful effects were identified.

Claims of various other effects deriving from the use of ultrasound range from retarded growth to increased rate of miscarriage. The concern is that the heat produced in foetal brain tissue by the process can cause irreparable cell damage and affect neurological functions. Another concern is that the sound may be painful to the baby's ears and be the cause of hearing and/or speech difficulties.

Practitioners are extremely sceptical of these concerns. Some argue that an average foetus in the modern world experiences comparable exposure daily – for example generated by cars and buses – to that generated by any scan.

READING

Ultrasound? Unsound – Beverley Lawrence Beech (MIDRS; 1994; £5; 1874413053) – *Information on the possible problems associated with use of ultrasound.* / AIMS, www.aims.org.uk.

Serum screening (blood) tests

A blood sample is taken from the mother (at about 15–17 weeks) to test the levels of one or more protein 'markers' that have crossed into the mother's bloodstream from the foetus (the first it produces) and from the placenta. These markers can indicate the likelihood of Down's syndrome (and, depending upon the type of test, other chromosomal abnormalities), plus neural tube defects (NTDs) such as spina bifida or anencephaly. Results normally take around 48 hours from receipt of sample.

The test's outcome is given as a risk probability level – a 'screen positive' (which indicates a greater than 1 in 250 chance of having Down's syndrome) or 'screen negative' (which indicates less than one in 250 chance). The result is calculated taking into account various factors including: the mother's age; the parents' ethnic groups; any family history of inherited disease; any previous difficulty in pregnancy; any personal illnesses, for example diabetes or epilepsy (and any drugs used for treating them); and environmental risks (for example from work, or if the parents drink excessively or smoke).

Mothers who screen positive (around one in 20) will be recommended to undergo amniocentesis.

DRAWBACKS TO SERUM SCREENING

A high proportion of 'positive' results occur when in reality there is no problem. These are known as 'false positive' results, and can be influenced by numerous factors, including: there being more than one baby; the baby being male; if you are black; if you smoke; if you had an early threatened miscarriage; or if you have viral hepatitis. As an added complication, levels of the proteins can vary even from day to day. The tables to calculate risk factors do not always take all these variables into account.

The test is only useful if your dates are accurate, as there is more protein for example at 18 weeks than at 16, with levels doubling every four weeks or so in the second half of pregnancy. If your dates are found to be wrong by more than 17 days, the test results will need to be reassessed.

TYPES OF SERUM SCREENING TEST

As the science of this form of testing has become more and more sophisticated, ever-more protein markers are being taken into consideration in assessing risk. In general, with the tests below, the fewer the number of markers, the older and the less commonplace the test. Effectiveness of the tests vary with the mother's age, with an increase in detection rates but also a marked increase in false positive results.

The accuracy of these tests is measured in terms of their detection rates and their false positive rates:

AFP (alpha-fetoprotein test): this test detects about 30% of Down's syndrome cases and there is a 5–10% false positive rate. Nine out of 10 women with high protein levels have healthy babies.

Double test: a more effective test than the AFP assessing the amount of AFP and one other protein 'marker' which is associated with an increased risk of Down's syndrome in the baby. The detection rate of Down's syndrome is 55%–60%.

Triple test and Triple-plus test (commonly called the Leeds test): as for the Double test, but measuring a third protein 'marker'. Other chromosomal abnormalities like Edward's syndrome may also be indicated; 60–70% accurate for Down's syndrome and 80% accurate for neural tube defects. The false positive rate is about 5%.

Bart's test/Quadruple test: as for the Triple-plus test but measuring a fourth protein. Detection rates at Bart's itself are reported as 75% for Down's syndrome, 85% for open spina bifida and almost 100% for anencephaly. The false positive rate is about 5%.

Biomark: measuring four markers, the detection rate for Down's syndrome is about 70%, with a false positive rate of about 5%.

Primark: the test currently favoured by Leeds University's test unit, can be conducted earlier in pregnancy than the Biomark and is often used in conjunction with a nuchal scan for greater accuracy. This combination gives the best detection rate and lowest false positive rate of all the tests listed for Down's and Edward's syndromes, the detection rate for the former being 81%, with a false positive rate of 2.5%.

Other foetal screening tests

Various tests can indicate the likelihood of other problems in your child. A good knowledge of your family medical history is useful here, as many of these conditions are not routinely screened for.

Tests generally given only if there is some reason to do so:

Cystic fibrosis: the commonest life-threatening inherited disease in the western world, found in one in 2,500 births in the UK, affects the lungs and digestive system. CF can be tested for from a blood sample or by a mouthwash that checks for four common gene mutations. If these are not found, the risk of being a carrier is considered low. Life expectancy of those with cystic fibrosis is 20–30 years with treatment. Around one in 25 white people are carriers and in about one couple in 500 both are. If both parents are carriers, the child has a one in four chance of being affected.

Toxoplasmosis: a blood test can detect whether the mother has had, or currently has the disease – a single-cell parasite found in animal faeces and raw meat. Discovery of a recent infection would trigger foetal testing.

Sickle-cell traits: approximately one in 10 people of African descent carry the gene for sickle-cell, which can be detected by a blood test. Sickle-cell anaemia is a serious blood condition which causes abnormality in red blood cells, leading to anaemia and joint pain. If both parents carry the gene, the child has a one in four chance of being a sufferer. Although painful, the disease is not necessarily fatal. If the mother is found to be a carrier the father will then be tested, and if this result is also positive further counselling is generally offered, possibly followed by a diagnostic test to check the foetus for the condition.

Thalassaemia traits: again, only a potential problem if both parents are carriers, which is usual only in parents of Mediterranean or Asian origin. If so, a child has a one in four chance of being a sufferer. The condition, which becomes evident in babies from around three months old, causes potentially fatal anaemia.

Tay–Sachs disease: predominantly found in the Jewish population, but others are also carriers. Children born of parents who are both carriers suffer cerebral degeneration and blindness from around six months and usually live no longer than four years.

Pelvimetry: measurement of the mother's pelvis by x-ray. Because of the risk of irradiation which may result in chromosomal abnormalities and increased risk of miscarriage, x-rays are not used in pregnancy unless absolutely necessary.

USEFUL CONTACTS

Association for Spina Bifida & Hydrocephalus (ASBAH),
☎ (020) 8441 9967, (020) 8449 0475 ⌁ www.asbah.org
/ HOURS Mon-Fri 9am-5pm; PUBLICATIONS *factsheets on both conditions, antenatal screeing, genetic counselling, vitamin supplementation for prevention.*

Cystic Fibrosis Trust, ☎ (020) 8464 7211 ⌁ www.cftrust.org.uk
Founded as a fund-raising organisation in the 1960s, the trust offers advice and support for sufferers and families through a network of 300 voluntary local groups. There is also a Family & Adult Support Service (FASS). / PUBLICATIONS *Fact sheets on carrier tests and tests during pregnancy and a good general one, Finding Out About Cystic Fibrosis. The trust have a publication list that can be ordered.*

Down's Syndrome Association, ☎ (020) 8682 4001
⌁ www.downs-syndrome.org.uk
A network of volunteer, parent-led groups supporting families of children with the condition (which affects approximately one in 1,000 babies).

Potter's Syndrome Support Group, ☎ (01938) 553755
⌁ www.geocities.com/potters_syndrome
Support for a condition which involves the absence of kidneys. It may be diagnosed by a foetal anomaly scan at 20 or so weeks. The pregnancy will continue but birth will be difficult partly because of the absence of amniotic fluid, which is produced by

the baby's kidneys. Many babies with Potter's syndrome are stillborn, or die after a few days due to underdeveloped lungs. / HOURS *early evening or during school holidays;* PUBLICATIONS *factsheet – free; tape of radio interview with doctor, £3.*

Sickle Cell Society, ☎ *(020) 8961 7795/4006* ⟨ *www.sicklecellsociety.org*

Information and counselling for sufferers and families of children with such disorders; financial assistance and educational grants; links with local support groups and specialist centres; holiday and recreational opportunities. The society is setting up a rapid information response service linking into a variety of local, regional and national databases. There are 9 support groups and centres across London. / PUBLICATIONS *Living with Sickle Cell Pain – advice for children and adolescents and their families; a general guide to Sickle Cell Anaemia.*

South East London Sickle Cell & Thalassaemia Centre, ☎ *(020) 7414 1357*

Screening for such disorders for those in Lambeth, Southwark and Lewisham, with non-directive counselling, advice on benefits and general support.

The Tay Sachs Screening Programme, ☎ *(0161) 795 7000, ext 5094*

The 'Manchester Screening Programme' offers screening by post for those who cannot reach a screening centre, together with information about this fatal genetic disorder and related 'storage' diseases. / PUBLICATIONS *Tay-Sachs & Allied Diseases.*

Tommy's, ☎ *(08707) 707070, Infoline (0870) 777 3060*
⟨ *www.tommys-campaign.org*

Advice and information to anyone concerned about toxoplasmosis.
/ PUBLICATIONS *Factsheets: Toxoplasmosis and Your Pet Cat – simple measures to avoid any risk of catching the disease; For Women with a Current Toxoplasma Infection During Pregnancy; After Your Baby is Born (SAE for free copies).*

The UK Thalassaemia Society, ☎ *(020) 8882 0011* ⟨ *www.ukts.org*

Formed by parents of thalassaemia patients, the society offers information on being a carrier or a sufferer of thalassaemia, together with support and counselling, and information about sickle thalassaemia. They conduct a major Asia-awareness programme (an ethnic group not traditionally associated with the disease) – literature is available in all major Asian languages as well as Greek. Life membership of the society is £100 (or £10 per annum).

Group B Strep (GBS)

Group B Strep is carried by around a third of the adult population at any one time, without any symptoms. It can be fatal to a newborn if carried by the mother at the time of birth, as it can lead to septicaemia, pneumonia and meningitis. About 500 babies a year in the UK are affected.

According to the Group B Strep Support group the risk to the baby of a woman carrying the infection can be significantly reduced by administering antibiotics to the mother from the onset of labour. Reliable tests for the infection are only just becoming available, however, and the GBSS suggests the precautionary use of antibiotics be considered where one of the risk factors below apply.

As of early 2004, the test available via the NHS is thought by the Group B Strep Support group to be so unreliable as to be pointless. The organisation does provide information regarding an alternative test – ECM – available privately for £18.

Risk factors are:
➢ A previous baby with Group B Strep infection.
➢ Where the pregnant woman has been found to carry GBS on a swab done for other reasons.
➢ Where GBS has been found in the urine.
➢ Where labour or membrane rupture is pre-term (before 37 weeks).
➢ Where rupture of membranes is prolonged (greater than 18 or 24 hours before delivery).
➢ Where the pregnant woman has a temperature of 37.8C or higher during labour.

USEFUL CONTACTS

Group B Strep Support, ☎ *(01444) 416176 (answerphone)*
🖰 *www.gbss.org.uk*
The organisation provides information regarding an alternative test to that available on the NHS (ECM – available privately for £18). / HOURS *Mon-Fri 9am-1pm.*

4. FOETAL DIAGNOSTIC TESTS

There is the possibility that some time in the future genetic abnormalities such as Down's syndrome will be accurately diagnosable by taking a sample of the mother's blood and testing those foetal cells which have crossed over into the mother's bloodstream from the placenta.

For the present, however, invasive tests – where a sample of amniotic fluid or of the baby's blood is taken for analysis – remain the only way to diagnose some conditions with reasonable certainty. (Note however, that even if the tests reveal nothing, there is still no cast-iron guarantee that your baby will be born without problems.)

Given the risk that they present to the unborn child, invasive diagnostic tests are only used where the foetus is judged to have a higher than average risk of abnormality. This is the case for all women in their late thirties (36 is the commonly used watershed), who are routinely offered amniocentesis on account of their higher than average risk of carrying a Down's baby.

Screening tests which indicate a potential problem are also a major factor in prompting further, diagnostic testing. However, there is some lack of consensus over exactly what screen positive rate is the correct basis from which to progress to invasive tests. A screen positive of 250 or more is a generally accepted figure, though Professor Kypros Nicolaides of King's College and the Foetal Medicine Centre prefers a borderline of 300. Some observers claim that extraneous factors can vary the correct interpretation of a given screening test's prediction of Down's syndrome in a child from one in 140 to one in 10,000. You may wish to try to assess these factors with your antenatal carers before going ahead.

Diagnostic tests can reveal chromosomal abnormalities that may have no obvious effect. An example is an extra X chromosome. Apparently around one in 400 newborns have a sex chromosome variation and most live relatively normal lives. Being told about such a situation can seem like bad news and can affect the way in which you relate to the child. You could ask not to be told of any chromosomal feature that would not have any obvious effects on your baby's wellbeing. If you do find out that this is an issue, you may want to seek genetic counseling to help you understand better all the implications.

Before proceeding with any such test, you may wish to investigate what the centre's miscarriage rate is subsequent to such procedures. Anecdotal evidence suggests that miscarriage rates after invasive tests vary shockingly between practitioners, from as low as 1% to as high as 4%.

The types of test

AMNIOCENTESIS
This test is routinely offered to all women whose screening tests have indicated a high risk of a problem; to those who will be aged 36 (or 37, depending on the hospital) or over at the birth; and to those with a family history of any chromosomal disorder.

Using a scan to locate the position of the baby, an extremely fine needle is used to remove approximately 20ml of the amniotic fluid surrounding the foetus. (In a few units, amnios are done 'blind' – without the scan. Try to avoid them – it's significantly more risky for the baby.) Cells from the baby in the fluid can then be cultured and tested for a range of disorders including Down's syndrome.

Amniocentesis is considered safest between 14 and 16 weeks. It has been carried out earlier, but there is an increased risk of miscarriage and leaks of amniotic fluid, particularly for older mothers.

It used to be that test results could take up to six weeks, but the FISH test (Fluorescent In Situ Hybridisation) can produce a result in 48 hours, revealing any extra chromosome and therefore the commonest problems (including Down's). This test does not produce false positives, but false negatives are possible so half of the sample is incubated over a two-week period, the cells harvested and individual chromosomes counted as a double check.

Provided the culture grows (there is a 2–5% chance of failure) amniocentesis does offer a high degree of certainty about major chromosomal abnormalities (with an estimated 0.5% possibility of error). Down's syndrome is correctly detected 90% of the time, and neural tube defects 80–90% of the time. Because an amniocentesis studies the DNA of the foetus, the sex can be determined (but may not always be revealed).

The risk of miscarriage is estimated at between one in 200 and one in 50, depending on the skill of the doctor and whether the mother rests afterwards. There is a 1 in 200 chance that a baby whose mother had an amniocentesis will have either a very low birth weight or neonatal respiratory problems. There is a small risk of introducing infection into the uterus via the needle, or of the baby being injured. In one case in 1,000, the needle misses the amniotic sac, and either punctures a blood vessel or the placenta. Some commentators also believe there is a risk of compression of the foetus with the removal of the fluid. As with CVS (see below), it is wise to check that the doctor performing the procedure performs at least 50 a year or otherwise is properly supervised. It is also worth bearing in mind that the risk is considered slightly higher if the test is done on a mother showing higher than average levels of alpha-fetoprotein (AFP).

Amniocentesis best practice:

➢ Should not be done 'blind', but watching simultaneously using ultrasound.

➢ The skin should be sterilised where the needle will enter so as not to introduce bacteria.

➢ Special fine needles should be used with special tips that are particularly visible to ultrasound scanners.

AMNIOFILTRATION

A form of amniocentesis carried out at around 11–12 weeks. Because of the dates, results are received earlier, but there is generally believed to be an increased risk of miscarriage. The procedure is usually only offered to women known to have a definite risk of a child with a chromosomal abnormality.

CORDOCENTESIS, ALSO KNOWN AS FOETAL BLOOD SAMPLING, OR PERCUTANEOUS UMBILICAL BLOOD SAMPLING (PUBS)

Similar to amniocentesis except that the needle goes into the umbilical cord at the point where it meets the placenta to gather a sample of the baby's blood. This is normally performed at 18 weeks, not before, and results after culturing the blood are available within two days. There is an estimated 2%-plus chance of miscarriage, plus placental and cord problems, so it is usually only used to confirm results of another test which has given serious cause for concern.

COELOCENTESIS

Similar to amniocentesis, this is a test researched at King's College that theoretically would be suitable earlier in pregnancy than amniocentesis or CVS. Research was halted as it was found to involve a higher risk of miscarriage. Subsequent research in Greece apparently runs counter to this finding and King's may restart work in this area. The test involves taking fluid from the cavity around the amniotic sac rather than puncturing the sac.

CVS (CHORIONIC VILLUS SAMPLING OR PLACENTAL BIOPSY)

Chorionic villi are small structures found in the first few weeks of pregnancy with the same chromosomal makeup as the foetus. They disappear by week 13, and the test is performed in weeks 9–12 (no earlier to avoid risk to the foetus).

Generally CVS is only carried out for women who have previously had grave problems with pregnancy, as it carries a higher risk of miscarriage than amniocentesis (2–3%) and also risks infection being introduced into the uterus.

A fine needle and tube are inserted into the womb either through the vagina and cervix, or through the abdominal wall (under local anaesthetic), and – using a scan for guidance – a few cells of the chorionic villi are extracted. (The abdominal route appears to have a lower failure rate and appears to cause less of the bleeding encountered in 10–25% of transcervical procedures.)

The test can reveal inherited diseases like sickle cell, thalassaemia, haemophilia, muscular dystrophy and Down's syndrome and chromosomal disorders, but not spina bifida or other neural tube problems. Preliminary results take 24–48 hours with full results available after two to three weeks.

The test can occasionally produce either a false positive or false negative result. In 2% of cases the test may be inconclusive because the mother's cells get mixed with the baby's. The rate of culture failure is estimated at up to 6%, three times that of amniocentesis.

There are a number of concerns about the effects of the procedure and as yet there has been no assessment of the potential damage of removing part of the tissue surrounding the embryo on the child's long-term health. One disturbing trial found CVS to be associated with serious injury or damage to babies.

In around half of all mothers tested, foetal blood leaks into the mother's system. Because of this some practitioners do not recommend the process for rhesus negative mothers.

5. TESTS AFTER BIRTH

In the 8 to 14 days after the birth, the baby will be given a Guthrie heel prick test. The drops of blood taken are analysed for a rare condition known as phenylketonuria (PKU), inherited from both parents, which, if left untreated, leads to brain damage. This is avoidable with treatment, principally dietary control. This same blood sample can be used to test for cystic fibrosis.

USEFUL CONTACTS

Cystic Fibrosis Trust, ☎ *(020) 8464 7211* ✆ *www.cftrust.org.uk*
Advice, support and information for parents whose children are diagnosed with cystic fibrosis, during pregnancy or after birth.

National Society for Phenylketonuria (NSPKU), ☎ *Helpline (0845) 603 9136, (020) 8364 3010, London & Home Counties (01279) 830162, Membership (0141) 954 6372* ✆ *www.nspuk.org*
Leaflets provide more information and advice on PKU.

6. EXTRA & PRIVATE TESTS

If you feel that you would like to have a certain test, but it is not offered by your antenatal clinic, it may be possible for your GP or consultant to refer you to a specialist unit within the NHS (such as The Harris Birthright Research Unit, see listings). Alternatively, all of the units listed in this section provide testing on a private basis.

Note that if you are having a blood test privately, accurate dating of the pregnancy is needed to improve the blood test's predictive value. You may know precisely when you conceived, or, if there is any doubt, an ultrasound scan can be used to assess your baby's gestational age.

Sample prices for private antenatal tests:

Fetal Viability Scan (5-10 weeks)	£100
Nuchal scan and blood test (11-13 weeks)	£130
with Chorion Villus Sampling (VCS) (11-15 weeks)	£400
Fetal anomaly scan (best performed at 20-24 weeks)	£170
with amnio (from 16 weeks onwards)	£400
with cervical assessment £23-24 weeks)	£200
with serum biochemistry (16-18 weeks)	£200
Fetal cardiac scan (13-24 weeks)	£150
Fetal wellbeing scan and Doppler (24-42 weeks)	£150
Fetal blood sampling (after 20 weeks)	£400
Pre-pregnancy counselling	£100
Amniocentesis or CVS in twin pregnancies	£550

NHS SPECIALIST UNITS

The Harris Birthright Research Centre, ☎ *(020) 7346 3040*
✆ *www.kingshealth.com/clinical/women/harris-birthright*
Under Professor Kypros Nicolaides, this is one of the leading units in the world for developing antenatal tests. To be tested you will require a referral from your GP or consultant. To be tested privately under Professor Nicolaides, contact the Fetal Medicine Centre.

PRIVATE TESTING UNITS

Antenatal Screening Service, ☎ *(020) 7882 6293*
✆ *www.smd.qmul.ac.uk/wolfson/epm/screening*
Offers the Barts Test for Down's syndrome and neural tube defects between 15 and 22 weeks (16–18 weeks being considered ideal to check for neural defects) with confirmation of dating by a scan. They do not encourage use of the test to 'second-guess' poor results from a previous test, say, from your antenatal clinic.

Babybond Ultrasound, ☎ *Booking line (0845) 35 111 55*

Private scans at studios in Ashford Kent (and also Rutland) from 16 weeks recorded for 30 minutes on to either video or DVD as a souvenir, along with a set of photographic images; price £130. At present, the purpose of the scan is completely non-medical (if you have any cause for concern, visit a hospital). In future the firm may consider introducing a more 'medical' test for re-assurance purposes.

Clinical Diagnostic Services, ☎ *(020) 7483 3611*

An ultrasound unit with close links to the Hospital of St John & St Elizabeth. Prices for the 12-week, 21-week and 34-week scans are £165-£180 (or £410 for all three), and amniocentesis costs £385.

Create Health Centre for Reproduction and Advanced Technology, ☎ *(020) 7486 5566* ⌂ *www.createhealth.org*

A centre specialising in all aspects of reproductive health. The centre's Professor Stuart Campbell has been involved in the development of a more sophisticated form of pregnancy scan, funded by a medical trust (Her Trust), which is continuing research into this area. The 3-D and 4-D (ie in real time) scanning techniques use digitally stored echoes, shaded to produce life-like pictures. In addition to showing greater physical detail, the images are more recognisable than traditional scans, complete with yawns, blinks and sometimes even apparently, smiles. A complete pregnancy scan (2D/3D/4D/Doppler) costs £275 and is recommended at around 28 weeks, although available between 20 and 36 weeks.

Doctor's Laboratory, ☎ *(020) 7460 4800* ⌂ *www.tdltlc.co.uk*

Cystic fibrosis 'carrier screen' test £72.50.

Fetal Medicine Centre, ☎ *(020) 7486 0476* ⌂ *www.fetalmedicine.com*

Run by Professor Kypros Nicolaides of King's (see Harris Birthright Research Centre above) – high standard of treatments backed up with informed counselling. Profits are used for further research by the Fetal Medicine Foundation, for example into the development of safer techniques for prenatal diagnosis. Screening scans: foetal viability scan (7–10 weeks, £100); nuchal scan (11–13 weeks, £130); foetal anomaly scan (20–24 weeks, £170); foetal wellbeing scan (24–42 weeks, £150). Diagnostic tests: amniocentesis (16–20 weeks, £400); CVS (11–15 weeks, £400).

Leeds Antenatal Screening Service, ☎ *(0113) 262 1675*

⌂ *www.leedsscreeningcentre.co.uk*
This unit – affiliated with Leeds University – is actively involved in developing new screening techniques. They offer the Beta Triple test (£59), although they currently favour the 'Biomark' test (£88). Other tests available are the Primark test (£185) and a cystic fibrosis blood test (£98); results are generally 7-10 days from receipt of sample (sampling packs are sent with instructions). / PUBLICATIONS *Free Patient Guides: Screening for Down's Syndrome; Screening for Cystic Fibrosis.*

Ultrasound Diagnostic Services, ☎ *(020) 7486 7991, (020) 7935 2243* ⌂ *www.uds.uk.com*
A full range of ultrasound scans including for early pregnancy dating (£95), nuchal translucency and biochemistry (£130) and foetal anomaly (£180).

CHAPTER 1.04

ANTENATAL CLASSES

1. **Introduction**
2. **Information-oriented classes**
3. **Active birth classes**
4. **Exercise classes**
5. **Mental preparation**
6. **Other forms of preparation**

(For information relating to common medical interventions and procedures in labour and options for pain relief, see chapter 4.03 Medical issues at birth. For books that discuss various aspects of pregnancy and the event of birth itself, see chapter 4.05 Finding out more.)

1. INTRODUCTION

Birth preparation classes give women and their partners the opportunity to learn more about the process of giving birth, from its physiological aspects to practical issues, such as what you can expect to find in a delivery room. Sometimes, the sessions also address basic parenting skills such as how to bathe a newborn.

Most hospitals provide some form of antenatal class, but there are also a good number of independent teachers and organisations (of which the NCT is the best known) which offer courses, all with their own angle. If you decide to give classes a go, it's worth giving some thought to finding the class and teacher which will suit you.

At their best, birth preparation classes can:
➢ Provide a background understanding about what goes on in a woman's body during birth.
➢ Inform pregnant women (and their partners) about common medical practices and interventions in labour, so that should any problems arise they can understand and participate in decisions on how the situation should be handled.
➢ Improve fitness and flexibility in preparation for the birth.
➢ Teach positions and exercises to help facilitate the birth.
➢ Build confidence, helping to reduce the stress and pain of labour.
➢ Give a few basic pointers about the practical day-to-day care of newborn babies.

Less obviously, perhaps, classes also offer an excellent chance to make friends with others in the same situation and to build up what can become an invaluable support network after birth.

With this in mind, when selecting a course it is sensible to consider whether you think you are likely to find congenial people on it, and particularly people whose approach to babies and children match your own. The average age can also be relevant. Above all, though, bear in mind that when you are adjusting to a new baby the proximity of your friends takes on a particular importance, so it is well worth trying to find a local group.

Classes fall broadly into the following three categories, with a large degree of crossover between each type:

Information-oriented classes: 'traditional' classes, such as those run by hospitals or the NCT, the core of which is discussing issues such as the physiological changes which take place during labour, possible medical interventions and options for pain relief.

Active birth classes: often much of the same ground is covered as in the more traditional classes, but the emphasis is much more on the physical aspects of, and preparation for, birth. Yoga-based exercises help to build strength and flexibility and promote ease and comfort in a variety of upright positions that can make giving birth easier.

Exercise classes: sometimes purely keep-fit. Many of the classes use yoga, where the aim is to learn positions that will help facilitate the birth.

Opting for one type of course does not, of course, preclude you from attending another. Whatever your choice, some form of exercise should probably be part of your antenatal preparation.

POSTNATAL PREPARATION (OR RATHER LACK OF IT)

Note that it is common for courses to ignore life on the other side of the birth, and those that do cover it do so in little detail.

It can be difficult to focus your mind on this in advance, but once plunged into the reality of being a mother some women wish they had given more thought to the subject in advance. It is worth looking out for the odd class that does actually tackle this area.

Book early

BIRTH PREPARATION CLASSES

Both information-oriented and active birth classes usually take the form of courses attended from around the 30th week of pregnancy. It is usually best not to leave starting these too late, in case the baby arrives early and you miss some. Most good classes are booked up well in advance so you should try to book as early as possible, certainly by the end of your third month.

Classes may be offered in the evening, during the day, or at week-ends. If you are still working and/or wanting to attend as a couple, a weekend option may be your best bet, especially given that in the later months of pregnancy women can find themselves very tired in the evenings.

EXERCISE CLASSES

It is recommended that you start building up your fitness from around the 12th week of pregnancy. Some classes are 'drop-in', requiring no advance thought, though the better ones usually have to be booked.

All regular classes (as opposed to set-length courses) should allow you a trial visit to see if the style suits you before you sign up for more regular attendance.

LISTINGS OF CLASSES IN THIS CHAPTER

No times are given for any of the classes listed in this chapter because they change regularly; and because – except in the case of exercise classes at leisure centres – most teachers strongly discourage drop-ins to their lessons. You are generally required to book a number of sessions at once.

SUMMARY OF YOUR ROUTINE APPOINTMENTS DURING PREGNANCY

YES — Have you had a baby before? — NO

✔✔	Before 12 weeks (may be 2 appointments)	• Give information on diet & lifestyle considerations, pregancy care services, maternity benefits, and screening tests. Your doctor or midwife should: • Find out if you need additional care • Tell you how taking folic acid (400 micrograms per day for up to 12 weeks) can reduce certain health risks for your baby. • Offer you screening tests and make sure you understand what is involved before you decide to have any of them. • Offer you an ultrasound scan to estimate when the baby is due. • Measure your blood pressure, height & weight. • Test your urine for the presence of protein. • Offer you help to stop smoking if you want it. • Offer you an ultrasound scan at 18-20 weeks to check the physical development of the baby.	✔✔
✔	16 weeks	• Your midwife or doctor should review, discuss and record results of any screening tests. • Measure your blood pressure. • Test your urine.	✔
	25 weeks	• Check on the size of your abdomen. Measure blood pressure & test your urine.	✔
✔	28 weeks	• Checks on the size of your abdomen, your blood pressure & test your urine • More screening tests for anaemia and red cell antibodies if you wish them. • If you are rhesus negative, first anti-D treatment if you wish it.	✔
	31 weeks	• Checks on the size of your abdomen, your blood pressure & test your urine.	✔
✔	34 weeks	• Checks on the size of your abdomen, your blood pressure & test your urine. • If you are rhesus negative, second anti-D treatment if you wish it.	✔
✔	36 weeks	• Checks on the size of your abdomen, your blood pressure & test your urine. • Check to see if the baby is head first – discuss options to turn the baby if it is feet first (breech position)	✔
✔	38 weeks	• Checks on the size of your abdomen, your blood pressure & test your urine.	✔
	40 weeks	• Checks on the size of your abdomen, your blood pressure & test your urine.	✔
	41 weeks	• Checks on the size of your abdomen, your blood pressure & test your urine. • Discuss option of membrane sweep. • Discuss whether you want your labour to be induced after 41 weeks.	

✔ Total appointments if you've had a baby before   Total appointments if you've not had a baby before **10**

2. INFORMATION-ORIENTED CLASSES

'Traditional' antenatal classes are primarily information-oriented. Most hospitals run such classes, and the National Childbirth Trust (NCT) has a formidable following for its courses.

This kind of class seems to be particularly useful for partners as they seem to be less motivated than mothers to do any reading up in advance. Couples' sessions in particular reassure men that they are not alone, and some courses offer a 'fathers only' evening. There are also classes solely for women should you prefer this.

Topics usually covered include:
➢ An explanation of what happens physiologically during labour.
➢ Terms used by the medical profession.
➢ Forms of pain relief.
➢ What you can do to help yourself, what your partner can do to back you up.

Useful additional topics worth looking for:
➢ An explanation of medical interventions, together with any issues about their relative risks and benefits.
➢ Looking after the baby (for example, how to breast-feed) and the post-natal period (including the emotional and psychological effects of birth on you and your relationship).

HOSPITAL-BASED CLASSES

Typically, NHS hospitals offer classes in a series of four to six (but sometimes more) sessions, also referred to as parentcraft or parent education classes. You should be guaranteed a place. The classes often focus on the particular approach preferred at that particular hospital and may have the advantage of allowing you to get to know more of the people who will be looking after you antenatally and at the birth. They will also probably be more revealing of that hospital's approach than the antenatal ward tour.

How good these classes are varies very much from hospital to hospital. Some hospitals, for example, offer specific classes on breast-feeding and some may also offer additional antenatal exercise and/or yoga classes, though this is not the norm.

THE NATIONAL CHILDBIRTH TRUST (NCT)

For many parents, membership of the NCT and attendance at its antenatal classes are part of the initiation rites of parenthood.

Now with over 50,000 members nationally (5,000 or so of whom live in London), the National Childbirth Trust, founded some 40 years ago, aims to provide parents with information and support in pregnancy, childbirth and early parenthood. Though perhaps best known for its antenatal teaching and breast-feeding counselling, it is also developing into a research-based lobbying organisation.

In their classes, NCT antenatal teachers cover the following: how the NHS works; pregnancy and birth; informed choice; preparing fathers-to-be; pain and pain relief; and postnatal life. Details of what is offered on each course vary from teacher to teacher, and from group to group.

To the extent that the organisation has a 'position', it is perhaps linked in many people's mind with natural childbirth and the avoidance of pain relief. Some people think that the 'N' in NCT still stands for 'Natural' rather than 'National' – even though the NCT changed its name within a couple of years of its foundation (four decades ago). The organisation has softened its line in this regard (though individual teachers may not have done), and these days puts more emphasis on informed maternal choice.

Without in any way denigrating the antenatal preparation classes run by the NCT, it is possibly its success as a 'networking' organisation for like-minded mums that really explains the strength of its membership. (You do not in fact even have to be a member to attend antenatal classes.) Given its strong appeal to some people, it is perhaps inevitable that it equally strongly turns others off, with perhaps the most common criticisms being that its ethos is 'preachy' and too middle-class.

What is undoubted is that the NCT embodies the concept that one of the most useful features of antenatal preparation is making new friends who are experiencing exactly what you are going through.

Contact central office for details of your nearest group running antenatal classes, and postnatal support groups, and for information and support for breast-feeding.

London branches are:

Barnet & District	Hillingdon
Bromley & District	Kingston
Central London	Lewisham & Greenwich
Chiswick	London Northwest
Clapham, Wimbledon	Newham
& Wandsworth	Putney & Fulham
Croydon & Coulsdon	Redbridge & District
Ealing	Richmond
Enfield	Southwark & Lambeth
Epsom & District	Sutton
Hackney & Islington	Tower Hamlets
Haringey	Twickenham
Harrow	Waltham Forest

INFORMATION-ORIENTED CLASSES

CENTRAL

Portland Hospital, Physiotherapy Unit
234 Great Portland St (opposite main hospital) W1N 6AH ☎ (020) 7390 8061
⌐ www.theportlandhospital.com
The hospital provides an antenatal preparation course (open to all, wherever you are having your baby) consisting of six weekly classes (two hours each) by a parentcraft midwife and obstetric physiotherapist (including a tour of the unit); evening and day classes available. There is also a condensed four hour weekend workshop covering labour for £84 and one-to-one sessions tailored to individual needs. / SEE ALSO *2.01 Postnatal; 2.03 Baby health; 4.02 Health practitioners.*

WEST

Sarah Bradley
11 Fielding Rd W4 1HP ☎ (020) 8994 0966
NCT-accredited advanced antenatal teacher offering evening classes and weekend workshops giving advice and information about all aspects of pregnancy and childbirth, including informed choice and self-help relaxation and pain-relief techniques; postnatal advice also given; up to £180. Sarah is also a member of the West London Teaching Group (NCT).

Heather Guerrini
30 Redesdale St SW3 4BJ ☎ (020) 7352 0245
Qualified nurse and NCT teacher, offering NCT classes in a variety of formats, including a concentrated course: two full-day workshops, plus an evening breast-feeding session and an evening for fathers. Courses for couples are £300 with a maximum of seven couples in a group. Other options include 'Refresher Classes' (for second and third time mothers); also one to ones. Class members are encouraged to socialise through reunions. / SEE ALSO *2.04 Childcare; 2.06 Baby & toddler activities; 4.02 Health practitioners.*

Christine Hill Associates
Strand End, 78 Grove Park Rd W4 3QA ☎ (020) 8994 4349
Obstetric physiotherapist Christine Hill's antenatal and postnatal courses are expensive, but they do produce many satisfied customers, who journey from all over town to attend. The full antenatal course is £440 and consists of eight weekly two-hour classes (including a class with Clare Byam-Cook, feeding specialist, and another held by the resident GP, Dr Tim Evans (ex-Medical Officer at the Portland Hospital). 'Refresher' courses are also available, £160.

Maud Giles
☎ (07939) 820651
Lactation consultant and ex-paediatric nurse offering breast-feeding and babycare lessons; partners welcome. Covers issues including what to do if you get mastitis, how to tell when your baby is getting enough milk, expressing, feeding twins, bathing, wrapping, handling the newborn, and postnatal consultations; £90 for one and a half hours. / HOURS 24hr answerphone; SEE ALSO 2.02 Feeding; 2.04 Childcare.

National Childbirth Trust (NCT)
Alexandra House, Oldham Terrace W3 6NH ☎ Enquiry line (0870) 444 8707
⊕ www.nctpregnancyandbabycare.co.uk; www.nctparentsconnect.co.uk
The UK's largest childbirth charity (see above), whose local branches are the lynchpin of most of its services. The organisation's largest areas of activity are mother-to-mother support (i.e. providing a social network), antenatal preparation and breast-feeding counselling, but exactly what is available depends on the branch: only some branches, for example, have nanny-share registers, postnatal training or groups for fathers. The trust is an enormous information reserve. At a local and national level it maintains an 'Experience Register' – lessons learnt by women who have faced unusual situations. It can also refer people with specific needs to other support organisations. You don't have to be a member of the NCT to take NCT antenatal classes, which are run on an area-by-area basis – call the central office and they will put you in contact with the person running the bookings for a given area (charges vary from area to area within a scale set by the central office). If the teacher you are allocated is not right for you it's worth trying to persuade the referral person in your local branch to transfer you to another class. Bear in mind however that classes get booked up months in advance. Information on classes and times can be found online. / HOURS Mon-Thurs 9am-5pm, Fri 9am-4pm; or answerphone; PUBLICATIONS Leaflets on most issues concerning childbirth; many local branches produce useful guides; large number of books (see NCT Maternity Sales); SEE ALSO 1.01 Where to have the baby; 2.01 Postnatal; 2.02 Feeding; 2.04 Childcare; 2.05 Travel; 2.06 Baby & toddler activities; 3.02 Baby equipment; 4.04 Miscarriage & stillbirth; 4.05 Finding out more; 4.06 Support groups.

The New Baby Company
8 Souldern Road W14 0JE ☎ (020) 7751 1152 ⊕ www.newbabycompany.com
Established in 2002, the company offers high quality antenatal courses, courses for couples and refresher courses in central and south west London; also a private one-to-one service. The stated aim ("our aim is to prepare you for motherhood – not just the birth") reflects the founders' belief that antenatal courses focus too much on preparation for the birth itself, rather than what happens next. / SEE ALSO 2.03 Baby health; 2.06 Baby & toddler activities.

Lolly Stirk
Holland Park W11 ☎ (01323) 422054
Lolly has been working in Holland Park for 15 years "encouraging parents to become active participants in the birth and infancy of their babies". Classes offered include birth preparation courses and breast-feeding workshops; also yoga; £14. / SEE ALSO 2.01 Postnatal.

NORTH

The Active Birth Centre ⌨
25 Bickerton Rd N19 5JT ☎ (020) 7281 6760 ⊕ www.activebirthcentre.com
'Preparing for labour and birth' is a five part course that partners can attend (£90 per person): it covers issues such as the choices of birth venue, normal birth, use of Syntometrine, monitoring, induction, foetal distress and learning assertiveness and negotiating skills. 'Your new baby: what nobody tells you', is more a parentcraft course than preparation for the birth: it explains how a child's development unfolds and is designed to help parents stay one step ahead of the game. / HOURS shop Mon-Fri 9.30am-6.30pm (Fri 4pm), Sat 10am-4pm; SEE ALSO 1.01 Where to have the baby; 1.06 Birth equipment; 2.01 Postnatal; 2.02 Feeding; 2.03 Baby health; 2.06 Baby & toddler activities; 3.01 Maternity wear; 3.02 Baby equipment; 4.02 Health practitioners; 4.05 Finding out more.

Julie Krausz

77 Hardinge Rd NW10 3PN ☎ (020) 8459 2903 ⌁ www.yogabirth.org
Active birth and yoga teacher whose birth preparation classes for couples comprise
a full weekend: topics include avoiding the cascade of intervention and coping with the
first few days after birth; £180 per couple. Advice on breast-feeding and relaxation can
be found on the website (Julie runs Body Comfort – see also). / SEE ALSO 2.01 Postnatal.

O&L Women's Health Physiotherapy Clinic

Fortis Green Health Clinic, 150 Fortis Green N10 3PA ☎ (020) 8920 9407
'Care in Pregnancy' classes cover comfortable ways of handling daily movements
(including sitting and turning in bed), relaxation to prevent pain, prevention of
incontinence and prolapse, exercises, advice on diet, breathing control, coping in
labour and breast-feeding. £70 for 4-5 sessions. / HOURS Mon, Tues, Weds, Fri: 8am-6pm; SEE
ALSO 1.06 Birth equipment; 2.01 Postnatal; 4.02 Health practitioners.

Yogahome

11 Allen Rd N16 8SB ☎ (020) 7249 2425 ⌁ www.yogahome.com
Birth preparation classes for individuals and couples by appointment, £30, including
massage and relaxation techniques for labour. / HOURS Call for hours; SEE ALSO 2.01 Postnatal.

SOUTH

Albany Midwifery Practice

*Peckham Pulse, 10 Melon Rd SE15 5QN ☎ (020) 7525 4995, Peckham Pulse (020)
7525 4999 ⌁ www.albanymidwives.org*
Antenatal discussion groups run by an NHS midwifery practice: one for women only
and one for couples; free. / SEE ALSO 2.01 Postnatal.

Sue Lewis Grad DB, MCSP, SRP

65 Vineyard Hill Rd SW19 7JL ☎ (020) 8946 8561
Obstetric physiotherapist Sue Lewis runs a wide range of classes. Birth preparation
covers pregnancy through to the first few weeks with the baby, complete with
information packs (£195 per couple, maximum five couples). Refresher courses for
second or third-time mums are also available. A 90-minute breast-feeding class with
a midwife includes coverage of a host of associated issues (bras, maternal diet, etc) for
£30. Also a Baby Confidence class – one and a half hours run by a midwife to help
establish good early feeding and sleeping habits with a new baby. / SEE ALSO 2.01 Postnatal;
2.03 Baby health; 2.06 Baby & toddler activities; 4.02 Health practitioners.

Mama-Rhythms

Wimbledon area ☎ (020) 8879 7081
Courses for couples by Angela Yates, an NCT teacher and assessor, health visitor and
reflexologist; offers sessions in relaxation, positions for labour, gentle exercise
incorporating discussions about birth and life with a new baby; £200 per couple. Also
postnatal classes and baby massage classes. / SEE ALSO 4.02 Health practitioners.

Val Orrow

31 Howard's Lane SW15 6NX ☎ (020) 8789 8885
Labour classes for couples, by arrangement.

Sarah Spoor (Baby Bliss)

127a Twickenham Rd Isleworth TW7 6AW ☎ (020) 8568 4913 ⌁ www.baby-bliss.com
Sessions for couples one evening a month, whose topics include how to choose your
hospital, hospital statistics, antenatal classes, and services offered by the NCT; £5 per
couple. / HOURS phone for appointment; SEE ALSO 1.06 Birth equipment; 2.06 Baby & toddler activities.

EAST

Arlene Dunkley-Wood

154 King's Head Hill E4 7NU ☎ (020) 8923 6452 (answerphone), (020) 8923 6452
An active birth teacher who offers one-day birth education classes either from home or
in Bethnal Green and Chingford (£100 per couple). / SEE ALSO 2.01 Postnatal; 2.06 Baby &
toddler activities.

Jayne Herbert

49 Mildenhall Rd E5 0RT ☎ (020) 8533 9925
Co-ordinator of childbirth preparation classes in Hackney and Islington, with various
teachers. A mixture of weekend and evening courses is available. The standard
eight-week course costs £155, which includes a year's membership of the NCT; shorter
intensive courses are priced pro rata, and concessions are available. / SEE ALSO
2.01 Postnatal.

3. ACTIVE BIRTH CLASSES

The Active Birth Movement was started in the late '70s by women who set out to encourage the then-relatively-novel idea (in the UK) of adopting upright positions for birth. It also proposed practising quite gentle, yoga-based positions, with awareness of breathing, relaxation and posture as part of preparation during pregnancy. The philosophy behind the classes is that they are for women who wish to play an active role in events, rather than be a passive participant in the process.

The Active Birth Centre is the most prominent advocate of this approach, and there is now a network of trained and certified active birth teachers throughout the UK. Some active birth teachers are also qualified NCT teachers.

Active birth classes differ from most other antenatal classes in encouraging pregnant women to start early. Twelve weeks is usually the recommended joining date, although it is never considered too late to start. The idea is to make the skills that are taught throughout pregnancy second nature, so that they can be used more easily during labour.

The main focus of active birth preparation is a weekly class of easy and relaxing yoga-based exercises (suitable for women with no previous yoga experience) together with a 'guided talk' on birth-related issues. This in effect combines training in practical skills to facilitate labour, with consideration of the situations you may face during pregnancy and labour – including the emotional and personal aspects of the process. Particularly useful is the practice of encouraging new mothers who have attended the class to return after the birth to talk through their experience of labour.

In addition to yoga classes, active birth teachers may offer information classes to be attended, with or without a partner, towards the end of a pregnancy. These cover birth options and breast-feeding, with more detailed information about active and water births. Some active birth teachers (and specifically the Active Birth Centre) offer one-day active birth workshops which cover labour and birth, rehearsal of birth positions, breathing, massage and partner support. These tend to book up early.

The active birth approach strongly supports promoting the natural process of labour. However, if such teaching places too much emphasis on the natural process it can make a genuine need for intervention seem rather more daunting than it might otherwise. A good teacher will not neglect to prepare the mothers for whom this will not be possible.

At its best, the active birth approach is designed to apply not just to a natural birth but – in fostering a flexible approach – to 'empower' women to take positive decisions about what is best for them, whatever the circumstances.

It seems that generally less emphasis is placed on getting the group to work together socially and to form a postnatal network than, for example, with NCT classes. Postnatal classes, where they are available, can help fulfil some of this role.

ACTIVE BIRTH CLASSES

WEST

Annabel Hargrave
SW19 ☎ *(020) 8287 5411* ✆ *www.yogabirth.org*
Qualified active birth teacher, working in Wimbledon and Southfields, who does yoga-based classes (max 10) to aid relaxation and prepare for birth; cost £10 for two hours; also Saturday morning workshops for couples (£50) to help them prepare for the birth and life afterwards. / HOURS *phone during office hours; SEE ALSO 2.01 Postnatal.*

NORTH

The Active Birth Centre 🏠
25 Bickerton Rd N19 5JT ☎ (020) 7281 6760 ◌ www.activebirthcentre.com
Active birth courses are run at the ABC itself but the centre also provides a list of
antenatal teachers qualified to teach in its style. There are two main types of active
birth course: the first comprises antenatal yoga classes (registration fee £10, then £20
per two-hour class with Janet, or £12 per class with other teachers) which include
discussion of the emotional and physical issues relating to birth; the other type of
course is more 'information-heavy' (see under Information-oriented classes).
Workshops on topics including practical skills for birth; massage for pregnancy and
labour; introduction to homeopathy; preparing to breast-feed are also offered (prices
vary). / *HOURS shop Mon-Fri 9.30am-6.30pm (Fri 4pm), Sat 10am-4pm; SEE ALSO 1.01 Where to have the
baby; 1.06 Birth equipment; 2.01 Postnatal; 2.02 Feeding; 2.03 Baby health; 2.06 Baby & toddler activities;
3.01 Maternity wear; 3.02 Baby equipment; 4.02 Health practitioners; 4.05 Finding out more.*

Jessica James
26 Kyverdale Rd N16 7AH ☎ (020) 8806 4820
Evening active birth classes with yoga and some discussion; also preparation courses
(with partners) which include strategies for getting the birth you want and
breast-feeding; £160 for eight classes; concessionary rates available. Best to book early.
Individual counselling is also available. / *SEE ALSO 2.01 Postnatal.*

Yvonne Moore
☎ (020) 7794 2056
An independent childbirth educator (co-founder of the Active Birth Association and
co-director of the Active Birth Teachers Training Course), Yvonne provides those who
attend her classes with useful extra information on all aspects of preparation for labour
and birth in groups or privately. She also offers one-to-one counselling sessions,
including on childbirth and help with handling any fears or problems from a previous
birth experience. Classes held in north London. / *SEE ALSO 2.01 Postnatal.*

EAST

Bridget Baker
116 Forest Rd E8 3BH ☎ (020) 7249 3224
A member of the Professional Association of Childbirth Educators. Classes include
exercise, but also a fair amount of information. Couples' classes take various formats,
typically nine weekly sessions for £150, or intensive weekend course, £100. Individual
sessions by arrangement.

4. EXERCISE CLASSES

Although you should make sure you get plenty of rest – particularly in
the first three months – it is sensible to keep fit during pregnancy.

Much of the incentive to do so relates to the period after the birth –
looking after a baby is physically demanding. In particular learning to lift
properly is vital, and pelvic floor (Kegel) exercises can help prevent incontinence, which affects an estimated one-third of all women after birth
(and some claim such exercises also help reduce the likelihood of a tear
or the need for an episiotomy).

Getting fit also seems to many women to be a logical way of preparing for labour. However – although there is a link between obesity and
problems at birth – statistically it does not actually appear that there is
any great relation between a woman's physical fitness and the length and
type of her labour. (There may, however, be benefits when it comes to
a speedier recovery from the labour.) What's more, it's important not to
over-do it, with a 2003 US study linking vigorous exercise in pregnancy
with lower birth-weight babies.

Few sports centres, including local authority ones, know much about
exercise in pregnancy (though they are improving), and it seems few doctors and midwives do either. That means that even if you are fit enough
to continue your normal class with appropriate adjustments, you may
not be allowed to do so. Women-only gyms, run by some local authorities,

are generally better informed and are more likely to help you, and increasingly the growing number of private gyms are catering to this kind of requirement as well.

Taking up exercise for the first time in pregnancy should be fine, provided it's a simple programme which doesn't increase your heart rate very much.

Particularly if you have not been in the habit of taking exercise, the recommended forms of activity are long, repetitive actions like walking or swimming. Exercise in water appears to be particularly beneficial, partly because the cushioning of the water minimises the likelihood of strain, and partly because the water supports the growing weight of the baby.

You should avoid:
➤ New forms of exercise or high-intensity, high-impact exercise, like running or sudden strenuous activity. (These can all divert blood from the uterus.)
➤ Exercising at all if you are feeling sick, tired, dizzy, are suffering from vaginal bleeding, or from any pain, including persistent headaches.
➤ Sports which could involve sudden impact, such as skiing, martial arts or squash.
➤ Long stretches, over-extension of joints and excessive bending. Stretching and twisting should be done with care as ligaments loosen in pregnancy making a strain more likely.
➤ Over-exercising to the point of exhaustion, getting overheated or dehydrated (forget the "no pain, no gain" approach for the moment).
➤ Lying flat on your back after 16–20 weeks (which can diminish the blood flow to and from the placenta).
➤ Exercising quite as much as you did before pregnancy. Alternatively, check that your pulse is below 120 five minutes after exercising and below 100 ten minutes afterwards – if not, you are doing too much.
➤ Continuing your normal exercise classes unless the teacher is professionally trained, knows you are pregnant and can allow for this by not involving you in any high impact or abdominal work.
➤ Exercising in hot weather unless you can drink plenty of fluid to avoid dehydration.

All the above precautions are, perhaps, even more important in the last three months of pregnancy, as there is some evidence that women who exercise a great deal in this period are slightly more likely to have low birthweight babies.

Benefits of exercise include:
➤ Improved posture.
➤ Controlled weight gain.
➤ Improved circulation, which helps to prevent varicose veins and leg cramps; (walking and swimming can be particularly helpful with this, combined with putting your feet up above the level of your head daily).
➤ According to some studies, alleviation of depression.
➤ According to some studies, improved general recovery after birth.
➤ The chance to join others in a similar situation from early in pregnancy, when you have most questions and may feel most in need of a support group.

GENERAL READING

Bathrobics for pregnancy – Jane Dorey, Justine Peek & Conny Jude (For health and vitality during and after pregnancy; Aqua Fitness; 1995; £11.99; 0-951951-77-7) – *Physiotherapist gives ideas for exercises in the bath.* / *Blooming Marvellous.*

Easy Exercises for Pregnancy – Janet Balaskas & Anthea Sieveking (Frances Lincoln; 1997; £9.99; 0-711210-48-9) – *Accessible work with wide appeal; ideas for a routine about twice a week.*

Essential exercises for the childbearing years – Elizabeth Noble (A guide to health and comfort before and after your baby is born; New Way of Life; 1995; £15.50; 0964118319) – *The fourth edition on exercises and posture for pregnancy and labour.*

Exercise for the Childbearing Year – Eileen Brayshaw & Pauline Wright (Butterworth-Heinemann Medical; 1996; £5.95; 1-898507-29-5) – *Written by two obstetric physiotherapists for use in pregnancy, in labour and after the birth. / Royal College of Midwives.*

Fit for Two – YMCA of the USA with Thomas W Hanlon (The official YMCA prenatal exercise guide; Human Kinetics – (0113) 278 1708; 1995; £9.95; 0873228286) – *RoSPA;T. McClurg Anderson*

The Mother and Baby Exercise Book – Emma Scattergood (Cassell & Co.; 1995; £9.99; 0706373928) – *Comprehensive exercise routines and complete instructions for a good fitness level to be maintained.*

Water Fitness During Pregnancy – Jane Katz (Human Kinetics; 1994; £14.95; 0-873224-95-7) – *Features 44 easy-to-follow exercises for women at all stages of pregnancy.*

Woman's Guide to Sport in Pregnancy (Maternity Alliance; 1994; £2.50; 0946741158) – *A Woman's Guide to Sport in Pregnancy.*

[Video] **The Y Plan Before & After Pregnancy** (1991; £12.99; AISN B00004CLHM) – *Approved by the Royal College of Midwives – Central YMCA fitness teachers take you through 12 minute blocks of exercise for different stages of pregnancy. / Lifetime Vision Ltd, Freepost 9 (WD 4616), London W1E 8AA – (020) 7577 7513.*

PILATES

Pilates for Pregnancy – Anna Selby (Gentle and Effective Techniques... for Before and After Birth; HarperCollins; 2002; £8.99; 0007133146) – *Suitable both in pregnancy and postnatally, a good all-round guide to the famous body-toning and posture-improving exercise programme,*

Pilates for Pregnancy – Michael King, Yolande Green (Toning Exercises for the Mother to Be; Mitchell Beazley; 2002; £10; 1840005408) – *Based on low-impact Pilates exercises, the guide tells you how to improve posture and increase back strength, using breathing and gentle stretching to strengthen the body's core muscles. Three versions of the original Pilates movements are suggested in step-by-step sequences for the three trimesters, as well as advice on exercise after birth.*

The Pilates Pregnancy – Mari Winsor with Mark Laska (A low-impact exercise programme for maintaining strength and flexibility; Vermilion; 2001; £10.99; 0-09-188289-3) – *A US title drawing on this system of exercise which is thought suitable both during pregnancy and after. There is an extensive section on the principles of the system, with specific programmes for each trimester. / www.randomhouse.co.uk.*

EXERCISE CLASSES

CENTRAL

Portland Hospital, Physiotherapy Unit
234 Great Portland St (opposite main hospital) WIN 6AH ☎ (020) 7390 8061
🖰 www.theportlandhospital.com
Antenatal, pilates-based, keep fit (suitable after 16 weeks pregnancy) supervised by an obstetric physiotherapist (consent of an obstetrician or GP is required if you wish to attend); £100 for six classes, or £18 per class. / SEE ALSO *2.01 Postnatal; 2.03 Baby health; 4.02 Health practitioners.*

WEST

Lysta Perry (RSA)
17 Turnham Green Terrace W4 1RG ☎ (020) 8994 8118
Specialist in ante and postnatal exercise: provides personal programmes at home (priced varies somewhat depending on distance), and personal aquanatal programmes. / SEE ALSO *2.01 Postnatal.*

Postnatal Shape Up Classes
44 Hartington Rd W4 3TX ☎ (020) 8994 0369
Personal trainer Rosemary Newman predominantly teaches postnatal Pilates-based exercise, but also runs prenatal classes. / SEE ALSO *2.01 Postnatal.*

West London Birth Centre
Northfields Community Centre, 71a Northcroft Rd W13 9SS ☎ *(020) 8567 2893*
Drop-in classes, comprising gentle stretching and exercise with the focus on breathing for pain relief and posture awareness, £5; Wednesday evenings, 8-9.45pm.

NORTH

Judy Di Fiore
☎ *(020) 8931 2085*
Antenatal fitness and Antenatal Pilates classes by private tuition only, £35 per session in Barnett area. / *SEE ALSO 2.01 Postnatal.*

Fit Start
Lancaster House, 6 Lancaster Rd N4 4PP ☎ *(020) 8374 7680*
Gentle antenatal workouts for all mothers-to-be are run by this north London-based organisation, which also offers a continuation of exercise for after the birth, with postnatal classes, baby massage classes and lively activity classes for kids. Classes (which run in terms the same length as school terms: 10-14 weeks) in Camden, Crouch End and Islington. / *SEE ALSO 2.01 Postnatal; 2.06 Baby & toddler activities.*

SOUTH

The Battersea Practice (Physio For All)
40 Webbs Rd SW11 6SF ☎ *(020) 7228 2141*
Antenatal exercise classes in small groups, with some discussion; locations in Battersea (maximum 8 people, £11) and Chelsea (maximum 4 people, £12). / *HOURS Mon-Fri: 9am-5pm, Sat: 9am-12pm; SEE ALSO 2.01 Postnatal; 4.02 Health practitioners.*

Sue Lewis Grad DB, MCSP, SRP
65 Vineyard Hill Rd SW19 7JL ☎ *(020) 8946 8561*
Antenatal preparation for birth classes with relaxation and breathing exercises: a course of five daytime classes with the option of bringing your partner to an evening session, £125. Also evening classes for couples; £195 for a three-week course. / *SEE ALSO 2.01 Postnatal; 2.03 Baby health; 2.06 Baby & toddler activities; 4.02 Health practitioners.*

London Academy of Personal Fitness
36 Carleton Ave, Wallington Surrey SM6 9LN ☎ *(0870) 4423231* ✆ *www.lapf.co.uk*
A team of 40 fitness trainers who can provide personally-tailored ante- and postnatal programmes, which include exercise, nutritional advice and stress relief. The programme director, who writes for a number of baby magazines on fitness issues (including Baby and Our Baby), allocates trainers and carries out initial fitness assessments and subsequent reassessments to check progress; £45 per session (£55 for two people); initial assessment is free if you sign up for 10 classes. / *HOURS 24 hour answerphone; SEE ALSO 2.01 Postnatal.*

Malden Leisure Centre
Blagdon Rd, New Malden Surrey KT3 4TA ☎ *(020) 8336 7770*
Weekly aquanatal classes from a qualified teacher: £43 for seven weeks (45 minute sessions); suitable from early to late pregnancy; crèche, yoga for pregnancy, £33 for five weeks, no experience necessary. / *HOURS Vary; SEE ALSO 2.01 Postnatal.*

World of Health
PO Box 23103 SE1 2GP ☎ *(020) 7357 9393* ✆ *www.worldofhealth.co.uk*
Health, fitness and lifestyle video and DVD supplier with some exercise titles. / *SEE ALSO 2.01 Postnatal; 2.02 Feeding; 2.06 Baby & toddler activities; 4.02 Health practitioners; 4.05 Finding out more.*

AQUANATAL CLASSES

WEST

Chelsea Sports Centre
Chelsea Manor St SW3 5PL ☎ *(020) 7352 6985*
Morning exercise classes in the toddler pool, £2.80. / *SEE ALSO 2.06 Baby & toddler activities.*

NORTH

Copthall Pools
Page St, Great North Way NW4 1PS ☎ *(020) 8457 9920*
Ante- and postnatal aquanatal classes, £4.45. / *SEE ALSO 2.01 Postnatal; 2.06 Baby & toddler activities.*

SOUTH

Amateur Swimming Association (ASA)
☎ (01509) 618 700
Joint ante-and postnatal aquanatal classes, with a midwife always present, £3.10. / *SEE ALSO 2.01 Postnatal; 2.06 Baby & toddler activities.*

Arches Leisure Centre
80 Trafalgar Rd SE10 9UX ☎ *(020) 8317 5020*
Aquarobic class followed by antenatal/postnatal discussion with an independent midwife. Partners are welcome to attend the evening sessions (morning classes are for women only); £5 per session (membership of £27 a year gives about 30% of prices). / *HOURS Mon-Sun 7am-8pm; SEE ALSO 2.01 Postnatal; 2.06 Baby & toddler activities.*

Splashworld Swimming Centre
Crook Log Bexleyheath, Kent DA6 8EQ ☎ *(020) 8303 5781* ⌁ *www.leisure-centre.com*
Aquanatal Thursday evening classes, £2.30 (£3.30 non-members; membership £27 per year). / *HOURS Mon-Fri 9am-9pm (Mon 9.30pm), Sat & Sun 8am-7pm; SEE ALSO 2.06 Baby & toddler activities.*

Yoga

As well as helping to keep you fit, yoga-based classes, especially less energetic ones, are particularly suitable for pregnancy. Different techniques focus on different aspects of bodily control, but in general yoga offers:

➤ Increased suppleness, and bodily awareness, a knowledge of certain positions and control of certain muscles, which together may facilitate birth.

➤ Focus on breath control as a conscious technique for reducing stress – a very relevant preparation for giving birth because, as a result, there may be less need for pain relief.

➤ Mental relaxation through calmed thoughts and emotions.

For maximum benefit, yoga is, like all exercise, recommended from around 12 weeks. The early start on breathing techniques (now taught in most antenatal classes for use during contractions) can be particularly useful. The longer they are practised the easier they are to use.

No prior experience of yoga is required for antenatal yoga classes and in fact it should be easier than normal as the hormones to relax the ligaments make stretching easier. It's an effect which works postnatally as well for as long as you continue breastfeeding.

READING

Easy Pregnancy with Yoga – Stella Weller (HarperCollins; 1991; £8.99; 0722519311)

The New Book of Yoga – Sivananda Yoga Centre (A complete step-by-step guide; Ebury; 1990, revised 2000; £14.99; 0091874610) – *Includes a sensible 14-page section on pregnancy, showing how standard poses can be modified by expectant women.*

Preparing for Birth with Yoga – Balaskas, Sabatini & Gordon (Exercises for pregnancy and childbirth; Element Books; 1994; £14.99; 1852304316)

[Video] **Simple Yoga for Pregnancy** (Little Gems Yoga; £15) – *Suitable for beginners (from 14 weeks of pregnancy); demonstrated by yoga teachers and pregnant women. / www.littlegemsyoga.co.uk Old Estate Office, Winchester Road, Sutton Scotney, Hampshire SO21 3JN.*

[Tape] **Yoga for Pregnancy** – Francoise Barbira Freedman (Cassell & Co.; 1998; £12.99; 0706376676) – *The tape comes with a booklet and wallchart.*

Yoga for Pregnancy – *Rosalind Widdowson (Antenatal exercises to tone, relax and prepare your body; Hamlyn; 2003; £5.99; 060060649X) – A useful guide for beginners and those wanting to adapt a standard yoga routine for pregnancy, covering the most suitable techniques for each stage, including how to prepare for birth. / www.hamlyn.co.uk.*

Yoga for Pregnancy – Wendy Teasdale (Gaia Books; 2000; £10.99; 1856751651) – *A guide which includes yoga postures to work into everyday life, to relieve backache, to increase suppleness, to strengthen the legs, and to loosen the hips in preparation for birth. It covers the trimesters individually and offers visualisations and a guide to meditation. / www.gaiabooks.co.uk.*

Yoga for Pregnancy (Travis Ltd; Travis Ltd, PO Box 23103, London SE1 2GP (020) 7407 3655 www.worldofhealth.co.uk) – *A video looking primarily at creating space in the abdomen, using safe and comfortable exercises.*

CENTRAL ORGANISATIONS

British Wheel of Yoga, ☎ (01529) 306851 ⌖ www.bwy.org.uk

The governing body for yoga in the UK, including hatha yoga – a type suited to pregnant women which focuses on body postures, breathing and relaxation. In return for an SAE the organisation can provide a list of representatives in your area who hold details of teachers and suitable classes. / *HOURS Mon-Fri 9am-4.30pm; PUBLICATIONS Yoga & pregnancy; Yoga & stress; Yoga & back pain.*

Network of Childbirth & Yoga Educators,
⌖ www.maternitybras.co.uk

A network of around 60 teachers throughout the country, including well-known names such as Lolly Stirk and Julie Krausz – the website, www.maternitybras.co.uk, lists all the teachers.

YOGA CLASSES
CENTRAL

Birth Light
Classes At October Gallery, WC1; HQ PO Box 148 Cambridge CB4 2GB ☎ (0771) 458 6153 ⌖ www.birthlight.co.uk

A charity founded by Françoise Barbira Freedman, focusing on an holistic approach to pregnancy, birth and babyhood using yoga and breathing methods. The website includes details of classes around the country. Sells a range of videos and books on yoga antenatally, postnatally and for babies, plus water exercise and swimming for babies. Prenatal yoga master class weekly near Holborn: £18.

Portland Hospital, Physiotherapy Unit
234 Great Portland St (opposite main hospital) W1N 6AH ☎ (020) 7390 8061 ⌖ www.theportlandhospital.com

Antenatal yoga and Pilates. / *SEE ALSO 2.01 Postnatal; 2.03 Baby health; 4.02 Health practitioners.*

WEST

Karen Fraser
Intergolf Ltd, PO Box 16-600 SW6 3ZU ☎ (020) 7731 7514 ⌖ www.just-yoga.com

Individual yoga sessions for pregnant women in their own home, £60 per hour. Karen also teaches groups at a number of health clubs around London, but you will need to be a member to join in.

The Ladbroke Rooms
8 Telford Road, Portobello Rd W10 5SH ☎ (020) 8960 0846 ⌖ www.theladbrokerooms.com

Antenatal yoga classes – kundalini yoga and hatha are both available. / *SEE ALSO 4.02 Health practitioners.*

The Life Centre
15 Edge St W8 7PN ☎ (020) 7221 4602 ⌖ www.thelifecentre.com

Yoga for pregnancy, £9 per 90 minute class. / *HOURS Mon-Fri 8am-9pm, Sat & Sun 9.30am-6pm; SEE ALSO 2.06 Baby & toddler activities; 4.02 Health practitioners.*

Lynne Pinette
25 Falcon Lodge, Carlton Gate, Harrow Rd W9 3TQ ☎ (020) 7286 7201

Holds antenatal yoga classes: on-going classes, which can be joined at any time. Classes in Notting Hill Gate and at the Portland Hospital.

Lolly Stirk
Holland Park W11 ☎ (01323) 422054

Lolly has been working in Holland Park for 15 years "encouraging parents to become active participants in the birth and infancy of their babies". Classes include: two-hour yoga-based antenatal classes; birth preparation courses; breast-feeding workshops; £14 per class. / *SEE ALSO 2.01 Postnatal.*

NORTH

Copthall Pools
Page St, Great North Way NW4 1PS ☎ (020) 8457 9920

Yoga in pregnancy, 6-week course, £49.80. / *SEE ALSO 2.01 Postnatal; 2.06 Baby & toddler activities.*

Julie Krausz
77 Hardinge Rd NW10 3PN ☎ *(020) 8459 2903* ☝ *www.yogabirth.org*
Active birth and yoga teacher who teaches on selected weekday mornings and
evenings: classes at Northcote Library; SW11, £13 and in NW6; £12. / *SEE ALSO
2.01 Postnatal.*

Yvonne Moore
☎ *(020) 7794 2056*
Antenatal yoga-based exercise, from an experienced and knowledgeable teacher;
venues in north London. / *SEE ALSO 2.01 Postnatal.*

Rena Nicholaou
31a Grantbridge St N1 8JL ☎ *(020) 7354 2450* ☝ *www.yogavision.co.uk*
Offers classes and private tuition in yoga, healing, meditation / deep relaxation,
antenatal, mother and baby yoga, plus yoga for children. She sells a Meditation / Deep
Relaxation / Guided Meditation CD £16.50 inc p&p.

Julie Tortora
☎ *(020) 8340 5366*
On-going (you can join the group at any time) yoga classes in Crouch End: the
approach includes visualisation for pregnancy and labour, £8.50 for 75 minutes (booked
by the month). Couples classes focusing on practical skills and coping in labour are
available subject to demand. / *SEE ALSO 2.01 Postnatal.*

triyoga
6 Erskine Rd NW3 3AJ ☎ *(020) 7483 3344* ☝ *www.triyoga.co.uk*
Yoga school with some classes for pregnant women; from £10 per hour; private
sessions also available by arrangement. Teachers include Simon Low and Peter
Walker. / *HOURS 6.30am-10pm; SEE ALSO 2.01 Postnatal; 2.06 Baby & toddler activities.*

Yoga for Pregnancy
IATE, Highbury Road House, 71 Ronalds Rd N5 ☎ *(020) 8699 0279*
☝ *www.yogavision.co.uk*
Gentle stretching, breathing exercises and deep relaxation in small groups run by Rena
Nicholaou who also runs other yoga classes, including deep relaxation
yoga. / *HOURS Classes held Tues evenings.*

Yoga Therapy Centre
90-92 Pentonville Rd, Islington N1 9HS ☎ *(020) 7689 3040* ☝ *www.yogatherapy.org*
Antenatal yoga evening courses which are ongoing (ie you can join at any point);
however, you must book for six weeks. / *HOURS Mon-Thurs 10am-6.30pm; Fri 10am-5pm.*

Yogahome
11 Allen Rd N16 8SB ☎ *(020) 7249 2425* ☝ *www.yogahome.com*
Weekly drop-in, £10, discount for a block of six; after-class discussions help to build up
a support network of other mums-to-be. / *HOURS Call for hours; SEE ALSO 2.01 Postnatal.*

SOUTH

Val Orrow
31 Howard's Lane SW15 6NX ☎ *(020) 8789 8885*
Active birth teacher offering yoga-based exercise classes, held in four weekly two-hour
sessions at £12.50 each; Putney.

Sivananda Yoga Centre
51 Felsham Rd SW15 1AZ ☎ *(020) 8780 0160* ☝ *www.sivanandayoga.org*
Yoga for Pregnancy, hour and half classes, £8 per class. / *SEE ALSO 2.01 Postnatal.*

World of Health
PO Box 23103 SE1 2GP ☎ *(020) 7357 9393* ☝ *www.worldofhealth.co.uk*
Health, fitness and lifestyle video and DVD supplier with some yoga titles. / *SEE ALSO
2.01 Postnatal; 2.02 Feeding; 2.06 Baby & toddler activities; 4.02 Health practitioners; 4.05 Finding out
more.*

EAST

Arlene Dunkley-Wood
154 King's Head Hill E4 7NU ☎ *(020) 8923 6452 (answerphone), (020) 8923 6452*
An active birth teacher, who offers morning 'yoga for pregnancy' classes (£12.50 a class;
booked in monthly blocks). / *SEE ALSO 2.01 Postnatal; 2.06 Baby & toddler activities.*

Wholebody
☎ (020) 8341 9973 mobile (07956) 156 051 ⏱ www.wholebody.co.uk
Specialists in massage, personal training and on site massage and yoga. Classes including poses for use in pregnancy and exercises to help with delivery. / HOURS *Flexible; phone for details; no calls after 8pm; SEE ALSO 2.06 Baby & toddler activities.*

5. MENTAL PREPARATION

Some experienced midwives feel that labour is 80% a matter of mental attitude, and only 20% physical. Such a claim is controversial, but few would dispute that time spent preparing yourself mentally for the birth, in whatever manner suits you best, is time well spent. Imagining what life will be like after the birth is also a useful activity and if focused on the practical may be a way of avoiding postnatal depression.

Some women take the 'mind-over-matter' philosophy further. Hypnosis as a method for pain-relief has devoted advocates, as do other complementary therapies.

Given the statistics on relationship breakdown during pregnancy, it is also a good idea to involve fathers in their own mental preparation for parenthood. Taking part in birth preparation classes and discussions may be a good start.

HYPNOTHERAPY

Straight hypnotherapy relies on the hypnotherapist being present during labour, which may be difficult to arrange.

Self-hypnosis avoids any such difficulties. The ability to enter a self-induced hypnotic state requires either a teacher, or there are tapes available for this kind of preparation for childbirth.

There are doubts about the standards of membership qualification currently required by some of the hypnotherapy governing bodies. The safest place to find an individual practitioner is the ICM (see chapter *4.02 Complementary medicine & Health practitioners*).

MENTAL PREPARATION

WEST

Rosey Grandage (SRP, MCSP, MBAcC)
40 St Dunstan's Rd W6 8RB ☎ (020) 8563 1330 home, Prospect Chinese Medicine and Physiotherapy Centre (020) 7381 5727 ⏱ www.prospect health.co.uk
Physiotherapist and complementary practitioner who runs courses for pregnant women. The course combines qi-gong, relaxation, and physiotherapy (using both eastern and western techniques) for both physical and mental preparation. Around £7 per session (dependant on size of class). / SEE ALSO *4.02 Health practitioners.*

Hypno Birthing
108 Westcott Crescent, Hanwell W7 1PB ☎ (0845) 1080 419 ⏱ www.hypnoclinic.co.uk
A specialist hypno-birthing clinic helping with a range of problems. Its website includes a list of FAQs and discussion of what hypnotherapy can do.

National Childbirth Trust (NCT)
Alexandra House, Oldham Terrace W3 6NH ☎ Enquiry line (0870) 444 8707
⏱ www.nctpregnancyandbabycare.co.uk; www.nctparentsconnect.co.uk
Sells a pair of Mum & Baby tapes or CDs of music, the first to encourage the mother to relax, the second to encourage the baby to sleep. Tapes £14, CDs £18. For list of prices see www.nctms.co.uk. / HOURS *Mon-Thurs 9am-5pm, Fri 9am-4pm; or answerphone; SEE ALSO 1.01 Where to have the baby; 2.01 Postnatal; 2.02 Feeding; 2.04 Childcare; 2.05 Travel; 2.06 Baby & toddler activities; 3.02 Baby equipment; 4.04 Miscarriage & stillbirth; 4.05 Finding out more; 4.06 Support groups.*

NORTH

Yvonne Moore
☎ *(020) 7794 2056*
An independent childbirth educator (co-founder of Active Birth Association and co-director of the Active Birth Teachers Training Course), Yvonne provides those who attend her classes with useful information on all aspects of preparation for labour and birth in groups or privately. One-to-one counselling sessions on childbirth and - how to help yourself, help with handling any fears or problems from a previous birth experience. Classes held in north London. / *SEE ALSO 2.01 Postnatal.*

Debra Sequoia
c/o Muswell Healing Arts, 169 Avenue Mews N10 3NN ☎ (07951) 215984, (020) 8365 3545
Childbirth educator providing individual sessions and classes to be attended with or without a birth partner; a single class may be sufficient for some relaxation in birth – a course is required if hypnosis is to be the sole means of pain management; £60 per session or £200 for a course of four sessions; also at Active Birth Centre.

Viveka
27a Queen's Terrace NW8 6EA ☎ (020) 7483 3788
See Jeyarani Centre under East – Dr Gowri Motha practices here two days a week; booking is via the Jeyarani Centre. / *SEE ALSO 4.02 Health practitioners.*

EAST

The Jeyarani Centre 🖼
34 Cleveland Rd E18 2AL ☎ (020) 8530 1146 ⌖ www.jeyarani.com
Obstetrician Dr Gowri Motha's 'Gentle Birth' programme can start before conception and combines training in self-hypnosis, reflexology, reiki, advice on ayurvedic herbal preparations to take, craniosacral therapy, and creative healing. Lifestyle adjustments including yoga and swimming are recommended. She also works at Viveka, (27a Queen's Terrace, NW8), and in Stamford Hill – see the website for details. Videos and tapes also available. Courses of four self-hypnosis classes introduce self-hypnosis with a simple explanation of all the organs work to prepare a mother for birth, with the aim of increasing confidence, deepening the bonding between mother, father and baby, and removing fear of the birth process. The course costs £75 and partners are welcome. After the first four classes participants are encouraged to attend as many follow-up classes as they wish. An audiotape can be used for further preparation. / *SEE ALSO 4.02 Health practitioners.*

OUTSIDE LONDON

Birth Psychology
The Association Fro Pre-& Perinatal Psychology And Health, PO Box 1398, Forestville CA, USA 95436 ☎ +1 707-887-2838 ⌖ www.birthpsychology.com/
A US site (run by a Californian educational organisation) covering the mental and emotional dimensions of pregnancy and birth in everything from scholarly articles to personal stories and 'late-breaking headlines'.

British Society of Clinical Hypnosis (BSCH)
125 Queensgate, Bridlingrton East Yorkshire YO16 7JQ ☎ (01262) 403 103 ⌖ www.bsch.org.uk/
A professional body of hynotherapists, whose database of members include details of specialisms for pregnancy and hypno-birthing.

Common Knowledge Trust
PO Box 892, Nelson New Zealand ⌖ www.commonkowledgetrust.com
Sells The Pink Kit: Essential preparations for your birthing body, made up of a 90 minute audio cassette, a video of close on two hours, and a book of 80-plus pages with illustrations and photographs.

Easy Birth
7 Overhill, Warlingham Surrey CR6 9JR ☎ (01883) 623 357 ⌖ www.Easybirth.co.uk
Weekend self-hypnosis for childbirth courses in central London, which emphasise that self-hypnosis is a state entered into daily, when day-dreaming for example. The website includes information on safety, what the hypnotic state feels like, what you remember and reassurance about not being under the influence of others.

Ecstatic Birth
6 Court Lodge, Lamberhurst Kent TN3 8DU ☎ (01892) 890614 ⌖ www.ecstaticbirth.com
Weekend antenatal classes run by US psychologist (and rebirthing expert) Binnie Dansby, in London and Hove featuring slides and videos about birth (particularly

water birth) information, breath control, visualisation and meditation, and the use of affirmations and declarations; the website provides course information online, plus ante and postnatal information. / HOURS 24hr answerphone; PUBLICATIONS Cassettes: *Having a baby is the Most Natural Thing in the World (a guided relaxation and visualisation designed to support easier pregnancy and childbirth, £9), Rhythm of Life (with life-enhancing thoughts for pregnancy, primitive and modern music and subliminal messages, £9). 'Ecstatic Birth ... conceive the possibility' CD-ROM (a multi-media pack with video, audio, music, photos, interviews and text; available from Connexions, No 4, 57 The Drive, Hove BN3 3PF (01273) 727588, +£2.50 p&p).*

Growing Needs 📖
11 Market Place Glastonbury BA6 9HH ☎ (01458) 833466
Specialist mail order supplier focussed on pregnancy, birth and childcare books that stocks a range of audio tapes on birth and relaxation. / HOURS *Mon 10am-5pm, Tue-Fri 9am-5.30pm; SEE ALSO 4.05 Finding out more.*

Healing Rebirthing Society
Flat 4, 57 The Drive, Hove East Sussex BN3 3PF ☎ (01273) 720853 ⏁ www.rebirth.dk
An organisation, with various local groups, which believes that women tend to repeat the pattern of their mother's pregnancy and their own birth. Workshops with lay midwife Binnie Dansby are open to all women (and partners) including those who are currently pregnant. Practitioners undergo three years training. / HOURS *Mon-Fri 9am-5pm;* PUBLICATIONS *Free information pack (send SAE).*

Natal Hypnotherapy
AIM Clinic, Bordon Hampshire ☎ (01428) 712 629 ⏁ www.natalhypnotherapy.co.uk
Sells a birth preparation CD by hypnotherapist Maggie Howell, combining guided visualisation, relaxation and hypnosis to prepare for pregnancy and birth. Other titles include pregnancy relaxation, VBAC preparation and post natal recovery. Also two-day weekend group hypnotherapy courses, and one to one sessions.

UK HypnoBirth Register
☎ (020) 8442 0105 ⏁ www.hypnobirth.info
A register of therapists who specialise in preparing mothers for birth. The therapists on the register offer a wide range of group and individual sessions for women and birth partners to learn how to give birth in a totally relaxed state of mind and body.

6. OTHER FORMS OF PREPARATION

READING
Having a Baby is the Most Natural Thing in the World – Binnie Dansby (Ecstatic Birth; 2000; £11.50 inc p&p) – *A tape containing messages designed to induce relaxation and mental preparation. (The same supplier has a CD ROM includes images of an Ecstatic Birth, plus information on how to achieve one yourself).* / *Binnie A Dansby, Colleens Oast, Lower Cousley Wood, Wadhurst, East Sussex TN5 6HE: 01892 785 102; www.ecstaticbirth.com.*

[Tape] **The Jeyarani Birth Programme** – *Self-hypnosis and Visualisation for Birth; Preparation for Birth (for use in the last two weeks); other tapes are available for use during labour, for postnatal toning and for relaxation. £10 each +p&p.* / *Jeyarani Centre – (020) 8530 1146.*

[Tape] **Rhythm of Life** – Binnie Dansby (Ecstatic Birth; £12 Cassette, £15 CD) – *Positive thoughts about birth, along with rhythmic music – primitive and modern; other titles along the same theme.* / *Binnie A Dansby, Colleens Oast, Lower Cousley Wood, Wadhurst, East Sussex TN5 6HE: 01892 785 102; www.ecstaticbirth.com.*

PREPPING THE BABY
Various sources indicate that a song repeatedly played to a baby while in the womb can be played postnatally to calm her when she cries. Any music or even a story would be suitable for this though there are some dedicated products available (see Books, Music and Videos 3.07).

WATER BIRTH PREPARATION
(For more information about pool hire companies and water birth in general, see chapter 1.06 Birth equipment.)
If you are considering using a birth pool at your hospital, you will not necessarily be offered anything in the way of special preparation by the hospital, and – should you wish to inform yourself further – may find the information offered by the pool hire companies useful. Most can provide details of various books, videos and events which they offer.

CHAPTER 1.05

RIGHTS

This area of employment law has been in constant flux over the past few years, with many changes, but also many ideas put forward and shelved.

The following details the position as we go to press but further changes are possible. It is a complex area, particularly when it comes to extra benefits for those on low incomes generally in the form of tax credits. Because of this these often go unclaimed. Given that the threshold for these has been raised significantly, it's worth double checking exactly what you may be entitled to.

The rights below apply to employees. If you are not sure of your employment status you should get advice. Agency workers, casuals, freelance and self-employed do not have the same rights but are still entitled to maternity pay and protection from sex discrimination. The Maternity Alliance (see listings) has specific information on their rights.

1. INTRODUCTION

Although there are a variety of benefits to which women become entitled when pregnant, the vital area of interest for many women is the protection that the law offers them with respect to their jobs.

Employees have a legal entitlement to paid time off for antenatal care throughout their pregnancy, including tests and birth preparation classes. They have the right to time off from work to give birth to the baby, and – perhaps most importantly – to be paid throughout this period.

Until recently, fathers enjoyed no legal right to paternity leave but this was introduced in April 2003. In December 1999, the UK adopted the EC Parental Leave Directive giving parents the right to 13 weeks unpaid parental leave per parent per child.

With the exception of pay and some pension issues, the law that primarily provides for a woman's employment rights when she is having a child is the Employment Rights Act 1996, though the 2002 amendments are described by the government as "the biggest change for 40 years". Pay, benefits and pensions provisions stem from the Social Security Contributions and Benefits Act 1992.

In addition to these laws, many decisions in this area come from employment tribunals. The Sex Discrimination Act also provides very important protection. As a result, the rules governing the finer points of mothers' rights in pregnancy are complex – not least because new judgments are changing the law all the time. If you have a specific problem you will need specialist advice (see Section 11, Further information).

One point the law is very clear on is time limits: for example, the advance notification that you are required to give your employer of the maternity leave you plan to take. It is important to respect these limits, particularly if you suspect that you may need the protection the law affords. If for some reason you have not been able to keep to the letter of these rules, your position may not be hopeless, but it will be more difficult.

Do not neglect to pay careful attention to your contract of employment. It may offer more than the legal minimum. The rights examined in this chapter are the minimum to which a pregnant woman is entitled. Employers and employees are free to agree on longer leave or greater pay entitlements on a voluntary or contractual basis.

ADOPTION

For the first time adoptive parents are being offered time off and pay when on leave, similar to that offered to birth parents. 26 weeks' leave is available at the same rate as SMP (£102.80 per week from April 2004-April 2005) and 26 weeks' unpaid leave, to one but not both adoptive parents. The other parent can take paternity leave.

NEW TERMINOLOGY:

The Department for Work and Pensions (DWP) was formed in June 2001 from parts of both the former Department of Social Security (DSS), and the former Department for Education and Employment (DfEE). The Benefits Agency of the former DSS (the agency directly responsible for maternity pay and child benefit) is also renamed as of April 2002. The new name (DWP) is used throughout this book.

In December 1999, changes to parental leave rights introduced new terminologies relating to maternity leave: what was Maternity Leave is now known as Ordinary Maternity Leave (OML); and what was formerly Extended Maternity Absence, which is now called Additional Maternity Leave (AML).

In addition, a new expression similar to Expected Date of Delivery (EDD) has been introduced. We still use 'EDD' in other parts of this book, but for this section, we will refer to Expected Week of Childbirth (EWC), the new term adopted by the Department of Trade & Industry (DTI).

Pay and pension law is the concern of the Department for Work & Pensions (DWP). Practically all other issues fall under the remit of the DTI.

Rights applying to all employees

Regardless of how long you have been working for your employer, or how many hours you work, you are entitled to:

➤ Ordinary Maternity Leave of 26 weeks.

➤ Paid time off during pregnancy for 'antenatal care' (appointments made on the advice of a registered medical practitioner, which include antenatal classes, medical check-ups, parentcraft and relaxation classes). After your first visit, you may need to show your employer a certificate signed by a GP, midwife or health visitor confirming your pregnancy, and also possibly an appointment card as proof of each appointment.

➤ If you are dismissed during this time, you are entitled to a written statement from your employer giving the reasons for your dismissal, regardless of whether you requested such a letter. It is automatically unfair to dismiss, or select for redundancy, a woman for reasons connected with her pregnancy and it is sex discrimination.

➤ Contractual benefits (such as accrual of annual leave) during ordinary maternity leave, apart from normal pay.

➤ Protection from conditions at work that might put your health or your baby's health at risk (see Section 9, Protection from hazardous work conditions, below).

➤ Facilities, in accordance with workplace regulations of 1992, "suitable … for pregnant women and nursing mothers to rest. They should be near sanitary facilities and where necessary include the facility to lie down." (This provision is merely an approved code of practice and as such carries less force than a statutory obligation.)

Relatively recent changes to maternity rights

EC PARENTAL LEAVE DIRECTIVE

In May 1998, the Government published a White Paper, *Fairness at Work*, setting out the legal framework for implementing the proposals of the EC Parental Leave Directive. The Employment Relations Act and the Maternity & Parental Leave Regulations 1999 have adopted these proposals, which affect all women having a baby on or after 30 April 2000.

Further changes introduced in October 2001 increased the parental leave allowance for parents of disabled children to 18 weeks, and extended the boundary of parental leave to include parents of children who were under 5 years old when the bill was passed (on 15 December 1999).

Outline provisions of EC Parental Leave Directive:

➤ Both mothers *and* fathers are eligible.

➤ The right to 13 weeks unpaid leave on the birth or adoption of a child. (This applies to *each* child – therefore a parent is entitled to up to 26 weeks parental leave for two siblings or twins, for example). The leave may be taken in blocks of one week, up to four weeks a year, with 21 days' notice to your employer, unless you have negotiated a preferable system. This is in addition to paid leave and statutory maternity or paternity leave.

➤ Protection from dismissal for taking parental leave, or for applying to take it.

➤ If the leave period is four weeks or less, the parent has the right to return to the same job at the end of the leave. If the leave period is more than four weeks, the job must be "the same or similar".

➤ Parents also have the right to "time off for dependants". This is the right to a reasonable period of time off to deal with "emergencies relating to dependents", such as serious illness or unexpected breakdown of childcare arrangements. (Note that employers may not be aware of this.)

Additional provisions of the Employment Relations Act 2002:

➤ 13 weeks parental leave available to all employees after one year's employment.

➤ Basic ('Ordinary') Maternity Leave extended to 26 weeks, in line with maternity pay (see pg 124).

➤ The qualifying length of service for Additional Maternity Leave reduced to 26 weeks by the 15th week before the baby is due (see below).
➤ Protection from dismissal for reasons connected with pregnancy.
➤ The legal right not to suffer 'detrimental treatment at work for reasons connected with pregnancy'.
➤ An employee's contract to be considered unbroken throughout both parental leave and Additional Maternity Leave (see below).

Relatively recent changes to maternity pay

BUDGET 1999

In April 1999, the Chancellor announced measures extending the eligibility conditions of Maternity Allowance (MA) to include women who earn between £30 a week and the lower earnings limits (LEL) for National Insurance (NI) contributions (£79 a week from April 2004–April 2005. Self-employed women are entitled to the same MA payments as employed women (see Section 3, Pay during time off).

Paternal rights to paid leave

Fathers are eligible for two weeks' paid paternity leave. This is paid at the same flat rate as Statutory Maternity Pay (£102.80 a week), and must be taken in one block of time, within eight weeks of the birth (or adoption) of a child.

(This is in addition to the 13 weeks unpaid 'parental leave' introduced by The EC Parental Leave Directive.)

2. TIME OFF WORK

Terms relating to time off:

Ordinary Maternity Leave (OML): previously known just as Maternity Leave. All employees in part or full-time employment – regardless of length of service – are eligible for 26 weeks Ordinary Maternity Leave.

Additional Maternity Leave (AML): previously known as Extended Maternity Absence. Women who have been employed for 26 weeks by the 15th week before the baby is due – regardless of the number of hours worked in this period – are entitled to Additional Maternity Leave, which is a further 26 weeks leave giving them a maximum of 52 weeks off.)

Compulsory Maternity Leave: an employer cannot allow a woman to return to work for two weeks, immediately following the date of childbirth (four weeks if she works in a factory).

Maternal rights to time off apply only to live births (even if the baby dies shortly afterwards) or still births after 24 weeks. Time off after a miscarriage (before 24 weeks) has to be taken as sick leave.

Ordinary Maternity Leave (OML)

ELIGIBILITY

All employed women are entitled to Ordinary Maternity Leave.

THE PERIOD OF TIME OFF TO WHICH YOU ARE ENTITLED

OML lasts for a maximum of 26 weeks. The earliest you can leave work is the beginning of the 11th week before the EWC, but thereafter the exact date at which you 'start the clock' is up to you.

If you give birth before the date you planned to start your OML, the leave is calculated as starting from the birth. There is no extra entitlement for a premature baby.

YOUR RIGHTS DURING ORDINARY MATERNITY LEAVE

While on OML you have a right to all the benefits of your employment, apart from your normal pay (see Section 3, Pay during time off, below).

➤ You have the right to come back to exactly the same job after the pregnancy.

➤ Your employer must continue to meet its pension obligations to you.

➤ You continue to earn holiday entitlement.

➤ You are entitled to retain perks such as a company car or mobile phone (unless they are provided for business use only).

➤ You have the right to have this period counted when assessing length-of-service payments or seniority rights.

YOUR OBLIGATIONS

You must notify your employer in the 15th week before EWC. You must give four weeks' notice of any changes. It is advisable to make the notification in writing, and your employer may request a copy of your maternity certificate (form MAT B1) which confirms the EWC. This certificate is available from whoever is running your antenatal care from 20 weeks of pregnancy. Your employer must respond to your notification.

If you are off sick for reasons connected with the pregnancy in the last four weeks of pregnancy your employer can start your maternity leave automatically from the first day of your absence even if you had planned to start your leave later.

If you plan to return to work at the end of your OML you do not have to give your employer any advance notice you simply turn up for work. If you plan to return to work earlier than the end of your OML period, you must give your employer 28 days notice. If you decide not to return to work you should resign in the normal way, giving your employer the notice required by your contract.

EXTENDING YOUR ORDINARY MATERNITY LEAVE

There is no right to extend your OML but if you are entitled to AML your employer should assume that you are taking it unless you give notice to return to work early. It is a good idea to check with your employer that they know you are taking AML. If you are off sick at the time when you have to return to work, you are entitled to sick leave and pay in the normal way and you should follow your employer's normal sickness procedures. You no longer have to return to work for a day to protect your rights.

Additional Maternity Leave (AML)

ELIGIBILITY

AML is an entitlement of all women employed for more than 26 weeks by the 15th week before the EWC.

THE PERIOD OF TIME OFF TO WHICH YOU ARE ENTITLED

AML lasts for 26 weeks from the end of the statutory Ordinary Maternity Leave period, giving a total potential amount of time off of 52 weeks.

YOUR RIGHTS DURING ADDITIONAL MATERNITY LEAVE

During AML, your employment rights do not enjoy the same degree of legal protection as during OML. Your actual job is still protected – you have the right to return to the same job but if your employer can show that it is not reasonably practicable for you to return to the same job they can you a suitable equivalent post on similar terms and conditions. This may be the case if your old position has become redundant.

YOUR OBLIGATIONS

There are no separate notice provisions for taking AML. You simply give notice by the 15th week before EWC that you intend to take maternity leave. It is advisable to do so in writing, and give your employer your maternity certificate (form MAT B1) which confirms the EWC. Your employer should write to you within 28 days confirming the date your maternity leave ends. If you are entitled to AML check that your employer has included the AML period. You do not have to decide whether you want to return to work at this stage. If you do decide not to return you should resign in the normal way giving the notice period required by your contract. You can 'work' your notice on your maternity leave. You do not have to give any notice to return to work you simply turn up at the end of your leave. If you decide to return early you must give 28 days notice.

If you resign from your job you do not have to repay ANY Statutory Maternity Pay. If you have been paid more than the legal minimum Statutory Maternity Pay (6 weeks at 90% of your average wages and 20 weeks at £102.80) – for example, if additional maternity payments were written into your contract – you may have to repay the difference if it was stated in your contract in advance.

SMALL FIRMS EMPLOYING FIVE OR FEWER PEOPLE

A woman working in a small firm employing less than five people does not enjoy exactly the same job protection as one in a large firm if she is eligible for, and chooses to take, AML. If your employer is able to provide a good enough reason why it is no longer able to offer you your original job or a suitable alternative, then there is no obligation to take you back.

EXTENDING YOUR TIME OFF

As for Ordinary Maternity Leave (see above).

3. PAY DURING TIME OFF

There are two main maternity benefits available to women:

Statutory Maternity Pay (SMP): paid by your employer, subject to you having a certain level of earnings and the required length of service (see below).

Maternity Allowance (MA): paid by the DWP, to pregnant women who are not entitled to SMP. A minimum wage of £30 a week is the qualification.

If you are not eligible for either of these benefits, you may be eligible for Incapacity Benefit (see below).

If you are eligible, you should also check your contract of employment. Some employers have more generous packages than the minimum statutory one.

Statutory Maternity Pay

ELIGIBILITY

You are entitled to Statutory Maternity Pay if:

➤ In the 15th week before the EWC (the 'Qualifying Week'), you have been continuously employed for at least 26 weeks (including the Qualifying Week itself). In layman's terms, this means you must have been in the job before the first week of your pregnancy.

➤ You are still employed in the Qualifying Week.

➤ Before the end of the Qualifying Week, you must have earned at least an average of £79 a week (the lower earnings limit for NI contributions) for eight weeks.

BENEFIT

SMP is a weekly payment to new mothers when they are off work, for a maximum of 26 weeks. It is payable during your OML and amounts to 90% of your average pay for the first six weeks off work, and then the basic SMP rate of £102.80 per week for 20 weeks.

SMP ceases to be paid when you return to work. Payment is usually made at the same time and in the same way as your normal wages, payable from the first Sunday after you cease work. You still have to pay income tax and NI contributions and all other usual deductions.

SMP is payable regardless of whether or not you decide to return to work. If you work for more than one employer you may be able to get SMP from both of them. If you are an agency worker you may be entitled SMP from your agency if you meet the normal conditions above.

YOUR OBLIGATIONS

To be paid SMP, you must write to your employer at least 28 days before you plan to stop work asking for SMP. It is a good idea to give notice for pay in the same letter as the one giving notification regarding your plans for time off in the 15th week before your baby is due. You will need to give your employer your maternity certificate (form MAT B1) to get SMP.

Maternity Allowance

ELIGIBILITY

If you don't qualify for SMP – for example if you don't work long enough hours, you are self-employed, or if you gave up work or changed jobs during pregnancy – you may be able to get a weekly Maternity Allowance from the Department for Work & Pensions (DWP). Apply on form MA1 from your local JobCentre Plus

You are eligible for Maternity Allowance if:

➤ You have been employed or self-employed in 26 of the 66 weeks before EWC, but are not eligible for SMP.

➤ You have earned a minimum of £30 a week in 13 of those weeks.

BENEFIT

MA is paid weekly, for a maximum of 26 weeks at a rate of £102.80 per week or 90% of your average earnings if that is less.

HOW TO APPLY

You need form MA1 (from your antenatal clinic or local JobCentre Plus). If you are employed you will also need a completed form SMP1 explaining why you are not eligible for Statutory Maternity Pay.

Incapacity benefit

If you are not entitled to SMP or Maternity Allowance you may be entitled to Incapacity Benefit from the DSS.

ELIGIBILITY

If you have worked and paid NI in the last three years but not in the last tax year, you may be eligible. The JobCentre Plus should automatically consider your claim for IB. If you do not qualify for MA, check that they have considered you for IB.

BENEFIT

IB is paid weekly, from six weeks before EWC and for two weeks after the birth. IB is £55.90 per week from April 2004-April 2005.

HOW TO APPLY

The DWP will automatically check if you are eligible for any Incapacity Benefit if your application for MA is not successful.

4. RETURNING TO WORK

Women have the automatic right to return to work after maternity leave. They also have protection from dismissal and unfair treatment relating to their pregnancy.

Returning after the basic 26 weeks' ordinary maternity leave entitles a mother to return to her original job under the same terms and conditions. Taking additional maternity leave the entitlement is to the same job but if the employer can show it is not reasonably practicable to a new post at least as favourable as the original one.

CHANGING WORKING HOURS

From April 2003 legislation has specified that employers must consider any request for family-friendly working arrangements from employees who have worked for them for 26 continuous weeks, with children under 6 or a child with disabilities under 18. Options include home-working, nine-day fortnights, and flexible hours. Some businesses have reported success with these, reducing staff turnover and staying open for longer hours. It remains to be seen how the rest react. The rights do not apply to agency workers or those in the armed forces.

Accepted grounds for refusal are additional costs, detrimental effect on ability to meet customer demand, inability to reorganise work among existing staff, inability to recruit additional staff, detrimental impact on quality, detrimental impact on performance, insufficient work during period employee proposes to work, or planned structural changes. Some commentators also note that whatever head office policy on the subject, this may take some time to filter down. The Department of Trade however estimates that four out of five applications to work flexibly will be accepted. According to the Maternity Alliance, an employer cannot simply state that there are no part-time vacancies, that the job is too senior, that continuity is crucial, or that last-minute overtime is essential. Arguments that part-timers are more expensive have to be proven.

The application must be made in writing and you must accept a permanent change to your terms and conditions of employment. Your employer must meet you within 28 days of your written request and must tell you their decision within the next two weeks, including any reasons for refusal. If your employer does not follow the correct procedure for considering your application you can make a claim in an employment tribunal.

If their refusal is unjustified you should seek advice about a claim for indirect sex discrimination. Under the Part-Time Workers' Regulations 2000, employers must give part-timers the same hourly rate as full timers in comparable jobs, and same pro rata benefits such as holidays.

Under the Working Time Regulations 1998, employees can no longer be forced to work more than 48 hours per week.

5. HEALTH BENEFITS

Free prescriptions and dental treatment for pregnant women and children are provided for by the NHS Charges for Drugs & Appliances Regulations 1989.

Free NHS prescriptions

ELIGIBILITY

All women during pregnancy, and for one year after the birth.

HOW TO APPLY

Ask your antenatal carer for form FW8. Complete the form and send it to the local Family Health Services Authority. You will receive a Health Authority Exemption Certificate (form FP92), qualifying you to free prescriptions until a year after the EWC. You may be asked to show this certificate when collecting prescriptions. For children, an official document showing their name and date of birth (such as an NHS medical card) may be required.

Free dental care

ELIGIBILITY

All women during pregnancy, and for one year after the birth.

HOW TO APPLY

Leaflet D11 is available from your dentist or the DWP. Alternatively you can simply sign the appropriate form when you have treatment.

Other health-related entitlements

Mothers on Income Support or Job Seekers Allowance can claim travel expenses to antenatal appointments, free sight tests and new glasses. See DWP leaflet HC11 for details.

Some families on a low income are also eligible to receive liquid and dried milk, plus vitamins for mothers (when pregnant and breast-feeding) and children under five. See DWP leaflet WMV:G1 for details.

6. MONEY FOR THE BABY

All regular benefits can be paid directly into the bank or building society account of your choice as well as by traditional order book or the new payment card at a post office.

For further information and advice, contact the local DWP, call one of the DWP freephone services (see below), or contact your local Citizens' Advice Bureau.

Child Benefit

ELIGIBILITY

Once you have registered the birth of your child, provided you have been living in Britain for at least six months, you can claim Child Benefit. The benefit accrues from birth. The latest time at which you can claim the 'back-dated' benefit is three months after the birth (though this period may be reduced).

Child benefit is paid for each child under 16, and each child under 18 who is studying or in work-based training full-time. It is not affected by income or savings.

BENEFIT

Payments at April 2004 are £16.50 a week for the eldest or only child, and £11.05 for each additional child. The rules of benefits payments and your individual circumstances determine the precise amount. (If you receive Income Support the Child Benefit will be deducted from your allowance total.)

Child Benefit is paid weekly or monthly at a post office or every four weeks directly into a bank or building society account.

HOW TO APPLY

There is an application form in the bounty pack that is given to all women who give birth in an NHS hospital. Forms are also available from midwives and from district offices of the Child Benefits Centre, or you can download one from the DWP website. Leaflet CH1 Child Benefit gives more information. Leaflet CH11 covers Child Benefit for lone parents.

Child Benefit Centre (Washington), ☎ *(0845) 302 1444*
⌁ *www.inlandrevenue.gov.uk/childbenefit*
Child benefit information and assistance; issue claim packs. / HOURS *7 days a week 8am-8pm.*

Sure Start Maternity Grants

ELIGIBILITY

Parents on Income Support, income-based Jobseekers' Allowance and parents on a low Income who are receiving Tax Credits are eligible for a Sure Start Maternity Grant (previously known as Maternity Payments).

Eligibility is affected by savings over £500 held by the parents (£1,000 if the parents are over 60).

BENEFIT

A one-off payment of £500 per baby, intended to help buy essentials for the newborn baby or newly-adopted baby under one year old.

HOW TO APPLY

You can apply from 11 weeks before the baby is due, up to three months after the birth, with form SF100 to be returned with MAT B1 or the baby's birth certificate. Parents adopting a child can apply up to three months after the adoption.

Tax benefits

There are two tax benefits for families:

➢ Working Tax Credit (WTC) for families with a combined income of under £63,000 pa; the credit is designed to top up income for those for whom it might not otherwise be financially worthwhile to work. It is also paid to low income mothers on maternity leave. The credit can include help towards childcare costs of up to £135 for one, or £200 for two children, or up to 70% of the weekly bill. Information is available from the WTC helpline on (0845) 300 3900 www.inlandrevenue.gov.uk or wwwdaycaretrust.org.uk.

➤ Child Tax Credit (CTC) paid to the main carer for families where the higher earning partner earns £58,000 per annum or less, or £66,000 for families with a children under one year. Further information is available on the helpline (0845) 300 3900.

Tax relief on the costs of childcare may also be available to working families. See chapter *2.04 Childcare* for details.

Other benefits
CTC replaces all previous benefits for those on low incomes but the following survive:
➤ Milk vouchers, due to be changed to vouchers for fruit, vegetables, cereal products or milk.
➤ New Deal for Lone Parents helping lone parents getting benefit with looking for a job, childcare and training.

BABY BOND
As the book goes to press, a baby bond of up to £500 for every child born in the UK has been announced. Details have yet to be finalised, but it will be paid for babies born from September 2002 onwards and will be available from April 2005.

USEFUL CONTACTS
Child Poverty Action Group, ☎ *(020) 7837 7979* ✆ *www.cpag.org.uk*
Campaigning, information and action group aiming to relieve poverty among families with children. / HOURS Mon-Fri 9.30am-5pm; PUBLICATIONS Welfare Benefits Handbook (£22 + £2.95 p&p, £6 for claimants) details potentially unclaimed benefits.

The Department for Work & Pensions (DWP),
☎ *(0800) 882200* ✆ *www.dwp.gov.uk*
Formerly the Department of Social Security (DSS) and the Benefits Agency: the governmental department responsible for maternity pay and benefits.

Inland Revenue, ☎ *CTC Helpline (0845) 300 3900, New Employers Helpline (0845) 607 0143* ✆ *www.inlandrevenue.gov.uk*
For a form to apply for Child Tax Credit, visit www.taxcredits.inlandrevenue.gov.uk.

7. PENSIONS
In order to qualify for the full basic state pension, women normally have to have been working and making payments into the state pension system for 39 years. Working for only 20 years, say, will entitle you to only 52% of the full pension.

It is possible, however, to make the period spent raising your children count towards your pension entitlement. This is done by applying for Home Responsibilities Protection (HRP) which – for the period spent raising children – entitles women to approximately half of the normal pension entitlement that they could have earned had they been in employment.

ELIGIBILITY
HRP is automatically given to everyone receiving Child Benefit for a child under 16. For more information see DWP leaflet CF411 'How to Protect Your State Retirement Pension If You Are Looking After Someone at Home'. This includes an application form.

Married women who have retained their right to pay reduced pension contributions cannot apply. Note that if a married woman either did not work, or worked but paid only the reduced contribution, she can still receive a pension based on her husband's pension contributions.

8. FATHERS' RIGHTS & RESPONSIBILITIES

Fathers married to the mother of their child share legal responsibility for that child up to the age of 18. If the parents of a child are not married, the legal responsibility is entirely the mother's, although the father has a financial duty towards the child's upbringing.

In the event that the father wants to take responsibility (or the mother wants him to) an application can be made through the courts for legal responsibility to be passed to the father. This will require help from a solicitor.

The Adoption and Children Bill 2001 under parliamentary consideration includes a clause which would give unmarried fathers parental responsibility if they register the child's birth with the mother.

Alternatively you can make use of the government publication *Children and Young Persons: The Parental Responsibility Agreement Regulations 1991* (amended 1994). This includes forms for completion by both parents who then have to get the agreement witnessed by an official of a court of law. There is no charge for this service. A copy is filed with the Principal Registry of the Family Division (a section of the High Court). The agreement can then only be ended by a court order or when the child reaches the age of 18.

Before proceeding, mothers (and fathers) may want to seek legal advice to clarify the implications of such an application.

If parents have separated, even before the birth of the child, the father is required to contribute maintenance. The calculations of the amount take into account the number of children, the income of the two parents, but should never total more than 30% of the father's net income, or 40% if in arrears. The main area for dispute is in working out the net income, for example deducting pensions contributions. The Child Support Agency can make a legal order for payments to be deducted from the father's wages if the mother raises the issue with them.

From April 2003 new legislation has enabled fathers who have worked at least 26 continuous weeks before the EWC to take paid paternity leave of up to two weeks. There is a statutory payment of £102.80 per week.

Employers will also have to consider any request for family-friendly working arrangements from employees with young children or a child with disabilities up to 18 years. (For more details see Returning to Work, above.) However, Parents at Work reports that to date only 36% of fathers have been successful in altering their work pattern in this way.

PATERNITY TESTS

Apparently the popularity of these tests has increased tenfold over the last decade, reportedly driven in part by the Child Support Agency which will pay for the test if it reveals that the claimed father is not so in fact. However, the Human Genetics Commission (HGC) the government adviser in this field, in 2002 recommended that taking a DNA sample by deceit (a hair, a glass from which the testee has drunk, etc) should be a criminal offence. Both parents would therefore have to approve before a sample could be taken from a child. A court order for sampling is required if the parent with care objects and an order may be issued if the court judges it in the best interests of the child.

USEFUL CONTACTS
LGC, ☎ *(020) 8943 7000* ⏆ *www.lgc.co.uk*
If you need to prove the paternity of your child, this company offers DNA testing.

9. PROTECTION FROM HAZARDOUS WORK CONDITIONS

Under the Congenital Disabilities (Civil Liability) Act 1976, your employer faces large financial liabilities if your baby is born with a handicap which can be shown to have been caused by conditions in your place of work.

To be entitled to special protection from hazards you must give your employer written notice of being pregnant. Should you wish to do this, it may also be a good idea to obtain a note (medical certificate) from your antenatal carers indicating its importance.

In response, your employer should then alter your working conditions or hours of work, offer you suitable alternative work, or suspend you on full normal pay for the period that the risk continues – probably the rest of pregnancy. However – if you refuse 'reasonable' alternative work – though you still have the right to suspension, you no longer have the right to full pay. Such protection also applies for an unspecified period after the birth and if breast-feeding.

Working with display screen equipment (VDUs) is not considered hazardous. (For more information see chapter *1.02 Looking after yourself*.)

Hazardous situations to avoid:
➢ Strenuous physical work and physical stresses such as vibration, noise and prolonged exposure to intense heat or cold.
➢ Mental and physical fatigue.
➢ Driving (or long periods of travelling) and night work.
➢ Being on your feet five hours or more a day (known to increase the chance of a low birthweight baby).
➢ Potentially dangerous situations, which include working with x-rays, contact with toxic substances such as biological toxins, lead, and (possibly) anaesthetics. Watch out in particular for substances labelled R61, R63 and R64 (or the old labels R40, R45, R46 and R49), which mean they are known to be potentially harmful in pregnancy. (Not all substances have been tested for this kind of risk.)

By law all employers must assess the risk to health and safety of all employees, and in the case of pregnant women, the risks to the unborn child. Your employer should be able, for example, to give you access to information (data sheets) on any chemical purchased for your work.

If you still need to handle toxic chemicals, ensure that you are supplied with good protective clothing and good ventilation to prevent inhalation of fumes.

If, after you have drawn your employer's attention to a potential hazard, you feel a risk is still being ignored, you can contact the Health & Safety Executive for advice (see listings below). This is important – for example, the Congenital Disabilities Act states that if parents in some way share responsibility for any disablement, damages will be reduced.

10. DETERMINING AND ASSERTING YOUR RIGHTS

The organisations and reading below can help to inform you of your rights, and on how to go about obtaining the protection they afford.

EMPLOYMENT TRIBUNALS

A common problem is that of an employer finding an excuse to dismiss you, or make you redundant because you are pregnant, or have taken time off for maternity.

In such a case, you can take your grievance to an Employment Tribunal. Application forms for arbitration are available from Citizens Advice Bureaux and Job Centres, but this is a complex area of the law, and – if you can – it's best to get some form of representation (see below).

The deadline for registering a claim is three months after you first learn of the problem. (Note, however, in some situations, you may be able to use the provisions of the Equal Pay Act to argue that a deadline of six months is more appropriate.)

It is worth bearing in mind that should you have been working part-time you have the same rights and benefits as full-timers.

Now that no-win, no-fee deals are permitted for UK lawyers, It may be possible to find a specialist willing to take your case on this kind of basis.

READING

Great Expectations (TUC Publications) – *A 180-page guide to maternity & paternity benefits. /* (020) 7467 1294, www.tuc.org.uk.

[Booklet] **Health & Safety at Work: Your Rights in Pregnancy & After Childbirth** (Maternity Alliance; £1) – *The rights that protect working women while pregnant, and in the six months after giving birth (or as long as they are breast-feeding). / The Maternity Alliance, www.maternityalliance.org.uk.*

[Booklet] **Maternity Rights** – DTI (free) – *A useful booklet, containing information on the legislation from the Employment Relations Bill 1999; available from Jobcentres. / www.dti.gov.uk.*

[Leaflet] **Money for Mothers and Babies** (free) – *Maternity and family benefits, who can claim and how to do it. / The Maternity Alliance, www.maternityalliance.org.uk.*

[Leaflet] **Pregnant at Work** (£1.50) – *Protection of your health, job, maternity pay and benefits; updated annually. / The Maternity Alliance, www.maternityalliance.org.uk.*

[Booklet] **Redundancy** (£1) – *From the angle of pregnant women and those on Maternity Leave. / The Maternity Alliance, www.maternityalliance.org.uk.*

[Booklet] **Sickness, Pregnancy and Maternity Leave: Your Employment Rights** (£1) / *The Maternity Alliance, www.maternityalliance.org.uk.*

The Which? Guide to Living Together – Imogen Clout (The law for cohabiting couples; Which? Books; 2002; £9.99; 0-85202-888-1) – *In addition to general issues like protecting the partners' financial and legal rights while in a relationship, the guide covers issues of parental responsiblity and adoption, and the position regarding children should the relationship break up. There is also a useful section on wills.*

Working Parents' Companion – Teresa Wilson (A National Childbirth Trust guide; Thorsons; 1998; £9.99; 0-722536-38-0) – *First published as Work and Home – parents talking about how they try to achieve the right balance between home and work, the pros and cons of different forms of childcare, a guide to care, plus financial, legal and emotional matters; one of the NCT's "core" titles.*

USEFUL CONTACTS

Advisory, Conciliation & Arbitration Service (ACAS),
☎ *Helpline (0845) 747 4747* ✆ *www.acas.org.uk*
The organisation's 'Public Enquiry Point' can advise on employment law problems and rights. / HOURS Mon-Fri 9.30am-4.30pm.

Child Support Agency (CSA), ☎ *National enquiry line (08457) 133133*
✆ *www.csa.gov.uk*
An executive agency of the DWP (formerly the DSS) which organises payments from absent parents for the upkeep of children whose parents live apart, in cases where the carer-parent receives state benefits, or in cases where there is no court order or other written agreement on maintenance. The organisation offers either just an assessment

of the amount which should be paid, or an assessment and collection service (both of which services can be applied for by either the carer or the absent parent). The agency's work includes tracing absent parents, and resolving paternity disputes; the website includes a guide 'For parents who live apart', and further advice is available on the helpline. / HOURS *Mon-Fri 8am-8pm, Sat 9am-5pm.*

Citizen's Advice Bureaux, ✆ www.nacab.org.uk; www.adviceguide.org.uk
Free, impartial, confidential advice; a useful starting point for referrals as to who you can approach with your problems and for help with copies of leaflets and forms. Your telephone directory will have details of your local branch, or use the website to locate one.

Department of Trade & Industry (DTI), ☎ (020) 7215 5000,
Booklets (0870) 1502 500 ✆ www.dti.gov.uk
The ministry responsible for employment legislation. / HOURS *Mon-Fri 8.30am-5.30pm (enquiries);* PUBLICATIONS *Maternity Rights – a guide for employers and employees (leaflet PL958).*

Employers for Work-Life Balance, ☎ (0870) 165 6700
✆ www.employersforwork-lifebalance.org.uk
A website with information illustrating the issues, with case studies, resources, a benchmarking system for your own company, and pointers on the business case.

The Equal Opportunities Commission, ☎ (0845) 601 5901
✆ www.eoc.org.uk
The people to contact if you feel you have faced discrimination after returning to work (say you were fired because you were unable to work at weekends in a job which is normally Monday to Friday). The commission can provide advice on your rights and how to process a claim. If you want to negotiate a return to work on a part-time basis the commission may be able to provide you with ammunition with which to argue your case. There is a three-month (less one day) time limit on claims under the Sex Discrimination Act. / HOURS *Mon-Fri 9am-5pm Helpline.*

Health & Safety Executive, ☎ Infoline (08701) 545500, Publications
(01787) 881165 ✆ www.hse.gov.uk

Law Centres Federation, ☎ (020) 7387 8570 ✆ www.lawcentres.org.uk
The HQ of the federation can give contact details of their 22 centres in London which provide free legal advice on, amongst other issues, employment law.

London Hazards Centre, ☎ (020) 7794 5999 ✆ www.lhc.org.uk
/ HOURS *helpline 10am-noon & 2pm-5pm (except Wed); 24hr answerphone.*

Maternity Alliance, ☎ Helpline (020) 7490 7639
✆ www.maternityalliance.org.uk
The organisation also has information on topics such as the rights of atypical workers, maternity allowance and incapacity benefit, redundancy and statutory maternity pay (SMP). / HOURS *helpline Mon & Thu 10.30am-12.30pm, Tue 6pm-8pm;* PUBLICATIONS *Leaflets: Pregnant at Work (protection of your health, protection of your job, maternity pay and benefits, SAE); Money for Mothers and Babies (SAE). .*

National Association of Citizens' Advice Bureaux,
✆ www.nacab.org.uk
Opening hours seem to get ever-shorter, but the bureaux do publish useful reports on issues like parental leave and working families tax credit, and give free confidential advice. Some can also help represent parents in tribunal cases. Check for local branch number on Web site.

National Council for One Parent Families (NCOPF),
☎ (020) 7428 5400, Helpline (0800) 018 5026 ✆ www.oneparentfamilies.org.uk
The helpline can offer information and advice on policy and rights to lone parents. Also publishes information on holidays for lone parents. / HOURS *helpline Mon-Fri 9am-5pm.*

Rights of Women, ☎ Advice line (020) 7251 6577, Admin (020) 7251
*65751*6 ✆ www.row.org.uk
Non-profit organisation offering free legal advice for women. / HOURS *Tues, Weds, Thurs 2pm-4pm & 7pm-9pm, Fri 12pm-2pm.*

Tailored Interactive Guidance on Employment Rights (TIGER), ✆ www.tiger.gov.uk
An interactive website (created by the DWP), designed to provide a user-friendly guide to UK employment law (including maternity leave and pay); also useful for employers.

The Trades Union Congress (TUC), ☎ (020) 7636 4030
⏀ www.tuc.org.uk

The Equal Rights department publish information aimed at helping women in pregnancy. Support in any dispute between a woman and her employer would be handled by the woman's individual union. / HOURS *Mon-Fri 9am-5pm; PUBLICATIONS List of publications available from TUC.* .

Work Foundation, ☎ (0870) 165 6700 ⏀ www.workfoundation.com

Formerly the Industrial Society, the foundation offers analysis and practical advice of working practices with the aim of producing ideas to make workplaces more effective and fulfilling. It publishes a number of relevant books – in 2002, they produced the Dads Army report: the Case for Father-Friendly Workplaces. / HOURS *Mon-Fri 8.30am-5.30pm.*

Working Families, ☎ (020) 7253 7243, *Helpline for legal advice (0800) 013 0313* ⏀ www.workingfamilies.org.uk

New Ways to Work and Parents at Work merged in 2003 to create this new charity which promotes flexible working arrangements – for example, job-sharing, flexitime, career breaks, working from home. It provides advice and information to individuals and employers, including on employment rights relating to maternity. / HOURS *Mon-Fri or answerphone; PUBLICATIONS Free information pack on flexible work patterns.*

CHAPTER 1.06

BIRTH EQUIPMENT

1. **Introduction**
2. **Birthing pools**
3. **TENS machines**
4. **Other equipment**

1. INTRODUCTION

The items detailed here are popular with mothers-to-be who are keen to play an active part in planning their birth, especially those who are organising a home birth.

Reasons you may wish to hire

➢ If you are planning a home birth.

➢ If you are planning a hospital birth, you may wish to be sure that equipment will definitely be available for the birth, and not in use by someone else.

➢ Even if you are fairly confident that the hospital will have facilities for you during your labour, if you want practice using the equipment beforehand.

In all cases, it is wise to give equipment a test run. The last thing you need to be doing during a contraction, is deciphering the instruction leaflet.

2. BIRTHING POOLS

Water birth

Water as a form of pain relief in childbirth is used in a number of cultures. Though it has traditionally been used in warm-climate countries, it has also been widely available in Russia and ex Soviet states for around 30 years. It is becoming more common in the UK and hire company Splashdown, believes that there are about 4,000–5,000 water births annually.

A Select Committee Report for the House of Commons in 1992 recommended that a birth pool be provided in the birthing environment of the mother's choice wherever practicable. Since that time, most NHS hospitals in London have installed birthing pools, though not all are used with any frequency. A 2004 report published by the British Medical Journal reported that women using the pool were less likely to request an epidural.

Benefits claimed for water birth:

Pain relief: research by one pool hire company found that 62% of those giving birth in water needed no other pain relief. In their survey, gas and air was used by 19% of the mothers, pethidine by 10% and an epidural by 4%. Another claims that around half the number of mothers giving birth in water (compared to giving birth without using water) require pain-relieving drugs.

Apparently lower incidence of tearing of the perineum: water birth guru Michel Odent reports that out of a sample of 100 births only 29 mothers tore and no episiotomies were performed.

Greater mobility: women often report enjoying the way water supports their by now rather heavy bodies, making positions like squatting easier. This support also lessens strain on the back (and possibly on the heart) and makes it easier to maintain a single position.

Faster labour: one pool hire company found that some of their sample of 116 mothers experienced astonishingly fast dilation once they entered the pool, making the time spent in the water a comparatively short part of the labour.

A gentler start in life for the baby: the rationale being that warm water is an environment similar to that in the womb. One hire company reports that babies born in water tend to be more alert and recover more quickly from birth, although believes it may simply be because the birth is usually gentler.

Limited interference with the mother: attendants tend to be limited to assisting rather than managing the birth. Monitoring and injections for example, require a higher level of maternal co-operation in water.

Although a normal bath can be pressed into action as a birth pool, it will seldom be big enough to be comfortable. Some mothers like to shower during labour, but most women attracted to water actually want to immerse themselves. Most hospitals have one or more large pools installed in the labour ward (see the hospital tables in chapter *1.01 Where to have the baby*), and many will also accept mobile birth pools if these are erected by a birthing partner. Use of hospital birthing pools is on a first-come-first-served basis, and so hiring your own pool is the only way of being 100% sure that one will be available for your use on the day.

Actual delivery in the water, though also known, is less common than the pool being used throughout the labour for pain relief, and then vacated for the birth. Some hospitals only like the latter option, and a good number of women prefer it anyway, as it allows them to give birth to the child using the full force of gravity.

Because birthing pools preclude the use of continuous foetal monitoring and generally make the woman in labour less accessible to her carers, some hospitals only encourage the use of water in births where no complications are anticipated, and where the woman is in spontaneous labour.

SAFETY

The 1992 Health Select Committee's report on maternity services recommended that all hospitals should provide women with "the option of a birthing pool where this is practicable". They were also suggested as an option in *Changing Childbirth*.

Although with a water birth, newborns emerge into water rather than air, babies can't actually breathe using their lungs until both head and rib cage have emerged – the point at which the ribcage can expand. Moreover it is reported that babies only seem to start trying to breathe on contact with the air. In any case the placenta (via the umbilical cord) offers a secondary supply of oxygen up to the point at which the cord is cut.

It seems that cases where water births have harmed the newborn have involved babies being kept under the water for a considerable period of time by over-enthusiastic converts to the concept. Once born, babies should be gently brought to the surface *immediately*.

It is important that the water in the pool should be at the right temperature: too hot, and it might cause brain damage in the baby; too cold and it may leave the mother unable to relax, and also might stimulate the breathing reflex in the newborn on emerging. The water should be blood temperature for delivery, and only a little hotter or colder during labour: 37–39 degrees Centigrade. Once full, pools cool slowly and the temperature can be maintained by topping up with relatively small quantities of hot water.

Arguments cited against water birth:
➢ The degree of relaxation may slow contractions. (Precautions are generally taken to counter this, in particular not using the water until labour is well under way: for example from the point when the cervix is 4cm–5cm dilated, or when the mother feels fully confident that labour is well-established).
➢ There may be greater risk of infection for mother, baby and midwife. However, Michel Odent reports no experience of such complications and believes that in hospitals water is probably a safer environment than air, given the high concentration of airborne bacteria. Concerns regarding infection are usually raised on account of the mother's faeces which may be expelled into the water by the pressure of the baby's head, but this also occurs out of water and water birth attendants usually simply scoop them out. Any residue is unlikely to present a risk to either her or the baby.
➢ That there is an increased risk of postpartum haemorrhage (though there seems little evidence).

Contra-indications for water birth
➢ Breech birth.
➢ Multiple birth.
➢ Signs of foetal distress.
➢ Unusually large baby.
➢ The mother being less than 38 weeks pregnant.
➢ The mother having haemorrhaged.
➢ The mother having high blood pressure.
➢ If the second stage of labour is particularly long.

In some of these cases it may be possible to use water as an aid to relaxation, or for pain relief earlier in labour.

THE PRACTICALITIES
If you plan to hire a pool, first ensure that you have a floor strong enough to hold up to a tonne of water (the weight of most oval or hexagonal pools) – i.e. about 100lbs per square foot, evenly distributed; the equivalent of eight people standing together. (Modern houses and flats, as well as hospitals, are generally designed to take concentrated floor loads equivalent to the weight of 12 people). Tranquil Waters reports no knowledge of a pool ever going through a wooden floor but recommends that if you are in doubt you should consult a structural surveyor (likely cost £150–£300 – they are listed in Yellow Pages).

Whatever room you choose should have sufficient ventilation to prevent a build-up of condensation or the room getting stuffy. It will also need access to water for filling and draining the pool. A bath or basin can be used for this (but may not drain as fast as most pumps can pump the water out).

It is useful to time how long it takes to fill the pool and to work out how to achieve the right temperature. Once full, the pool can be a pleasant place to spend time in the days before the birth – a time when lying down is uncomfortable for many women.

All mains electric equipment in the pool's proximity must be protected by an RCD (Residual Current Device) circuit breaker, to cut off the current in case of a fault.

There are a range of types of birthing pools designed for use away from birthing centres and hospitals:

Oval/round: the most expensive pools; moulded PVC fibreglass panels slot together to create the pool; a liner fits over the surface; oval generally provides more space than round.

Hexagonal: a popular and relatively economical option; a liner is draped over a frame constructed around steel tubes or wooden panels.

Inflatable: effectively a large paddling pool, but with sides manufactured using a material of similar strength to that used for life rafts.

Semi-flexible: rather than being constructed from parts, the pool is flexible and transported whole; the pressure of being filled with water and a clip-on rail provide the bath with rigidity.

Non-dismountable rectangular: like a large household bath.

There are some differences of opinion between suppliers as to exactly what equipment is needed:

Liners and cleanliness: most companies supply a new liner for each hirer to ensure cleanliness. Birthworks, although it offers the option of a new liner, believes it to be unnecessary if the pool is disinfected between uses, to which end it supplies a German disinfectant system, which uses oxygen rather than chlorine. The company states that with the aid of this disinfectant the pool can be used for relaxation in the days before the birth and also for the birth without having to change the water. (Notwithstanding this, it still advises users not to keep the same water at body temperature for more than 24 hours as this will stimulate bacterial growth, and to drain and refill the pool if you do.) Doubters of the disinfectant system point to the porosity of the PVC which makes up the sides of the pool, believing it is almost impossible to sanitise completely without soaking it in quite concentrated disinfectant.

(A further note on cleanliness: many hire companies sanitise the hoses supplied with the pool, but not all of them do – it's worth checking with the company.)

Leakage: a double liner system provides extra security against leakage.

Heating units: Birthworks offers a recirculating heater unit for maintaining a constant water temperature (it also functions as a pump for emptying the pool). Aqua Pools, on the other hand, will not offer such equipment, pointing to NHS studies indicating that all types of recirculating filtration heating systems are potential breeding ground for bacteria. (The problem is said to be that liquids such as blood are able to pass through the filter to the heater where the heat encourages bacteria to breed. The bacteria are then pumped out into the fresh water the next time the system is used.)

Inflatable vs non-inflatable: Aqua Pools argues that inflatable pools are unsuitable for birthing because they do not provide support, are more likely to spill and may puncture. Splashdown, on the other hand

– working with advice from the Royal College of Midwives – does provide an inflatable option, which, it claims, is strong enough to be leant on with the whole body, and can be inflated in five minutes. Whatever the virtues of these claims, any pool used for birth should have sides which are solid enough to be sat on, or leaned against.

Integral steps: extremely helpful for getting in and out, and safer than a stool or similar.

Hire companies

Most hire companies take bookings well in advance and the majority of mothers make contact from 30 weeks. Late bookings are usually an option but one that will probably incur an express delivery fee. When deciding on the hire period, bear in mind that most mothers deliver in their 41st week and that you might like a couple of days after the birth to get round to packing the pool up and sending it back.

When selecting a pool, dimensions are obviously a key feature. Allow sufficient space around it for birth attendants, and in case you wish to deliver out of the water. The taller you are, the larger the pool you will probably want.

If you are taking a pool into hospital, speed of assembly is an issue. Most pools take 5–15 minutes to assemble and do not require tools; filling them takes 15–30 minutes, depending on the water pressure.

Most pools are packed in a box or holdall and are transportable in a hatchback or family saloon. However, do check with the hire company, as some pools do not dismantle, and require an estate car or roof-rack for transport.

The following may be included with the pools or may be charged extra:
➢ Hoses for filling and emptying the pool – 0.5 inch or 0.75 inches for home use, 1 inch for hospital use.
➢ A water heater.
➢ A thermometer.
➢ A water maintenance kit.
➢ Adaptors to connect the hoses with your taps.
➢ A low stool or stools for birth attendants to sit on, to help the mother step into and out of the pool and possibly to sit on in the pool.
➢ A clean liner.
➢ Insurance covering damage to the pool.
➢ A heat-retaining cover.

Further useful items include:
➢ A bucket.
➢ Disinfectant.
➢ Mats or something soft for birth attendants to kneel on.
➢ A sieve for removing any stray matter in the water.
➢ Cleanable mats for stepping on to when getting out of the water.

In addition to the books and videos listed below, most of the hire companies run events and talks for women considering a water birth. In some cases they will also be able to put you in touch with other women in your area who are having or have had a water birth.

The prices included in the listings below are only a general guide because companies differ in what they offer in their basic 'packages'. To make an exact comparison between companies you must make a detailed assessment of exactly what equipment you need and then determine whether it is included in the package or would involve an additional charge.

READING

[Video] **A Guide to Water Birth** (John Radcliffe University; £25 or hire £13 (with £12 returnable deposit), £1 p&p) – *A guide mainly for professional use, showing how to set up a water birth pool in hospital, featuring footage of a water birth.* / Splashdown Water Birth Services – (020) 8422 9308.

[Booklet] **Choosing a Water Birth** (£4.50) – *Pool rental; midwives' code of conduct; advice on overcoming obstacles.* / AIMS, www.aims.org.uk.

[Video] **How to Prepare for a Safe & Easy Water Birth** – Dr Gowri Motha (The Jeyarani Birth Programme; £15) – *The progression of several underwater births by the obstetrician who introduced water births to the London NHS. (The video is also part of a starter pack that includes a hypnosis audio tape and herbal products, £20)* / www.jeyarani.com.

Labour and Birth in Water (How and why you might use water ; NCT; 2003; £2.50) – *A 20-page booklet on planning a water birth and hiring a pool, plus relevant research supporting the benefits of this form of pain relief.* / NCT Maternity Sales, (0870) 112 1120; www.nctms.co.uk.

[Video] **Water & Birth** – Janet Balaskas & Amy Hardie (Active Birth Centre; £19.95 (free with pool hire)) / www.activebirthcentre.com.

[Video] **Water Babies** (Splashdown Water Birth Services; 1997; £27.50 (also available on six-week hire for same price; £15 refunded on return)) – *Belgian obstetrician and water birth specialist Dr Herman Ponette introduces footage of water births. The video also shows water birth of breech babies and twins.* / (020) 8422 9308, www.splashdown.org.uk.

Water Birth – Janet Balaskas & Yehudi Gordon (The concise guide to using water during pregnancy, birth & infancy; HarperCollins; 1992; £9.99; 0-722527-88-8) – *An excellent practical title, which includes a look at the psychological role of water and its relevance to pregnancy and childbirth.* / Active Birth Centre.

The Water Birth Handbook – Dr Roger Lichy & E Hertzberg (The gentle art of waterbirthing; Gill & Macmillan; 1993; £8.95; 0-946551-70-7) – *By a doctor who has been at the forefront of water birth in Britain since 1985. All aspects of birth in water including safety, choice of pools and arranging the birth.* / Splashdown Water Birth Services – (020) 8422 9308.

Waterbirth – Melanie Lines (What I need to know; M Lines; 1992; £4.50; 0951970003) – *A 50-page guide on the advantages of water births and the practicalities of arranging them.* / Melanie Aqua Birth Pool Hire + 50p p&p.

Waterbirth Unplugged – Beverley A Lawrence Beech (Midwives Press; 1996; £14.50; 1-898507-53-8) – *Proceedings from the First International Waterbirth Conference – one of the few books on the subject with an emphasis on research supporting water birth.* / AIMS, www.aims.org.uk.

USEFUL INFORMATION

Waterbirth, ⏁ www.waterbirth.org
Run by an US-based, not-for-profit organisation, this site provides a wealth material as well as a well-stocked, online store with numerous books and videos.

BIRTHING POOL HIRE COMPANIES

The Active Birth Centre
25 Bickerton Rd London N19 5JT ☎ *(020) 7281 6760*
⏁ *www.activebirthcentre.com*
The centre runs what they claim to be the largest nationwide pool hire business in the UK – nay, the world! Hexagonal, oval or round pools are available, with related equipment such as squatting stools; call for prices; the hire period is typically 14-18 days (min 1 week). / HOURS shop Mon-Fri 9.30am-6.30pm (Fri 4pm), Sat 10am-

4pm; SEE ALSO 1.01 Where to have the baby; 1.04 Antenatal classes; 2.01 Postnatal; 2.02 Feeding; 2.03 Baby health; 2.06 Baby & toddler activities; 3.01 Maternity wear; 3.02 Baby equipment; 4.02 Health practitioners; 4.05 Finding out more.

Aqua Pools
25 Bickerton Rd London N19 5JT ☎ *(020) 7482 5554*
🖰 *www.activebirthcentre.com*
See Active Birth Centre.

BirthWorks
58 Shalmsford Street, Chartham, Canterbury Kent CT4 7RH ☎ *(01227) 730081*
🖰 *www.birthworks.co.uk*
Hexagonal and fixed or folding rectangular pools are available, with disposable liners. Rental can be by the week but the company recommends a four-week hire period: rectangular £200, hexagonal £240. Optional insurance against loss or damage is £6 per week (advised if not covered on domestic contents policy or if taking to hospital). Collection and delivery can be arranged. / *HOURS Mon-Fri 9am-5pm, or answerphone.*

Gentle Water
50 North Way Lewes BN7 1DJ ☎ *(01273) 474 927* 🖰 *www.gentlewater.co.uk*
Oxagonal pools designed by the director of the company including a lockable thermal cover to keep children and pets safe and reduce condensation in the room. The pool dismantles and can be packed into two transport boxes (51cmx61cmx63cm). Included is a dedicated water heater that runs off a domestic 13 amp power supply, a digital thermostat, lightweight insulated side walls for greater temperature retention, reinforced liner with optional disposable inner liner, and cushioned top edges and floor for greater comfort. A filtration system includes replaceable filter elements for maximum hygiene and can be used for seven days constantly. Price for four weeks' hire is £290, a disposable liner £40. / *HOURS 9am-12pm, 24hr answerphone.*

Melanie Aqua Birth Pool Hire
122 The Grove, Moordown Bournemouth BH9 2UA ☎ *(01202) 518152*
Oval pools (£160): the company guarantees to better any comparable pool hire price quoted elsewhere. Transport, if required, is £75. Hire period four weeks – two either side of EDD. Longer or shorter periods also available with an extension charged by the day. / *HOURS 24hr answerphone.*

Sarah Spoor (Baby Bliss)
127a Twickenham Rd Isleworth TW7 6AW ☎ *(020) 8568 4913*
🖰 *www.baby-bliss.com*
Heated Genesis pool, also hexagonal and rectangular pools; from £200. / *HOURS phone for appointment; SEE ALSO 1.04 Antenatal classes; 2.06 Baby & toddler activities.*

3. TENS MACHINES

Developed in the late 1960s and introduced to the UK from Sweden in 1976, TENS (Transcutaneous Electrical Nerve Stimulation) machines are found by some women to be an effective form of pain relief in labour, although no one fully understands the mechanism by which they work.

The set-up comprises a battery-powered transmitter and four electrodes taped to your back: two just above the buttocks and two higher up.

The transmitter generates a voltage (approximately 9V) and a pulse of current passes through the electrodes, the timing of you control via a pushbutton handset. The sensation is likened to a tingling sensation or pins and needles.

It is thought that these electric pulses somehow disrupt the transmission of pain along the nerves; or that TENS stimulates production of the body's natural painkillers (endorphins).

Pain relief is not guaranteed, and some women find TENS more effective than others. When set up, TENS takes 10 to 20 minutes to take effect. To stand the highest chance of success, the technique should be used from early in labour – it is thought that the longer the stimulus, the greater the pain relief.

TENS is often used together with gas and air or other forms of pain relief. It cannot be used in water.

The Obstetric TENS Hire Service at the New Road Clinic reported the following responses from a sample of 2000 customers:

Effectiveness in first stage of labour

Very good	Good	No answer	Not effective
58%	31%	4%	7%

Effectiveness in second stage of labour

Very good	Good	No answer	Not effective
18%	31%	3%	48%

Would use TENS again

Yes	No	Possibly
88%	5%	7%

This is by its nature a self-selected group. Other reports indicate a success rate varying from 10–70% (with few women, for example, using TENS when pushing out the baby's head).

You will need to make sure you are familiar with the controls on your model. Some have a frequency control and some have a boost button for extra relief at the peak of a contraction. Machines come with either disposable, self-adhesive electrodes or more old-fashioned, reusable, gel-and-tape electrodes (which have to be disinfected between uses). If you opt for the former, you will probably need an extra set for practising.

Depending on the supplier, in addition to the machine you may need:
➤ A new battery.
➤ Tape to attach the electrodes in place.

Benefits claimed for use of TENS
➤ TENS has no side effects for mother or baby.
➤ Control of pain relief is in the hands of the mother.
➤ No drugs are used.

➢ It is non-invasive.

➢ The normal course of labour is unaffected.

➢ The mother's consciousness is unaffected.

➢ The mother retains mobility.

➢ TENS can be combined with other forms of pain relief, which was found to be 75%–80% effective in one survey.

➢ TENS can also be used on either side of a Caesarean scar to help dull any pain relating to the wound.

Reasons against the use of TENS:

➢ It may be unsafe to practise with a TENS machine before 36 weeks of pregnancy.

➢ TENS should not be used by those with cardiac pacemakers, epilepsy or heart disease.

➢ Electronic foetal monitoring equipment can be affected by the use of a TENS machine. Should foetal monitoring be judged necessary, this can interrupt the ability to use TENS for pain relief. If the interruption comes late on in labour, the effectiveness of resuming use of TENS thereafter is severely diminished.

Most TENS machines are available for hire for four weeks – two weeks either side of the due date. Free extensions are usually possible and some hirers offer a basic hire period of six weeks.

TENS MACHINE HIRE COMPANIES
Ameda Egnell
Unit 1 Belvedere Trading House, Taunton Somerset TA1 1BH ☎ (01823) 336362
🖰 www.ameda.demon.co.uk
Model with boost button; £25 for four weeks (£25 returnable deposit); make contact three weeks before your EDD. Extension of period free with notification. Free cancellation if notified before dispatch. / HOURS Mon-Fri 8am-5pm; SEE ALSO *2.02 Feeding*.

BabiTENS
Rehabilicare (UK) Limited, Fairview Estate, Reading Rd, Henley-on-Thames Oxfordshire RG9 1HE ☎ (01491) 578446 🖰 www.rehabilicare.co.uk
Model with boost button; £27.50 for one months; make contact four weeks before your EDD. Extension of period free with notification. Free cancellation if notified before dispatch.

Babycare Tens
108 George Lane, South Woodford London E18 1AD ☎ (020) 8532 9595
🖰 www.babycaretens.com
Rents the 8040b machine at £24.50 for 30 days' hire, with detachable hand-held booster button to change the mode from burst to continuous and with a pulse rate facility to increase or decrease the speed of pulses. Lady Tens at £22 for 30 days' hire is preset except for the strength of the pulse, which can be controlled by dial. There is a preset burst mode for use in early labour and between contractions, and can then be switched to constant mode. Hire is extended for one week without charge if the baby has not yet arrived, with further weeks charged at £5.

Natures Gate
PO Box 371, Basingstoke Hampshire RG24 8GD ☎ (01256) 346060
🖰 www.naturesgate-uk.com
The supplier claims that its Tens machines offer 50% more power than some competitors. Units are sent out three weeks before EDD for six weeks, with extension usually free with notification (£1 per day otherwise); priority handling service available, £1.50. Silver service (£22) comes with six standard self-adhesive disposable electrodes; Gold service (£26) has reusable electrodes and hand held boost button, also usable for after pains or back pain after the birth, and useful if you are concerned about false starts; prices include alkaline battery with expected 60+ hours energy.

O&L Women's Health Physiotherapy Clinic

Fortis Green Health Clinic, 150 Fortis Green London N10 3PA ☎ *(020) 8920 9407*
Hires TENS machines for use in labour. / HOURS *Mon, Tues, Weds, Fri: 8am-6pm; SEE ALSO 1.04 Antenatal classes; 2.01 Postnatal; 4.02 Health practitioners.*

Obstetric TENS Hire

The New Rd Clinic, 128 New Rd, Portsmouth Hampshire PO2 7RJ ☎ *(023) 9282 8998*
Normal hire period six weeks (delivered three weeks before EDD), £17.50 + P&P £2.70 – free extension with notification. £3 cancellation charge. Recorded delivery must be used for return. / HOURS *Mon-Fri 9am-5pm, or answerphone.*

Obtens

53 Linden Road, Wesbury Park Bristol BS6 7RW ☎ *(0117) 924 1982*
🖰 *www.obtens.co.uk*
Six week hire period, £19, plus 50p for each day thereafter; supplied with battery and either reusable silicone rubber electrodes or disposable self-adhesive electrodes. Certificate of posting included for return. / HOURS *24hr answerphone.*

Pulsar

Spembly Medical, Newbury Rd, Andover Hampshire SP10 4DR ☎ *(0800) 515413, (01264) 365741* 🖰 *www.pulsar-tens.com*
One of two suppliers recommended by the NHS and also by the NCT. Machines can be set at the highest comfortable level by the mother and a hand-held boost button increases the rate of stimulation pulses. The careline offers support in the use of the machines. 35-day rental, £26.99 – with a free extension if notified in advance (£6 per extra week otherwise). Freepost label included plus battery and disposable electrodes. Full cancellation if notification given before machine is sent out or £13.50 refund if baby born while Pulsar in post (if returned unused within 7 days).

Septrim Medical

164 Old Woolwich St London SE10 9PR ☎ *(0500) 710071, (020) 8314 1117*
🖰 *www.contentbaby.co.uk*
'Birthmate' TENS machines available to hire online or buy (NHS-approved model); £20 for six weeks (hire is free if you pre-book a breast pump).
/ SEE ALSO *2.02 Feeding.*

4. OTHER EQUIPMENT

The Active Birth Centre

25 Bickerton Rd London N19 5JT ☎ *(020) 7281 6760*
🖰 *www.activebirthcentre.com*
The centre sells a variety of items including a 'birth ball' (£30). See the website for details. / HOURS *shop Mon-Fri 9.30am-6.30pm (Fri 4pm), Sat 10am-4pm; SEE ALSO 1.01 Where to have the baby; 1.04 Antenatal classes; 2.01 Postnatal; 2.02 Feeding; 2.03 Baby health; 2.06 Baby & toddler activities; 3.01 Maternity wear; 3.02 Baby equipment; 4.02 Health practitioners; 4.05 Finding out more.*

BirthWorks

58 Shalmsford Street, Chartham, Canterbury Kent CT4 7RH ☎ *(01227) 730081*
🖰 *www.birthworks.co.uk*
As well as pools (see above), this company can supply a birthing stool, designed not to inhibit movement and to leave the backbone and hips free. £45 for four weeks' hire. / HOURS *Mon-Fri 9am-5pm, or answerphone.*

Ruth White Yoga Centre

Church Farm House, Spring Close Lane Cheam SM3 8PU ☎ *(020) 8644 0309*
🖰 *www.ruthwhiteyoga.com*
Suppliers of mats used in some maternity units, based on yoga mats, providing a warm, non-slip surface for mothers who want to use a squatting position for delivery; perforated to allow liquid to drain away. Machine washable standard £22; lightweight £19. / HOURS *Mon-Fri 8am-4pm.*

CHAPTER 1.07

TIMETABLE & WHAT TO PACK

1. Timetable
2. What to pack

Part of the stress that many women feel during their first pregnancy is – on top of all the new issues which crop up and must be dealt with on a daily basis – not having a good feel for what happens next.

The following schedule provides a 'rough guide', assuming a normal pregnancy – one not affected by issues that would require, say, frequent medical attention.

1. TIMETABLE

How your due date is calculated

Pregnancy is generally measured in weeks and the prevailing British rule of thumb is that a 'normal' pregnancy should last 40 weeks. This is quite a rough yardstick, however, and a duration of one or two weeks more or less is very common. Some Continental countries, for example, take 41 weeks as the norm.

The only exception to this rule is twins, which are sometimes considered full term at 37 weeks. (Consequently, some consultants like to admit mothers of twins to hospital between 30 and 36 weeks for observation and rest.)

Approximately 30% of babies are 'early', 70% 'late', with only 2% arriving on the estimated due date (the EDD); 6% of babies arrive before 38 weeks and 4% after 42 weeks.

The calculation of the EDD has traditionally been an extremely inaccurate science, based on the date of the last menstrual period (LMP). This is being phased out, however, in favour of estimates based on ultrasound scans. In October 2003, new NHS guidelines recommended that in future all women should be offered a scan (ideally between 10 and 13 weeks) to determine gestational age.

THE TRADITIONAL SYSTEM (LMP)

The starting week for the calculation is taken from the first day of the last period before conception. Thus, as most women ovulate in the middle of their cycle, the calculated duration of your pregnancy typically includes two weeks when you weren't pregnant. That's just how it's done. If your cycle is longer than four weeks it's even more a matter of guesswork when exactly you conceived, and there is theoretically a greater likelihood of your pregnancy lasting a little longer than 40 weeks.

Antenatal carers have for years used obstetric 'wheels' to calculate the EDD for them. These wheels can be inaccurate so it is well worth doing your own calculations.

AGE ASSESSMENT BY ULTRASOUND

The developmental stage of the foetus as seen and measured by ultrasound is now felt to provide a good mareker of how far the pregnancy has progressed and, where available, is now generally considered the preferred estimate.

The calculation does have consequences

Because induction is routinely advised for 'overdue' babies, the result of a miscalculated EDD is sometimes a baby artificially caused to be born prematurely.

Point out to your carers as early as possible if you disagree with their EDD.(If you know the date on which you conceived, or noticed symptoms of pregnancy (feeling 'different', constipation and/or nausea, swollen or tender breasts, feeling tired, going off foods or drinks like coffee and alcohol, needing to go to the toilet more often), mark it in your diary in case there is any doubt further down the line. It is the sort of detail that is difficult to remember eight months later.)

Some mothers, if they are worried about being induced on the basis of what is a somewhat inexact calculation, lie about the date of the first day of their last period, indicating that it was a week later than it actually was. (Early dating scans can scupper this strategy, but they do at least offer a more accurate EDD.)

To avoid rising tension if the baby's birth goes over the due date (for yourself, your partner, and other interested parties like prospective grandparents), some carers suggest that you mark the baby's projected arrival in your diary as a two week period either side of the 'official' due date, rather than as a particular day.

The run-up to the birth

The following tasks are unrelated to any particular timetable, and answer to the description: "it's never too early to start thinking about ...".

➤ If you want to have private antenatal classes, including with the NCT, book early – places on the good courses go quickly.

➤ Review how suitable your home is for having a family. Some 40% of couples move in the run-up to a birth. Why? Because even though it is a pain moving when pregnant, it is even worse after the birth, with the demands of looking after a small baby or toddler.

➤ Home improvements are best done now to avoid having to care for a newborn in rooms full of paint pots or even rubble. Furthermore, consider how to arrange your home so that a crawling baby will not cause havoc. With builders, insist that all work is completed well before the last month of pregnancy so that you do not feel fraught or invaded in the run up to the birth. It may be worth including a completion date in the deal, with penalties if it is not met.

➤ The top maternity nurses get booked up eight months ahead of time. Experienced nannies look for their next placement up to six months in advance (though there are no hard and fast rules). A sensible objective would be to check out all the potential options at an early stage, to save yourself time and energy once the baby arrives.

➤ If you have pets, plan who will look after them at the time of the birth and consider how they will be cared for immediately afterwards. The RSPCA recommends maintaining feeding and exercise routines to reassure pets and to reduce their potential stress or frustration (see chapter *2.01 Postnatal*).

➤ Write a will and get your finances in order (see chapter *2.08 Finance*).

➤ Discuss childcare issues with your partner. You may differ in your approaches and the sooner you discuss any differences the better. Bear in mind that each child is different and has different needs; and your views once you have a baby may be very different from what you imagine them to be in advance (see information on parenting courses, see chapter *2.01 Postnatal*).

➤ Preposterous as this sounds, if you are thinking of childcare in a day nursery you need to be thinking about it now. There's a serious short-age of places and the sooner you book one the better. Similarly if you want to have a reasonably guaranteed crack at one of the better regarded nursery schools in your area you need to start thinking now, and, even more ridiculously, the same is true of some private schools. (see chapter *2.07 Education*).

Week-by-week timetable

WEEK 0
Starts the first day of the last period before conception.

WEEK 5
This is the week in which you would normally start your next period. DIY tests are available which, starting from the day after a missed period, give a good indication as to whether or not you are pregnant. Note, how-ever, that it is not uncommon to experience a late period that results from a pregnancy that miscarries at a very early stage. In such cases any preg-nancy test carried out before the miscarriage would still have given a positive result.

WEEKS 6–10
Verifying the pregnancy should now be possible with greater certainty.

➤ You may get a free pregnancy test at your GP's practice (though some-times there is a charge for instant results), at an antenatal clinic, or at an NHS family planning clinic. Other family planning organisations and chemists will also carry out the test for a charge. These, like home tests, are of ever-increasing accuracy and, when they fail, tend to indi-cate you are not pregnant when in fact you are, rather than vice versa. If you've done a home test, don't be surprised if your GP doesn't seem very interested in an 'official' one and just takes your word for it.

➤ It is possible to confirm pregnancy with an early ultrasound check from week 4, but this is not usually considered necessary unless there have been problems in previous pregnancies. Not all practitioners can do this accurately.

➤ Some people want to announce the pregnancy just as soon as they know. Others prefer to wait until after three months (week 13) as mis-carriage is less likely after that stage. If an amniocentesis is required, some people wait until they have had the test results at around weeks 14–16. When telling others about the expected birth, midwives some-times suggest giving an estimated due date of two weeks after the real one to avoid grandparents and the like pestering you incessantly to find out if the baby has arrived.

As soon as possible, start thinking about:
➤ Where you want to have the child (see chapter *1.01 Where to have the baby*).
➤ Whether you want the foetus to be tested for abnormality (and where you stand on termination). Are there any specific antenatal tests that you would like performed? If you would like a nuchal scan (see weeks 11-14) and your chosen or local hospital is one of the few where it is

not available, start making the necessary arrangements (see chapter *1.03 Tests*). All the tests that are routinely available to pregnant women are listed in this timetable, but it is up to you whether you have them or not.

➤ Book a maternity nurse if you want one. The best take bookings eight months in advance. An agency can generally find someone at less than a month's notice but at this stage you have to take what you can get.

WEEK 8

➤ Once your GP has accepted that you are pregnant, the practice should provide you with information about your NHS birth options. Unless you are going private or considering a home birth, your GP will refer you to your chosen hospital who may then contact you directly (though London hospitals may need some chasing).

➤ Your first, 'booking' appointment is generally some time between week eight and week 12. This is usually the longest visit of the pregnancy at between one and two hours, and will probably involve a number of tests to assess your general health (see chapter *1.03 Tests*). It may be split up into two separate visits. You do not have to go via your GP. If you know which hospital you would like to handle your birth, you may be able to go direct to the hospital's antenatal clinic, but some hospitals – particularly popular ones – insist you do go through a GP.

➤ If you want to have your care handled by community midwives (and that, by definition, includes home births), arrange this as early as possible as capacity tends to be limited. This will probably be via the hospital.

➤ You are now eligible for free prescriptions and dental care, subject to filling out the appropriate forms (see chapter *1.05 Rights*).

➤ From now to between weeks 28 and 32 you will have antenatal check-ups every four weeks (see chapter *1.03 Tests*).

WEEKS 10–1 2

➤ Start looking into antenatal classes and possibly parenting classes. NCT classes in particular book up fast, so the sooner you put your (and possibly your partner's) name down, the better. (See chapter *1.04 Antenatal classes*). If you are expecting twins it is sometimes suggested that you book classes earlier than usual as twins are generally born a little early.

➤ If you are going to need maternity clothes for work or evenings this is a good time to start looking and ordering mail order catalogues (see chapter *3.01 Maternity wear*).

WEEKS 11–14

➤ The usual date at which the initial ultrasound scan (nuchal scan) screening for neural tube defects, and foetal anomaly scan are carried out (see chapter *1.03 Tests*).

WEEK 12

➤ As the greatest risk of a miscarriage is past, this is a good time to start antenatal yoga or exercise classes.

➤ From around now it should be possible to hear the baby's heartbeat at antenatal checks. If nobody offers, ask – it can be very reassuring.

➤ This is a good time to look into what maternity benefits you may be due (see chapter *1.05 Rights*).

➤ Whenever you reveal that you are pregnant, people will start telling you labour stories. It can seem as though women who have good labours are almost ashamed of relating them and you will tend to hear the horror stories instead. Combine this with images of birth on film and television and you could well be terrified. A little 'reprogramming' can be very effective – read positive birth stories (such as Nicky Wesson's *Home Birth* – see chapter 1.01 *Where to have the baby*), or attend an antenatal exercise or yoga class where women come back to talk about their experiences.

➤ Qualified, experienced nannies are starting to be booked up for the period after your due date.

WEEKS 14–16
➤ The usual dates for an amniocentesis, which is only routinely offered to women considered 'high risk' (see chapter *1.03 Tests*).

WEEKS 14–20
➤ Serum screening tests, on a maternal blood sample, to check for chromosomal abnormalities in the foetus will be conducted around now (see chapter *1.03 Tests*).

WEEK 16
➤ You should be invited to your first antenatal appointment after your initial ones to discuss any screening test results, decide if you need iron supplementation and test your blood pressure and urine.

WEEKS 18–20
➤ If you agree, an ultrasound scan will be performed to detect structural anomalies in the foetus.

WEEK 22
➤ Babies born prematurely at this point now have a very small (5%) chance of survival.

WEEKS 24–42
➤ Although more usually between weeks 32–36, you may be offered a detailed ultrasound scan, also called a foetal wellbeing scan, around now (see chapter *1.03 Tests*).

WEEK 25
➤ Antenatal check (first time mothers only): measure and plot symphysis–fundal height; test blood pressure and urine.

WEEK 26
➤ You must have been employed for six months before this point (the "Qualifying week") in order to qualify for Statutory Maternity Pay.
➤ If you wish to start your time off from work at Week 29 (the earliest you can do so), you must inform your employer now in order to give the necessary 21 day notice. If you are eligible not just for Ordinary Maternity Leave, but also for Additional Maternity Leave and wish to take it, then you must inform you employer that you are planning to do so (also stating your intention to return to work thereafter).

WEEK 28
➤ Antenatal check (all mothers): screening for anaemia; consider iron supplementation; offer anti-D to rhesus negative women; measure and plot symphysis–fundal height; test blood pressure & urine.

WEEK 29
➤ Almost all (95%) of babies born prematurely at this point survive.

➤ You can start Ordinary Maternity Leave or Additional Maternity Leave any time from now. When to stop working is a very individual decision. Don't try to judge too far ahead – you may find yourself feeling very tired and not up to working at your normal pace. There are other considerations: it is argued by some, for example, that rest during the day becomes increasingly important for the baby, as it allows greater blood flow to the placenta, and research indicates that if you are unhappy or particularly stressed by work, this can trigger labour prematurely.

As soon as you have left work, start to make preparations for the labour, as your tummy will only continue to grow from now on, making activity more of an effort. The more you can organise now, the less hassle you will face in the immediate run up to, or after, the birth. The following is a checklist of things you might like to get out of the way:

➤ Pack a bag for the hospital (see Section 2, What to pack).
➤ Order any equipment you are planning to use during the birth (see chapter *1.06 Birth equipment*).
➤ If you are planning to breast-feed, buy some nursing bras (see chapter *3.01 Maternity wear*).
➤ Do a bit of reading up on life after birth, and looking after a baby (See chapter *4.05 Finding out more*).
➤ Stock up on shopping (washing powder, toilet rolls etc.), and cook for the freezer, or buy ready-made meals (ideally not too spicy or anything linked to giving babies colic – see chapter *2.02 Feeding*) for after the baby arrives. You might like to experiment with home shopping (see chapter *2.02 Feeding*) – a real boon once you have a child.
➤ If you don't have one, consider getting a mobile phone (and a cordless one for your home).
➤ Set up as many direct debit payments as possible to minimise paperwork.
➤ If going back to work in three months, start finalising your plans concerning childcare (see chapter *2.04 Childcare*).
➤ If you wish to consider cord blood donation, or private cord blood banking (see chapter *2.03 Baby health*).
➤ Pamper yourself with plenty of time with friends, trips to the cinema and candlelit dinners. Getting your hair cut, legs waxed and other 'treatments' you fancy is also a good idea as you will find it much more difficult after the baby has arrived.
➤ Get plenty of sleep, including – if at all possible – daytime catnaps.

WEEK 31
➤ Antenatal check (first time mothers only): measure and plot symphysis–fundal height; test blood pressure and urine.

WEEKS 32–36
➤ Some hospitals may carry out a foetal wellbeing scan (see chapter *1.03 Tests*).

WEEK 34
➤ Antenatal check (all pregnant women): offer a second dose of anti-D to rhesus-negative women; measure and plot symphysis–fundal height; test blood pressure and urine.
➤ Items of equipment like prams and car seats are often not kept as stock items by shops. Especially if getting a specific model is important to you, get your order in by now to allow six weeks for delivery (see chapter *3.02 Baby equipment*). Note this is especially a factor for autumn

babies, as prior to the arrival of new models, retailers tend to operate with depleted stocks.

WEEK 36

➤ 90% of babies are born after this week.

➤ Antenatal check (all pregnant women): measure and plot symphysis–fundal height; test blood pressure and urine; check position of baby; if babies are breech, consider ECV.

➤ Arrange how you are going to get to wherever you are having the baby. Driving yourself is not recommended. If you have a companion, are not in too much pain and are close enough, then walking is a possibility and may help labour progress. If you plan on using a taxi company, check in advance that they don't mind transporting a woman in labour (many do mind). Ambulances may simply take you to the nearest hospital rather than the one you are booked into. Note that if you are to be attended by a community midwife you will not be able to use her car (for insurance reasons).

➤ Consider who you will want to visit you after the birth and how visits are going to be staggered. Make sure you and your partner agree on this so that – if they are at all numerous – some form of 'slot allocation' can be arranged at the same time as any birth announcement. This is particularly important after a Caesarean.

➤ If worried about your waters breaking on your mattress, put a waterproof sheet on it – one that can be later used by the toddler would be useful though you may want to keep it on your own bed while starting breastfeeding to protect against leaking milk.

➤ List the phone numbers of everyone who's offered to help, and what they've offered to do in case you're too sleep deprived later to remember.

➤ If you have another child or children make sure all childcare cover is in place, plus entertainment and meals for the period after the new baby has arrived.

WEEK 38

➤ Antenatal check (all pregnant women): measure and plot symphysis–fundal height; test blood pressure and urine.

WEEK 40

➤ It's time, but don't expect the baby to arrive on the due date. Plan plenty of flexible, relaxed activities. Waiting for a baby can seem to go on forever and it's good to take your mind off the birth.

➤ Antenatal check (first time mothers only): measure and plot symphysis–fundal height; test blood pressure and urine.

➤ You might like to make sure you don't have varnished nails when you go into labour. Nail colouring is used as one of the indicators of patient wellbeing under anaesthetic.

WEEK 41

➤ Antenatal check (all pregnant women): consider a membrane sweep; consider induction of labour; test blood pressure and urine; measure and plot symphysis–fundal height.

TO WEEK 42

➤ 70% of babies arrive after the EDD, and 4% of pregnancies go more than a fortnight overdue. Stay relaxed – you might like to try an 'alternative' induction method (see chapter *4.03 Medical issues at birth*) or a complementary therapy (see chapter *4.02 Complementary medicine &*

Health practitioners). According to circumstances, your carers will probably be reluctant to 'wait and see' beyond this point.

After the birth

Giving birth, however well it goes, tends to leave new mothers feeling rather unfocused. This makes it more difficult to ask for what you want, and especially hard to stand up to those in authority who occasionally take advantage of this fact when pushing for the courses of action they think best (or who simply don't have the time to spare to a new mother who is feeling somewhat at sea). Even within a single institution, you may receive conflicting advice, particularly about feeding and sleeping. Try to make sure your partner is aware of the likelihood of this and is in a position to back you up should any issues emerge.

Although live-in help, paid or related, may be invaluable for a time, it can arrest the development of the 'family' unit. This kind of help might therefore be best organised for after the father has returned to work.

ONE DAY AFTER THE BIRTH

➢ The earliest that women tend to leave hospital after giving birth is six hours. Mothers with an uncomplicated birth tend to leave in one or two days.

TWO DAYS AFTER THE BIRTH

➢ As you come home from hospital and/or the milk comes in you may suffer the baby blues – a heightened emotionalism, vulnerability to doubts about your mothering, and general tearfulness. When or whether this strikes is unpredictable – 30% of women report it as a problem after 10 days, reducing to 10% after a month. Make sure your partner knows this may happen (see chapter *2.01 Postnatal* for information and remedies).

➢ Whether you give birth privately or on the NHS, one of your community midwives will visit you most days for the 10 days after you get home, and advise you on issues such as feeding, bathing, routines, etc.

➢ Expect calls from your health visitor for up to 14 days after the birth. Try to anticipate this and book them in for a convenient time.

FIVE DAYS AFTER THE BIRTH

➢ Women who have had a Caesarean section typically leave hospital around this time.

8–14 DAYS AFTER THE BIRTH

➢ A Guthrie heel prick test will be carried out on the baby (see chapter *1.03 Tests*).

10 DAYS AFTER THE BIRTH

➢ If you have a problem with stitches – they can sometimes fall out – and the problem persists beyond this point, get yourself checked out as soon as possible. Don't allow anyone to tell you that it's not worth fussing about. Badly healed stitches/scars can ruin your sex life and the sooner they are sorted out the better.

BEFORE WEEK 6

➢ Register the birth. All births, including stillbirths, must be registered within 42 days at the registry office of the borough in which the child was born. If this is problematic you can go to another registry office in

England or Wales, which will then forward the information. (See chapter *2.09 Naming & ceremonies*.)

6–8 WEEKS

➤ It is usual for you and your baby to have a check-up with your GP. If you are going to have your baby immunised, this may be when the first set of jabs – Hib, DPT, meningitis C and polio – are administered. DPT stands for diphtheria, pertussis (whooping cough) and tetanus; Hib for Haemophilus influenzae type b – a bacteria that causes a type of meningitis, and also pneumonia, and ear infections. You will be notified of the timetable for subsequent injections. If you wish to delay or to avoid having the injections given at all you should probably write in advance to the GP with whom the baby is registered explaining your position. (See the information on immunisation in chapter *2.03 Baby Health*).

➤ Boredom and a sense of loneliness may set in around this time. If you are not yet part of a mother and baby network, this is a good time to join up. This is also a suitable time to start going to postnatal and baby activity classes. (See chapter *2.01 Postnatal*).

BEFORE WEEK 7

➤ Most mothers who return to work do so between now and six months after the birth. (See chapter *1.05 Rights*.)

➤ Write to your employer stating that you will be returning to work. Many people advise that you do this even if you don't actually intend to return, in order to keep your options open. Life with a baby is a whole new ball game and you don't know how you're going to feel, or how your priorities may change even after just a month or so.

WEEKS 12–16

➤ Further vaccinations (DPT booster shots) are given at this time. A 12-week postnatal check may also be introduced.

WEEK 26

➤ Deadline for collecting Child Benefit accrued since birth.

WEEK 29

➤ Maximum end-point for Additional Maternity Leave.

8 MONTHS

➤ Development check for the baby; (this will include a hearing check if one was not conducted earlier – see chapter *2.03 Baby health*).

12–18 MONTHS

➤ MMR vaccination (see chapter *2.03 Baby health*, immunisation, for information if you have concerns on this point).

2. WHAT TO PACK

It is wise to pack a bag of things you will need in hospital well before the EDD – at least four weeks in advance is sensible. Even if you are planning a home birth, it is a good idea to have a bag prepared in case you need to, or choose to transfer to hospital. Whatever the case, this may prove a useful checklist.

You might want to pack two bags – one for labour and one for after. The second can then be left at home for your partner to bring in whenever it is required.

Note that many NHS hospitals have very limited storage space for patients – often just a small locker or cupboard by your bed – and prefer for you only to have with you items which you are actively using. That means your partner may have to take home any surplus items as soon as possible after the birth, and be made responsible for bringing in all the going-home stuff shortly before you are due to leave.

The following is a list of suggestions of the 'including-the-kitchen-sink' variety. The idea is to pick whatever appeals to you. You certainly don't need everything on the list.

Hospitals prefer you not to take valuables in with you and if you feel you must, suggest that you hand them over for safe-keeping.

For you

MOST IMPORTANT
➤ Your maternity records, if you are holding your own notes.
➤ A birth plan, if you have one.
➤ Two or more loose garments/nightdresses/large T-shirts – one to give birth in and the others for afterwards – with front openings if you are planning to breast-feed. Cotton is probably best as you may feel sweaty. You could use a hospital gown for the messy business of giving birth if you can be bothered to change but these generally open up the back, making immediate breast-feeding more complicated and making the wearer feel a bit institutionalised. Bear in mind that you will probably get blood on your nightdresses.
➤ Jumper, dressing gown and socks to keep warm if the labour is long.
➤ Slippers or shoes to walk around in.
➤ Bottled water, apple juice (citrus juices are considered – by some experts, too acidic to drink at this stage) or herb tea fortified with honey, and something to eat if your hospital allows food: point them to *Birthrights* (see Reading in chapter *4.03 Medical issues at birth*) if you want to argue this point in advance. Glucose tablets can be useful for extra energy although fructose tablets (available from health food stores) might be better as they offer a slower release of energy. Bendy straws are handy. Take biscuits or other snacks for after the birth.
➤ Hairbrush and hairband to keep your hair out of the way.
➤ A supply of snacks and drink for your birth partner. You may have no appetite in labour, but your companion may get hungry and thirsty.

OPTIONAL
➤ Birth equipment you are planning to use, i.e. birth pool or TENS machine.
➤ Music tapes/CDs and a player if the birthing rooms are not equipped with them.
➤ Any complementary products that you are planning to use: homeo-pathic/aromatherapy products such as arnica (useful for swelling and bleeding); or Bach Flower Rescue Remedy (for shock, injury or trauma).
➤ A bucket to sit on (sounds bizarre but is comfortable) and/or a bean-bag, large floor cushion or inflatable gym ball, plus possibly a pad, piece of foam or yoga mat for kneeling on.
➤ Ice cubes in a thermos to suck on (could be made of fruit juice or rasp-berry leaf tea), and/or an ice pack.
➤ In hot weather, a fan.
➤ Flannels or small sponges for refreshing your face, or a water spray.
➤ A lip moisturising stick for dry lips.

➤ Massage oils. (Wooden massage rollers or even a tennis ball are some-
   times useful for pain relief.)
➤ A mirror – useful if you want to see the baby's head emerging.
➤ A hot flannel to help the perineum stretch (ask about facilities for
   heating water or take a kettle for your partner to do this).
➤ A watch for timing contractions.
➤ A video recorder if the hospital is agreeable.
➤ Champagne to celebrate (the nurses may be willing to put this in a
   fridge for you).

For the baby

MOST IMPORTANT

➤ If you have decided to bottle-feed, formula milk and bottles.
➤ Nappies – newborn size (or mini if you've been told it's a large baby).
   Although the hospital may supply some it's best not to rely on this.
➤ Two stretchsuits and vests (you can get more brought in if necessary).
➤ Plenty of cotton wool or soft muslin for cleaning.

OPTIONAL

➤ Oils such as olive or almond are good for dry baby skin.

For afterwards

MORE IMPORTANT

➤ Disposable pants (available from NCT Maternity Sales, Boots and
   Mothercare), avoiding paper ones which are uncomfortable and tend
   to disintegrate. Go for stretchable ones. Alternatively use lots of old
   cotton ones which you can throw out when you are ready for something more cheerful. In either case you will need something
   comfortable to hold sanitary towels and possibly ice packs in place.
   Larger are better and vital if you have a Caesarean scar.
➤ Sanitary towels, some of which are specifically maternity ones. Slimline
   versions such as the Always Ultra brand are much less bulky, but the
   one-way coating may stick to stitches and the 'dry' surface may feel
   uncomfortable. Look for those without a woven surface and go for
   those labelled 'classic' or 'soft-covered'. Stick-on pads are convenient
   but 'winged' pads may tear disposable knickers. You may need as
   many as two packs in the first two or three days.
➤ Nursing bras if you are planning to breast-feed and breast pads even if
   not, plus possibly some cabbage leaves (recommended for engorgement – yes, people swear they help).
➤ Toiletries – toothbrush, toothpaste, tissues, perfume, make-up, soap,
   shampoo etc.
➤ Soft towels for you and the baby if you are going to be in for a few
   days.
➤ Change for the payphone, or a mobile phone (though the latter cannot
   actually be used on the ward, as they interfere with monitoring equipment).
➤ A camera and – if you haven't yet gone digital – fast (400ASA) film to
   avoid needing flash (this causes newborns to close their eyes). If you
   expect that the baby may be taken into special care before you see it
   (for example if you are having twins), a Polaroid camera can be a good
   way of letting you see what the new arrival looks like should you be
   immobilised.

OPTIONAL

➤ A soft cushion to sit on after the birth, or possibly a Valley cushion
  (see listings in chapter *2.01 Postnatal*).

➤ High-fibre nibbles are good if you get hungry, and will help with constipation (a common complaint).

➤ Writing paper/cards and stamps.

➤ Books/magazines or playing cards.

➤ Radio/Walkman.

➤ Bath cleaner and cloth, plus antiseptic wipes in case lavatories, baths
  and bidets are not clean enough for you. Antiseptic wipes or disposable
  toilet seat covers are useful to avoid contracting infections if you have
  a tear. Maternal Infections postnatally have been rising so without
  these you should limit your contact with these areas as far as possible.

➤ Eye shades to help you sleep.

➤ Change for the hospital car park.

➤ Any complementary products you wish to use: perhaps arnica cream
  for a bruised perineum; raspberry leaf tea, calendula or Hypercal tincture to help heal stitches; herbal balm to aid healing; witch hazel
  (reputedly helpful if you suffer from haemorrhoids after the birth);
  Bach Flower Rescue Remedy as a 'pick-me-up'; aromatherapy oils
  etc. Salt in the bath works as a natural antiseptic.

➤ Your partner may want a change of clothes, toiletries and some food
  as well.

For going home

➤ Comfortable clothes – you will be about the size you were at six
  months pregnant. As some women lose a lot of blood at first you
  might like to opt for darker colours.

➤ Shawl or blanket and (depending on the season) snowsuit for the baby
  to go home in. If you're at all likely to get nostalgic about these items,
  bear this in mind when choosing.

➤ Car seat for the baby (required by law); possibly one fitted with a
  'head hugger'.

Parenting Basics

CHAPTER 2.01

POSTNATAL

1. **The best of times... the worst of times**
2. **Postnatal depression**
3. **Other potential problems**
4. **Looking after yourself**
5. **Parenting**

(For information on postnatal childcare – maternity nurses, doulas, and so on – see chapter 2.04 Childcare.)

1. THE BEST OF TIMES... THE WORST OF TIMES

Both physically and psychologically birth is an upheaval for the mother – as well as for the baby.

There may be great highs, but possibly also significant lows. If you don't fall in love with your baby at first sight, for example, that's perfectly common. Some people find it takes time, sometimes considerable time.

Especially with a first child, you are likely to feel different from usual and – temporarily – a lot less sure of yourself. This range of complex feelings can make the contradictory advice that you may receive from 'experts' (friends and health professionals) more than a little worrying. If you have been able to do some reading up and preparation in advance, all well and good. If not, it can be useful to look for a couple of people whose opinion you feel is valid, and rely primarily on their views. Do not be afraid to disregard everyone else's opinions and trust your own instincts about what is best for your baby.

Pain is felt by around 70% of mothers after birth – either the after-pains of the uterus contracting to its pre-pregnancy size, or discomfort from bruising, tearing, an episiotomy or a Caesarean. You are perfectly within your rights to ask for help with this – for example through the pre-scription of painkilling drugs. You might also consider using a TENS machine if you have access to one, or a complementary treatment or product.

One temporary problem can be loss of short-term concentration and short-term memory. This may be due to a flood of hormones designed to wipe out memories of any difficulties during the birth and/or the extreme fatigue that may occur after the physical effort of labour plus broken nights' sleep. Some women suffer from this 'cheese brain' state for just a day or so. Others find it lasts longer.

You may also have to contend with physical problems after the birth – such as backache, headaches, neck and shoulder pains, incontinence and haemorrhoids. At least as important, and less easily defined, is a 'thin-skinned' quality – useful for picking up every tiny message from the baby, but leaving you vulnerable to the merest hints of criticism. Forewarn your partner that a little wobbliness (sometimes more than a little) is likely in the days and weeks after the birth.

The NCT's The More Things Change… report in 1999 found that postnatal care and support – as well as help with breast-feeding – was one of the aspects of care most in need of improvement. You may have to make a fuss to get it, but it is important that you receive psychological support and medical help if you feel you need either or both – even after the medical profession has signed you off as fit (usually at the six-week check). Looking after a baby is hard work and it is a good investment to remedy any complaint as soon as possible.

Should you encounter a health professional who tells you it's nothing to worry about, try somewhere else, even if it's another GP in your health centre. However grateful you may be to your carers for having helped you and the baby through pregnancy and labour, you owe it to your child to be in the best possible state of health.

As soon as you feel up to it, it can be useful to find things to do with the baby outside the house so that you don't feel too housebound. (For ideas, see chapter *2.06 Baby & toddler activities*.) When you feel ready (usually after the six-week check, perhaps later if you had a Caesarean) you can try a postnatal exercise class. Some classes combine activities for both the mother and the child.

Do arrange for as much help as possible for as long as possible, whether from family or friends or some form of paid help. Statistically, in the short term this reduces the likelihood of postnatal depression, and in the long term reduces stress (there is, for example, a link between low levels of help and child abuse).

If you are a first-time parent, it is probably a good idea to jettison any idea of 'getting life back to normal' after the birth. You will find that getting even the simplest thing done now can be much more complicated than it was of old. New babies tend to rule the agenda for their parents and it can be a while – sometimes years – before this changes. You may find life less taxing accepting this basic truth, rather than trying to fight it.

READING

(For titles aimed at fathers rather than mothers, see chapter 4.05 Finding out more.)

All Change (A woman's guide to life after having a baby; Maternity Alliance; £2.50) – *Part of the organisation's Women's Guides series, offering personal accounts of the worries and concerns which may arise on becoming a parent, and issues like looking after yourself and communicating with your partner. / The Maternity Alliance, www.maternityalliance.org.uk.*

Baby and You – compiled by Rosalyn Thiro (The Real Life Guide to Birth and Babies; Blue Island Publishing; 2002; £11.99; 0-9540802-1-1) – *Thoughts and comments on the issues and practicalites of pregnancy, birth and parenthood. It includes contributions from 50 parents, plus Sheila Kitzinger, Kate Figes and more. It offers ideal reading for those who want to consider different scenarios and approaches, or simply to read up other mothers' thoughts on pregnancy, birth and new parenthood. / www.blueisland.co.uk.*

The Best Friend's Guide to Getting Your Groove Back – Vicki Iovine (Loving your family without losing your mind; Bloomsbury; 2001; £9.99; 0-747551-84-7) – *Latest in the series from the zippy, best-selling American writer on pregnancy.*

The Best Friend's Guide to Motherhood ★ – Vicky Iovine (Surviving the First Year; Bloomsbury; 1999; £9.99; 0-747536-48-1) – *An antidote to the wave of authors who are unhappy to find parenthood is not what they expected – American information/opinion in a humorous tone.*

Callie's Tally – Betsy Howie (An Account of a Baby's First Year (Or, What My Daughter Owes Me); Piatkus; 2003; £7.99; 0-7499-2028-9) – *An entertaining look at the hidden costs of child rearing - extra caffeine intake, photo processing bills and membership of Weight Watchers. It considers whether babies should be billed for postnatal chocolate binges and for the travel expenses they incur in being shown off to in-laws.*

The Fat Ladies Club – Hilary Gardener, Sarah Groves, Lyndsey Lawrence, Andrea Bettridge, Annette Jones (The Indispensible Real World Guide to Pregnancy; Penguin; 2002; £6.99; 0-141-00789-3) – *Originally self-published, the accounts of five friends who met at antenatal class. They tell all, covering the gamut from stretch marks to labour, their sex lives and when the authors first felt like mums. With five to choose from, most readers can find an experience which makes personal sense. A subsequent volume published in 2003, sub-titled Facing the First Five Years, covers issues like sibling rivalry, the family bed, juggling work and children, food, and more.*

The Fat Ladies Club 2 – Hilary Gardener, Andrea Bettridge, Sarah Groves, and Lyndsey Lawrence (Facing the first five years; Penguin; 2003; £7.99; 0141012927) – *One of the original five fat ladies has died of cancer, but the remaining four again distill the wisdom of their different approaches and experiences of childcare covering issues like sleep and sex, flab and fashion, andn toilets and tantrums (a chapter with some laugh out loud moments).*

From Here to Maternity – Joan McFadden (The ultimate survival guide for new parents; Mainstream Publishing; 1997; £6.99; 1-85158-941-4) – *A bracing account of what to expect, based on a first person narrative, but with added information. It's a bit like getting advice from a friendly older sister.*

Help! I'm a Parent! – Gwen Rankin (How to cope with the first year; Piatkus 2nd edition; 1996; £10.99; 0749913827)

The Parenting Puzzle – Candida Hunt (How to Get the Best Out of Family Life; Family Links; £14.99; 2003; 0954470907) – *Based on a 10-week course called the Nurturing Programme (which has been running for 10 years), whose idea is to encourage parents to get the best out of family life. It includes feedback from attendees and ideas for activities in explaining how emotions influence our actions, hot to guide children and how to boost self-esteem in parents and children.*

Partners Becoming Parents – Christopher Clulow ed (Jason Aronson; 1997; £16.95; 0765700247) – *Twelve essays about – among other things – co-habiting, marriage, the effects of infertility on men and on women, fighting after the baby arrives, step-families; a range of theories is offered.*

The Sixty Minute Mother – Rob Parsons (Hodder and Stoughton; 2000; £6.99; 0-340630-61-2) – *Follow-up to the Sixty Minute Father, taking different mothers as examples; the highs and lows plus issues such as whether to go back to work, raising a child alone, guilt, favouritism, and illness.*

For those who feel that this is not what you expected

A Life's Work – Rachel Cusk (On becoming a mother; Fourth Estate; 2002; £6.99; 1841154873) – *A slightly self-indulgent account of coming to grips with the realities of birth and a new baby. Consoling for other educated women who know nothing about babies.*

I'm Okay, You're a Brat – Susan Jeffers (Freeing ourselves of the guilt-making myths of parenthood; Hodder & Stoughton; 1999; £9.99; 0340708573) – *Popular with child-free adults who like their life that way – a far from upbeat assessment of the joy of parenthood.*

Life After Birth – Wendy Blumfield (Every woman's guide to the first year of motherhood; Element Books; 1994; £6.99; 1852303514) – *A look at the physical and emotional changes of life with a baby in the first year.*

The Mask of Motherhood – Susan Maushart (Rivers Oram Press/Pandora Press; 1999; £9.99; 0-863584-07-1) – *Written by an American/Australian social scientist on the premise that – while the experience of becoming a mum is different for everyone – the stereotyped image of perfect motherhood peddled by the media and parenting books puts a great deal of extra pressure on women; similarly the divide between those who do and those who don't have kids.*

The Year After Childbirth – Sheila Kitzinger (Prentice Hall; 1994; £19.95; 0-684196-15-8) – *Shfity downbeat coverage of the various problems which may beset you.*

Postnatal care

MIDWIVES

Regardless of where you have given birth, for the 10 days after you return home from hospital (or, if you delivered at home, for the 10 days following the birth), you are visited by midwives from your local community midwife service. This is generally based at your nearest hospital. Visits are often daily, particularly for first time mothers, but if you are obviously confident well may be less frequent.

The midwives check that the mother's uterus is contracting appropriately, that any tear or stitches are healing properly and will help with any breast-feeding issues or other queries and concerns.

They will also check that the baby is well, that the umbilical stump is healing, offer reminders about baby care, and may administer, for example, the Guthrie heel prick test.

The midwives may also weigh the baby, but given that a weight loss is expected in the first few days, as a policy some teams will only do this on request, because they feel that the results can worry the parents unnecessarily.

HEALTH VISITOR

Based at a child health clinic, health centre or GP's surgery, a health visitor is a qualified nurse who has completed further training in community health. The main responsibility is to support families that have children under five: they may run ante- and postnatal classes, for example.

As well as supporting parents, health visitors also perform a social rôle in protecting children: for example from neglect or mistreatment by their parents. Vital though this task may be, it is perhaps inevitable that as a result even some excellent mothers feel conscious of being judged by their health visitor.

A health visitor pays a visit to all new mothers at home, within two weeks of the birth. She will provide advice on baby care, feeding, weaning and immunisation and should be able to offer information on welfare rights and services in the area. She should also have counselling skills to help both the mother and partner.

Many health visitors do sterling work in helping mothers who are unaware of standard current advice on health, safety and nutrition. However, in some areas their training is not especially deep; and it is not unusual to hear of mothers who feel they have been worried unnecessarily by their health visitor. What's more, some health visitors pointers on nutrition are old-fashioned and product- (if not nowadays brand-) led.

If your health visitor tells you anything about your baby, or about your own health, which you doubt or which causes you any concern, don't dismiss the advice, but don't treat it as gospel either. If the issue is an important one, seek a second opinion as soon as possible.

Try to ensure that your health visitor always makes an appointment to see you. Some occasionally drop in unannounced.

2. POSTNATAL DEPRESSION

(As with so may other things, where depression is concerned, prevention is better than cure. For organisations that help mothers create social networks and avoid feelings of isolation, see Section 4, Looking after yourself, below.)

CAUSES

Depression is not unusual at times of great life change – which of course a birth is – but susceptibility to the condition after having a baby is exacerbated by a whole variety of factors.

Physical factors:
➢ Hormone imbalance (particularly if you experienced elation in late pregnancy in which case the chemical change in your body is likely to be particularly marked).
➢ The tiredness which follows the physical exertion of labour and then the lack of sleep which often follows a birth. Extreme tiredness some-

times leads GPs to diagnose depression when the real problem is exhaustion (or vice versa).
➤ Anaemia: an iron-rich diet or supplementation may help (see chapter *1.02 Looking after yourself*).
➤ A deficiency of potassium (which is found in bananas, orange juice and tomatoes).
➤ Strict dieting, which – when it results in low blood sugar – is depressive.
➤ Use of the contraceptive pill (known to be an aggravating factor).

Emotional factors:
➤ The shift from being the centre of attention to playing second fiddle to the baby.
➤ The overwhelming emotions which accompany such an important life experience – including intense love for the baby.
➤ The recognition of the complete change of lifestyle that you have undergone – the loss of personal autonomy, freedom and financial independence; the sheer drudgery of looking after a small child.
➤ A sense of anticlimax.
➤ A sense of loss of control during the birth; depression is thought to be more common after a highly interventive and technological birth.
➤ Lack of support from those around you, including professional carers. No-one to talk to – particularly in situations when the new mother's own mother is absent, and even more so if she is no longer active.
➤ Strain in your relationship with the father.
➤ Fear and anxiety about coping with the baby.
➤ Difficult memories of childhood triggered by the arrival of your own baby.
➤ Depression over your physical appearance.

External factors:
➤ Financial worries.
➤ The disempowerment of hospital life (one piece of research found depression around four times higher among mothers who had given birth in hospital compared with those who gave birth at home).
➤ A change of location (the onset of depression seems most common on the day of returning home from hospital).

Those with lower expectations of pregnancy and parenthood seem less prone to depression, while those with an unsupportive partner or anyone who had been trying to become pregnant for two or more years may be more susceptible. Migraine sufferers are, on average, twice as likely to suffer.

BABY BLUES
Baby blues, also known as childbirth, puerperal, or postnatal blues, affects more than half (some believe more than three quarters) of women a few days after the birth, when tearful, anxious and irritable feelings are all common. As a rough guide you should take the matter seriously if it continues for more than 10 days.

Treatment includes:
➤ Simply talking (in the framework of professional counselling if preferred). The earlier for this the better. The NCT for example reports that early acknowledgement of the mother's feelings lead to a swifter recovery.
➤ Vitamin supplements, and zinc supplements.
➤ Evening Primrose oil supplements.

➢ A range of complementary therapies – particularly homeopathy which takes into account mental as well as physical symptoms, and also aromatherapy.

➢ Time spent with the baby – as long as possible, as soon as possible, preferably in physical contact – according to some reports appears to help avoid or lift the blues. If nothing else, it helps you tune into the baby's signals so she feels a little less 'alien'. Some people find carrying the baby in a sling helpful when they need to get things done (see chapter *3.02 Baby equipment*). The importance of this sort of physical closeness is further suggested by research which shows that more new mothers can identify their baby by smell than by cry.

➢ One much-talked-about solution is to eat a little of the placenta (you can cook it) because it is rich in hormones, the lack of which are blamed for postnatal depression. Few mothers do this but the placenta is yours and you are entirely within your rights to ask for it to take home.

POSTNATAL OR PUERPERAL DEPRESSION

Postnatal or puerperal depression is a far more serious condition than the 'blues' and can develop at any time during the first year after giving birth. It seems to be something like continuous baby blues along with lethargy, anxiety, sleep and appetite disturbance, sometimes poor concentration, and indifference to (or excessive concern for) the baby. If you aren't crying you may be agitated, or abnormally energetic. According to reports at a 1996 conference on the subject, between 10% and 15% of women suffer the start of depressive illness in the early months after birth, with mothers under 24 particularly at risk. However, only a small proportion of these cases are identified.

In this state of mind it can be difficult to recognise your condition, but if you are suffering persistently negative feelings about any aspect of your situation you can try the solutions mentioned for baby blues, plus those listed below.

Treatments for postnatal depression:

➢ Progesterone treatment.

➢ A course of anti-depressants and/or therapy, this second potentially with a practitioner specialising in the field.

➢ Lightboxes – little used currently in the UK but more popular in the US.

POSTNATAL OR PUERPERAL PSYCHOSIS

Considerably more serious again than the above, puerperal or postpartum psychosis affects an estimated one woman in 500 and amounts to full-blown psychosis, with dramatic mood swings and bizarre behaviour, such as hallucinations and rejection of the baby. This condition appears to be more clearly linked than the others to previous mental health or personality disorders – it is important that you inform your carers and health professionals if you have any history of mental health problems.

In such a situation hospitalisation may be the only answer – ideally with the baby, though there are a limited number of centres that offer this.

Under the Disability Discrimination Act 1995 it has been established that depression can amount to disability. This is relevant if you cannot return to work as planned. The Maternity Alliance has published a booklet covering the most pressing questions and has been offering support in a landmark case against an employer whose dismissal in a case like this is considered illegal.

POST TRAUMATIC STRESS DISORDER (PTSD)

It has been recognised that some mothers are actually traumatised by the birth of their babies, generally as a result of feeling out of control.

Symptoms include:

➢ Recurrent thoughts and images of the birth, intruding on your thoughts.

➢ Recurrent dreams of the birth.

➢ Avoidance of any reminders of the birth.

➢ Flashbacks to previous traumas such as a car crash.

➢ Amnesia relating to periods around the birth.

➢ Increased levels of anger and diminished levels of concentration.

Treatment is generally in the form of counselling, psychotherapy or some similar approach. Your hospital may offer this especially if it has acknowledged it was at fault. See also the section on Counselling and Talking treatments under chapter *4.02 Complementary Medicine & Health Practioners*.

DEPRESSION AMONG FATHERS

An estimated one in three to one in four fathers suffer postnatal blues or depression, which may manifest itself as withdrawing from the situation. A significant proportion admit to feeling jealous and, at times, inadequate.

Possibly this is a reaction to such a major life change, fatigue, and a sense of isolation from the mother and the baby. One theory is that fathers who rely on their spouse for reassurance are likely to find the new arrival more difficult. Alternatively, if the mother copes splendidly a father who planned to play the supportive role can feel a bit superfluous.

READING

Antenatal & Postnatal Depression – Siobhan Curham (Practical advice and support for all sufferers; Vermilion; 2000; £9.99; 0091856078) – *Written by a sufferer and including plenty of firsthand comments from mothers. Loooks at possible causes and strategies, both after the birth and before, fears and their causes, and nutritional ideas to help with symptoms.* / www.randomhouse.co.uk.

[Tape] **Coping with Depression** – Royal College of Psychiatrists (Talking Life; 1998; £13.99; 1901910202) – *Two-cassette pack produced with the help of the Royal College of Psychiatrists offering strategies for dealing with depression on a daily basis; shorter version also available.* / Talking Life, PO Box 1, Wirral, L47 7DD tel: 0151 632 0662 www.talkinglife.co.uk.

Depression After Childbirth – Katherine Dalton and Wendy Holton (How to Recognise, Treat and Prevent Postnatal Depression ; OUP; 2001; £10.99; 0192632779) – *By one of the experts in the field, a new edition of the classic text,including chapters on careers and motherhood, coping with stress, a look at the role the partner can play and the effects PND can have on him. There is also a chapter examining maternal behaviour in animals.*

Feelings after Birth – Heather Welford (The NCT Book of Postnatal Depression; NCT; 2002; £5.99) – *A new edition of the NCT's title on the subject, explaining postnatal depression in all its forms, its triggers and the possible courses of action.*

Is there Sex After Childbirth? – Juliet Rix (HarperCollins; 1995; £7.99; 0722529570) – *Aiming to help couples keep their emotional and sexual lives in tact after a birth.*

Life After Birth – Kate Figes (Penguin; 2000; £7.99; 0-140252-63-0) – *An ideal read for those who feel they've been short-changed by the system - from antenatal classes to society at large, leaving them in the dark about the physical and emotional dark days of new motherhood. Tales of others hiding behind a wall of competence offer some consolation to those who feel they are struggling.*

Perfect Mothers, Invisible Women – Susan Van Scoyoc (Learning to be a good mother without losing your identity; Robinson Publishing; 2000; £7.99; 1841191345) – *For those who are finding new motherhood hard work and in particular who feel they have lost themselves in the role, a helpful tome from a chartered psychologist and family therapist. Using case studies, it addresses the root causes (from a feminist perspective), and suggests ways of overcoming the problems.*

Postnatal Depression – Paula Nicolson (Facing the paradox of loss, happiness and motherhood; John Wiley & Sons; 2001; £8.99; 0471485276) – *Based round the experiences of 24 women coming to terms with motherhood, a practical guide explaing PND, theories of its causes, and what to do if it affects you. To sum up, the theory is that with a better understanding of the realities of motherhood, including both the spychological and biological aspects, new mothers will develop better self-awareness which will put them in a better position to deal with the emotional and practical challenges of being a parent.* / www.wiley.com.

The Year After Childbirth – Sheila Kitzinger (Prentice Hall; 1994; £19.95; 0-684196-15-8) – *Perhaps rather downbeat coverage of the various problems which may beset you.*

USEFUL CONTACTS

As well as the organisations below, local health authorities are becoming more alive to the issue and may have a service in place, probably run by health visitors, to pick up on sufferers and offer support.

Action on Puerperal Psychosis, ☎ *Department of Psychiatry (0121) 678 2354 or (0121) 678 2361*
For those diagnosed with Puerperal Psychosis – researcher Jackie Benjamin (j.f.benjamin@bham.ac.uk) is building a national panel of women who have experienced the problem, together with helping to publicise information about the condition and research into its causes, prevention and treatment.

Anna Freud Centre, ☎ *(020) 7794 2313* ⌁ *www.annafreudcentre.org*
The Parent and Infant Project, run by the centre, provides support for new mothers, particularly those suffering postnatal depression or any other emotional/psychological issues affecting their relationship with the child. A financial contribution is appreciated but not required. / *HOURS 9am-6pm.*

Association for Postnatal Illness (APNI), ☎ *(020) 7386 0868*
⌁ *www.apni.org*
A nationwide network of volunteer supporters, all of whom are ex-sufferers of postnatal illness; they can put one of their local volunteers in one-to-one telephone contact with a current sufferer. / *HOURS Mon-Fri 10am-5pm; PUBLICATIONS Booklet on postnatal depression (send SAE).*

Depression Alliance, ☎ *(020) 7633 0557, Postnatal depression helpline (0845) 120 3746* ⌁ *www.depressionalliance.org*
"The leading UK charity for people affected by depression", whose website offers details of symptoms and treatments, as well as campaigns and local groups. / *HOURS Mon-Wed 10am-5pm, Thurs 10am-1pm, Fri 1pm-5pm.*

The Marcé Society, ☎ *(01270) 752110* ⌁ *www.marcesociety.com*
An organisation primarily for professionals, but a useful source of information on research into puerperal mental illness.

Maternity Alliance, ☎ *Helpline (020) 7490 7639*
⌁ *www.maternityalliance.org.uk*
After speaking to many women suffering from postnatal depression and to those who advise and counsel them, the Maternity Alliance put together a free 'Postnatal Depression and Work' fact sheet. It answers the most pressing questions from new mothers thinking about their return to work and explains what happens at the end of maternity leave. / *HOURS helpline Mon & Thu 10.30am-12.30pm, Tue 6pm-8pm.*

Meet a Mum Association (MAMA), ☎ *National info line (01525) 217 064, Helpline (020) 8768 0123* ⌁ *www.mama.org.uk*
The organisation aims to help mothers and mothers-to-be avoid feeling isolated and lonely (often precursors to postnatal depression) by putting them in touch with one of their local networks. Help is also available via their postnatal illness helpline (staff are not medically trained, but are all women who have suffered PND). / *HOURS helpline Mon-Fri 7pm-10pm; PUBLICATIONS Leaflets on postnatal illness.*

National Association for Mental Health (MIND), ☎ *(020) 8519 2122* ⌁ *www.mind.org.uk*
The local London branch of this national mental health charity, provides supported housing, drop-in centres, counselling, befriending, advocacy, employment and training schemes. / *HOURS Mon-Fri 9.15am-5.15pm; PUBLICATIONS Leaflets (mostly £1) on anxiety, caring, childhood distress, depression, eating distress, postnatal depression, Seasonal Affective Disorder (feeling more tired and depressed in winter than summer), How to Assert Yourself, How to Cope with Panic Attacks, How to Cope with Relationship Breakdown, How to Survive Family Life; books for survivors of child abuse, coming off tranquillisers, and other problems.*

National Childbirth Trust (NCT), ☎ Enquiry line (0870) 444 8707

🖰 www.nctpregnancyandbabycare.co.uk; www.nctparentsconnect.co.uk
Some NCT branches run groups for postnatally depressed women; ask your local
branch for details. / HOURS Mon-Thurs 9am-5pm, Fri 9am-4pm; or answerphone.

National NEWPIN, ☎ (020) 7407 7255 🖰 www.newpin.org.uk

The charity provides group therapy and, where appropriate, one to one
counselling. / HOURS Mon-Fri 9am-5pm.

The Parent Infant Clinic, ☎ (020) 7433 3112

🖰 www.infantmentalhealth.com
The psychotherapists at the clinic can provide help for women with postnatal
depression (and more serious problems).

Parentline Plus, ☎ Freephone parent Helpline (0808) 800 2222, Textphone

(0800) 783 6783 🖰 www.parentlineplus.org.uk
Free national telephone support service, Parentline, for parents who are under stress
and/or experiencing problems with their children. / HOURS helpline Mon-Fri 2pm-5pm & 7pm-
8pm.

Samaritans, ☎ Helpline (08457) 909090 🖰 www.samaritans.org

Telephone confidential emotional support for depression, crises and problems of all
kinds. / HOURS 24 hrs.

Talking Life, ☎ (0151) 632 0662 🖰 www.talkinglife.co.uk

A leading supplier of self-help health programmes on audio cassette to the NHS (the
tapes produced in conjunction with specialist doctors and health charities). Prices are
from £8.50 per tape. Coping with Depression (recommended by the Depression
Alliance) uses cognitive techniques to turn negative thoughts to positive ones,
and setting targets and goals; other titles include Coping with Anxiety and The
Relaxation Kit.

3. OTHER POTENTIAL PROBLEMS

Incontinence

Postnatally you may find your pelvic floor muscles have lost some tone
with consequences for your bladder control. If this is still the case after
six weeks consider seeking professional help. Physiotherapists report a
70% success rate in this area. (See chapter *4.02 Complementary medicine &
Health practitioners*).

USEFUL CONTACTS

Continence Foundation : The Helpline Nurse, ☎ (020) 7831

9831 helpline, (0845) 345 0165 🖰 www.continence-foundation.org.uk
Referral is provided to local advisers; you can also e-mail for advice on
continence-help@dial.pipex.com. / HOURS Mon-Fri 9.30am-1pm; PUBLICATIONS Leaflet on pelvic
floor exercises for use during pregnancy or after birth, together with advice on bowel problems which can
result from episiotomies.

PRODUCTS

Aquaflex

Simpla Continence Care ☎ contact your local Boots 🖰 www.ssl-international.com,
www.aquaflexcones.com
Exercise cones (a set costs about £20) placed in the vagina like a tampon, to help locate
the right muscles to prevent incontinence. You may be able to ask for these, or
a similar product, to be prescribed on the NHS. Boots is now the primary stockist for
this product. / HOURS Mon-Fri 9am-5pm.

NEEN HealthCare

100 Shaw Road, Oldham Lancashire OL1 4AY ☎ (0161) 925 3180
🖰 www.neenhealth.com
Mail order supplier (largely to health professionals) of products (monitors, exercisers),
books and tapes aimed at overcoming the condition.

READING

Keeping Control – Jane Smith, Raj Persad, Philip Smith and Anne Winder (A Practical Guide to the Prevention and Treatment of Stress Incontinence; Vermilion; 2001; £6.99; 0091852196) – *A co-operative venture between a consultant urological surgeon, a consultant obstetrician, a gynaecologist and a continence adviser. It looks at management of the problem, and treatments available.*

Regaining Bladder Control – Eileen Montgomery (1989; £2.50; 185457003X) – *The causes of stress incontinence; exercises to combat it. / NCT Maternity Sales, (0870) 112 1120; www.nctms.co.uk.*

Residual discomfort

A small percentage of women may still have pain in the perineum as long as three years after the birth and, although this is more likely after an episiotomy, tears can also create this problem.

If after three or four months you have healed but are still uncomfortable, specialist physiotherapists (members of the Association of Chartered Physiotherapists in Women's Health, see chapter *4.02 Complementary medicine & Health practitioners*) may be able to help. One form of treatment is the use of ultrasound, typically three times a week for six weeks – a technique which may work even nine months after the birth. Another treatment is the use of Pulsed Electromagnetic Energy (PEME) to help with hardened scars or even incomplete healing. Specialist advice, exercises and massage instruction are other reasons you might wish to visit a physiotherapist.

A DIY remedy to suppress such pain is a compress of witch hazel or chamomile, the latter perhaps in the form of tea in ice cubes. If you have a problem with sex, a lubricant can help but if the problem persists you should seek specialist advice.

The following are reported to help:

➢ Coarse, for example Dead Sea, salt in the bath.
➢ Ice packs.
➢ A cold compress of wet fabric, cooled in the freezer.
➢ In the early days, when opening your bowels, firm pressure with a soft sanitary pad on the stitches to support the stretchy perineum may help the stitches to stay in place.

USEFUL CONTACTS

The Avon Episiotomy Support Group, ☎ (020) 8482 1453

A voluntary helpline which includes a support counsellor for women with problems with episiotomies and tears (including emotional difficulties). They may be able to offer pointers for dealing with a problem; however, official medical advice in this area is very divided, so they can only give personal opinions. Whatever the difficulty, they recommend going for help as soon as possible.

Valley Cushions, ☎ (01709) 872 137 *or your local NCT branch*

🖑 www.valleycushions.co.uk
The Vally Cushion™ has two inflatable pads and a central channel, allowing for circulation and pressure relief. (It is an alternative to a simple rubber ring, which tends to restrict circulation). Complete with hygiene covers, they are generally hired through the NCT via local agents (at around £10 for five days, and £1.20 a day thereafter). The website, though, gives you further information, and allows you to buy direct. / *HOURS 24 hour answerphone.*

PRODUCTS

NCT Maternity Sales

239 Shawbridge St Glasgow G43 1QN ☎ *(0870) 112 1120, Breatfeeding helpline (0870) 444 8708* 🖑 *www.nctms.co.uk*
'Feme' pads contain cooling gel for easing discomfort, £12 (refills £5); also 'Breast Soother' re-usable gel packs for cold or warm use, £10. The 'Valley Cushion' (see also) can be hired from local NCT agents – it comes with a hygienic Cooltech cover for each user. / *HOURS Mon-Fri 9am-5pm; Helpline 8am-10pm; SEE ALSO 2.02 Feeding; 3.01 Maternity wear; 3.02 Baby equipment; 3.04 Baby clothes; 3.06 Toys; 4.06 Support groups.*

Oscar & Dehn
Unit 7, Burmarsh Workshops, Marsden St London NW5 3JA ☎ (020) 7267 6110
🖰 www.oscardehn.com
Natal Nurse (£15) is for women who have had an episiotomy or bad tear – a soothing
gel pack with a sleeve, worn like a sanitary towel that can be used cool to soothe
bruising and warm to help healing. / HOURS *9am-5pm;* PUBLICATIONS *Leaflet available;* SEE ALSO
2.02 Feeding.

Pets

Dogs and cats in particular may feel curious about and/or jealous of a
new baby. The RSPCA recommends introducing pet and baby gently and
ensuring that the animals get special attention whenever possible so that
they don't feel neglected.

As the baby grows you will need to help your child and pets understand each other and not hurt or irritate each other. The RSPCA for
example highlights that children should not be allowed to tease or disturb an animal when sleeping or eating, and that it is unfair for them to
carry food around in front of a pet.

READING

Your Dog & Your Baby – Silvia Hartmann-Kent (A practical guide; Dog House
Publications; 1996; £12.95; 1873483228) – *A slim book (but with a level of
information rare elsewhere) on introducing a baby to a home where there is an
established dog.*

USEFUL CONTACTS

Cats Protection, ☎ *Helpline (0870) 209 9099* 🖰 *www.cats.org.uk*
Providers of useful leaflets and telephone advice; membership £12 per year;
concessions for children ('kittens') and over 60s; lifetime membership £175. / HOURS *Mon-
Fri 9am-4.30pm;* PUBLICATIONS *Cats and Babies, dos & don'ts for first-time parents with a cat; also a free
leaflet on toxoplasmosis.*

**Royal Society for the Prevention of Cruelty to Animals
(RSPCA)**, ☎ *(0870) 333 5999* 🖰 *www.rspca.org.uk*
Produces a useful Animal Care leaflet with advice on dealing with pets and a new
baby. / HOURS *Mon-Fri 9am-5pm, 24 helpline;* PUBLICATIONS *Leaflet: Your pets, your children and you.*

4. LOOKING AFTER YOURSELF

Support networks

Support organisations can offer help in a variety of ways – anything from
a boost to your social life to a vital lifeline – and they can be invaluable
for new parents. It is worth getting in touch and building up contacts as
soon as you feel up to it.

The biggest network is the NCT, which organises regular get-togethers for mothers all over the country. The organisation may have someone
local to you who acts as a co-ordinator for groups of new mothers to meet
and do activities such as going swimming once a week (half the mothers
in the pool, half baby-sitting the babies at the side). These sessions may
turn into child-minding or baby-sitting groups – useful if you want to contain the cost of going out, though you will need a partner who can baby-sit
your child when returning the favour on another evening.

How much these groups do beyond pure socialising depends on the
enthusiasm of those running them, but some have a library of books relevant to new mums, offer local first aid courses, and run specialist
networks: for example of mothers who had Caesareans.

The contact name and number for many local parent-run groups
(those not connected with national networks) often changes every 12

months, so ask your health visitor or other local parents for up-to-date details.

NATIONAL NETWORKS

The Active Birth Centre, ☎ (020) 7281 6760

🕆 www.activebirthcentre.com
Mothers Talking: a structured weekly discussion for mothers led by a counsellor, £5. Some feel that the discussions focus a little too much on potential problems. / HOURS *shop Mon-Fri 9.30am-6.30pm (Fri 4pm), Sat 10am-4pm.*

Caesarean Support Network, ☎ (01624) 661269

A network of contacts, and telephone information service giving practical, non-medical advice for women who have had or expect to have a caesarean delivery. / HOURS *after 6pm and at weekends;* PUBLICATIONS *Exercises following a Caesarean (from the week thereafter), Home Helps, Breast-Feeding and Emotional Difficulties – all 50p.*

Careline, ☎ (020) 8875 0500 🕆 www.careline.org.uk

Based in Wandsworth - a confidential telephone information service for all ages, which holds details of local support groups for different needs (for example, one suited to a young mum feeling isolated and depressed). Careline refers callers to a list of counselling services (and its website likewise contains extensive lists of contacts). / HOURS *Mon-Fri 10am-8pm & Sat 7pm-10pm.*

Full-time Mothers, ☎ (020) 8670 2525 🕆 www.fulltimemothers.org

Call or check online for details of local groups.

Home-Dad Link, 🕆 www.slowlane.com/groups/homedadlink

A relatively new organisation (formerly Househusband Link) aiming to establish contact between full- and part-time househusbands and single fathers, in order to counter their isolation; one local group at present – with more hoped for. / PUBLICATIONS *Quarterly newsletter 'Him Indoors' (£10 or £5 for low family income annually).*

Home-Start UK, ☎ Head office (0116) 233 9955, London (020) 7831 7023

🕆 www.home-start.org.uk
National family-support charity based in Leicester (London regional office details given); local support groups all over London. / HOURS *Mon-Fri 9am-5pm.*

Hornsey Vale Community Centre, ☎ (020) 8348 4612

Post-Natal support group.

Meet a Mum Association (MAMA), ☎ National info line (01525) 217 064, Helpline (020) 8768 0123 🕆 www.mama.org.uk

National network of eighty or so local groups of mothers for friendship and support (and if there is no local group, then with an individual); may be particularly useful to mothers who have moved to a new location, or to previously working women who now find themselves at home, or any mother who finds herself isolated or lonely while pregnant or after giving birth. Also runs a postnatal depression helpline. / HOURS *helpline Mon-Fri 7pm-10pm.*

Mother's Union, ☎ (020) 7222 5533 🕆 www.themothersunion.org

Almost 125 years old, this international Christian organisation has local branches attached to many churches and its mission statement is to promote the wellbeing of families worldwide. At a local branch level the organisation runs parenting courses, mother and toddler groups, new baby groups, and baptism preparation classes, though projects vary by region; call the number listed to find your local branch.

National Childbirth Trust (NCT), ☎ Enquiry line (0870) 444 8707

🕆 www.nctpregnancyandbabycare.co.uk; www.nctparentsconnect.co.uk
/ HOURS *Mon-Thurs 9am-5pm, Fri 9am-4pm; or answerphone.*

National Women's Register, ☎ (0845) 450 0287 🕆 www.nwr.org

Started in the '60s as the Liberal-minded Housebound Housewives Register, the organisation is no longer exclusively made up of housewives. It aims to put women in touch with each other for friendship and informal discussion through a network of local groups – particularly useful when moving to a new area. The website lists local groups. Members usually meet in each others' homes. Membership £14. / HOURS *Mon-Thurs 9.15am-3.30pm.*

LOCAL GROUPS

Albany Midwifery Practice, ☎ (020) 7525 4995, Peckham Pulse

(020) 7525 4999 🕆 www.albanymidwives.org
Postnatal discussion groups run by an NHS midwifery practice, for mothers with babies up to six months old.

Ealing 135, ☎ *(020) 8825 5588, Ealing Council's childrens infoservice*
A west London-based group (established over 25 years ago) for parents and carers of
children under five; regular newsletter, magazines and activities; local discounts for
members; membership from £12 a year (concessions).

Haringey Parents
Founded in the '60s, the organisation provides a newsletter (six times
a year), courses, playgroups and events to its 750 members based in
Muswell Hill, Crouch End, Wood Green and sometimes further afield.
Membership is £10 (£5 if on income support). The current membership
secretary's number is to be found advertised in local libraries and health
centres.

Jayne Herbert, ☎ *(020) 8533 9925*
Co-ordinator of breast-feeding support and postnatal groups (and some courses) in
Hackney and Islington.

Jessica James, ☎ *(020) 8806 4820*
Six week postnatal daytime course (two weeks to three months after giving birth)
where mothers can discuss their feelings and learn strategies for coping with their new
baby; £50. Groups are encouraged to meet up for self-help thereafter. Individual
counselling is also available.

Tufnell Park Parents Support Group (TPPSG), ☎ *(020) 7485
7625*
Voluntary organisation of around 250 families living in or not far from Tufnell Park,
around half of whom have children of preschool age. The main activities are
twice-weekly tea and play sessions held in members' homes that any other members
can attend. There are also summer and Christmas children's parties and an evening
meeting for members every quarter. Whilst not a campaigning group, it sometimes
provides representatives for local authority consultation
procedures. / PUBLICATIONS *Quarterly newsletter (40pp) containing articles, recommended babysitters,
trades lists of recommended tradespeople and a weekly guide to ongoing drop-in mother and child groups in
the area.*

Women's Centre, ☎ *(020) 8422 1100*
Counselling for all women's problems, including postnatal depression and relationship
problems; based in north London. / HOURS *Mon, Wed, & Fri 10am-3pm, Sat 10am-noon.*

FATHER'S GROUPS
Dads UK, ☎ *(07092) 391489, (07092) 390210* ⌂ *www.dads-uk.co.uk*
For single (be it through separation or bereavement) and gay dads – advice from those
who have found themselves in similar situations, including tips on divorce, custody and
being without your children. It includes a forum. / HOURS *Helpline Mon-Fri 11am-10pm.*

Families Need Fathers, ☎ *(020) 7613 5060* ⌂ *www.fnf.org.uk*
This national charity is one of the main organisations providing information and advice
on parenting issues for parents – not just men – who no longer live together – perhaps
more accurately it should be called families need parents and grandparents. It promotes
continuing the relationships of all of the above with children after a divorce or
separation (statistically, within two years of separation or divorce, almost half of the
children involved lose all contact with one parent). / HOURS *Office Mon-Fri 9.30am-4.30pm.*

Fathers Direct, ⌂ *www.fathersdirect.com*
"The best thing to happen to Fatherhood since Eve entered Paradise" – a website
aimed at fathers (not just in single parent families), offering news, information and
games; in early 2003 launched Dad magazine with contributors like Tony Parsons and
profiles of father of five Pierce Brosnan and Beckham with son Brooklyn.

Home Dad UK, ☎ *(07752) 549 085* ⌂ *www.homedad.org.uk*
The only UK group for dads staying at home to bring up their children, full-time,
part-time or raising kids on their own (of whom there are apparently over 150,000).
The website includes a magazine section and a forum.

Exercise
Don't overdo it. It can take up to six months for levels of the relaxant in
your body (which loosened your ligaments ahead of the birth) to return to
normal, longer if breastfeeding. However, some gentle exercise is likely to
make you feel better about yourself.

Many antenatal teachers also run postnatal classes for women. (The listings below include many teachers also included in chapter *1.04 Antenatal classes*.)

MOTHER & BABY CLASSES

CENTRAL

Portland Hospital, Physiotherapy Unit
234 Great Portland St (opposite main hospital) W1N 6AH ☎ *(020) 7390 8061*
🖰 *www.theportlandhospital.com*
Four-week course aiming to provide both information and support; topics include baby massage and development, sleeping and routines and starting solids. / SEE ALSO *1.04 Antenatal classes; 2.03 Baby health; 4.02 Health practitioners.*

NORTH

Harringay Club
50 Tottenham Lane N8 7EE ☎ *(020) 8348 2124* 🖰 *www.harringayclub.org.uk*
Weekly Baby Club morning for under twos and their parents/carers. / HOURS *Mon-Sun 9am-5pm;* SEE ALSO *2.06 Baby & toddler activities.*

O&L Women's Health Physiotherapy Clinic
Fortis Green Health Clinic, 150 Fortis Green N10 3PA ☎ *(020) 8920 9407*
Mother and baby support and exercise classes: tone up tummy muscles; learn about a baby's physical development; baby massage. / HOURS *Mon, Tues, Weds, Fri: 8am-6pm;* SEE ALSO *1.04 Antenatal classes; 1.06 Birth equipment; 4.02 Health practitioners.*

Julie Tortora
☎ *(020) 8340 5366*
Mother and baby exercise classes – one hour plus half an hour for chat; all exercises are structured with baby participation in mind (with a short stretch session for babies at the end); £7.50 per session. / SEE ALSO *1.04 Antenatal classes.*

triyoga
6 Erskine Rd NW3 3AJ ☎ *(020) 7483 3344* 🖰 *www.triyoga.co.uk*
'Mummy and me' mother and baby yoga classes; suitable for babies from 40 days old to walking; £10 an hour. / HOURS *6.30am-10pm;* SEE ALSO *1.04 Antenatal classes; 2.06 Baby & toddler activities.*

Yogahome
11 Allen Rd N16 8SB ☎ *(020) 7249 2425* 🖰 *www.yogahome.com*
Postnatal drop-in yoga classes at which babies up to crawling age are welcome; £10 for two hours. / HOURS *Call for hours;* SEE ALSO *1.04 Antenatal classes.*

EXERCISE CLASSES

CENTRAL

Portland Hospital, Physiotherapy Unit
234 Great Portland St (opposite main hospital) W1N 6AH ☎ *(020) 7390 8061*
🖰 *www.theportlandhospital.com*
Exercise class, incorporating a crèche to help regain pre-pregnancy strength and shape. / SEE ALSO *1.04 Antenatal classes; 2.03 Baby health; 4.02 Health practitioners.*

WEST

Annabel Hargrave
SW19 ☎ *(020) 8287 5411* 🖰 *www.yogabirth.org*
Qualified active birth teacher giving classes in postnatal yoga and baby massage. Classes are in Wimbledon and Southfields; £10 for two hours. / HOURS *phone during office hours;* SEE ALSO *1.04 Antenatal classes.*

Lysta Perry (RSA)
17 Turnham Green Terrace W4 1RG ☎ *(020) 8994 8118*
Personal training at home. / SEE ALSO *1.04 Antenatal classes.*

Postnatal Shape Up Classes
44 Hartington Rd W4 3TX ☎ *(020) 8994 0369*
Gentle Pilates-based exercise (in groups of eight or less) for those with babies of four weeks up; £80 for five classes; a baby massage instructor also teaches for part of the course; crèche. / SEE ALSO *1.04 Antenatal classes.*

Lolly Stirk
Holland Park W11 ☎ *(01323) 422054*
Postnatal yoga, exercise and baby massage classes, £14 per class. / SEE ALSO 1.04 Antenatal
classes.

NORTH

The Active Birth Centre 🖼
25 Bickerton Rd N19 5JT ☎ *(020) 7281 6760* 🖰 *www.activebirthcentre.com*
Postnatal yoga classes (with crèche for babies) for new mothers, £9. / HOURS shop Mon-Fri
9.30am-6.30pm (Fri 4pm), Sat 10am-4pm; SEE ALSO 1.01 Where to have the baby; 1.04 Antenatal classes;
1.06 Birth equipment; 2.02 Feeding; 2.03 Baby health; 2.06 Baby & toddler activities; 3.01 Maternity wear;
3.02 Baby equipment; 4.02 Health practitioners; 4.05 Finding out more.

Copthall Pools
Page St, Great North Way NW4 1PS ☎ *(020) 8457 9920*
Ante- and postnatal aquanatal classes £4.45. / SEE ALSO 1.04 Antenatal classes; 2.06 Baby &
toddler activities.

Dax Moy Personal Training Studios
21 St Albans Place N1 0HZ ☎ *(020) 7354 3550*
A personal trainer who works with a team specializing in pre- and post-natal
exercise. / HOURS by appointment.

Judy Di Fiore
☎ *(020) 8931 2085*
Postnatal exercise classes at St Mary's Church Hall, Hendon Lane, Finchley, courses of
six weeks available for £45; also beginners Pilates classes suitable for postnatal women
at John Keble Church Hall in Edgware; courses of six weeks available for £45; private
sessions also offered, £35. / SEE ALSO 1.04 Antenatal classes.

Fit Start
Lancaster House, 6 Lancaster Rd N4 4PP ☎ *(020) 8374 7680*
Exercise classes, in Camden, Crouch End and Islington, to help new mothers get back
into shape and re-energise; 10-12 week terms. Babies welcome; the company also runs
baby massage and antenatal exercise classes. / SEE ALSO 1.04 Antenatal classes; 2.06 Baby &
toddler activities.

Julie Krausz
77 Hardinge Rd NW10 3PN ☎ *(020) 8459 2903* 🖰 *www.yogabirth.org*
Active birth and yoga teacher: postnatal classes on weekday afternoons, NW6; £12; also
held at Northcote Library SW11; £13. / SEE ALSO 1.04 Antenatal classes.

Yvonne Moore
☎ *(020) 7794 2056*
Yoga-based classes; group or private tuition available. / SEE ALSO 1.04 Antenatal classes.

Park Road Pools
Park Rd N8 8JN ☎ *(020) 8341 3567*
Postnatal water exercise, £3.70. / SEE ALSO 2.06 Baby & toddler activities.

Sequin Park
240 Upper St N1 ☎ *(020) 7704 9844* 🖰 *www.sequinpark.co.uk*
Women only gym, which offers pre and postnatal classes.

Sunstone Health & Leisure Club
16 Northwalk Rd N16 7HR ☎ *(020) 7923 1991, (0800) 083 2272*
🖰 *www.sunstonewomen.com*
Woman-only north London health club and beauty salon whose offering includes
creche and pre- and postnatal classes, and massage for pregnancy; some facilities are
open to non-members.

Yoga Junction
Unit 24, City North, Fonthill Road, Finsbury Park N4 3HF ☎ *(020) 7263 3113*
🖰 *www.yogajunction.co.uk*
Postnatal yoga classes.

SOUTH

Amateur Swimming Association (ASA)
☎ *(01509) 618 700*
Joint ante-and postnatal aquanatal classes, with a midwife always present, £3.10. / SEE
ALSO 1.04 Antenatal classes; 2.06 Baby & toddler activities.

Arches Leisure Centre
80 Trafalgar Rd SE10 9UX ☎ *(020) 8317 5020*
Friday morning (10.30-11.30) exercise class, £4 (crèche available, 9.30am-3pm). Also aquanatal classes, £5 (followed – in term-time only – by discussion sessions). / *HOURS Mon-Sun 7am-8pm; SEE ALSO 1.04 Antenatal classes; 2.06 Baby & toddler activities.*

The Battersea Practice (Physio For All)
40 Webbs Rd SW11 6SF ☎ *(020) 7228 2141*
Postnatal exercise classes in small groups. Locations in Battersea (where babies are welcome) £11 and Chelsea £12. / *HOURS Mon-Fri: 9am-5pm, Sat: 9am-12pm; SEE ALSO 1.04 Antenatal classes; 4.02 Health practitioners.*

Sue Lewis Grad DB, MCSP, SRP
65 Vineyard Hill Rd SW19 7JL ☎ *(020) 8946 8561*
Five-week course of one-hour classes to tone the pelvic floor and abdomen, and to exchange advice on life with a new baby. Cost £70, including crèche. Suitable from a few days after birth or two weeks after a Caesarean. Advanced course (more Pilates-style, less chat) cost £65. Breast-feeding classes also offered. / *SEE ALSO 1.04 Antenatal classes; 2.03 Baby health; 2.06 Baby & toddler activities; 4.02 Health practitioners.*

London Academy of Personal Fitness
36 Carleton Ave, Wallington Surrey SM6 9LN ☎ *(0870) 4423231* ⏚ *www.lapf.co.uk*
A team of 40 fitness trainers provide individually-tailored postnatal fitness programmes, £45 per session, including free initial fitness assessment and regular progress checks. / *HOURS 24 hour answerphone; SEE ALSO 1.04 Antenatal classes.*

Malden Leisure Centre
Blagdon Rd, New Malden Surrey KT3 4TA ☎ *(020) 8336 7770*
Weekly aqua classes for mums and babies six months and up. Creche and baby massage. / *HOURS Vary; SEE ALSO 1.04 Antenatal classes.*

Sivananda Yoga Centre
51 Felsham Rd SW15 1AZ ☎ *(020) 8780 0160* ⏚ *www.sivanandayoga.org*
General yoga classes suitable for postnatal exercise (specific prenatal courses are also run, otherwise inform your teacher you are pregnant), £8. Drop-in classes are held throughout the day. / *SEE ALSO 1.04 Antenatal classes.*

World of Health
PO Box 23103 SE1 2GP ☎ *(020) 7357 9393* ⏚ *www.worldofhealth.co.uk*
Health, fitness and lifestyle video and DVD supplier with postnatal exercise titles. / *SEE ALSO 1.04 Antenatal classes; 2.02 Feeding; 2.06 Baby & toddler activities; 4.02 Health practitioners; 4.05 Finding out more.*

EAST

Arlene Dunkley-Wood
154 King's Head Hill E4 7NU ☎ *(020) 8923 6452 (answerphone), (020) 8923 6452*
An active birth teacher, who offers yoga-based exercise classes in Bethnal Green, Wanstead and Chingford (£12.50). / *SEE ALSO 1.04 Antenatal classes; 2.06 Baby & toddler activities.*

OUTSIDE LONDON

David Lloyd
PO Box 888 Dunstable LU5 5XA ☎ *(01582) 844 899* ⏚ *www.davidlloydleisure.co.uk*
Facilities at 45 clubs include crèches offering qualified care for children aged 3 months-5 years.

Esporta
Trinity Court, Molly Millars Lane, Workingham Berkshire RG41 2PY ☎ *(0800) 0377 678, Head office (0118) 912 3500* ⏚ *www.esporta.com*
An international group of health clubs, with 9 branches dotted around London; some have crèches and most have numerous activity classes for kids. Membership costs £200–£300 per person with discounts for family membership.

Fitness First
58 Fleets Lane, Fleetsbridge, Poole Dorset BH15 3BT ⏚ *www.fitnessfirst.com*
Gyms with creches for children 3 months to five years.

Virgin Active
Active House, 21 North Fourth St Central Milton Keynes MK9 1HL ☎ *(01908) 546600* ⏚ *www.virginactive.co.uk*
Family friendly gym complexes throughout the country (and in London in Acton, Islington and Wandsworth); many clubs have crèches and children's classes.

READING

Back in Shape – Sally Lewis (The 10-week post baby recovery plan; Hamlyn; 2003; £5.99; 0600606503) – *Designed to fit around a baby's daily schedule, a week-by-week routine starting four weeks after birth, including exercises, nutritional advice, beauty tips and advice on relieving physical and emotional problems. Also relaxation and complementary self-help techniques. / www.hamlyn.co.uk.*

The Complete Guide to Postnatal Fitness – Judy DiFiore (The official YMCA programme; A & C Black; 1998; £13.99; 071364852X) – *Very thorough, being aimed at teachers as well as new mothers.*

[Video] **Getting Back** – Deborah Makin (The complete guide to reshaping your body after childbirth; NCT; 1999; £12.99) – *A video including mini-workouts, plus how to eat well and lose fat. / NCT Maternity Sales, (0870) 112 1120; www.nctms.co.uk.*

Weight management and Fitness Through Childbirth – Theresa Francis-Cheung (Hodder & Stoughton; 2001; £6.99; 0-340-75693-4) – *As well as pregnancy, the guide covers the postnatal period when women are apparently physiologically designed to lose their earlier weight gain. There are also pointers on what to do if your Body Mass Index doesn't return to normal in six months or so, which is the usual expectation. / www.madaboutbooks.com.*

Your Health After Birth – Judy Sadgrove (Marshall Publishing; 1998; £9.99; 1840281006) – *One of a series of factfiles with advice on getting back into shape, and relevant exercises.*

Osteopathy

(For listings of practitioners and more general information, see chapter 4.02 Complementary medicine & Health practitioners.)

A check-up with an osteopath anything from a few days to several weeks after the birth can be useful to make sure your bones and viscera have gone back into their correct alignment.

Osteopathic treatment has been found specifically useful for the realignment of the pelvis and vertebrae, speeding up the process of resettling the body after birth, and some women report a boost to their energy reserves after such treatment.

Particularly if labour was difficult, mothers can face problems like backache, a frozen sacrum, or a dislocated coccyx, which make sitting and lifting uncomfortable. Sometimes the uterus doesn't quite return properly into place, which can create problems years later. Osteopathy can be helpful with all these problems as well.

As parents of babies and young children do more lifting than usual, it is important that they remember to do so without straining their back (bend the knees and tuck in the tummy). This is particularly important for the mother, whose back will be particularly vulnerable postnatally because of the hormone changes of pregnancy. Always sit, therefore, with your back well supported. Also, arrange nappy changing and the cot base at a comfortable height to prevent excessive back strain.

Massage for mums

See chapter 4.02 *Complementary medicine & Health practitioners.*

5. PARENTING

(Many of the hundreds of books on this subject are listed in chapter 4.05 Finding out more. For reading and support groups relating to working parents, see chapter 2.04 Childcare.)

In the past five years there has been a boom in parenting books, organisations and courses, and now even the government has given this a stamp of approval. The chair of the Youth Justice Board has recommended setting up 300 parenting programmes across England and Wales following research showing that children of parents who attend these courses committed 50% fewer offences in the subsequent year.

Starting earlier, the effectiveness of such courses is likely to be greater because they alert parents to issues before they have become a problem.

Parenting courses are particularly good at focusing attention on potential causes of problems, and useful long-term techniques for dealing with them. Courses are also particularly useful for those parents with reservations about the way they themselves were parented. There seems to be considerable evidence that, without effort to prevent it, patterns in child-rearing behaviour are passed on from generation to generation.

USEFUL CONTACTS

Anna Freud Centre, ☎ (020) 7794 2313 ⟁ www.annafreudcentre.org
The centre's Parent and Infant Project provides support for new parents who may be struggling to develop a relationship with their baby. / HOURS 9am-6pm.

British Institute of Learning Disabilities (BILD),
☎ (01562) 723010 ⟁ www.bild.org.uk
Publishers of the I Want to Be a Good Parent books on parenting for those with learning disabilities, written in simple English with pictures to help. / HOURS Mon-Fri 9am-1pm & 2pm-4.30pm; PUBLICATIONS What's it like to be a parent?; Children need healthy food; Children need to be clean, healthy and warm; Children need to be safe; Children need love. £10 each, £37.50 for the set (audio cassette of all five, £40).

Children are Unbeatable, ☎ (020) 7713 0569
⟁ www.childrenareunbeatable.org.uk
An alliance of more than 350 professional and religious bodies, and also individuals. It was formed in 1998, and campaigns for children to have the same legal protection against being hit as adults, and promotes positive, non-violent discipline. / HOURS Mon-Fri 10am-3pm.

Children's Hours Trust, ☎ (01483) 578454
⟁ www.childrenshourstrust.org.uk
Promoters of the idea of regularly devoting a set period of time (say, an hour) to a child, where the child does what it wants (within sensible limits) and the parent offers undivided attention and listens hard to what the child has to say. The system has proved beneficial for both 'normal' and special needs children (such as those with autism). The trust is currently formulating workshops and training for parents and interested professionals.

The Children's Project, ☎ (020) 8546 8750 ⟁ www.childrensproject.co.uk
Private counselling for parenting problems in Kingston and Richmond postcodes, and also Wandsworth and Putney. The initial consultation is free, then £30 per half hour or £50 per hour.

Liedloff Continuum Network, ☎ (01600) 861816
⟁ www.continuum-concept.org
A support group and network for those interested in the ideas of Jean Liedloff, author of the parenting book, The Continuum Concept. They advocate what they describe as a more natural, respectful approach to child-rearing which encourages extended breast-feeding, sharing your bed with your baby or small child and 'baby wearing' – carrying babies constantly as well as a belief that babies are naturally social and don't need to be taught how to behave. / HOURS calls no later than 9pm.

Natural Nurturing Network, ☎ (0116) 288 0844
A non-profit making organisation which provides a network for like-minded parents in the area of relationships – particularly those with children – and encourages, for example, bonding at birth, long term breast-feeding, children sleeping in the family bed, baby carrying and responding to children's cries. Send an SAE for more details. / PUBLICATIONS Newsletter (with book reviews, articles by members, personal accounts of problems and solutions, noticeboard).

Parentline Plus, ☎ Freephone parent Helpline (0808) 800 2222, Textphone (0800) 783 6783 ⟁ www.parentlineplus.org.uk
Free national helpline for parents, offering a listening service for any parent requiring emotional support. A changing range of publications are produced. Advice for stepfamilies is a particular strength. / HOURS helpline Mon-Fri 2pm-5pm & 7pm-8pm.

Parents in Partnership – Parent Infant Network (PIPPIN),

☎ *National office (01727) 899099* ⏚ *www.pippin.org.uk*

"Promoting positive early family and parent-infant relationships" – this charity is concerned with all new families, and aims to help all members of the family cope with the emotional and social upheavals that a new birth brings (an area where the charity feels people are left with little help at present). The organisation does not promote a 'right' way of parenting, but rather aims to build parents' confidence to pursue the parenting practices that that feel are right. This, they feel, is particularly important for fathers, who seldom receive much in the way of preparation. Groups and free classes are planned across the country, forming social networks for new parents – see the website for details. / HOURS *Mon-Fri 9am-5pm;* PUBLICATIONS *Newsletter (free to download from the website).*

Positive Parenting Publications, ☎ *(023) 9252 8787*

⏚ *www.parenting.org.uk*

A charity which publishes literature and offers training courses and resource materials to equip parents to offer confident parenting (including materials for families and professionals working with special needs children). It runs one-day practical training days for would-be facilitators on the Positive Parenting course and also parent workshops for schools. / HOURS *Mon-Fri 9am-5pm;* PUBLICATIONS *Leaflets for new parents and dads (free with SAE); booklet for parents of young children (£3 inc p&p), available via the website or phone.*

RaisingKids, ☎ *(020) 8883 8621* ⏚ *www.raisingkids.co.uk*

A one-stop shop for parents to get information on anything on food for a picky toddler to education. The site includes a discussions forum, Ask an Expert, and has writers on parenting, nutrition, education and skin. / HOURS *24 hour online.*

Sarah McGuinness, ☎ *(020) 8299 4872*

Parenting coaching – a variant on the better known life coaching – taking each case individually and helping parents find their own way.

Susan Kennard, ☎ *(020) 7690 6171 mobile (07966) 434 701*

⏚ *www.soul-purpose.org*

A parent and family consultant offering individual sessions and 8-week courses aimed at parents of 0-6 years. They cover listening skills, difficult behaviour and the like, and offer parents practical, emotional, non-directional support. Also offers encouragement on sleep routines, food and sibling rivalry.

World of Health, ☎ *(020) 7357 9393* ⏚ *www.worldofhealth.co.uk*

Health, fitness and lifestyle video and DVD supplier whose list includes a number of 'parentcraft' titles – from touchy feely issues to practical guides (e.g. how to choose equipment).

PARENTING CLASSES

(Note that a number of the organisations listed above also run parenting courses as detailed.)

Baby Basics, ☎ *(020) 8455 8966* ⏚ *www.babybasics.me.uk*

Run by two mothers, who offer two-hour evening seminars in Finchley with big names including Penelope Leach (how to look after a child), Eileen Hayes (behavioural management and what is going on in baby and children's minds) and Miriam Stoppard (general and health advice). Sessions cost £15 per person and take place across London.

Care for the Family, ☎ *(029) 2081 0800* ⏚ *www.care-for-the-family.org.uk*

The organisation offers the Parentalk video-based course to be used with groups of parents. For those with slightly older boys 'Dads and lads' is a sports-based parenting project encouraging fathers to get involved with their sons.

The Children's Project, ☎ *(020) 8546 8750* ⏚ *www.childrensproject.co.uk*

Parenting Classes with their roots in current physchology research offering an in-depth look at the impact of modern life on the developing child. They aim to maximise the pleasure of being a parent to make children happy, social, confident and eager to learn. The aim is to raise parental self-confidence, show how to avoid conflict, and how to listen and empathise with children. Courses are of 12 one-hour sessions over six or 12 weeks include a course pack with recommended reading, websites, and contacts; £70.

Crêchendo, ☎ *(020) 8772 8120* ⏚ *www.crechendo.com*

Run workshops on child development and understanding your child's behaviour, £99 each.

The Family Caring Trust, ☎ *(028) 3026 4174* ⏚ *www.familycaring.co.uk*

The trust writes and supplies programs for 6–8-week parenting courses for 8–12 people. The courses are used worldwide and endorsed by, amongst others, The Health Visitors' Association, and the NSPCC. Options include courses on parenting children up to six years old and a 'married listening' course for couples. Elements of the parenting courses include how to withdraw attention from bad behaviour and give it to good behaviour, how parents can attend to their own needs, and sharing experiences with others in the group. The parenting course pack includes video tapes or DVD and costs £58; books for the individual participants are £5.95 each, and videos or DVDs are £37. / HOURS Mon-Fri 9.15am-4pm.

Heart of Parenting, ☎ *(020) 8749 1964* ⏴ *www.spectrumtherapy.co.uk*
Psychotherapist Judy Hargreaves, who has also worked at the Active Birth Centre, runs a series of ongoing parenting workshops and hosts a monthly group, 'Family Matters'.

Marilyn Kaye (Dip ION), ☎ *(020) 8954 2222*
Nurse, health visitor and nutritionist who runs classes in Stanmore and Hampstead Garden suburb as well as advising at home within the area on "anything connected with baby health". Problems related to poor potty training (and associated constipation) are sometimes referred to her by GPs. Weaning sessions include 'Quick Solutions' sessions – how to produce good food in minimum time. Other examples include allergies and sleep problems. £30 for an hour and a half to two hours (divided between the group). / HOURS *answerphone.*

The New Learning Centre, ☎ *(020) 7794 0321* ⏴ *www.TNLC.info*
Parenting skills course 'Calmer, Easier, Happier Parenting' – fees vary. Coaching and on-going support for parents and children, to develop motivated, confident children; suitable for parents of children up to the age of four. Introductory talks run throughout the year and courses are held every week. Call for details.

The Parent Company, ☎ *(020) 7935 9365* ⏴ *www.theparentcompany.co.uk*
Specialists in seminars (held in London and Surrey) on parenting topics, £45 per seminar, £60 for two. Subjects include Discipline – finding a balance; Building self-esteem with children; Raising girls/boys; Success with a Nanny; Feeding children; Is my child sick?.

Parentalk, ☎ *(020) 7450 9073* ⏴ *www.parentalk.co.uk*
A charity aiming to help parents enjoy parenthood and to help good parents do an even better job. It publishes a good series of guides and offers Parenting Principles Course packs for use by up to 10 people at home, in parent and toddler groups, etc. Anyone can lead the course (£50), which is in eight video-led lessons: Be yourself; Love them and let them know; Look and listen; Remember it's good to talk; Defend the boundaries; Choose your battles; Parent with elastic; Back to the future. / HOURS Mon-Fri 9am-5.30pm; PUBLICATIONS *Parentalk guides – fun, down to earth practical information.*

Parentline Plus, ☎ *Freephone parent Helpline (0808) 800 2222,* Textphone *(0800) 783 6783* ⏴ *www.parentlineplus.org.uk*
The organisation aims to improve child-adult relations through parent support groups and practical programmes. It runs courses, including the highly-regarded Parenting Matters, a 12-week general parenting course, and Being a Parent, a shorter version over six sessions – both offered in modules. Issues such as squabbling, food and untidiness are tackled, and fathers are particularly welcome. Seminars, talks and a national freephone helpline are also offered (see above). / HOURS *helpline Mon-Fri 2pm-5pm & 7pm-8pm.*

Squiggle Foundation, ☎ *(020) 8882 9744* ⏴ *www.squiggle-foundation.org.uk*
The foundation studies and cultivates the tradition of D W Winnicott, the paediatrican and psychoanalyst who specialised in the mother-infant relationship and primary creativity. The website lists the resources available, including courses (10 weeks, £200).

www.ocado.com

I want **£30 off** my grocery shopping.
A service that delivers in one-hour slots.
And a paddling pool. Full of jelly.

Be more demanding. Thousands of shoppers have already switched to
Ocado, the online supermarket in partnership with Waitrose. We would
love you to join them, so we're offering you £30 off your shopping –
that's £10 off each of your first 3 shops over £75. So, if you'd like to
save time and money go to **www.ocado.com** and change the way
you shop today. To claim your discount all you have to do is enter the
following codes when you checkout at the end of each of your shops.
Shop 1: VOU2546156   Shop 2: VOU2586646   Shop 3: VOU2631733

ocado

in partnership with **Waitrose**

Supermarket shopping, the way it should be.

Codes must be used within 8 weeks of your first shop. Offer ends 01/04/05. For more
information and terms and conditions, please visit www.ocado.com or call 0845 399 1122.

CHAPTER 2.02

FEEDING

1. **Introduction**
2. **Breast vs bottle**
3. **Breast-feeding**
4. **Bottle-feeding**
5. **Solids**
6. **Drink**
7. **Home food shopping**
8. **Organic food**

(For information relating to food allergies, see chapter 2.03 Baby health. For information on nutritionists, see chapter 4.02 Complementary medicine & Health practitioners).

I. INTRODUCTION

Feeding is a big deal. With a young baby, it consumes a large portion of the day (and the night) and is more wearing than expectant parents generally imagine. As children grow and are taught to feed themselves, it also surprises many parents to discover just how complicated this seemingly simple process can turn out to be.

Not just every mother but practically everyone you come into contact with will probably have opinions on how you should feed your baby. Whether the issue is breast or bottle, milk or solids, feeding on demand or by timetable, or organic versus factory production, baby feeding is a subject which gets people frightfully steamed up. (The bottom line is, of course, to feed your baby in the manner that seems right to you.)

Especially in the early months, feeds are sufficiently regular that they tend to drive the whole family's schedule. Feeding on demand has many strong advocates who argue that this is the best way of feeding a young baby, and it can head off bouts of tiring protracted screaming. However, some mothers feel a need for some form of structure, at least later if not at first.

The amount babies eat is, of course, related to how much weight they gain, though the link is not as obvious as might be thought. Weight gain is one of the chief (though rather broad-brush) measurements of newborn development, and as such comes in for a good deal of attention. In some cases the issue is arguably focused upon to an excessive extent (see Concerns over weight gain in newborns, in Section 3, Breast-feeding below).

Once the baby moves on from milk, no matter how much rubbish parents may have become accustomed to eating, the responsibility of feeding their baby often provokes a re-examination of questions such as the desirability of organic produce, twinned with a suspicion of factory food and food additives.

GENERAL

The Food Magazine (The Food Commission; £20 (1 year subscription)) – *Independent research into all aspects of food and drink. Related back issues include issue 38, Jul/Sep 1997 (GM Baby Food & UK Companies, also polyfiller additive research); issue 48, Oct/Dec 1998 ('Toothkind' drinks); issue 51 Oct/Dec 2000 (healthy eating for children; junk food in packed lunches). See website for further back issue listings.* / Food Commission 020 7837 2250; ourworld.compuserve.com/homepages/foodcomm/.

The Food We Eat – Joanna Blythman (Penguin; 1998; £6.99; 0-140273-66-2) – *If you are seriously concerned by the quality of food on general sale, this title appears to confirm some of your worst suspicions.* / Food Commission 020 7837 2250; ourworld.compuserve.com/homepages/foodcomm/.

The New Shopper's Guide to Organic Food – Lynda Brown (Fourth Estate; 2002; £9.99; 1841154253) – *A comprehensive guide of what organic food to buy and where (including online retailers and box schemes). Also an A-Z of organic food and drink.*

Our Children's Toxic Legacy – John Wargo (How science and law fail to protect us from pesticides; Yale University Press; 1998; £13.95; 0-300074-46-8) – *Recommended by The Pesticides Trust – traces the history of pesticide law and usage, and discusses our long-term failure to protect ourselves and our children from pesticide contamination of food, soil, water and air. Heavy-going but pretty much all the ammunition you need should anyone feel you're being unduly fretful.*

Superbug, Nature's Revenge – Geoffrey Cannon (Virgin Books; 1996; £9.99; 0-863699-34-0) – *By the author of The Food Scandal and The Politics of Food, a book looking at the widespread use of antibiotics in farming and medicine and their likely effects for human health.* / The Society for the Promotion of Nutritional Therapy.

Tinned paste and polyfiller (Baby foods in the 1990s; The Food Commission - 0207 837 2250; £10 for members, £30 non-members) – *A 40-page report on problems with commercial baby food.* / ourworld.compuserve.com/homepages/foodcomm/.

2. BREAST VS BOTTLE

After years of bottle-feeding being promoted as a better, more modern way of feeding newborn babies, medical opinion both in the UK and internationally has swung strongly behind the policy of breast is best.

On the back of campaigning to bolster breast-feeding, the number of women in the UK who do so has been growing – 71% of new mothers breast-fed after birth in 2003. (The figures drop off significantly, though, over the first couple of months.) Social background is an influence: according to a report in *The Times* over 90% of mothers in the highest social classes start by breast-feeding.

With the practice becoming more commonplace once more, there has been a shift in attitudes in society. Large retailers, for example, now take a more positive attitude to breast-feeding than they did ten years ago.

The scientific arguments for breast-feeding (and against bottle-feeding) are sufficiently overwhelming that advertising for newborn formula milk is not allowed in the UK. Nor is any claim permitted in manufacturers' promotional material to link the concept of health with formula milk.

As an expectant first-time mother, it is easy to assume that breast-feeding should be as easy as falling off a log. For many women it is, but for a significant proportion it is not. This is an issue that the breastfeeding lobby has often chosen to gloss over in the past, but is beginning to address now it feels the main battle is won.

While the vast majority of mothers should be able to breastfeed (97% do in Norway for example), two factors can work against success.

The first is lack of moral support and know-how. Older relatives and to a lesser extent midwives and health visitors, may have no firsthand experience of breastfeeding. They may have little practical advice to offer and – as it was not how they raised their own children – wittingly or otherwise undermine the process.

The second is physical pain – generally due to difficulties latching on. The trick is to get expert advice fast – something which may also help with the emotional issues.

Counselling and books can play an invaluable part in helping to overcome any difficulties. However, if your child is losing weight, the same hospital that told you shortly after birth that breast is best, may well advise you to start adding in formula feeds.

If – for whatever reason – you decide at the outset that breast-feeding is not right for you, be prepared for a rough time. This is an issue that arouses strong passions in some quarters, and some mothers (and midwives) are vociferous in their opposition to bottle-feeding. Even if nothing is said, bottle-feeding in a group of breast-feeding mothers can be an uncomfortable experience.

Advantages of breast-feeding/ disadvantages of bottle-feeding

➤ All experts regard breast-milk as the best food for a baby. A plethora of studies show breast-feeding to offer benefits including: improved immunity against disease; resistance to allergies; stronger bone structure; and better mental development and psychological support. Breast-milk is incredible stuff: for example, mothers produce a different type of milk if they have given birth to a premature baby or one at full term. In addition, on the basis of tests with calves, it appears that an infection in the baby may even trigger the production of milk with specific antibodies to fight it. Colostrum, the early milk, is particularly valuable, and the breast-milk continues to change in composition as the baby grows.

➤ Formula is a very adequate substitute, but has its shortcomings; bottle-fed babies are more likely to suffer gastro-intestinal infections and, for example, may suffer an increased incidence of eczema. There are also periodic scares about chemical contamination of one sort or another.

➤ Breast-feeding offers instant comfort to an unhappy baby.

➤ It was reported in the *British Medical Journal* that breast-feeding acts as a pain reliever for the baby.

➤ Breast-feeding can help the bonding between mother and baby.

➤ Breast-feeding is an extremely convenient way to feed a baby – no time or equipment is required to sterilise and make up bottles (particularly tiresome for night feeds and when travelling).

➤ Breast-feeding can be a lot cheaper than bottle-feeding, even allowing for the mother's increased appetite.

➤ A breast-fed baby's nappy is less messy and smelly – mother's milk produces far less waste. This generally means less discomfort for the baby (not to mention the obvious benefits for carers).

➤ Breast-feeding can help with regaining your pre-birth figure because it burns up the extra stores of fat laid down during pregnancy. (Some women, though, feel that this is outweighed by the substantial amounts they feel they need to eat to feed successfully.) It also helps the uterus contract to its pre-pregnant size, and protects against pre-menopausal breast cancer (a 5% reduction for every six months' feeding according to one recent study), ovarian cancer and osteoporosis.

➤ There is less danger of overfeeding – babies tend to take what they want and stimulate milk to meet their needs by sucking. For the first four–six months a baby needs nothing else – even water is superfluous. With bottle-feeding there is more danger of overfeeding ('come on, finish the bottle').

➤ Breast-feeding requires babies to exercise their facial muscles, which according to some reports leads to better jaw lines and fewer problems with dentition than amongst bottle-fed babies. In a similar vein, protracted bottle-feeding of toddlers (i.e. to too great an age) is thought to lead to maladjusted facial muscles and even speech difficulties.

➤ Breast-feeding is environmentally friendly, needing no packaging, processing or transport and could, it is claimed by many, save the NHS £35m a year on gastroenteritis in bottle-fed babies alone.

➤ It is sometimes argued that formula feeding will help a baby to sleep through the night, but a recent report (published in an NCT publication) disputes this.

Disadvantages of breast-feeding/ advantages of bottle-feeding

➤ Weight-gain is – in general – slower for breast-fed babies than for bottle-fed ones, and anxiety about whether the weight-gain is sufficient is more common. Any anxiety is exacerbated by the fact that, whereas with bottle-feeding you can see how much milk babies are taking, with breast-feeding it can be difficult to know if a child is 'eating properly'.

➤ Some mothers produce insufficient milk to breast-feed properly (though cases where this is genuinely so are rare than those where a woman's confidence has been eroded for some reason – it is worth seeking advice from a lactation consultant.)

➤ Though some women find breast-feeding a doddle, for a reasonable number it may start out distinctly uncomfortable, or even very painful (if this happens get expert help quickly). This problem peaks for most at around three or four days. (In most cases, the problem is likely to be the baby failing to latch on properly.)

➤ Only the mother can feed a breast-fed baby. Unless she devotes time to expressing milk, or combines breast-feeding with formula (the latter being only advised after four weeks so the baby gets time to stimulate regular milk production and learn to suck), the mother cannot be left to sleep through the night. Bottle-feeding can enable others close to the child to get involved and a chance for mum to catch up on some much-needed sleep.

➤ Some babies take an age to breast-feed during the first few (say six) weeks (anything from every four hours to every hour) and this is very time-consuming. Even thereafter, breast-feeding – particularly if you are feeding on demand – can take up a major part of the day, making it difficult to get on with other things. This is a particular issue where there are other kids to look after.

➤ Breast-feeding is feared to lead to sagging breasts. (Experts, however, report that sagging is the result of changes that occur within the breasts as they enlarge during pregnancy.)

➤ There may be embarrassment if breast-feeding in public.

➤ Some men regard their partner's breasts as their territory and resent the baby's use of them.

➤ Some women find the whole experience too animal.

➤ If the baby has colic, a breast-feeding mother may have to restrict her diet: (see Mother's diet & wellbeing in Section 3, Breast-feeding below).

➤ Some argue that formula is an important source of iron. However, this is much disputed, and breast-milk, though less iron-rich, may actively aid the absorption of iron.

➤ If the mother's own mother bottle-fed there will be no issue about going about things differently.

Undisputed reasons to bottle-feed

➤ A baby 'failing to thrive' because the mother is – for whatever reason – not producing enough milk. This may result from the mother being too tired or under stress (and is often a consequence of a Caesarean section). Failure to thrive is the kind of condition best diagnosed by a paediatrician as – for example – it is very common for all babies to lose weight after the birth. This is an area where many people, less qualified health professionals included, don't know what they're talking about.

➤ Serious illness and/or infection in the mother, as breast-feeding will debilitate her.

➤ The mother taking certain medications that could pass into the breast-milk (though apparently there are few of which this is true).

➤ If the baby suffers severe lactose intolerance (see Section 4, Bottle-feeding below), no form of human or cow's milk can be offered.

➤ If the baby suffers cleft lip or cleft palate, breast-feeding may be difficult, but CLAPA (see chapter *2.03 Baby health*) can help with this. See www.breastfeedingnetwork.org.uk.

➤ A mother who is a drug addict should not breast-feed.

➤ If the mother is HIV positive, it is possible that the infection may be passed to the baby by breast-feeding.

Hospital policy

The vast majority of the NHS hospitals surveyed for this guide are working towards 'Baby-Friendly Status' – a breast-feeding policy laid out by the WHO and UNICEF. The midwives at such hospitals are required by the policy to actively promote breast-feeding and have target quotas which they aim to meet.

Criteria for hospitals achieving 'Baby-Friendly Status':

1. Have a written breast-feeding policy that is routinely communicated to all health care staff.
2. Train all health care staff in skills necessary to implement this policy.
3. Inform all pregnant women about the benefits and management of breast-feeding.
4. Help mothers initiate breast-feeding – possibly within half an hour of birth.
5. Show mothers how to breast-feed and how to maintain lactation even if they should be separated from their infants.
6. Give newborn infants no food or drink other than breast-milk unless medically indicated.
7. Practise 'rooming in' – allowing mothers and infants to remain together 24 hours a day.
8. Encourage breast-feeding on demand.
9. Give no artificial teats or dummies to breast-feeding infants.
10. Foster the establishment of breast-feeding support groups and refer mothers to them on discharge from the hospital or clinic.

There is still some way to go. In recent times the UK has been pulled up by the committee of the UN Convention on the Rights of the Child for having breast-feeding rates among the lowest in Europe. It was suggested that this might be because advertising of formula is still permitted. The committee recommended the adoption of the international code for marketing of breast-milk substitutes (a code adopted by all other countries except the UK, US and Somalia). In addition Unicef is calling for better training of midwives and health visitors in the UK after discovering that even newly qualified members of those groups lacked the relevant knowledge and skills.

3. BREAST-FEEDING

If you choose to breast-feed your baby it is important to remember that this is (at least in part) a learned, not an instinctive, activity – for both mother and baby. Moreover, the prime time to start is reportedly within 30 minutes of birth. After that apparently the baby's urge to suck diminishes until around 48 hours later.

Personal advice can be invaluable, especially when getting started, and is available either over the phone or in person from midwives, counsellors, and support groups (see reading and listings below), as well as friends and family. Beware, though – even on a postnatal ward – of ill-informed and conflicting advice. Try to find someone who you find sympathetic and beware of interventions from midwives and doctors who don't know what they're doing. One cack-handed latching-on attempt in the first couple of days can leave you very sore and get the whole process off to a bad start. Breast-feeding is not a process governed by hard and fast rules: find a solution that suits you.

Note that babies that do not latch on properly won't get enough food or liquid and may then be too tired and dehydrated to eat properly. Get help to sort out any problems quickly.

Attending a talk before the birth (see chapter *1.04 Antenatal classes*) can be useful preparation. It is difficult, however, to retain the instructions in the meantime without a baby to practise on.

PAIN

Ignore midwives who tell you that breast-feeding is bound to cause pain. Many have not breast-fed themselves and many are of a generation that took little interest in it. That said, some women may find it painful (some extremely so) and days four and five after the birth are those most likely to be difficult with potential bruising, cracked skin, or engorgement. This is the time when many women give up. As counsellors will tell you, this phase does pass and you shouldn't feel pain for more than four to seven days, although it can take three weeks to a month to feel really on top of things and in the early days getting it right really does take concentration.

The main cause of pain and problems while breast-feeding is incorrect positioning (see Equipment for breast-feeding, below). Other causes could be any old scar tissue in the breast, or a thrush infection of the milk ducts. Relaxation exercises as used for labour can help alleviate discomfort, for example if the let-down of the milk is painful.

If you suffer from mastitis (which can occur after a few weeks of breast-feeding, not just at the start), expressing milk or applying local heat in the form of a poultice or hot water bottle can help, as can aromatherapy and homeopathy. If you try a complementary therapy to alleviate this condition, you should get to a practitioner quickly (see chapter *4.02 Complementary medicine & Health practitioners*). If you have a temperature, contact your GP immediately to check if your breast (or breasts) has become infected. Any medication should be taken as soon as possible.

Once again, do make sure that you avoid advice from anyone who does not know about breast-feeding (possibly including health visitors, relatives and even some doctors). For example, with mastitis you must continue to feed (or at least take milk) from the inflamed breast or the blockage is likely to get worse. The reverse is often suggested. Breast-feeding counsellors are the ideal advisers as they are specialists in the subject and can, for example, suggest when extra tests might be appropriate.

SUPPLY AND DEMAND
The constant cycle by which the baby's demand for milk stimulates milk production by the mother is an important part of the process, and one which you must be aware of. 'Use it or lose it' is a useful mantra.

Beware, for example, of well-intentioned offers by midwives on your postnatal ward to give your baby a bottle so that you can get some sleep. This will mean your child will not be hungry enough to stimulate milk production from you.

If your baby is not sleeping next to you, you can pin a note to the cot requesting that she be brought to you for feeding.

Some hospitals have a policy that newborns must breast-feed within a specified period after the birth, or be given a bottle. Others are considerably more relaxed. If you are at one of the former, your baby hasn't fed and you don't want formula given, you can ask for a high glucose solution to be given by syringe In the mouth to keep the blood sugar level up until the baby is ready to feed.

Extra milk supplies will take a day, or, very occasionally, two to arrive. If your baby is premature (or unwell) and has to go into special care, you can ask for cup-feeding to be used with top-ups by tube so that the child does not get used to using a bottle and forget how to 'work' for breast-milk.

If you feed on demand for the first few weeks to establish your supply of milk, this supply will continue to match demand, generally seven or more feeds a day. (Note that feeding on demand is not the same as encouraging snacking and after the first few weeks you may need to encourage the baby to eat a full meal at each feed, keeping her awake with a nappy change if necessary; and then not feeding again until she is sufficiently hungry to eat in reasonable quantities again.)

As the baby grows, some women experience increased demand (every four to six weeks) for more regular feeds, especially at night, to stimulate increased milk production. Once the amount of milk available has increased, the regularity of feeding will return to its usual level.

According to some breastfeeding experts, few babies are too big to get adequate milk from their mothers. If there are concerns, seek advice from a breast-feeding counsellor who can tell you if this really is the case, and can advise you on boosting your supply. Midwives and health visitors do not generally have expertise in this area, nor do most paediatricians. There may be concerns about whether a large baby's blood sugar is stable – instability could be a reason for giving extra fluids. Here a paediatrician is the person to ask.

Small babies are likely to want to feed particularly regularly, as their stomachs are so tiny that they can only take in a little food at a time.

MIXING BREAST- AND BOTTLE-FEEDING
Some people speak rather glibly about mixing breast- and bottle-feeding. To do so successfully, though, does require a modicum of planning.

Breast-feeding for four–six weeks or so is required before the supply of milk is sufficiently well-established that most women can start to substitute one bottle feed a day for a breast feed without jeopardising their supply of milk. This is generally a first small step on the road to weaning. In the short term it allows mothers to feel less constantly tied to the baby, though this may also be achieved by them expressing milk and leaving it for later bottle-feeding.

If you do plan some mix of breast- and bottle-feeding (say, because you are planning to work) note that, while it is important not to lose your supply by introducing the bottle too early, introducing it too late may mean your child is reluctant to co-operate with the switch.

MOTHER'S DIET & WELLBEING
The mother's diet will be consumed indirectly by the baby, so it is important – both for you and the baby – to eat well while breast-feeding, and not to get run down. Ideally, eat lots of small meals, as a long period without food means your milk supply will drop temporarily. An NCT study found that a daily intake of less than 1,500 calories per day for a week reduced milk production: 2,200 to 2,700 calories per day is recommended, depending upon your activity levels.

Different babies are intolerant of different foods, so it may be worthwhile avoiding certain foods while breast-feeding. Possible culprits include eggs, beans, carbonated drinks, highly seasoned dishes and monosodium glutamate. Caffeine (in coffee, tea, cola and chocolate) can make the baby irritable. Artificial sweeteners can make the baby over-excited. Unsurprisingly, nicotine and alcohol can also have undesirable effects – nicotine can cause diarrhoea or vomiting, and alcohol can affect the baby's development. Sage, dried lentils and mint are believed by complementary practitioners to cause some drying-up of the milk supply (worth bearing in mind when you want to stop the breast-feeding). Consumption of strongly flavoured food, for example a whole tube of extra strong mints, may cause temporary refusal of the breast.

In addition, when breast-feeding you need:

Plenty of rest: not a self-indulgence, but the way to ensure you will have plenty of milk: resting just for a day should mean your supply goes up.

Plenty to drink: but do not force yourself into this, as paradoxically it seems that over-hydrating your system can actually decrease your milk supply. The rule is drink to thirst.

Concerns over weight gain in newborns
Especially in the early weeks, it is standard practice to weigh newborns regularly at visits by health visitors and midwives and at baby clinics. The weight is plotted on a chart and assessed against similarly-aged babies as a measure of your child's development. Your child's weight relative to the accepted standard is expressed as a 'percentile': i.e. which hundredth of the population your child falls into, so the 50th percentile is the 'average'.

Although monitoring babies in this way should be a good idea, failure to gain weight in accordance with these charts can easily become cause for anxiety, and there are far more babies about whom the process raises concerns than there are babies with real problems.

The original charts were developed drawing on information from a small group of white, American, bottlefed babies. They do not, therefore, always offer a useful marker for babies who are differently fed and from different cultures and ethnic groups.

Breast-fed babies are far more likely to generate anxiety than bottle-fed ones, which can heighten the stress of an already difficult learning phase. Having been bombarded with propaganda about the virtues of breast-feeding, some new mothers all of a sudden find themselves under the opposite pressure from carers to 'top up' feeds with a bottle, resulting in confusion, further anxiety and feelings of failure.

If this looks like a potential problem you should ask for the baby to be assessed against one of the newer, breast-fed baby charts which are designed to show the different pattern of weight gain compared with formula fed babies.

It is important to remember that different health visitors (and even doctors) have different levels of training in this area, different opinions and may give different advice. Some health professionals seem focused on the chart rather than the child, perhaps forgetting that the charts are based on relatively crude assumptions. For example little account is taken of genetic makeup (a baby of slight parents is likely to be slight as well). Furthermore, it is relatively common for babies to lose weight compared with their starting percentile and then quite happily in their own time to 'regress to the norm'. This is another pattern ignored by many who use the charts.

There are a number of other markers of wellbeing in addition to weight. These include length, sufficient wet nappies daily, and that the baby remains bright-eyed and alert.

If the prime source of your anxieties derives from your carers rather than your own perception of the appearance of your child, you might like to ask for a 'thrive line check' (see Child Growth Foundation below). This is not necessarily something your carers will have heard of, and you may need to introduce them to the idea.

READING

[Leaflet] **A Beginner's Guide to Breast-feeding** (Community Practitioners & Health Visitor's Association (CPHVA); 2001; £1.85) – *A sensible leaflet. / c/o TG Scott (01732) 884023.*

Best-feeding ★ – Mary Renfrew, Chloe Fisher & Suzanne Arms (Getting breast-feeding right for you; Celestial Arts; 1990, revised 2000; £9.99; 0890879559) – *Clear and accurate information, including good advice on positioning for breast-feeding. One of the best titles for first-timers.*

Breast is Best – Drs Penny & Andrew Stanway (The authoritative book on breast-feeding; Pan; 1996; £6.99; 0-330347-53-5) – *Comprehensive tome with 465 pages of information.*

[Video] **Breast-feeding** (B-Line Productions; 1993; £35.25) – *Presented by Maggie Philbin – 60 minutes of advice from professionals and mothers. / B-Line Productions, 45 Muswell Road, London N10 2BS; (020) 8444 9574; www.b-lineproductions.co.uk.*

[Video] **Breast-feeding** (Coping with the first week; Mark-It Television; 1996; £19.95) – *One of a series of breast-feeding videos – recommended by NCT reviewers as a positive production that helps mothers to overcome difficulties. / Mark-It Television Associates, (0117) 939 1117; www.omikron.freeserve.co.uk/markit/.*

Breast-feeding Your Baby – Jane Moody, Jane Britten & Karen Hogg (A National Childbirth Trust guide; Thorsons; 1998; £9.99; 0-722536-35-6) – *A clear guide (with specialist sections on, for example, twins) which covers all possible scenarios from not having enough milk to producing too much. Case histories back up the thorough background research. One of the NCT's "core" titles.*

[Booklet] **Breast-feeding – A Good Start** (NCT Publishing; 2001; £2.50) – *20-pages of advice for beginners.*

[Booklet] **Breast-feeding: How to express and store your milk** (NCT Publishing; 2000; £2.50) – *A leaflet of practical, illustrated information. / NCT Maternity Sales (0870) 112 1120; nctms.co.uk.*

Breastfeeding (Coping with the First Week; Travis Ltd) – *Produced in association with the Royal College of Midwives, a guide featuring mothers dealing with the emotional and practical aspects of breastfeeding. / TRavis Ltd. PO Box 23103, London SE1 2GP (020) 7407 3655 www.worldofhealth.co.uk.*

Breastfeeding - Your Guide (Prohealth; £14.99) – *A 63-minute audio CD for parents.* / *Prohealth Publishing, Unit 3, The Priory, London Road, Canwell, Sutton Coldfield, West Midlands (01543) 481 523 www.prohealthpublishing.com.*

[Video] Coping with the First Week – Mark-It Television with the Royal College of Midwives (1996) – *Some feel the advice is prescriptive but it usefully focuses on the key issue of positioning; one of a number of videos produced by the Mark-It production company on this subject.* / *(0117) 939 1117, www.omikron.freeserve.co.uk/markit/.*

The National Childbirth Trust Book of Breast-feeding – Mary Smale (Vermilion; 1999; £7.99; 0091825695) – *Aims to address every aspect of breast-feeding from initial discomfort and concerns (such as failing milk supplies) through to successful weaning.*

NCT Breastfeeding for Beginners – Caroline Deacon (Thorsons; 2002; £6.99; 0-00-71308-0) – *The NCT's big title on a subject which is close to its heart.* / *NCT Maternity Sales, (0870) 112 1120 www.nctms.co.uk.*

The Politics of Breast-feeding – Gabrielle Palmer & Sheila Kitzinger (Pandora HarperCollins; 1988; £9.99; 0863582206) – *A title for those who are, or who want to be committed to the cause; a politicised (and fascinating) look at the hows, whys and wherefores of the practice worldwide.*

Practical Parenting - Breastfeeding – Jane Chumbley (Nursing your baby and introducing bottles; Hamlyn; 2003; £5.99; 0600606627) – *A pretty comprehensive guide, covering: getting started; how to overcome problems like engorgement and soreness; frequent feeders and premature babies; moving from breast to bottle with advice on expressing, sterilisation and weaning.* / *www.hamlyn.co.uk.*

Practical Parenting Problem Solvers: Breast-feeding – Felicity Tucker (Macmillan; 1999; £5.99; 0-330370-48-0) – *Outlines why 'breast is best' and explains basic methods and how to deal with any problems. Takes a new mother through the entire breast-feeding experience.*

What to Expect When You're Breastfeeding... and What if You Can't – Clare Byam-Cook (How to feed and setle your baby and have a life of your own; Vermilion; 2001; £7.99; 0091856744) – *By a midwife who works with Christine Hill's antenatal practice in Chiswick, offering classes and home visits. The book offers solutions to the problems encountered on those visits, including a practical and detailed section on bottlefeeding* / *www.randomhouse.co.uk.*

SOURCES OF ADVICE

The Active Birth Centre, ☎ (020) 7281 6760
✆ www.activebirthcentre.com
Regular breast-feeding classes at the centre, which also sells breast-pumps. / HOURS *shop Mon-Fri 9.30am-6.30pm (Fri 4pm), Sat 10am-4pm.*

Association of Breastfeeding Mothers (ABM), ☎ (020) 7813 1481 ✆ www.abm.me.uk
A charity offering advice to mothers and health workers and which runs support groups for members who are breast-feeding or wish to breast-feed. They can supply the numbers of local counsellors around the country. Alternatively send an SAE for more information or written counselling. Electric breast pump hire is offered in conjunction with Ameda Egnell (see Equipment for breast-feeding). Operates a 24-hour voluntary helpline (020) 7813 1481. / PUBLICATIONS *Quarterly magazine; leaflets (including Breast refusal; Coping with too much milk, 60p-£1.70).*

Baby Milk Action, ☎ (01223) 464420 ✆ www.babymilkaction.org
An organisation campaigning for informed choices about infant feeding, full support for breast-feeding and ethical behaviour by baby food companies. Nestlé has been a particular target of the organisation's wrath, against which it co-ordinates a boycott in 70 countries on account of Nestlé's continuing failure to comply with UN directives on promoting formula, particularly in the Third World. (According to UNICEF one and a half million babies die every year because they are not breast-fed.) / PUBLICATIONS *Information and publication list (SAE).*

Breastfeeding Network, ☎ Helpline (0870) 900 8787
✆ www.breastfeedingnetwork.org.uk
Charity aiming to provide support and education of new mothers, health workers and professionals, free from commercial bias. The free national helpline is manned by volunteers. The charity maintains an exhaustive website which is a mine of information and links on every aspect of breast-feeding. It has FAQ and discussion sections, but also numerous links, product recommendations, details of breast-pump suppliers and so on.

International Lactation Consultants Association (ILCA),
⏚ www.ilca.org
A US-based organisation set up to serve as an advisory body for women's and
children's health, to stimulate and support research in all aspects of lactation and infant
feeding, and to support the implementation of the International Code of Marketing of
Breast-milk Substitutes plus subsequent relevant resolutions.

Lactation Consultants of Great Britain, *⏚ www.lcgb.org*
A UK-based organisation for those working to support breast-feeding in a variety of
fields. The website includes a number of interesting links. If you need a consultant,
e-mail them and they will provide details of someone in your area.

La Leche League of Great Britain, *☎ Helpline (0845) 120 2918,*
(020) 7242 1278 ⏚ www.laleche.org.uk
An international voluntary organisation headquartered in the US but which operates in
60 countries. Gives information, support and counselling on breast-feeding plus
information for those in special circumstances e.g. blind mothers, babies with cleft or
soft palate, premature babies, multiple births, Downs Syndrome. They have 90 local
groups in the UK providing mother-to-mother support with trained counsellors and
have a sizeable catalogue, primarily of publications, as well as a small amount of
equipment (they also advise health professionals). Membership is £18 (£10
concessions). Call for details of local contacts. / PUBLICATIONS *Publications catalogue includes: A
Mother's Guide to Milk Expression; Breast Pumps.*

Maud Giles, *☎ (07939) 820651*
Lactation consultant and ex-paediatric nurse who provides help and education for all
feeding and baby-related problems including sore nipples, low weight gain, colic,
reflux, and sleeping; £90 for one and a half hours. / HOURS *24hr answerphone.*

National Childbirth Trust (NCT), *☎ Enquiry line (0870) 444 8707*
⏚ www.nctpregnancyandbabycare.co.uk; www.nctparentsconnect.co.uk
The trust provides trained counsellors who are available to help all mothers, not just
NCT members – the Breast-feeding Line (0870 444 8708) puts callers in touch with
a counsellor, seven days a week (8am-10pm). The NCT also holds a Breast-feeding in
Special Situations register for people with special requirements (such as breast-feeding
twins or triplets, nursing a toddler and a baby at the same time, recurrent mastitis or
feeding after breast surgery). Access to this register should be via a breast-feeding
counsellor rather than direct. / HOURS *Mon-Thurs 9am-5pm, Fri 9am-4pm; or answerphone;*
PUBLICATIONS *Leaflets: Breast-feeding – a good start; Breast-feeding after a Caesarean; Breast-feeding a baby
in a Special Care Unit; How to express and store milk; Returning to work; Making plenty of milk for your
baby.*

Promom (Promotion of Mother's Milk), *⏚ www.promom.org*
The site of a US nonprofit organisation, featuring 101 reasons to breast-feed, discussion
forums and breast-feeding information.

Sainsbury's/Wellbeing Eating for Pregnancy Helpline,
☎ (0845) 130 3646 ⏚ www.shef.ac.uk/pregnancy-nutrition
The helpline provides general information on nutrition while breast-feeding and can
advise on specific points. / HOURS *10am-4pm.*

World of Health, *☎ (020) 7357 9393 ⏚ www.worldofhealth.co.uk*
Health, fitness and lifestyle video and DVD supplier with titles to show – rather than
just tell – you how to breast-feed.

USEFUL CONTACTS
Child Growth Foundation, *☎ (020) 8995 0257, (020) 8994 7625*
⏚ www.heightmatters.org.uk
This foundation, founded in 1977 produces useful 'thrive' acetate sheets that fit over
standard growth charts and are designed to facilitate a better reading. Some health
visitors have access to such acetates, and if there are concerns about your child's weight
gain compared to the charts, you could ask for a 'thrive line check'. You can purchase
the acetates yourself direct from the foundation (£5 per set – one each for boys and
girls). A similar set of acetates exists for those with the opposite concern – that of
over-feeding their baby.

Equipment for breast-feeding
A pillow or cushion to raise the newborn baby to the nipple and to support
the mother's back can be all that is needed for breast-feeding, and even
that is not always necessary.

You may, though, wish to consider some of the following products.

Breast-feeding aids:

Nursing bras: these make life considerably easier if you normally wear a bra and/or if your breasts have become sufficiently large that you now need one. Two or three will probably suffice.

A feeding chair: a comfortable chair can make all the difference to the comfort of feeds – ones with arms and firm upholstery are generally found best. Some people treat themselves to a rocking chair, or there are some super-comfortable glider-rockers specifically designed for feeding.

Special cushions: shaped to facilitate feeding – can also be useful for propping up the baby and beforehand for support in pregnancy.

Breastpads: to absorb milk spilling into your clothes. Reusable ones are cheaper, but at least three sets are a good idea. Avoid plastic-backed pads, as these can leave nipples soggy, which can lead to problems. A recent innovation is breastpads in fine wool treated with lanolin, that wick moisture away and are breathable (the lanolin offers extra protection). Silk ones backed by terry are also available designed to take advantage of the fabric's reported natural healing properties. A towel or mattress protector under your bed sheets is also worthwhile, to protect your mattress.

Nipple shells: enable you to catch the milk that comes out of one nipple when feeding from the other. This spare milk can then be frozen for when you are not around to feed (though only the less important foremilk is caught).

Breast pump: see below.

Nipple creams: see below.

Cabbage leaves: widely recommended as the best thing for engorged breasts (honest).

Nipple shields: designed to protect sore nipples, these shields come in two types: latex, which act as an extra skin with more solid central nipple; or the now less popular silicone, which are rigid with a teat. Use of the rigid variety in particular can reduce the amount of milk the baby gets which normally means feeding takes longer; they can make it difficult for the baby to latch on properly, increasing rather than diminishing soreness; and they can be difficult to wean a baby from. Some people feel they are best avoided except as a last resort, but they can be extremely useful for example if you have inverted nipples or other conditions which hamper easy feeding. For more advice contact a breast-feeding counsellor.

Sterile milk freezer bags: useful for any surplus milk that you produce, enabling you to leave supplies for when you are away from the baby (although freezing does destroy antibodies). There are hollow 'bottles' into which you can insert these bags directly once defrosted, onto which a teat is screwed, providing an instant bottle. (Alternatively you could donate surplus milk to a local hospital human milk bank – see Milk banks, below).

Mineral and vitamin supplements: ideally prescribed by a qualified practitioner, to supplement both mother and (indirectly) the baby (see chapter *4.02 Complementary medicine & Health practitioners* – Nutrition for details of the better quality brands).

EQUIPMENT BRANDS
Cannon Avent
*Cannon Rubber Ltd, Glemsford Suffolk CO10 7QS ☎ Product advice line (0800) 289064
⏱ www.aventbaby.com*
The largest UK manufacturers of bottle-feeding and breast-feeding equipment, stocked in many major chains and supermarkets; provides a product advice line and mail order service. All bottles fit the Avent breastpump. There is also a range of associated products including Niplette for flat or inverted nipples and an out-and-about breastpump set, including cool packs. / *HOURS 8.45am-5pm.*

Dr Brown's (BFree)
☎ *(020) 8731 7776* ✆ *www.BabyBFree.com*
This company specialises in Bisphenol A-free products (see Bottle-feeding);
the hand-operated breast pump, £20, comes with an adapter and bottle.

Lanowool
42 Fordington Rd London N6 4TJ ☎ *(020) 8444 9061* ✆ *www.lanowool.com*
Suppliers of breast-feeding pads made of fine merino wool treated with highly purified
lanolin to help protect the nipples and keep the breasts at a constant temperature. They
are also breathable, moving moisture away from your body. They cost £10, but it is
thought that for average milk production you should need no more than one pair (or
possibly two if you want to wash one while you wear another). See the website for
further information.

Lansinoh
Lansinoh Laboratories, Inc, Prospect House, 32 Sovereign St Leeds LS1 4BJ ☎ *(0113) 389
1038* ✆ *www.lansinoh.co.k*
The UK outpost of a market-leading US firm (founded by a mom in 1984), dedicated to
the promotion of breast-feeding and the supply of relevant equipment – breastmile
storage bags, nursing pads, breast-feeding tops. Visit the website for full information.
The company's leading product, claimed to be "the worlds purest Lanolin" (used to
treat cracked nipples) is available at Waitrose.

Maws
Jackel International, Dudley Lane, Cramlington Northumberland NE23 7RH ☎ *Helpline
(0500) 979899*
Breast-feeding starter kit of breast pump, pads and accessories.

Medela
Central Medical Supplies, CMS House, Basford Lane, Leekbrook Staffs ST13 7DT
☎ *(01538) 399541* ✆ *www.centralmedical.co.uk*
A brand of breast pump for sale or hire from Expression Breastfeeding (see also, under
breast pump hire companies). The range includes products for specific problems
including a silicone teat for babies who can swallow correctly but have sucking
difficulties, and a Supplemental Nursing system, used for cleft palate, premature and
weak babies who have difficulties breast-feeding. The nipple shields are recommended
by at least one breast-feeding expert as particularly good because they are cut away at
one side, allowing the baby to feel and smell the breast with her nose while feeding,
and they come in different sizes.

Niplette
Cannon Rubber Ltd, Glemsford Suffolk CO10 7QS ☎ *Product advice line (0800) 289064*
✆ *www.aventbaby.com*
A product designed to suck out inverted nipples painlessly. In one to three months
continuous wear the manufacturers say nipples will stay permanently erect. Stocked by
Boots and independent chemists; you should use them between pregnancies or in the
first six months, as once you start producing colostrum they will fall off.

Tommee Tippee
Jackel International, Dudley Lane, Cramlington Northumberland NE23 7RH ☎ *Helpline
(0500) 979899*
The Pur Natur range includes a hand breastpump with a wide based bottle for stability,
teat, spare valve and nipple adapters for a good fit. / *HOURS Mon-Thu 9am-4.45pm, Fri 9am-
2pm; SEE ALSO 3.03 Nursery decor.*

Tyco Healthcare
154 Fareham Road, Gosport Hampshire PO13 0AS ☎ *(01329) 224 150*
✆ *www.tycohealthcare.com*
Manufacturer of hydrogel breast-feeding pads known as MotherMates, designed to
reduce pain and discomfort when breast-feeding. The company has no direct retail
presence, but you can visit the US parent company website for further information.

USEFUL CONTACTS
Back 2
28 Wigmore St London W1H 9DF ☎ *(0800) 374604, (020) 7935 0351*
✆ *www.back2.co.uk*
Stockists of 'Glider Rockers' and v-shaped feeding pillows. Also stock special chairs for
breast feeding. / *HOURS Mon-Fri 9am-5.30pm, Sat 10am-6pm, Sun noon-5pm; SEE ALSO 1.02 Looking
after yourself; 3.02 Baby equipment.*

Grobag
Fusion House, Union Rd, Kingsbridge Devon TQ7 1EF ☎ *(01548) 854 444*
✆ *www.grobag.com*
Vendor of the Theraline Maternity and Nursing pillow in various styles, suitable for

feeding and supporting babies as they learn to sit up. / HOURS Mon-Fri 9am-7pm, Sat 10am-1pm; SEE ALSO 1.02 Looking after yourself; 3.01 Maternity wear; 3.02 Baby equipment; 3.03 Nursery decor; 3.08 Nappies.

Oscar & Dehn
Unit 7, Burmarsh Workshops, Marsden St London NW5 3JA ☎ *(020) 7267 6110*
🖰 *www.oscardehn.com*
Company producing thermal health and beauty products such as breast nurse packs (designed in consultation with the NCT and ABM) which can be chilled to reduce inflammation and help mastitis or warmed to help blocked ducts; made of soft vinyl filled with a temperature retaining gel and small enough to slip into a nursing bra; from Boots, John Lewis, NCT Maternity Sales and Blooming Marvellous, cost £12.50 or you can buy by mail order. / HOURS 9am-5pm; SEE ALSO 2.01 Postnatal.

Nipple creams

Creams and sprays to help avoid cracked and sore nipples are widely sold, but there are some issues raised in connection with their use.

Concerns relating to nipple creams:

➤ Babies recognise the smell of your breasts and introducing a foreign smell may not be desirable.

➤ Some query whether these products may contribute to nipple trouble when learning to feed.

➤ Given the likelihood that some of the product will be ingested by the baby it is important to know exactly what it contains.

Specific products which some experts suggest avoiding:

➤ Peanut oil (also listed as arachis) is found in some brands of nipple creams (although manufacturers are phasing it out). Its use may help explain the increased incidence of peanut allergy under the age of five years.

➤ Lanolin – may cause an allergic reaction in itself (or the reaction may be a result of the chemicals used on the sheep from which it is derived).

➤ Products containing alcohol are said to dry the nipple.

➤ Soap may dry the skin.

One widely suggested preventive is a little of the fattier hindmilk (the last of a feed) rubbed over the nipple plus plenty of fresh air. You should avoid allowing your nipples to remain damp from leaked milk – use breast pads, or wear natural fabrics. It is recommended that you wash with plain water.

Some commentators suggest daily massage with almond, grapeseed or wheatgerm oil as preparation for breast-feeding.

Breast pumps

Expressing milk is much easier for some women than it is for others. If it works for you, it can be useful for a variety of reasons: if you are producing more milk than you need; in order to allow bottle-feeding with breast-milk when you are not around; or if you are unable to use your milk because you are on medication but want to maintain your supply; to supplement feeds; and so on.

Different forms of pumps:

It is worth checking before hiring or buying that the pump features a universal thread to fit all standard baby bottles (or, if not, that there is a practical way for you to handle the milk produced).

Hand pumps: the cheapest option, but some models can be unreliable; difficult to keep clean, slow and sometimes tricky to use. They do allow very easy adjustment of the pumping rate; up to £20.

Battery and small mains operated pumps: a bit easier to use but not suitable for more than two or three uses a day as they can cause painful nipples; prices around £45.

Slightly larger electric pumps: cost around £70 or £80.

Hospital-quality electric pumps: (weighing 10kg), a large pump powerful enough to stimulate milk production without actually breast-feeding the baby at all, so potentially the best choice if you need to express most or all your milk. Very pricey to buy (about £450), they can be hired for under £10 per week. Some women find their mechanical appearance rather intimidating.

BREAST PUMP HIRE COMPANIES
Ameda Egnell
Unit 1 Belvedere Trading House, Taunton Somerset TA1 1BH ☎ *(01823) 336362*
🖰 *www.ameda.demon.co.uk*
The supplier of the electric breast pumps that are hired by voluntary NCT agents also runs a scheme for hiring direct. The Lactaline pumps are designed to mimic the suckling pattern of a baby and encourage let down; a dual lightweight pump is designed to reduce collection time and can even be powered from the electric lighter of a car. / HOURS *Mon-Fri 8am-5pm; SEE ALSO 1.06 Birth equipment.*

John Bell & Croydon Chemists
50-54 Wigmore St London W1V 2AU ☎ *(020) 7935 5555* 🖰 *www.johnbellcroydon.co.uk*
Hire heavy duty electric breast pumps, £110 deposit, £1.10/day hire, purchase of tubes and bottle £9.50.

Expression Breastfeeding
Central Medical Supplies, CMS House, Basford Lane, Leekbrook Staffs ST13 7DT
☎ *(01538) 399541* 🖰 *www.centralmedical.co.uk*
Sole distributors in the UK of Medela breast-feeding products (whose top-of-the-range pumps are used by many hospitals). Items for sale include a mini electric breast pump (£45 including p&p). The company also hires large pumps for £18 a month, plus a £35 initial charge to cover equipment that must be bought by the mother (and carriage). The company also sells a range of breast-milk freezer bags, nipple shields and carry bags. / HOURS *Mon-Fri 8.30am-5.30pm.*

La Leche League of Great Britain
BM 3424 London WC1N 3XX ☎ *Helpline (0845) 120 2918, (020) 7242 1278*
🖰 *www.laleche.org.uk*
Breast pumps are available to hire from the local support groups – call for details of your nearest group. / SEE ALSO *4.05 Finding out more.*

NCT Maternity Sales
239 Shawbridge St Glasgow G43 1QN ☎ *(0870) 112 1120, Breatfeeding helpline (0870) 444 8708* 🖰 *www.nctms.co.uk*
Ameda Egnell operates a hire scheme in conjunction with the NCT; hand-operated and electric pumps, and Medela bra pads are also available for sale. / HOURS *Mon-Fri 9am-5pm; Helpline 8am-10pm; SEE ALSO 2.01 Postnatal; 3.01 Maternity wear; 3.02 Baby equipment; 3.04 Baby clothes; 3.06 Toys; 4.06 Support groups.*

Septrim Medical
164 Old Woolwich St London SE10 9PR ☎ *(0500) 710071, (020) 8314 1117*
🖰 *www.contentbaby.co.uk*
In operation since 1993, this company hires (and sells) professional electric expressing machines by the day. Guaranteed delivery and optional demonstration; same day replacement in case of failure. Feeding accessories also available (breast milk storage bottles, sterile teats, disposable sterilising bags). / SEE ALSO *1.06 Birth equipment.*

Milk banks

In 1990 it was estimated that if every baby in a UK neonatal unit had been fed breast-milk, 100 of them would not have died. Hospital milk banks used to be relatively common and helped with this problem (largely one of gut infections), but concerns about the transmission of infectious diseases, including HIV, caused many to close. Now that the breast-milk is pasteurised and screened, a few hospitals have opened milk banks again. However, currently only three operate in Greater London and there are some in neighbouring areas.

Those milk banks that do operate often suffer a severe shortage of milk and are constantly looking for new donors.

You don't have to be someone who produces masses of milk to donate. Some babies in neonatal units take no more than a couple of millilitres of milk at a time so smaller but regular donations are always welcome.

If you would like to donate you need:

➢ To be willing to undergo blood tests and screening for infection.

➢ To be a non-smoker.

➢ Not to be taking any routine medication or herbal remedies.

➢ Space in your freezer to store milk. Most hospitals can only afford to collect milk at intervals.

➢ To have a baby under six months old. The composition of breast-milk changes as your baby grows and for babies in neonatal units only the earlier milk is suitable.

➢ A willingness to express milk, though no more than once a day. Milk leaked from one breast while you feed from the other is considered less useful because it is only foremilk so with a lower energy content. On the other hand as little as 30ml–50ml a day of expressed milk – a couple of tablespoonfuls – would be sufficient: a process which should take around 10 minutes. Many donors only do this every second day.

➢ A willingness to express over a period of time, so that the hospital gets some return on its investment in your screening tests.

USEFUL CONTACTS
Kingston Hospital Milk Bank, ☎ *(020) 8974 5390*
⌂ www.kingstonhospital.nhs.uk

St George's Hospital Milk Bank, ☎ *(020) 8725 1937*

United Kingdom Association for Milk Banking (UKAMB), ☎ *(020) 8383 3559* *⌂ www.ukamb.org*
Check the web for your nearest milkbank and details of how to become a donor; you can call, but resources to handle such enquiries are limited.

4. BOTTLE-FEEDING

There is not the same steep 'learning curve' – for either mother or baby – in relation to bottle-feeding as there is for breast-feeding. Such 'learning curve' as there is relates more to how to organise the daily task of cleaning bottles, making up new bottles, and organising the paraphernalia required for feeding on the move, rather than the actual process itself.

Some women bottle-feed their children from their child's first day of life, while others come to the process later on to supplement breast-feeding to give themselves more freedom. Some mothers who plan to bottle-feed for the most part will still breast-feed for the baby's first few days of life, because of the exceptional protective qualities and high protein content of the milk produced immediately after the birth (known as colostrum).

Formula milk

Formula milk is available from most chemists and supermarkets. The three big brand names in the UK are SMA, Cow & Gate and Milupa (these last two being under common ownership).

The EU's Infant Formula and Follow-on Formula Regulations 1995 dictate what manufacturers can include in formula and set strict nutritional specifications. The manufacturers do tinker with their respective 'brews', but their ability to differentiate their products is limited.

Given this – and the fact that the law bans advertising for all but follow-on milk – any claims as to which brand is better (for example, that one brand is less likely to cause allergies) are primarily a matter of urban legend. (Some mothers do look out for fortification with LCPs – Long Chain Polyunsaturated fatty acids – which are claimed to contribute to development of the brain and nervous system).

For most mothers, the key to choosing a brand of formula is which one the baby likes the taste of best. It is not unknown to find that a baby who would not be weaned from the breast on to one brand will happily take another.

Once you have found formula that does not cause your baby problems, the advice is to stick to it. Bottle-fed babies appear not to be keen on change and a different formula could upset their digestion.

Formula milk comes in a range of styles, designed to cater for babies at different stages of their growth.

Stage one formula is primarily made from the whey part of cow's milk. Whey is easier to digest so this is considered suitable for newborns and babies of up to weaning age.

'Follow-on' milk (and also brands of stage one formula 'for the hungrier baby') include more of the less digestible curds part of the milk (high in the protein casein) and are aimed at babies up to one year old (the age at which the feeding of normal cow's milk is no longer discouraged).

The idea with follow-on milk is that it is more substantial than the stage one formula. Many people question its worth, however. It is no more nutritious than standard formula, which is a perfectly acceptable way of feeding babies up to the age of one.

Formula is available as powder to be made up with cooled, boiled water, or ready-mixed, in small cartons – expensive but convenient when out and about.

SOYA-BASED AND OTHER ALTERNATIVES TO STANDARD FORMULA

(For more information regarding allergies and lactose-intolerance, see chapter 2.03 Baby health.)

If your child has a lactose intolerance, a doctor may recommend that you try a formula based on soya (used by 2–3% of babies in the UK).

Additionally, these products are also used by very committed vegetarians and are also sometimes touted as a cure for colic. There is no scientific proof that soya milk helps with colic, however and it is worth bearing in mind that these formulas contain sugar which can lead to tooth decay and is held by some to undermine immunity. Soy also apparently encourages production of mucus. In addition there are concerns based on research on mice that a chemical found in soy milk – genistein – may compromise the immune system, possibly because it mimics the hormone oestrogen. More research is expected.

The general advice (from the government and the American Association of Pediatricians to name two sources) is only to use a soya-based formula if recommended to do so by a doctor. Another alternative basis for formula is goats' milk. As with a soya-based product, it is recommended that you only use such formulations if advised to do so by a doctor.

With older babies who have moved on from formula, alternatives to cow's milk include soya milk, goat's milk and rice milk – all generally available in health food shops and some supermarkets. If you choose to go with one of them – some research is sensible to ensure you are achieving a balanced diet for your child.

FORMULA MILK BRANDS

Cow & Gate
White Horse Business Park, Trowbridge Wilts BA14 0XQ ☎ Careline (08457) 623623
🖰 www.cow-gate.co.uk
As well as its very widely stocked standard brands such as Cow & Gate Premium, the firm produces a number of specialist formulas including a dairy-free variety (Infasoy). / *HOURS information service Mon-Thu 8.45am-5.15pm, Fri 8.45am-4.30pm; PUBLICATIONS 10 page booklet: A positive approach to early labour (free).*

Enfamil
🖰 www.enfamil.com
Produced by US giant Mead Johnson – the largest formula brand in the world; generally it is its specialist formulations which pop up in the UK in chemists and specialist food shops, in particular ProSoBee (a soya-based formulation). The firm also does an iron-enriched formula, LactoFree (a milk-based infant formula, but without lactose) and Nutramigen (both designed to be anti-colic).

Farleys
🖰 www.tinytums.co.uk
Though better known for its rusks and so on, the baby products division of food giant Heinz does make a number of formulas, both standard and soya-based. The 'tinytums' website offers a fair amount of advice and the ability to email the experts.

Isomil
🖰 www.ross.com
US brand of soy-based formula from US drug giant Abbott Laboratories.

Milupa
Newmarket Ave, White Horse Business Park Trowbridge BA14 0XQ ☎ Careline (08457) 623628 🖰 www.milupa.co.uk
Manufacturers of Aptamil and Milumil; the brand also encompasses a number of products for feeding pre-term infants, and for fortifying milk. This brand and also Cow & Gate are owned by Nutritia.

Nanny
c/o Vitacare, Unit 1 Utopia Vilage, 7 Chalcot Rd London NW1 8LH ☎ (0800) 328 5826
🖰 www.dgc.co.nz, www.vitacare.co.uk
Goat's milk based infant formula, produced by the Dairy Goat Co-operative of New Zealand.

SMA
Huntercombe Lane South, Taplow, Maidenhead Berks SL6 0PH ☎ Careline (0845) 776 2900 🖰 www.smanutrition.co.uk
The largest UK brand of formula milk runs a customer careline staffed by mothers to answer questions about feeding. In addition to the regular formulations, such as SMA Gold, there are specialist formulas including Wysoy – a soy-based one. / *HOURS Mon-Fri 8am-6pm.*

ORGANIC FORMULA MILK BRANDS

Ecolac
Elysium Natural Products, Unit 12, Moderna Business Park, Mytholroyd Halifax HX7 5QQ ☎ (01422) 885523
Organic-certified infant formula, from the same Dutch brand as produces baby-cereals for lactose-intolerant children.

HIPP
165 Main St, New Greenham Park Berks RG19 6HN ☎ (0845) 050 1351
Best known for its jars of organic baby food, the company now also produces organic follow-up formula. / *HOURS Mon-Fri 9am-5pm.*

Holle

Elysia Natural Skin Care, Unit 27, Stockwood Business Park, Stockwood, Redditch Worcs B96 6SX ☎ (01386) 792622, Elysia (01527) 832863
Organic baby milk and follow-on milk, as well as weaning and adult foods (see also Organic home shopping). / HOURS *Mon-Fri 9am-6pm.*

Organico

☎ *(0118) 951 0518 ⏁ www.organico.co.uk*
French brand of organic infant milk and follow-on milk (for babies up to six months); trial tin of infant formula delivery service available.

Equipment for bottle-feeding

To bottle-feed you will need:

➤ 6–10 bottles/teats/caps.
➤ Formula milk.
➤ A bottle brush for cleaning.
➤ A smaller brush for cleaning the teats can be useful.
➤ A method of sterilising the bottles, for example: boiling; using sterilising tablets or solution in cold water; an electric steam steriliser; or a microwave steriliser (a relatively quick and cheap option, if you have a microwave). Make sure the bottles fit into your chosen sterilising container.
➤ A bottle and baby food warmer if you don't like the idea of heating up bottles in hot water – at least at night. Some experts criticise these as encouraging the breeding of bacteria (though you can obviate this problem to an extent by heating just the water and adding the powder afterwards).
➤ Despite advice on packaging to the contrary, many mothers heat bottles in the microwave. If you do so you must shake the milk vigorously after heating and ensure that there are no 'hotspots'.

You may also wish to consider:

➤ A travel case for transporting bottles at a constant temperature (bearing in mind the comments above on breeding bacteria).
➤ A powder holder (for holding pre-measured amounts of formula to be mixed with water just before use).

Bottles

Bottles come in standard, narrow and wide-necked designs. The latter, while easier to clean and fill, are more liable to leak and may be difficult for older babies trying to feed themselves. They will also not fit onto breast-feeding pumps which are generally designed to take only standard bottles.

Design refinements include snazzy patterns, heat sensitive materials, and unusual shapes (such as easy-to-hold-designs or angled 'anti-colic' bottles). Beware anything too out-of-the-ordinary which may not fit in your steriliser, will be difficult to clean, and may not fit standard teats.

The standard size is nine ounces. Four ounce bottles are also available which may be useful for small quantities of drinks in between feeds – whether of expressed milk, boiled water or chamomile. Look out for self-sealing (leak-proof) options, and designs without difficult-to-clean corners.

Most bottles are made of polycarbonates which, especially once scratched and discoloured, can leach a chemical known as Bisphenol A. (Use of microwaves to heat bottles may accentuate the process, because of their capacity to create small areas of high temperature). In recent years, concern has been raised that even small quantities of this substance may be harmful. It is a claim that is disputed, but specialist suppliers provide bottles free of this substance and some big suppliers are said to be looking at reducing its content in their products. At the least it seems a sensible precaution to throw out worn bottles.

TEATS

Teats are specified by different flow speeds. The idea is to start out with 'slow' and move to faster speeds if required as your baby grows or if she is used to a fast flow when breastfeeding. You can always widen the teat hole manually, with a heated needle, if you don't want to buy another set. Take care, however, as flow that is too rapid for a baby can cause choking.

The materials used to manufacture teats are either silicone (clear) or latex (the original, brown material). The latter is softer and often the preferred choice of babies, who may however chew through it. 'Anti-colic' silicone teats appear to last better than latex ones in sterilisers, though some experts doubt that any anti-colic design actually achieves what is claimed for it. One recent variant is a silicone teat with little bumps designed to soothe and massage a baby's gums.

Different babies drink at different speeds. Restlessness at feeding time may be due to the hole in the teat allowing too fast or too slow a flow of milk.

There are also teats designed to let the baby control the flow rate (again with reducing colic in mind), and orthodontic teats designed to minimise wind problems and to stimulate the development of mouth and jaw muscles in a way similar to breast-feeding (see listings for details). Standard teats are not recommended for children over the age of one because of the risk of dental decay arising from the way a teat distributes liquid in the mouth.

BRANDS

Baby and You
108 George Lane, South Woodford London E18 1AD ☎ (020) 8532 9595
⌂ www.babyandyou.com
Stockists of Core steam steriliser, and bottle and food warmers. / SEE ALSO 3.02 Baby equipment.

Cannon Avent
Cannon Rubber Ltd, Glemsford Suffolk CO10 7QS ☎ Product advice line (0800) 289064
⌂ www.aventbaby.com
The largest UK manufacturers of bottle-feeding and breast-feeding equipment, stocked in many major chains and supermarkets; provides a product advice line and mail order service. Products include a bottle to take disposable bags and a teaching spout to fit reusable bottles to convert to non-spill training cups, as well as a range of sterilisers and travel items. / HOURS 8.45am-5pm.

Dr Brown's (BFree)
☎ (020) 8731 7776 ⌂ www.BabyBFree.com
Bottles with a patented air flow system ('Natural Flow'), made from Bisphenol A-free material; designed to eliminate the vacuum in the bottle chamber, and bubbles in the liquid (potential causes of colic); variety of teats for different ages and flow speeds.

Lindam
Hornbeam Square West, Hornbeam Park, Harrogate North Yorkshire HG2 8PA
☎ Customer care (01423) 855 833 ⌂ www.lindam.co.uk
Warmers, sterilisers, and feeding equipment. / HOURS 9am-5pm; SEE ALSO 3.02 Baby equipment; 3.03 Nursery decor.

Maws
Jackel International, Dudley Lane, Cramlington Northumberland NE23 7RH ☎ Helpline (0500) 979899
(The name originates from the inventor of the first baby feeding nipples in 1807. Maws products are part of Newcastle-based Jackel International.) Wide-neck 'anti-colic' bottle; vari-flow nipple which adjusts flow according to a baby's sucking strength; heat-sensitive strips on bottles (and spoons) to tell you if the milk is too hot; steriliser pack.

Steribottle
Eardley House, 182-184 Campden Hill Rd London W8 7AS ☎ (0500) 979899
⌂ www.steribottle.com
What claims to be the first affordable, pre-sterilised, single-use feeding bottle; made
from recyclable plastic, it's freezer-friendly, available in 125ml and 250ml sizes with
a medium or fast flow teat; stocked, among others, by Boots.

5. SOLIDS

When to wean

Thirty years ago it was common to start children on solids after only a
couple of months (and there are still competitive parents who start early
to show how fast their child is developing). However, the most recent
recommendation from the Department of Health is to start a child on
solid foods no earlier than six months. (Meanwhile, food manufacturers,
reluctant to lose sales, continue to emphasise the earliest possible ages.)

For bottle-fed babies, there are arguments in favour of starting solids
earlier – some sources think that formula does not offer sufficient iron
for babies, and it is thought that unless babies start to chew, there could be
problems with speech later on.

For breast-fed babies, however, iron is not an issue, and breast-feeding
develops the strength of facial muscles in a manner that bottle-feeding
does not. Breast milk provides all nutrients a baby needs for the first nine
months of life, and The World Health Organisation (WHO) recommends
that solids are introduced no earlier than at six months as prior to this
time they "do not confer any growth advantage over exclusive breast-
feeding". This is supported by the DOH because the baby rice and purees
suitable at this stage offer a narrower range of nutrients than either formula or breast-milk, which continue to be the prime source of nutrients for
the first year.

Giving solids too early is known to increase risk of eczema and wheezing. For this reason it is now recommended that babies in families with
these problems are weaned later. The reason may be connected to the
mechanism that some believe is behind food intolerance; 'leaky gut' – a gut
which may allow small particles of food out into the bloodstream. In a
baby this may occur because the gut is not yet complete functional.

Introducing solids later also means that the body will have the necessary neuro-muscular co-ordination to start handling more than just
liquid, and the kidneys will not be unduly stressed.

Signs of readiness for solids include the disappearance of the tongue
thrusting reflex when the baby puts anything in her mouth, and reaching for food. The appearance of teeth is not thought to be much of a
marker.

Bottle-feeding is not recommended for babies over one. WHO recommends supporting mothers who breast-feed into the second year,
although some babies stop spontaneously around ten or eleven months.
Two years is probably the natural cut-off point, as around this time the
larynx shifts lower, improving speech but ending the ability to suck and
breathe simultaneously.

Even after weaning, it is recommended that milk should still be part of
your child's diet. This could be breast-milk, but otherwise for a one-year
old, at least 12oz of milk per day is recommended. This should be cow's
milk rather than formula and the Health Education Authority stresses
that it should be *full fat* – not semi–skimmed or skimmed.

An advisory committee to the Department of Health reporting on feeding young children, recommended giving supplemental vitamins from six months if breast-feeding, one year if bottle-feeding, and in all events to at least five years. Given that an estimated 84% of children under four are iron deficient with one in eight meeting the clinical definition for being anemic, an iron rich diet would also be wise, together with vitamin C to aid absorption. (Symptoms include loss of appetite, lethargy and developmental delay.)

READING

The New Contented Little Baby Book – Gina Ford (The secret to calm and confident parenting from one of the world's top maternity nurses; Vermilion; 2002; £9.99; 0-091882338) – *Controversial scourge of the feed-on-demand school of thought – an advocate of highly-structured feeding and sleeping routines (which she claims will lead your newborn to sleep through the night by 10 weeks old). Those who hate the book feel its methods are akin to treating your child like Pavlov's dog, but even some doubters find the basic ideas behind the routines useful. Others in the same vein include the contented Little Baby Book of Weaning, and From Contented Baby to Confident Child.*

Practical Parenting - Weaning and First Foods – Sara Lewis (Which foods to introduce and when; Hamlyn; 2003; £5.99; 0600605647) – *A guide to introducing solids (whether bought or homemade) into the diet. It includes advice on cooking methods and food fads, and how to recognise when your baby is ready for more milk. Common problems are also addressed. / www.hamlyn.co.uk.*

[Video] **Weaning** (B-Line Productions; 1993; £35.25) – *Mothers, health professionals and nutritionists give tips, advice and information on solid food. / B-Line Productions, 45 Muswell Road, London N10 2BS; (020) 8444 9574; www.b-lineproductions.co.uk.*

When do I start my baby on solids (NCT; 50p) – *One of a series of NCT advice sheets. / NCT Maternity Sales (0870) 112 1120, www.nctms.co.uk.*

How to go about it

Starting babies on solids is messy and time-consuming, particularly if you prepare separate meals for them. One school of thought advocates feeding babies from their parents' plates. This is certainly relatively easy and has the advantages of showing them that the food is palatable and of getting them used to eating with others. On the other hand, babies need a high-calorie diet, including fats. The high-fibre, low-fat diet of some adults is therefore unsuitable (for example, fibre can affect a baby's ability to absorb nutrients). Also there are types of food which are advised against before nine months to a year (see below).

Because the idea is to teach the baby to chew, solids should not be offered from a bottle but with a spoon or clean fingers.

EQUIPMENT FOR FEEDING
(Details of high chairs are covered in chapter 3.02 Baby equipment.)

Types of bib:

Terry towelling: the larger the better – best with a Velcro fastening. They tend to stain but are very suitable for catching early baby dribble and possets, and can be hot washed.

Plastic backed: as above but they can't be hot washed, so are more prone to stains.

Plastic with arm slots: ideally including a front pocket to catch spilt food, these can be sponged down after each use. Again the larger the better.

Full length sleeves: all of the above are available with full-length sleeves, which are more expensive but save enormously on laundry.

Pelican bib: hard plastic with a front lip to catch spilt food. They have no arm cover, look a mite uncomfortable, but are otherwise very practical. Unsuitable for young babies. A new variant is made with a more comfortable cotton 'body' attached to the plastic lip.

Napkin clips: transform a normal napkin into a bib (although usually a small knot will do the same).

Unless you go for the hard plastic variety, about half-a-dozen bibs is ideal. If you want to use the hard ones, you should probably start early as slightly older babies don't seem to adapt well to them.

Other handy items:

Small electric mixers: easier than the sieve and wooden spoon method, an electric hand blender can be very useful for producing purees.

An ice cube tray: so that you can cook extra food in advance and defrost it in the tiny quantities that most babies consume when they start on solids.

Plastic spoons: because they don't hold heat from hot food. You can also get angled ones that help babies feed themselves. However, some are better designed than others.

Drinking cups: children differ in what they like. Some go straight from bottle to open cup, though this is often messy. Others will graduate to a soft spouted cup. Many parents swear by hard spout cups that prevent spills. Those with seals on the spout are particularly handy for when out and about. Leak-proof spouts prevent children from experimenting with liquid pouring, but may take time for some children to master.

Plates and bowls: options include dishes with suction bases, with lips to aid the scooping of food, dishes manufactured from heat sensitive materials (that change colour if the food is too hot), and, of course, dishes with pretty pictures to be discovered when all the food has been eaten up.

USEFUL CONTACTS

The Ellie Nappy Company
PO Box 16, Ellesmere Port Cheshire CH66 2HA ☎ *(0151) 200 5012*
⌨ *www.elliepants.co.uk*
Stockists of magic mats for high chairs which help stop utensils sliding around. / HOURS
Mon-Fri 8am-8pm, Sat 8am-1pm; 24hr answerphone; SEE ALSO 3.04 Baby clothes; 3.08 Nappies.

Miriam Stoppard Lifetime
Greencoat House, Francis St London SW1P 1DH ☎ *(020) 7630 1400*
⌨ *www.miriamstoppard.com*
Funky looking Always Learning feeding items (with different colours and textures) –
available through Boots. / HOURS *Mon-Fri 9am-6pm; SEE ALSO 3.04 Baby clothes; 3.06 Toys.*

Tommee Tippee
Jackel International, Dudley Lane, Cramlington Northumberland NE23 7RH ☎ *Helpline*
(0500) 979899
Feeding equipment including plastic bowls, plates and cutlery (some of which change
colour above a certain temperature). / HOURS *Mon-Thu 9am-4.45pm, Fri 9am-2pm; SEE ALSO*
3.03 Nursery decor.

Tommee Tippee
Jackel International, Dudley Lane, Cramlington Northumberland NE23 7RH ☎ *Helpline*
(0500) 979899
The Pur range originating in France, includes clear silicone teats with a valve in the
base to allow a steady milk flow and reduce wind; a range of bottle styles, including
Nipper Grippers, in the shape of an elongated doughnut to allow better grip, and wider
mouthed, squat items for more convenience when out and about. A disposable system
consists of sterilised bags which can be fitted into plastic bottles which are closed with
teat and lid. Accessories include a microwaver sterilising tray and bottle brushes.
/ HOURS *Mon-Thu 9am-4.45pm, Fri 9am-2pm; SEE ALSO 3.03 Nursery decor.*

V&A Marketing
Charlesworth House, Andrews Rd, Llandaff North Cardiff CF14 2JP ☎ *(029) 2057 5600*
⌨ *www.tuff-n-tumble.com*
Manufacturers of the Anywayup Cup – a modern design classic brand of feeding cup
(over 10 million sold in the last decade). It's easy to hold and – thanks to a patented
valve – will not leak other than when sucked on by a child; different designs for

children at 6, 9 and 12 months; from £3. Other products include 'Easy Eaters' products for spill-proof mealtimes; plates, bowls, cutlery and bibs. / *HOURS Mon-Fri 9am-5pm; SEE ALSO ; 3.04 Baby clothes; 3.08 Nappies.*

What to feed babies

(For information on allergies, see chapter 2.03 Baby health.)

Because babies can only eat small amounts of food it is particularly important that what you give offers good nutritional value. However, as with recommendations on what you can and cannot eat during pregnancy, the goalposts are constantly moving and, as with most nutrition, every individual has different needs.

The following are some current pointers but, as ever, the best advice is to do as you see fit. From 12 months, you can feed your child pretty much anything, within reason, unless there is a family history of diet-related problems.

Recommendations from the COMA Working Group on the Weaning Diet (note, COMA was the forebear of the Scientific Advisory Commission on Nutrition – an advisory body to the Department of Health):

Salt: avoid all salt, as it can put undue strain on the baby's kidneys (and – not in the report – salt intake as an infant is thought by some experts to cause higher blood pressure in later life). Processed foods are generally very high in salt, and should be treated with caution. If you do use salt in cooking some complementary practitioners recommend the use of sea salt.

Non-milk extrinsic sugars: avoid all sugars except the natural ones in milk or uncrushed fruit until the baby is six to seven months old. Sugars on the blacklist include: from fruit juices; in rusks; and in a large number of baby drinks. As well as tooth decay and being implicated in gut problems and even depressions of the immune system – the logic being that a baby's system has to make a disproportionate effort to produce insulin to handle sugar highs and lows – early exposure to sugar can cause problems by creating a lasting taste for sweet things. Words to look out for on lists of ingredients include sucrose, glucose, dextrose, syrup, honey or any other word ending in -ose (other than, of course, lactose), plus weasel descriptions like "evaporated cane juice". Products stating 'no added sugar' may still contain natural sugars such as those from fruit juices and hydrolysed starch that also cause tooth decay. The British Association of Tooth Friendly Sweets (BATS) has a logo of an umbrella over a tooth indicating that the contents of the pack should be safe for teeth, though there has been controversy over the quality of this blessing. The official advice on giving anything sweet is to do so at meal times when the saliva is active in washing out the mouth.

Cereals containing gluten: avoid in babies under six months old as Coeliac disease (see chapter *2.03 Baby health*) may be triggered by eating gluten (found in wheat, oats, rye and barley.) According to COMA the problem 'commonly manifests itself during the weaning period'. There are also more controversial claims about a connection with allergies (see chapter *2.03 Baby health*).

Concerns have also been raised regarding the following:

➤ Nuts and seeds, particularly if there is a family history of allergy, as they can cause severe allergic reactions (see chapter *2.03 Baby health*).

➤ Eggs, a potential allergen, should be introduced into your child's diet with caution.

➤ Fruit (particularly citrus fruit) juices, being sugary and acidic, may cause nappy rash. Some sources suggest not giving fruit juices to babies under six months old, and even after then dilute one part juice to five parts water with no more than 170ml per day to the age of six. Citrus fruits, particularly oranges, do not agree with a number of babies.

➤ Fizzy drinks are blamed (in one report) for contributing to loss of appetite, poor weight gain and poor behaviour at meals. They are also well known to contribute to tooth decay, and therefore are better drunk in one go than sipped over a period of time.

➤ Saccharin-flavoured squashes should be well-diluted to avoid over-concentration of the sweetener.

➤ Honey contains bacterial spores which are harmless to adults but which can grow and produce toxins which could be harmful to a baby under 12 months old.

➤ Soft cheeses may contain listeria.

➤ Additives considered most likely to cause trouble include E210, E211, E220, E250, E251, E320, E321 and flavour enhancer E621. Some like Tartrazine (E102) have been found to deplete the body of zinc, potentially triggering hyperactivity. (Research by the Asthma and Allergy Research Centre on 277 three-year-olds indicated that removing artificial colourings and preservatives from children's diets results in improved concentration and better behaviour. Consumption of the same additives showed immediate behaviour problems in a quarter of the children studied.)

➤ Hot spicy foods.

➤ Mineral water containing more than 20mg of sodium per litre.

➤ Anything containing nitrites, most commonly found in processed meats – for example bacon and ham: these inhibit the carriage of oxygen in the blood. For this reason they are banned in food specifically for babies.

➤ Toxins of various kinds in fish, notably mercury. The Food Standards Agency now recommends that shark, swordfish and marlin for example be avoided by children under 16. There are also concerns over potential carcinogens in farmed fish including dye that may be implicated in damage to children's eyes. EU legislation is due to reduce the amount of dye permitted while some toxic chemicals, although still present in some cases, are now outlawed.

It is a good idea to introduce new foods one at a time in case there is any kind of adverse reaction.

Research has shown that babies do enjoy different tastes, although they have much subtler palates than adults so may be able to find interest where an adult cannot. Adding fresh herbs is an easy way of subtly changing the flavour of a baby's food.

Research has also indicated that children given family food from an early age, puréed if necessary, were less likely to have feeding problems later in life. Initial disgust is quite likely to change to liking if a food is offered at intervals of a few days.

USEFUL CONTACTS

(For organisations specifically concerned with organic food, see Section 7, Organic food below.)

The Active Birth Centre, ☎ *(020) 7281 6760*

🖰 *www.activebirthcentre.com*
Nutrition workshops covering (among other issues) how to wean your baby, and when. / HOURS *shop Mon-Fri 9.30am-6.30pm (Fri 4pm), Sat 10am-4pm.*

British Nutrition Foundation (BNF), ☎ (020) 7404 6504
⏱ www.nutrition.org.uk
An organisation working closely with DEFRA to promote knowledge of nutritional issues.

The Food Commission, ☎ (020) 7837 2250 ⏱ www.foodcomm.org.uk; www.parentsjury.org.uk
An organisation independent of the government and food industry, which campaigns for safer, healthier food for all and on specific issues such as irradiation, additives and pesticides; operates a Parents Jury which compiles parental comments and votes on good and bad foods marketed to children. / HOURS Mon-Fri 9.30am-5.30pm; PUBLICATIONS *Annual subscription, £22: quarterly magazine with updates on additives (eg, on excessive use of artificial sweeteners in children's drinks), baby food, genetic engineering, and pesticides; back issues £3.50; issue 48, Jan 2000 'Good for sales, bad for babies'.*

The Food Standards Agency, ☎ (0845) 606 0667
⏱ www.foodstandards.gov.uk/
The government agency responsible for monitoring food safety and standards, and supposed to offer consumer independent and balanced advice. The new consumer-focused website aims to be "a one-stop-shop for reliable nutritional and health information". / HOURS *Helpline 9am-5pm;* PUBLICATIONS *Inherent Natural Toxicants in our Food, paper no. 51 £14.99.*

Pesticide Action Network UK (PEX Action on Pesticide Exposure), ☎ (020) 7274 8895, (020) 7274 6611 ⏱ www.pan-uk.org
A non-profit action group working to eliminate the hazards of pesticides and promote sustainable alternatives with regular coverage of issues relating to pregnancy and babies in the organisation's journal. / PUBLICATIONS *Publishes Pesticide News covers pesticide problems and alternatives in the UK, European and worldwide (https://secure.virtuality.net/panukcom/subs.htm) £20 a year with three free issues for new subscribers. Also free on-line pesticide information update service. .*

SUSTAIN, ☎ (020) 7837 1228 ⏱ www.sustainweb.org
The result of a merger between the National Food Alliance and the Safe Alliance, an organisation which publishes a newsletter with round-ups of news relating to health and food issues.

The Vegan Society, ☎ (01424) 427393 ⏱ www.vegansociety.com
The society can advise on providing a vegan diet for babies. / PUBLICATIONS *'A Practical Guide to Veganism During Pregnancy & Throughout Childhood', £1.50; 'Pregnancy, Children & the Vegan Diet' by Dr Michael Kalper, £7.95.*

Vegetarian Baby and Child, ⏱ www.vegetarianbaby.com
A nicely presented US online magazine, offering lots of free advice and information.

The Vegetarian Society, ☎ (0161) 928 0793 ⏱ www.vegsoc.org
An information officer can help with advice on vegetarian diets for women who are breast-feeding, and for children during weaning and thereafter. / PUBLICATIONS *Free information sheets: weaning vegetarian babies; pregnancy; vegetarian nutrition for children.*

HEALTHY EATING

Boost Your Child's Immune System ★ – Lucy Burney (What you need to know about allergies, vaccinations, antibiotics and diet, including over 160 recipes; Piatkus; 2001; £10.99; 0-7499-2114-5) – *By a nutrition consultant and children's health specialist (and parent of three), a guide with useful information on how a child's immune system works, an essential diet, and an A-Z guide to beneficial foods. Liquid requirements and foods to avoid are among other topics covered. The author's web site www.lucyburney.com provides further up-to-date information and a forum for discussing particular concerns and issues.*

Dump the Junk! – Mary Whiting (The book of over 300 tips that encourage children to eat healthy food; Moonscape Ltd; 2002; £7.99; 0-9544324-0-1) – *The sooner you start the better for your children – that's the theme of this guide which aims to empower beleaguered parents. Chapters include: How to be in charge; How to get children to eat more vegetables; and How to deal with schools and nurseries. Numerous comments and practical contributions from parents are included. / Moonscape Ltd, Shaleshurst, Shalesbrook Lane, Forest Row RH18 5LS (01342) 825 845 www.moonscapebooks.com.*

[Posters] **Food Commission Posters** (£2.50 per poster) – *Four posters handy for the kitchen aimed at parents and carers – Children's Food; Additives; Reading Food Labels; GM Foods. / Food Commission 020 7837 2250; ourworld.compuserve.com/homepages/foodcomm/.*

The Food Our Children Eat – Joanna Blythman (How to get children to like good food; Fourth Estate; 2000; £7.99; 1841154776) – *The introduction to this book says: "This book is for people who have the gut reaction that, however ubiquitous and common it might have become, the typical children's diet is unacceptable: first, because it drastically limits children's food horizons, and second, because it deviates so much from any notion of good nutrition, that it stores up problems for their long-term health."* It has some sobering facts – chapters include 'The rot begins with those little jars', 'You Know Best' and 'Introducing the World of Food'.

Healthy Food for Kids – Bridget Swinney (Meadowbank; 1999; £6.95; 0881663360) – *Written by a nutritionist on cooking healthy meals and creating healthy attitudes to food.*

Readymade baby food

When in early 2004 Tony Blair floated the idea of regulating advertising of food aimed at children, the spotlight was turned yet again onto the quality of processed foods.

The Food Commission, an independent non-profit organisation campaigning for safe food, regularly produces reports on baby food. Its news is seldom good. Back in 1992 it reported on manufacturers marketing weaning foods to babies too young to digest them. In 1995 it was saying almost exactly the same things. 'It leaves only one defence for a baby: a vigilant parent'. A further Food Magazine investigation in January 2000, entitled 'Good for sales, bad for babies' again reported very little change and the conclusions of a May 2000 report for Which? were very similar.

Gluten and extrinsic sugars are highlighted as particular problem ingredients, even in 'savoury' dishes. The Commission's survey of leading brands (including Cow & Gate, Boots, Heinz and Farley's) found that, of more than 400 products examined, the majority failed on one or more counts to meet the recommendations of the COMA group. The Which? report found that a number of items for babies under six months contained gluten, an ingredient which should be avoided before that age.

Manufacturers were also criticised by the Commission for bulking out around 70% of the products on the market with low-nutrient starches and added water. EU legislation permits this practice, so 'meat-only' dishes, for example, can contain 60% non-meat fillers and 'mainly meat' dishes can contain 90% non-meat fillers.

There is further concern that in some instances food may be cooked up to four times, severely diminishing its nutritional value. Boosting the calorie content with fat or oil is permitted. Label claims such as 'wholesome', 'nutritious' and 'natural goodness' are meaningless.

From 2002 some pesticides have been banned for use on crops destined for use in babyfood. Some parents, though, still prefer to go organic on account of the many pesticides that are are still permitted to be used.

By law artificial colours and preservatives are not allowed in baby foods, though they are common in processed food products aimed at older children. MSG for example is reported by Susan Clarke (author of *What Really Works for Kids*) to act as a neuro toxin in the brain.

Before feeding a jar of baby food to your child, it's no bad idea to taste a bit of it. Some well-known brands deliver insipid flavours and queasy-making textures, whereas others manage to be much more consistently appetising. On the other hand be aware that children can find interest where adults do not. They have almost three times as many tastebuds and much more interest in texture than older eaters. And while adult palates may expect salt and sugar, babies' don't.

Preparing it for yourself

Fresh food is of course generally preferable to that which has to be pre-served, offering elements like enzymes and amino acids that are only incorporated with difficulty in pre-processed foods. Even if you are no great whiz at the stove, there is still much you can do in the way of simple food preparation and, in addition to the nutritional bonus, and it is con-siderably cheaper than buying pre-prepared food. Puréed cooked vegetables and stewed fruit are simple and easy to make, and – stored in the freezer in ice cube trays – make excellent building blocks for meals.

Within a month or two, babies are ready to move on to more chal-lenging fare. If you are already a competent cook you will probably be perfectly able to cook for your child without a specialist cookbook. However, the recipe books listed below may give you ideas if you feel you are running short on inspiration, or try a cookery course. (Note though, if you have a fussy child, cooking a lot of special food that just gets rejected can cause more irritation than it's worth). Cooking meals for the whole family without salt and sugar, and then adding them after you've removed a baby portion for liquidising, is one effort-saving strategy.

Avoiding Problems

According to some sources, a third of children have mild to moderate eating problems by the time they are five, and seven in 10 babies have an eating problem that continues to the age of four – for example selective eating only.

A child psychiatrist specialising in eating disorders recommends ignor-ing the behaviour rather than rewarding it with attention, while another expert in the field likens the problem to bed wetting – fine in a toddler but not when a child is older.

The best cure seems to be prevention. Research in Philadelphia showed that children exposed to specific flavours either before birth or in breast-milk favoured those foods when they started eating for them-selves. So a mother who eats well and widely should, with any luck, have a child who does the same.

COURSES

Eileen Fairbane
London NW2 ☎ *(020) 8450 2470, mobile 07956 553924*
Hale Clinic aromatherapist, who also runs 'detoxification' cookery courses specialising in wheat-free, diary-free and sugar-free cookery. / *HOURS Phone for details; SEE ALSO 4.02 Health practitioners.*

Marilyn Kaye
Stanmore Middlesex ☎ *(020) 8954 2222*
Nutritionist who – in the Stanmore and Hampstead Garden Suburb areas – provides 'Quick Solutions' sessions for individuals or groups, which show you how to throw together nutritious food quickly; £30 for an hour and a half to two hours (divided between the group). Member of the Association of Physical and Natural Therapists. / *HOURS answerphone; SEE ALSO 2.01 Postnatal.*

Penrhos Court
Kington Herefordshire HR5 2LH ☎ *(01544) 230720* ⏚ *www.greencuisine.org*
A hotel in Herefordshire offering courses (two days full-board £200) in organic meat-free cooking suited to babies (and also in pregnancy), as well as yoga and baby massage. / *SEE ALSO 1.02 Looking after yourself.*

READING

Annabel Karmel Baby & Toddler Meal Planner – Annabel Karmel (Over 200 quick, easy and healthy recipes; Ebury; revised 2001; £12.99; 0091880882) – *Ten-year old best-selling title, whose author now has a stable of similar titles; if your level of cooking is such that you can't effortlessly make a roux, you wont find all the recipes 'quick and easy'.*

Baby and Child Vegetarian Recipes – Carol Timperly (Ebury; 1997; £10.99; 0091853001) – *More than 150 meat-free recipes (checked by a nutritionist) that are not too time-consuming; also menu charts, and description of the stages of development in a child's eating.*

Cooking for Coco – Sian Blunos (Naturally delicious babyfood recipes from a chef's kitchen; Carroll and Brown; £12; 1-903258-70-7) – *A trained chef (and wife of Michelin-starred chef Martin Blunos), provides recipes parents could eat too – say meatballs in tangy tomato sauce, with warm mango and cardomon puree, and semolina pudding with caramelised bananas. Most can be cooked in advance and frozen. Also outline pointers on weaning issues.*

Eat Up – Mark Hix with Suzi Godson (Food for children of all ages; Fourth Estate; 2000; £16.99; 1841161475) – *A glossy tome from a London chef (The Ivy, Le Caprice and J Sheekey) with children; around half the ideas are suitable for babies but basically these are nursery food recipes for all the family.*

Food Boosters for Kids – Amanda Cross (Hamlyn; 2002; £14.99; 0600604209) – *Main meals to snacks to juices and smoothies. The guide includes suggestions for boosting the immune system, for convalescents, to encourage a good night's sleep and so on. / www.hamlyn.co.uk.*

The Food Doctor for Babies and Children – Vicki Edgson (Nutritious Food for healthy Development; Collins and Brown; £14.99; 1843400006) – *A child health nutritionist gives advice on the food and nutrients that children need for optimal health, energy, immunity, brain growth and healthy bones. Identifies food allergies and intolerances, includes recipes and meal planers, including first foods, family meals and easy options, and addresses the issue of children who are fussy eaters.*

Good Food for Kids – Dr Penny Stanway (Hamlyn; 2000; £14.99; 0-600600-79-3) – *From the author of 'Breast is best', dinners for children from six months up. It includes advice on the creation of a balanced diet, weaning, foods for common ailments and allergies, as well as a range of recipes. / (0600) 600 793.*

Healthy Eating for Babies & Toddlers – Anne Sheasby, Jill Scott & Mark Buckingham (Illustrator) (Colour Library Books; 1998; £9.99; 1858333997) – *A guide to recipes and menus for children from weaning to five years old; includes over 100 recipes.*

How to Eat – Nigella Lawson (The pleasures and principles of good food; Chatto and Windus; 1999; £17.50; 0-701169-11-7) – *The domestic goddess's tome includes sensible writing on the subject of feeding babies and children, including some recipes.*

Little Red Gooseberries – Daphne Lambert (Organic recipes from Penrhos; Orion Trade; 2001; £16.99; 0-752838-44-X) – *A collection of recipes from 'the UK's leading organic country house hotel & restaurant'. / www.greencuisine.org.*

NCT First Foods and Weaning – Ravinder Lilly (Thorsons; 2002; £6.99; 0-00-713607-2) – *Easy recipes for a range of suitable dishes plus timesaving tips. / NCT Maternity Sales (0870) 112 1120; www.nctms.co.uk.*

Nursery Food Book – Mary Whiting & Tim Lobstein (Arnold; 1998; £13.50; 0-340718-94-3) – *Written by two Food Commission staff (both specialists in related fields) – an invaluable teaching text for nannies and nursery nurses, this book is also a useful tool for parents of children spending lots of time in childcare. It covers healthy nutrition, nursery provision, special diet and multicultural provision, food-related activities and recipes.*

The Organic Baby and Toddler Cookbook – Daphne Lamber & Tanyia Maxted-Frost (Green Books; 2000; £6.95; 1-870098-79-X) – *From weaning to three years, with the emphasis on seasonal, raw or lightly-cooked wholefoods; it includes juice recipes for babies and breast-feeding mothers, blender salads, and toddler savouries.*

Planet Organic Baby & Toddler Cookbook – Lizzie Vann (Dorling Kindersley; 2000; £9.99; 0-751329-07-X) – *One of the most popular titles on the subject, by the founder of Baby Organix. Includes the Top 10 'superfoods' for each age group, foods for common ailments and a collection of recipes, with nutritional details of each meal.*

Superfoods for Children – Michael van Straten & Barbara Griggs (Books your child's health and brain power with over 120 nutrient-packed superfoods; Dorling Kindersley; 2001; £9.99; 0-7513-1264-9) – *Not just a recipe book, but also a look at what foods are best for your kids; with its simple ideas, it's useful if you aren't really into cooking, but want to ensure your kids are eating well.*

6. DRINK

Partly in order to discourage a taste for sweeter flavours and partly to protect baby teeth, water and milk are generally recommended as the main drinks for a baby either in the first six months or the first year, different health professionals taking different views. Baby blackcurrant drinks, fruit juices and herbal drinks with added sugar also generally contain acid which contributes further to tooth decay. Juice, if given, should therefore be heavily diluted. Suggested proportions range from one part juice to five or even 10 parts of water, and should not exceed 170ml per day.

The teats and spouts used at this age deliver liquid to parts of the mouth where they cause more tooth decay than if drunk adult style. For this reason the COMA report on feeding young children recommended using a cup if you choose to give anything other than water or milk. You should particularly avoid giving alternatives to these between meals when there is less saliva to protect the teeth. Later on fizzy drinks are implicated in osteoporosis in girls.

7. HOME FOOD SHOPPING

Immediately after having a baby, getting out and about can seem rather difficult. Indeed, even after that, if your toddler is of the variety who won't stay in the supermarket trolley or is given to escape stunts, having food, nappies and so on delivered can seem like an eminently sensible luxury.

There are two main varieties of home delivery services. These are: order services, where you phone, fax or e-mail your order from their list (supplied either in catalogue form or online); and box schemes which, for a set price, supply a range of goods, chosen by the supplier from what is currently best priced at market (usually seasonal goods). With the latter schemes in particular, value for money varies widely from supplier to supplier so check carefully what you can expect to receive before committing to more than a sample order.

Organic home shopping services, box schemes and mail order companies are listed in the Organic food section, below.

SUPPLIERS
Ady's Catering
☎ (020) 7794 4580
Party caterer – also available to fill the freezer for before/after the baby arrives.

The Food Ferry
B24-B27 New Covent Garden Market, Nine Elms Lane London SW8 5HH ☎ *(020) 7498 0827* ◌ *www.foodferry.com*
Not the cheapest but one of the better-quality home delivery services with a range of 2,400 supermarket (and some deli'-style) items, with a list of 600 best-selling items to help with ordering. Your first order is free of delivery charges. Same day deliveries may be available on orders placed before 10.15am. Minimum order £20. / *HOURS Mon-Fri 8am-8pm, Sat 9am-2pm.*

Food Glorious Food
16 Fentiman Rd London SW8 1LF ☎ *(020) 7582 9947*
Readymade meal supplier, specialising in 'Emergency rescue packs' – meals for the first weeks of motherhood, all freshly-made to order, labelled with cooking instructions (some suitable for freezing). The company can also stock your fridge for when you arrive home from hospital, with basics (including "that long-awaited piece of blue cheese"). Eight main course meals, £95.

Goodness Direct
South March, Daventry Northants NN11 4PH ☎ *(0871) 871 6611* ◌ *www.GoodnessDirect.co.uk*
Specialist website supplier also offering health and news features, eco-friendly cleaning

materials and fair trade products – stocks over 3,000 products including organic baby foods, non cow's milk infant formulas, gluten-free foods and foods for those with allergies. / *SEE ALSO 4.02 Health practitioners.*

Nappy Express
128 High Rd London N11 1PG ☎ *(020) 8361 4040* ⌂ *www.nappyexpress.co.uk*
Cover most London postcodes and deliver between two and five times a week (Mon-Fri). The company specialises in baby foods (excluding fresh foods) and does an organic range which they are constantly expanding. Some books, puzzles, videos, decorative items and household goods – from cleaning liquids to drinks (standard brands) – are also sold. / *HOURS Mon-Fri 9.30am-5.30pm.*

Ocado
☎ *(0845) 399 1122* ⌂ *www.ocado.com*
Launched in partnership with Waitrose, this fast growing online delivery service ("Be more Demanding") covers most of greater London and the south east (and now also part of the Midlands). They offer Waitrose-quality groceries and the convenience of one-hour delivery slots. The range includes a good array of organic baby foods.

Sainsbury's
General enquiries ☎ *(0800) 636262, Orderline (0845) 301 2020*
The home shopping service, Sainsbury's To You, operates across most of London. You place your order online – anything from the store can be delivered (including toys, etc) – and it is delivered to you at a charge of £5. / *HOURS mostly 8am-8pm, Sun 10am-4pm.*

Somerfield
General enquiries ☎ *(0117) 935 9359*
Register for a 'Home Delivery Card' and – at larger stores – it enables you to shop as normal, and then have all your purchases packed and delivered free (if your shop is over £25, for a £3 charge if not); if you're outside the designated area for home delivery, delivery may still be possible at a £5 surcharge. / *HOURS mostly 8am-8pm.*

Tesco
☎ *General enquiries (0800) 505555, home shopping (08457) 225533*
Tesco Direct: Freepost SCO652 DD1 9XW
☎ *(08457) 024024, (08457) 031031*
Home food shopping now covers about 96% of the UK; orders are placed over the Internet, and delivered for a charge that varies from £3.99 to £5.99 depending on which day you pick. / *SEE ALSO 3.01 Maternity wear; 3.04 Baby clothes; 3.06 Toys.*

Waitrose
General enquiries
☎ *Customer service (01344) 424680*
98-101 Marylebone High St W1M 4DD
☎ *(020) 7935 4787*
196 Kings Rd SW3 5XP
☎ *(020) 7351 2775*
2 Alexandria Rd W13 0NL
☎ *(020) 8579 3379*
Gloucester Arcade, 128 Gloucester Rd SW7 4SF
☎ *(020) 7370 2424*
1305 High Rd N20 9HX
☎ *(020) 8446 0323*
199 Finchley Rd NW3 6NN
☎ *(020) 7624 0453*
273 Ballards Lane N12 8NR
☎ *(0800) 188 884 (020) 8343 7303*
32-39 Temple Fortune Parade NW11 0QS
☎ *(020) 8458 6645*
366 Holloway Rd N7 6PA
☎ *(020) 7700 3717*
Brent Cross Shopping Centre, Hendon Way NW4 3FQ
☎ *(020) 8203 9711*
292 Upper Richmond Rd West SW14 7JG
☎ *(020) 8878 4792*
Putney Exchange Shopping Centre, High St SW15 1TW
☎ *(020) 8246 6848*
The home delivery service is offered by most stores in London, though to a limited range of postcodes; go to a store, book a time for delivery (available all day, including evenings, six days a week) and do your shopping, and it will be delivered to your door. Free for orders over £25, £3 charge otherwise. One of the best supermarkets for organic produce – over 500 items.

8. ORGANIC FOOD

Despite its cost, an increasing number of parents choose to feed their children organic food due to ever more regular food scares. Organic products are now reported to make up to 15% of the market.

The residual level of pesticides in food is one common concern. Manufactured baby food is generally no better on this score than factory-made food for adults – a survey in the States in the '90s apparently found 16 different pesticides in the eight main baby food brands.

Where such toxins are concerned, the official 'acceptable' level for consumption is calculated on the intake of a ten-stone adult. Therefore, in some circumstances, babies and toddlers ingest a much higher proportion of toxins for their bodyweight than is acceptable in an adult.

Note that products marked as being organic may not be entirely so. Those certified as organic must be at least 95% so. Products marked 'including organic products' must be at least 75% organic. Note too that ingredients may be imported from countries with rather laxer rules about what constitutes organic, notably the US.

The question of whether organic food is 'better' than non-organic food, or is becoming just another way supermarkets can achieve premium pricing, has become very contentious. Given the growing lack of confidence in factory farming, however, there seems no doubt that organic produce is set to take a growing market share, especially of food fed to children.

READING

The New Shoppers' Guide to Organic Food – Lynda Brown (Fourth Estate; 1998; £8.99; 1-857028-40-6) – *Well-regarded guide with details of shops, box schemes, farm suppliers and so on.*

The Organic Baby Book – Tanya Maxted-Frost (Green Books; 2003; £7.95; 1903998212) – *Reasons for going organic, plus a lot of practical information on products, suppliers, breast-feeding, etc; how to 'green' your home. / www.greenbooks.co.uk.*

The Organic Directory – Clive Litchfield (Green Earth Books; 2000; £7.95; 1-870098-84-6) – *Listings of close to 1,000 suppliers across the UK (including smaller suppliers in London) of food and other organic produce, together with background information. Produced in conjunction with the Soil Association; also lists restaurants and accommodation. NB NEW EDITION DUE 2002/3*

USEFUL CONTACTS

Department for Environment, Food & Rural Affairs (DEFRA), ☎ (020) 7238 5915 ⊕ www.defra.gov.uk/farm/organic/
Government department (fka MAFF) responsible for organic standards in the UK. It is the authorising body for organic certification and award the right to use 'organically certified' symbols, working through the main organic standards organisations, which include The Soil Association (see also); see the website for the other organisations. / HOURS 9am-5pm.

Henry Doubleday Research Association (HDRA), ☎ (02476) 3035171 ⊕ www.hdra.org.uk
One of the largest organic organisations in Europe, promoting organic gardening. / HOURS open all week.

Links Organic, ☎ (020) 7590 9272 ⊕ www.linksorganic.com
An online directory of more than 2,200 organic businesses and organisations, including home delivery services, retailers, manufacturers and organic farmers.

The Soil Association, ☎ (0117) 929 0661 ⊕ www.soilassociation.org
One of the main organisations which supervises the standards for organic produce in the UK, promotes organic farming and food, organises relevant campaigns (GMOs, antibiotic use, etc) and runs an accreditation system. Over 6000 members (individual membership £18; family £25). / PUBLICATIONS Living Earth magazine; guides to organic shopping.

Organic meat

Concerns following the BSE crisis have made many parents much more
interested in organic meat. (See below for suppliers.)

The Soil Association (see above) is the organisation responsible for
accrediting organically raised meat in the UK. The association banned
feeding of all animal proteins to cattle and sheep as early as 1983. It continues to impose stringent requirements on meat that it labels as organic.

Although not yet in the spotlight, non-organic poultry may soon
become a cause for public concern. The use of antibiotics in feedstuffs – a
practice which may have led to a rise in resistance to antibiotics – is one
issue that has already caught the attention of regulators.

Regulations are making it more difficult to slaughter animals on site.
Ideally organic meat is butchered at an organic-only or mobile abattoir.
Where this is not possible, to prevent contamination, meat sold as organic
must only be slaughtered in slaughterhouses registered with the Soil
Association. Requirements include a separate slaughter line, slaughtering at a time separate from non-organic animals, washing down after
slaughtering of non-organic meat and a separate storage area for organic
meat.

Note that, despite the widespread concerns about the use of nitrates,
these are still permitted additives in organic meat.

It is also worth remembering that organic baby foods, like non-organ-
ics, can be bulked out with cheaper (albeit organic) ingredients such as
rice starch and with sugars which can be added in the guise of apple or
pear juice concentrate.

Shopping

In addition to the shops and brands listed below, big-name brands and
supermarkets are increasingly moving towards producing and selling
organic goods, produce and groceries.

ORGANIC BABY FOOD BRANDS
Baby Organix

Organix Brands Plc, Freepost BH1 336, Christchurch, Dorset Dorset BH23 2LU
☎ Customer line and mail order (0800) 393511, (01202) 479701
🖰 www.babyorganix.co.uk
Founded in 1992 – one of the two largest baby organic food companies in the UK,
known particularly for its cereals, but also producing ready-made meals in jars, plus

bread sticks, pasta shapes, rice cakes and dried fruit. The helpline can provide details of stockists (which include all the big supermarkets), or you can order everything, except the jars, direct. Full labelling information for all the company's products can be found on the website, which claims that Baby Organix never adds processed sugars, salt, thickeners, processing aids and unnecessary fillers to its baby foods. / *HOURS Mon-Fri 8.30am-5.30pm.*

Beechnut
♨ www.beechnut.com
A highly respected US range found in health food and organic food shops.

Boots
General enquiries
☎ *Customer services (08450) 708090*
Organic Mother's Recipe range. / *SEE ALSO 2.03 Baby health; 2.05 Travel; 3.01 Maternity wear; 3.02 Baby equipment; 3.04 Baby clothes; 3.05 Shoes; 3.06 Toys; 3.08 Nappies; 4.02 Health practitioners.*

Community Foods
Micross, Brent Terrace London NW2 1LT ☎ (020) 8450 9411
♨ www.communityfoods.co.uk
Dried fruit, nuts, pulses and more – contract grown and mostly organic. No direct consumer service.

Fresh Daisy Organic Babyfood
Meadow Green, PO Box 34483, Hammersmith London W6 8XF ☎ (0870) 240 7028
♨ www.daisyfoods.com
Organic, frozen and chilled babyfoods, designed to retain natural taste, colour and nutrition, and made without salt, sugar or preservatives. Ingredients include peach, plus and vanilla, squash and red lentil, or potato, parsnip and pear. Most come from Eostre Organics, an East Anglian fair trade farming co-op. The website lists stockists, or you can order online.

Green & Organic
Unit 2, Blacknest Industrial Estate, Blacknest Rd, Blacknest, nr Alton Hampshire GU34 4PX ☎ (0871) 425 2405 ♨ www.greenandorganic.co.uk
Importer of a range of organic foods including the Biobambini range from Germany (the first company to make organic baby food in the 1950s). Stocks around 2,500 products. Ring for details of stockists or mail order. / *HOURS office Mon-Fri 9am-5pm, shop Wed-Fri 10am-4pm; SEE ALSO 3.08 Nappies.*

Heinz
♨ www.tinytums.co.uk
Proof positive that organic food has joined the mainstream: the firm's organic jars increasingly seem as familiar as the traditional Heinz range.

HIPP
165 Main St, New Greenham Park Berks RG19 6HN ☎ (0845) 050 1351
Widely stocked organic brand (one of the UK's two largest) – known particularly for its jars, and fruit juices, though they now also have bags of dried foods. / *HOURS Mon-Fri 9am-5pm.*

Miniscoff
☎ (07798) 526090 ♨ www.miniscoff.co.uk
Frozen ready meals for toddlers; sold by outlets that include Planet Organic and the Bluebird food market; options include minced organic beef Old MacDonald's Pie; lamb with apricots, orchard chicken, pork cannonballs, and a 'Munch of the Month'; call or see the website for other stockists.

Organico
☎ (0118) 951 0518 ♨ www.organico.co.uk
French organic fruit and vegetable meals, infant cereals and teething biscuits; trial tin delivery service available.

pots for tots
Unit WHE 112, The Wandsworth Business Village, 3-9 Broomhill Road London SW18 4JQ ☎ (0845) 450 0875 ♨ www.potsfortots.co.uk
Soil Association approved, 100% organic food for babies and toddlers that can be eaten cold, reheated and frozen within its sell by date. There's a broad range of dishes, some gluten, milk and lactose free. Check out the website for stockists, or order online.

Simply Organic
21 Dryden Vale Boston Glen EH20 9HN ☎ (0131) 448 0440
♨ www.simplyorganic.co.uk
Manufacturer of Original Fresh Babyfood Company branded products (as well as soups and pasta sauces) available in Tesco throughout the UK and also in local food shops, health stores and delicatessens.

Truuuly Scrumptious
Unit 2, Charmborough Farm, Charlton Road, Holcombe Radstock BA3 5EX ☎ *(01761)*
239 300 🖃 *www.bathorganicbabyfood.co.uk*
A company set up by a Norland nanny and a specialist in food marketing sciences.
Frozen organic baby meals, without added sugar or salt, in recipes selected for
nutritional value. There is a range of sweet and savoury options from 4, 6 and 12
months. Deliveries in London and Bath, and available through some health food shops.

Suppliers

As with the shopping directory (see *chapter 3.14*) a mailbox symbol indicates
a supplier who will sell by mail order.

The listings are divided as follows:
➢ Organic suppliers
➢ Organic butchers

ORGANIC SUPPLIERS

CENTRAL

Alara Wholefoods
58-60 Marchmont St WC1N 1AB ☎ *(020) 7837 1172*
Organic fruit and vegetables, dry goods, baby foods. Also Solgar supplements,
and vitamin products. / HOURS *Mon-Fri 9am-6pm, Sat 10am-5pm.*

Fresh & Wild
🖃 *www.freshandwild.com*
BRANCHES AT:
  69-75 Brewer St W1R 3FL ☎ *(020) 7434 3179*
Wholefood organic stores with groceries, breads, ready meals, wines and beers; also
complementary healthcare, baby foods and baby products. Some branches also have
delis and juice bars. / HOURS *Mon-Fri 7.30am-10.30pm, Sat 8.30am-10.30pm, Sun 11.30am-8.30pm;*
SEE ALSO 0 .

GNC

☎ *(01483) 410600, 02476 244 400* 🖃 *www.gnc.co.uk*
BRANCHES AT:
  104 Marylebone High St W1U 4RR ☎ *(020) 7935 8412*
  The Plaza, Oxford St W1D 1LT ☎ *(020) 7323 1990*
  Unit G14, West One Centre, Oxford St W1C 2JS ☎ *(020) 7629 8535*
An American vitamin and mineral supplement franchise: most shops stock a selection
of organic products including goat's milk formula. / SEE ALSO 0 .

Neal's Yard Bakery
2 Neal's Yard WC2H 9DP ☎ *(020) 7836 5199*
Organic breads, biscuits, cakes and fruit bars. (Many products also available from Fresh
& Wild and Planet Organic.) / HOURS *Mon-Sat 10.30am-5pm.*

Planet Organic
BRANCHES AT:
  22 Torrington Place WC1A 7JE ☎ *(020) 7436 1929*
One-stop "natural food supermarkets", whose range includes organic fruit, vegetables,
meat, fish, groceries, dairy products, cheese, wine, frozen goods, take-away snacks,
supplements and confectionery with natural sweeteners. / HOURS *Mon-Fri 10am-8pm, Sat &*
Sun noon-6pm; SEE ALSO 0 .

Revital Health Food Store
(0800) 252875 🖃 *www.revital.com*
BRANCHES AT:
  3a The Colonnades, 123 Buckingham Palace Rd SW1 9RZ ☎ *(020) 7976 6615*
🖃 *www.revital.com*
If you're looking for a hard-to-find health product, it's worth checking out the website
linked to these two shops: it offers over 40,000 lines, neatly organised by brand
name. / HOURS *Mon-Fri 8.30am-7pm, Sat 9am-6pm; SEE ALSO 0 .*

Waitrose
☎ *Customer service (01344) 424680* 🖃 *www.waitrose.com*
BRANCHES AT:
  98-101 Marylebone High St W1M 4DD ☎ *(020) 7935 4787*
This supermarket whose range of organic produce is one of the best among the major
retailers, offers a home delivery service (some stores), internet shopping and a box
scheme. / HOURS *Mon-Sat 8.30am-9pm, Sun 11am-5pm; SEE ALSO 0 .*

WEST

As Nature Intended
201 Chiswick High Rd W4 2DR ☎ *(020) 8742 8838* ⌂ *www.asnatureintended.uk.com*
Wide-ranging organic supplier, offering fruit, vegetables, dairy, dry goods, ready meals,
natural remedies, baby foods and non-food household goods. / HOURS *Mon-Fri 9am-7pm,
Sat 9am-6pm, Sun 11am-5.30pm.*

Bushwacker Wholefoods
132 King St W6 0QU ☎ *(020) 8748 2061*
Organic baby food, fruit and vegetables, dry goods, dairy produce, complementary
health products and prenatal nutrients; also water filtration equipment. / HOURS *Mon-Sat
9.30am-6pm (Tue 10am).*

Food for Thought
154 High St Hounslow TW3 1LR ☎ *(020) 8572 0310*
Organic wholefoods. / HOURS *Mon-Sat 9am-5.30pm;* SEE ALSO *4.02 Health practitioners.*

Fresh & Wild
⌂ *www.freshandwild.com*
BRANCHES AT:
 210 Westbourne Grove W11 2RH ☎ *(020) 7229 1063*
See write-up in central.

The Fresh Food Co 🖰
The Orchard, 50 Wormholt Rd W12 0LS ☎ *(020) 8749 8778* ⌂ *www.freshfood.co.uk*
Nationwide home delivery service for organic fresh food (no dry goods): meat, fruit,
vegetable and confectionery, sold through a variety of box schemes. Nutritional and
culinary advice, as well as recipes, are given on the website, which lists over 4000
items. / HOURS *Mon-Fri 9am-5.30pm (Thu 7pm).*

The Grain Shop
269a Portobello Rd W11 1LR ☎ *(020) 7229 5571*
Veggie (non-organic) take-away, which is also an organic bakery, and stocks organic
baby food, vitamins, supplements and soya milk. / HOURS *Mon-Sat 9.30am-6pm.*

Health Foods
767 Fulham Rd SW6 5HA ☎ *(020) 7736 8848*
Health food shop with large organic selection (including Hipp, Babynat and Baby
Organix baby foods); also sells goat's formula milk, supplements, vitamins,
homeopathic remedies and babycare products (including teething
granules). / HOURS *Mon-Sat 9am-5.30pm.*

Here
Chelsea Farmers' Market, 125 Sydney St SW3 6NR ☎ *(020) 7351 4321*
New store offering a wide range of goods; free local delivery. / HOURS *Mon-Sat 9.30am-8pm,
Sun 10am-6.30pm.*

Luscious Organic
☎ *(020) 7262 9492*
BRANCHES AT:
 11 Fulham Broadway SW6 ☎ *(020) 7381 8010*
Stockists of Truuly Scrumptious baby food. The shops features juice bars, coffee bar,
groceries, and frozen food. / SEE ALSO *0 .*

The Organic Grocer
17 Clifton Rd W9 1SY ☎ *(020) 7286 1400*
Fruit, vegetables, dairy products, dry goods, and baby products (including Vitacare
goat's milk, Chow Baby fresh baby food, Yofu Junio and Vrai Bébé children's
desserts). / HOURS *Mon-Sat 9am-8pm, Sun 10am-8pm.*

Planet Organic 🖰
22 Torrington Place WC1E 7HJ ☎ *(020) 7727 2227*
BRANCHES AT:
 42 Westbourne Grove W2 5SH ☎ *(020) 7727 2227, Deliveries (020) 7221 1345*
See write-up in central.

Portobello Wholefoods
266 Portobello Rd W10 5TY ☎ *(020) 8968 9133*
Vegetarian (mainly organic) supplier of bread, fruit and vegetables, complementary
health products and baby foods. / HOURS *Mon-Sat 9.30am-6pm, Sun 11am-5pm.*

Sloane Health Clinic 🖰
27 Kings Rd SW3 4RT ☎ *(020) 7730 7046*
Organic foods, snacks and baby food, homeopathic remedies and essential oils; there's
a clinic downstairs. / HOURS *Mon-Fri 8.30am-7pm, Sat 9am-7pm;* SEE ALSO *4.02 Health practitioners.*

Stockwells Pharmacy & Natural Health Clinic
Stockwells Pharmacy, 75 New Broadway, Ealing W5 5DA ☎ *(020) 8567 0678*
The shop includes a wide range of organic baby food. Feeding information is also available. / *SEE ALSO 4.02 Health practitioners.*

Waitrose
☎ *Customer service (01344) 424680* ⌐ᵈ *www.waitrose.com*
BRANCHES AT:
  Gloucester Arcade, 128 Gloucester Rd SW7 4SF ☎ *(020) 7370 2424*
  196 Kings Rd SW3 5XP ☎ *(020) 7351 2775*
  2 Alexandria Rd W13 0NL ☎ *(020) 8579 3379*
See write-up in central.

NORTH

Alternatives Health Store
1369 High Rd N20 9LN ☎ *(020) 8445 2675* ⌐ᵈ *www.naturesalternative.co.uk*
Organic and diet foods and alternative treatment products. / *HOURS Mon-Sat 9am-6pm.*

Bumblebee 🔐
30 Brecknock Rd N7 0DD ☎ *(020) 7607 1936* ⌐ᵈ *www.bumblebee.co.uk*
Fruit (fresh and dried), vegetables, dairy products, baked and dry goods. Also organic baby foods. / *HOURS Mon-Sat 9.30am-6.30pm (Thu 7.30pm).*

Fresh & Wild
⌐ᵈ *www.freshandwild.com*
BRANCHES AT:
  49 Parkway NW1 5PN ☎ *(020) 7428 7575*
  32-34 Stoke Newington Church St N16 0LU ☎ *(020) 7254 2332*
See write-up in central.

GNC
☎ *(01483) 410600, 02476 244 400* ⌐ᵈ *www.gnc.co.uk*
BRANCHES AT:
  Bennet & Luck, 212 Upper St N1 1RL ☎ *(020) 7226 3422*
  243 Muswell Hill Broadway N10 1DE ☎ *(020) 8444 7717*
See write-up in central.

The Haelan Clinic
41 The Broadway N8 8DT ☎ *(020) 8340 1518* ⌐ᵈ *www.haelan.co.uk*
Wholefood store (mainly organic) selling fruit and vegetables, groceries and dairy produce; a complementary health clinic is attached. / *HOURS Mon-Fri 9am-6pm (Fri 6.30pm), Sun noon-4pm; SEE ALSO 4.02 Health practitioners.*

Hendon Health Food Centre
125 Brent St NW4 2DX ☎ *(020) 8202 9165*
Organic bread from South London Bakery Company plus baby food (including infant tea and vegetarian options), organic ice cream, goat's milk formula, vitamins and supplements. / *HOURS Mon-Fri 9am-6pm, Sat 10am-2pm.*

Just Natural
304 Park Rd N8 8LA ☎ *(020) 8340 1720*
Organic fruit and veg, dairy and dried goods; also Baby Organix and Hipp.

Just Organics 🔐
113 Wilberforce Rd N4 2SP ☎ *(020) 7704 2566*
Fruit and vegetable box scheme, offering 10 and 15 lb boxes of mixed fruit and vegetables; all evening deliveries, mainly to N, NW and E postcodes.

London Farmers' Markets
6 St Paul St N1 7AB ☎ *(020) 7704 9659* ⌐ᵈ *www.lfm.org.uk*
If you want to look the people who are producing your food in the eye, there's no substitute for patronising one of the growing range of farmers' markets, where all the produce is grown within 100 miles of the M25, and sold directly by the producer. Markets are usually open on Saturday or Sunday: visit the website for details of your nearest.

Mother Earth Organic Market
5 Albion Parade, Albion Rd N16 9LD ☎ *(020) 7275 9099*
Fruit, vegetables and dairy products; also baby food, nappies and other baby products, purified water, supplements and homeopathic remedies. / *HOURS Mon-Fri 9.30am-8pm, Sat 9.30am-7pm, Sun 11am-7pm.*

Natural Health
339 Ballards Lane N12 8LJ ☎ *(020) 8445 4397* ⏚ *www.naturesalternative.co.uk*
Health store and clinic, selling food supplements, aromatherapy oils, homeopathic remedies and the Weleda range of baby products. / HOURS *Mon-Sat 9am-5.30pm;* SEE ALSO *4.02 Health practitioners.*

The Olive Tree
84 Willesden Lane NW6 7TA ☎ *(020) 7328 9078*
Organic fruits, vegetables, wholefoods, supplements and herbal remedies; also baby foods and nappies. / HOURS *Mon-Sat 10am-6.30pm (Wed closing 1pm).*

Peppercorns
193-195 West End Lane NW6 1RD ☎ *(020) 7328 6874*
Wholefoods and baby foods. / HOURS *Mon-Sat 10am-7pm.*

Revital Health Food Store
☎ *(01895) 629950, (0800) 252875* ⏚ *www.revital.com*
BRANCHES AT:
  35 High Rd NW10 2TE ☎ *(020) 8459 3382, Mail order (0800) 252875*
⏚ *www.revital.com*
See write-up in central.

Temple Health Foods �’
17 Temple Fortune Parade NW11 0QS ☎ *(020) 8458 6087* ⏚ *www.templehealth.co.uk*
The wholefoods range of this shop includes some organic items, plus vitamins, supplements and baby food. / HOURS *Mon-Fri 9am-6pm, Sat 9am-5.30pm, Sun 10am-2pm.*

Victoria Healthfoods 🖒
23 The Broadwalk, Station Rd Edgware HA8 7PD ☎ *(020) 8905 6931*
⏚ *www.victoriahealthfoods.com*
Health food shop, stocking organic baby foods; also a range of supplements and toiletries. / HOURS *Mon-Sat 9am-6pm, Sun 10am-4pm.*

Waitrose
☎ *Customer service (01344) 424680* ⏚ *www.waitrose.com*
BRANCHES AT:
  Brent Cross Shopping Centre, Hendon Way NW4 3FQ ☎ *(020) 8203 9711*
  273 Ballards Lane N12 8NR ☎ *(0800) 188 884 (020) 8343 7303*
  366 Holloway Rd N7 6PA ☎ *(020) 7700 3717*
  199 Finchley Rd NW3 6NN ☎ *(020) 7624 0453*
  32-39 Temple Fortune Parade NW11 0QS ☎ *(020) 8458 6645*
  1305 High Rd N20 9HX ☎ *(020) 8446 0323*
See write-up in central.

SOUTH

Abel & Cole 🖒
Unit 8-13, MGI Estate, Milkwood Rd SE24 0JF ☎ *(020) 7737 3648*
⏚ *www.abel-cole.co.uk*
A general organic home delivery service. A box service is available – the range includes a weaning box. / HOURS *9am-5pm.*

G Baldwins & Co
171-173 Walworth Rd SE17 1RW ☎ *(020) 7701 4892, Mail order (020) 7703 5550*
⏚ *www.baldwins.co.uk*
General health food store stocking organic dry goods. / HOURS *Mon-Sat 9am-5.30pm;* SEE ALSO *4.02 Health practitioners.*

Balham Wholefood & Health Store
8 Bedford Hill SW12 9RG ☎ *(020) 8673 4842*
Suppliers of organic baby food, including 'Vitacare' goat's milk formula powder. / HOURS *Mon-Sat 9.30am-1.30pm & 2.30pm-6pm (Tue & Thu close 7pm).*

Borough Market
Borough High St SE1 ☎ *(020) 7407 1002* ⏚ *www.boroughmarket.org.uk*
Fast establishing itself as one of London's top foodie attractions, Borough Market offers a comprehensive range of produce, much of it free range or organic. / HOURS *Fri noon-6pm, Sat 9am-4pm.*

Brixton Whole Foods
59 Atlantic Rd SW9 8PU ☎ *(020) 7737 2210*
Vegetables; dry goods; bread; baby food and eco-friendly groceries (together with a selection of massage oils and herbal remedies, vitamins, nappies and teething products).

Dandelion Health Foods
120 Northcote Rd SW11 6QU ☎ (020) 7350 0902
Organic vegetables, groceries, herbs and baby food; goat's milk; also homeopathic products, vitamins and supplements and baby bodycare products. / HOURS *Mon-Sat 9am-6pm, Sun noon-3pm.*

Farm-a-Round 🔄
Offices B134-143, New Covent Garden Market, 9 Elms Lane SW8 5DZ ☎ (020) 7627 8066 ⌐ www.farmaround.co.uk
Originally known for a box scheme deliveries (across London, and now also in Yorkshire) of seasonal vegetables and fruit, this firm now offers a general organic grocery service. / HOURS *Mon-Fri 9am-5.30pm.*

Fresh & Wild
⌐ *www.freshandwild.com*
BRANCHES AT:
   305-311 Lavender Hill SW11 1LN ☎ (020) 7585 1488
See write-up in central.

GNC
☎ *(01483) 410600, 02476 244 400 ⌐ www.gnc.co.uk*
BRANCHES AT:
   151 Putney High St SW15 1SU ☎ (020) 8788 0944
   31 Tranquil Vale SE3 0BU ☎ (020) 8318 0448
   Unit 201, Court Shopping Centre, 4 Queens Rd SW19 8YE ☎ (020) 8947 3583
See write-up in central.

Greenlands 🔄
Unit 3a Greenwich Market SE10 9HZ ☎ (020) 8293 9176
Wholefoods, organic produce and baby foods (including Babynat); vitamins, essential oils and Weleda homeopathic remedies. Also Babynat food. / HOURS *Mon-Sun 9.30am-6.30pm.*

Greenwich Organics 🔄
86 Royal Hill SE10 8RT ☎ (020) 8488 6764 ⌐ www.greenwichorganic.co.uk
Organic fruit and vegetables, dairy products, breads. teas and coffees. / HOURS *Mon-Sat 10am-6pm.*

Provender
103 Dartmouth Rd SE23 3HT ☎ (020) 8699 4046 ⌐ www.provender.org.uk
Organic wholefoods, fruit and vegetables, dairy produce and organic baby food are all sold, alongside home-baked bread and cakes. Also café. / HOURS *Mon-Sat 8.30am-6pm.*

SG Manning
34-36 New Park Rd SW2 4UN ☎ (020) 8674 4391
Mainly organic dry goods and dairy products, plus baby food and a range of baby milks. / HOURS *Mon-Fri 9am-6pm, Sat 9am-1pm.*

Sheel Health & Herbal
312-314 Lewisham Rd SE13 7PA ☎ (020) 8297 1551
Organic dry foods, baby foods and complementary health products. / HOURS *Mon-Fri 9am-7pm, Sat 9am-6pm.*

Simply Organic 🔄
196 The Broadway SW19 1SN ☎ (0845) 1000 444 ⌐ www.simplyorganic.net
Established in 1999 with over 2,000 certified organic products offered, including Hipp and Baby Organix, as well as baby toiletries and nappies. Regular box deliveries are also available.

Today's Living 🔄
92 Clapham High St SW4 7UL ☎ (020) 7622 1772 ⌐ www.todaysliving.co.uk
Heath foods, supplements, dry goods, baby foods and complementary health products. / HOURS *Mon-Sat 9am-6.30pm.*

Vitality Health Foods
The Savacentre, 1 Merton High St SW19 1DD ☎ (020) 8544 9433
General health food store, stocking some organic products and a range of gluten-free products. / HOURS *Mon-Sat 9am-9pm, Sat 9am-8pm, Sun 11am-5pm.*

Waitrose
☎ *Customer service (01344) 424680 ⌐ www.waitrose.com*
BRANCHES AT:
   292 Upper Richmond Rd West SW14 7JG ☎ (020) 8878 4792
   Putney Exchange Shopping Centre, High St SW15 1TW ☎ (020) 8246 6848
See write-up in central.

Wellbeing Foods
19 Sydenham Rd SE26 5EX ☎ *(020) 8659 2003*
Dry goods, fruit and vegetables; juices; vitamins and supplements. Baby foods (by the case) by advance order only. / HOURS *Mon-Sat 9am-6pm.*

The Wholefood Shop
96-98 High St Croydon CR0 1ND ☎ *(020) 8686 6167*
A broad range of vegetarian items, including dry goods and dairy products; also supplements. Baby food by advance order only. / HOURS *Mon-Sat 10am-6pm, Weds 11am-6pm.*

EAST

Apple Jacks 🖃
28 The Mall, The Stratford Centre E15 1XD ☎ *(020) 8519 5809*
⌐ www.applejacks.co.uk
Organic products, wholefoods and nutritional supplements; the mail-order service apparently has customers worldwide. / HOURS *Mon-Sat 9am-6pm (Thu & Fri 7pm), Sun 11am-5pm.*

Fresh & Wild
⌐ www.freshandwild.com
BRANCHES AT:
  196 Old St EC1V 9FR ☎ *(020) 7792 9020*
See write-up in central.

Friends Organic
83 Roman Rd E2 0QN ☎ *(020) 8980 1843*
Health food shop whose range includes organic fruit, vegetables and bread. / HOURS *Mon-Sat 9.30am-6pm (Fri 7pm).*

Granary Health Foods
165 High St North E6 1JB ☎ *(020) 8552 5988*
Wholefoods; organic produce; vitamins and supplements; aromatherapy oils and herbal remedies. / HOURS *Mon-Sat 9am-6pm.*

The Organic Delivery Co. 🖃
70 Rivington St EC2A 3AY ☎ *(020) 7739 8181* *⌐ www.organicdelivery.co.uk*
Vegetarian grocery items, bread, fruit and vegetables; also nappies, baby care products, books and homewares. / HOURS *deliveries Mon-Fri after 3.30pm.*

Peaches Health Foods 🖃
143 High St E11 2RL ☎ *(020) 8530 3617*
Pastas, dry goods, chilled foods, prenatal supplements and baby products. / HOURS *Tue-Fri 9am-6pm, Sat 9am-5.30pm.*

The Spitalfields Market
Brushfield St E1 6AA ☎ *(01279) 444663 (market organiser)*
Large covered market with an all-organic section. A range of produce is available, from baked goods to fresh juices, but fruit and vegetables predominate. / HOURS *Sun 10am-4pm (some stalls throughout the week).*

Spitalfields Organics
103a Commercial St EC1 6BG ☎ *(020) 7377 8909*
Vegetarian and organic dry goods shop within the covered marketplace (many of the stalls there sell organic produce, see also). Dairy products, breads, baby foods and nappies are among the ranges stocked. / HOURS *Mon-Sun 10am-7pm.*

Vita Health Food
565 Lea Bridge Rd E10 7EQ ☎ *(020) 8539 3245*
Organic breads, pastries and dry goods plus milk formula (but not baby foods). / HOURS *Mon-Sat 9am-6pm.*

The Wholemeal Shop
190 Well St E9 6QT ☎ *(020) 8985 1822*
Organic breads, pastries, beverages, conserves, and dry goods; vitamins and mineral supplements; baby foods. / HOURS *Mon-Sat 9am-6pm.*

OUTSIDE LONDON

A Lot of Organics
Absolute Web Solutions, Douglas House, 33 Douglas Road, Caversham Reading RG4 5BH
☎ *(0118) 375 9375* *⌐ www.alotforganics.co.uk*
A search engine designed to help consumers find organic, ethical, eco-friendly, vegetarian and special diet produce in the UK. / SEE ALSO *3.04 Baby clothes.*

Graig Farm 🖼
Dolau, Llandrindod, Wells Powys LD1 5TL ☎ *(01597) 851655* 🖱 *www.graigfarm.co.uk*
Dairy products, bread, groceries, vegetables, fruit and non-food items are among the
items available – from the website or by mail order. / HOURS *Mon-Sat 9am-5.30pm, or
answerphone.*

Holle 🖼
Worcs BB0 2NF ☎ *(01386) 792622, Elysia (01527) 832863*
Holle, sold by Elysia Natural Skin Care (see also), is a range of Swiss products produced
to stringent (Demeter) organic standards. The range offers formula milks (see also),
cereal porridge mixes (suitable for babies over six months old), rusks and unrefined
whole cane sugar. Some of the cereal mixes are also gluten free. / HOURS *Mon-Fri 9am-6pm.*

Longwood Farm Organic Farmers & Butchers 🖼
Tuddenham St Mary, Bury St Edmunds Suffolk IP28 6TB ☎ *(01638) 717120*
This company primarily sells meat, but other products including fruit, vegetables, dairy
and dry goods are also available. / HOURS *Mon-Fri 9am-5pm, or answerphone.*

The Village Bakery 🖼
Melmerby, Penrith Cumbria CA10 1HE ☎ *(01768) 881515* 🖱 *www.village-bakery.com*
A website operator offering "almost certainly the largest range of organic baking
available by mail order in the UK"; the website also has a useful directory of retailers of
their products. / HOURS *Mon-Sat 8.30am-5pm, Sun 9.30am-5pm.*

The Watermill 🖼
Little Salkeld, Penrith Cumbria CA10 1NN ☎ *(01768) 881523* 🖱 *www.organicmill.co.uk*
A mail order service offering a wide range of organic flours and organic baking
products. / HOURS *shop 10.30am-5pm (tea room Mar-Nov only).*

West Country Organic Foods 🖼
Natson Farm, Tedburn, St Mary Exeter EX6 6ET ☎ *(01647) 24724*
🖱 *www.westcountryorganics.co.uk*
A website offering a high-tech way of buying low-tech organic food direct from small
farmers in the West Country. You can also order by telephone, post or fax. / HOURS *24hr
answerphone.*

ORGANIC BUTCHERS

WEST

As Nature Intended
201 Chiswick High Rd W4 2DR ☎ *(020) 8742 8838* 🖱 *www.asnatureintended.uk.com*
Meat and fish supplier: also frozen foods. / HOURS *Mon-Fri 9am-7pm, Sat 9am-6pm, Sun 11am-
5.30pm.*

The Fresh Food Co 🖼
The Orchard, 50 Wormholt Rd W12 0LS ☎ *(020) 8749 8778* 🖱 *www.freshfood.co.uk*
Organic fish and meat, sold in boxes or individually: salmon, smoked fish, all meats,
including venison, bacon and burgers. / HOURS *Mon-Fri 9am-5.30pm (Thu 7pm).*

C Lidgate 🖼
110 Holland Park Ave W11 4UA ☎ *(020) 7727 8243*
Celebrated Holland Park butcher much of whose range is organic, with the remainder
mainly free-range. All pies, pâtés and quiches are made on the premises. / HOURS *Mon-Sat
7.30am-6pm (Sat 5pm).*

Macken Brothers 🖼
44 Turnham Green Terrace W4 1QP ☎ *(020) 8994 2646*
Well-known quality butchers with a good selection of free range produce. / HOURS *Mon-
Sat 7.30am-6pm.*

Randall's Butchers
113 Wandsworth Bridge Rd SW6 2TE ☎ *(020) 7736 3426*
Organic and free-range meats. / HOURS *Mon-Fri 7am-5.30pm, Sat 7am-4.30pm.*

Stenton Family Butcher 🖼
55 Aldensley Rd W6 9PL ☎ *(020) 8748 6121*
Organic or free range meat and poultry from the Brackenbury 'Village' butchers;
sometimes also organic honey and cheese. / HOURS *Tue-Fri 8pm-6.30pm (Thu 1pm), Sat 8am-
5pm.*

Thorogood Butchers 🖼
113 Northfields Ave W13 9QR ☎ *(020) 8567 0339*
Suppliers of organic additive-free meat. Sausages can be made to order to
accommodate special dietary needs. / HOURS *Tue-Sat 8am-5pm.*

NORTH

BMC Foods 🖻
258 Kentish Town Rd NW5 2AA ☎ (020) 7485 0346
Fishmonger that also stocks organic meat from the Pure Meat Company. / HOURS Mon-Sat 8am-5pm (no fish on Mon).

SOUTH

Moen's
24 The Pavement SW4 0JA ☎ (020) 7622 1624 ⊘ www.moen.co.uk
Exclusively organic and free-range butcher. / HOURS Mon-Fri 8am-6.30pm, Sat 8am-5pm.

Organic World 🖻
23 Friar's Stile Rd Richmond Hill TW10 6NH ☎ (020) 8940 0414
Exclusively organic butchers. / HOURS Mon-Sat 7.30am-5.30pm.

Simply Organic 🖻
196 The Broadway SW19 1SN ☎ (0845) 1000 444 ⊘ www.simplyorganic.net
Fish, shellfish, smoked fish, meat and poultry.

OUTSIDE LONDON

Eastbrook Farm Organic Meats 🖻
Bishopstone, Swindon Wilts SN6 8PW ☎ (01793) 790460
⊘ www.helenbrowningorganics.co.uk
A range of organic meats and sausages by mail order – order from the website or by phone. Some products are available from supermarkets (particularly, under the Helen Browning brand, from Sainsbury's). / HOURS Mon-Fri 8.30am-5pm.

Graig Farm 🖻
Dolau, Llandrindod, Wells Powys LD1 5TL ☎ (01597) 851655 ⊘ www.graigfarm.co.uk
Meat, fish and pies. / HOURS Mon-Sat 9am-5.30pm, or answerphone.

Longwood Farm Organic Farmers & Butchers 🖻
Tuddenham St Mary, Bury St Edmunds Suffolk IP28 6TB ☎ (01638) 717120
Retail operation in Suffolk, with mail order business. Delivery within a week of ordering, either frozen or vacuum packed. On Sundays, the farm has a stall at Spitalfields Market (Thursdays on Portobello Market). / HOURS Mon-Fri 9am-5pm, or answerphone.

Pure Meat Direct 🖻
Home Place, Fruit Farm, North Cot, Launceston Cornwall PL15 9RQ ☎ (01409) 211127
⊘ www.puremeatdirectonline.co.uk
Additive-free and organic pork, beef, lamb, poultry and game, by mail order or through the website.

The Real Meat Company 🖻
East Hill Farm, Heytesbury Warminster BA12 0HR ☎ (01985) 840562
⊘ www.realmeat.co.uk
Free-range additive-free beef, lamb, pork and chicken, from the website or by telephone order. / HOURS 24hr answerphone.

Swaddles Green Farm 🖻
Hare Lane, Buckland St Mary, Chard Somerset TA20 3JR ☎ (01460) 234387
⊘ www.swaddles.co.uk
One of the best-known organic businesses in the country: website-based service offering high-quality meat, poultry and fish, sausages and burgers, babies and children's food (including organic versions of 'junk' food), ready meals, dairy produce and groceries. / HOURS 24hr answerphone.

West Country Organic Foods 🖻
Natson Farm, Tedburn, St Mary Exeter EX6 6ET ☎ (01647) 24724
⊘ www.westcountryorganics.co.uk
See Organic shops. / HOURS 24hr answerphone.

CHAPTER 2.03

BABY HEALTH

1. **Introduction**
2. **Cot death**
3. **Meningitis**
4. **Immunisation**
5. **Cord blood banking**
6. **Colic & restlessness**
7. **Sleep problems**
8. **Allergy**
9. **Developmental issues**
10. **First aid**
11. **Injuries**
12. **Teeth & teething**
13. **Other issues**

(For information on sun protection and insect repellents see chapter 2.05 Travel; for alternative treatments see chapter 4.02 Complementary medicine & Health practitioners; for a comprehensive listing of support groups for children with severe injuries, genetic abnormalities or serious physical conditions, see chapter 4.06 Support groups.)

1. INTRODUCTION

Babies are notoriously susceptible to a range of common maladies. Coughs and colds may be rife in the early months, and the hint of a rash or spot can seem sinister. Matters are not helped by the fact that babies have no way of telling you how they feel.

Some parents manage to be completely laid back about their child's physical well-being – others just can't stop worrying. Although this may be your first baby, and you may not wish to appear over-fretful, have confidence in your own judgement. If you feel sure all is well you are probably right. If on the other hand you have a serious concern, don't be fobbed off. You know better than anyone else whether your child is well.

Just after the birth, your midwife team can be an excellent source of advice on any problems. Thereafter health visitors can offer some guidance, though they are not trained to the same extent as midwives and for more serious complaints it would be wisest to consult your GP.

One of the frustrating things about baby-related complaints like colic, is that, as with pregnancy-related problems, orthodox medicine often has no solutions to offer. For such problems, many mothers turn to complementary techniques (see chapter *4.02 Complementary medicine & Health practitioners*).

Having a good reference book or two to hand is a good idea – they can help set your mind at rest over the significance of various symptoms. As well as the suggestions listed below, some of the titles in the Childcare section of chapter *4.05 Finding out more* have sections devoted to baby health.

READING

Baby and Child Health Care – Dr Miriam Stoppard (Dorling Kindersley; 2001; £9.99; 0751305014) – *An A–Z of common childhood complaints, symptoms and treatment; when to seek further advice.* / www.dk.com/uk.

Beyond Antibiotics – Michael Schmidt (50 (or so) ways to boost immunity and avoid antibiotics; 1994; £15.99; 1556431805)

Does My Child Need The Doctor? – Loraine Stern (Bloomsbury; 1994; £9.99; 0747517533) – *Easy to use guide of more than 200 problems that parents face.*

Health Education Authority Guide to Child Health (1995; £9.99; 0-752102-59-1)

Natural Healthcare for Children ★ – Karen Sullivan (How to raise happy, healthy children from 0-15; Piatkus; 2000; £17.99; 0-7499-2115-3) – *Probably the best single handbook for parents wanting the holistic/complementary approach, covering the mainstream alongside the complementary alternatives on anything from mouth ulcers to autism. Among other sections includes pointers on the conflicting advice given to parents, healthy eating, and natural boosters for the immune system. There is also an extensive section on vaccination.*

NCT Book of Child Health – Dr Morag Martindale (Thorsons; 2000; £5.99; 0722540140) – *Compiled by a family doctor, an A-Z guide for children up to 12 years; symptoms and illnesses are cross referenced with pointers on remedies and when to call the doctor.*

Practical Parenting - What's That Rash? – Priscilla Middlemiss (How to identify and treat childhood rashes; Hamlyn; 2003; £6.99; 0600605132) – *Everything you need to know about rashes, including incubation periods, symptoms, diagnoses and medical treatments. Colour illustrations and photographs illustrate the appearance of rashes, and a diagnosis chart in each chapter indicates possible causes. The guide includes suggestions for complementary and self-help treatments.* / www.hamlyn.co.uk.

Practical Parenting A-Z Guide to Children's Health – David Hoslam (Metro Publishing; 1999; £7.99; 1-900512-68-8) – *Covers all relevant topics in an accessible format.*

Royal Society of Medicine Encyclopedia of Children's Health ★ – Robert Youngson MD (Bloomsbury; 1997; £8.99; 0747533024) – *With 546 entries, a glossary of medical terms and a reference on child health matters, from newborn to teens; includes psychological and behavioural issues.*

Total Health for Children – ed David Elliman & Helen Bedford (Marshall Publishing; 1999; £15; 1840282835) – *From birth to 12 years old, a review of potential health problems together with suggestions both for both prevention and treatment.*

Treat Your Child the Natural Way – Amanda Cochrane & Mary Loveday (Everyday remedies & first aid; Harper Collins; 2001; £9.99; 0007110731) – *A guide to complementary therapies for children, from first aid to preventative treatments. For each condition or symptom, the author lists alternative remedies and gives an indication of what a GP would diagnose and prescribe (including advice on when hospital or GP treatment would be required).*

When Your Child is Ill – Dr Bernard Valman (A Home Guide for Parents; Dorling Kindersley; 2002; £9.99; 0751339741) – *Authorised by the British Medical Association. Includes easy-to-use flow charts of potential problems and how to handle them.*

The Which? Guide to Children's Health – edited by Dr Harry Brown (Which? Books; 1997; £9.99; 0-852026-55-2) – *An extensive reference work, including an A-Z of illnesses, tips for their prevention, details of behavioural and emotional problems, how to give first aid and how to get the best from health professionals.*

Your Child's Health – Dr Hilary Jones (Everything you need to know to keep your child healthy from birth to twelve years old; Hodder & Stoughton; 1996; £12.99; 0340654007)

USEFUL CONTACTS

Baby Check, ☎ (01603) 784400

Suppliers of a booklet developed with funding from the Foundation for the Study in Infant Death with 19 simple checks to help you interpret how ill your child actually is, and whether you should be consulting a doctor. Suitable for babies up to 6 months old, it includes a checklist of symptoms devised by paediatricians at Addenbrooke's Hospital. All profits are used for research. £2.75; can also be supplied with a thermometer, at additional cost.

Child Accident Prevention Trust (CAPT), ☎ (020) 7608 3828

⏚ www.capt.org.uk
This charity sees itself as the first port of call for parents where issues of child safety are concerned; it is committed to reducing the number of children and young people killed, disabled or seriously injured as a result of accidents. It covers all aspects of safety

and organises high profile public safety campaigns, including Child Safety Week; parents can contact the trust with specific queries regarding safety equipment and accident prevention; factsheets are available on the website. / HOURS *Mon-Fri 9am-5pm.*

Department of Health, ☎ *(0800) 555777* 🖑 *www.doh.gov.uk*
Can supply copies of useful booklets. / PUBLICATIONS *Meningitis C Under 24; Cot Death & Reducing the Risk of Cot Death.*

Medic Alert Foundation, ☎ *(0800) 581420, (020) 7833 3034*
🖑 *www.medicalert.org.uk*
Providers of an internationally-recognised emergency identification system (started in 1956) using symbols on bracelets or pendants for people with hidden health problems. In the event of an emergency, a 24-hour helpline provides paramedics with a complete medical history. Membership £30, plus £15 a year for the following year. Small bracelets for children; steel £20; 9ct gold £129.

Medical Advisory Service, ☎ *(020) 8994 9874*
Provides information on health care services and puts people in touch with appropriate specialists. / HOURS *Mon-Fri 6pm-8pm.*

NHS Direct, ☎ *(0845) 4647* 🖑 *www.nhsdirect.nhs.uk*
Advice is available over the phone, and so in straightforward cases is a diagnosis, though referral is often made to your GP all the same. The website provides links from a comprehensive database of support groups.

There are now a number of online medical information sources:

READING – INTERNET

The Patient's Internet Handbook – Robert Kiley & Elizabeth Graham (Royal
    Society of Medicine Press; 2001; £9.95; 1853154989) – *Designed to help people to
    find safe medical information on the internet, with a chapter devoted specifically to
    pregnancy, childbirth and infant care. Corrections and updates are published on their
    website (www.patient-handbook.co.uk) – these can also be e-mailed to you if you
    register.* / *(01235) 465500.*

USEFUL CONTACTS – INTERNET

E-med, ☎ *(020) 7806 4028* 🖑 *www.e-med.co.uk*
A 'virtual surgery' – for a joining fee (£20), and a £15 per consultation fee, you can e-mail (or telephone) symptoms to a doctor, who can diagnose and prescribe medication (even e-mailing a prescription to a local pharmacy). In cases where one-to-one diagnosis is required, patients can visit the surgery in St. John's Wood – information on NHS care can be given if the suggested private treatment would prove too costly. Useful for busy and working parents. / HOURS *Mon-Fri 9am-6pm.*

Independent Pharmacy, 🖑 *www.independentpharmacy.co.uk*
An 'independent UK health resource' website: use the directory of pharmacies to find one local to you; also health and beauty tips and a section looking at common health problems in children.

MedicDirect, 🖑 *www.medicdirect.co.uk*
"The only interactive website hosted by leading UK medical consultants providing comprehensive health information online", says the home page. It is apparently designed for use by professionals as well as the public – there is no dedicated section on babies or children, but you could look up specific problems.

NetDoctor, 🖑 *www.NetDoctor.co.uk*
What claims to be the UK's leading consumer health website includes a section on pregnancy and birth (examples of topics include amniocentesis, anaemia, assisted conception, adoption, calculating dates, constipation, prolapse, sleep problems, and diet in pregnancy); also discussion groups, health service listings and relevant news items.

NHS Direct, ☎ *(0845) 4647* 🖑 *www.nhsdirect.nhs.uk*
Online advice from the team that provide the NHS telephone advice service.

Surgery Door, 🖑 *www.surgerydoor.co.uk*
Website venture from firm supplying touchscreen health information kiosks to the NHS, with an online pharmacy, health-related books, mother and baby products, and 'healthy' foods. Site includes advice for new parents, plus local health service listings and maps. There are specific sections on Pregnancy and Parents, New Parents and Children 0-5.

Registering your baby with a GP

It is sensible to register your baby with a GP as soon as possible, although emergency treatment is always available from A&E departments at local hospitals. Normally when you register the birth at your local registry office you will also be given a form to send off for an NHS card for the baby. If you are not given a form, you can complete one at the baby's six-week check-up.

The most natural choice is to register your baby with your own GP. If for some reason you will be choosing a new GP with whom to register your child – perhaps because you have just moved house – try to look for a doctor who will do telephone consultations and ideally one with his or her own children.

Local health centres and baby clinics

A local health centre – possibly the same venue as for your postnatal check-ups – will usually offer a range of clinics and services that include a weekly baby clinic. (Such centres often also offer therapies, paramedical services, sale of welfare food and special advisory, immunisation and vaccination clinics.)

These regular sessions provide the opportunity for your baby to be weighed and undergo other simple checks, and for you to air any worries or doubts. However, if your baby is bright-eyed, responsive, with good skin colour, and producing wet nappies, you may wish to limit your attendance to the more comprehensive development check-ups at six to nine months and 18 months to two years (see below, in Section 8, Developmental issues).

Health visitors are also based at health centres. Every new baby and mother are assigned a named health visitor who will visit you at home, as well as seeing you at the clinic.

Many health centres run series of postnatal talks, sometimes limited to first-time mothers, on subjects such as sleeping, feeding and resuscitation. They are also a good way of meeting other new mothers. If your own centre does not run talks, ask to be put in touch with another centre that does. Most are happy to welcome mothers from outside their area.

USEFUL CONTACTS

NHS Direct, ☎ (0845) 4647 🖱 www.nhsdirect.nhs.uk

This telephone information service should be able to answer queries about NHS services – e.g. dentists, hospitals, specialist NHS doctors and centres which specialise in particular conditions.

What the system provides

The NHS Patients Charter Services for Children & Young People stipulates that when you have a baby you can expect the following:

➤ Your newborn should have a physical examination by a paediatrician, midwife or your GP.

➤ The baby should have a further physical examination at six–eight weeks.

➤ You should be invited to visit a local child health clinic or GP surgery regularly for the first few months of the baby's life, where a health visitor, GP or clinic doctor will check the baby.

➤ The baby should have further developmental checks at six to nine months (incorporating a hearing test if your baby did not have one of the increasingly common computerised tests shortly after birth), then at 18 months to two years, and at three to four and a half years.

➢ You should be given the name and telephone number of your health visitor within your first week at home with the new baby.

➢ You should receive a call from the health visitor between ten and 14 days after the birth of your baby or within five working days if newly-registered with a GP (and having children under five years old).

➢ You have a right to be given an explanation of any proposed treatment including its related benefits and risks and of any alternatives.

➢ You can expect your child to be cared for at home whenever possible – though in practice in London this is rare. If treatment is in hospital it should be under the supervision of a consultant paediatrician or paediatric specialist.

➢ If you need to take your child to the Accident & Emergency unit of a hospital you should have your child seen immediately, have the need for treatment assessed, and if required be given a bed in no more than two hours.

➢ If your child is referred by your GP to a consultant you should be seen within three months, or at most six months.

Your child's entitlement to free treatment:
    Dental treatment: children up to 18 are entitled to free treatment with an NHS dentist. However, fewer and fewer dentists in London offer NHS treatment and you should make it clear from the outset if this is what you want.

    Sight tests: free for children up to 16, and NHS spectacle vouchers help with the cost of any glasses prescribed. However, a first sight test is usually not conducted on under-threes. You can get a list of opticians from your doctor or the Yellow Pages.

2. COT DEATH

In 1991 the Foundation for the Study of Infant Deaths (FSID) introduced its Reduce the Risk of Cot Death campaign, and the following year the UK experienced a halving in the number of babies dying as a result of cot death (also called SIDS – Sudden Infant Death Syndrome). The initiative was hailed as one of the most successful health promotion campaigns ever.

A further campaign to educate parents in 1998 led to a further fall of 25%. Since that time the incidence of SIDS in the UK has generally been in the range of 0.5–0.6 in 1000 (0.48 in 1000 in 2002 – 342 cases). Cot death remains, however, the leading cause of death in babies over the age of one month killing approximately one a day.

The time of greatest risk is three to four months, with a large majority of cases before six months.

The key recommendation of the Reduce the Risk campaign was for babies to be placed on their backs rather than on their fronts for sleeping (the exact reverse of the advice in our parents' day). Other key recommendations relate to temperature (for it seems that overheating is one of the key risk factors), and smoking.

The current thinking on cot death is:
➢ Positioning: babies should go to sleep on their backs or their sides with the lower arm forward to prevent them rolling over until they are able to do this by themselves in their sleep ('back to bed').

➤ Put babies' feet at the foot of the cot ('feet to foot') to prevent them slithering down under the blankets and overheating.

➤ Temperature: babies should be kept warm but not too warm – about room temperature (15–20°C/65°F). One sheet and three blankets is the recommended set-up for the cot, blankets being recommended for bed-clothes as they can be added to and taken away as necessary. The best blankets are 'cellular' ones with holes (to prevent overheating/suffocation if the baby wriggles underneath them). Duvets, hot water bottles and electric blankets are advised against for babies under one year old because of the possibility of overheating. Sheepskins are also thought by some to fall into this category

➤ A baby's body does not regulate temperature as well as an adult's. Note that it is especially important not to overheat an unwell baby who will probably need to lose excess heat, especially from the head. A layer between the baby and a plastic-covered mattress should also help prevent overheating. Check for temperature by touching the baby's trunk or neck, not hands or feet.

➤ Avoid smoking in the vicinity of the baby – one of the biggest risk factors implicated in cot death. Ideally no one should smoke in the house, nor in front of the baby, and especially not in the same room as the cot. (If you are a smoker who would like to quit, there is a listing of self-help groups in chapter *1.02 Looking after yourself*).

➤ Don't sleep with the baby in your bed if you are a smoker, drunk, very tired, take drugs or medication, or the baby is less than 8 weeks old. It is considered very dangerous to sleep together on a sofa, armchair or settee.

➤ Always keep the baby's head uncovered indoors. Babies should be no more dressed than adults in the same environment either in or outdoors.

➤ Sleep the baby in the same room as you for the first six months.

Despite all the attention that this topic has received in recent years, a relatively recent Department of Health study showed that the vast majority of people still do not know, for example, that duvets and quilts double the risk of cot death. If you employ a nanny, or leave your baby in the care of a mother's help, babysitter or anyone else, ensure that they are fully up-to-date on current thinking.

The laundry list of other potential causes of cot death include: a delayed reaction to drugs used at the birth; baby medicines, including those sold over the counter; delayed development of reflexes; some other developmental problem, possibly resulting from pregnancy or a bacterial infection.

Premature babies

Premature babies are seven times more likely than average to suffer cot death.

Research reported in 2001 found that such newborns are at reduced risk, however, if they start out in life sleeping *on their fronts* – i.e. in direct contradiction of the general advice to parents.

The Foundation for the Study of Infant Deaths is now funding research by King's College Hospital to determine at what age such children should switch to sleeping on their backs.

READING

Cot Deaths – Jacquelynn Luben (Coping with Sudden Infant Death Syndrome;
NCVO Publishers; 1989; £6.95; 0-719912-64-4) – *One of a number of titles sold by the
Foundation for the Study of Infant Deaths. (Others help explain what has happened from
a young child's perspective.) / www.sids.org.uk.*

USEFUL ORGANISATIONS

Cot Death Society, ☎ (01635) 38137, Monitor helpline (0845) 6010234
☞ www.cotdeathsociety.org.uk
Not a bereavement society or helpline: this charity believes in promoting the use of
monitors for all babies at risk. Monitors (and now sometimes video monitors) are sent
out free within 24 hours of receiving a medical referral. / *HOURS 24hr answerphone.*

Foundation for the Study of Infant Deaths (FSID),
☎ (0870) 7870885, Helpline (0870) 7870554 ☞ www.sids.org.uk/fsid
The foundation runs a helpline which provides information on current research
relating to cot death and how to avoid it; also for bereaved families (and those helping
to support them), which can refer parents to local support groups. The foundation also
runs CONI (Care of Next Infant) – a scheme run in conjunction with the NHS for
parents having a child subsequent to losing one through cot death, to help them with
their anxieties. The organisation sells a liquid crystal nursery thermometer indicating
the suitable temperatures for babies (£2.75). / *HOURS Mon-Fri 9am-11pm, Sat-Sun 6pm-11pm;
PUBLICATIONS fact sheets relating to most areas of concern to parents; BabyZone – good infant care practice;
Questions and Answers About Cot Death; all send SAE.*

USEFUL CONTACTS

Coghill Research Laboratories, ☎ (01495) 752 122
☞ www.cogreslab.co.uk
Roger Coghill claims to have discovered a strong correlation between cot deaths and
sources of electromagnetic energy such as tube lines, power lines and electrified
railways (even electric radiation heaters), and also believes that such radiation may be
connected to hyperactivity and/or fussiness in babies. The 'Mouse' sold by his
company Coghill Laboratories (£343.63; or hirable from website or from The Healthy
House £41.13) designed to measure such fields. / *PUBLICATIONS Something in the Air (£18).*

3. MENINGITIS

*(As a general rule, this book steers clear of covering the symptoms and treatment
of specific childhood illnesses. The general childcare books listed in chapter 4.05
Finding out more are packed with such details, as are many of the general information sources listed at the start of the chapter. However, such is the fearsome
reputation and concern regarding this disease that it seems appropriate to give
it a section of its own here.)*

Meningitis is the inflammation of the tissues which cover the brain and
spinal cord. It comes in a number of varieties (Hib, type B, type C, etc),
and its cause can be viral or bacterial (the latter being more serious).

Though vaccines can protect against certain variants (Hib and type
C, for example), no immunisation yet exists for the type B form of the
disease – the type most common in the UK.

In its most severe form, meningococcal meningitis, the condition is
allied with septicaemia – blood-poisoning which causes blood to leak
under the skin in bruises, blisters and spots. This condition causes such
fear because it is the only infectious disease in the UK where – within
hours of the first symptoms manifesting themselves – a previously fit and
healthy baby or child (or adult) could be in intensive care fighting for survival. For reasons that are not fully understood, children are relatively
more susceptible than most other age groups.

Meningococcal meningitis and septicaemia affects about 2,000 children a year in the UK. The national death rate is 20%–50%, though at
specialist units continuing improvements in care mean that the survival
rate is now approaching 100%.

CONTACTS
Meningitis Research Foundation, ☎ *Helpline (0808) 800 3344*
🖰 *www.meningitis.org*
The organisation's helpline offers information on the signs and symptoms of the disease, if a child is sick and it seems meningitis could be the cause. Note, however, that the operators cannot diagnose over the phone. The organisation's website includes numerous photographs of different manifestations of the disease. / *HOURS 24hr helpline;* PUBLICATIONS *Meningitis & Septicaemia Am I At Risk?; Meningitis- Baby Watch; Meningitis - Tots Watch Symptoms in tottlers; leaflets for those bereaved due to meningitis; symptom cards for your wallet (all free, send SAE).*

National Meningitis Trust, ☎ *(0845) 6000 800*
🖰 *www.meningitis-trust.org.uk*
Support for sufferers of the illness and their families. / *HOURS 24hr helpline;* PUBLICATIONS *Leaflets and symptom cards (and information packs for health workers) – free.*

St Mary's Hospital, ☎ *Helpline (0845) 4647* 🖰 *www.st-marys.nhs.uk*
One of the two top units in the country for treating meningitis. Local hospitals are encouraged to call St Mary's immediately with a case, and the hospital can usually have a mobile unit to them in 60-100 minutes. / *HOURS 24 hr answerphone.*

4. IMMUNISATION

All children in the UK are routinely offered an immunisation programme. There is a timetable for these recommended by the Department of Health, but exact details may vary by area. A typical timetable up to the age of two would run as follows:

At 2 months:
   Hib: Haemophilus influenzae type b – the illnesses caused by this infection includes one type of meningitis.
   DPT: diphtheria, pertussis (whooping cough) and tetanus.
   Meningitis C.
   Polio.

At 3 months:
   DPT: booster shot.

At 4 months:
   DPT: booster shot.

At 2-18 months (usually before 15 Months):
   MMR: measles, mumps and rubella.

(As we go to press further vaccinations are being discussed for inclusion in the programme above, including another meningitis jab, and also immunisation against chicken pox.)

Further vaccinations are then typically given around the time of beginning school, at between three and five years of age.

The justification for vaccination is that the risk of death or serious damage from a disease in the order of x in 1,000 is swapped for a risk of death or serious damage from its vaccine in the order of x in 1,000,000. Where vaccinations became controversial, it is invariably due to a perception that the risk from the vaccine has been under-estimated, so upsetting this whole risk/benefit calculation.

An overwhelming majority of health professionals are strong advocates of immunisation and many view any undermining of confidence in the system as irresponsible scaremongering. Many argue that parents who do not immunise their children are jeopardising the standards of public health, and increasing the risk of the re-emergence of epidemics of certain diseases.

It is widely reported that parents who refuse to have their children immunised risk the child being struck off their GPs' lists – or if the GP knows in advance, not taken on in the first place. It has been suggested that part of the explanation for this may be that GPs risk losing a bonus of £2,865 per annum if less than 90% of two-year-olds on their list are unvaccinated. Although the BMA "strongly advise all parents to give their children the MMR vaccine" they "would not support any GP who strikes a patient off" for failing to do so.

'Big picture' issues regarding vaccination

Arguments cited in favour of immunisation:

➤ For those who have faith in the scientific/medical process, there is overwhelming evidence regarding the efficacy of vaccination in protecting babies against potentially fatal diseases.

➤ Immunisation is believed to protect not just the individual but also the 'herd'. For this reason, in countries such as France and the USA, penalties are imposed on parents who refuse to have their children vaccinated (In France welfare payments are available only to parents of vaccinated children. In certain US states, unvaccinated children may not go to school, and parents are liable to prosecution if their children do not attend school).

➤ Any danger to the individual is judged by the overwhelming majority of doctors and healthcare professionals to be both lower than the risk of the disease itself, and also to be worth the protection to the herd.

Arguments cited against immunisation:

➤ Doubts have been raised as to the validity of the analysis of risks versus benefits – particularly in respect of some specific vaccines – both for the individual and the 'herd': for example, as to whether all potential side effects (such as an increase in autism in relation to MMR) have been given due weight in official risk calculations.

➤ Among complementary practitioners in particular, there is a belief that vaccination may damage the immune system and may be a factor in the rise in allergies and other chronic childhood ailments. They believe such damage must be factored into the risk/benefit analysis.

➤ The profits made from vaccination raise doubts about the impartiality of some of those who advocate them.

➤ Sceptics of the scientific/medical process question the orthodox view that immunisation is responsible for conquering disease in the West, citing better sanitation and diet as two significant factors.

Another common concern expressed by some who are not against vaccination per se, is whether the increasingly common practice of giving many vaccines at once is really wise.

Everyone agrees that vaccination is inadvisable if:

➤ There has been any suppression of the baby's immune system, for example with certain medical treatments such as chemotherapy.

➤ If the baby is suffering an infection, for example of the respiratory tract.

➤ Some practitioners feel that vaccination is inadvisable if the child is known to suffer from certain allergies or severe handicaps, particularly fits or spasms.

➤ Some practitioners offering single jabs recommend waiting until the child is slightly older than is usual in the UK. In this way, they say, there is a better chance of ensuring maternal antibodies have cleared from the child's system. If they have not, apparently this can interfere with the immunisation process.

Most doctors give short shrift to the counter arguments to immunisation, and parents who are sceptical on the subject will need to research for themselves.

The orthodox medical view of immunisation is presented by practically all childcare texts – the reading lists below represents a variety of opinions.

For the most part, the 'Useful contacts' listings include support groups for children damaged by vaccines, organisations campaigning for further research into all areas of immunisation, and medical establishments prepared to diverge from the government's recommended programme.

READING

A Guide to Childhood Immunisations – Health Promotion England (Health Promotion England; 2001; 50p; 0752119648) – *Information on immunisations, their recognised side effects and the arguments in favour.* / *Available from GPs or health visitors, or directly* – *(01235) 465 565.*

An Educated Decision – Christina J Head (One approach to the vaccination problem using homeopathy; Lavender Hill Publishing; 1995; £9.99; 0953575802) – *An accessible discussion of vaccination and homeopathy, the immune system and a range of case studies.* / *Lavender Hill Homeopathic Centre.*

Homoeopathic Alternatives to Immunisation – Susan Curtis (Winter Press; 1995; £5.95; 1874581029) – *For those who want to try homeopathic alternatives to conventional vaccination, with pointers on treatment for parents who have decided not to vaccinate.* / *Neals Yard Remedies, or 29 Horniman Drive, London SE23 3BJ.*

Vaccination and Immunisation – Leon Chaitow (Dangers, delusions and alternatives: What every parent should know; 1988; £6.99; 0-852071-91-4)

The Vaccine Guide – Randall Neustaedter (Making an informed choice; North Atlantic Books; 1996; £14.99; 1556432151) – *Comprehensive coverage of the subject from an American physician.*

Vaccines – Dr Paul A Offit & Dr Louis M Bell (What every parent should know; MacMillan; 1999; $12.95; 0028638611) – *Two experts on infectious diseases put the case for vaccination.*

Vaccines - Are They Really Safe and Effective? – Neil Z Miller (A parent's guide to childhood shots; New Atlantean Press; 1996; $8.95; 1-881217-10-8) – *A multitude of facts and figures back up a sceptical review.*

What Doctors Don't Tell You – Lynne McTaggart (The truth about the dangers of modern medicine; Harper Collins; 1996; £9.99; 0722530242) – *400-page general text, of which about a third is devoted to vaccines, including general issues, and the necessity and efficacy of individual vaccines. At the back is a vaccine consent form for parents who feel they are being coerced into vaccination against their wishes. This requires those administering the vaccine to take full responsibility should any problem result.*

USEFUL CONTACTS

The Active Birth Centre, ☎ (020) 7281 6760
🖰 www.activebirthcentre.com
A talk is given, approximately four times a year; 'On Vaccination', by Michel Odent at the Active Birth Centre, £16 a head. / *HOURS shop Mon-Fri 9.30am-6.30pm (Fri 4pm), Sat 10am-4pm.*

Association of Parents of Vaccine-Damaged Children,
☎ (01608) 661595
Founded in 1973, this small organisation claims to be the longest-established pressure group in this area, responsible for the campaign which culminated in the Vaccine Damage Payments Act of 1979: in June 2000 the payments scheme was finalised, so the campaigning was successful. / *PUBLICATIONS 4 leaflets covering all common vaccinations (send SAE).*

Immunisation.org.uk, ☎ NHS Direct (0845) 4647
🖰 www.immunisation.org.uk
Website promoting the government's position on vaccination.

The Informed Parent, ☎ (0190) 321 2969 🖰 www.informedparent.co.uk
A society for parents with doubts about childhood immunisation. / *HOURS 24 hour answerphone; PUBLICATIONS Free information pack (send SAE); four newsletters a year (membership, £15).*

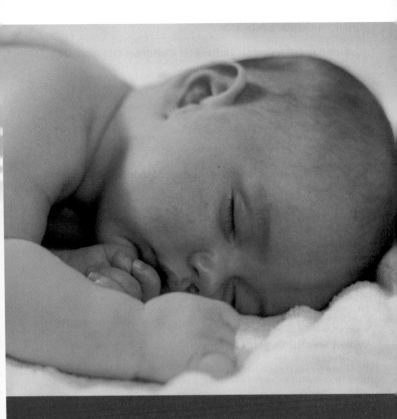

Justice for All Vaccine Damaged Children UK (JAVDC),
☎ (0117) 955 7818

Providers of telephone advice to parents on what they can do if anything goes wrong with a vaccination. It emphasises that doctors may be slow to diagnose any problem, and suggests getting a copy of the child's clinical notes and noting the batch number of the vaccine as soon as possible before making a claim. If a baby suffers any adverse reaction to a vaccination the JAVDC advises parents to report this to the doctor immediately and to ensure that an entry is made on the 'Yellow Card' and sent to the Committee on Safety of Medicines. The entry should record the reaction, the batch number and the name of the manufacturer of the vaccine. / HOURS helpline 9am-9pm; PUBLICATIONS Fact sheets and HB3 claim form – SAE.

Justice, Awareness & Basic Support (JABS), ☎ (01942) 713565
⌐ www.jabs.org.uk

Run by the parents of a vaccine-damaged child, not an anti-vaccination group but one which campaigns for better information and awareness, as well as support for families of vaccine-damaged children. The association can provide general information and advice if you have a vaccine-damaged child about what you should do next.

Salli Rose, ☎ (07940) 470284

A homeopath who runs a seven-step programme with parents to decide about immunisation and alternatives to it. These sessions are either private or in groups.

Vaccine Damage Payments Unit, ☎ (01772) 899756
⌐ www.dwp.gov.uk

To claim a one-off payment under the Vaccine Damage Payments Act 2000, send for claim form VAD 1A. / HOURS Mon-Fri 9am-5pm; PUBLICATIONS Leaflet HB3: information about making a claim and qualifying conditions for a claim.

World Health Organisation (WHO), ☎ (+ 41 22) 791 2111
⌐ www.who.int

The United Nation's heath agency. You can trawl the website for the organisation's views on immunisation (and on many other health topics of worldwide importance).

Concerns regarding the MMR vaccine

Concerns regarding potential side effects associated with vaccinations have hit the headlines over the last few years, primarily in respect of the MMR vaccine. Two studies in 1995 and 1999 from Hampstead's Royal Free Hospital linked the vaccine with the onset of autism and bowel problems.

The scares over the MMR vaccine have caused a sharp decline in the number of parents taking their child to be immunised (to the great concern of health officials). In 2003 the uptake rate dipped to a new low of 78% (in areas of London the rate being closer to 70%).

This uptake rate compares very unfavourably with the 94–95% rate of uptake for other childhood immunisations.

In Spring 2004, a new twist was given to the controversy with the news that both *The Lancet* (which first published it) and 10 of the 12 researchers who wrote the original report now wished to disown it. Whether this will be enough to win parents back to the MMR remains to be seen.

Government advice, the advice of most doctors, and the accepted practice in Europe and the US is to administer the MMR vaccine.

THE 'SINGLE' JAB

From 1999, the government has forced the issue of MMR for parents – and fuelled the whole controversy – by making it much more difficult to obtain the monovalent ('single') jabs for measles, mumps and rubella. Effectively the attempt has been to force parents to choose the recommended vaccination or no vaccination. Predictably parents chose no vaccination.

The efficacy of the single jabs is a disputed point. Some feel the government's statements come close to 'rubbishing' them, whereas quite a number of doctors say they are reasonably efficacious, just not as good as MMR. Much of the reason for preferring MMR is that parents do not need to be trusted to organise six vaccinations rather than just one.

Private clinics and some 'renegade' GPs offer the single jabs, and some parents have visited clinics on the Continent to secure them – cheaper than in the UK where prices range from £40 to £100 per jab. The vaccines may also be more easily located than in the UK where demand plus government limits on imports have created waiting times of up to six months.

In late 2001, a GP in the north of England was reported to the GMC for giving the single inoculation in private clinics. The GMC decided not to proceed to a full conduct committee against the doctor.

MMR – FURTHER INFORMATION

Direct Health 2000, ☎ *(0870) 200 0999* ⌁ *www.dh2.co.uk*
Private clinic providing 'single' jab mumps, measles and rubella vaccines, price £80 per vaccination; only parents agreeing to all three vaccinations are given; a blood test (£98) can identify whether the child already has immunity to any of the three diseases. / HOURS *Mon-Sat 9am-5pm, closed Sun.*

Justice, Awareness & Basic Support (JABS), ☎ *(01942) 713565*
⌁ *www.jabs.org.uk*
The organisation can – via their helpline or website – provide details of local doctors who will give the single jab for measles, mumps and rubella.

National Autistic Society, ☎ *Helpline (0870) 600 8585* ⌁ *www.nas.org.uk*
Excellent information pack on the MMR vaccine with detailed background information, and a thorough statement of the society's position. / HOURS *helpline Mon-Fri 10am-4pm.*

5. CORD BLOOD BANKING

This practice is sometimes referred to rather misleadingly just as cord collection. It refers to the storage of blood taken from umbilical cords, which is rich in haemopoietic stem cells (HSC). Such cells can be used instead of bone marrow transplants for the treatment of leukaemia and some other life-threatening conditions (in particular cancers).

In the fullness of time, it may be that they are the basis for a wide range of potentially life-saving treatments – for example Alzheimer's disease – the subject of large research projects around the globe. This and the already-proven success in fighting Leukemia has inspired the creation of a number of private medical facilities who collect these cells at birth and store them for use, in case your child should need them and be able to benefit from advances in medicine. (The current limit for effective storage is about 20 years,. though some expect this to lengthen).

The potential benefits of keeping and storing such blood has also led to the initiation of a programme by the National Blood Service to collect such blood. Parents are encouraged to donate their child's umbilical blood in the same spirit as blood marrow donors (so-called 'altruistic' donation). An international database is maintained of blood held in public banks to help those in need to make a match.

The ethics and efficacy of commercial blood banking has been the subject of some controversy.

Issues relating to commercial umbilical blood banking:

➢ Though revolutionary in fighting leukemia, most of the other possibilities for such banked cord blood remain speculative.

➢ For families with a history of leukemia, doctors are supportive of private cord blood banking.

➤ For low-risk families the issue is more complex – the price is significant and the risk is small; it comes down to individual parental assessment as to whether the price is worth paying to 'insure' against a rare but life-threatening condition (and perhaps others should the research pay off).

➤ There have been claims that marketing campaigns run by some companies ("like freezing a spare immune system") have been unduly emotive.

➤ Collecting the blood can be time consuming; should it be carried out by an attendant midwives or doctors – in the absence of a clear need – it raises issue of whether this is an appropriate use of resources. There is also a legal liability question should the collection fail due to the negligence of a carer. For these reasons, some hospitals insist that parents who wish to collect the blood do so themselves.

USEFUL CONTACTS

Cells4Life
Sussex Innovation Centre, Science Park Square, University of Sussex, Falmer Brighton Beast Sussex BN1 9SB ☎ (01273) 234 676 ⁀ www.cells4life.co.uk
The company – founded in 2002 and starting operations in 2003 – claims to be the first such company to offer storage actually in the UK; five years storage costs £895, and 25 years £1,150; if cells are not stored successfully only £50 is payable.

Future Health Technologies
3 Faraday Building, Nottingham Science & Technology park, University Boulevard Nottingham NG7 2QP ☎ (0115) 907 8610 ⁀ www.futurehealth.co.uk
The first company to have applied for accreditation as a private umbilical cord blood stem cell bank in the UK, apparently. It charges £120 for the cord blood collection and shipping kit and delivery, then £475 for transport within the UK, processing, cryopreservation and first year storage. The subsequent annual storage fee is £58. Alternatively, on top of the processing fee, pay up-front for 10 years storage (£650), or 20 years (£750).

National Blood Service
☎ (020) 8732 5442 ⁀ www.blood.co.uk
"Altrustic" cord blood donations are currently only possible in some outer-London hospitals (at Barnet, Northwick, Luton & Dunstable hospitals and also in Belfast and Glasgow; and then only on certain days. Please note: the service will offer NO information about private blood banks.

Smart Cells International
60 Marylebone High St London W1U 5HU ☎ (020) 7486 4686 ⁀ www.smartcells.com
The "UK's leading umbilical cord blood bank & stem cell storage provider" (to quote their website) charges £995 for 20 years storage of which £900 is payable only after the successful storage of your baby's stem cells. The cells are processed within 72 hours.

UK Cord Blood Bank
1 Harley St, Suite 102 London W1G 9QD ☎ (020) 7291 4569 ⁀ www.cordbloodbank.co.uk
The UK subsidiary of the New England Cord Blood Bank, which claims to have been the first company to offer commercial blood banking in the UK. Enrollment charge £130, processing £220 and then storage £50 per annum; pre-paid 20 years storage, £700. / HOURS Mon-Fri 9am-5pm.

6. COLIC & RESTLESSNESS

Most small children experience the above to some degree. However, serious cases can not only cause concern about the baby, but also take parents to their wits end.

The causes of these conditions are only hazily understood, and this is another area where some mothers turn to complementary techniques to help: in particular cranial osteopathy (see chapter *4.02 Complementary medicine & Health practitioners*) and baby massage (see chapter *2.06 Baby & toddler activities*).

STEM CELLS

SMART CELLS INTERNATIONAL is the UK's leading provider of safe storage of umbilical cord stem cells.

Stem cells are very smart master cells that develop into all other specialised cells in the body: the entire blood system, heart cells and all other organs, nerves, muscle, bone and the body's immune system.

The use of stem cells has proven to be more and more important in the treatment of a number of serious diseases such leukaemia and anaemia.

Until recently, in the event of a disorder such as leukaemia, doctors would resort to bone marrow transplants, hoping to increase the healthy cells in the patient. Unfortunately, it is very difficult to find a matching bone marrow donor and, moreover, apparently successful transparents are rejected in nearly 50% of cases.

By preserving your newborn's stem cells, they are immediately available if needed and they can be transplanted with no symptoms of rejection - these are your baby's own cells.

Research into therapeutic uses for stem cells is growing almost exponentially. Stem cells may one day help to treat a myriad of diseases and disorders such as diabetes, stroke, malignant tumours, Parkinson's and Alzheimer's Disease.

SMART CELLS safely stores your baby's stem cells for at least 20 years in their fully accredited laboratory, using a vapour nitrogen cryogenic process. Preserving your baby's umbilical cord stem cells is an extraordinary opportunity not to be missed.

If you require any further information about preserving umbilical cord stem cells, contact **SMART CELLS INTERNATIONAL** and the team will be pleased to assist you. You can also obtain information about the new adult stem cells collection service.

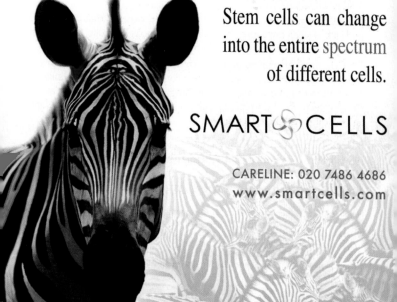

Colic

Constant crying, and any related bad temper are the symptoms ascribed to the condition referred to as colic. It seems to affect about 30% of babies in the UK – often later in the afternoon, in the evening or at night – from shortly after birth to about three months.

Broadly there are three schools of explanation:

Digestive problems, including possibly wind: some research indicates that as many as a third of all colicky breast-fed babies are helped by their mother cutting milk and dairy products out of her own post-birth diet. Other products that it may be helpful to avoid are those containing caffeine (coffee, tea, colas and chocolate), beans, strawberries and spices. Onions and garlic appear on some blacklists, but other research indicates that babies seem to positively enjoy the taste of these foodstuffs in the milk, drinking more when they are present. For bottle-fed babies changing formula might just help, but it's a longshot. There are some baby products which aim to alleviate the problem by reducing the bubbles in the milk in the baby's stomach. However, according to research in Texas, colic medication may itself trigger problems such as the suspension of breathing. Some parents swear by giving their baby chamomile or peppermint tea, and Susan Clark (author of What Really Works for Kids,) suggests giving a probiotic.

Physical tensions: Some people suggest that the condition results from tensions created in the baby's body by the stress of the birth. Cranial osteopathy is generally recommended as a solution, see chapter *4.02 Complementary medicine & Health practitioners).*

Immaturity, particularly of the nervous system: Harvey Karp, author of The Happiest Baby, highlights the fact that colic is unknown in the Third World. He argues that human babies are born immature and may be unable to 'self-calm' and may be helped by soothing traditional techniques including swaddling, gentle movement, and repetitive noise. Separate research does indicate that holding babies more than average at both six weeks and five months results in babies who cry less, offering indirect support for Karp's theory.

MISDIAGNOSED COLIC

Tracey Hogg, author of the Baby Whisperer, believes that overfeeding and lack of sleep can cause something which looks like colic, and suggests a fixed sequence to reassure the baby of what will happen next.

Continual heartburn in babies (more properly called reflux or gastroesophageal reflux) can also create a condition like colic. It is linked to constant crying, vomiting, back-arching, food intolerance and ear and throat infections. If untreated it can lead to inflammation of the oesophagus, bit it can be hard to diagnose.

PRODUCTS TO COUNTER COLIC

Gripe waters and similar colic remedies are sold in chemists. How effective they are is debatable.

Birth & Beyond, ☎ *(01869) 811099, (0870) 905 7878*
🖳 www.birthandbeyond.co.uk
Suppliers of the Bettersleep, an innovative hammock-style bed on a frame; suitable until a baby is 12 months old (or 12kg, or until a baby can kneel/stand/sit). Designed in Australia to promote calm in colicky or unsettled babies, the idea is that newborns feel continuously cuddled (as in the womb) and can be easily rocked. It is used in maternity units, nurseries and hospitals for babies with respiratory conditions; expert endorsements claim it encourages development generally. Foldable and lightweight (around 9kg), it can be used in the home and as a travel cot; cost from £195 or rent

(£25/month, minimum three months) with an option to buy (deducting rental to date); organic cotton version (from £250), sheets and mattress covers also available. / HOURS Mon-Fri 9.30am-6pm (Sat 1pm).

Inconsolable crying

This situation can make parents' lives hellish, with colic often blamed as the cause.

READING

The Happiest Baby ★ – Harvey Karp (Michael Joseph; 2002; £9.99; 0718145348) – *Karp, who runs a clinic in California, believes that Nature brings children into the world earlier than they are really ready for, and suggests reproducing babies' pre-birth experience after birth, thus developing what he calls the 'calming reflex'. The technique refers to five 'Ss' - swaddling, placing the baby on his side or stomach, shushing (producing relatively loud white noise), gentle swinging (mirroring pre-birth movement), and sucking. He argues that the absence of these techniques in the West makes our babies cry, and that their use should encourage the child to be more relaxed during the first three or four months of life, and therefore easier later on. Some of the ideas are also used by others, not least Gina Ford, but this system is more adaptable.*
/ *www.thehappiestbaby.com Karp's web site sells a DVD or video of the technique, plus 'womb service'. .*

[Booklet] **Colic & other Manifestation of Food Intolerance in Normal Breast-fed Infants and Their Families** – Maureen Minchin (£1) / Action Against Allergy (020) 8892 2711 – SAE to PO Box 278, Twickenmham TW1.

Crying – Anna McGrail (Simple steps to cope; NCT/Thorson Books; 1999; £5.99 (order 0870 900 2050); 0722536097) – *Why babies cry; the difficult process of differentiating the different meanings of different sounds; also feeding, colic, teething, and advice on when to consult an expert.*

Practical Parenting Problem Solvers: Crying – Eileen Hayes (Macmillan; 1999; £5.99; 0-330370-51-0) – *Why babies cry, what they are trying to communicate and how to cope with it.*

Secrets of the Baby Whisperer – Tracy Hogg with Melinda Blau (How to calm, connect and communicate with your baby; Vermilion; 2001; £9.99; 0-09-185702-3) – *As a babycare book this has the major advantage of recognising that babies don't all behave or react in the same way, and offers basic categories (Angel, Textbook, Touchy, Spirited and Grumpy) and their likely needs and preferences. For complete novices, there are pointers on what different types of cries might mean. The overall tone is warm but firm. A further title covers similar issues for toddlers.*
/ *www.randomhouse.co.uk the author's web site www.babywhisperer.com sells an audio tape for breastfeeding mothers, designed to reduce anxiety. .*

USEFUL CONTACTS

Cry-sis, ☎ Helpline (020) 7404 5011 ⏱ www.cry-sis.com
Cry-sis, a voluntary self-help group run by parents who have experienced the problem of a crying, sleepless or particularly demanding baby (or young child). A network of volunteers offer practical advice, reassurance and a sympathetic ear. / HOURS Mon-Sun 9am-10pm; PUBLICATIONS Information on why babies cry excessively, or sleep poorly and possible solutions – SAE.

National Society for the Prevention of Cruelty to Children (NSPCC), ☎ Helpline (0800) 800500 ⏱ www.nspcc.org.uk
Offers a leaflet on how best to handle babies (for example not holding them with their head unsupported or shaking them). / HOURS 24hr helpline.

Why Cry, ☎ (01903) 889 520 ⏱ www.why-cry.co.uk
Hand held electronic unit to analyse why a baby is crying. It gives a read out in 20 seconds and comes with a guide with pointers on rectifying the situation. Apparently, it has a 95% success rate. The point is not to replace a parent's natural ability to understand their child, but to create an awareness of the importance of interpreting crying, so aiding emotional development and increasing IQ. The unit costs some £70, including delivery.

7. SLEEP PROBLEMS

(Sleep problems are often linked with developmental difficulties – for details of which see below.)

There are an estimated 30-plus sleep clinics across London designed to help parents get their children to sleep at what they consider appropriate times and for appropriate periods.

Some sleep clinics are only open to parents registered with the health centre at which the clinic operates. Others will see anyone interested in attending. Some clinics operate as drop-ins, others require appointments.

If your child has sleep problems your health visitor should be able to refer you to a sleep clinic. These can offer the intensive support which can help parents rebuild any lost confidence over the matter of sleeping.

Approaches all basically feature the introduction of some form of routine, but diet and supplements are also sometimes discussed.

READING

The Good Sleep Guide for You and Your Baby ★ – Angela Henderson (Hawthorn Press; 2003; £5.99; 1-903458358) – *An up-dated edition of a word-of-mouth bestseller on getting babies of 0-18 months to sleep. It's short, and simple enough for exhausted parents to be able to follow, summarising the best known approaches and experts, and then summarising that information in pointers; there's also a sleep diary to help monitor progress and extra tips for example on diet. / www.babysleepguide.co.uk.*

[Tape] **Coping with Children's Sleep Problems** – Royal College of Psychiatrists (Talking Life; 1998; £8.50 inc p&p; 1901910172) – *A self-help programme for parents. / Talking Life, PO Box 1, Wirral, L47 7DD tel: 0151 632 0662 www.talkinglife.co.uk.*

How to Get a Good Night's Sleep – Heather Welford (Thorsons; 1995; £4.99; 0-722531-10-9) – *A slim volume, with a number of reassuring first-person accounts.*

[Video] **Its Time To Sleep UK** – *A step-by-step guide one how to teach babies and toddlers to sleep independently, and through the night; produced in Australia in association with Rhonda Abrahams a mothercraft nurse who won a small business award for creating a Baby Sleep and Settling Centre in a Melbourne Hospital. / 20 Kingsmead, Sawbridgeworth, Herts, CM21 9EY, 01279 600702, http://www.itstimetosleepuk.com/.*

NCT Book of Sleep – Penney Hames (Harper Collins; 1999; £5.99; 0722536089) – *A baby's sleep needs; bedtime routines; deciding where the baby sleeps; managing broken nights; parental sleep needs.*

NCT Help Your Baby to Sleep – Penney Hames (Thorsons; 2002; £6.99; 0-00-713605-6) – *Information and practical steps to help babies sleep through the night; covers a baby's requirements for sleep, bedtime routines, where the baby sleeps, broken nights and meeting your own sleep needs. / NCT Maternity Sales (0870) 112 1120 www.nctms.co.uk.*

Night-time Parenting – William Sears (How to get your baby and child to sleep; Leche League International; 1999; £9.95; 0912500530) – *A US title relying on 'attachment' parenting options – i.e. not just leaving the child to get on with it – including practical ideas and strategies. / La Leche League Books Ltd.*

The Parentalk Guide to Sleep – Kate Daymond and John Byrne (Hodder & Stoughton; 2001; £5.99; 0340785411) – *A small book with simple explanations of the different ways to help your child sleep well. It encourages parents to trust their instincts.*

Sleep – Siobhan Stirling (Helping your child to sleep through the night; Hamlyn; 2003; £5.99; 0600606643) – *A guide full of strategies for getting the child to sleep through, including how to deal with nightmares, early waking, and bed wetting (plus steps to minimise the risk of cot death). The format is notably user-friendly. / www.hamlyn.co.uk.*

Sleepless Children – Dr David Haslam (A handbook for parents; Piatkus; 1992; £7.99; 0-749911-24-7) – *Practical advice from a doctor who has suffered himself with sleepless babies; a relaxed approach, that considers the options in a consoling manner.*

[Video] **Snoozie Babe** – Manchester Sleep Clinic (A parent's guide to better sleep for children; Trafford Area NHS; £9.99 + £2.99 p&p) – *Produced by an NHS clinic – a 15-minute video using case histories showing how to handle problems step by step. / Snoozie Babe, PO Box 70, Didsbury, Manchester M20 2EX.*

Solve Your Child's Sleep Problems – Dr Richard Ferber (A practical and comprehensive guide for parents; Dorling Kindersley; 1986; £7.99; 0863181228) – *Written by an American paediatrician who runs a sleep clinic in Boston and who has done a lot of research into children's sleep patterns. His advice is rigid and will not suit all parents or children but he's become well enough known for the verb to Ferberize to have entered the American language.*

Calms crying babies

Nothing causes parents more unhappiness, distress and exhaustion than a baby crying inconsolably. Happily there is an answer - the **'Jaygee Babysooth'**® CD with its unique rhythmic sounds and background of 'pink noise'. This Award winning product soothes over 90% of crying babies in minutes, pacifies babies when they are overtired and fretful and takes over when cuddling and rocking etc.fails. It also comforts through colic and teething and helps babies drift off to sleep so making night time waking and feeding less stressful.

It works

In fact the **Jaygee Babysooth** -® CD. aids parent/ child bonding by lowering tension, which allows you to relax and enjoy your new baby.

Originally the **'Jaygee Babysooth'** CD was **'The Baby Soother'** cassette. This under went 10 months of testing on 324 babies in maternity hospitals and homes. Astounding results emerged. Using only sounds to settle babies was a new and proven reality.

for more peaceful night ...

- enjoy your new baby ...

Following the discovery of the **'Jaygee Babysooth'**® sounds 25 years ago the media around the world including the UK's "News at Ten";radio's "You and Yours",& the 'World Service', "The Sunday Times", "The Times",the "Daily Mirror", most baby mags and relevant professional journals hailed them a pioneering 'breakthrough in babycare'. Since then hundreds of thousands of families worldwide have benfitted. Parents generally say it's a 'Godsend'. Why not join them?

MUST BE STARTED WITHIN 12 WEEKS OF BIRTH - SOOTHES FOR MONTHS

Jaygee Cassettes, Dept. C., 5, Woodfield, Burnham on Sea, Somerset. TA81QL

PHONE USING VISA/MASTERCARD FOR 24 HOUR ORDERING & 24 HOUR DESPATCH

01278 789352

CD- £9.99 / cassette-£6.99
(add £1p & p - all orders sent First Class Mail)

I enclose a cheque payable to Jaygee Cassettes for a 'JaygeeBabysooth' C.D. £10.99 (includes p & p.) ( ) or 'Baby Soother'cassette' -£7.99 (includes p & p.) ( )

NAME...

ADDRESS..

Jaygee Cassettes, Dept C, 5, Woodfield, Burnham on Sea, Somerset, TAB 1QL

Also available from www. amazon.co.uk; www. whsmith.co.uk ; www. blackwells. com; www. pickabook. co.uk

Full details &/or immediate download of an MP3 version

- www.babysooth.com-

Three in a Bed – Deborah Jackson (The benefits of sleeping with your baby; Bloomsbury; 1999; £12.99; 0747542953) – *Argues that the natural place for parents to sleep is in physical contact with their children and that approaches to the contrary stem from no more than Victorian prejudices and slum standards of hygiene. Ideal reading for those who want to be convinced.*

Through the Night – Dilys Daws (Helping parents and sleepless infants; Free Association Books; 1993; £14.95; 1-853430-69-2) – *Second edition by a consultant child psychotherapist at the Tavistock Clinic. The approach is based on the working of the family as a whole.*

USEFUL CONTACTS

Andrea Grace (RGN, RMN, BA, Dip HV), ☎ *(020) 8348 6959*
Independent health visitor who specialises in such problems in babies and children and the creation of individual sleep plans; her approach aims to be practical, child-centred and not to cause trauma (to child or parents). £90 package, in-home one hour consultation with unlimited telephone support thereafter; Discount for North Londoners.

Baby Sleep Guide, ☎ *Orderlinen (0702) 092 2750*
⏱ *www.babysleepguide.co.uk*
An online and mail order source of the eponymous publication (plus a CD of New Age music called Baby Sleep). / HOURS *10am-9pm 7 days a week.*

The Healthy Start Clinic, ☎ *(020) 7411 5660, (020) 7411 5686*
An NHS clinic open to all, providing help with skills like massage and improving parenting skills. Issues covered include persistent infant crying, sleeping and feeding difficulties, toddler management, behaviour management, and positive parenting. Also operates in Streatham Common. Clients in Lambeth only. Phone advice open to all. Two evening clinics a week on Monday and Thursday. Call for an appointment. / HOURS *Clinic: Wed-Fri 9.30am-5pm.*

Talking Life, ☎ *(0151) 632 0662* ⏱ *www.talkinglife.co.uk*
A leading supplier of self-help health programmes on audio cassette to the NHS (the tapes produced in conjunction with specialist doctors and health charities). Prices are from £8.50 per tape. Coping with Children's Sleep Problems – produced with the Royal College of Psychiatrists – offers strategies to deal effectively with some of the most common childhood sleep problems.

The Tavistock Clinic, ☎ *(020) 7435 7111* ⏱ *www.tavi-port.org*
NHS psychotherapeutic centre where treatment is available to those living in certain areas of London, subject to a referral from a health professional. The clinic's under-5s counselling service is reported as being particularly good at dealing with sleeplessness. / HOURS *Mon-Fri: 9-5.30pm for enquries, longer hours for appointments.*

8. ALLERGY

According to a Finnish study, 19% of babies are allergic to something at 12 months old, 27% at three years old and 8% at six years old. The Paediatric Allergy Clinic reports that 15–18% of children are now allergic to something and a report by the Royal College of Physicians in 2003 indicated that numbers are continuing to grow. In occasional, very severe cases, simple skin contact with the allergen can provoke an attack

Various sources blame a laundry list of causes for childhood allergy. These include: overheated or small rooms, poor ventilation, modern washing techniques (no more boiling of fabrics or very hot washes), air pollution, population density, cigarette smoke, petrol fumes, pollen, house dust and related mites, gas, paint, man-made fibre bedding, plus chlorine in water.

There is growing speculation that over-cleanliness may be to blame with lower rates of asthma, for example among children living in the country or with pets. On this basis, anti-bacterial soaps may be best avoided.

Once sensitised to one trigger, it seems that sensitivities to others may follow. Antibiotics have been found on occasion to trigger temporary lactose intolerance and may be implicated in other temporary allergies.

The role of diet is controversial, particularly as food intolerance is often mistaken for allergy. (An allergic reaction involves the immune system and the effect is rapid, whereas intolerance generally involves the endocrine system, indicating a lack of the required enzymes to digest food and takes a few hours to develop.) A more widely recognised cause of allergy is if either parents' family has a history of atopy, i.e. asthma, hayfever or eczema.

Symptoms indicating allergies or intolerances are multifarious but the AAA lists vomiting, colic, fevers, snuffles, persistent coughs, wheezing, eczema, asthma, regular ear and other infections, frequent colds, altered sleep patterns, bloating, blood in stools, poor appetite, sweating, hyper-activity or lethargy, dry skin and easy bruising as possible signs. In children allergy may also cause an accumulation of fluid in the middle ears, leading to reduced hearing.

There isn't really a cure for allergy. The idea is that the carers help you find out exactly what to avoid, or what drugs to use to alleviate the symptoms. However, some of the techniques detailed under Eczema and Environmental allergy below may also help. Given the limitations of tra-ditional medicine in this area, some parents turn to complementary practitioners (see chapter *4.02 Complementary medicine & Health practi-tioners*).

READING

The Allergy Handbook (What Doctors Don't Tell You; 1998; £7.35 inc p&p; none) – *A round-up of recent investigations into the subject by researchers looking for alternatives to conventional wisdom.* / WDDTY (020) 8944 9555, www.wddty.co.uk.

Allergy Solutions – Suzannah Olivier (You Are What You Eat; Pocket Books; 2001; £6.99; 0671773135) – *A look at possible causes of the general increase in allergies, as well as the role of the immune system, how allergy tests work, the effects of pollution and the possible role of diet.*

The Daily Telegraph The Complete Guide to Allergies – Pamela Brooks (All your questions answered on allergies, their symptoms, causes and treatment; Robinson Publishing; 2001; £9.99; 1-84119-161-2) – *Most useful for the A-Z of potential allergens which makes up most of the book, the guide also includes details of different types of allergy testing, possible symptoms and treatments. An explanation of what actually happens in an allergic reactions is also given.*

Is This Your Child? – Doris J Rapp MD (Discovering and treating unrecognised allergies in children and adults; Quill; 1992; $15; 0688119077) – *A quick reference answering all questions which you are likely to want to ask.*

Your Child: Allergies – Bridgid McConville (Practical and easy-to-follow advice; Element Books; 1999; £5.99; 1-862044-99-6) – *Designed to help parents understand, support and care for their child.*

USEFUL CONTACTS

Action Against Allergy, ☎ (020) 8892 2711

The association encourages diagnosis and treatment through the NHS and maintains a register of resources. It also acts as an information centre on all aspects of allergy and allergic illness, treatments, and offers a specialist referral service to your nearest NHS allergy clinic or private allergy specialist (£5); membership is £15. / PUBLICATIONS AAA *Suppliers' List details sources of additive-free natural foods; leaflets on allergy –* SAE, Mothers, Babies and Young Children, £2; *Pesticides in Food & the Environment factsheet, £1;* Anaphylaxis – the Extreme Allergic Reaction, 80p; Introducing Formula and Solids to Babies, 50p.

Allergy UK, ☎ (020) 8303 8525, Allergy helpline (020) 8303 8583

✆ www.allergyfoundation.com
Founded by a group of medical specialists, the organisation (formerly known as the British Allergy Foundation) is concerned with all allergies; deals with parents' queries and supplies patient information and product advice; membership £10. / HOURS helpline Mon-Fri 9am-5pm (manned by allergy specialist nurse); PUBLICATIONS *Excellent leaflets on milk; managing peanut allergy; avoiding house dust mites; a product information sheet gives details of cleaning sprays and foams, vacuum cleaners, contacts for wooden flooring and bedding systems.*

The British Institute for Allergy & Environmental Therapy, ☎ (01974) 241376 ⏁ www.allergy.org.uk

Previously called the Institute of Allergy Therapists (and known locally as Ffynnonwen Natural Therapy Centre) – a group of therapists and health professionals, both in orthodox and alternative medicine, who have undergone specialist training in the diagnosis and treatment of food, chemical and environmental allergy. The organisation offers members of the public brief advice and a referral list for more detailed consultation.

The British Society for Allergy & Clinical Immunology, ☎ (020) 7637 9711 ⏁ www.soton.ac.uk/~bsaci/

A medical association, primarily for doctors: they can supply details of NHS allergy clinics for GP referral – write giving details of your GP, and information on the member clinics will be sent to your GP; for basic advice, they refer to the British Allergy Foundation (see also).

British Society for Allergy, Environmental & Nutritional Medicine, ☎ Advice line (0906) 302 0010 ⏁ www.bsaenm.org

Previously known as the British Society for Nutritional and Environmental Medicine, this organisation provides information to GPs rather than the general public. If your GP is not an allergy specialist it can refer your GP to someone who is; they can also supply a list of 'environmental practitioners' near you; their recommended doctors have experience and an interest in the health impact of environmental factors and food sensitivity; (the advice line is charged at 50 per minute). / PUBLICATIONS *Effective Allergy Practice, Effective Nutritional Medicine – £5.*

Ecozone, ☎ (020) 8777 3121 ⏁ www.ecozone.co.uk

A supplier of cleaning products low in chemicals, plus a bagless vacuum cleaner with water filter to trap the dirt. Also Medibed products designed to prevent the passage of mites but not the flow of air.

Merton Books, ☎ (020) 8892 4949 ⏁ www.mertonbooks.co.uk

Offers a mail order service covering self-help health titles, with a wide range on allergy. / HOURS *Mon-Fri 9:30am-5pm.*

National Society for Research into Allergy, ☎ (01455) 250715 ⏁ www.all-allergy.co.uk

Founded in 1980, this charity offers a telephone helpline, magazine, information pack and expert help on diets, nutrition and treatments, including a dietary elimination and re-introduction programme for babies and children; £15 for one-year membership, £10 thereafter.

Paediatric Allergy & Immunology Clinic, ☎ (020) 7886 6384

An NHS clinic providing consultation, skin-testing and treatment for patients under 16 years old. GP referral is necessary.

Sensitif Products, ☎ (0800) 074 8445 ⏁ www.sensitif.co.uk

Suppliers of 'anti-allergen' products – from domestic cleaning products to shampoos and hand gels – without pesticides, caustics, volatile organic compounds, sodium laurel sulphate, petroleum distillates, glycol ethers, benzyl benzoates or perfumes. / HOURS *Mon-Fri 10am-6pm.*

Space Air Solutions, ☎ (01483) 252 240/504 8883 ⏁ www.spaceairsolutions.com

Sells the Siesta photocatalytic air purifier from Daikin which is designed to collect dust, pollen, pet hairs, smoke, and other pollution, to kill germs, and even to balance ions. A filter sheet lasts 6-8 months and the filter roll 4-7 years. The machine can be remote controlled and wall mounted or free standing. Retail price is £359.

Asthma

This condition is not necessarily, but may be, triggered by an allergy. Asthma affects the airways of the lungs, sensitivity to any number of triggers causing the airways to tighten and swell, making the breathing difficult – potentially causing the 'wheezing' commonly associated with asthmatics. Other symptoms may include coughing (particularly at night or after exercise), a 'whistling' noise in the chest, and getting short of breath.

Asthma or wheezing affects an estimated one in seven children under five years in the UK with around two-thirds outgrowing the condition by school age. It is difficult to diagnose asthma in children as a pattern of symptoms must be studied before a doctor can do so conclusively.

The tendency to develop asthma is known to run in families. Until recently, breast-feeding for at least four months was suggested as a way that that parents with asthma could reduce the chances of their child developing the condition. (Also keeping the house smoke-free and keeping the child away from potential allergens, such as furred or feathered pets, pollen or house-dust mites). However, a recent study suggested that breast-feeding might not offer the protection once thought, suggesting that lack of vitamin D might be more of a problem. Breastfeeding mothers are therefore recommended to take additional vitamin D, or two teaspoons of cod liver oil.

Air pollution is not thought to cause asthma, but can worsen symptoms already present.

Asthma is treated with two types of medicines: one to relieve breathing difficulties, and another to protect the airways and prevent attacks. Both are administered through inhalers – 'preventer' medicines are taken daily, and 'reliever' medicines administered whenever the child becomes wheezy, or before exercise. Preventers contain low-dose corticosteroids (not the same as anabolic steroids).

Complementary therapies may help if used in conjunction with inhalers. Swimming is an excellent form of exercise for children with asthma.

READING

Asthma: The Complete Guide for Sufferers and Carers – Deryk Williams (Piatkus; 1997; £9.99; 0749916060) – *Ranges from background information to everyday procedures.*

Your Child: Asthma – Erika Harvey (Practical and easy to follow advice; Element Books; 1998; £5.99; 1-86204-207-1) – *Living with a child with asthma, the treatments available, the practical steps to take and how to cope positively.*

USEFUL CONTACTS

Action Asthma, ⌂ www.actionasthma.co.uk
An Internet-based programme sponsored by drugs company Allen & Hanbury's (part of Glaxo Wellcome) with personal diary and "online health tools"; paper-based newsletter also available.

Kingston Natural Healing Centre, ☎ (020) 8546 5793
⌂ www.surrey-online.co.uk/knhe
This complementary health clinic offers a specialist treatment for the relief of asthma, called Buteyko; originating from Russia, the treatment focuses on breathing control. / HOURS Mon-Fri 9am-5pm.

National Asthma Campaign, ☎ Helpline (08457) 010203
⌂ www.asthma.org.uk
The leading national charity in the area provides a helpline (manned by asthma nurses) and information booklets for parents (as well as for teachers and medical professionals). / HOURS Helpline Mon-Fri 9am-5pm; PUBLICATIONS *A booklet covers causes, diagnosis, different patterns, medicines, preventing onset and management; Asthma & Pregnancy covers the issue for mothers suffering from the problem; factsheets (also online) on asthma and babies, under 5s and diet.*

Eczema

Eczema appears to be the most common form of allergy in babies and its incidence appears to be on the increase. However, it does not usually persist, with two out of five who suffer as babies growing out of the condition by the age of two, and eight out of ten by the age of five. (However, that still leaves an estimated one in five schoolchildren suffering it to some degree.)

Broadly speaking, types of eczema fall into two categories: atopic eczema (to which there is a genetic predisposition and a link with hay fever and asthma); and contact eczema, which is caused by direct contact with a substance which causes the skin to react badly. (There is also a condition called seborrhoeic eczema, which is most common in the first three months of life and typically doesn't persist for more than a few months. On the scalp it is known as 'cradle cap', but it also can affect the nappy area, face, neck or armpits.)

One of the problems with eczema is that its causes are many and varied. In the case of contact eczema sufferers, the substances that may be responsible include washing powders, oils, foods, nickel, rubber and even some plants. Being a condition with multiple causes, there is no one solution to suit everyone.

Pointers:

➤ Emollients (specialist moisturisers) for the skin and steroids (used with caution) are the main treatments, though sometimes these become ineffective with time.

➤ Note washing dries skin so bathing should be swift and not too hot; olive and almond oil in the water are good moisturisers. Avoid perfumed soaps or bubble baths, and wash hair separately to avoid skin irritation from shampoo. Try bath oil rather than soap. Alternatively some of the suppliers listed under Chapter 3.09 *Lotions & potions* have relevant products.

➤ Baking soda (sodium bicarbonate) added to a lukewarm bath is suggested as a mild antiseptic, opening pores and relieving itching and irritation in a 10-20-minute soak; hanging a clean cotton sock filled with porridge oats in the bath water apparently works on a similar principle.

➤ If the condition is particularly bad there are 'wet wraps' – gauze wrapped over creams.

➤ Discomfort is often linked to clothes and fabric irritating the skin. Temperature can also play a big part so cotton and other natural fabric clothing is often recommended. Specialist clothes (see opposite) are available to minimise irritation and for optimum results need to fit firmly – to avoid bags and creases – without being too tight.

➤ Avoid clothing and bedding labelled as easycare, stain resistant, non-iron or crease resistant, as the chemicals used may cause problems. Similarly avoid nightdresses sold in the UK or any nightwear from the US (by law they must be dipped in flame-proofing chemicals).

➤ Avoid washing clothes and bedding at low temperatures and with biological detergents and fabric conditioners.

➤ Be sensitive to room temperature, particularly at night-time.

➤ Minimise environmental irritants (see pg. 250).

➤ Diet is believed by some to play a role with tips including cutting out dairy products except butter (in the mother if breastfeeding a pre-weaned child), while eating other calcium-rich foods like green, leafy vegetables, sesame seeds, beans and pulses. Additionally essential fatty acids (such as those found in nuts, seeds and oily fish) are reported helpful. Given that some children turn up their noses at such ingredients, an alternative is to use a supplement.

➤ Excitement can exacerbate the problem, so it can be helpful to keep levels down.

It may be worth visiting your GP and asking for a referral to a dermatgist (skin conditions are not part of a GP's standard training). Becauseof a shortage of specialists expect a wait; even when going privately it can take around six weeks.

Some people also turn to complementary therapies such as herbalism, homeopathy and acupuncture *(See chapter 4.02 Complementary medicine & Health practitioners.)*. Complementary practitioners generally see the problem as an attempt by the body to eliminate material it can't handle – whether foods, substances like soap or nappy chemicals, or prescribed drugs. The practitioner will look for a suitable product to nourish the skin but also generally seek to boost the immune system.

USEFUL CONTACTS

Eczemavoice, ⌁ www.eczemavoice.com
A website for support and exchange of information.

National Eczema Society, ☎ Infoline (0870) 241 3604 ⌁ www.eczema.org
Eczema (estimated by the society to affect one person in 10) is closely linked to asthma and hay fever and involves sensitivity to a wide range of environmental factors. The society offers pointers on the problem, advice and information on treatments, and a list of potentially useful products (cotton clothes, and so on). Membership at £20 provides local contacts, together with a quarterly magazine with the latest news and tips from other members; the NES also administers the Skin Care Campaign. / HOURS *Mon-Fri 9am-5pm;* PUBLICATIONS *free information sheets (subjects include cradle cap, wet wrapping and Chinese medicinal plants for treatment); diet information packs (one covers birth-12 years, with information on general care and management, £10 or free to members).*

The Psoriasis Association, ☎ *(01604) 711129*
⌁ www.psoriasis-association.org.uk
Advice for parents about how best to handle this skin condition which is different from, but bears similarities to eczema. Although it is rare in children under four,
and generally diagnosed later on in life, over 1.5 million people in the UK are known to be affected. It is neither infectious nor contagious, and is caused by a massively accelerated skin replacement process; symptoms include raised red patches of skin covered with silvery scales; treatments vary according to the severity of attacks. / HOURS *Mon-Thurs 9.15am-4.45pm, Fri 9.15am-4.15pm;* PUBLICATIONS *Leaflet: Psoriasis in Children; Guttate Psoriasis; Sore Throats and Psoriasis; newsletter available to members.*

Talk Eczema, ⌁ www.talkeczema.com
Set up by the mother of an eczema sufferer to bring together families affected by the condition; information sources, recommendations of books and products, and online chat.

SPECIALIST CLOTHING SUPPLIERS

E Sharp Minor, ☎ *(020) 8858 6648* ⌁ www.esharpminor.co.uk
Clothes sold by this firm are suitable for most children with eczema. / HOURS *shop & mail order enquiries Tue-Sat 10am-4pm.*

The Healthy House, ☎ *(01453) 752216* ⌁ www.healthy-house.co.uk
Baby suits (as well as creams and gloves). / HOURS *9am-5pm. 24 hr message.*

Over The Moon Babywear, ⌁ www.overthemoon-babywear.co.uk
This online retailer of clothes for under-twos lists all clothes made using only natural fibres in a separate section.

Pure Cotton Comfort, ☎ *(01524) 730 093* ⌁ www.eczemaclothing.com
100% Edo-Tex standard cotton, suitable for high-temperature washes, with flat seams inside and out, removable labels and soft-ribbed edges and seams sewn with cotton thread. Items include underwear, nightwear, reusable nappies, hats, mittens, T-shirts and sleepsuits. It is produced by the mother of a child with severe eczema who notes that not all organic cotton is suitable as the fabric may still include itchy particles of cotton husk.

Schmidt Natural Clothing, ☎ *(0845) 345 0498*
⌁ www.naturalclothing.co.uk
Nappies and clothing made from untreated organic cotton, silk and wool; a specialised sleepsuit has enclosed hands and feet to prevent scratching and further irritation from eczema. / HOURS *Mon-Fri 9am-6pm, 24hr answerphone.*

Silk Story, ☎ *(01869) 277181* ⌁ www.silkstory.com
Pure silk jersey baby and childrenswear – absorbent, soft and light, it allows skin to breathe, reduces rashes and irritation, and may be helpful for babies with eczema. Machine washable. / HOURS *24hr answerphone.*

SPECIALIST PRODUCTS

Kobashi
2 Fore St, Ide Devon EX2 9RQ ☎ *(01392) 217628* ⌁ *www.kobashi.com*
The Kobashi baby lotion with lavender, chamomile, Aloe Vera, borage and natural
vitamin E is claimed to be useful in treating eczema. / HOURS *Mon-Fri 8:30am-6pm; SEE ALSO*
4.02 Health practitioners.

The Natural Bodycare Company
27 High St, Redbourn Herts AL3 7LE ☎ *(01582) 794993* ⌁ *www.natural-bodycare.com*
Natural, fragrance free and non-allergenic products, recommended for children with
eczema; gift baskets from £1.65-£20. / HOURS *Mon-Fri 8am-6pm, or answerphone.*

Verde
3 Princes Close, Old Town SW4 0LQ
☎ *Mail order & advice line (020) 7720 1100, Office (020) 7720 1122*
15 Flask Walk NW3 3HG
☎ *(020) 7431 3314*
75 Northcote Rd SW11 6PJ
☎ *(020) 7223 2095*
Chamomile Baby Body Balm is recommended for eczema and cradle cap. / HOURS *Mon-*
Sat 10am-6pm (SW11 opens at 9.30am), Sun noon-6pm (NW3 only); SEE ALSO 3.09 Lotions & potions;
4.02 Health practitioners.

Weleda
Heanor Rd, Ilkeston Derbyshire DE7 8DR ☎ *(0115) 944 8200* ⌁ *www.weleda.co.uk*
Calendula baby moisturising cream is suitable for children with eczema. / HOURS *Mon-Fri:*
9am-5pm ; SEE ALSO 3.09 Lotions & potions; 4.02 Health practitioners.

Environmental allergy

Some allergies, rather than being caused by internal problems (notably
food), are caused by external factors. Examples include a wide range of
substances if they come into contact with the skin (metal is just one) but
also airborne materials such as pet hairs and dust mites. Dust mites are
commonly cited as the most likely cause of many allergies, and are an
obvious factor to try to eliminate should your child be suffering this kind
of problem.

Warmth and damp both encourage mites so should be discouraged.
Washing at 60°C or more kills these bugs, so consider such a fortnightly
wash for all sheets, pillowcases and duvet covers (and possibly even curtains). Freezing also kills them – a suitable treatment for soft toys is leaving
them in the freezer for at least six hours. Pillows, mattresses, carpets and
soft furnishings also tend to harbour mites, and you will need a high-effi-
ciency vacuum cleaner to suck them out of the fibres – ideally when the
child is out of the house. The British Allergy Foundation (see listings,
above) offers a list of approved models. In the intervening periods wet
dusting can be helpful.

Micro-porous membrane covers for mattresses, pillows and duvets
offer a barrier to house dust mites and their droppings but still allow moisture through, but are generally only available full size. So-called 'air
cleaners', (for example, those produced by Honeywell, see listings below)
may be helpful with airborne allergies.

USEFUL CONTACTS

Air Improvement Centre, ☎ *(020) 7834 2834*
⌁ *www.air-improvement.co.uk*
Wide range of air cleaners starting at £70. / HOURS *Mon-Fri 9am-5pm, Sat 10am-1am.*

Allerbreathe, ☎ *(01752) 662317*
A soft, breathable form of protective bedding to protect against dust mites –
manufactured by a non profit-making organisation providing jobs for the disabled;
available by mail order.

The Healthy House, ☎ (01453) 752216 ⌁ www.healthy-house.co.uk

Mail order suppliers of dust mite barrier cases for mattresses and pillows; boil-washable pillows; wool pillows and duvets; unbleached and undyed sheets and organic cotton duvets. / HOURS 9am-5pm. 24 hr message.

The Wholistic Research Company, ☎ (01438) 833100
⌁ www.wholisticresearch.com

Mail order suppliers of a range of 'health' products, including dust mite control aids using a tannic acid spray which the company claims is less dangerous than standard chemicals. / HOURS Mon-Fri 9am-5pm; PUBLICATIONS Leaflets (for example with suggestions for avoiding high heat and humidity).

Food allergy

A study reported in 2001 by the British Nutrition Foundation found that only 1–2% of adults are food intolerant, but 5–8% of children are (with a US study suggesting it is commoner in boys than girls). However, 90% of intolerances are reported outgrown by the age of three.

The number of sufferers appears to be increasing, although the explanation for this is not obvious. The only thing that can be said for certain is that this is a field where nobody definitely has the answers, but a lot of people claim that they do.

The foods most commonly cited as potential triggers include: wheat, corn, soy, nuts (and nut oils), eggs, tea, coffee, citrus fruit, sesame seeds, tomatoes, pepper and yeast, plus certain food additives. Cow's milk (see below) and goat's milk are also on the potential 'hit list', along with fish.

Some commentators recommend avoiding problematic foods entirely for at least the first nine months of a baby's life, if not the first year, particularly if there is any history of allergy in the family. The logic is that the infant gut is more permeable than an adults' and allows material to pass through, which it would not in a more developed system, thereby causing reactions which may result in allergy.

Any early eczema would be an indicator for proceeding carefully with food and bodycare products, including skin creams (for example, those including arachis – an oil made from peanuts or groundnuts), unless treated to remove potential allergens (see chapter *3.09 Lotions & potions*). However, eliminating basic foods from the diet can cause significant nutritional deficiencies, and you will probably need the help of a qualified nutritionist or dietician if you are considering this strategy to any significant degree.

There is an argument that cutting out foods, and then reintroducing them can increase sensitivity. An opposing one argues that eliminating a problem food for three months allows the body to recover so there will be no reaction when it is reintroduced.

With very high-risk cases – i.e. with severe allergy already in the family – breast-feeding mothers are also sometimes recommended to avoid doubtful foods. Whether allergens are transported in breast-milk (or through the placenta) is still much debated however.

Allergy testing is done by GP referral by a skin prick test or blood test. Based upon these results, testing the elimination of certain foods from your child's diet may be suggested.

If you know there is a problem it is also helpful to get a RAST (radioallergosorbent) test as soon as possible so you know its magnitude. The test measures the level of antibodies in an individual to a specific substance.

NUTS, EGGS AND SHELLFISH (ANAPHYLAXIS)

Nuts and their derivative oils – particularly peanuts and sesame seeds – and also eggs and shellfish, are possible causes of anaphylaxis. This life-threatening reaction is the most severe of allergies. Symptoms in young children include: abdominal pain; vomiting; swelling of the lips, tongue and face; rashes; shortness of breath; possibly falling blood pressure; and loss of consciousness. Peanut butter is therefore now positively discouraged as a food for weaning and should probably be avoided until after your child is three years old – seven years old according to some sources, and 12 years old in families where there is a known history of allergies. Sensitisation, it is suggested, may occur with the use of nipple creams containing peanut oil.

MILK AND FORMULA MILK (ANAPHYLAXIS; LACTOSE-INTOLERANCE)

(For information on brands of soya-based and other specialist formulas, see chapter 2.02 Feeding.)

Milk is thought by many commentators to be an allergen and in rare cases – as with nuts and eggs (above) – it can trigger an anaphylactic shock. Casein intolerance is also linked (anecdotally, but not scientifically) with apparently unrelated problems such as autism.

Estimates vary, but it is claimed that one in five babies is allergic to cow's milk (up to 90% of adult Asian and black people are also estimated by some sources to be lactose intolerant). Such commentators believe bottle-feeding can produce symptoms such as diarrhoea, wind, stomach cramps, runny nose, sore throat, ear infections and possibly as many as 60% of cases of asthma. One theory is that the human digestive system turns the casein in cow's milk into indigestible, solid curds. Heating milk helps avoid this process, hence milk used in cooked foodstuffs is not thought to be problematic.

Soya milk and soya-based formula is usually the recommended alternative to cow's milk and standard formula. However, some estimates put the level of allergy just as high for soya milk as for cow's milk and they usually contain sugar which can cause tooth decay. (Moreover some questions have been raised about the safety of soya products, as they contain phytoestrogens – substances similar to oestrogens.) Soya-based formula is available without a prescription, but general advice is only to feed it to your baby if advised to do so by a doctor.

As well as soya-based formulas, there are also hypo-allergenic brands from which the allegedly allergenic proteins of cow's milk have been removed. These milks generally require a prescription. Moreover they are said not to be very palatable, so they are probably best introduced before weaning, after which time it may be difficult to persuade a baby to start drinking them.

Goat's milk is sometimes suggested as an alternative, but the British Allergy Foundation reports that this, like sheep's milk, is unsuitable for a young baby. The organisation further cautions that goat's milk should be treated with care because goats are not subject to the strict hygiene controls enforced on dairy cattle.

CEREALS (COELIAC DISEASE)

Gluten – a protein found naturally in cereals such as wheat – can trigger coeliac disease, especially if eaten before six months. The condition makes it difficult for the digestive system to absorb vitamins and minerals. Sufferers can get gluten-free foods on prescription.

The condition is not classified as an allergy – it is an inflammation of the lining of the small intestine that leads to failure to gain weight, vomiting and diarrhoea. These symptoms do not show from birth, but from after eight or nine months when gluten starts to form an increasingly significant part of the diet. However, these symptoms may have other causes and this should be investigated. Once coeliac disease is diagnosed, the main treatment is a strict gluten-free diet (no wheat, oats, barley or rye) for life.

If you suspect your baby has this condition, the Coeliac Society recommends continuing to feed the child food with gluten as this makes the symptoms 'classic', and diagnosis easier. However, the society does recommend that no solids containing gluten should be given in families with another sufferer until the baby reaches six months.

There has been huge change in the level of awareness and diagnosis of the condition. Only a few years ago, only 300 new childhood cases would be diagnosed each year. The level of diagnosis in the population as a whole is now estimated at 1 in 1,000 on the society's website and in early 2004 research reports in the press suggested the incidence may be as high as 1 in 100.

FOOD ADDITIVES

Research in 2002 on 273 children on the Isle of Wight indicated something many parents have worked out empirically, that additives permitted in children's food cause deterioration in concentration and behaviour. Further research is need but the substances most often cited as likely to be problematic are: sodium benzoate; Tartrazine (E102); Sunset Yellow (E110); and Annatto (E160b).

READING

Allergy Prevention for Kids – Leo Galland (A nutritional guide; Bloomsbury; 1991; £7.99; 0-747510-40-7) – *Nutritional advice for mothers and babies.*

Caring For Your Child With Severe Food Allergies – Lisa Collins (John Wiley & Sons; 1999; £8.99; 0-471347-85-X) – *Emotional support and practical advice from a parent who's been there. / www.wiley.com.*

Caring for Your Child with Severe Food Allergies – Lisa Cipriano Collins (Emotional support and practical advice from a parent who's been there; John Wiley & Son ; US$10.95; 0-471-34785-X) – *By the founder of the US website 'Food Allergy Matters', this title dwells very much on the potential for crisis. However it includes helpful hints about possible signs of allergy (such as an eczemous reaction to eggs or lentils); sound practical advice on how to tackle the issue – including check lists – and how to be aware of the effects of the condition on the whole family.*

Complete Guide to Food Allergy and Intolerance – Dr Jonathan Brostoff & Linda Gamlin (Bloomsbury; 1993, revised 1998; £6.99; 0747534306) – *The intricacies of elimination diets are included in this comprehensive tome, considered the best lay work on the subject; also provides detailed explanation of allergies, chemical sensitivities, the possible role of candida and giardia, causes of food intolerance, and food problems in children; notes that the medical establishment is reluctant to accept as genuine problems which are non-specific and don't always cause the same symptoms, because that runs counter to the causal system which has been in vogue since the discovery of germs.*

Dairy-free, Lactose-free Diet Plan – Carolyn Humphries (Foulsham; 2001; £7.99; 0572026838)

[Magazine] **The Inside Story: Food and Health** (£34.95 a year) – *Information about allergy-related products, research and recipes. / Berrydale House, 5 Lawn Road, London NW3 2XS – (020) 7722 2866.*

USEFUL CONTACTS

Allergy Induced Autism (AIA), ☎ *Helpline (01733) 331771*
🖰 *www.autismmedical.com*
A type of autism linked with food intolerance (and possibly low levels of sulphate in the body) which is usually noticed at 18 months to two years in children who previously showed no sign of such a problem. The organisation is funding research which may

lead to pre- or neonatal screening for the condition. Membership is £10 per annum. / *HOURS Mon-Fri 9am-3.30pm; PUBLICATIONS Leaflet (send SAE); membership (includes information pack and newsletter, £10).*

The Anaphylaxis Campaign, ☎ *(01252) 542029*

www.anaphylaxis.org.uk
"Fighting for those with potentially fatal food allergies" – a campaign to raise the awareness of life-threatening allergies: particularly to dairy products, fish and shellfish, nuts and seeds (including pressing for better labelling of foods). It provides information for those affected on treatments and a midwife/health visitor pack; £5 annual membership (includes newsletter).

The Coeliac Society, ☎ *Helpline (0804) 448804* *www.coeliac.co.uk*

A charity for those suffering from this illness (a sensitivity to gluten that hinders the absorption of food). The advice that the organisation provides includes an annually-updated list of gluten-free food. (Note that membership cannot be made available until a firm diagnosis has been made.) / *HOURS Mon-Fri 9am-5pm.*

Food & Chemical Allergy Association

Free advice – by letter only – on all forms of allergic illness, relating to (among other issues) preconception, pregnancy and newborns showing signs of allergy to milk and other foods. The comprehensive booklet available focuses on the role of sensitivities triggered by a build-up of chemicals in the body from food and the environment, and looks at vitamin therapy as a treatment. / *PUBLICATIONS Understanding Allergies (£2 with A5 SAE).*

Food Intolerance Databank, ☎ *(01372) 376761*

www.leatherheadfood.com
Ask your GP if you need information from this database (accessible only by state registered dieticians and medical practitioners), which holds data on milk, wheat, egg, soya, and Azo-free foods, together with product information on dairy, wheat, soya, egg and additives, such as benzoates and sulphur dioxide. / *HOURS Mon-Fri 9am-5pm.*

Galactosaemia Support Group, ☎ *(0121) 378 5143*

www.gsgnews.tripod.com
The group provides contacts for families, a helpline, food lists and a newsletter for members with this life-threatening and life-long metabolic disease (not an allergy) which renders the sufferer intolerant to milk, due to a missing enzyme.

Health Screening, ☎ *(01823) 325023* *www.healthscreeningltd.com*

A company specialising in testing people (including babies on solids) for allergies and food intolerances. Testing uses acupuncture principles which are claimed to be non-invasive and painless, with instant results. (Formerly called Allergycare, this company no longer sells foods for people with allergies – see Ultrafarm.) / *HOURS Mon-Fri 9am-5pm.*

Kidsaware, ☎ *(01480) 869 244* *www.kidsaware.co.uk*

An online and mail order supplier of awareness products for children with nut allergies. A donation from sales is made to the Anaphylaxis Campaign and Allergy UK. The products aimed at helping young children avoid nuts includes a selection of t-shirts (including tighter fitting for girls), baseball shirts for boys, sweats, caps, stickers, badges and bags, plus bibs and a teddy. The items carry slogans like 'Have a nut free day', and 'Nut Free Zone'. T-shirts start at £8.99 and stickers from £3.50 for 12.

Ultrafarm, ☎ *(01491) 578016*

A mail order company specialising in basic foods for people on special diets, including those with allergies.

9. DEVELOPMENTAL ISSUES

(For information and books on development in relation to play, see Reading in chapter 3.06 Toys. For information on educating children with special educational needs see chapter 2.07 Education.)

All children grow at different rates. Some walk at eight months, some at over two years; some talk before a year – others don't make much sense until they are three. It usually doesn't mean much but especially in today's hyper-competitive society it is incredibly easy to worry about children, and whether they are 'normal' – especially as little Billy down the road appears to be progressing faster.

What is much more difficult is to work out when a child has a true developmental difficulty. The argument that the object of your concern "will grow out of it in time" sounds common-sensical and is often true. But it can also be a dangerous false reason to waste time. This is particularly the case as a state of denial (that there is a true problem) is common in parents – and particularly in fathers and grandparents – of children with developmental problems. Another common concern is that receiving an official diagnosis may stigmatise a child and prejudice the future.

If your child does actually have a problem then early help and intervention can make all the difference in the long term and inaction just squanders that opportunity. What's more, for many parents who have received a serious diagnosis, the grief and shock of the process and worries about stigma are generally quickly outweighed by the relief that comes from accessing resources to help the child.

If you do come to think there may be a serious issue to address, seek an expert diagnosis at the very earliest opportunity as it can take ages for the system to grind into motion, wasting valuable time. By acting well before school age is reached, it may be possible to limit difficulties which might otherwise hamper your child's progress and confidence down the line. Part of these children's problems as they grow is not just their disadvantages, but the poor self-image they develop: in effect there's a risk they just give up.

Don't worry unduly about experts finding problems when there aren't any, especially if you are on the NHS. A diagnosis of a serious developmental difficulty can cost the state many tens of thousands of pounds – failure to have a real problem recognised is a much more common complaint than concerns raised when there aren't any.

Standard developmental checks

Your local surgery or health clinic will invite you to developmental health checks at six to nine months (which may incorporate a hearing test), 18 months to two years, and three to four and a half years. These are very broad brush tests and conducted to varying standards, depending on the health visitor who carries them out. Parents, though, of children where there are concerns have usually developed worries of their own by this stage, however: that their child just doesn't seem to be developing how they expected/like their peers.

HEARING TESTS

Hearing difficulties – in particular undiagnosed ones – can have profound implications for speech and related development, including social development. About 1% of children have some form of significant impairment at birth.

As part of the six to nine month test it has until recently been standard practice to give babies hearing tests. These are notoriously unreliable, however, and are being phased out to be replaced by the Oto-Acoustic Emission Test (OAE), conducted in the first few weeks of life (at the earliest on the postnatal ward). Under the Newborn Hearing Screening Programme (NSP) this should be available across the country by 2005.

The test measures the 'echo' produced by the ear in response to sounds heard. It is extremely accurate and any potential problems are checked with the more detailed Audiological Brainstem Response (ABM). With this early diagnosis, any problems can be tackled from the very start.

In the lifespan of this edition of this guide, however, some readers' babies will still receive the traditional 'distraction' test. Don't be overly alarmed if your child fails this test (which amounts to little more than a carer whispering in your child's ear), nor the first follow up. This test has an extraordinarily high failure rate. On the other hand, if you have reason to be concerned about your child's hearing and have only had one of the old-style tests, push for one of the new ones as well.

If your child fails either test and you have concerns about your child's hearing, ask for a referral to an audiology clinic: 50% of deaf children are currently not diagnosed until 18 months or older, and 23% remain undiagnosed until they are over three.

EYE TESTS

Opinions differ on the right age for a first eye test. Some optometrists say three years, others 18 months. Many parents feel it is only necessary to go for a test if there seems to be a problem.

If you have any concerns, the earlier you go the better. Eye tests are provided free on the NHS until the age of 16, with most opticians being able to provide the necessary application forms.

Note that tests given at baby clinics or health centres are without specialised equipment and carried out by people not qualified to diagnose eye problems.

The optometrist should thoroughly examine children's eyes to check for a visual defect such as long sight, short sight or astigmatism. Sometimes the problem is only in one eye and the child's sight has appeared to be functioning normally on the strength of one good eye.

Problems are most common in children with certain syndromes, those with a low birth weight, or those who were premature babies. An eye co-ordination defect such as a squint or a tendency to squint may be caused by a hereditary factor but is sometimes caused by forceps. Rarely a child may be born with an eye health problem or develop an eye disease in early life.

Diagnosis of more serious concerns

Unless you take your child privately, your GP or health centre will refer you to a member of the local child development team, who will assess whether your concerns have any possible grounding. If appropriate there will then be referrals to a paediatrician or other specialist units.

The endpoint in the diagnostic process is generally a 'multi-disciplinary assessment' where numerous professionals, having submitted reports on your child, gather to give you their collective diagnosis. No matter how worried parents may have become about their child, many are unprepared for the emotional impact of receiving an official label for their child's condition. A period of 'grief' afterwards is not uncommon, despite the obvious fact that the child is just the same child as before any diagnosis.

There tends to be a somewhat messy overlap of responsibilities in the diagnostic process between health and education professionals. Although educational psychologists are involved, the people who lead diagnoses are often doctors and paediatricians. But the 'treatment' and consequences of a diagnosis can have much more to do with the impact on decisions as to how to educate your child than the application of any medication (often there is none).

For more on the issue of finding the right school, see Special needs in chapter *2.07 Education*.

NUTRITIONAL SUPPLEMENTS

There is a growing amount of research into the role that nutritional supplements can play in supporting development. Essential fatty acids for example have been used with some reported success in treating children with learning difficulties. The problem is that too much of any supplement may be toxic and little research has been done on assessing safe quantities for young children. Similarly gluten-free and dairy-free diets are anecdotally reported helpful by many parents of special needs children. Yet depriving a young and growing child of such large food groups needs to be handled with care. Before trying significant supplementation you should obtain expert advice from a practitioner (see chapter 4.02 *Complementary Medicine & Health practitioners*) and possibly a second opinion as well.

CONDITIONS COVERED IN THIS SECTION

Sections below include:
➢ ADHD.
➢ Autism (& Asperger's syndrome).
➢ Dyspraxia.
➢ Dyslexia.

DIAGNOSIS

There are no blood or similar tests for these conditions – diagnosis takes place as part of a multi-disciplinary assessment whereby professionals observe your child, fill out detailed questionnaires and score the answers according to rigidly defined diagnostic scoring systems.

CAUSES

These conditions are still all relatively new to medical science, still quite poorly understood, and in many cases are overlapping. In fact, some doctors see the distinctions between the conditions as a fraction artificial and view the situation, instead, as a 'cloud of problems' with differing children – while falling loosely into one diagnostic camp or other – suffering their own individual 'packages' of difficulties.

GENERAL CONTACTS (FOR INDIVIDUAL DISORDERS SEE SPECIFIC SECTION)

America Hyperlexia Association, ☎ +1 773 216 3333
⌂ www.hyperlexia.org
Hyperlexia is a developmental disorder – akin to autism and ADHD – where alongside normal or heightened intelligence and curiosity a child exhibits a set of traits including noise hypersensitivity and diminished social awareness. The Association's website offers a fund of information about it.

Association for All Speech-Impaired Children (AFASIC),
☎ (020) 7490 9410, Helpline (0845) 355 5577 ⌂ www.afasic.org.uk
An association concerned with children experiencing speech and language difficulties (about one in 10 children encounter some such problem at one time or another): offers information on assessment and diagnosis of any problem; campaigns on the issues; and runs a helpline and local support groups. (A pure language impairment is termed dysphasia; dyspraxia describes difficulty making the movements which produce speech; there are other possible causes of such conditions, for example difficulty with listening.) / HOURS Mon-Fri 11am-2pm; PUBLICATIONS Free publications list and leaflets.

British Stammering Association, ☎ (020) 8983 1003, Helpline (0845) 603 2001 ⌂ www.stammering.org
Stammering tends to develop around two-and-a-half to three years of age. This national organisation provides information and counselling for health professionals and for those worried that their children may have such a problem. For the latter, the association produces a free information pack which helps determine whether you should seek a referral to a speech and language therapist from your GP, and will advise you on going about this. The organisation emphasises that it is important to seek advice on such a potential problem as soon as possible, but also points out that

labelling pre-schoolers as stammerers can cause an early communication difficulty to develop into a confirmed problem. / HOURS *Mon-Fri 9am-5pm, helpline Mon-Fri 10am-4pm;* PUBLICATIONS *Free information pack.*

Child & Family Consultation Centre, ☎ *(020) 8355 1984*
Part of the NHS, the centre is for parents who feel worried about their child's emotional development or behaviour. Must be referred by a professional. / HOURS *9am-5pm.*

Cleft Lip & Palate Association (CLAPA), ☎ *(020) 7431 0033*
🕈 *www.clapa.com*
Such a condition affects one in 700 babies, and the association gives support and information on problems relating to feeding (specialist feeding bottles are available, though breast-feeding can be possible with tuition), hearing, speech, dental care and facial appearance – home visits postnatally may be offered; call for details of local branches. / HOURS *Mon-Fri 9am-5:30pm;* PUBLICATIONS *Help for Parents, a useful general leaflet (as well as ones relating to specific issues).*

Enuresis Resource & Information Centre (ERIC), ☎ *Helpline (0117) 960 3060* 🕈 *www.eric.org.uk*
The organisation provides support and information on enuresis (bed-wetting), as well as soiling and daytime wetting (including information relating to special needs children); it also sells protection against bed-wetting (and alarms for older children). / HOURS *Mon-Fri 10am-4pm.*

Fragile X Society, ☎ *(01371) 875100* 🕈 *www.fragilex.org.uk*
Fragile X results from a 'fragile' area on the X chromosome. Children with it are similar to those with an autistic diagnosis, with mild to severe language and learning difficulties and other characteristics of abnormal development. It may go undiagnosed until the child is older, but unlike many development disorders can be diagnosed with a blood test. It may be found that relatives, though asymptomatic, are carriers. / PUBLICATIONS *Newsletter three times a year.*

Gifted Children Information Centre, ☎ *(0121) 705 4547*
🕈 *www.ukindex.info/giftedchildren.co.uk*
A private centre specialising in assessing gifted, dyslexic and left-handed children, as well as children with Asperger Syndrome and ADHD. The centre offers advice and guidance, publications, legal help and the services of a senior psychiatric social worker to advise on dealing with schools and local authorities. Also psychological, scholastic and IQ assessments, followed by counselling sessions for parents.

I CAN, ☎ *(0845) 225 4071* 🕈 *www.ican.org.uk*
Formerly known as Invalid Children's Aid Nationwide, this organisation works with children with speech and language difficulties, including the provision of special schools. / HOURS *Mon-Fri 9am-5pm.*

Look, ☎ *(0121) 428 5038* 🕈 *www.look-uk.org*
National federation of families with visually impaired children, providing support with local support groups and a quarterly newsletter, and via family support officers. Areas of expertise include explanations of medical terms, applying for benefits, suitable toys and games, and finding further information. / HOURS *Mon-Fri 9am-4pm.*

MENCAP, ☎ *Helpline (0808) 808 1111* 🕈 *www.mencap.org.uk*
The largest UK organisation for people with learning disabilities and their families. Apart from campaigning to raise the profile of learning disability issues, the society's activities and services include the provision of residential services, training, employment services, clubs, leisure opportunities and individual support for families and carers of people with learning disabilities. The national centre can redirect people to local affiliated bodies, some of which are able to provide advice and counselling. Publications and leaflets can advise parents on which health professionals are able to offer help, from social workers to occupational therapists. / HOURS *Mon-Fri 9am-5pm;* PUBLICATIONS *Leaflets, including 'You and Your Child'. .*

National Association for Mental Health (MIND), ☎ *(020) 8519 2122* 🕈 *www.mind.org.uk*
The national mental health awareness charity provides information on mental health problems in children, and information for carers. / HOURS *Mon-Fri 9.15am-5.15pm;* PUBLICATIONS *Leaflets: Understanding childhood distress; Children and young people and mental distress; Understanding ADHD (all £1). Email publications@mind.org.uk.*

The National Association for Special Educational Needs (NASEN), ☎ (01827) 311500 ◌ www.nasen.org.uk

The association promotes the development of children and young people with special educational needs and supports those working with them via branches for teachers, parents and governors throughout the UK. / PUBLICATIONS *Range of publications concerning children with special needs (largely aimed at professionals but some are suitable for interested parents).*

Speech, Language & Hearing Centre, ☎ (020) 7383 3834

◌ www.speech-lang.org.uk

Assessment and therapy centre for children under five with delays in speech, language or communication, and those with hearing impairments. / HOURS *Mon-Fri 9am-5pm (school terms only).*

Young Minds, ☎ Helpline (0800) 0182 138, (020) 7336 8445

◌ www.youngminds.org.uk

An organisation which aims to increase awareness of the mental and emotional needs of children and their families. The helpline is for anyone worried about the emotional well-being of a child, with a professional call-back service for parents seeking advice. / HOURS *Mon-Fri 9:30am-5:30pm;* PUBLICATIONS *Leaflets: What are Child and Family Consultation Services?; How can Family Therapy help my Family?; Tuning into our Babies. (all £1).*

Hyperactivity (ADD, ADHD)

There is much dispute about the causes, appropriate treatment, and even diagnosis of this condition. Estimates of how prevalent it is vary, but some claim it affects 1 in 10 children, and few estimates go below 1 in 30. Often it is mid-diagnosed as autism (see also) and vice versa.

Your child need not necessarily be zooming around like a whirligig to have this treatable disability. Increasingly the focus in diagnosing it is on the lack of attention and lack of social awareness that goes with such a state. The labels used to describe hyperactive children are increasingly Attention Deficit Disorder and Attention Deficit/Hyperactivity Disorder.

A child may display a lack of focus and failure to engage with children, and activities that goes beyond 'normal'. This lack of comprehension is often associated with low self-esteem, frustration, crying and aggression.

As with many concerns regarding children these days, it currently appears to be on the increase. Whether this is a result of the condition being more prevalent, or that it is rather a result of greater consciousness of the condition is unclear. Moreover, it is also yet another tempting label for a worried parent to think about putting on what may be nothing more than a naturally disruptive youngster.

Where present, hyperactivity can make life extremely difficult for parents and is not much fun for the child, either.

Diagnosis is sometimes possible with babies, but usually takes place at the age of two or older over a period of time, with observation – sometimes in a nursery setting – by developmental experts. There is some evidence that diet may be a cause, with a variety of food additives and sugar most commonly implicated.

In the US, the condition is often medicated using the drug Ritalin which, despite widespread use, remains controversial (it's a powerful amphetamine, whose nickname is "The Chemical Cosh"). An alternative is a nutritional approach notably with zinc, which is often deficient, and avoidance of natural salicylates which inhibit use of polyunsaturated fatty acids and most importantly essential fatty acids.

Certain other measures may also be helpful. A survey by the Hyperactive Children's Support Group found that 45% of ADHD children reacted to perfumes, 80% to the colourants in medicines, 53% to preservatives in medicines, 58% to coloured toothpaste, and 41% to coloured bubble bath. Given this, it seems best to avoid any avoidable additives including in washing products, air fresheners, deodorants, and fabric conditioners.

USEFUL CONTACTS

ADHD National Alliance, ☎ *(020) 7608 8760* ⏱ *www.adhdalliance.org.uk*
A body which aims to bring together different approaches to ADHD and lists a variety of groups with different approaches – from those that are pro treatment through medication to those recommending the use of complementary techniques.

Children & Adults with Attention Deficit Hyperactivity Disorder (CHADD), ⏱ *www.chadd.org*
US charity with comprehensive website including frequently asked questions, fact sheets, and information on research.

Feingold Association, ☎ *+1 631 369 9340* ⏱ *www.feingold.org*
Respected US charity that promotes the research and diet pioneered by American paediatrician Dr Benjamin Feingold. It is dedicated to helping apply dietary techniques to improve behaviour, learning and health.

Hyperactive Children's Support Group (HACSG),
☎ *(01243) 551313* ⏱ *www.hacsg.org.uk*
For parents of Hyperactive/ADD/ADHD children (symptoms in babies include screaming, restlessness, thirst, head-banging, cot rocking and unwillingness to feed). The group offers contact with families of other afflicted children, and members can request details of companies selling relevant nutritional supplements. Membership £10-£15 per annum. / *HOURS Mon-Fri 10am-1pm; PUBLICATIONS Diet sheets and introductory information – SAE; ADHA Hyperactive Child: A Guide for Parents (£5; p/p included). .*

READING

The ADD Book – William Sears & Lynda Thompson (New understandings, new approaches to parenting; Little Brown; 1998; $17.95; 0-316778-73-7) – *A positive guide to understanding and assisting ADD children.*

The ADD Hyperactivity Workbook For Parents, Teachers and Kids – Harvey C Parker (Speciality Press; 1996; £12.99; 0-962162-96-5) – *Simple and effective strategies to help parents understand and manage a child with ADD/ADHD.*

Helping Children Cope With ADD – Patricia Gilbert (Sheldon Press; 1998; £6.99; 0-859697-84-3) – *One of a well-known series of layman's guide to medical conditions – symptoms, treatments, medications and dietary approaches.*

The Hyperactive Child – Belinda Barnes Irene Colquhoun (Attention Deficit Hyperactivity Disorder - A practical self-help guide for parents; HarperCollins; 1997; £5.99; 0722508832) – *By parents for parents, explaining causes and suggesting remedies.*

Understanding ADHD – Dr Christopher Green & Dr Kit Chee (A parent's guide to Attention Deficit Hyperactivity Disorder in children; Vermilion; 1997; £9.99; 0091817005) – *One of the writers is the author of Toddler Taming – facts are livened up with a sprinkling of humour.*

Why Your Child is Hyperactive – Ben Feingold MD (Behaviour and learning problems caused by food; Random House; 1985; $14.95; 0394734262) – *Diet with a lengthy track-record of tackling hyperactivity in children.*

Autism (and Asperger's syndrome)

Autism (literally self-ism) is a lifelong developmental disability that affects the way a person communicates, and makes it more difficult for those with the condition to relate to others.

In the UK and the US, the number of diagnoses has increased so significantly in the last 10 years (by a factor of 10x) that many people consider there to be an autism epidemic. As of early 2004, The National Autistic Society quotes a figure for the incidence of autism as 91 in 10,000 births. Three out of four are boys. What is unclear is whether the increased number of diagnoses relates to more awareness amongst nursery staff and doctors, or reflects some real change in the number of children with developmental issues.

Much is made in the press of sudden 'regressive' or 'disintagrative' autism linked to vaccinations such as MMR (see Immunisation above), where a normally developing child is knocked backwards. But this is not the general pattern. For the most part, the differences that mark a child's development out as different from their peers gradually start to manifest themselves at 18 months to three years and increase progressively (often reaching a high watermark of difference from the 'norm' aged about five).

Autistic children display a so-called 'Triad of Impairments' – difficulty in social interaction, in imaginative play; and rigidity or repetitiveness of habits. Often these are tied in with problems with sensory processing – e.g. over- or under-sensitivity to sounds, or touch – and a low general level of arousal. This last often ties in with autistic children engaging in self-stimulatory activities such as hand-flapping or at the extreme head-banging.

The term 'autism' covers a huge spectrum of difficulties – from so-called 'higher functioning' autistic children, who can be practically indistinguishable from their normally developing peers; to those lower down the spectrum who cannot speak and will require support throughout their lives. (To many people the term evokes the film 'Rain Man' or associations with exceptional skills. This can be the case, but is a rarity.)

Many (though not all) doctors now consider the similar Asperger's syndrome (which similarly affects many more boys than girls) to be part of the autistic spectrum, and some see it as practically synonymous with higher-functioning autism.

CAUSES OF AUTISM

Autism is a syndrome – that is a description of a set of common symptoms – rather than a condition with a unique underlying cause. It seems probable that what is lumped under the catch-all term autism relates to different factors in different children. The hunt for the exact mechanism that triggers autism in its various manifestations is the focus of intensive research around the globe.

With the huge rise in diagnoses, much has been made in the UK in recent years of a hypothetical link with the MMR vaccine (and in the US there has been a similar controversy over Thiomersal – a mercury-based liquid that used to be used as a suspension for vaccines). In early 2004 the spotlight has been turned onto tuna and other oily fish on the basis that they are prone to contamination with mercury.

Whatever the rights and wrongs of these debates, they are clearly not the whole story as the uneven split between boys and girls and studies of identical twins point to a genetic component (though this does not rule out the possibility of 'environmental triggers' such as vaccines or pollutants). It may be that were a link to be established between autism and MMR, say, that it might only apply to a small subset of vulnerable children who suffer regressive autism as a result.

TREATMENTS FOR AUTISM

There is no cure for autism (and – if you have a child who may be affected – you should be most sceptical of any organisation which claims to offer you one). Some drugs-based treatments are being tested, but all are in their infancy, built on science's as yet very hazy understanding of the condition and highly speculative. Some parents report dramatic successes from gluten-free and dairy-free diets, though again there's no clear medical explanation of why they may work.

What is increasingly clear is that early intervention – the earlier the better – with, for example, speech or occupational therapy – can make an enormous difference to the outcome in adult-hood. Pioneered in California, a system called Applied Behavioural Analysis (ABA) is increasingly popular, and there are one or two special schools in London that have sprung up with ABA principles at their core. There is a tendency, though, for different exponents of ABA to claim that theirs is the One True Way, whereas what may be most important is a high level of input delivered in an intelligent manner. There is also a concern that some ABA regimens make the child good at the therapy, without what has been learnt generalising into real-life situations.

It is hard to be definitive about prognoses. The term autism has existed for less that 50 years. As a result, many (perhaps most) adults who are higher functioning have never been diagnosed. Consequently there is very little information for parents as to where to set their expectations for their child.

USEFUL CONTACTS

Allergy Induced Autism (AIA), ☎ Helpline (01733) 331771
🖰 www.autismmedical.com
See Food allergy, above. / HOURS Mon-Fri 9am-3.30pm.

National Autistic Society, ☎ Helpline (0870) 600 8585 🖰 www.nas.org.uk
As well as autism, this highly regarded charity also supports people with related disorders such as Asperger syndrome which are together classified as autistic spectrum disorders (ASD), but with a biological base. The society runs six special schools throughout the UK and holds details of other affiliated ones. There is a library facility which has to be booked first. The society can also re-direct people to local groups, and provide information on TEACCH (treatment and education of autism and related communication-handicapped children). This was devised in the '70s in the US to get the best out of autistic children and enable them to integrate into the community. Though symptoms for autism usually only appear from 18 months the charity will offer free information to anybody who feels concerned (and has a recently updated website). / HOURS helpline Mon-Fri 10am-4pm; PUBLICATIONS Reading list, books, leaflets , journal, newsletter, catalogue and many videos.

Jessica Kingsley Publishers, ☎ (020) 7833 2307 🖰 www.jkp.com
One of the leading publishers internationally in the area of autism and special needs in general – from general background, to texts for therapists to self-help manuals for parents (including home ABA courses). / HOURS Mon-Fri 9am-5pm (school terms only).

Speech, Language & Hearing Centre, ☎ (020) 7383 3834
🖰 www.speech-lang.org.uk
Though not primarily a centre for treatment of autism, this specialist nursery treats a fair number of children up to the age of five on the autistic spectrum (for whom speech and language difficulties are often one of the most obvious differences in their development). / HOURS Mon-Fri 9am-5pm (school terms only).

Dyspraxia

Once known as 'Clumsy Child Syndrome', Dyspraxia (loosely 'problems with doing') describes a condition whereby certain children's brains have difficulty in processing information. This impairs their perceptions and ability to communicate.

According to the Dyspraxia Foundation Dyspraxia affects 10% of the population to some degree, 2% severely. Its effects can manifest themselves from babyhood with an ineptness at feeding. In toddlerhood and early childhood this translates into poor gross motor skills such as pencil grips, drawing and writing; clumsiness dressing; language difficulties; messiness and general poor manual skills.

Verbal Dyspraxia describes the condition when it relates particularly to the inability to properly co-ordinate the larynx and muscles that create speech. This can lead a child's words to be unintelligible even to close family. In the US this condition is sometimes termed apraxia.

As with say ADHD (and autism), there can be a very high level of physical activity and excitability, and poor levels of concentration. The processing difficulties dyspraxics experience seems to relate to some abnormality/immaturity in the development of the neurones in the brain. Far more boys than girls are affected, by a ratio of 4:1.

Treatment tends to be via occupational therapy, physiotherapy, games and PE aimed at building skills in areas that are pinpointed as being lacking.

USEFUL CONTACTS

The Dyspraxia Foundation, ☎ *(01462) 454986 (Helpline)*
⌁ *www.dyspraxiafoundation.org.uk*
The foundation runs a network of countrywide support groups for children with the condition and their families. / *HOURS Helpline Mon-Fri 10am-1pm; PUBLICATIONS Wide range of leaflets and publications (modest charge).*

Dyslexia

Dyslexia is a congenital condition that can occur at any level of intellectual ability. As well as a difficulty with reading, writing and spelling it is often linked with difficulties with spoken language and sequencing of concepts.

Although some traits of dyslexia are often spotted by parents in early infancy, it generally manifests itself at school, and as such falls outside the general scope of this book.

USEFUL CONTACTS

British Dyslexia Association (BDA), ☎ *Admin (0118) 966 2677,*
Helpline (0118) 966 8271 ⌁ *www.BDA-dyslexia.org.uk*
Representing the estimated 2 million dyslexics in the UK, the association works with health professionals and parents to promote early identification of the problem. Befrienders, contactable via the helpline, aim to enable parents to get the right help. Annual subscription to mailing list £35. / *HOURS helpline Mon-Fri 10am-12.45pm, 2pm-4.45pm; PUBLICATIONS Dyslexia Journal, £45 for 4 issues a year on new developments and recommended reading; resources lists and events lists; regularly updated 'Help Available in London' sheets offer pointers on how to ask for referral to a specialist (and where) plus details of other specialist help.*

Dyslexia Institute, ☎ *(01784) 222 300* ⌁ *www.dyslexia-inst.org.uk*
An educational charity, founded in 1972, for the assessment and teaching of people with dyslexia and for the training of specialist teachers. It is now the only national dyslexia teaching organisation in the world.

Chirocare, ☎ *(01202) 768508*
A physical treatment for dyslexia and similar learning difficulties, founded in the belief that these conditions are caused by problems with the nervous system due to, for example, a difficult birth, early head injury, or early exposure to toxins (or immunisations). The organisation points to the frequent discovery in sufferers of the misalignment of certain bones and joints and related co-ordination difficulties. / *HOURS Mon-Sat (not Wed) 9am-2pm.*

10. FIRST AID

Children are particularly vulnerable to accidents, and occasionally first aid carried out before expert emergency treatment arrives can make a significant difference to the outcome. Even if never used, knowledge of this kind can give parents, especially first-timers, peace of mind.

If you have any specific queries about child safety you can contact the Child Accident Prevention Trust (see below), the fire prevention officer at your local fire station, your health visitor, the health education unit at your local health authority or the home safety officer in the trading standards department (or the environmental health department) of your local council.

READING

Baby First Aid – Dr Miriam Stoppard (The essential quick reference guide; Dorling Kindersley; 2003; £5.99; 1-4053-0143-0) – *Another title from the Stoppard stable.*

[Video] **The Breath of Life** (St John's Ambulance; 2002; £12 (booklet £1.50); Product code: P20200) – *Overview of the procedures for the resuscitation of babies and children.* / *www.stjohnsupplies.co.uk, (020) 7278 7888.*

The Fast Guide to First Aid for Babies and Toddlers (St John's Ambulance; £4.95) – *A quick guide to the most common problems on a laminated A3 folding sheet.* / *www.stjohnsupplies.co.uk, (020) 7278 7888.*

First Aid for Children Fast – Caroline Greene (Emergency procedures for all parents and carers; Dorling Kindersley; 1999; £9.99; 0751311618) – *Quick reference index; step-by-step guide with photographs.* / *The Red Cross, 9 Grosvenor Crescent, SW1X 7EJ – (020) 7235 5454.*

Safe Kids – Vivian K Fancher (A complete child safety handbook and resource guide for parents; Wiley & Sons Ltd; 1991; £11.99; 0-471529-73-7)

Courses

The listings include details of various first aid courses. In addition some adult education centres run evening classes in first aid – for details see *Floodlight* (available from local newsagents and bookshops), although bear in mind that there are different resuscitation and first aid procedures for adults, as distinct from babies and children. A basic adult first aid course would therefore not be sufficient. Practical teaching is most effective in small groups, so look for somewhere offering this.

USEFUL CONTACTS

The Active Birth Centre, ☎ (020) 7281 6760
🖰 *www.activebirthcentre.com*
Resuscitation & First Aid for Babies (£20), run approximately every month. / *HOURS shop Mon-Fri 9.30am-6.30pm (Fri 4pm), Sat 10am-4pm.*

Best Bear, ☎ (020) 7352 5852 🖰 *www.bestbear.co.uk*
The website holds a list of first aid courses available, aimed at both parents and carers.

Sue Lewis Grad DB, MCSP, SRP, ☎ (020) 8946 8561
Baby Safety Classes, taken by a Norland nanny, developed in conjunction with the Association for Child Accident Prevention: administration of first aid, crisis response, the principle causes of accidents, and resuscitation; £40; crèche, £5 (evening only).

Marie Askin, ☎ (020) 7603 8103
First aid classes: taught by registered nurse with many years experience teaching; held at a mutually convenient venue, three-hour classes for four to ten people; two-part courses: dealing with an unconscious child (possible causes, and resuscitation techniques) and general first aid (everything from burns and fractures to poisoning); exact details are tailored to meet the requirements of the group.

Portland Hospital, Physiotherapy Unit, ☎ (020) 7390 8061
🖰 *www.theportlandhospital.com*
Two and half hour classes in baby first aid, led by the parentcraft midwife, are held on a regular basis.

Red Cross, ☎ (020) 7933 3601 🖰 *www.redcross.org.uk*
The organisation's training department will give details of local contacts at one of the 46 London centres for organising a certificated childcare course covering resuscitation, bleeding, asthma and other baby ailments, either over two weekend days or over three evenings (12 hours in total). The total price for up to 12 people is £390 + VAT – either a group of 12 can club together and organise a course or you can join other groups. (Trainers are happy to teach in nurseries, schools, church halls and the like – they do not recommend homes because of the lack of space.)

St John Ambulance, ☎ (0870) 010 4850, Courses (020) 7324 4000
🖰 *www.sja.org.uk*
First aid kits and manuals are sold by the famous first aid charity, which also runs courses. Individual bookings for small groups are not generally available (but you may be able to find a tutor who is happy to oblige). Courses specifically aimed at parents are run in some areas – call for details. / *HOURS Mon-Fri 9am-5pm.*

USEFUL CONTACTS

Child Alert, ☎ *(020) 7384 1311* ⌁ *www.childalert.co.uk*
An independent directory website providing information and advice on child safety and wellbeing; also safety products (including a 'babyproofing' service), first aid courses, helpline listings, parenting networks and information for disabled parents and disabled children. / HOURS *Mon-Fri 9am-5pm, 24-hr Web site.*

Crêchendo, ☎ *(020) 8772 8120* ⌁ *www.crechendo.com*
One-day courses (£99) on first aid for babies and children.

A Nelson & Co, ☎ *(020) 7629 3118, Mail order (020) 7495 2404, Stockists (020) 8780 4200* ⌁ *www.nelsonbach.com, www.nelsonandrussell.com*
Manufactures a range of creams to help with first aid, including for bruises, for cuts and sores and for dermatitis. / HOURS *Mon-Sat 9am-5.30pm (Sat 4pm).*

The New Baby Company, ☎ *(020) 7751 1152* ⌁ *www.newbabycompany.com*
Three-hour course in Wandsworth or Hammersmith, £48.

Prohealth, ☎ *(0121) 353 4633* ⌁ *www.prohealth.sageweb.co.uk*
A baby and child first aid kit (£35), containing 70-plus items, and an 80-minute audio CD about childhood injuries and illnesses. Half a dozen emergency first aid cards also included.

Safe & Sound, ☎ *(020) 8449 8722* ⌁ *www.safe-and-sound.org.uk*
First aid child safety courses for parents, au pairs, nannies, and baby-sitters. Courses taught by a qualified medical professional. / HOURS *Mon-Fri 9am-6pm.*

Medicine chest

All medicines should be kept under lock and key, and even then in a kitchen cupboard rather than one in the bathroom as adults are more often around in the kitchen thus are more able to foil exploration attempts. Look for containers with child resistant caps and take particular care with foil packs.

How many medications you want to purchase is up to you. The magazine *Natural Parent* reported that at least 95% of baby ailments are self-limiting: i.e. heal themselves. However, treating the child often makes the parent feel better while recovery takes place.

You should check with your GP before giving aspirin to children under 12 years old or paracetamol to children under three months old.

Ideas for a first aid kit:

➢ Different sizes of sticking plasters.
➢ A thermometer (the tape-on-forehead variety is less accurate than the mercury or digital types).
➢ Sterile dressings and surgical tape (in particular brands which don't hurt when pulled off and are hypo-allergenic).
➢ Scissors.
➢ Tweezers (for splinters, stings, etc).
➢ Bandages (for the psychological reassurance of the child if nothing else).
➢ Calpol (or a similar brand containing paracetamol) is widely seen as the baby equivalent of taking an aspirin. Avoid using these products more than twice a week over a period of months (or daily for more than a week).

THERMOMETERS

Baby Echos (& Rad Pad), ☎ *(01270) 255 201* ⌁ *www.babyechos.co.uk*
BebeSounds Ear Thermometers (£25), which display temperatures in large figures (in just one second) and display a smiley face when the temperature is normal. The probe is washable, avoiding the extra cost of disposable probes. A Remote Fever Monitor (around £45) allows a baby's temperature to be checked even while sleeping. The monitor clips to the front of a nappy or pyjama waistband and sounds an alarm on the parents' monitor if it reaches a pre-programmed level.

Boots, ☎ Customer services (08450) 708090 ◁ www.boots.com; www.wellbeing.com
Own-brand plastic digital thermometer; may not be as accurate as some, but it is much cheaper then the Braun (£7.55) and can be inserted in the mouth (or in the armpit), with none of the anxiety associated with a glass and mercury alternative.

Braun, ☎ Consumer relations (0800) 783 7010 ◁ www.braun.com
One of the best makes of thermometer – the Thermoscan takes temperatures from the ear in one second using infra-red technology similar to the Omron; the top model is about £40; contact them for details of local dealers. / HOURS Mon-Fri 9am-5.30pm.

Omron Healthcare, ☎ (01273) 495033 ◁ www.omrom-healthcare.com
In a test on thermometers run by The Independent newspaper, this one came out top, with praise for its ease of use. A little-known Japanese brand, it uses infra-red technology to take the temperature next to the ear drum within three seconds (the temperature corresponds most closely to that of the brain which reflects core temperature). A cover protects the measurement probe, and you have to change these with each use – 20 come with the thermometer: the GT1 (Gentle Temp) costs around £40. / HOURS Mon-Fri 9am-5.30pm.

COMPLEMENTARY TREATMENTS

If you are interested in complementary treatments you could obtain a complementary first aid kit. You might also like to consider also the following remedies, bearing in mind that aromatherapists recommend restricted use of essential oils for very young babies. (See chapter *4.02 Complementary medicine & Health practitioners* for therapists and chapter *3.09 Lotions & potions* for details of stockists.)

➤ Tea Tree products (oil, cream, lotion, gel or soap) – for cuts, grazes, thrush, sunburn, and wherever anti-fungal, anti-bacterial and anti-viral properties are required.

➤ Chamomile essential oil has anti-inflammatory properties and is a gentle sedative.

➤ Arnica for bruises.

➤ Bach Flower Rescue Remedy for shock.

➤ Sun protection cream, ideally one using a physical screen such as titanium dioxide rather than a chemical screen.

➤ Sunburn products (natural yoghurt will also relieve sunburn).

➤ Aloe Vera gel for skin problems, including burns.

➤ If you use homeopathic remedies it is useful to have these to hand as they always seem to be required when the shops are shut. Readymade complete first aid kits are available – for details see chapter *4.02 Complementary Medicine & Health Practitioners*.

11. INJURIES

The following are support groups for babies children unlucky enough to have suffered some form of major injury.

USEFUL CONTACTS

Association for Spinal Injury Research, Rehabilitation & Reintegration (ASPIRE), ☎ (020) 8954 5759 ◁ www.aspire.org.uk
Spinal cord injuries usually occur to those aged 18-35 (through skiing, riding, etc) but can occur at any time. The charity can advise parents of children with spinal injuries on issues such as finding playgroups, schooling, adapting the home, and so on. Their rehabilitation centre provides help not only to those with spinal injuries, but also to those with similar problems arising, for example, from a birth defect.

Brain Injury Association (HEADWAY), ☎ (0115) 924 0800
◁ www.headway.org.uk
An organisation (formerly called the National Head Injuries Association) aimed at babies, children or adults who sustain any form of head injury (not birth trauma). Contacts are provided to other charities and local support groups, including the Child Brain Injury Trust (see also); call for an information pack.

Child Accident Prevention Trust (CAPT), ☎ *(020) 7608 3828*
⌁ *www.capt.org.uk*
Accidental injury is one of the leading cause of death and disability in childhood (due to
the large reduction in infectious diseases and other causes of child mortality). This
charity aims to promote the prevention of accidents in the home and outside, by
promoting safe play and safety in the home and has much information for parents on
safety in the home. / *HOURS Mon-Fri 9am-5pm; PUBLICATIONS Free leaflets (send SAE).*

Child Brain Injury Trust, ☎ *(01865) 552467, Helpline (0845) 601 4939*
⌁ *www.cbituk.org*
For children with head injuries caused by an accident after birth, the organisation
(formerly called the Children's Head Injury Trust) offers advice on where to get help
with physical, financial, emotional and medical problems (questions requiring specialist
knowledge can be referred); referrals to local support networks. / *HOURS Mon-Fri 9.30am-
5pm; PUBLICATIONS Free information pack; access to database of specialist provisions; also provide CD
ROM / video and book for siblings free to families. .*

12. TEETH & TEETHING

It is suggested that children should have their teeth cleaned twice a day
from the moment the first ones appear so that they get used to the idea
sooner rather than later. It may be years, however, before your child can
brush without your help – some say that (unless using an electric brush) it
takes until the age of six to have the necessary manual dexterity to do a
good job.

Special children's toothbrushes offer small heads with soft bristles and
an easy grip handle for the child or an adult to hold. For really tiny babies
a fresh flannel, clean handkerchief wrapped round a finger, or cotton bud
may be all that is required to convey the idea.

Visits to the dentists can start as soon as you like, on the same principle, letting the child accompany you on your visits and climb on to the
seat to open their mouth when they are ready.

According to the 1995 National Diet and Nutrition Survey 30% of
children between three-and-a-half and four-and-a-half years old have tooth
decay and 45% of five-year-olds according to the UK Child Dental Health
Survey have decayed, missing or filled teeth.

PREVENTION RATHER THAN CURE

Frequent exposure to any acidic or sugary foods or drinks (particularly
fruit juices and fizzy drinks) can erode tooth enamel. Brushing teeth soon
after consumption of such items (within an hour say) actually worsens
the situation, spreading sugars over the teeth while the enamel is still softened.

Not all parents wish to avoid such foods and drinks entirely, but you
can still take steps to limit their damage.

Tips for cutting the damage done by acidic and sugary drinks:
➤ Prevent your children from sipping such drinks over a long period of
time.
➤ Don't put them into a feeding bottle with a teat.
➤ Don't allow them to be consumed at bedtime as saliva flow is reduced
during sleep.
➤ The best time for consumption is at meal times when saliva is most
active.

If the child is prone to tooth decay even milk in bed after brushing can
cause problems. Note also that syrupy medicines can also cause decay
and often there is a sugar-free alternative – albeit with artificial sweeteners which carry their own concerns.

FLUORIDE TOOTHPASTES (AND FLUORIDATION OF WATER)

A compound of fluorine – one of the most abundant elements in nature – fluoride inhibits tooth decay and plaque.

Fluoride toothpastes were introduced in the 1960s and 1970s and – while fluoridated water is very common in the US – it is becoming more widespread in the UK. At present fluoridation is found in about 1/10 of the country – mostly in the Midlands – but the government's current long-term aim is to make this coverage universal.

Though dentists and politicians promote general use of fluoride there are some scientists who question whether fluoride's undoubted benefits in preventing tooth decay outweigh the potential risks presented by use of such a toxic substance, even in trace quantities. Too much fluoride causes mottling in young teeth leading to dental fluorisis – a condition that affects quite a number of children in areas where water is fluoridated. Research has also associated excess fluoride with more significant problems, including growth disorders, glandular problems, and cancer.

Toothpaste with fluoride has been generally recommended for children over seven. Before seven years the British Dental Association, recommends using products containing only 0.11% sodium fluoride or 0.38% sodium monofluorophosphate, ruling out most adult fluoridated toothpastes. This advice is not universal, however. Health visitors in some areas with low levels of fluoride in the water recommend using adult toothpaste in small quantities to promote dental health.

An opposing school of thought is that children under 3 should not be exposed to anything other than the tiny quantities of naturally occurring fluoride in food and un-treated water.

Dependent on the level of fluoride in your area, and your own thoughts on the issue, you will need to choose whether you go for adult toothpaste in tiny quantities, child's toothpaste or a non-fluoride toothpastes. Whatever your view, given some children's fondness for eating toothpaste as well as using it for brushing, this is clearly a habit worth discouraging.

Another potential concern with toothpaste is the level of artificial sweeteners and sodium laurel sulphate they contain – the latter being a potential carcinogen. (see *chapter 3.09 Lotions and Potions*).

FINDING A DENTIST

Look for a dentist with children's toys and books in the waiting room and/or one who first tells a child what they are going to do, then shows them before actually doing it.

A paediatric dentist will be specialised and see children from birth on. There is no need for a formal referral letter as they are primary providers of preventive and therapeutic oral health care. They have specialised training and experience to evaluate and treat deviations from normal dental growth, tooth decay, dental erosion, and so on.

General dental treatment is free on the NHS. Treatment, or supervision of treatment by a specialist paediatric dentist is similarly available through referral to a dental training hospital and sometimes through the community dental service.

DENTISTS

British Dental Association, ☎ *(020) 7935 0875, Patients' Helpline*
(0870) 333 1188 ⏚ *www.bda-findadentist.org.uk*
The BDA website has a 'Find-a-Dentist' section which includes a list of 'frequently
asked questions'. A helpline manned by nurses and hygienists can be useful for parents
with queries about teething or their child's first visit to the dentist. / HOURS *helpline Mon-
Fri 9am-5pm.*

Dental Help Line, ☎ *(0845) 063 1188* ⏚ *www.dentalhealth.org.uk*
A dental helpline run by the British Dental Health Foundation to answer questions
from the public about dental issues, including any relevant to children. / HOURS *Mon-Fri
9am-5pm;* PUBLICATIONS *leaflets on children's health and mother and baby; free.*

General Dental Council (GDC), ☎ *(020) 7887 3800* ⏚ *www.gdc-uk.org*
The regulatory body of the dental profession. Its website has specialist lists, including
paediatric dentistry. / HOURS *Mon-Fri 9am-5pm.*

READING

Practical Parenting - Your Child's Teeth – Jane Kemp and Clare Walters with kate
    Barnard (How to keep your child's teeth and gums healthy; Hamlyn; 2003;
    £5.99; 0600606651) – *Lots of practical questions and answers, tips and a checklist.*
    / *www.hamlyn.co.uk.*

TEETHING

The period when a tooth is coming through (often two steps forward and
one back) may or may not be difficult. If it is you will want to relieve your
child's anguish / spare yourself the howling.

There are over-the-counter gels sold to soothe teething. Some contain little more than sugar syrup, though, and how effective they are is
debatable.

Other teething remedies:
    Something cold: this could be teethers designed for chilling; or for
better flavour cold lumps of fruit or vegetables (make sure the baby won't
be able to break big chunks off) – two suggestions are carrots and bananas.
    A soft toothbrush: offers hard and soft textures to chew on.
    Teething biscuits: probably best only for older children, or you could
make your own by baking bread at low temperatures until it hardens.
    Junior paracetamol (Calpol): used by some parents for its soothing
(and quieting) properties.
    Teethers: PVC-free teethers are made by all the major baby product
manufacturers.
    Homeopathic and complementary remedies: see chapter 4.02
Complementary medicine & Health practitioners.

13. OTHER ISSUES

In this section:
➤ Head lice.
➤ Toxocariasis.
➤ Avoiding dangerous plants.
➤ Circumcision.
➤ Birth marks.
➤ Supplements.

Head lice

The Department of Health estimates that at least one in ten primary
school children is affected by head lice every year, and figures for younger
children who attend nursery groups seem unlikely to be very different.

Epidemics occur at intervals, particularly in the autumn. Girls (and their mothers) and blondes are reported most susceptible.

The simplest preventative measure is cutting or tying the hair back. A weekly check is wise, covering the hair in conditioner, possibly with relevant essential oils, then. combing with a fine-toothed nit comb, possibly dipped in a bowl of vinegar, or with vinegar in the final hair rinse. Combs are available from pharmacies and need to be pale or bright coloured to show up the little beasties as you comb them out.

If the child has lice, repeat the treatment every day for ten days (the life-cycle of the louse). If infestation is a recurrent problem consider using lavender oil on collars and Vaseline smeared round the back of the neck and behind the ears.

Chemical treatments for lice contain organophosphates, but lice in some areas have developed tolerance. The treatments may cause rashes and/or headaches, and are not recommended for young children. The growing problem of lice has led to a boom in complementary products to treat them. The vast majority of these rely on aromatherapy oils, which may not be suitable for use on under-two-year olds. Although good quality oils are expensive, in the long term it will be cheaper and safer to make up your own mix with suitable oils in a perfume-free conditioner. Lavender and camomile may be helpful if the scalp is sore and potentially infected. For more ideas, see the suggested reading in the Aromatherapy section of chapter *4.02 Complementary medicine & Health practitioners*.

USEFUL PRODUCTS

Argos, ☎ (0870) 600 3030, Direct home shopping (0870) 600 2020
⌂ www.argos.co.uk
Stocks a battery-powered comb which electrocutes head lice as it is drawn through the hair. / HOURS vary.

Boots, ☎ Customer services (08450) 708090 ⌂ www.boots.com; www.wellbeing.com
The reusable Bugbuster kit to cure head lice is available at larger stores, £4.50.

Bug Buster, ☎ (020) 7686 4321 ⌂ www.nits.net
A 'Bug Buster' kit contains specialist combs (which you use with your usual shampoo) to help prevent or eliminate head lice; kit includes instructions, cape and stickers for children, £6.40; also information on threadworm, scabies and Toxocara (roundworm found in dog faeces). / HOURS helpline Mon-Fri 10am-5pm.

Community Hygiene Concern, ☎ Helpline (020) 7686 4321
⌂ www.chc.org
A health and education charity which aims to provide information and advice on parasites such as head lice and worms (see also). / HOURS helpline Mon-Fri 9.30am-5pm.

Head Lice Info, ⌂ www.HeadLiceInfo.com
A US site offering a 'Head Lice to Dead Lice' programme – a treatment backed by the Harvard School of Public Health, that uses olive oil to smother and kill the lice; the site includes pointers on the potential problems with chemical treatments.

READING

Head lice to dead lice – Roberta MacPhee & Joan Sawyer (The non-toxic solution that really works; Newleaf; 2001; £6.99; 0717132269)

Toxocariasis

Toxocariasis can be caught from grass, plants or soil where infected animals have defecated (even long after the faeces have withered). Symptoms may include general aches and pains, asthma, epilepsy and occasionally damage to sight. Protection measures include covering sand-pits, and de-worming dogs every three months (though about half the cases in the UK occur in families without a dog or cat).

USEFUL CONTACTS
Community Hygiene Concern, ☎ *Helpline (020) 7686 4321*
⌁ *www.chc.org*
A health and education charity which aims to protect people and pets both from parasites and also from potentially toxic treatments, particularly those of doubtful effectiveness; the website offers information and products for sale. / HOURS helpline Mon-Fri 9.30am-5pm; PUBLICATIONS Free information pack (send SAE + 3 first class stamps); leaflet: The Toxocara & People (information and protection measures).

Avoiding dangerous plants

Children are given to sticking plants, leaves, sticks and twigs into their mouths. Some – for example yew tree seeds – are extremely dangerous. If you have a garden, you may wish to identify exactly what varieties of plants and fungi grow there.

Some plants cause an instant adverse reaction, while with others your child may only fall ill 24 hours later. If you suspect your baby has eaten something poisonous you should take the child, *and a sample of the plant and the vomit,* to the local casualty department.

READING
Do It Safely In the Garden – *How to make gardens safe for children.* / Consumer unit, DTI – (020) 7215 0383.

[Leaflet] **Take care, be plant aware leaflet** (Kew Gardens together with RoSPA)

USEFUL CONTACTS
Guy's Hospital (Poisons Unit), ☎ *(020) 7955 5000*
⌁ *www.hospital.org.uk*
The medical toxicology laboratory at Guy's is the largest in the UK, and runs the National Poisons Information Service, which provides information to assist with diagnosis of suspected poisoning following exposure to any kind of chemical product, venomous animal or poisonous plant, and also subsequent patient management. / HOURS 24 hr.

Birth Marks

True birth marks, as opposed to the red 'stork bites', or 'Mongolian blue spots' which fade with time, are caused by abnormal blood vessels or pig-mentation.

Strawberry naevus generally disappear, half by the age of five, 90% by the age of nine. Port wine stains are flatter and larger and will grow with the child unless treated.

In either case you should ask your GP for referral to a specialist. Laser treatment may be offered from as young as six weeks. However, as this field is developing very rapidly it is worth considering waiting in order to benefit from ever-more-effective treatments.

Circumcision

This procedure is no longer available on the NHS because it is not now considered medically necessary. Poor genital hygiene in men and early sexual activity are implicated in cervical and penile cancer, rather than failure to circumcise.

Some specialists believe that a non-retracting foreskin may require circumcision but others think that this is almost never necessary as the situation rectifies itself with growth (the foreskin is in fact non-retracting in most newborns, according to NORM – see listings). If there is still a problem at the age of 17 it can be dealt with then and some practitioners feel that this has the added advantage of not causing trauma to a young child (which appears to have the effect of lowering their pain threshold). There are complications in one in 250 circumcisions.

USEFUL CONTACTS

NORM UK, ☎ National HQ (01785) 814044, London office (020) 7274 0086
🖰 www.norm-uk.org
Charity which offers information and support to parents seeking to counter any
pressure to circumcise, and to those who have already had their child or themselves
been circumcised. Also offer pointers on conservative remedies for foreskin disorders in
boys. / PUBLICATIONS *Free leaflets: Alternatives for circumcision; Your birthright – your foreskin and you;
Infant Circumcision, Answers to Your Questions; can also recommend videos and books.*

Supplements

Vitamin drops for babies and toddlers are often sold in health centres but
these tend to be among the cheapest available and not of the best quality. Such products may also contain artificial sweeteners, which are
generally considered unsuitable for children. For suppliers of alternative
supplements see chapter *4.02 Complementary medicine & Health practitioners.*

CHAPTER 2.04

CHILDCARE

1. **Choosing childcare**
2. **Nannies & nanny shares**
3. **Day nurseries**
4. **Childminders**
5. **Au pairs & mother's helps**
6. **Postnatal care: Maternity nurses & doulas**
7. **Ad hoc childcare**
8. **Baby-sitting**

1. CHOOSING CHILDCARE

(For information about toddler groups and one o' clock clubs see chapter 2.06 Baby & toddler activities; for information on pre-schools (or playgroups), see chapter 2.07 Education; for details of local publications, see chapter 4.05 Finding out more.)

If both parents want or need to work, study, or keep up any activity outside the home, they will need childcare. If you have decided to look after your children yourself, childcare is not as vital an issue, but can still be useful, if only as a helping hand.

There are numerous childcare options, some of which are rather hazily defined, and a number of which overlap. The primary distinction is between those best suited to unsupervised care – i.e. with an element of child-rearing rather than just childcare – and those which are more a case of taking some of the work off mum's hands.

The UK is widely reported to have the highest childcare charges in Europe. The average cost a year in London is around £10,600 (70% more than the rest of the country), and can be much more. If you plan to return to work the first calculation you should make is how much money you will have left once you've paid your carer.

Despite a £300m government investment in 900 neighbourhood nurseries across the UK, availability remains patchy (largely because of the extremely low pay in the sector). In London the mayor has launched a childcare strategy to help address this.

For the moment you may finally figure out what you would like, only to find it is more expensive than you can afford, or unattainable in your area (particularly in the case of day nurseries, which book up fast). A degree of flexibility is therefore essential.

Whatever you opt for, start looking as soon as the baby is born, if not sooner. That way you will be on top of the issues sufficiently to improve your chances of getting what you want.

If you are returning to work, whatever system of care you use you should probably keep some holiday in reserve in case the carer is ill (or, if your child is at nursery in case she becomes ill, as if she does the nursery will not take her). Even better, if you can manage it, is to spend a day or even half a day a week working at home with childcare – an option which allows for greater flexibility in terms of practicalities and availability for emergencies.

SAFETY

Stories of babies damaged or even killed by their carers naturally make big headlines. (Tragically, though, statistics indicate that a parent or other relative is far more likely to be culpable of this kind of behaviour.)

There are perennial calls for the establishment of a register of nannies with some suggestion that it be administered by Ofsted (in the same way that childminders are now regulated by that agency). Even if the system does tighten up further, though, it is always wise to ask questions. Staff in nurseries for example (which are already regulated by Ofsted) may not be police checked unless the nursery itself has requested it.

As of spring 2003 ministers have also been looking at the regulations governing those who care for children and it is very probable that smacking by childminders and nannies will be outlawed.

The carer options

Carers capable of sole charge:

Nanny: not registered under the Children Act – anyone can call themselves a nanny. Usually the term is applied to a trained nursery nurse (see Childcare qualifications below) and/or someone with several years of childcare experience able to take sole charge of children and be responsible for all duties in relation to them. She may live in or out of your home. She may do some baby-sitting and pre-arranged chores though most qualified nannies (with the exception of the relatively rare breed of housekeeper/nanny) are unwilling to undertake household duties.

Day nursery: regulated under the Children Act, and – since September 2001 – inspected by OFSTED. Requirements are laid down regarding – amongst other issues – the ratio of children to carers, and staff training. Some nurseries will take babies as young as six weeks, but six months is much more common and many only take children over two years old. Different types of day nursery are: private, council/local authority run, workplace and community; all of which are discussed in more detail in the relevant section. (NB: although the word crèche is sometimes used to refer to day nurseries, in the UK the term is properly used to describe a place to leave children temporarily at gyms, leisure centres, restaurants, etc.)

Childminder: regulated under the Children Act, and – since September 2001 – inspected by OFSTED; a self-employed childcarer working within her own home.

Reciprocal care: an arrangement with a friend or family member in which cash does not necessarily change hands. The arrangement might be that one family will look after your children part of the week in return for your family looking after their children in another part of the week. An alternative is a group of three or more friends for a day or half day a week, say two mothers looking after four babies on each occasion.

A family member: most obviously one of the grannies. Having your mother or mother-in-law around the place may not always seem ideal, but – if they are willing – may be your best option, especially for a part-time solution. There have even been suggestions that the government will extend childcare tax credit to remunerate grandparents, though so far nothing has come of this (to claim at present grandparents must be registered as childminders).

Carers requiring supervision:

Au pair: literally 'on equal terms'; traditionally (and in everyday speech) the term used to describe young girls – usually foreigners, usually untrained – who help with childcare and light housework in exchange for accommodation, food, a modest wage and the opportunity to learn English. Now that under European Law any EC national can work in the UK with nothing more than a passport, the term – as used by the Home Office – has a narrower, technical meaning that only refers to nationals of certain European (non-EC) countries who are allowed to enter the UK solely to work as au pairs. To the Home Office, therefore, there is no such thing as a 'French au pair' or an 'Australian au pair'. Commonwealth citizens working under the 'Working Holidaymaker Scheme' are better termed mother's helps and are generally more expensive to employ.

Au pair plus: someone who works longer hours, takes on more duties, and is paid somewhat more than a traditional au pair; must be an EC national, as there is no work permit category accommodating those from outside the EC.

Mother's help: generally untrained, young women who help with childcare and housework under the supervision of the mother. Australians and New Zealanders working while travelling through London often come into this category and some have childcare training. Being generally inexperienced, however, this is not a category of carer that is generally suited to sole care. Mother's helps can be hard to find but are financially worthwhile as rates are 30–40% less than for qualified nannies. May live in or out.

Carers whose job is assisting the mother in the period around the birth:

Maternity nurse: usually a live-in position for a person with or without qualifications who is on-call 24 hours a day after the birth. The role focuses on helping the mother with the child and usually the issue of establishing a routine. It does not generally encompass household chores.

Doula: a live-out position: an American idea that is beginning to catch on here. A full doula is an experienced mother employed to act as a helper and advisor before and during as well as after the birth. The idea is that a doula mucks in with jobs such as housework and supports rather than replaces the mother as the primary care giver to the child. In the UK the term may also refer to a post just covering the post-birth period and is a kind of glorified mother's help.

Making the choice

Points to consider when choosing a suitable type of childcare:

➤ What can you afford? See the table (pg. 276) for a comparative guide to the costs of different types of childcare.

➤ Could you manage with part-time childcare or do you need a full-time solution?

➤ Will you need a carer who can work unsupervised? Are you able to be at home and oversee what's going on?

➤ How many children do you have who need looking after? Care in the home rather than at, for example, a nursery is more cost-efficient when you have more than one child.

➤ What sort of qualities are you looking for in a carer? Would you prioritise childcare qualifications or a natural flair with kids? See below for a guide to childcare qualifications.

YOUR OPTIONS FOR CHILDCARE

LONG TERM CARE

	Salary/hour (net)	Salary/week (net)	Salary/annum (gross)	Age of child	Capable of sole charge	Live in	Other duties	Trained	1+ children	Hidden costs	Holiday
Nanny – live in	£7.70	£308	£21,343	0+	Y	Y	Y	Y	N	Agency fees/ advertising/car insurance	Go with family
Nanny – live out	£9.62	£384	£27,320	0+	Y	N	Y	Y	N	Agency fees/ advertising/ babysitting	
Nanny share	£4.50	£180	£10,800	0+	Y	Y/N	Y	Y	Y		
Private day nursery	n/a	£135	£7,000	6 months+	Y	N	N	Y	Y	After school care if both parents work	
Local authority day nursery	n/a	£0–£60	£0–£3,000	6 months+	Y	N	N	Y	Y		
Childminder	n/a	£110	£5,700	0+	Y	N	N	N	Y	Retainer over holidays	Retainer payable
Au pair	n/a	£30–£40	n/a	0+	N	Y	Y	N	N	Agency fees/ car insurance	
Au pair plus	n/a	£30–£60	n/a	0+	N	Y	Y	N	N	Agency fees/ car insurance	
Mother's help – live in	£3.75	£150	£9,000	0+	N	Y	Y	N	N	Agency fees/tax/National Insurance	
Mother's help – live out	£5.50	£220	£14,000	0+	N	N	Y	N	N	Agency fees/tax/National Insurance	

SHORT TERM CARE

	Salary/hour (net)	Salary/week (net)	Salary/annum (gross)	Age of child	Capable of sole charge	Live in	Other duties	Trained	1+ children	Hidden costs	Holiday
Maternity nurse	n/a	£400	n/a	0–3months	N	Y	N	N/Y	n/a	Agency fees	
Doula	£10	n/a	n/a	0–3months	Y	N	Y	N/Y	n/a	£250–£400 fee for attending the birth	
Babysitter	£5	n/a	n/a	0+	Y	N	N	N	N	Travel home	

> Where do you want your child to spend time – the familiar environment of your own home or somewhere where it's possible to meet other children? See below for a detailed comparison of care in and out of the home.

There are books which can help you tackle some of these questions (see Reading – Advice on choosing childcare, below). As soon as you have an idea of what you need, you should start looking. As any deadline approaches – for example, your return to work – you may find you have to widen your definition of what is acceptable.

It seems that babies are flexible about who looks after them until they are about nine months old. After that age they find it much harder to adapt to new people and will need a settling-in period with someone new.

Four pitfalls to look out for when contemplating childcare:

> Worrying about what your peers and parents will expect, rather than thinking about what your child needs, and what you would like.

> Deliberately choosing a carer who is not as good with the child as you are, so that they won't undermine you in the eyes of your child. (Even with an excellent childcarer, babies still know that she is not a parent.)

> Changing childcare any more than is necessary. Children like and benefit from continuity.

> Choosing a carer with whom you can't communicate effectively.

In choosing childcare it is sensible to keep half an eye on the issue of education, and what kind of pre-school choices you will be making. These choices may in turn be important in determining options for primary education (see chapter *2.07 Education*).

USEFUL CONTACTS

Best Bear, ☎ *(020) 7352 5852* ✆ *www.bestbear.co.uk*
This website aims to be a definitive directory of the country's best childcare providers, including nanny and au pair agencies, tested by an experienced nanny. The site also provides a fair amount of general childcare information, lists first aid courses, has information on choosing a school, a 'nanny tax calculator' and an online shop (mostly links to recommended shopping sites).

Childcare Link, ☎ *(08000) 960296* ✆ *www.childcarelink.gov.uk*
New government-backed service to provide information to parents. Via its website, it provides a fair amount of background information. Geographical searches are possible using maps, and a fair amount of local contact details for childminders, nurseries and pre-schools are supplied. As part of the same initiative, councils are to be obliged to set up childcare information centres on the High Street. / PUBLICATIONS *Factsheets on your childcare options from the freephone number.*

Daycare Trust, ☎ *(020) 7840 3350* ✆ *www.daycaretrust.org.uk*
The organisers of the National Childcare Campaign promote affordable, accessible, equitable, educational, flexible and diverse childcare (and offer advice on where to find it). The telephone helpline (accessed through the number given) has access to a computerised database of local childcare information services. / HOURS helpline Mon-Fri 10am-5pm; PUBLICATIONS *Childcare Now, a quarterly journal about the latest developments in childcare; Checkout Childcare, a very helpful and informative pack containing 20 topic sheets relating to childcare including sample questions for interviewing a nanny – £5 (up to two of the topic sheets can be ordered free).*

National Association of Children's Information Services (NACIS), ☎ *(020) 7935 0088* ✆ *www.nacis.org.uk*
Formerly known as Choices in Childcare – a national network of children's information services that promotes access to information on childminders, private nurseries, local authority nurseries, crèches, playgroups, parent-toddler groups, nannies, health and support services and leisure activities.

National Association of Early Years Professionals (NAEYP), ⏚ www.nann.freeserve.co.uk

Though the association (formerly the National Association of Nursery Nurses) primarily supports nannies, it does provide some services for parents, including training evenings held in Central London covering a wide range of childcare issues. / PUBLICATIONS *How to employ a nanny.*

Office of Standards in Education (OFSTED), ☎ (020) 7421 6800

⏚ www.ofsted.gov.uk

This government department most associated with school inspections is also responsible for the inspection of all childcare facilities (childminders, crèches, nurseries). Most of the information provided by Ofsted in this area is directed at professionals, with parents directed to the government's Childcare Link service.

USEFUL CONTACTS – BALANCING HOME & WORK

It is estimated by 2010 eight out of 10 mothers will be working, albeit some of them part-time. The decision to return to work is governed by multiple issues, including finances, your feelings about the baby, and the type of work you do.

According to at least one specialist in adult careers advice, if yours is a knowledge-based job, the longest you can drop out is two years. If it is skills-based you can return when you like. The exceptions to these are where contacts are an important element of the job – in the media for example.

From April 2003 the tax regime has been altered in favour of businesses helping employees with work at home expenses and there is increasing pressure from campaign groups to permit more flexible working hours – ideal if it can be achieved by both parents.

Better Business, ☎ (01291) 641222 ⏚ www.better-business.co.uk

A network for people whose office is in their home; the website lists services and offers advice. / PUBLICATIONS *Factsheets on starting a business and working more effectively from home – SAE £72 p/a 10 editions can get first free.*

Flametree, ☎ (020) 7804 8878 ⏚ www.flametree.co.uk

A consultancy specialising on managing the work-life balance; since it started it has become much more 'b2b' (ie corporate consultancy), but it continues to offer individual life coaching for parents.

Working Families, ☎ (020) 7253 7243, Helpline for legal advice (0800) 013 0313 ⏚ www.workingfamilies.org.uk

New Ways to Work and Parents at Work merged in 2003 to create this new charity which promotes flexible working arrangements – for example, job-sharing, flexitime, career breaks and working from home. It provides a free helpline and various publications on the subjects of childcare and employment rights. / HOURS *Mon-Fri or answerphone;* PUBLICATIONS *Employees Guide to Flexible Working (£3.99); Working Parents Handbook (£6.99); Balancing Work and Home.*

CAMPAIGNS

Full-time Mothers, ☎ (020) 8670 2525 ⏚ www.fulltimemothers.org

A non-profitmaking organisation, founded in 1991, that exists to help mothers who would like to look after their children themselves. It aims to promote understanding of the child's needs for a full-time mother, to raise the status and self-esteem of mothers at home and to campaign for changes in both employment policies and in the tax and benefits system to support that choice. Membership costs £7.50 (concessions £1) which secures a quarterly newsletter and invitations to two open meetings a year.

READING – ADVICE ON CHOOSING CHILDCARE

[Info Pack] **Check Out Childcare** (£5) – *20 sheets on a range of childcare services with tips including an action checklist, and what to do when arrangements break down.* / *Daycare Trust.*

Choosing Childcare – Ann Mooney (A guide for parents and providers; Ashgate Publishing Group; 1997; £10.50; 1-857423-61-5) – *Topics include childcare providers, choosing the best for your child, and how the law affects childcare service.*

[Booklet] **Choosing What's Best for Your Pre-school Child** – *A useful booklet.* / *National Early Years Network.*

[Booklet] **Free to Work Childcare Guide** – Free to Work Childcare Guide (£2.90 to members) / Gingerbread.

Mothercare Othercare – Sandara Scarr & Judy Duynn (Penguin; 1987; £4.99; 0140227601) – *Research indicating that the mother–child relationship is not uniquely important, but that what is more important to a baby is quality and continuity of care.*

READING – ADVICE ON BALANCING HOME & WORK

The 24-Hour Family ★ – Polly Ghazi (A Parent's Guide to Work-Life Balance; Women's Press Ltd; 2003; £9.99; 0-7043-4763-6) – *Probably the most thorough book on the subject, covering all kinds of possible work options and their financial ramifications. Includes clear and thorough summaries of your legal position and potential tax break as well as general issues like changing needs as your children grow, and how to win over your employer. Very extensive resource directory.*

Balancing Work & Home – Sarah Litvinoff & Lucy Daniels (Parents at work: a practical guide to managing stress; Parents at Work Publications; 1994; £5.50; 0-950879-29-0) – *A sensible publication with plenty of information on how to deal with handling work and children.*

Carol Smillie's Working Mum's Handbook – Carole Smillie with Eileen Fursland (Virgin; 2003; £11.99; 0-7535-0746-3) – *Slick, but straightforward title that covers all the bases with quotes from Carol and other working mums: ideas on the work-life balance, getting organised, choosing childcare, maternity leave and pay, and tax credits.*

How to Succeed as a Working Parent – Steve Chalke (Hodder & Stoughton; 2003; £7.99; -340-86120-7) – *From the Parentalk expert, how to divide home and work, how to reassess commitments regularly, how to take control of your money, and how to choose the right childcare.* / www.madaboutbooks.com.

Madonna and Child – Melissa Benn (Towards a new politics of motherhood; Vintage; 1999; £7.99; 0099272539) – *Somewhat controversial book by Tony Benn's daughter, arguing that the lives of modern mothers are "glamourised and disposed, sentimentalised and over-looked"; attacks the 'Cosmo' theory about "having it all", and investigates the "unrecognised social revolution" in the role of motherhood in the 1990s.*

The Smart Woman's Guide to Staying at Home – Melissa Hill (How to walk away from the working world and keep your independence; Vermilion; 2001; £9.99; 0-09-185596-9) – *An upbeat read for those dubious about their decision to step off the career ladder. As well as practical ideas about day-to-day issues sorted (including how to agree on sharing tasks), it offers some interesting ideas on how to look for and do new things to do with your time. Some readers will find it full of good advice, others that it is irritatingly New Age.* / www.randomhouse.co.uk.

Take A Career Break – Astrid Stevens (Bringing up children without giving up your future; Need2Know; 1996; £4.99; 1861440243)

Working Mum – Lindsay Cook (The Survival Guide; Simon & Schuster; 2000; £6.99; 0-684-86623-4) – *By the managing editor of the Daily Express, a densely written guide focusing on how to make sure you don't lose your rung on the career ladder. It also covers all the nitty gritty, right down to how to tell your boss and colleagues of your pregnancy, and how to organise your return to work.*

Working Parents' Companion – Teresa Wilson (A National Childbirth Trust guide; Thorsons; 1998; £9.99; 0-722536-38-0) – *Ideas from parents about juggling work and home, at different stages of family life; one of the NCT's "core" titles.*

The Working Parents' Handbook – Irene Pilia (A practical guide to the alternatives in childcare; Parents at Work Publications; 1994; £6.99; 1-898676-05-4) – *Includes pointers on interviewing, handover of care, and workplace care.*

FINANCIAL HELP WITH CHILDCARE

Part of the Working Tax Credit for families *(see chapter 1.05 Rights)* is help with the costs of childcare for families on lower incomes under the Childcare Credit scheme (details available from the Inland Revenue). Up to 70% of the eligible costs can be paid to a maximum of £90 a week, leaving parents to find 30% themselves – around £40 a week.

An innovation in the April 2003 budget was the introduction of childcare taster sessions for single parents thinking of returning to work.

In accordance with the Children Act if your child is 'in need', your local social services department has a duty to provide daycare. This could be in a local authority day nursery, a subsidised place in another nursery, a playgroup, or with a childminder. Individual local authorities define 'in need' differently, but broadly speaking, it includes children whose health or development would be seriously affected without daycare, and children with disabilities.

USEFUL CONTACTS

The Department for Work & Pensions (DWP),
☎ (0800) 882200 ⏚ www.dwp.gov.uk
Formerly the Department of Social Security (DSS): the freephone number provides details of all benefit entitlements.

Style of care: inside vs outside the home

Affordability is too often the dominant concern in choosing childcare, but is by no means the only factor to consider. One of the key issues is whether your child should spend most of the time at home, or be cared for somewhere else with other children.

CARE IN THE HOME:
(NANNIES, AU PAIRS, ETC)

Advantages:
➤ Inside the home the child does not have to leave the security of a familiar environment.

➤ Your child will be the prime focus of the carer's attention, and will receive lots of one-to-one attention.

➤ You choose the individual looking after your child.

➤ There is no more convenient form of childcare. You can seek someone willing to work hours to suit you. There is no rush to get the baby/children ready in the morning, and hurrying back to pick them up afterwards.

➢ You can direct how the child's time is to be spent.

Disadvantages:

➢ When you are out, there is no supervision of the carer. You leave your child in the care of just one adult in whom you place total trust.

➢ Your child may lack playmates, and may not develop social confidence, and the confidence of being out and about. (Of course you can always – as many mothers do – organise activities to counter this, though this involves additional expense which needs to be factored into the overall equation).

➢ A sick carer will mean having to find someone to cover, or you taking time off work.

➢ You become an employer, with all the responsibilities which that entails regarding tax, redundancy obligations, and so on.

CARE OUTSIDE THE HOME:
(DAY NURSERIES & CHILDMINDERS)

Advantages:

➢ The child socialises with other children on a daily basis, and becomes accustomed to being away from home.

➢ With a nursery (but not a childminder), the presence of a number of staff offers a degree of supervision of the carers.

➢ With a nursery (but not a childminder), there is usually a good degree of cover if an individual carer is sick.

➢ With both nursery and childminder, you may be more likely to achieve continuity of care than with a nanny (sackings and resignations of nannies being relatively commonplace).

Disadvantages:

➢ Your child is not the prime focus of attention and is away from the familiarity of home. Pre-schoolers, in particular boys, do not always socialise well, and tend to benefit from more one-to-one attention.

➢ You need to travel to and from the nursery/childminder (although one or two nurseries will pick children up in the morning). Moreover with a nursery (but not necessarily with a childminder), there is little flexibility over hours. The nursery may not open early enough to leave much time to get to work, and similarly may close at a time which means leaving work early.

➢ Ill children are generally not welcome at nurseries or childminders – which means making alternative arrangements or a parent taking time off work. There is also the chance of infection from the other children.

➢ Your child may – in the absence of proper supervision – be at the mercy of older and tougher children.

➢ There may be less opportunity for the child to invite friends home, and to be invited to friends' houses.

➢ With a childminder, her commitments to her own home and family may limit her chance to provide stimulation for your child.

REGULATIONS APPLYING TO CHILDCARE
OUTSIDE THE HOME

Under the Children Act 1989 all forms of childcare (other than those in your own home) with a duration of more than two hours per day have to be registered. Inspections used to be the responsibility of the local authority, but since September 2001, both the registration of all new childminders and day nurseries and the annual check on their standard of care are now conducted by OFSTED.

Close relatives are exempt from the requirement to register. Note though that if you are eligible for the Working Families Tax Credit and use grandparents for childcare, then, if they register as childminders, you may be eligible for Childcare Tax Credit.

Full-time childcare establishments are subject to regulations covering health and safety, staffing levels, food safety and hygiene, space, light, access, staff-training and so on. The Children Act sets out guidelines to good practice in all forms of childcare. Some of the Act's most important facets are the provisions limiting the number of children who can be looked after by a single carer. (Trainee-carers should not be counted. In the case of childminders, numbers include the carer's own child.)

Recommended ratios of carers to children:
➤ birth–two years old: one adult to three children.
➤ two–three years old: one adult to four children.
➤ three–five years old: one adult to eight children.

OPTIONS INVOLVING FAMILIAR HOMES AS WELL AS – OR INSTEAD OF – YOUR OWN

The following are better suited to part-time than full-time care:
➤ A nanny share.
➤ A grandmother or other relative (though this can lead to difficulties over who is ultimately in charge).
➤ A friend (however, you might be wise to pay a decent rate for this or to offer a carefully negotiated exchange of services).
➤ Swapping childcare with another mother ('reciprocal care'). Note: reciprocal care is difficult at times when either child is ill.

Childcare qualifications

Qualifications tend to be of somewhat greater interest to those employing individual childcarers (nannies, childminders, etc), rather than those employing nurseries where you buy into more of a system. Having said that, the qualifications of the staff at a given nursery give some indication of the kind of system you are buying into.

Regarding nannies in particular, not everyone is convinced of the benefits of qualifications. Some excellent nannies are just women who have had lots of experience with kids and/or have a natural empathy with them irrespective of formal training. Much depends on what style of care you are looking for. Qualifications can bring with them more rigid ideas about how things should be done, which can clash with the mother's own, plus an unwillingness to do anything extra, such as emptying a dishwasher.

There is a bewildering array of childcare qualifications. Note that these awards may not indicate much expertise of actually working with children – in particular, someone straight out of college may only have made a largely theoretical study of the subject.

CACHE (see listings below) is the only 'awarding body' (what used to be called an examination board) which specialises in childcare. It offers arguably the most widely recognised and well-accepted qualification on the market: what used to be called (and is still widely referred to as) the NNEB – now the CACHE diploma in nursery nursing.

CACHE can verify any of its own certifications if you can provide the awardees' name, certificate number and place of study.

CACHE qualifications:

CCE (CACHE Certificate in Childcare and Education): a one-year course that may be completed over two years on a part-time basis. It combines theory with practice and covers both physical and emotional care. The award indicates a carer requiring supervision, and is generally suited to a nursery assistant.

CACHE Diploma in Nursery Nursing (the old NNEB): two years' full-time study or the equivalent part-time, with two days a week practical experience in, say, a nursery or maternity unit. The course provides training in the development of children (from birth to just under eight years old) and in promoting emotional, physical, intellectual, linguistic and social development. Assessment is by written and practical tests. This qualification indicates someone capable of working largely unsupervised – namely a nanny or a more senior nursery position.

CACHE Level 3 Certificate in Childminding Practice (CCP): developed with the National Childminding Association (NCMA), this qualification is for those who are or are looking to become a registered childminders.

ADCE (Advanced Diploma in Childcare and Education): professional development for those who have been working in childcare for several years, or who are already well qualified. This qualification indicates someone suitable to work unsupervised. Nannies will only rarely be this qualified – the qualification is more likely to be held by senior nursery staff.

CACHE Level 2 Certificate in Pre-school Practice: developed with Pre-school Learning Alliance (PLA), a part-time course taken over 240 hours (plus at least 150 spent in contact with children and families). It is suitable for those who wish to work at a supervised level in the pre-school field.

CACHE Level 3 Diploma in Pre-school Practice: As for level 2, above, but for those who wish to work unsupervised or at a supervisory level in the pre-school field.

NVQS

CACHE, BTEC and City & Guilds are among organisations awarding National Vocational Qualifications (NVQs) in Early Years Care and Education.

NVQ level 2: for assistants in nurseries and schools, playgroups/pre-schools, and crèches. Also a suitable qualification for mothers' helps.

NVQ level 3: for playgroup/pre-school leaders, childminders, nannies, and workers in nurseries and schools (such as nursery nurses).

No higher NVQ yet exists in this area. (Nor a level 1 qualification, as this covers only routine and predictable work – impossible in childcare…)

BTEC qualifications:

BTEC National Certificate in Childhood Studies (Nursery Nursing): a two-year, full-time course including 800 hours of practical work in at least four different types of workplace with children of 0–2, 2–5 and 5–8 years old. Optional subjects include first aid & safety, nutrition & diet and learning activities & play. Experience working in a private home would be the most useful for a nanny (for whom this is a suitable qualification).

BTEC National Diploma in Childhood Studies (Nursery Nursing): a two-year, full-time course including 800 hours of practical work and a period spent in 'professional practice'. Marginally more academic than (but similar to) a CACHE diploma.

NAMCW qualifications (see note below):

National Association of Maternal and Child Welfare (NAMCW) Advanced Certificate in Childcare and Education: a one-year course, equivalent to an NVQ level 2.

NAMCW Diploma: a two year, full-time course designed to support the development of practical experience to NVQ Level 3.

NAMCW Diploma in Nursery Nursing: a two-year programme equivalent to NVQ level 3.

Note: in 2002, the NAMCW ceased to exist, having been subsumed by CACHE. The certificates listed above have a two-year life span, so you may still see them in use.

Other qualifications:

AMI Diploma (Montessori Training Organisation): an intensive one year course for candidates educated to at least A-Level standard.

Diploma in Nursery Nursing & Early Childhood Teaching (Montessori Centre International): foundation course in Montessori teaching.

USEFUL CONTACTS

City & Guilds, ☎ *(020) 7294 2425* ⌖ *www.city-and-guilds.co.uk*
The organisation offers NVQs in Early Years Care. The City & Guilds course in Family & Community Care is no longer run, but is a qualification you may come across.

Council for Awards in Children's Care & Education (CACHE), ☎ *(01727) 847636* ⌖ *www.cache.org.uk*
The council provides a list of its courses (NVQs) for childminders and nannies, and where they can be studied.

Montessori Centre International, ☎ *(020) 7493 0165*
⌖ *www.montessori.ac.uk*
This organisation trains teachers to teach in the Montessori style, and awards the International Diploma in Early Childhood Teaching.

Montessori Training Organisation (AMI), ☎ *(020) 7435 3646*
⌖ *www.montessori-ami.org*
The only training organisation in the UK to be authorised by the Association Montessori Internationale (AMI – see Montessori Society in 2.07 Education). The AMI diploma can be obtained after an intensive 1-year or 2-year course, which focuses on the child under six, using the theory originally developed by Maria Montessori. You may come across other, similarly-named qualifications but these are not authorised by this organisation as there is a lack of patent control over the Montessori name.

Qualification & Curriculum Authority (QCA), ☎ *(020) 7509 5555* ⌖ *www.qca.org.uk*
Previously the National Council for Vocational Qualifications, NCVQ – the accrediting body for all NVQs, which can provide information on who runs childminder NVQs.

TRAINING

If she doesn't already have first aid qualifications, you might like to ask your carer if she would be prepared to take an appropriate course. See chapter *2.03 Baby health* for details of first aid courses.

2. NANNIES & NANNY SHARES

Images of old-fashioned, Mary-Poppins-style nannies have sometimes in recent years given way to scare stories in the media about not just irresponsible, but even violent nannies. In part this situation has not been helped by the government's continuing resistance to the establishment of a national nanny register.

It remains the case, however, that for those who can afford to employ a nanny, this often remains the best childcare option, affording parents with demanding jobs the maximum flexibility. (A nanny should not, however, work more than 10 hours a day and must have a minimum of one-and-a-half days and three evenings off a week.) It also gives parents a great deal of control over the details of their child's care.

Different nannies have different likes and dislikes. For example some don't like shared care: i.e. looking after a child or children where the mother is also around. Older nannies offer experience but may be more old-fashioned in their approach and possibly have children of their own who may need looking after. Younger nannies may be more up-to-date with child-raising theory but less experienced in practice.

WHO CAN CALL THEMSELVES A NANNY?

Anyone. According to the Professional Association of Nursery Nurses about half the 100,000 nannies working in the UK are unqualified. In many cases the lack of qualifications does not indicate a lower standard of care, but it does make checking references of paramount importance.

LIVE-IN VERSUS LIVE-OUT

As with most forms of childcare, finding a good carer ends up being most parents' chief preoccupation (of which more below). Before you get to that stage, however, you need to refine your ideas further as to exactly what you are looking for, in particular whether your nanny is to live under your own roof.

Live-in nanny:

➤ The cheaper alternative, though the cost of board including the extra wear-and-tear on your house must be factored into your calculations.

➤ Hours are generally slightly longer (up to approximately 55 a week) often with one or two nights' baby-sitting thrown in. When nannies live in there is no danger of late arrivals, although there is the potential problem of a blurring between working and non-working time. Live-in nannies tend to work even when they are slightly unwell.

➤ You will need a separate, suitable room for the nanny, ideally with a television and bathroom.

➤ Unless you have a house with plenty of space, a live-in arrangement inevitably cuts down the already limited time which you and your partner can spend privately.

➤ Nannies working in such an arrangement usually give plenty of notice of leaving.

Live-out nanny:

➤ The more expensive option.

➤ You and your partner enjoy greater privacy.

➤ Hours are normally only around 45 hours a week and baby-sitting has to be negotiated as an 'extra'. Days lost to sickness tend to be greater. However, a live-out nanny is more likely to view all the time spent with the child or children as work time, and is consequently less tempted to go about her own business during those hours.

➤ Little notice may be given of plans to quit.

THE CONTRACT

The golden rule is to decide what you want the nanny to do and to tell her this both in advance and also while she is working for you. Communication should avoid most problems, and any that surface should be discussed as soon as possible.

It is a good idea to write up a contract or job description before you even start trying to recruit. In that way you will save time interviewing unsuitable applicants.

Once you've found the right person make sure you both sign the contract before she starts so you know where you both stand.

Subjects for the contract or job description to cover:

➤ Proposed starting date.

➤ Live-in or live-out.

➤ Working hours (you may wish to allow for 15–30 minutes cushion at each end of the day for a handover, discussion and any unforeseen lateness).

➤ An outline of the weekly timetable including any work expected at the weekend, and evening baby-sitting requirements.

➤ Free time (if live-in).

➤ Whether time is to be spent with the child/children outside the house, and if so where and doing what.

➤ Any cooking required, and the type of food to be given to the children, including any diet restrictions. Specify whether meals are included for live-out nannies, and whether meals are to be eaten with the family.

➤ Any cleaning duties required and a specification of those not required (the latter may reassure a non-cleaning nanny).

➤ Any other household duties, e.g. ironing, keeping the children's rooms tidy.

➤ Whether the carer will be required to drive the children anywhere. (Check for a clean driving licence and include the carer on your car insurance.)

➤ Exact financial details relating to the position, including net pay and when and where this will be paid (weekly or monthly, by cash, standing order or cheque). Decide on whether you are talking net or gross and do your sums carefully before you start interviewing to avoid taking on someone who turns out too expensive. A salary review is usually expected after a year.

➤ Sick pay.

➤ Unless you plan to offer a pension or other benefits it would be wise to make it clear that no such terms are offered with the job.

➤ Holidays (standard is four weeks) including any restrictions on timings of holidays, for example to coincide with your own. Will the nanny be expected to accompany the family on holiday?

➤ Sackable offences, e.g. theft, dishonesty, drunkenness, incompetence, bad time-keeping, physical or mental cruelty to the child, and endangering the child's life. State which of these you consider grounds for instant dismissal.

➤ Rules on smoking in the house/in front of the children.

➤ Guidelines regarding how you expect the carer to treat the child, for example the types of entertainment or discipline you prefer.

➤ Any house rules, for example about visitors, especially boyfriends, staying out all night, etc.

➤ Use of the phone.

➤ Any restrictions on use of different rooms in the house.

➤ Guidelines on your child's watching of television.

➤ Trial period on both sides.

➤ Notice period on both sides.

➤ The possibility of looking after other siblings, e.g. older children in the school holidays, new babies etc.

➤ Confidentiality.

USEFUL CONTACTS

The Professional Association of Nursery Nurses (PANN),
☎ (01332) 372337 ✆ www.pat.org.uk
The section of the Professional Association of Teachers trade union relevant to child carers – nursery nurses, nannies and classroom assistants. / PUBLICATIONS 'All you need to know about Working as a Nanny', contains a model nanny employment contract, £5.

READING

The Nanny Handbook – Karen House, Louise Sheppard (How to Find and Keep the Best Nannies and Au Pairs; Simon & Schuster; 2001; £12.99; 0684866366) – *A guide offering detailed practical advice, particularly on how to make the relationship work, especially in the important first week. Also, the importance of ground rules.*

The New Good Nanny Guide – Charlotte Breese & Hilaire Gomer (Complete handbook on nannies, au pairs, mother's helps, childminders and other childcare options; Ebury; 2000; £14.99; 0-0918-2535-0) – *Now in its fifth edition, the best-known reference on the subject by author–mothers who originally worked as nannies; it includes a directory of more than 100 interviewed nanny and au pair agencies, and also covers childminders, mother's helps and nurseries; advises on areas from the practical to the more "touchy feely".*

[Magazine] **Nursery World** – *A weekly magazine aimed at childcare professionals – job adverts for nannies are taken on Fri. It often runs articles on contracts, National Insurance and other aspects of nanny employment. Ring for details of back issues. (The publication occasionally includes The Professional Nanny, which compiles an annual survey of salaries reported by nanny agencies.) / www.nursery-world.co.uk.*

The Top Notch Nannies' Guide – Jean and Jasmine Birtles (A quick, easy, fun guide to hiring a nanny; Summersdale; 1999; £4.99; 1-902320-12-3) – *As you'd expect from the boss of one of the most successful nanny agencies (and her daughter), information which is practical and to the point. If you think you will need a nannycam, she says, you shouldn't be employing a nanny. There are questions for the interview, a sample contract, and a table with the sobering statistics on children killed in Britain by parents as opposed to nannies - and former are far more likely culprits than latter. / www.summersdale.com or www.topnotchnannies.com.*

AIDS FOR NANNIES

The Nanny Diary (Applejack Nanny Ltd; 2002; £30) – *A hardback A4 volume with a page per day incorporating entries for meals, appointments, after hours baby-sitting requirements, expenditures, medications, other instructions; and space for noting what the children did that day. / 308 Upper Richmond Road West, East Sheen SW14 7JE – (020) 8878 5778.*

Nannyboard *(£4.99) – An emergency list that can be stuck to the fridge, with various pieces of information of potential use to anyone looking after your children: from your childrens' allergies, to contact numbers, to where to find the fuse box. It is endorsed by St John Ambulance (ten first aid procedures are on the back). / PO Box 29961, London SW6 6FT; www.childalert.co.uk.*

Finding a nanny

Note: the avenues for recruiting a nanny – agencies and places to advertise – are in many cases similar to those for finding an au pair, mother's help, or maternity nurse. Lead times however may differ.

LEAD TIME

Allow four to six weeks through an agency and up to 12 weeks if advertising yourself. Be prepared for a tiring round of interviews, particularly if you are advertising independently, and note that agencies will begin to consider you difficult if you haven't found someone suitable after half a dozen interviews. Good people may well be employed currently so you need to allow further time for them to finish their current job. If you find someone you like, move fast; the best nannies go quickly. But do note that the most expensive is not by any means necessarily the best.

AGENCIES

As with all types of recruitment, it can be surprising just how long advertising a post and interviewing applicants can take. If you can afford one, a good agency may save you time. The better firms will provide some pre-vetting of applicants.

Modest expectations in this area are essential. These are businesses that are notorious for variability both of their service and of the quality of people that they supply. It remains to be seen how government plans to regulate this area might improve matters.

Some agencies send along candidates without checking their references (or only doing so cursorily), regardless of what they are telling you to the contrary. A 1997 investigation by The Sunday Times famously found three out of six agencies failed to pick up on a candidate who had been convicted of manslaughter and, indeed, positively recommended her to parents.

Membership of the Recruitment and Employment Confederation (REC) – a federation of all kinds of recruitment agencies – is interpreted by some people as a good sign, but is no cast iron guarantee of standards. Members are supposed to abide by a code of conduct but some still seem to be very lackadaisical.

The final fee is usually a percentage of the agreed salary, though (particularly with au pairs) a fixed fee may be charged instead. This is not a cheap way of finding an employee. An agency's total fees for providing a full-time nanny will seldom leave much change from £1,000, and £1,500 is probably nearer the mark. In addition, some are introducing a registration fee, similar to that charged by au pair agencies. Fees are often quoted excluding VAT, so be sure to factor this into your calculations. Remember that, as with estate agents, there is an incentive for agencies generally to 'talk up' rates.

Some agencies will provide a draft contract for you and the nanny to sign but this usually needs amending. Few agencies are up to speed on employment law, insurance regulations or on how to arrange to pay tax and NI directly. You are paying for an introduction and that's that.

When dealing with nanny agencies:

➤ Do read the terms and conditions (and run a mile if they are not readily forthcoming).

➤ Bear in mind that if the nanny doesn't work out, most refund periods expire well before this will become apparent.

➤ Look for a good information pack indicating what you can expect of the agency, and the nanny – usually only offered by agencies of longer standing.

➤ A good measure of the agency's quality is how much detail they take from you about your requirements. An excellent sign is if they send someone to see you in person.

➤ Check that the agency interviews all candidates in person and checks their references and any gaps in employment.

➤ Look for detailed information about candidates and introductions only to suitable ones.

➤ Expect to be contacted after an interview to see how it has gone.

➤ Ideally look for somewhere offering 'after-sales' service in case there are any problems.

➤ Beware of agencies charging a registration fee. There's no guarantee they will do anything to earn it.

➤ If you want a live-out nanny, a local agency may be more useful than a big name but agencies open, shut and change hands constantly. As ever, word of mouth is the best recommendation.

READING

South West & North West London Parents' Directories (free) – *Bi-annual listings (May and November) of relevant local services, including extensive nursery school and nanny agency details.* / (020) 8785 2430.

USEFUL CONTACTS

(In addition to the sources listed below, perhaps the best places to find agencies are local publications and magazines such as the NCT newsletter – see chapter 4.05 Finding out more.)

Best Bear, ☎ (020) 7352 5852 ✆ www.bestbear.co.uk
In 1999/2000 it investigated more than 1,000 agencies of which it considered that fewer than 150 made the grade. Information covers using agencies, placing ads and general advice on hiring. There is also a section on the site for carers.

Department for Education & Skills (DfES), ☎ (0870) 000 2288
✆ www.dfes.gov.uk
Formerly the Department for Education & Employment (DfEE): the website lists information about how to find a nanny.

nannyjob, ✆ www.nannyjob.co.uk
Simple but effective website, which – as well as a directory of nanny agencies and nursery schools – offers a noticeboard for advertising/finding nanny positions.

Recruitment & Employment Confederation (REC),
☎ (020) 7462 3260, (0800) 320588 *for agencies* ✆ www.rec.uk.com
The industry organisation for employment agencies of all kinds (the majority being nothing to do with childcare). Some people take membership to indicate a basic level of professionalism (members are supposed to abide by the REC Code of Good Recruitment Practice) although there are indifferent agencies which are members, and sensibly-run agencies which are not. The organisation can provide a list of member agencies specialising in childcare.

ADVERTISEMENTS

If you are prepared to do the leg-work required by advertising and interviewing then this is a much cheaper way of finding a carer than using an agency.

A nanny in a current job will probably have to give a month's notice and your advertisement may take up to a fortnight to appear, so you should start placing ads eight to 12 weeks before you actually need someone.

If you give a telephone number, rather than an address, you will usually get more responses but this requires that you do a lot of interviewing over the phone, which can be wearing. For phone responses you will need to be prepared with a job description and set of basic questions.

If you use a box number you will get fewer responses but will be more protected against weirdos.

The advertisement should state:

➤ Whether the post is live-in or live-out.

➤ Exact details of the nature of the job: is it just childcare or do you wish housework to be included?

➤ Number and age of children (no further description is helpful at this stage).

➤ A preferred level of experience.

➤ Any further requirements: e.g. driver, non-smoker.

PLACES TO ADVERTISE

Ealing Gazette & Ealing Leader
134–136 The Broadway London W13 0TL ☎ *(01895) 451027*
⌁ www.ealinggazette.co.uk
Free newspapers distributed throughout the boroughs of Ealing, Hammersmith and Fulham. Line ads: £5.80 per word (+ VAT); minimum 10 words; runs in both newspapers for one week; place ad by Wednesday 4pm. Display box approximately £50.

Families Magazines
PO Box 4302 London SW16 1ZS ☎ *(020) 8696 9680* *⌁ www.familiesmagazine.co.uk*
Publishers of a number of local free-sheets whose total circulation is over 200,000. Ads in the small 'Childcare' section are free, but only a limited number are published, on a first come, first served basis. Free classified ads can also be placed on the website for a month. / SEE ALSO *2.06 Baby & toddler activities; 2.07 Education.*

The Ham & High
100a Avenue Rd London NW3 3HF ☎ *(020) 7433 3888* *⌁ www.hamhigh.co.uk*
Ads in London's largest local newspaper tend, perhaps, to attract people simply looking for a job, including a proportion of foreign students, rather than specialists: £1 per word + VAT; min 10 word, max 50. In the same group are Broadway Ham & High (Crouch End), Highbury & Islington Express, and Wood & Vale Express (St John's Wood and Maida Vale).

The Lady
39-40 Bedford St London WC2E 9ER ☎ *(020) 7379 4717* *⌁ www.lady.co.uk*
The classic place to advertise: first 10 words £21, every further five words £9.50 including VAT; deadline Wed 3pm for following Tue edition.

nannyjob
⌁ www.nannyjob.co.uk
Simple but effective website, which – as well as a directory of nanny agencies and nursery schools – offers a noticeboard for advertising/finding nanny positions.

Nursery World
Admiral House, 66-68 East Smithfield London E1W 1BX ☎ *(020) 7782 3000*
⌁ www.nursery-world.com
Weekly publication aimed directly at childcare professionals. Advertising deadline is Friday for publication the following Thursday. Nanny advert rates: minimum 6 lines (£4 per line); minimum total £25 + VAT.

Simply Childcare
16 Bushyhill Rd London SE5 8QJ ☎ *(020) 7701 6111* *⌁ www.simplychildcare.com*
Listings of nannies, nannyshares, childminders, after-school carers and baby-sitters that are free to the carers and to subscribers. The magazine covers childcare London-wide and in some more outlying areas (to the M25). Minimum subscription of three issues over six weeks, £35 (including an advertisement). A childcare information pack is also available for £9.95. / HOURS *9.30am-5.30pm.*

TNT

14-15 Child's Place London SW5 9RX ☎ *(020) 7373 3377* ⌁ *www.tnt-live.com*
Free magazine aimed at travelling Antipodeans – some parents' preferred choice for childcare as they are usually much less fussy about the details of the job and are more light-hearted in their approach than those making a career of nannying; on the other hand some have no interest in children and are only looking for some money to travel. It is wise to check how long a given applicant is permitted to stay in the country. 3 lines (12-15 words) £81.50 + VAT, deadline midday Thursday. This will be entered to TNT on Monday, Wednesday and on website for a week. Other local papers may be useful but not are as well recognised as a forum for this kind of position.

NOTICEBOARDS

Noticeboards in shops and libraries are a cheap way to advertise, and a good way of finding someone local.

Places to look for noticeboards:

➤ Children's shops.

➤ The children's section of the local library.

➤ Newsagent shop windows, particularly in areas where many families have nannies.

➤ Some supermarkets have boards.

➤ The local Jobcentre. This is free and though not traditionally some-where to find a qualified nanny, it can be a potential source of mother's helps.

➤ Local parent support groups usually have regular newsletters which take advertisements (see chapter *2.01 Postnatal*).

➤ Some NCT branches run a nanny share register (see below).

➤ For a part-time carer, generally only for six months, local language schools, either on their noticeboard or through the head office. For schools listings try the British Council (see Au Pairs below) or Yellow Pages.

NANNY TRAINING COLLEGES

If you are prepared to forego experience, then recruiting direct from one of the colleges can be a relatively economical way of employing a nanny.

Newly-trained nannies tend to be more up-to-speed on the latest advice and theories concerning childcare. They are also generally more flexible, both in adapting to the mother's theories and in doing non-child-care work. Availability is naturally subject to the seasonality of courses (which usually end in June).

If you are looking to economise further, consider employing a nanny actually in the course of her training. To qualify as nursery nurses, students must have practical experience and for these periods can be employed at a reduced rate or simply given work experience though availability is usually limited by the other requirements of their course. If interested, contact a local college (bearing in mind that you are unlikely to get someone qualified to provide unsupervised care.) Degrees of inexperience vary, but for, say, a 'probationer' nanny you get pretty much a fully qualified nursery nurse – just one who has never had sole charge of a child before.

A useful option if you only require part-time care would be to find someone looking for employment while completing a part-time course.

You can get a current list of approved colleges from CACHE (see listings). If you want a nanny with a serious training pedigree, the main private training colleges are listed below.

USEFUL CONTACTS

The Chiltern College, ☎ *(0118) 947 1847* ⌕ *www.childcarelink.gov.uk*

This well-known private training college runs a register of potential employers for
graduates and former students with career experience. An introduction fee is charged
(from £400); nannies are placed all over England but demand is high.

Norland College, ☎ *(01225) 466 202* ⌕ *www.norland.co.uk*

The big 'name' in nanny training – the college provides parents with a list of qualified
nannies and runs a placement service. Fees for use of the service: £1200 + VAT for
a full-time permanent position; £860 + VAT for a newly trained nanny (one year post);
£60 per week for a temporary nursery nurse.

When interviewing you will need to find out about the applicants.

Issues like the following are relevant:

➤ Where did she grow up?

➤ Does she have siblings and what do they do?

➤ Where and what has she studied/where did she go to school?

➤ Does she have a boyfriend or husband?

➤ Where does she socialise?

➤ What was her last job and why did she leave?

➤ What does she most like/dislike about looking after children of this
age?

➤ What experience does she have of working with children of this age?

➤ What is her approach to discipline?

➤ How would she plan to entertain/occupy children of this age?

➤ What is the minimum period she can commit to staying with you?

➤ If there are any gaps on the CV (common in girls from Continental
Europe, who rarely produce British-style CVs), what was she doing
then?

➤ Can she cook?

➤ Can she drive?

➤ What is her ideal family?

➤ What is she planning to move on to?

➤ Check all references carefully, remembering the acknowledged fact
that British parents are reluctant to hurt future employment prospects
even of nannies they have sacked.

➤ Ask open questions – what kind of play do you encourage?

➤ Check (for a live-out nanny) that the commute is manageable.

➤ Invite the nanny to spend half a day with you before signing the contract. This means you can combine a formal interview with watching
her in a more hands-on situation (for example, handling bath-time).

➤ Bear in mind that if you get the right person and treat her well she's
likely to stay, saving you time and money in the long run.

Nanny shares

A nanny share can mean either a nanny looking after different people's
children on different days of the week, or a nanny looking after children
from different families simultaneously, potentially all week long.

In the second case, the idea is that both families pay less while the
nanny gets paid more. The exact details have to be negotiated, with the
rate of pay depending on the nanny's experience and the number of children involved. However, note that some nannies find in practice that
looking after two sets of children is too much to handle.

Nannies who work for more than two families are subject to the regulations of the Children Act (see Section 3, Day Nurseries below), which
involves registration and inspection by OFSTED.

Considerations for nanny shares with another family:

➤ Whether you would like the children from the other family to be the same age as your baby, or different, giving more sense of family.
➤ Whether any newborn babies are included.
➤ The other family's approach to childcare and issues like discipline and food.
➤ Whether time will be spent in your house or the other family's house. Note that getting the child to the other house and back can be time-consuming and inconvenient. Nannies generally do not like to be involved in dropping-off and picking-up arrangements.
➤ If a simultaneous share is to be in just one family's house, will the division of the nanny's salary be adjusted to cover the higher food and heating bills of that family, or will the convenience of everything happening under that family's roof militate against this?
➤ How responsibility for tax is going to be shared.
➤ If the nanny is to be provided with a car, how payment for insurance and petrol will be split.
➤ If extra equipment has to be bought, how the cost will be split.
➤ How food, toys and nappies will be organised.
➤ What will happen if a child or the nanny is sick?
➤ What will happen during either family's and the nanny's holidays?

Finding a nanny share

Noticeboards (see Finding a nanny, above) are a particularly appropriate way to look for a suitable nanny-sharing arrangement or some form of reciprocal care. Networking at NCT and other support group meetings or baby activity classes may also prove helpful.

USEFUL CONTACTS
National Childbirth Trust (NCT), ☎ *Enquiry line (0870) 444 8707*
⌖ www.nctpregnancyandbabycare.co.uk; www.nctparentsconnect.co.uk
Some NCT branches run a nanny share register (and branch publications can also be a fertile source of childcare, and baby-sitting contacts). Contact your local branch for details. / HOURS *Mon-Thurs 9am-5pm, Fri 9am-4pm; or answerphone.*

SW London Nannyshare Register, ☎ *(020) 8677 3015*
Run mailing lists for SW London families requiring a nanny, families with a nanny to share, and for nannies looking for work; £15 to register for free list every 2 or 3 weeks; free for nannies to join. Send your name, address and telephone number along with the age and sex of your child(ren), the start date, brief details of the arrangements sought together with a cheque.

Tax & other liabilities
(For proposed changes to maternity rights, see chapter 1.05 Rights.)
The law precludes a nanny from setting up as a self-employed outside contractor responsible for her own tax. Therefore, you, as the employer, will be responsible for PAYE. The Inland Revenue runs what used to be known as a 'Q scheme' – the 'simplified PAYE deductions scheme' for employers of domestic workers (see below). This removes the need for all the complicated employment forms (P45s, P60s etc) and allows quarterly rather then monthly tax returns to be submitted.

If – as is likely – your nanny (or other carer) is paid above the tax threshold of £4,535 per annum, your obligations as an employer include liabilities for Statutory Sick Pay (SSP) and maternity pay.

Under Small Employer's Relief (SER), if you pay less than £20,000 national insurance a year the maternity pay is actually paid by the Inland Revenue which hands it to the employer in a lump sum plus 4 1/2% to cover administration. The payments are then passed to the nanny by you the employer at appropriate intervals for the full period the maternity pay is claimed, whether the nanny is returning to work with you or not.

SSP is payable if the carer is sick for four or more days in a row, regardless of how long she has worked for you.

Your responsibilities under PAYE:

➤ To set up a PAYE scheme with the Inland Revenue's PAYE tax office for income tax and National Insurance (NI).

➤ To make quarterly payments of tax and NI to the Inland Revenue.

➤ To provide weekly or monthly payslips to your employee (depending on how she is paid), setting out the PAYE deductions from the gross pay.

➤ To submit to the Inland Revenue an annual declaration and summary of deductions and payments. This is put together using a Deductions Card that must be completed every time you pay her. See below for details of how to obtain one.

➤ To maintain PAYE records.

Note that even if tax and NI are not due you still have a legal duty to keep records of all payments and to give an itemised payslip showing gross pay, deductions and net pay. Payment record books and payslips are available from business stationers.

Payroll agencies

PAYE is a notoriously fiddly area – one for which many commercial organisations use outside specialists. The new simplified PAYE Q scheme aims to alleviate much of the time-consuming paperwork involved, but there are agencies who can take it off your hands entirely if you prefer.

Some nanny agencies will provide this service for a fee or there are specialists. Generally these firms will set up the PAYE scheme, provide payslips and an annual declaration, tell you how much to pay the nanny each month and specify the amount for a quarterly cheque to the Inland Revenue. They will also provide a P45 for the nanny when she leaves. Some services require payment in advance, which is not refundable, and some agencies will charge for a change of nanny.

USEFUL CONTACTS

Inland Revenue, ☎ CTC Helpline (0845) 300 3900, New Employers Helpline (0845) 607 0143 ✍ www.inlandrevenue.gov.uk
The helpline for New Employers (open Mon-Fri 8am-8pm, Sat & Sun 8am-5pm) will send you a New Employer's Starter Pack. The office can help with queries regarding the Inland Revenue and the Contributions Agency and should be able to give the latest details on anything from Statutory Maternity and Sick Pay to PAYE.

Lamburn & Turner, ☎ (01582) 834850 ✍ www.lamburnandturner.co.uk
£35.25 per quarter for weekly or monthly payments.

Nanny Payroll Services, ☎ (01536) 373111 ✍ www.nannypayroll.co.uk, www.paydayservices.co.uk
The Nanny Payroll Service is just part of their business; £130 per year (including VAT) for monthly-paid wages. They claim particular expertise in splitting paycodes for nanny shares. The website has information files to download. / HOURS Mon-Fri 9am-5pm.

Nannytax, ☎ (0845) 226 2203 ✍ www.nannytax.co.uk
Claims to have been the first payroll service dedicated to nannies in the UK and charges a total per year (including VAT) of £211.50. for either monthly or weekly wages. Call or visit the website for a free information pack.

Taxing Nannies, ☎ (020) 8882 6847 ✍ www.taxingnannies.co.uk
Charges are £15 per month (including VAT) for wages paid monthly.

Administrating PAYE by yourself

Ring to register as a new employer and you can do so on the phone requesting the simplified deduction scheme. You can then, if youwish, request a visit from a business advisor to show you the paperwork and calculations required. This advisor will then offer ongoing support if required.

Insurance

Note that if your employee injures herself in your home, you could be liable to pay compensation. Cover for this may already be included in your household insurance under the personal liability section but – if not – you will need additional cover. If the injury is caused as she goes about her employment for you, then you are vicariously liable for any damage caused. Again this might fall under your household cover. Note also that household policies do not generally cover work outside the UK should the nanny come on holiday with you.

Another issue is liability cover, in case the nanny herself causes an injury. It may also be wise to check whether she has her own cover and, if not to suggest that she contemplates it. PANN (see listings, below) offers its members a policy.

You should also check that your car insurance covers your nanny. If the nanny is under 25 years old this can add considerably to costs. If she uses her own car you should check that it is insured for business purposes.

USEFUL CONTACTS

The Professional Association of Nursery Nurses (PANN)
2 St James' Court, Friar Gate Derby DE1 1BT ☎ (01332) 372337 ✆ www.pat.org.uk
The section of the Professional Association of Teachers trade union relevant to child carers – nursery nurses, nannies and classroom assistants. Members have a code of practice and are insured for up to £5 million for incidents in the course of their work.

Redundancy

A nanny who has worked for you for at least two years is entitled to redundancy pay. If aged between 22 and 40 years old, she will be entitled to one week's pay for each year of employment.

Dismissal

If you are dismissing the nanny, it is wise to make sure that the dismissal follows the procedure agreed in the contract. Failing to do so may leave you open to a claim for breach of contract and – if the nanny has been employed for over a year – unfair dismissal.

Investigating nannies

A few agencies claim to be able to offer police checks for potential employees, plus List 99 checks (of those people blacklisted by the Department of Education).

USEFUL CONTACTS

CUonPC
349 Brighton Road, South Croydon Surrey CR2 6ER ☎ (020) 8680 4009
✆ www.CUonPC.com
A vendor of nanny-cams, security cameras and voice-alert systems.

Spymaster
3 Portman Square London W1H 6LB ☎ (020) 7486 3885 ⊘ www.spymasteruk.com
Bugging devices and nannycam systems (which can be hidden in, for example, clocks);
the bugging equipment is designed to work over a far greater distance and more
efficiently than any standard baby monitor, but prices start at around £300 + VAT.
/ HOURS Mon to Fri 9.30am-6.30pm, Sat 10am-5pm.

3. DAY NURSERIES

*(For regulations applying to childcare outside the home, see above under Choosing
Childcare. For information regarding nursery schools, see chapter 2.07 Education.)*
Day nurseries are one of the biggest growth areas in childcare. The
number of places in registered nurseries in the UK mushroomed between
1988 and 1998/99 from 36,000 to 247,000, and in December 2003 stood
at 280,000. And yet demand still outstrips supply, as shown by the number
of parents who undertake 'Mission Impossible' journeys daily because
they were unable to secure a suitable place nearer home (or who feeling
they have to go for second best).

The scarcity of places makes early registration with nurseries essential, and you may have to pay a fee just for the privilege of maintaining
your name on a lengthy waiting list.

Although some nurseries take babies from as young as six weeks, six
months is a more common starting age. However, numbers are very limited for the under-twos and – for babies especially – places generally have
to be booked at least three months ahead, and in some areas before the
baby is even born.

Nurseries report that most children are better settled if they spend at
least three and preferably four or five days of the week at the nursery.
Priority is given to those seeking full-time places and some establishments
only offer these. However, because of the part-time nature of many mothers' work, market pressures mean it can sometimes be easier to secure a
part-time place.

Hours vary: from 7am/8am to 5pm/6pm is typical. Some private
establishments are beginning to open even later, though a number of
these impose a limit on the maximum length of time you can leave your
child.

Day nurseries are usually open all year excluding bank holidays, a
week at Christmas and a week (or more) in the summer.

Types of nursery:

Private day nurseries: the cost for one child is comparable to that of a
student or unqualified nanny. For more than one child, however, it can
easily work out more expensive than an experienced nanny.

Local authority day nurseries (children's centres): generally provide full
or part-time places for children from birth to five years old. There are not
very many in existence (only enough for less than 2% of under-threes by
one estimate), places are normally only available to children referred by
Social Services, and there are usually long waiting lists. Reasons for which
Social Services might refer a child include parental illness, to help a wid-
owed parent, or difficult home circumstances. Priority is often given to
children with special needs or learning difficulties. At least 50% of the
staff should have childcare qualifications plus possibly qualifications in
social work and special needs. Fees for means-tested parents rise to £130
per week or there are private places, usually for around £5 or £10 more, if
there is space. Single parents usually pay less. Notification of availability of
a place is usually only available about three weeks in advance. To find
out more, contact your local Social Services department.

Community nurseries: these are run by local childcare organisations, charities, special interest groups (such as churches) or by social services on their behalf. There are around 250 In England. Such nurseries tend to be cheaper than average, but there are not usually many places, and they often only take children from a specified catchment area. Not many take under-twos. As such organisations are generally non-profit-making, the cost of using them is usually comparable to that of using a childminder. Parents are expected to contribute time to administration and fund-raising.

Workplace nurseries: Some workplace nurseries are open to the general public. They are sometimes called crèches, a term more commonly used in the UK to refer to short-term childcare (for example in a sports or shopping centre, or a supermarket). Workplace nursery places benefit from the employer contributions being tax-free. Occasionally colleges offer subsidised childcare on a similar principle for students. The number of workplace nurseries, which once looked set to grow, has failed to do so. However, as standards are often high, should one be available to you it is likely to be a good option.

Finding a nursery

LEAD TIME
Nowhere in London is well supplied with nurseries and some parts are even worse than others. At best you can expect a waiting time of a couple of months – and even then availability will almost certainly be restricted to certain days. In some areas six months-plus is nearer the mark.

FINDING THE OPTIONS
There is, at the time of writing, no definitive printed guide to day nurseries and nursery education in the capital, though some books do exist and the amount of information on the web is increasing. The national rating system for nurseries and playgroups under the investors in children scheme may improve matters.

Local councils (see chapter *4.01 London boroughs*) should provide parents, on request with a complete list of nurseries in the borough. It may also be worth requesting lists from neighbouring boroughs, and the borough in which you work, if relevant.

Advertisements are to be found in all London-based baby and children publications, including NCT newsletters.

MAKING A CHOICE
Bear in mind that typically nurseries are run by youngish women who often leave to have children of their own. The heads are generally the key to the quality and style of the nursery and if they move on you may be looking at a very different establishment from the one you thought you had chosen. Some gentle questioning around the subject can be useful.

Once you have arrived at a first choice, try to confirm your child's place as quickly as possible. If no place is available it may be worth putting your child's name on the waiting list and making regular checks to see if a place comes free. Mothers' arrangements change all the time, and somewhere with no prospect of a free place one week, may be in touch the next.

USEFUL CONTACTS
Best Bear, ☎ *(020) 7352 5852* ⏚ *www.bestbear.co.uk*
An on-line directory of over 20,000 nurseries nationally.

The Bright Horizons Family Solutions, ☎ (020) 7253 9620

🖰 www.bright-horizons.com
Group of nurseries; also runs a consultancy service, recommending other
nursery/childcare solutions.

Families Magazines, ☎ (020) 8696 9680 🖰 www.familiesmagazine.co.uk

Regular round-ups, plus advertisements for nurseries in the relevant catchment area
(including much of London, and of other major cities). They also run the Education
Advisory Service (see also).

National Day Nurseries Association, ☎ (01484) 723 322

🖰 www.ndna.org.uk
Association of nursery owners – representing approximately one-sixth of private day
nurseries in the country – which will provide details of members in your area. The
organisation publishes guides to help parents selecting nurseries.

Office of Standards in Education (OFSTED), ☎ (020) 7421 6800

🖰 www.ofsted.gov.uk
Although the Children's Act inspections (the general inspections that used to be carried
out by the London boroughs) are not yet available on the website, most nurseries also
receive Nursery Education inspections, details of which are available.

Nursery checklist

The following is a fairly comprehensive checklist of questions and issues
that you may want to bear in mind when you go about your nursery
visits.

Note that all nurseries receive regular inspections (previously by the
local borough, now by OFSTED) and a well-run nursery should have no
objection to showing you a copy of the latest report.

Bear in mind that you will probably want to have one or two settling-
in sessions to acclimatise your child to this new setting. Keep this in mind
when you discuss timing with the nursery.

Staffing & set-up:

➤ How stretched are the carer-to-child ratios? For example, is there a
cook, or will one of the staff in your child's room have to leave at
intervals to prepare/wash bottles, cook food, etc.

➤ How long have staff been with the nursery? Does it have a fair number
of middle-aged women who have been there for years, or are they all
youngsters who have been there five minutes and are likely to move
on?

➤ To what extent is the nursery using/dependent on temporary staff?
Are the temps from an agency, or people with whom the nursery has
an on-going relationship?

➤ How are the different age groups organised? – smaller groups are
easier to manage than larger ones.

➤ Does the nursery operate a "key-worker" scheme: i.e. a specific carer
to whom your child is officially attached. If so how many such children are there per key-worker. If not, is the set-up such that your child
will have familiar faces to relate to, and someone who will be your
point of contact in following your child's progress.

Atmosphere & style:

➤ Do staff focus all their attention on you, or do they show an interest in
your child? Do the adults talk to everyone including babies?

➤ Does it feel like a happy, well-run place? How does your child react
to the atmosphere? Do the other children look busy, happy and
friendly with the staff?

➤ Does the nursery take steps (for example through noticeboards, or a
daily report book) to keep parents well informed about their child's
activities – for example what they have eaten today, what they did,
and so on?

➢ What activities are offered? Messy activities are a good idea as this saves tired parents from tidying up at home. Is there an increased range of activities for older children including any pre-school teaching? Are there outings such as swimming, music, dance etc, and if so are they charged extra? Is the children's artwork displayed and can it be taken home? Do the children watch TV and if so what kind?

➢ For older children, is there a policy on discipline, or bullying?

➢ Where a nursery has a 'baby room' and a 'toddler room', or some similar segregation, how flexible is their attitude to when to make the move between the two? Is the equation as simple as 'this week you are one, so it's time to move to the toddler room'? How much attention do they pay to advanced periods of settling-in?

Environment:

➢ Are the rooms warm, safe, reasonably spacious and well lit? Are the floors clean and suitably surfaced for different activities?

➢ Is the housekeeping up-to-scratch? For example, what are the nappy changing facilities and loos like?

➢ Is there a safe, clean and securely fenced outside play area with any play equipment? If not, is there any regular programme of taking the children out for a walk?

Practicalities:

➢ Opening hours. When can you drop off? What happens if you are late collecting the child? Particularly if commuting by train, look for some flexibility here in case of delays – though there may be an extra fee payable.

➢ How convenient is the venue for you, as you will be doing a lot of ferrying to and fro. If you are driving, how easy is parking?

➢ What food is offered and can your preferences or any allergies be catered for?

➢ Does the nursery provide milk, nappies, sheets, etc and charge you, or do you have to buy these things and take them?

➢ What happens if your child is sick?

4. CHILDMINDERS

(For regulations applying to childcare outside the home, see above under Choosing Childcare.)

Childminders are usually self-employed mothers who take care of children, including their own. They are limited by the local authority and legislation to a maximum of six children under eight years old, including their own. Some will be registered for fewer. Many cater for babies.

Costs range widely and some childminders offer a discount for two or more children from the same family. Meals may or may not be included in the price, and you should assume that you will have to provide nappies. Most childminders will ask for a 50% retainer to reserve a place before your child starts, and also while you are on holiday.

Hours are usually between 7.30am and 7pm but if you work odd hours it might be possible to find someone who can be more flexible.

The regulation of childminders shifted in autumn 2002 from the Social Services department of local borough councils to Ofsted, with whom all childminders are now obliged to register by law. On registration, all childminders are checked by the Criminal Records Bureau and have health checks as well as checks to see that their home is safe.

Parents should ask to see copies of the registration before making a final decision. It is worth remembering that registration is not a guarantee of high standards and the responsibility for finding someone suitable and safe is almost entirely up to you.

Childminders are required to have safety procedures in place and to keep records of the children in their care.

The majority of childminders, while experienced, lack the general childcare qualifications common amongst staff in many nurseries and nannies. However all childminders must now attend a training course to register and must have first aid training and public liability insurance as part of the new national standards. There are also now childminding qualifications, such as the Certificate in Childminding Practice.

Ofsted has started publishing reports on all registered childminders on its web site. The NCMA has argued that because entries include address details this may result in a drop in the number of childminders.

GRANDPARENT CHILDMINDERS

Note that if you are eligible to receive Working Tax Credit (WTC), then you can claim Childcare Tax Credit if you are using registered childcare. If care is provided by your parents, therefore, it may be worth encouraging them to register with Ofsted. For eligible families this can be worth up to £135 per week for one child. (See also Section 1, Choosing childcare, above for details of the Inland Revenue helpline and free publications.)

Childminder checklist

In addition to seeing your potential childminder with her own children you need to see how she relates to your child.

As with a nanny, you need to find someone whose attitudes to childcare issues (discipline, potty training, diet, sweets etc) mirror your own as closely as possible. You are unlikely to be the sole employer and are therefore less able to dictate terms (than say with a nanny), so agreement on these issues from the start is even more important.

The checklist below covers the sort of points you may want to cover. You may wish also to enquire about the last OFSTED inspection, and see if references are available from other parents. By far the most important test, however, may be how your child and the childminder seem to hit it off.

Personal qualifications:
➢ Is the childminder registered (ask to see their certificate)? To be operating as a childminder without registering is illegal.
➢ How long has she been childminding? Why did she become a childminder and does she have any relevant recent training?
➢ Is she a member of the National Childminding Association (NCMA, see below) which offers its members insurance?
➢ Previous work experience and plans for the future.
➢ Is there a first aid box? Is there an emergency drill in place?
➢ Is she a member of a local childminder group – useful for regular updates on playgroups, toy libraries etc?

Set-up:
➢ How many other children are there, and how old are they?
➢ Do other people live in or visit the house. Do they, for example, smoke? (Childminders have to keep a smoke-free environment when they are childminding. Any other people over 16 that live in the house

or who visit regularly have to be checked by the Criminal Records Bureau, just as the childminder has to be).

➤ Are parents free to drop in?

➤ Are there any routines your child would have to fit into, including dropping other children at school?

➤ When does the housework get done? If it's during childminding hours are the children involved in an educational sense in any way or are they just left to occupy themselves.

➤ What activities and outings are the children offered?

➤ What is the approach to discipline/potty training/play etc?

Environment:

➤ Is the house clean, safe and warm?

➤ What are the toys and any equipment such as garden play equipment like? Will your child be allowed to bring toys from home?

➤ Is the TV on for much of the day? What restrictions are placed on viewing?

➤ Are there any pets in the house?

➤ Is there somewhere to rest?

Practicalities:

➤ What kind of food is provided?

➤ Are there extra charges for food and activities?

➤ Does play include physical exercise, stories, and messy games e.g. with water, sand and paints?

➤ Does the childminder have any flexibility on hours? Does she charge an overtime rate and when would it come into effect?

➤ Are alternative arrangements organised for when the minder is sick or on holiday?

➤ Is a retainer payable when your child is sick or on holiday, and how much is it?

➤ What is the notice period on either side?

Contract

In addition to relevant points mentioned for a nanny contract (see above) you should consider including:

➤ Rates for overtime including evenings and public holidays.

➤ Arrangements for when the childminder is sick.

➤ Who will provide nappies and food.

➤ Where the child can be taken.

➤ Whether the child can travel in the childminder's car.

Finding a childminder

LEAD TIME

Allow 8–12 weeks for finding a childminder. This will give you scope to visit a few times and to settle the child in. The task is more difficult in some areas than others as the availability of childminders varies quite significantly according to where you live.

PLACES TO LOOK

In the absence of personal recommendations, the best way of finding a childminder is by calling the Children's Information Service of your local council (see chapter 4.01 *London boroughs*). It is a good idea to get in touch some months beforehand, to get an idea of availability in your area. The department should be able to provide a list of registered childminders or better still a vacancy list. Note that it is not unusual for a quarter of the registered childminders in a given area not to be currently childminding.

If there is a shortage in your area you could try to recruit your own childminder by advertising locally (see noticeboards under Nannies). However, the childminder must register before starting to look after your child.

USEFUL CONTACTS

Childcare Link, ☎ *(08000) 960296* ⌐ *www.childcarelink.gov.uk*
An online database, searchable by area.

Families Magazines, ☎ *(020) 8696 9680* ⌐ *www.familiesmagazine.co.uk*
Regular round-ups of nurseries in areas covered, which now include much of London (and of other major cities).

The National Childminding Association (NCMA),
☎ *(020) 8464 6164, (0800) 169 4486* ⌐ *www.ncma.org.uk*
This organisation promotes qualified registered childminders and aims to improve the quality of childcare available by improving resources and training available; can supply information concerning local childminder's groups, the checks made on applicants for childminding, how to negotiate a contract and how to maintain a good working relationship. To promote quality registered childminding, the organisation has launched Children Come First – a scheme to set up Approved Childminding Networks and to provide support and training for registered childminders, run by local authorities and Early Years Development teams. / PUBLICATIONS *Choosing a Childminder: A Guide for Parents (£4 inc p&p); updated annually.*

5. AU PAIRS & MOTHER'S HELPS

For mothers who are around in the home, the ability to leave the child in sole charge of someone else is not such an issue. This opens up the pos-sibilities of certain cheaper forms of childcare which take some of the work off the mother's plate, and provide help with running the home, while leaving the raising of the child or children largely to the mother. However, it is worth reiterating that au pairs should not be left in charge of babies and some recommend not in sole charge of any children under three.

Au pairs

Au pairs generally either arrive in September and stay until June, or arrive in June and stay until September, though there are exceptions to this.

August is reported to be a good time of year for local recruiting as most potential employers are on holiday. September is bad but October onwards better again as au pairs unhappy with their current family look to move on.

As the position is generally treated as a fill-in job, girls will usually give priority to other options which arise, like offers of study courses or even blandishments of boyfriends back home. The general understand-ing is usually that you should be able to provide them with details of local English language schools. Pointers about live-in nannies apply though, unlike most nannies, au pairs can expect to eat with the family.

Although most learn, you should assume zero knowledge of children, cleaning, big cities and health & safety issues. Written notes are there-fore invaluable, as is a list of unbreakable rules – e.g. no smacking.

HOME OFFICE DEFINITION OF AN AU PAIR

The term technically only refers to nationals of certain European – but non-EC – countries (see the Carer options in Choosing Childcare above). Nationals from these countries may enter the UK to help with childcare and light housework for up to 25 hours a week in exchange for accommodation, food, a modest wage and the opportunity to learn English.

On arrival, they must be unmarried without dependants, and aged between 17 and 27 (most are 19–21 years old). Male au pairs have been allowed since 1993 though the vast majority are girls. The maximum stay is two years and most stay six months to a year.

Home Office regulations allow citizens of the following countries to enter under 'au pair status':

➢ Andorra.
➢ Bosnia-Herzegovina.
➢ Croatia.
➢ Cyprus.
➢ Czech Republic.
➢ Estonia
➢ The Faroes.
➢ Greenland.
➢ Hungary.
➢ Latvia
➢ Lithuania
➢ Liechtenstein.
➢ Macedonia.
➢ Malta.
➢ Monaco.
➢ Poland
➢ Republic of Bulgaria
➢ Romania
➢ San Marino.
➢ Slovak Republic.
➢ Slovenia.
➢ Switzerland.
➢ Turkey.

Visitors from other countries are not entitled to 'au pair' status. Of course, EC nationals don't need special status to work in the UK and may prefer to work longer hours because it means earning more money.

Visitors to the UK with 'au pair' status should have an au pair visa and should be able to show you their passport to demonstrate that this is the case. If you advertise for someone in the UK however, around half the applicants you attract will probably only have a student visa. Under Home Office regulations, those with a student visa should not work more than 20 hours per week during term time unless the work placement is part of their study.

If you employ someone without the correct status and are found out you may be liable for prosecution and a fine of up to £5,000. The au pair will be deported to her home country.

Finding an au pair

LEAD TIME
In general, once registered with an agency, au pairs are keen to find a placement as soon as possible. Lead time can be as short as a fortnight, but might occasionally involve a delay until the end of an academic term. You will need to allow a further fortnight for settling in and learning how to look after the children.

If recruiting directly, lead time will depend largely on whether the girl already has a job and how soon she plans to leave.

WHERE TO LOOK

Agencies generally charge a registration fee of £10-£20, and a set fee if they offer a successful introduction. As au pairs are often still living in their home country when they register with an agency, they can generally only be interviewed by phone, which is rather a handicap to the recruiting process.

Publications advertising nanny agencies often include details of au pair agencies too (see under Nannies).

If you are happy to put in the time, the web can be a useful source of leads. You may have to look through a large number of applications and will need to send a detailed letter about your family, house and job requirements to potential candidates before sifting out a few more by e-mail and then a phone call if a candidate seems suitable. An exchange of photos is also useful.

If you want someone on the spot who you can interview, au pairs can sometimes be found through foreign churches and youth groups, and cards in the windows of newsagents, particularly in smarter parts of town. Local language schools are another potential source. The Yellow Pages lists language schools, so it is easy to find schools near you (also useful for finding courses for your au pair to attend).

In all cases you need to follow up references very carefully.

INTERVIEWS

As a minimum try to interview a prospective au pair by phone, or if their English is not good enough, by fax or e-mail (though on the hop you are more likely to get honest answers).

The questions for nannies are a good starting point, but others worth covering are:

➢ Does she have a boyfriend and if so how are they likely to find being separated?

➢ What does she eat?

➢ Why does she want to be in London/the UK?

➢ What would she do if a child were injured in her care?

It is worth looking at the contract pointers for nannies, and including those you feel are relevant in the job offer for a potential au pair. As with nannies, the more you can clarify before the job starts, the better.

USEFUL CONTACTS

AuPairs, ☞ www.aupairs.co.uk
The website is a matching service (not an agency) for families and au pairs. You can runs a free advertisement for three weeks and then you will be charged £45 for a month.

British Council, ☎ Information centre (0161) 957 7755, (020) 7930 8466
☞ www.britishcouncil.org, www.englishinbritain.co.uk (British schools site)
Call or email for a thorough list of recognised English-language schools.

Home Office, ☎ (08706) 067766, Recorded information (020) 8649 7878
☞ www.homeoffice.gov.uk
The information line provides details on immigration requirements for the non-EC countries listed above.

International Au Pair Association, ☎ (+45) 3317 0066
☞ www.iapa.org
Founded in 1994, an international trade association for au pair agencies, set up to protect the interests of au pairs and host families through a code of conduct. The site includes links to member agencies' websites.

READING

The New Good Nanny Guide – Charlotte Breese & Hilaire Gomer (Complete
    handbook on nannies, au pairs, mother's helps, childminders and other childcare
    options; Ebury; 1997; £14.99; 0-0918-2535-0) – *See write-up under nannies.*

Successful Au Pairs – Hilli Matthews (Sheldon Press; 2001; £6.99; 0-85969-849-1) –
    *What to get if you're planning to get an au pair; the author set up and ran an au pair
    agency for 20 years and has distilled her experience and those of her clients; the book
    covers the practicalities, expectations of both au pairs and employers, house rules, free
    time, problems, legalities and some contact details.*

Mother's helps

For many women who spend a good deal of time at home, the ideal
employee is someone who combines looking after the children with help
looking after household chores: known as a mother's help.

For the most part, the only childcarers prepared to take on a significant
burden of household duties are unqualified. This makes mother's helps
less suited to unsupervised care, though this depends on the individual.
Being useful but cheaper than a nanny, good mother's helps tend to be
in short supply.

Finding a mother's help

LEAD TIME

Given the supply and demand imbalance, allow longer to find a mother's
help than you would for a nanny or au pair.

WHERE TO LOOK

Because of the unskilled nature of the work, and its relatively informal
nature, many people find helps in the same way as they would a cleaner –
through local contacts, noticeboards and local publications – rather than
using more formal methods such as an agency. The agency route and
advertising can be useful, however, particularly if you are looking for
someone with some form of childcare experience. (see Finding a nanny,
above for suggested points of contact).

6. POSTNATAL CARE: MATERNITY NURSES & DOULAS

Maternity nurses

A maternity nurse is a woman who specialises in the care of newborns.
About half have some form of childcare qualification, usually the old
NNEB (now the CACHE Diploma in Nursery Nursing).

The role of the maternity nurse is to help the new mother learn to
look after her baby on return from hospital, allowing her to gain confidence and also to get some sleep (particularly useful if you have twins).
Maternity nurses are live-in carers, usually on call 24 hours a day except
Sundays. Generally the baby will share a room with the nurse who will
bring the baby to the mother if she is breast-feeding and will do all the
night feeds if she is not.

A maternity nurse usually stays for four to eight weeks, but also anything from two weeks to six months. There is an argument in favour of
them staying no more than a month as their long-term presence can undermine a woman's faith in her own ability to cope.

Some maternity nurses expect not to have to cook or do domestic
chores (although they will usually assume responsibility for keeping baby
equipment clean) and may expect to eat with the new family, impinging

on your time together. Exact details of the timetable should be agreed in advance and it would be wise to discuss also how much childcare guidance they are going to offer. You will need to get clear in advance anything you have definite feelings about, for example breast- or bottle-feeding and exactly what care the maternity nurse will undertake.

As maternity nurses are usually older than nannies (average age 35, the more prestigious ones older), their experience can be intimidating. This may not help you gain confidence, particularly with a first baby. They may also hold old-fashioned ideas about baby care, significantly out of synch with current beliefs.

Be somewhat cautious of anyone who assures you that before leaving they will have the child in a fixed routine. This may well be at the expense of your supply of milk if breast-feeding, for example if she tops up feeds with bottles. Also some babies will co-operate, but others will not, which can cause tension if you feel the nurse is upsetting your newborn.

Finding a maternity nurse

LEAD TIME

Because maternity nurses are relatively scarce they need to be booked up well in advance (good ones may be booked eight or nine months in advance, so you really do need to move quickly if you have a particular person in mind). Agencies should be able to find someone as late as a month before the birth, perhaps even later, but standards here are variable.

WHERE TO LOOK

See Finding a nanny, above.

Doulas

American medical anthropologist Dana Raphael coined the word 'doula', derived from the Greek for servant or handmaiden. Its modern usage embodies the concept of a woman experienced in childcare (usually a mother herself) who acts as helper to the mother.

In the States help before and during birth as well as afterwards is central to the concept. In the UK, the role of a doula is sometimes restricted to the period after the birth.

In both countries, the idea is that the doula provides moral support, particularly around birth, even if she is not actually to attend; helps the mother tackle unfamiliar activities such as breast-feeding; and helps out with running the house and generally keeping the whole show on the road. The aim is to support the mother in the unfamiliar and demanding role of looking after a baby, but following her lead. (This contrasts sharply with the part played by maternity nurses, whose traditional role is to take the baby away as much as possible to allow the mother to rest and in some cases obliging the mother to follow a predetermined system.)

Given how stretched the maternity services are currently, doulas who attend antenatally and birth can offer a much-needed supplement to the standard NHS provision. With private, consultant-led births, they can also help provide continuity of care and moral support where it might otherwise be lacking.

Finding a doula

LEAD TIME

You should book a doula three to four weeks in advance, although as they are relatively rare, it is sensible to enquire well ahead of this. Charges are around £7 to £10 an hour, generally at least four hours a day. Birth doulas cost around £200 for the birth, regardless of the time it takes.

USEFUL CONTACTS

British Doulas
Flat 2, 49 Harrington Gardens London SW7 4JU ☎ (020) 7244 6053 or (0870) 757 5353 ☞ www.britishdoulas.co.uk
A sister company of Top Notch Nannies; runs doula training courses in London, and can provide doulas; advice and information about hiring a doula can be found on the website.

Doula UK
PO Box 26678 London N14 4WB ☞ www.doula.org.uk
Formerly Birth & Bonding International, this organisation "for doulas, run by doulas" is a non-profit organisation, providing information on what doulas do, information on booking agencies and a 'Find a Doula' service (many of the better-known names of the baby world are referenced); there is also a section on questions you should ask prospective birth or postnatal doulas.

Heather Guerrini
30 Redesdale St London SW3 4BJ ☎ (020) 7352 0245
Heather is a trained doula and reflexologist who operates through the NCT; call for details of doula service. / SEE ALSO *1.04 Antenatal classes; 2.06 Baby & toddler activities; 4.02 Health practitioners.*

Maud Giles
☎ (07939) 820651
A former paediatric nurse and breast-feeding specialist who offers short-term daily maternity nursing (9am-5pm) to help with a baby, similar in style to a postnatal doula, £12 per hour. / HOURS *24hr answerphone; SEE ALSO 1.04 Antenatal classes; 2.02 Feeding.*

Millennia Doulas
82 Lawn Rd London NW3 2XB ☎ (020) 7586 1028 ☞ www.millenniadoulas.com
An informal network managed by childcare educator Ruth Tamir (who is a doula herself and a breast-feeding supporter), who trains doulas and can place doulas with families: referrals are largely to ex-pupils and she can recommend both 'birth doulas' (to accompany women in labour) and 'postnatal doulas'. A flat fee of £25 is charged if a doula is found; contracts are individually agreed between the doula and the employer. A birth doula may cost £250-£400 for the whole package of care; postnatal doulas cost £10-£15 per hour.

Night nurses

These are maternity nurses who only work overnight, particularly recommended for parents who do not have a spare room for anyone to live in. They work eight to twelve hours payable hourly, and are sometimes hired in conjunction with a doula for day-time help.

Finding a night nurse

Most agencies offering maternity nurses should be able to arrange a night nurse, or contact the specialists listed.

USEFUL CONTACTS

Night Nannies
3 Kempson Rd London SW6 4PX ☎ (020) 7731 6168 ☞ www.nightnannies.com
Offering 10-hour cover through the night, plus advice on getting the baby to sleep, if required.

7. AD HOC CHILDCARE

If something goes wrong with your childcare arrangements, or for some other reason you need childcare in a hurry, your first ports of call should be contacts of your current carer or nursery. Individuals may have friends who your child has already met who are able to help at short notice, particularly over holiday periods when their usual charges may be away. Similarly, nurseries may have temporary vacancies over holiday periods and might be willing to take your child for a short period.

Nanny agencies can help with a temporary nanny, but this can be expensive. Nanny training colleges may be able to supply someone close to being qualified who would value the work experience.

There are one or two 'drop-in' nurseries that will take children with little notice (sometimes on the same day). As with temporary nannies, such arrangements are not cheap.

USEFUL CONTACTS

Hopes & Dreams, ☎ *(020) 7833 9388* ✆ *www.hopesanddreams.co.uk*
A day nursery with a crèche which may be used on an impromptu basis; all staff have NNEB (or equivalent) or Montessori qualifications; also provides baby-sitters in the home, or at hotels; also have full-time nannies.

Pippa Pop-Ins, ✆ *www.pippapopins.com*
Nursery schools offering an ad hoc crèche facility, a school-run service, holiday excursions, and the provision of baby-sitters and nannies.

8. BABY-SITTING

Even for the relatively undemanding role of baby-sitting, finding someone to whom you feel comfortable entrusting your baby can still take a surprising amount of time and nervous energy.

Agencies are one answer (see below), but not everyone feels comfortable with such an anonymous route to finding a temporary carer. A member of the family, or close friend is obviously best of all, or at least a word-of-mouth recommendation. In their absence obvious routes include.

Suggestions for baby-sitters:
➢ A friend's au pair or nanny, or one of their friends (many of whom will be au pairs or nannies).
➢ If your child attends a day nursery, members of staff often provide baby-sitting services.
➢ A baby-sitting club – for suggestions see below.
➢ A local parent support group; some list baby-sitters in their newsletters.

If you use a baby-sitter who is not personally recommended it is vital to take up references first. The going rate is about £5–£8 an hour, often with the cost of a taxi home on top of that.

A few pointers to bear in mind:
➢ Love of children is not enough in an emergency. You need to make sure the sitter knows how to contact a doctor and how to get hold of you.
➢ The sitter will need to know where the baby equipment and supplies are kept including nappies, clean clothes, bedding, drinks, books and toys.
➢ With babies over about four months it is wise to give them a chance to get to know the baby-sitter before you go out in case they wake before you return.

➤ A good sign is someone who has a little fun with the child on arrival but can be firm about bedtime.

➤ Make your position on visitors clear from the outset.

➤ Under-16s, being minors, cannot be held responsible for their actions. Indeed the parents of the baby may be held responsible for the baby-sitter while in their home.

➤ Unless the baby-sitter lives nearby, you should be prepared to run them home or organise a taxi.

USEFUL CONTACTS

Childminders, ☏ (020) 7935 3000 ⁂ www.babysitter.co.uk
Founded in 1967, the company ("the world's largest baby-sitting service") has over 1,000 registered sitters – many are nurses, nannies and primary school teachers. Sitting is bookable on a same day basis, though two or three days in advance is preferred; yearly joining fee is £59+VAT. Evening hourly rates for sitters are £5.20-£6.40 (depending on which day) and £6.80 during the day. All bookings must be for a minimum of four hours, and reasonable travel expenses (and a taxi after 10pm) are also payable.

Kasimira, ☏ (020) 7581 8313 ⁂ www.kasimira.com
Comprehensive service incorporating baby-sitting, tuition, parties and activities (for older children). The organisation is categorical that baby-sitters have been police, health and reference checked. Membership £95 per year or £35 per quarter plus VAT. One-off joining fee of £25 +VAT.

nannnease, ☏ (020) 8544 8025 ⁂ www.nannease.com
Covering west and south west London, this Wimbledon-based agency supplies baby-sitters (£50 joining fee) – £4 booking fee and then £5–6 per hour; (also an agency for child carers and nannies).

Sitters, ☏ (0800) 389 0038 ⁂ www.sitters.co.uk
Agency (member of REC) providing "mature women recruited from the childcare profession – teenagers are not accepted". The idea is that families get to know two or three local baby-sitters to cover most of their bookings. The service covers the whole of England. There is a membership fee of £12.75 for three months in addition to a £4 booking fee and payment to the baby-sitter of £4.50-£5.25, depending on where you are in the country (£5-6.25 Saturday) per hour (minimum four hours). / HOURS Mon-Fri 8am-7pm, Sat 10am-2pm.

South of the River, ☏ (020) 7228 5086 ⁂ www.southoftheriver.co.uk
A membership baby-sitting service operating in south west postcodes south of the river. It takes bookings up to three months in advance. All sitters are said to be experienced in working with children, interviewed personally and with two references relevant to childcare followed up. Annual subscription is £65 and a small booking fee applies except for same-day bookings. Sitters must be walked home or a taxi paid for in addition to the fee for baby-sitting.

Top Notch Nannies, ☏ (020) 7259 2626 ⁂ www.topnotchnannies.com
Runs a service worldwide; all staff are nannies, teachers, maternity nurses or doulas; one-off baby-sitters, join for a year and receive the telephone numbers of four local sitters to call on when you need to; sitters hourly rates from £6-8 an hour. Some sitters can do domestic work, tutoring and party helping for extra pay. Evening baby-sitting register available.

Universal Aunts, ☏ (020) 7386 5900
An organisation supplying temps for a wide variety of tasks (shopping, errands etc), which can supply babysitters and carers for travel and outings. Evening babysitting (after 6pm) £5 per hour, daytime £7 per hour; minimum 4-hour booking. A fee is payable per booking.

Babysitting circles

By exchanging babysitting, parents get a chance to go out without the extra cost of a paid babysitter. You can do this informally with another couple, but if you would like a wider group to draw on the following is a suggested system for a points-based system.

Before 7pm: 2 points per quarter hour.
7pm-midnight: 1 point per quarter hour.

After midnight: 2 points per quarter hour.

How it might work:
➤ Each member starts with 100 points.
➤ Points in deficit on leaving the circle are charged at 25p each.
➤ The circle meets regularly to share information and up-date lists (say at least once every three months).
➤ The circle operates open house times when parents and children can meet potential babysitters.
➤ The beneficiaries of the babysitting are expected to provide suitable refreshment for the sitters.
➤ The sitters are responsible for finding a replacement sitter should they cancel an agreement to baby-sit.
➤ Members keep their own notebooks.

With young babies, it is possible for the babysitting to be at the house of the babysitters, the parents collecting the baby on their way home. However, generally the babysitting is done at the child's house: this means that the babysitting parents require a partner to be at home looking after their own children.

CHAPTER 2.05

TRAVEL

1. **Introduction**
2. **Holidays which suit kids**
3. **Health issues**
4. **Making the journey**

The author of this book is a travel journalist of 17 years' standing. She runs a website, www.family-travel.co.uk, which provides information and listings in greater depth than included here. Family Travel has a policy of not accepting advertising and, unusually, accepts no press trips from tour operators. The Rough Guide to Travel Online described it as a "stylish, independent UK site... which deals with everything you need to know when planning a holiday with kids, whatever their age and whatever your budget", and the Sunday Times as "One of the least glitzy, but possibly the most useful family travel site ... very easy to navigate".

(For information on travelling when pregnant, see chapter 1.02 Looking after yourself.)

1. INTRODUCTION

Travel with children can be hard work, but is not without compensations. Having kids along can open new doors by providing an instant rapport with other families with children – both locals and other travellers. And although children seldom take much interest in what you have come away to enjoy, simple things like palm tree leaves in the breeze can offer little ones quite unexpected amounts of pleasure.

Keeping an eye on children in unfamiliar territory can be the greatest concern. Babies are at their safest while still immobile, so you might find it worth taking a holiday before they start crawling. Travel with toddlers is particularly hard work, but the cost of flying with them shoots up at two years, so if you can it's worth scheduling a trip before that watershed.

Getting a passport

If you are travelling abroad, you must these days get your baby an individual passport, which is valid for five years.

Processing may take at least a month, though you can pay for speedier service. A standard application costs £16, a fast-track application (seven-day turnaround) £30, or premium application (four-hour turnaround) £45. As always, you also have the option of visiting the passport office in person, rather than posting your application (for an additional £15).

Complete an application form, available from main Post Offices and branches of some travel agents. The form needs to be submitted together with the child's birth or adoption certificate (copies are not accepted) and two photographs must be counter-signed (and dated) by a UK 'professional person' (such as a teacher or police officer). The professional concerned must be someone who can certify that the photograph is a true likeness.

Given restrictions on the required photograph and the difficulty of manoeuvering babies in photo booths, a professional shot may seem the easiest way of obtaining these. However, there are alternatives.

You can lay your baby on a white sheet or similar, take a series of head shots from above, have two sets of prints developed and cut the most appropriate shot to the size required. (If you have a digital camera and/or scanner plus a programme such as Photoshop this should be an easy task). Alternatively some stores have booths that can be adjusted for babies and toddlers.

Note that more documentation is needed for proof of citizenship if the child was not born in the UK – this might include the parents' birth certificates and/or marriage certificate.

USEFUL CONTACTS

London Passport Office
Globe House, 89 Ecclestion Square London SW1V 1PN ☎ National enquiry line (0870) 521 0410, Application request line (0901) 470 0110 ⏚ www.ukpa.gov.uk, www.passport.gov.uk
The website contains useful travel advice and information on local passport offices. Application forms can also be obtained via the site, which shows a regularly updated estimate on how long applications are taking to process. / *HOURS Mon-Fri 7.45am-7pm, Sat 9.15am-3.15pm (appointments only).*

Insurance

Taking out adequate travel insurance takes on new significance when travelling with children, given their propensity to go down with childhood illnesses.

Take, for example, a situation where your child contracts a condition like chicken pox when you are abroad. No airline will take you on the return trip until a doctor certifies your baby 'Fit to Fly' because of the risk of infecting other passengers (a particular hazard as airliners are so heavily air-conditioned). If you do not have adequate insurance you will have to bear the costs of accommodation for your forced extended stay, and – if you don't have a transferable return – a new return ticket. Such unforeseen costs can easily double the cost of the holiday itself.

(You might be tempted to be antisocial and risk the trip anyway, but bear in mind that due to the potentially serious consequences of chicken pox – including brain damage to unborn children – cabin crews are increasingly encouraged to spot ill people and are under instructions to return the aircraft to the gate at any time before take off should they do so.)

Some companies offer free travel insurance for children under two as part of a parent's policy. Special family policies for two adults and one or more children work out cheaper than individual cover.

For once, it's worth reading the small print. For example, a policy offering "Family cover" probably means that each member of the family is covered as an individual, *not* that the family as a unit is covered. Take the example above of having a child with chicken pox. "Family cover" might only cover the additional costs for the ill child and mother. Dad and other fit children might not be covered: i.e. they might have to return home before the others, or pay their own way to stay on.

If your child has an on-going condition such as asthma, check carefully how the policy deals with pre-existing conditions.

2. HOLIDAYS WHICH SUIT KIDS

There is a whole set of new issues to consider when you start planning holidays with children. If things go wrong, it's a lot less tolerable than when you are on your own. Careful forward thinking is therefore advisable.

Factors to consider

Which of the following factors are more important depends on your own priorities, but all bear consideration.

WHAT THE PARENTS WANT

The classic formula for a successful family holiday is to make sure the youngest is happy and work up from there. This is a good start, but parents need to be taken into consideration as well – looking after children is hard work and parents need to look after themselves to make sure then can give it their best shot. It is therefore useful to think through what you really want – culture, peace and quiet, good food, sport, time with your children, or away from them. Look for somewhere which will supply what you want *and* provide for the child's requirements as well.

CHILDCARE

When it comes to childcare, requirements vary widely – from fulltime to none. You need to decide how much you want – and how much your child will be happy receiving.

From around eight months children can suffer separation anxiety. Some parents feel that they just have to get over this. Others find that they are wasting expensive pre-booked childcare because they don't have the heart to leave a wailing infant. (There are also reports from parents that in some places they are made to feel like wimps if they take the second view.)

Note also that there is no requirement for childcare overseas to adhere to British standards, even if provided by a British tour operator. Only local legislation applies and in some countries provision is totally unregulated. This means standards can sometimes fall well short of even the minimum expectations at home. Staff may be unqualified and because the pay is poor, many girls regard the job as a kind of holiday and may turn up for work hungover or unslept. The safety of the childcare area is also very variable, as is the quality of entertainment offered.

Broadly the options are:

Just somewhere child-friendly: if on reflection all you want is the chance of some pleasant evening meals, an obvious option is a child-friendly hotel with a decent restaurant and your baby monitor. If you want local colour, the Eastern Mediterranean, notably Greece and Turkey, offers places where people may be only too happy to fuss over a small child while you eat.

Somewhere with child-friendly companions: possibly with relatives or another family, this offers the chance of a bit more childcare cover. However it can be wise to discuss the detail in advance, and for it to be successful, you need to be of reasonably like minds, particularly when it comes to parenting styles.

Taking a nanny or au pair: this should make life a lot easier for parents, though it is a good idea to work out in advance exactly what hours and work will be required. It is not always successful. Some families feel that they just can't relax as much with a relative stranger as they do on their own. And of course an extra person adds considerably to costs.

Childcare provided by the tour operator: this is becoming more widely available as more operators cotton on to demand from parents. However, whether such care is included as part of an all-in price or charged extra, you do pay quite handsomely. Whether it is worth the money depends on a number of factors including whether you feel the care is sufficiently well run and whether the timing of its provision is going to be convenient. Note also the comments on safety above.

Childcare arranged on the spot: this can be possible in smaller hotels and sometimes in self-catering properties. However, to know whether it is an option you will have to book through a specialist tour operator where they really know the places they are selling.

Baby-listening: this is not generally found outside the UK, largely because it is considered insufficiently reliable and hotels do not want to take responsibility without proper access to the child or children. A possible solution might be to take your own monitor, but bear in mind that claimed ranges are often optimistic – the reality in a hotel with thick and/or RSJ reinforced walls plus electric generators may be much less impressive. Though rather specialist and more pricey, you might consider investing in the sort of short-range radios used in small boats (see 3.02 Baby Equipment) which offer a more reliable connection.

Using organised childcare of any kind you need to:

➢ Feel happy that there is an appropriate ratio of staff to children and that all staff are competent.

➢ Ensure that the physical area is well set up, with lots of space out of the sun in hot climates, for example, and places where babies and toddlers can sleep if they want to.

➢ Check what kind of activities are offered, what meals and equipment provided, and what provision there is for time spent both in and out of doors.

➢ With slightly older toddlers you need to feel happy that the child feels he or she can communicate well and is comfortable with the other children there. This can be an issue in crèches run in non-English-speaking resorts or hotels.

CLIMATE

Babies and toddlers do not tolerate places with extremes of climate particularly well so unless you have a particular reason to choose such a destination (to ski, for example), these are best avoided. If rain is likely (and it is in all of Europe, even in the height of summer) you should be prepared for some time indoors.

HEALTH

Even more important than climate is that you make sure you pick somewhere your child is unlikely to get sick and that you are happy about using the health services should anything go wrong. Worry levels vary markedly in parents and unless you stay well within your own tolerance limits, it won't be much of a holiday.

If you are less than confident about travel abroad, it might be best to holiday in Britain until you feel happier about venturing further afield.

If you do go abroad it is unwise to do so without health insurance. Even in countries with reciprocal health agreements with the UK, the service is seldom as comprehensive as with the NHS, and with a sick baby or toddler you do not want to risk slower or lower quality advice.

BUDGET

Travel agents generally consider 'family' and 'cheap' as synonymous, but there are ways to make your budget go further without going for the tackiest options in the big name brochures.

Go out of season: you will be stuck with planning your life around school holidays soon enough. While you still have the freedom, it makes sense to holiday out of season when travel is cheaper and destinations less crowded. What's more, out of season the weather in southern Europe is more suitable for babies and toddlers.

Book only what you need: don't pay for anything that you are not actually going to use – notably childcare but also an all-inclusive meals package.

Choose a less mainstream destination: for example, think about holidaying somewhere well away from a beach, where accommodation is much cheaper than anywhere equivalent on the coast.

Child discounts: these are rarely as attractive as they appear. They usually apply only to children sharing a room with two full paying members of the party and may feature inconveniences like no baggage allowance and no seats on flights for children under two. In addition all supplements such as airport taxes are payable on top of the quoted rate.

Standards: don't be more budget-conscious than you really have to be. Food and accommodation can be so bad that you end up spending extra on eating out, hiring a car to get away and in bad cases, moving to other accommodation.

Types of holidays

Holidays for parents and children are becoming increasingly sophisticated, with new schemes being launched every year. The following are some of the better-known options but there are also some surprising alternatives even with babies, including cruising, cycling, and other activities.

Beware, however, glowing reports on family-oriented tour operators in national newspapers and magazines: they are almost invariably the result of a free family holiday for the writer.

GENERAL LISTINGS
BUPA
Russell Mews Brighton BN1 2NR ☎ *(1273) 208181* ✆ *www.bupa-intl.travel-guides.com*
The organisation's website includes a travel guide with – amongst other things – useful introductory information to health issues (required vaccinations, commonly occurring diseases) on a country-by-country basis.

Family Travel
1 Hargrave Rd London N19 5ST ☎ *(020) 7272 7441* ✆ *www.family-travel.co.uk*
Probably the most comprehensive British site on the subject, with both general travel advice and a wide-ranging database of destinations and types of holiday.

LISTINGS – SPECIALIST COMPANIES
Holiday Care Service
7th Floor, Sunley House, 4 Bedford Park Surrey CR0 2AD ☎ *(0845) 124 9971*
✆ *www.holidaycare.org.uk*
Holds data on all aspects of accessible tourism and travel for the disabled, covering accessible accommodation, visitor attractions, transport, low-cost holidays, children's holidays and holidays for one-parent families. Produces accessible accommodation guides. / HOURS *Mon-Tues 9am-5pm, Wed-Fri 9am-1pm.*

READING
[Newsletter] **Family Travel Times** ($39 for 1 year ($49 for two)) – *Ideas for travel in the US.* / Family Travel Times, 40 Fifth Ave, New York, NY 10011, USA – 00 1 212 477 5524; *www.familytraveltimes.com.*

List of Seaside Award beaches in the UK & Blue Flag beaches (available in return for an SAE) – *Maps of blue flag beaches and marinas all over Europe can be found on the website. / European Blue Flag Campaign, Tidy Britain Group, Lion House, Muspole Street, Norwich NR3 1DJ, www.blueflag.org.*

Travel with Children – Maureen Wheeler (Lonely Planet; 1995; £6.95; 0-864422-99-7) – *A sensible look at the subject, especially long-haul flights. Consoling for parents who want to continue to adventure.*

Travellers' Health – ed Dr Richard Dawood (How to stay healthy abroad; OUP; 2002; £12.50; 0-192622-47-6) – *An incredibly thorough sourcebook covering individual diseases and hazards, infectious diseases by area, and including travel with children. Useful if venturing into the wilds, otherwise perhaps unnecessarily depressing. If you are going to be off the beaten track see the chapter on Children Abroad which covers issues like hepatitis, swimming hazards, walking barefoot, assessing fevers and respiratory infections and immunisation.*

HOTELS

Despite boasting among their number some of the least child-friendly establishments in the world, the UK's hotels are becoming more welcoming to kids, especially at the very top end of the market.

Specialist family hotels usually involve drawbacks. Standards of décor tend to be low, the children's food tends to be uninspired, and meals with other people's children can tend to lowest common denominator standards. In some cases, widespread advertising and parental desperation seem the only possible explanation for their continued success.

There are however a small number of more expensive hotels which, responding to changing demographics, are offering an attractive and relaxing experience to suit all members of the family.

Overseas, as a general rule, only the larger hotels or 'aparthotels' (200 units plus) provide facilities like a crèche or early evening meal sittings. Care may not be by staff with fluent English. As in the UK, where childcare is provided, parents may well not be allowed to leave the premises.

It is worth thinking about whether you really need these facilities. If your baby is too old to be happy left with strangers and too young to need a kid's club, you might find yourself better suited by a small hotel with flexible, friendly staff. These might be able to baby-sit for you once your child has got to know them. Smaller specialist tour operators are good at suggesting suitable hotels for this kind of holiday.

Local agencies may be able to provide a babysitter if the hotel does not – important if you will want to leave the premises for example for an evening meal. It might be wise to check out the standard of in-house catering if you are not going to be able to eat elsewhere.

READING

Harden's Hotel Guide – Richard Harden, Peter Harden (Harden's Limited; 2003; £12.50; 1-873721-55-2) – *First edition of this new independent guide to the best places to stay based upon a survey of ordinary travellers. Unlike most hotel guides, it does not exact payment in return for a listing ("Unusually independent" – The Times). It includes, amongst other details, any restrictions on children staying, and lists of child-friendly establishments.*

SELF-CATERING

Self-catering sounds like a great idea when with children – you don't have to worry about disturbing the neighbours or getting everyone dressed for meals. On the other hand, it does involve almost as much housework as when living at home – unless you pick somewhere that is convenient for eating out.

There are a number of villa companies which offer properties with hotel style service, though you do pay extra for this. The widest range used to be in the Caribbean but the idea is developing in Europe as well.

However, given that you can't get out like you used to you need to pick any companions for self-catering particularly carefully. Perhaps renting two adjoining properties might work best. You also have to consider any area outside the villa. If there is a pool, will you spend all your time worrying about your crawling child falling in?

Some holiday complexes are extremely closely packed so noise disturbance can be a real problem, particularly in hot weather when doors and windows are open.

CAMPING

Sites with ready-erected tents are both convenient and popular for family holidays. However, in the school holidays they are very busy so you need to book well ahead.

Advantages include the informal atmosphere and the proximity of plenty of other children (less of an advantage with very small ones). Some even have dedicated children's couriers. However, the larger sites do not make the most visually attractive places to holiday ("like Tesco's car park", to quote one parent). Noise carries, which can make it harder to get children to sleep, particularly in a sociable camp (check for weekly discos for example). The smaller and therefore quieter sites may be better for parents of younger children, though these do offer fewer central facilities.

LISTINGS

Canvas Holidays
12 East Port House, Dunfermline Fife KY12 7JG ☎ *(01383) 629000*
⌂ *www.canvas.co.uk*
A family-run company claiming to be pioneers of self-drive European camping holidays, offering a wide range of sites. / HOURS Mon-Fri 9am-8pm, Sat 9am-2pm, Sun 10am-4pm.

Carisma Holiday
Heronsgate Rd, Chorleywood Hampshire WD3 5BB ☎ *(01923) 284235*
⌂ *www.carisma.co.uk*
A small range of selected French beach sites where you are likely to have a less British experience than at some of the larger sites. / HOURS Mon-Fri 9am-5:30pm.

Eurocamp
Hartford Manor, Greenbank Lane, Northwich Cheshire CW8 1HW ☎ *(01606) 787000*
⌂ *www.eurocamp.co.uk*
The big-name operator which makes a particular point of offering a range of services for families, including those with babies. The company has bought out a number of other brands over the last few years including Keycamp, for which bookings are made separately (see below), and Sunsites. / HOURS Mon-Fri 8am-10pm, Sat 8:30am-5:30pm, Sun 9:30am-5am.

Haven Europe
PO Box 30, Bognor Regis W Sussex PO21 1XY ☎ *(0870) 242 7777*
⌂ *www.haveneurope.com*
A major British operator which owns eight camping sites in France, and sells holidays in around 40 others in France, Spain and Italy. / HOURS Mon-Fri 9am-9pm. Sat 9am-7.30pm, Sun 9am-6pm.

Keycamp Holidays
92-96 Lind Rd, Sutton Surrey SM1 4PL ☎ *(0870) 7000 123* ⌂ *www.keycamp.co.uk*
Another larger operator (part of the Eurocamp group) targeting the family market with better quality accommodation. Some sites are specifically recommended for toddlers. / HOURS Mon-Fri 9am-8.30pm, Sat 9am-5pm, Sun 10am-4pm.

Mark Hammerton
Spelmonden Old Oast Goudhurst Kent TN17 1HE ☎ *(01892) 525456*
⌂ *www.markhammerton.com*
Run by someone whose original company was bought up by Eurocamp, this company focuses on mid-sized sites.

Sandpiper Holiday Ltd

Walnut Cottage, Kenley Shropshire SY5 6NS ☎ (01746) 785123
🖰 www.sandpiperhols.co.uk
A small specialist holiday operator, which knows its few sites well (they are all within five minutes of a beach).

Select France

Fiveacres, Murcott, Kidlington Oxford OX5 2RP ☎ (01865) 331350
🖰 www.selectfrance.co.uk
A family-run operator offering only four-star sites in the Dordogne, and other areas of France, all either on or near the beach. / *HOURS Mon-Fri 9am-5.30pm.*

BED & BREAKFASTS

The scale of most B&Bs both in the UK and overseas can make them good places to stay with children, especially in the country where there should be plenty of outdoor space. Success partly depends on the host family and to a lesser extent on other people staying. For practical reasons it is wise to pick somewhere which offers meals and to avoid anywhere too elegant.

FARM HOLIDAYS

Farm stays are generally a family-friendly form of bed and breakfast, with evening meals usually included and the chance to spend time watching how a farm works.

READING

RAC Farm Holiday Guide, Great Britain & Ireland – RAC (RAC Publishing; 1993; £6.99; 0-862112-06-0) – *Self catering, caravanning, camping and B&B on farms.* / FHG Publications, 18 High Street, Paisley PA1 2BX – (0141) 887 0428.

Stay on a farm (Jarrold Publishers; 1999; £7.95; 0711708711) – *Details of over 1,000 self-catering and B&B options on farms.* / Farm Holiday Bureau, National Agricultural Centre, Stoneleigh Park, Warwickshire CV8 2LZ – (01203) 696909.

HOMESWAPS

These schemes can be a relatively cheap way of taking a holiday with only transport and day-to-day expenses to pay for. Aim to swap with a family with children of the same age so that equipment and toys should be suitable, the house will be 'child-proofed' and there is the possibility of making use of their babysitter. This should not be too difficult, as many of those keen to participate are families with young children.

You will need to make sure that your household insurance covers you for homeswapping and that the family with whom you are swapping have made the same checks. You can also swap cars, and the same concern applies.

Swappers can use up more electricity than you and could rack up some high phone bills, so make arrangements for bill swapping

LISTINGS

Home Base Holidays

7 Park Ave London N13 5PG ☎ (020) 8886 8752 🖰 www.homebase-hols.com
In operation for over 19 years, working with the worldwide First Home Exchange Alliance; £29 for one year's online registration or £39 for 2 years online.

Homelink International

Linfield House, Grose Hill Rd, Virginia Water Surrey GU25 4AS ☎ (01344) 842642
🖰 www.homelink.org.uk
Perhaps the best-known home-swapping organisation; over 12,500 members in 50 countries; £95 a year (plus £10 for a photograph of your house) gives you a website listing and entry into five directories. / *HOURS 8.30am-6pm.*

Intervac International Home Exchange Service
24 The Causeway Chippenham SN15 3DB ☎ (01249) 461101 ⌁ www.intervac.co.uk
The 'other' name in home swaps, started in 1953 and of comparable size to HomeLink International; £99 a year for entry on website and in directories; website-only listing costs £60.

Latitudes Home Exchange
16 Rowe Ave, Peacehaven East Sussex ☎ +1 800 877 8723 ⌁ www.home-swap.com
Australian-based company with UK agents, offering homes all over the world. Member of the International Home Exchange Association (IHEA). Service through the Internet – very user-friendly website. US$50 a year (plus US$6 for a photograph of your home; US$15 for a second home). Guaranteed exchange in your first year. Custom-matching service available at extra cost.

National Childbirth Trust (NCT)
Alexandra House, Oldham Terrace London W3 6NH ☎ Enquiry line (0870) 444 8707
⌁ www.nctpregnancyandbabycare.co.uk; www.nctparentsconnect.co.uk
The NCT Homeswap Register, which has been active for over 25 years, costs £25.85 per year (non-NCT members are welcome, but you must have one child under 11 to join). Mainly UK properties – London homes are surprisingly popular, and the service is expanding, so more overseas homes may appear; registers are sent out three times a year (fortnightly e-mail updates on request). Non profit-making – all monies are directed back into the NCT. Contact Denise Tupman on (01626) 360689. / *HOURS Mon-Thurs 9am-5pm, Fri 9am-4pm; or answerphone; SEE ALSO 1.01 Where to have the baby; 1.04 Antenatal classes; 2.01 Postnatal; 2.02 Feeding; 2.04 Childcare; 2.06 Baby & toddler activities; 3.02 Baby equipment; 4.04 Miscarriage & stillbirth; 4.05 Finding out more; 4.06 Support groups.*

TIMESHARE

Despite a name tarnished by dubious selling techniques, this option is popular with some families, particularly those who have bought into one of the smarter timeshare schemes. You would be unwise to buy a property without visiting first, but some UK-based companies offer a fly-buy programme with the flight cost refunded on purchase. Some UK resorts offer a night's accommodation on an inspection visit.

There are properties available for timeshare in the USA, Spain, Portugal and France but also in less expected places like northern Africa, Egypt, Turkey, South Africa, Kenya and Latin America – perhaps more suitable destinations once your child is older.

Second-hand purchases are often better value for money than new ones as around 40% of the initial purchase price generally goes to pay for marketing.

A major feature of some timeshare options is that you don't have to go back to the same property year after year – for an extra fee you can swap with other timeshares. Two of the largest companies organising this are Interval International and RCI.

An alternative is to buy into a points-based holiday scheme. This does not involve one specific site but an entitlement to take holidays in one of the properties belonging to the network you buy into.

With both these options you do need to be willing to tie up your money and plan your holidays in advance. However, once you have made the payment your annual holiday outlay need be only the management fee (typically around £200 per week) plus transport and food. Note that whatever you buy into you should not regard it as an investment. Re-sale is difficult and while trying to sell, generally at a loss, you will have to continue to pay service charges.

LISTINGS
Holiday Property Bond
HPB House, Newmarket Suffolk CB8 8EH ☎ (01638) 660066 ⌁ www.hpb.co.uk
Each £1 you invest in the company buys you one index-linked point. (Minimum investment is £3,000 but a family wanting summer holidays plus a couple of other half-term breaks would need to invest more like £7,500.) Points can be spent annually (or saved up) at a range of locations in the UK and abroad, many in Europe. In addition

to the points 'spent' there is a user charge to pay per holiday, dependant on dates, location and the size of the accommodation – for two bedroom accommodation in spring this might be £250 a week. Properties owned by the company range from small apartments to three-bedroom villas, plus options like narrowboats. Advantages are that most sites have good facilities, including baby equipment, children's play areas, toy and video libraries. Disadvantages are that popular places get booked up well in advance and working out the points system can be difficult.

Organisation for Timeshare in Europe (OTE), AISBL
78-8 Rue Defacqz, 4th Floor, B-1060 Brussels Belgium ☎ +32 2533 3069
🖰 www.ote-info.com
The European timeshare watchdog: worth contacting before you sign on any dotted lines. The organisation sets professional standards and investigates any complaints against its members. It is unwise to deal with any timeshare organisation which does not belong. OTE can provide pointers on successful timeshare buying and selling timeshare and points-based holidays, as well as lists of timeshare developers, timeshare marketers and re-sale specialists. A helpsheet is available in return for an SAE with, if relevant, details of the resort or company any specific query relates to. The website is a very useful first point of contact.

FAMILY-FRIENDLY HOLIDAY PROGRAMMES

The tour operators which sell through high street travel agencies are trying to market themselves better to the family market and are now offering more options for families. These are largely in well-known resort areas, based around self-catering developments of at least 200 units.

Details vary as the operators alter their packages each year to offer more alluring deals. Much is made of discounts for children but these are generally more apparent than real and the additional family services are of variable standard.

HOLIDAY VILLAGES

These self-catering resorts with central facilities are one of the main options marketed to families. Notwithstanding some grumbles – including cramped accommodation, and variable standards – particularly in southern European properties, some parents who might once upon a time never have contemplated such an option find them useful, especially for short breaks. Childcare is more geared up for slightly older children but may also be available at some villages for babies and toddlers at an extra cost. Babysitting may also be offered.

There are numerous options but the following are popular.

LISTINGS
Center Parcs
Kirklington Rd, Eakling Notts NG22 0DZ ☎ (08705) 200300 🖰 www.centerparcs.co.uk
Started in the '60s in the Netherlands and imported to the UK in the '80s, this company has centres at Longleat, Elveden and Sherwood Forest. On the continent there are five in the Netherlands, two in Belgium, two in France and one in Germany. The basic concept is that the park is set in greenery with some outdoor activities, plus central, heated facilities with lots to do and a big pool usually a feature. / *HOURS Mon-Fri 8.30am-10pm, Sat-Sun 9am-9pm.*

Perfect Places
Hartford Manor, Greenbank Lane, Northwich Cheshire CW8 1HW ☎ (01606) 787776
🖰 www.perfectplacesonline.co.uk
Part of the Eurocamp group, an operator offering self-catering family holidays at centres operated by Pierre & Vacances, Maeva/Latitudes, VVF Vacances, Gran Dorado and Roompot in variously France, Spain, Italy, Holland and Germany. / *HOURS Mon-Fri 8:30am-8pm, Sat 8:30am-5:30pm, Sun 9:30am-5pm.*

FAMILY RESORTS

Some parents feel that these all-inclusive or near-all-inclusive resorts are overpriced for what you get. Others swear by them, and particularly by the extensive childcare which they offer.

Prices are more affordable if you can travel outside the school holidays. Even in May, however, an adult sharing a room will pay around £500 for a week, with prices for under-ones around £100 and under-twos perhaps £250. For exhausted parents with babies and toddlers, they do provide an uncomplicated, eminently 'do-able' package with lower childcare costs than many DIY packages.

In addition to the multi-centre operations like those listed there are also independent resorts

LISTINGS

Club Med
Kennedy House, 115 Hammersmith Rd London W14 0QH ☎ *(020) 7581 1161*
⌁ *www.clubmed.com*
The original all-inclusive holiday village concept, with sites all over the world. A number of resorts have Baby Clubs and Mini Clubs (some resorts have lower age limits of four or six years old; others are adults only); children and family special offers are available. The European resorts are less likely to provide English-speaking staff. Accommodation is at a range of standards; crèches are daytime only (9am-5pm), and must be pre-booked as space is limited, and there is no evening baby-sitting.

Mark Warner
10 Old Court Place, Kensington Church St London W8 4PL ☎ *(0870) 770 4227*
⌁ *www.markwarner.co.uk*
A tightly-run operation with some devoted followers, largely professionals and their families, particularly from London and the Home Counties. In addition to the winter ski operation, the company also runs all-inclusive beach resorts in Turkey, Greece and Corsica. Childcare for 4 months to 17 years. Childcare included for 2 to 17 for summer holidays. Extra charges for childcare during winter.

Sunsail
The Port House, Port Solent, Portsmouth Hampshire PO6 4TH ☎ *(023) 9222 2222*
⌁ *www.sunsail.com/uk*
Not strictly all-inclusive like the other two, so guests feel able to stray outside the Sunsail perimeters. Thought by some people to be less aspirational/exclusive than the competition. There are clubs in Turkey, Greece and Antigua. / HOURS *Mon-Fri 9am-5.30pm, Sat 9am-12pm.*

SKIING

This is one of the key areas where operators have really grasped the demand for quality holiday childcare.

You can 'DIY' of course – families with older children, or with a non-skiing childcarer in the party will find that independent self-catering accommodation is considerably cheaper. For families with only babies and toddlers, and no non-skier or childcarer, there is always the option of resort-run crèches. However, standards of these are very variable: they may not offer English-speaking staff; and (especially at either end of the season) there is no guarantee that they will be open.

If you want more backup, the following operators run their own childcare services with crèches and/or dedicated nannies.

LISTINGS

Handmade Holidays
South Floor, Carpenters Building, Carpenters Lane, Cirencester Glost GL7 1EE ☎ *(01285) 648518* ⌁ *www.meriski.co.uk*
Specializing in luxourious facilities in Meribel. Offers crèche, chalet care and childcare. / HOURS *Mon-Fri 9am-5pm.*

Mark Warner
10 Old Court Place, Kensington Church St London W8 4PL ☎ *(0870) 770 4227*
⌁ *www.markwarner.co.uk*
An operation of long standing with childcare in Courmayeur, Verbier, La Plagne, Val d'Isere, Courchevel, Meribel and St Anton.

Powder Byrne
250 Upper Richmond Rd London SW15 6TG ☎ *(020) 8246 5300*
⌂ *www.powderbyrne.co.uk*
Smart operator offering crèche care plus up-market accommodation. / HOURS *Mon-Fri 9am-6pm.*

Simply Ski
Kings Place, Wood St Kingston upon Thames KT1 1SG ☎ *(020) 8541 2209*
⌂ *www.simply-travel.com*
Free baby-sitting one night a week and British qualified nannies at Courchevel and La Plagne ; private nanny service in Verbier. / HOURS *Mon-Fri 9am-7pm, Sat 9am-4pm, closed Sun.*

Ski Beat
Metro House, Northgate, Chichester W Sussex PO19 1BE ☎ *(01243) 780405*
⌂ *www.skibeat.co.uk*
Runs crèches in La Plagne, Les Arcs and La Tania, and a nanny service in Tignes and Val d'Isere.Ski school and afternoon care are available in La Plagne, Les Arcs, and La Tania. Children qualify for discounts but still get their own rooms. / HOURS *Mon-Fri 9am-6pm, Sat 10am-3pm.*

Ski Esprit
185 Fleet Road, Fleet Hampshire GU51 3BL ☎ *(01252) 618 300* ⌂ *www.ski-esprit.co.uk*
"The family specialist" (though not the largest), offering a wide range of activities and childcare in Morzine, Chamonix, Courchevel, La Plagne, La Rosiere and Verbier.
/ HOURS *Mon-Fri 9am-6pm, Sat 9am-4pm.*

Ski Famille
Unit 2, Claire Hall, Parsons Green, St. Ives Cambridgeshire PE27 4WY ☎ *(0845) 644 3764* ⌂ *www.skifamille.co.uk*
Family specialist – separate kids' rooms with night lights and kids' décor, in Les Gets (in Portes du Soleil). / HOURS *Mon-Fri 8am-6pm.*

Ski Scott Dunn
Fovant Mews, 12 Noyna Rd London SW17 7PH ☎ *(020) 8767 0202*
⌂ *www.scottdunn.com*
Qualified nannies at Courchevel, Val d'Isere, Meribel and Zermatt. During school holidays, children's ski classes are offered. / HOURS *Mon-Fri 9am-6pm.*

Is it right?

Once you have narrowed down your choices of potential destinations, you will want to evaluate how well the proposed accommodation will suit your needs, especially in terms of how child-friendly and safe the location is.

The following is a laundry list of practicalities, some of which you may feel are important enough that you should enquire about them before making a decision

Safety

➢ Are there balconies and if so can these be blocked off by doors, screens or windows? (However high the railings, a climbing child can use furniture such as a chair to get over them.)
➢ Are there full-length glass doors or low windows?
➢ Are there steps inside the rooms?
➢ Are there any open staircases?
➢ Are the floors carpeted or tiled?
➢ Will there be heaters which could burn a child or be knocked over?
➢ Is there water anywhere easily accessible (pond, pool, stream)?
➢ If there is a gate, can it be opened easily?

Accommodation:

➢ Where exactly will the room be? Distant annexes are not suitable if you want to eat in the restaurant in the evening while using the baby monitor.
➢ What is access like? Is the area buggy-friendly? Is there a lift?
➢ Give some thought to trying to find a good layout. For example, if you want to get a cot into your room, it may allow you a little more

sleep in the morning if the cot can be out of eyeshot of your bed? You might want to enquire about the option of a small en suite room for the child or connecting rooms.

➤ Is there somewhere separate to sit in the evenings when the baby is sleeping?

➤ If there is a kitchen for self-catering, how big is it (some are designed for little more than breakfast preparation). If no kitchen, is there a kettle or stove and/or a fridge?

➤ Can a cot with bedding be provided (and – in warmer climates – a mosquito net)? What type of cot will it be (not all are entirely safe – say, with bars of a size a baby's head could get stuck). If you are travelling by car it might be better to take a travel cot.

➤ Is there a bath if your child is unhappy in a shower?

➤ Is there drying space (sometimes a problem in smart hotels which don't like the balcony being used for this purpose).

➤ What kind of noise can be expected? (Is there a disco, noisy service entrance, bar or busy road nearby?)

Food:
➤ Will there be food your child likes to eat?

➤ Will babies be allowed to eat in the restaurant at all times?

➤ Are out-of-hours meals available, such as high tea?

➤ Is food freshly cooked or is it served on a buffet? (If the latter this is probably not hygienic enough for very young children.)

Location:
➤ How far is the accommodation from the beach/garden/pool, and how are they reached?

➤ Are there any steps or steep slopes to be negotiated when moving around with a buggy?

➤ Is it possible to avoid the noonday sun by making excursions in the early morning and late afternoon?

➤ If at the seaside: how steep is the beach? Is it sand or shingle? How far is it to the water (buggies are hard work in sand)? How calm is the water likely to be? Is the water warm and clean? What is offered on the beach (umbrellas, cafés, showers)?

Services & facilities:
➤ Is there anywhere nearby where you can buy nappies, formula etc?

➤ Are there babysitting or baby listening services?

➤ What is there to do if it rains?

➤ How many high chairs are available? (You don't want a daily race for the only one.)

➤ Do they have a fenced-in area and any facilities specifically for children: for example a kids' pool? If not, are children allowed in any adult pool? There is sometimes a lower age limit for this or a requirement for certain types of swimsuits.

➤ Are there any extra charges for any of the facilities?

3. HEALTH ISSUES

Different parts of the world are home to different bugs. These may be harmless if familiar, but are more of an issue when encountered for the first time by a baby or toddler whose immune system is not yet fully developed. A few basics worth remembering are listed below.

General pointers:
➤ Take particular care in warmer climates.

➢ Always boil water for a baby (for 10 minutes ideally) and sterilise utensils. Note that hot water from a hotel kitchen may only have been heated, not boiled. Alternatively consider one of the portable travel filters now available.

➢ Don't eat food that has been on a buffet or other display in warm weather, especially if there are flies. Tepid dishes like casseroles may have been kept warm for some time.

➢ Avoid shellfish unless you are sure that it is fresh and from clean water.

➢ Avoid salads, unpeeled fruit or other raw food unless you are certain it has been washed in clean water. Peel fruit yourself and if you have reservations rinse it in a disinfectant solution such as Milton.

➢ Avoid ice unless you are sure it is made with clean water.

➢ Avoid ice cream unless you are sure it has been properly stored at low temperatures.

READING

Your Child's Health Abroad – Dr Jane Wilson-Howarth & Dr Matthew Ellis (A manual for travelling parents; Bradt Publications; April 1998; £8.95; 1898323631) – *Written by adventurous parents, this guide includes information on different medical kits for different regions, preventive care, common and less common ailments, basic medical questions translated into five languages, and potential health risks region by region. It also covers issues like hepatitis, swimming hazards, walking barefoot, assessing fevers or respiratory infections and immunisation. An ideal reference book.*

Food & drink

If your baby is still being breast-fed it makes sense to delay weaning until after any holiday. Breast-feeding is convenient and offers a much better guarantee of hygiene than the alternatives.

If you are bottle-feeding, single feed readymade cartons of formula can be very handy. Make sure that you have an adequate supply of formula with you, especially if your child uses anything non-standard. Alternatively, check what local brands are available with your operator.

For making up formula, using bottled water can be a handy option, but only if it is a brand with a suitably low mineral content. The UK government advice is that you should still boil it first and ideally filter it (though neither safeguard is common on the Continent).

You can keep pre-mixed feed in a thermos, though this should probably not be kept hot for fear of bacteria multiplying. A much better option is to keep hot water in a thermos, to mix with pre-measured powder as required. You can buy hard plastic containers for this purpose. Disposable bottle bags can save on sterilising or there are 'travel kits' on the market, with disposable teats and bottles plus re-sterilising solution.

If the baby is weaned on to solids, bringing food from home means you won't have to spend too much time experimenting or tracking down suitable items. Note that baby foods sold on the Continent generally include more salt and sugar than is standard in the UK.

Immunisation

Even if you have reservations about immunising your child fully in accordance with travel guidelines, practitioners particularly recommend vaccination against polio and tetanus if a child is travelling outside western Europe and North America.

Note that if you wish to travel anywhere with endemic Yellow Fever, immunisation is considered vital for Caucasians. The shot is seldom given to young children, however, and not at all to children under nine months so you may be well advised to avoid such destinations.

USEFUL CONTACTS

Hospital for Tropical Diseases

*Mortimer Market, Capper St, Off Tottenham Court Rd London WC1E 6AU ☎ Healthline
(09061) 337733, Clinic (020) 7388 9600 ⏚ www.thehtd.org*
The hospital runs a travel clinic that offers pre-travel advice and post-travel screening
(for tropical travellers); appointments must be made. They also offer a 24 hour
advisory helpline (50p per minute; average call seven minutes) and a 24 hour fax-back
advice service (£1.50 per minute; average call two minutes). / HOURS *Mon-Fri 9am-4.30pm.*

Medical Advisory Service for Travellers Abroad (MASTA)

*Moorfield Road, Yeadon Leeds LS19 7BN ☎ Helpline (0906) 8224100, General (0113)
238 7501 ⏚ www.masta.org*
Telephone advice line (60p per minute) – they can send out individual country Health
Briefs with information on immunisations, malaria protection, and up to 84 other
potential health hazards. Briefs are updated daily and validated by the London Hospital
for Tropical Diseases. / SEE ALSO *1.02 Looking after yourself.*

Mosquitoes

Biting insects can make life uncomfortable for children, but in Britain and
most of Europe they are generally no more than a nuisance – even babies
will probably take no more than a couple of weeks to develop tolerance to
mosquitoes.

However, efficient protection against mosquitoes is vital in more
exotic climes given that they can carry not just malaria but other diseases
such as dengue fever, sleeping sickness and Lyme disease. Healthway
Medical reports that In some areas malaria, which until 10 years ago was
relatively easy to prevent, has become resistant to virtually all drugs.

Repellents containing Deet (Diethyl toluamide) are the only really
effective mosquito deterrents. However, the safety of Deet may be in
question, especially in combination with another chemical called perme-
thrin. A 1988 report in *The Lancet* advised parents not to use a repellent
made up of more than 50% Deet for babies (and children under two years
old) because of their thinner skin and greater ratio of skin surface area to
body mass. Some repellents for children contain under 50% Deet (see listings), but a concentration below 25% may not be sufficiently effective.
Breast-feeding women are recommended not to use Deet repellents either.

Alternatives are either equally unsuitable for under-twos or are based
on products like essential oils. (See listings for products.) However, note
that Neal's Yard Remedies warns that the skin of children under 18 months
reacts to essential oils differently from older children and adults. Using
essential oils before this age may result in permanently sensitising the
child's skin.

Most insect repellents considered acceptable for under-twos rely on
citronella essential oil, though there are variants. Where these products are
effective (and they are not always) it is only usually for between 30 and
60 minutes, though manufacturers may otherwise claim differently.

In case of any adverse reaction, it is a good idea to check any product on your child's skin before you travel.

Non-chemical protection measures:

➤ Stay scent-free: i.e. avoid any perfumed products including shampoos
and sunscreens.

➤ Cover the skin as completely as possibly with long sleeves, long
trousers and shoes etc.

➤ Wear neutrals and avoid dark shades, especially blue. Bees and wasps
are attracted to bright colours.

➤ Mosquitoes can bite through lightweight fabrics so a certain density of
clothing is preferable.

➤ Avoid stagnant water (which attracts mosquitoes) and food (which attracts bees and wasps). Placing something like jam away from where you are sitting can draw bees away.

➤ Take particular care at dawn and dusk when mosquitoes tend to bite. Blackflies tend to bite in the morning, and midges when the light is not bright, i.e. grey and cloudy weather and at dawn or twilight.

If you do use a repellent bear in mind that the aroma that attracts mosquitoes is believed to come from certain points on the human body, so the best approach is to treat these. Apply product on the child's ankles, backs of the hands (not the fingers, to avoid ingestion) and either side of the neck.

To keep repellent use to a minimum, keep as much of the child's skin covered as possible. Whichever option you go for, avoid aerosol sprays which mean the product may be inhaled. Instead use either a lotion or a pump spray. Insect repellent should not be used under clothing.

After returning indoors the treated skin should be washed in soap and water. This is especially important when use is repeated within a day, or on consecutive days.

If a baby gets a mosquito bite use cool water to soothe it and a suitable lotion such as aloe vera. Heat or rubbing will make itching worse so keep clothing light. A mild antiseptic may be useful on larger bites. In the case of stings it can be useful to have first aid instructions to hand. You should seek help immediately with any stings inside the mouth, in case of swelling.

USEFUL CONTACTS & PRODUCTS

Alfresco
PO Box 7401 London N6 6BQ ☎ (020) 8348 6704 ⌂ www.alfresco.uk.com
Moisturiser that is also an insect repellent using botanical ingredients melissa, geranium and lavender; a medic from the London School of Hygiene and Tropical Medicine reportedly says of it: "in the developed world where you are not exposed to malaria, it's very effective … compared to other plant-based products"; apparently safe to use on children and babies.

Burt's Bees
Natural Fact, 192 King's Rd London SW3 5XP ☎ (020) 7352 4283
⌂ www.burtsbees.com
US products from the Carolinas, including Lemongrass Insect Lotion; available from Natural Fact.

Medical Advisory Service for Travellers Abroad (MASTA)
Moorfield Road, Yeadon Leeds LS19 7BN ☎ Helpline (0906) 8224100, General (0113) 238 7501 ⌂ www.masta.org
Stockists of Mosi-Guard (see also) as well as Deet-based insect repellents and wrist bands. / SEE ALSO 1.02 Looking after yourself.

Mosi-guard
Moorfield Rd, Yeadon West Yorkshire LS19 7BN ☎ Mail order (0113) 238 7575
⌂ www.mosi-guard.com
Natural insect repellent, made from lemon eucalyptus oil, clinically tested by the London School of Hygiene and Tropical Medicine. Suitable for all the family, it is said to be fully effective for two-three hours, and to have some effect for up to six hours. Aerosol, pump spray, lotion and stick formats, from £5.59. Available direct, through MASTA (see also) or from most UK pharmacies. / HOURS Mon-Fri 9am-5.30pm.

Mozzie Patch
Bioconcepts Ltd, PO Box 15, Havant Hants PO9 1RQ ☎ (023) 9249 9133, 24 hr info line (023) 9249315 ⌂ www.mozziepatch.com; www.bioconcepts.com
A fabric patch containing citronella which can either be attached to a bed or pram, or placed in a small plastic holder round the wrist or on a belt (a 'gizzmo'). The USP is that there is no direct contact with the skin. You can buy direct – a 24-pack is £4.99. Alternatively the product is sold in pharmacies (including Boots, from August-October, or orderable any time – product code 46-31-056). Gizzmos must be purchased separately through Bioconcepts. / HOURS 9am-5.30pm.

Natrapel
Ardern Healthcare, Pipers Brook Farm, Eastham, Tenbury Wells Worcs WR15 8NP
☎ *(0800) 195 7400* ⌁ *www.ardernhealthcare.com, www.bens100.com*
The top-selling Deet-free repellent in the US (the company listed are the UK suppliers).
/ HOURS *Mon-Fri 9am-5pm.*

Sun protection

(See also chapter 3.04 Baby clothes, for stockists of sun protection items.)
As children have thinner skin (which develops fully from puberty) they
are in particular need of protection from the sun.

Sunburn in babies may be related to the development of skin cancer in
later life. By one estimate, six serious bouts of sunburn as a child double the
chances of developing skin cancer one day. The younger the child is when
sunburn occurs, the greater the risk. Use of adequate protection is therefore very important.

Sunburn can occur in the UK as well as overseas, if only because ultraviolet (UV) rays can penetrate clouds. Start your holiday using total
sunblock with creams and clothing, exposing young skin very gradually,
and remembering to count all time spent outside as well as on the beach.

Note that there are some concerns about the safety of some sun protection screens. In addition to general issues regarding ingredients in
cosmetics (see chapter *3.09 Lotions and Potions*), some commentators feel
that not enough is known about the workings of chemical sunscreens,
some of which are known to cause skin reactions. Recommendations
therefore include sun avoidance (i.e. using shade and long, loose clothing for protection), or use of products which rely for their effectiveness
on creating a physical block: for example with titanium dioxide. This last
is the traditional thick, white product, but can be very finely ground to
make it less visible.

In case of any adverse reaction, it is a good idea to check any product you plan to use on your child's skin before you travel.

Sun protection advice:

➤ Keep babies under 12 months old out of the sun completely. Bear in
mind that an estimated half of all UV rays falling on the skin are
reflected (i.e. are not the result of direct sunlight), so you need to use
sunscreen even in the shade. Reflections from water, snow and sand
are particularly strong. Some suppliers of sun protection clothing (see
chapter *3.04 Baby clothes*) also supply protective sun pods which help
guard against UV from all angles.

➤ The sun is strongest between 11am and 3pm (when your shadow is
shorter than you). This is the period requiring greatest care, when
older children will also need particular protection against the sun.
Encourage siestas, or at least staying in the shade.
Consider buying a pop-up sun-safe 'cabana' either just for children,
or big enough for adults too.

➤ Dress babies and children in loose fitting cotton clothes. Fabric should
be in close weave (as fabric stretches protection is diminished), and
sleeves and trousers or skirts should be long.

➤ Hats with wide brims that don't fall off are essential. The National
Radiological Protection Board (NRPB) does not recommend baseball
caps, which leave the neck exposed – a hat that covers both the ears
and the back of the neck is ideal. Particularly for babies who may have
little hair, a dense or lined fabric is necessary and not all baby sunhats
provide this.

➤ In the case of babies in buggies, make sure the sunshade is adequate
(parasols are generally not suitable for proper sun protection). Move

the buggy as the sun moves round. The canopy may need to be extended or even lined in bright sunlight.

➤ Babies in slings will need protection with a parasol (in practice an umbrella) as may those in backpacks – some models have optional shades to attach.

➤ Some experts recommend swimming in T-shirts because of the UV reflected by water. Soggy cotton is apt to be chilly on windy days, however – see chapter *3.04 Baby clothes* for suppliers of Lycra UV safe clothing.

➤ Use a cream offering good protection from both UVA and UVB rays. Protection from the second is indicated by the sun protection factor (SPF).

➤ Take a high protection factor cream. There is no universal standard for SPFs, but a minimum SPF of 15 (UVB protection), plus 3 or more stars (UVA protection) is recommended for babies, and factors of up to 45 are available, though higher numbers do not necessarily offer more protection, particularly in cheaper, lesser known brands. Advice is that sunscreen should not be the primary method of protection.

➤ When swimming, a waterproof high factor cream is recommended particularly for faces, reapplied frequently. Water 'resistant' creams are not suitable for prolonged periods in water.

➤ Temperature is also an issue. Babies can overheat fast (see below for symptoms of heat exhaustion). As a preventive measure, keep a supply of cool drinks available all the time.

➤ Bright sunlight can hurt the eyes, particularly when reflected from snow. Some suppliers of sun safe baby clothing also supply baby sunglasses (see chapter *3.04 Baby clothes*). Look for glasses with a UV filter.

➤ Darker skins have less of a problem with sunburn but even black skin can still burn.

➤ Polymorphic light eruption (PMLE), a rash that occurs as a result of photosensitivity, is apparently often misdiagnosed as prickly heat, and affects 15% of all the UK population. The symptoms are a burning sensation or itch that lasts several days. Serious cases should be referred to a dermatologist. Sometimes PMLE only occurs with the first major UV exposure of the summer and may not return.

BRANDS

Boots
General enquiries ☎ *Customer services (08450) 708090*
Their own-brand sun protection, Soltan, is an effective and inexpensive product, easy to apply even at high factors, and is available in three types: original; sensitive skin; with added insect repellent; SPF 4-60. / *SEE ALSO 2.02 Feeding; 2.03 Baby health; 3.01 Maternity wear; 3.02 Baby equipment; 3.04 Baby clothes; 3.05 Shoes; 3.06 Toys; 3.08 Nappies; 4.02 Health practitioners.*

Dr Hauschka Skin Care
Elysia Natural Skin Care, Unit 27, Stockwood Business Park, Stockwood, Redditch Worcs B96 6SX ☎ *(01386) 792622* ⌂ *www.drhauschka.co.uk (skin care only)*
The Dr Hauschka range of organic skincare products produces a sun protection cream for children, SPF 22, £14; sunblock stick SPF 30, £6 and after sun cream, £9; available at Farmacia and via mail order. / *HOURS Mon-Fri 9am-5:30pm; SEE ALSO 3.09 Lotions & potions.*

Forever Living Products
55 Amity Grove, Raynes Park London SW20 0LQ ☎ *(020) 8947 6528*
⌂ *www.foreverliving.co.uk*
The world's largest grower and distributor of aloe vera products. The aloe-based suntan lotion has an SPF of 30. Aloe vera gelly or lotion can be effective on sunburn. / *HOURS 24hr answerphone; SEE ALSO 3.09 Lotions & potions.*

Linco Care
Linco House, Manchester Rd Carrington M31 4BX ☎ *(0161) 777 9229*
⌂ *www.calypsosun.com*
Wide range of sun protection creams, including a coloured roll-on cream for kids; SPF

20, with 3* UVA rating and UVB filters; disappearing colour shows where lotion has been applied; also gels, creams, sprays, after sun products, insect repellent and adult tanning products; up to SPF 40. / HOURS *9am-5.30pm; SEE ALSO 3.08 Nappies.*

Sun E45
Moorfield Rd, Yeadon West Yorkshire LS19 7BN ☎ *Mail order (0113) 238 7575*
☝ www.masta.org
"Non-irritant, mineral-based sunscreens which form a protective shield on the skin to reflect away sunlight"; claimed to be ideal for infants, though the product's density can give the impression of a badly made-up geisha; available from MASTA (see also) or call for details of stockists. / HOURS *9am-5.30pm.*

USEFUL CONTACTS
National Radiological Protection Board (NRPB)
Chilton, Didcot Oxon OX11 0RQ ☎ *(01235) 831600* ☝ *www.nrpb.org.uk*
The organisation produces a number of leaflets relating to UV radiation and sun protection. / PUBLICATIONS *Info on how to protect baby skin from the sun.*

Sun-Togs
Direct Offers Ltd, Litton House, Saville Road, Westwood, Peterborough Cambridgeshire PE3 7PR ☎ *(01733) 765 030* ☝ *www.sun-togs.co.uk*
In addition to clothing sells sun protection cabanas, buggy-, pram- and stroller-covers, and car sun blinds; buggy covers £30. / HOURS *Mon-Fri 9am-5pm, or answerphone; SEE ALSO 3.04 Baby clothes.*

Wellbeing Screening
Barham Court, Teston, Maidstone Kent ME18 5BZ ☎ *(01622) 618 725*
☝ *www.personal-screening.com*
Sells single use sun/UV patches (15 for £7.99), allowing wearers to assess the degree of protection offered by their sun block or screen. The patches change colour after a fixed period of exposure; if smeared with the relevant sun screen cream the reading will adjust appropriately.

READING
[Leaflet] **Shades of Summer** (NRPB; Free) – *Detailed information on fabric and sun protection. / National Radiological Protection Board (NRPB) – (01235) 831600.*

Other health problems

Diarrhoea: usually caused by contaminated food or water, but also sometimes by too much heat/sun. Replacing lost fluids is the most important thing. Dehydration in a baby is most commonly marked by drowsiness, a dry tongue and less urine than usual. Readymade rehydration products are available, but anti-diarrhoea agents (found in over-the-counter products) should be avoided in children under five – Lomotil in particular – and antibiotics rarely help. Flat cola can be used for rehydration, or make your own mix with a finger pinch of salt and a teaspoonful of sugar to 250ml – around 1 mugful – of boiled water (the final solution should be no saltier than tears). If possible, add a squeeze of fresh orange. Simple foods are best after diarrhoea but not milk because the lactose cannot be digested.

Earache: often triggered by swimming. Once it has occurred, it is recommended to keep the ear completely dry for at least a week or two. Ear plugs or a headband designed to keep ears dry can help with this. A complementary approach for prevention and treatment is to put a drop of garlic oil in the ears before and after each swim.

Altitude: can be a problem for children with a heart problem or asthma so beware of rides up to the top of mountains where altitude sickness can strike.

Prickly Heat: occurs typically on the trunk and neck and is due to the sweat glands becoming blocked. It results in the skin becoming inflamed and itchy. Ensure the skin stays clean and dry. Loose-fitting cotton clothes will help with this as will a cool wash at the end of the day, taking care to dry afterwards and perhaps using a little dusting powder.

Heat exhaustion: can occur very quickly, especially in babies, with excessive sweating and failure to replace perspiration with liquid. Severe tiredness, headache, nausea, and cold and clammy skin are symptoms. Water, ideally with half a teaspoon of salt per pint, is the recommended antidote. Heat stroke follows heat exhaustion. In hot conditions, keep a supply of cool drinks available.

Hypothermia: can strike in cooler climates where parents are moving so keeping warm, but the child is not because seated in a buggy or backpack.

Constipation: although everyone is aware of the problems of diarrhoea, it is also important to avoid the opposite problem. Ensure a good supply of fresh fruit and vegetables and enough liquids.

POSSIBLE INCLUSIONS IN A MEDICAL KIT
➢ Plasters and sterile dressings, plus a small roll of porous tape.
➢ Antiseptic solution (TCP or Tea Tree Oil).
➢ Paracetamol (not Aspirin for under-12s): i.e. Calpol or Disprol.
➢ Cooling spray/treatment for insect bites.
➢ Scissors, tweezers and safety pins.
➢ Thermometer.
➢ Rehydration sachets.
➢ Treatment for burns and sunburn (calamine/aloe vera).
➢ Cough product.
➢ Arnica cream (good for bumps and bruises).

For babies
➢ Preferred teething product.
➢ Colic remedy.

LISTINGS
Hospital for Tropical Diseases
Mortimer Market, Capper St, Off Tottenham Court Rd London WC1E 6AU ☎ *Healthline (09061) 337733, Clinic (020) 7388 9600* ⏱ *www.thehtd.org*
Travel products (mosquito repellents, sunscreens, water treatment tablets) and first aid kits are available to buy in the clinic. / HOURS *Mon-Fri 9am-4.30pm.*

Nomad Travellers Store & Medical Centre
40 Bernard St London WC1N 1LJ ☎ *(020) 7833 4114* ⏱ *www.nomadtravel.co.uk*
Run by a couple who have travelled with their own children, including destinations well off the beaten track. Among other useful items, it can provide a tailor-made family first aid kit to tackle the potential problems of different destinations. You can call in advance to discuss your requirements, and collect it once it has been put together. / HOURS *Mon-Fri 9.30am-6pm.*

See chapter 4.02 *Complementary medicine & Health practitioners* for homeopathic travel kits and others that make use of alternative products.

4. MAKING THE JOURNEY
The following general principles apply no matter what form of transport you are taking.

General pointers:
➢ Once your baby is too old to sleep anytime, anyplace, anywhere, it is easiest to timetable journeys around sleeping and waking patterns.
➢ Incorporate the logistics of feeding into your timetable – take extra food in your hand luggage in case of delays.
➢ Try to plan on giving your child a quiet day before and after travelling.
➢ Allow plenty of time for each section of a trip to help avoid over excitement or tiredness (and nausea in children given to travel sickness).

➤ Consider how long any transfers are likely to take. One hour with a toddler in a coach is ample for most parents.

➤ It is particularly worth remembering that on the return journey you may have to leave your accommodation by midday, so evening departures are not ideal unless you can arrange a late checkout or temporary accommodation.

➤ Some people contemplate sedating their children for long journeys, particularly on board planes where an excitable or nervous child may irritate fellow passengers. However, sedatives commonly have the side effect of making the child grizzly or very woozy on waking which makes the next phase even more difficult. Sometimes products simply make the child more hyper, with attendant problems, without actually causing them to sleep.

Travel by air

Babies should not fly in their first 48 hours of life because their heart and lungs can't cope with the reduced levels of oxygen at altitude.

Fears were raised a few years ago (1998) that even beyond this time babies who fly run an increased risk of cot death. Proof of such claims remains elusive – The Foundation for the Study of Infant Deaths says there is no evidence for it – but you may wish to seek reassurance on this point from your GP.

Deciding which airline to use – particularly on a long-haul flight – is not a clear-cut affair. Staff tolerance, or even better, liking of babies, is an important advantage. Airlines from more developed countries often provide more in the way of physical facilities but you might well encounter less staff support than on a less swish carrier based in the developing world.

REDUCED RATES

Children under two travel more cheaply in an adult's lap – in general at a cost of 10% of a full adult fare – but have little or no luggage allowance, and all surcharges, e.g. departure taxes, must be paid in full. You may be allowed to bring on board a carry cot/basket (a maximum weight of 10kg is typical) but baby clothes, bedding and food will be treated as part of the accompanying adult's luggage allowance.

From the age of two, children are charged around two-thirds of the full fare (although this varies from airline to airline) and qualify for their own seat and a baggage allowance.

BASSINETS

On longer flights, young babies are usually provided with a bassinet (an on-board cot of varying designs), though there are a limited number of places on a given aircraft that can accommodate one so availability is not guaranteed. Smaller babies take priority over larger ones, but frequent fliers who have asked for a certain type of seat seem to come highest of all in the pecking order, so if you want a place which will take a bassinet you would be well advised to check in early.

The design and size of bassinets vary, as do the regulations about the age and weight of children allowed to use them. Some designs are soft-sided, variously described as a hammock or duffle bag. Some are strapped on to a shelf; others bolt into the wall. Some are, in effect, open-topped cardboard boxes, unsuitable for children over six months.

For children who have outgrown the use of a bassinet, even if they are young enough still to qualify to travel on your lap, you may find the price of their own seat is a worthwhile investment, especially on long journeys.

BOOKING A SEAT

It is a good idea to try to pre-book your seats, but not all airlines will guarantee an exact position. On flights where smoking is permitted, avoid seats at the rear, which is where the smoking section is usually located. If you can't pre-book your seats, then it is a good idea to be more than usually diligent about turning up in good time for the check-in. That way you can at least ensure you are seated together with your partner and avoid getting stuck at the rear of the plane.

If you ask for a bassinet you will almost certainly be given a bulkhead seat. If you are organising a long flight, it is worth a little investigation into the configuration of the aircraft that you will be taking. On newer craft these seats can be some of the better options on the plane. On older ones, however, they are sometimes right under the film screen which may disturb the baby and the seat arms may not lift (so getting yourself in and out when the bassinet is in place can be difficult.).

Bassinets are usually located near each other, so they can be a noisy option. Particularly if you have a toddler, seats at the side of the aircraft may be a better bet. The windows offer a little distraction and the wall makes corralling slightly easier. However, bear in mind that children may want to get up and walk around, which is troublesome for the person in the aisle seat if you're in a row of three.

Travellers with babies may on some carriers receive priority for places near emergency exits for safety reasons. It may, however, not be possible to secure a seat in the row right by the exit because of an obligation to keep the route to the exit clear, and because passengers in those seats may be required to open the door in an emergency.

HEALTH ISSUES

Airlines will not carry children with infectious diseases, severe cases of middle ear infection, or sinusitis. You should in any case consider avoiding air travel with a child with a particularly heavy cold or any form of ear infection or sinusitis – the changes in air pressure during the flight may cause pain from unequal pressure on either side of the eardrums. Painkillers and/or nasal decongestants can help. Repeated swallowing also relieves the pain, so it is an idea to provide drinks for the baby (or something else to suck on) during take-off and landing. You could also ask for two paper cups filled with paper napkins soaked in hot water to put over the ears. This helps relieve the pressure. If all else fails crying provides relief so it is a good idea not to resist it.

Because of dehydration when flying, you should give your child plenty of uncarbonated drinks. If you are breast-feeding you yourself should also drink plenty of water.

Given that the body swells when in the air it is not a good idea to travel with a limb in plaster as this can stop the blood flow. If your child is in plaster you will have to discuss this with your doctor.

MEALS

Special baby meals may be provided as long as you (and any booking agent) remember to request them in advance. It is worth checking what these are made up of as they may not be suitable for the age of your child and/or may be of inferior quality to the adult option.

It is better if children's meals are served before the adults' so you don't end up juggling two trays at the same time or even worse, two trays plus a toddler on your lap. If either of these is a likely case scenario you might find it easier to take your own food for either you or the child, to eat at your own convenience.

BOARDING

Some airlines offer families with young children pre-boarding. This means fewer people to squeeze past and first choice of where to put your possibly copious hand luggage so that it is easily accessible during the flight.

Buggies are not generally allowed on board, though there may be the odd exception for umbrella-folding styles. Usually the buggy is taken from you at the gate and placed in the hold. Well-organised airlines can then return the buggy or a substitute to you as you disembark. The majority don't do so until you get to the luggage carousel. This can be a long hike without wheels.

A backpack or sling may be handier than a buggy. Slings in particular are always allowed on board and so generally are backpacks. One or the other will ensure you have immediate transport at the other end.

CHILD SAFETY

Safety measures for babies and children vary markedly between airlines, partly because of the different jurisdictions in which they operate.

Not all airlines offer the 'belly belts' that are specially designed for children in parents' laps, fearing that in the event of an accident they might do the child more harm than good. It is correct that this style of belt could cause significant damage, but an unbelted child – as in a car accident – will almost certainly fly forwards, causing injury to herself and possibly others. Most airlines that do offer them insist they are worn.

Some airlines offer a specially-designed seat for infants from six months old. Alternatively you might be allowed to use your own car seat (see Travel by car, below) though not all seat models fit airline seats. Also, though a car seat might prove more secure in the event of an accident than just having a child on your lap, they do limit the amount of space the child has, and on long flights the lack of mobility in a five-point harness can prove frustrating

On certain routes (inbound to Australia for example), plane interiors are routinely sprayed with insecticides. The World Health Organisation says visitors should not have to be sprayed if it would be detrimental to their health. You could claim this for a baby but you would have to argue the point with the airline well in advance and the author is unaware of how practically they could accommodate this.

Baby changing tables are becoming more common but are still not universal, particularly on short-haul routes. It is therefore wise to be prepared for doing without.

POINTS TO CONSIDER

When booking flights:
➤ What child/family fare deals are available?
➤ Cot/bassinet availability, size and type.
➤ Are seats pre-bookable?
➤ Do families with children have priority for boarding?
➤ Are buggies allowed on board?

➤ Special baby meals: are they suitable for the current age of your baby? Are they served before the other meals (advisable)? Do baby meals have to be booked in advance?
➤ Are there bottle-heating facilities?
➤ Are there on-board changing facilities? Some airlines have changing tables in all lavatories, others in none or just one.
➤ Check which seat belts/other safety measures are available.

Facilities and what to take onboard:
➤ Freebies for children are less common on short-haul flights, though some offer small toys. On long haul routes, toddlers are often offered activity packs with toys, crayons and cards. (You may even get free nappies or a small pack of baby powder, cream etc.) However, pack a sufficient supply of nappies, books and toys in case freebies are not forthcoming.
➤ Blankets to protect against fierce air conditioning and for in-flight sleeps. These are often provided by the airline.
➤ Dense fabric for shielding any bassinet from the light.
➤ If no bassinet is available, suitable material e.g. sheepskin for the child to lie on the floor in front of a seat if feasible. Fabric can then be draped over an open seatback table to provide darkness.

Travel by car

As most parents swiftly discover, young babies are almost always lulled to sleep by the motion of a car, making it an excellent form of transport. It becomes a less attractive option once the child needs entertaining on long trips, when a second adult comes in handy.

It can be helpful to timetable drives to coincide with children's sleeping times, and to plan breaks at your child's usual snack and meal times. Almost all motorway service stops in the UK and Europe offer changing facilities, and many have children's play areas.

To avoid motion sickness try to ensure the child can look ahead rather than out of the side window, which gives a greater sense of movement.

Suggested items for car journeys include:
➤ Music cassettes can be invaluable for long journeys, especially with toddlers. Bear in mind you will hear several renditions of any tape.
➤ Toys hung from the rear grab handles so they can't fall out of reach. (Avoid noise-making toys.)
➤ An extra rear-view mirror (available at many baby equipment stockists) to check what is going on in the back seat when driving.
➤ A blind for protection against the sun. (A piece of fabric wedged into the top of the window will substitute.)
➤ The best entertainment of all – an adult in the back seat.

HIRE CARS

If you are fly-driving, or hiring a car you may wish to check that it has child-proof locks, and that an appropriate car seat can be provided. Reputable car hire companies will hire a seat at around £25 per week (occasionally hire is included in the standard price.). Provision of a child seat is never absolutely guaranteed and a report by Family Travel found a worryingly high proportion of companies unaware that a baby seat involved in a collision should be discarded.

You may prefer to take your own. If you have booked a separate plane seat for your child you may be able to take your car seat to use on board. However, if it doesn't fit the airline's seat or seat belts, it'll have to go in the hold, This incurs some risk of damage and you would do best to use a polystyrene model (suitable for 18 months-plus), which can tolerate a higher level of mistreatment.

Travel by train

If you don't have too much baggage, rail trips can be an ideal option for travel with kids, providing space and the possibility of movement on board, plus plenty of things to watch out of the window.

When booking seats it is wise to request one close to the door for easy access to the toilets (though not too close if the child is walking and prone to exploration). Sitting close to the buffet car is also sensible as shopping trips break up the journey (although walking through crowded carriages can be difficult for toddlers).

If you are breast-feeding you may prefer to book one of the airline style seats, but with slightly older children, a seat with a table is useful for entertainment – a clip-on seat can make the table more accessible for a younger child and also deters attempts to escape.

The UK rail network offers a family rail card for £20 a year offering one third off rail prices for one or both of two named adults travelling with up to four children who are entitled to travel anywhere for up to 60% off. (Discounts do not apply on first class tickets and some peak time services.) Some operators, for example Great Western, now operate family carriages.

USEFUL CONTACTS
National Rail Enquiries
☎ (08457) 48 49 50 ⬦ www.nationalrail.co.uk
Timetable details for all the UK train operators.

Trainline
⬦ www.thetrainline.com
Web-based UK train timetable and booking service.

Travel by sea

Offering plenty of space to move around, ferries are usually good for toddlers. The keen competition between operators means that bargain fares are almost always on offer, and there is increasing availability of play areas, crèches, changing and feeding rooms.

Cruising, contrary to its image, is also becoming a notably family-friendly option, certainly if you find the right ship.

Ideas for what to take

The following lists are prompts rather than a specific recommendation of what you should take.

For the journey:
➢ Toys. One or two familiar toys for younger children, and possibly a couple of books (you don't need more – they will read them over and over again). Older children can be allocated their own case to be opened at intervals for them to pick the next toy. Avoid toys with bits that will get lost (down the side of seats, in the sand, etc), noisy toys, and very large toys. You can now get very cheap toddler personal stereos, which help pass the time.
➢ Layered clothing, to take into account changes in temperature, including chills on board planes.
➢ Blanket and/or bedding.

> A picnic plus extra food and drink to cover the journey and any delays. Even on board a ferry or train catering facilities may be busy and your own food will be better and/or cheaper. Small items like baby sandwiches take longer to eat and help pass the time. For older children little packets of nibbles/treats (in-flight meals are a good source of small items) are useful but avoid salty and sweet foods which create thirst (raisins, crackers and non-dripping fruit are good choices). Biscuits are good if travel sickness is likely. Deep-frozen drinks cartons stay fresh in a picnic bag for at least 24 hours but can be difficult once opened. A screw top bottle minimises spillage.
> Spoons, bibs and cleaning-up items.
> A cool bag and pack, which will also be useful at the destination. Wide-necked vacuum flasks are useful for reheating by immersion.
> Bottles or training mugs (even if no longer strictly necessary they help to keep things much drier).
> Lots of plastic bags – for rubbish, snacks, anything wet etc. The clear zip-lock ones are particularly useful.
> Wet wipes and tissues or cloths for spills.
> A plastic box with lid or plastic bag in case of motion sickness.
> Preferred teething-relief product for babies.
> Transport – sling, buggy or backpack plus a canopy for sun and/or rain cover.
> A change or two of clothes (depending on the length of the journey) in case of vomiting and spills. Include a change of clothes for adults who may be caught in any fallout.
> More changes of nappies than you think you will need, plus cleaning materials, nappy cream and nappy sacks.
> If you use aromatherapy, lavender oil may help sleeping on long haul flights or if suffering from jetlag on arrival.

Ingenious gadgets for warming bottles in the car and car toy tidies are available from various suppliers and catalogues (see chapter *3.02 Baby equipment*).

For your stay:
> Nappies. Pack a suitable supply in black bin bags – they can be checked in with your luggage (label them clearly).
> Formula milk – your usual brand may not be available. Related feeding and sterilising gear.
> Favourite spoons, especially for babies starting to feed themselves.
> Appropriate clothes – ideally allowing for layering. Ski chalets are often hot so the child may need no more than a T-shirt indoors; Mediterranean countries are cool at night and the odd rain item is wise. In warmer climes remember sun protection clothes and products.
> Travel wash powder, laundry line and pegs (travel shops sell a good twisted-elastic alternative to traditional pegs).
> If not provided and your child is not sleeping in your bed, a travel cot (also doubling as a playpen). In hot climates a basket or cot is better than many carrycots because of the greater ventilation.
> A sheepskin or favourite cot blanket, useful for creating a familiar sleeping spot.
> In areas with mosquitoes, a net to put over the cot.
> A portable coil immersion heater for boiling water (buy a good one as cheap models can be both dangerous and slow).
> Clip-on/portable safety seat.

➤ Masking tape for the base of the bath if you fear slipping (or use a towel).

➤ A baby monitor. (Note that not all work overseas. You will also need to check the equipment's range.)

➤ A stairgate for self-catering accommodation if appropriate.

Out and about:

➤ A large drinks bottle or individual sealable cups for refreshment on the move.

➤ A large beach umbrella or sunscreen pod. The latter will generally be lighter and offer better protection. If you can be bothered, taking your own can prove a real bargain. Some beaches in the more crowded parts of Europe, however, will not allow you to bring your own.

➤ Swimming floats.

➤ Beach/summer toys.

➤ Beach shoes to protect against hot sand, rocks etc.

➤ A large waterproof bag for wet swimming things.

TRAVEL EQUIPMENT STOCKISTS

See also Travel cots in the Sleeping equipment section of chapter 3.02 Baby equipment.

Samsonite Baby Travel

Weybury Hildreth Ltd, 2 St Leonards Close, Bridgnorth Shropshire WV16 4EJ ☎ (01746) 769676 ⌁ www.baby-travel.com

Produces a range of items ranging from nappy changing bags (carry case, shoulder and packback varieties, a baby wardrobe case including insulated bottle and food pocket as well as baby garment bag, plus pop-up travel cot and travel bed suitable until the baby can sit unaided.

Tots Away

Globe House, 3rd Floor, Southall St Manchester M3 1LG ☎ (0870) 751 0640 ⌁ www.totsaway.co.uk

Sells a pre-packed rucksack for trips with a baby, contents including disposable Steri-bottles, disposable cold water sterilising bag, a car bottle and food warmer to plug into a car cigarette lighter, disposable bibs, travel bowls, travel wipes, plastic bag for mess, and wipe clean changing mat. The rucksack is £29.99, refills of the disposable items, £5.99. Further bags are planned along with clothes, all related to travel with little ones.

Travelling with Children

30a Old Street, Upton upon Severn Worcester WR8 0HW ☎ (01684) 594 831 ⌁ www.travellingwithchildren.co.uk

Not just a retailer, but this website offers a range of products particular suited to travellers. Products range from aromatherapy oils to baby carriers, via harnesses, travel cots, luggage, toilet equipment and UV protection.

CHAPTER 2.06

BABY & TODDLER ACTIVITIES

(For information on pre-schools for toddlers, see chapter 2.07 Education. For suggested books on playing with children, see chapter 4.05 Finding out more.)

1. INTRODUCTION

Early stimulation of all kinds enhances children's learning – both physical and mental – promoting confidence as they grow.

It appears that babies are born with billions of brain cells: many more than they have at the age of three, and almost twice as many as adults. Stimulation is believed to trigger the building of connections between cells: the more connections the better. However, the ability to form links appears to diminish with age, and those parts of the brain which do not get 'wired up' seem to atrophy.

Playing, singing, reading, talking ... – all are obvious ways for mothers to stimulate babies and children without recourse to classes. However, even relatively young babies enjoy new people and a change of scene. The same is, perhaps, even more true of mothers feeling trapped at home, for whom classes present some of the best opportunities to get out and about, socialise, and pick up useful local information (on nanny share opportunities, nurseries, schools, ...).

For parents who feel a structured system of learning must be better for their child, some classes are arranged in a progressive series. Be alert, however, to the issue of placing too many demands on your child too early.

In the first year the danger of 'hot-housing' – ambitious parents pushing their children into intensive learning – is not really an issue. Babies are excellent at letting anything they find uninteresting wash over them. With toddlers this is less the case and the brighter ones in particular can feel a pressure to perform, or to be sociable.

If your child just doesn't like a particular class, don't stress – back off and try something different; or try the same again, but in a couple of months. Many teachers will allow you to attend a class to see if it suits you before signing up. Mix learning with fun, and keep time in the day for doing nothing in particular.

Good classes get booked up, so it is worth putting your baby's name down in advance. Don't assume, though, that just because a course is expensive, or over-subscribed, that it is necessarily any good.

CHOOSING SAFE ACTIVITIES

Have Fun & Be Safe (NSPCC; free) – *A guide to help parents and carers choose children's activities. It is mainly aimed at slightly older children but points are still valid for younger ones in playgroups and crèches. Available to download from the NSPCC website (code 0188). / www.nspcc.org.uk.*

MAKING UP YOUR OWN GAMES

Baby Minds – Linda Acredolo & Susan Goodwyn (Brain-building games your baby will love; Bantam; 2000; £9.99; 0553380303) – *The title makes it sound rather 'hot-housing', but this book (put together by development experts) gives a fair amount of intriguing information about the intellectual abilities of newborn babies; it includes ideas on talking to your baby with sign language.*

Baby Play and Learn Pack – Dr Miriam Stoppard (Give your baby a flying start in life; Dorling Kindersley; 2000; £19.99; 0 7513 0612 6) – *The premise is that just one hour of structured play a day with your baby helps develop crucial "brain connections"; the pack provides a parent guide, activity cards, and black and white drawings.*

Baby Signs – Linda Acredolo & Susan Goodwyn (How to talk with your baby before your baby can talk; Vermilion; 2000; £12.99; 0-09-185168-8) – *By two child psychologists – a programme for working on signs to communicate better with pre-verbal children; a US best-seller.*

Brain Games for Babies, Toddlers & Twos – Jackie Silberg (140 fun ways to boost development; Hamlyn; 2003; £9.99; 0600605825) – *A selection of 150 games designed to stimulate brain development up to the age of 3. Each game is acccompanied by an explanation of how the game promotes brain activity. As the child grows, aims include increasing vocabulary, encouraging musical ability and improving balance and co-ordination. / www.hamlyn.co.uk.*

Bright Baby – Dr Richard C Woolfson (Understand and stimulate your child's development; Hamlyn; 2001; £14.99; 0-600-60071-8) – *Pricey but interesting, this guide by a child psychologist covers development patterns (including hand-eye coordination, language and social interaction), as well as practical suggestions for stimulating children, from birth to 15 months. / www.hamlyn.co.uk.*

Bright Toddler – Dr Richard C Woolfson (Understand and stimulate your child's development; Hamlyn; 2001; £14.99; 0-600-60249-4) – *Covering 15 to 36 months, more pointers on development and how to stimulate it. In the same series is 'Bright Child' covering, 21/2 to 5 years. / www.hamlyn.co.uk.*

Dorothy Einon's Pre-school Play Book – Dorothy Einon (Bloomsbury; 1999; £11.99; 0747540918) – *Prolific childcare and parenting author's suggestions for over 100 games broken up into three sections – the first two years, the pre-school years and for ages 6-10.*

Entertaining and Educating Babies & Toddlers – R Gee and S Meredith (Usborne; 1992; £5.99; 0-7460-0006-5) – *A popular book, which has been around for more than 10 years. It offers simple ideas for playing with babies and young children, none requiring a great deal of preparation or equipment. / www.usborne.com.*

The Genius of Play – Sally Jenkinson (Celebrating the Spirit of Childhood; Hawthorn Press; 2001; £11.99; 1-903458-04-8) – *A look at what play means for children, what they express through it and how it helps them develop. The title is written from a Steiner perspective, but offers insights unrelated to that educationalist's philosophy.*

[Video] **Heuristic Play with Objects** – Elinor Goldschmied & Anita Hughes (Children of 12-20 months exploring everyday objects; National Children's Bureau; £25.85; 2000) – *A 20-minute video showing how children from 1 to 20 months satisfy their need for exploratory play, using a City nursery as an example; price includes an explanatory leaflet. / www.ncb-books.org.uk.*

Learning Early – Dorothy Einon (Everything parents need to encourage and develop their child's learning skills from birth to six years of age; Marshall Publishing; 1999; £14.50; 1840280921) – *Games and activities designed to develop potential in pre-schoolers.*

Let's Play Together – Mildred Masheder & Susanna Vermaase (Over 300 co-operative games for children and adults; Merlin Press; 1989; £7.99; 1-854250-13-2)

Sign with Your Baby – Joseph Garcia (How to communicate with infants before they can speak; Northlight Communication; 2000; £49.95; 0966836731) – *A comprehensive kit with book, training vido, signing guide (British version) and quick reference guide. It is designed for use from around eight months.* / NCT Maternity Sales (0870) 112 1120; www.nctms.co.uk.

You Are Your Child's First Teacher – Rahima Baldwin (Celestial Arts; 2000; £12.99; 0890879672) – *The author argues that creative play and fantasy, together with a sense of aesthetics is important to a baby's development; includes ideas on how to nourish creativity, and artistic and musical ability.*

You Are Your Child's First Teacher – Rahima Baldwin Dancy (What parents can do with and for their children from birth to age six; Celestial Arts; 2000; $14.95; 0890879672) – *The author argues that creative play and fantasy, together with a sense of aesthetics, is important to a baby's development. The title looks at how to encourage these, and so to develop a child's artistic, musical and general creativity.*

Your Child at Play: 2 to 3 Years – Marilyn Segal (Nurture your child's intelligence thorugh language and imagination; Vermilion; 2001; £7.99; 0091825016) – *Pointers on games, and their importance.*

Your Child At Play: Birth to 1 Year – Marilyn Segal (Discovering the senses and learning about the world; Newmarket Press; 2001; £7.99; 093785851X) – *A title explaining how play can spur brain development and offering different practical play ideas.*

Your Child at Play: One to Two Years – Marilyn Segal (Vermilion; 1999; £7.99; 0091827604) – *Follow-on edition, showing how play aids development and including information on managing problems.*

USEFUL CONTACTS

Families Magazines, ☎ *(020) 8696 9680* ⌂ *www.familiesmagazine.co.uk*
Excellent series of local publications, which include a wealth of information and advertising. They produce local listings of playgroups, pre-schools, parent & toddler groups and one o'clock clubs.

London4kids, ⌂ *www.london4kids.com*
Website promising up-to-date and comprehensive information on entertaining kids in and around London.

World of Health, ☎ *(020) 7357 9393* ⌂ *www.worldofhealth.co.uk*
Health, fitness and lifestyle video and DVD supplier with a range of different videos on stimulating and entertaining babies.

GETTING AROUND BY TUBE

It can seem as if the main challenge to organising baby activities is not finding somewhere to go, but just getting there. This is particularly the case if you are reliant on the tube.

Unfolded buggies are not, theoretically, permitted on the Tube Mon-Fri, 7.30am-9.30am and 4pm-7pm. Currently just 40 Tube stations are 'step free': i.e. it is possible to get from platform to street level without the use of steps or an escalator. In central London, only Westminster qualifies. More stations are being made step free over the next 20 years.

USEFUL CONTACTS

Transport for London, ☎ *(020) 7222 1234, Mobility information (020) 7941 4600* ⌂ *www.londontransport.com, www.thetube.com*
General service details and information on mobility issues relating to public transport in London.

2. BABY MASSAGE

(See chapter 3.09 Lotions & potions, and chapter 4.02 Complementary medicine & Health practitioners for stockists of suitable massage oils.)
Massage is an excellent form of communication with a baby that is too young to play with toys, and is becoming increasingly popular as an activity for parents with their newborns. Part of the rationale for the activity is the view of some child experts that being touched is vital both to the mental state of babies and also their physical wellbeing.

Reported benefits of massage

➤ Alleviation of colic, restlessness and irritability; it is also said to be useful with posseting babies (as it relaxes muscles) and with encouraging overtired babies to get off to sleep.

➤ Improved muscle tone and co-ordination.

➤ A good way for fathers to get to know their baby better (it is said to help both parents with bonding).

➤ Compensation for the loss of contact with or absence of a parent caused by a spell in special care, illness, or even just daily separation on account of work.

➤ Child experts such as Bruno Bettelheim (author of *A Good Enough Parent*, see chapter *4.05 Finding out more*) point to the need to help children develop a healthy and positive attitude to their bodies and believe activities such as massage help this.

➤ One US study found premature babies massaged gently three times a day grew more rapidly than those who were not massaged.

Very gentle massage is recommended in the days after birth, graduating to firmer and more complex strokes as the baby grows. Babies may not enjoy massage when they are learning to crawl, but generally return to it when past this stage, if offered.

Caesarean babies, or those born after a short labour are said, initially, to be more resistant to the activity, perhaps because they have had less experience of squeezing sensations. However, like most babies, they usually grow to enjoy it.

Classes are usually of a drop-in nature. You will need a changing mat, towel and a suitable massage oil.

CENTRAL BODIES

Guild of Infant and Child Massage, ☎ *(01889) 564 555*
⌁ *www.gicm.org.uk*
Send a parent pack which gives basic information about the benefits and possible courses in the local area.

International Association of Infant Massage (IAIM) UK,
☎ *(07816) 289 788* ⌁ *www.iaim.org.uk*
Specialists in baby massage may have trained with this organisation, which can provide lists of local practitioners and instructors. Please send an SAE or visit the website (the phone is only manned intermittently).

LISTINGS

CENTRAL

Neal's Yard Remedies
☎ *(0845) 262 3145* ⌁ *www.nealsyardremedies.com*
BRANCHES AT:
 15 Neals Yard WC2H 9DP ☎ *(020) 7379 7222*
At the Elgin Crescent branch.

WEST

Rob Blanks (ITEC, LCM)
34a Overstone Rd W6 0AB ☎ *(020) 8741 8136*
Baby massage and home tuition in west London, from £20; emphasises the importance of the bonding opportunity of baby massage for fathers. / HOURS *Mon-Sat 9am-6pm.*

Heather Guerrini
30 Redesdale St SW3 4BJ ☎ *(020) 7352 0245*
Baby massage classes, with an introduction to simple reflexology techniques. / SEE ALSO *1.04 Antenatal classes; 2.04 Childcare; 4.02 Health practitioners.*

The Life Centre
15 Edge St W8 7PN ☎ (020) 7221 4602 ◌ www.thelifecentre.com
Baby massage class suitable for babies from eight weeks to six months. Some soft gymnastics and stretching for the mothers (to restore physical shape and induce relaxation) also included; from £9.50 per 90 minute session; must be booked in advance. / HOURS *Mon-Fri 8am-9pm, Sat & Sun 9.30am-6pm; SEE ALSO 1.04 Antenatal classes; 4.02 Health practitioners.*

Neal's Yard Remedies
☎ (0845) 262 3145 ◌ www.nealsyardremedies.com
BRANCHES AT:
  Chelsea Farmers Market, Sydney St SW3 6NR ☎ (020) 7351 6380
  ◌ www.nealsyardremedies.com
    9 Elgin Crescent W11 2JA ☎ (020) 7727 3998
See write-up in central.

The New Baby Company
8 Souldern Road W14 0JE ☎ (020) 7751 1152 ◌ www.newbabycompany.com
Three sessions from after babies are 8-weeks old, £48. / SEE ALSO *1.04 Antenatal classes; 2.03 Baby health.*

Urban Escape
Jo McCallum (RGN) ☎ (07976) 701041 ◌ urbanescape@msn.com
Home visits and group or individual course; IAIM certification. / SEE ALSO *4.02 Health practitioners.*

Peter Walker
PO Box 8293 W9 2WZ ☎ (020) 7289 8196 ◌ www.thebabywebsite.com
The big name in baby massage (who worked with staff from St John's & St Elizabeth Birth Unit, the Life Centre and the Active Birth Centre) is a trained yoga teacher and physical therapist whose teaching aims to strengthen your baby's survival system, relieve colic and fractiousness, improve feeding and sleeping rhythms and help your child secure a strong flexible body and good posture.He specialises in treating special needs babies, especially those with cerebral palsy; a one-hour one-to-one session is £40, although concessions can be made. He recommends starting as early as four weeks.

NORTH

The Active Birth Centre 🖰
25 Bickerton Rd N19 5JT ☎ (020) 7281 6760 ◌ www.activebirthcentre.com
Courses run by Beth Winslet and Lynn Murphy, for babies 'from newborn to sitting', followed by postnatal yoga; £75 for four classes. Baby massage classes (without yoga), £10 (must be booked in advance). / HOURS *shop Mon-Fri 9.30am-6.30pm (Fri 4pm), Sat 10am-4pm; SEE ALSO 1.01 Where to have the baby; 1.04 Antenatal classes; 1.06 Birth equipment; 2.01 Postnatal; 2.02 Feeding; 2.03 Baby health; 3.01 Maternity wear; 3.02 Baby equipment; 4.02 Health practitioners; 4.05 Finding out more.*

Amber White Dip Cot, ITEC, RZT
81 Pert Close N10 2RZ ☎ (020) 8442 0992
Teaches parents massage in series of four weekly sessions, with small groups. / SEE ALSO *4.02 Health practitioners.*

Angel Chiropractic Clinic
18 St Alban's Place, Upper St N1 0NX ☎ (020) 7288 2999
Sessions for parents on a one-to-one basis. / SEE ALSO *4.02 Health practitioners.*

Fit Start
Lancaster House, 6 Lancaster Rd N4 4PP ☎ (020) 8374 7680
Baby massage classes in Camden and Islington (more London venues planned). Part of a wider programme of fitness sessions for mother and baby; run in 10-12 week terms. / SEE ALSO *1.04 Antenatal classes; 2.01 Postnatal.*

Harringay Club
50 Tottenham Lane N8 7EE ☎ (020) 8348 2124 ◌ www.harringayclub.org.uk
Afternoon baby massage classes, £3.50(£2 members; membership £25). / HOURS *Mon-Sun 9am-5pm; SEE ALSO 2.01 Postnatal.*

Hornsey Vale Community Centre
60 Mayfield Rd N8 9LP ☎ (020) 8348 4612
Baby massage and playgym. / SEE ALSO *2.01 Postnatal.*

Jane Waller
Crouch End N8 ☎ (020) 8342 8136, Mobile (07752) 037669
Five-week courses with qualified IAIM practitioner, £40. / HOURS *Ring for details.*

Kailash
Centre of Oriental Medicine, 7 Newcourt St NW8 7AA ☎ *(020) 7722 3939, 020 4833476.* ᕳ *www.orientalhealing.co.uk*
Runs a short course in massage for children, taught to small groups, £25-£40 for three hours' tuition. / HOURS *Mon-Sat 9am-7pm; SEE ALSO 4.02 Health practitioners.*

London College of Massage
Correspondence – Diorama, 34 Osnaburgh Street, London NW1 3ND; Venue – D2 Diorama, 3-7 Euston Centre NW1 3JG ☎ *Enquiries (020) 7813 1980, Clinic 0870 990 5828* ᕳ *www.massagelondon.com*
Workshops for parents and caregivers cover the basic techniques of massage for babies and include simple muscle-strengthening exercises; £30. A home service may also be available – call for information. / HOURS *Mon-Fri 9am-9pm; SEE ALSO 4.02 Health practitioners.*

Neal's Yard Remedies
☎ *(0845) 262 3145* ᕳ *www.nealsyardremedies.com*
BRANCHES AT:
  68 Chalk Farm Rd NW1 8AN ☎ *(020) 7284 2039*
See write-up in central.

Park Road Pools
Park Rd N8 8JN ☎ *(020) 8341 3567*
Baby Massage sessions. / SEE ALSO *2.01 Postnatal.*

triyoga
6 Erskine Rd NW3 3AJ ☎ *(020) 7483 3344* ᕳ *www.triyoga.co.uk*
Baby massage classes are offered at this north London yoga centre, from £12 for a 90-minute class. Book ahead. / HOURS *6.30am-10pm; SEE ALSO 1.04 Antenatal classes; 2.01 Postnatal.*

Wholebody
N8 ☎ *(020) 8341 9973 mobile (07956) 156 051* ᕳ *www.wholebody.co.uk*
Courses teaching parents how to massage their baby, either one to one or in groups. / HOURS *Flexible; phone for details; no calls after 8pm; SEE ALSO 1.04 Antenatal classes.*

Yoga Babies
Crouch End N8 ☎ *(020) 8883 3234, (020) 8364 9868* ᕳ *www.yogababies.co.uk*
The massage course lasts six weeks including a session of postnatal yoga and a father's Sunday session, demonstrating a combination of Swedish and Indian massage techniques. The five-week infant yoga class is considered a follow-on class with adapted Hatha yoga postures for phyisical stimulation. There are also songs and relaxation.

SOUTH

City Health Partnership
37 Oxford Rd SW15 2LH ☎ *(020) 8789 0607* ᕳ *www.cityhealth.biz*
Courses of five sessions, £60-£75, depending on size of class. / HOURS *Mon-Fri 8am-8pm, Sat 8am-12pm; SEE ALSO 4.02 Health practitioners.*

CC (Kiki) von Eisenhart-Goodwin (BSc Phys, MCSP, SRP, Pg Dipl, CNAA)
Kiki's Children's Clinic,133 Thurleigh Rd SW12 8TX ☎ *(020) 7207 4234* ᕳ *www.kikisclinic.com*
Paediatric physiotherapist who uses massage. / HOURS *Mon-Fri 9am-5pm, Sat 9am-1pm; SEE ALSO 4.02 Health practitioners.*

Sue Lewis Grad DB, MCSP, SRP
65 Vineyard Hill Rd SW19 7JL ☎ *(020) 8946 8561*
Regular baby massage courses taught by a qualified midwife, including various techniques designed to help with colic; £40. / SEE ALSO *1.04 Antenatal classes; 2.01 Postnatal; 2.03 Baby health; 4.02 Health practitioners.*

Clare Mundy
SE14 ☎ *(020) 7639 2397* ᕳ *www.blissfulbaby.co.uk*
London College of Massage-trained teacher of a range of simple techniques based on traditional Indian baby massage; offers two-hour sessions in your own home for babies aged from two weeks to six months; demonstrates strokes, the most effective pressure and special techniques for colic; recommends oils (supplied) and provides a written copy of the routine; individual sessions, or groups of 2-3 or 4-8 people (prices vary).

Neal's Yard Remedies
☎ *(0845) 262 3145* ᕳ *www.nealsyardremedies.com*
BRANCHES AT:
  6 Northcote Rd SW11 1NT ☎ *(020) 7223 7141*

32 Blackheath Village SE3 9SY ☎ (020) 8318 6655
15 King St Richmond TW9 1ND ☎ (020) 8948 9248
See write-up in central.

Sarah Spoor (Baby Bliss)
127a Twickenham Rd Isleworth TW7 6AW ☎ (020) 8568 4913 ⏚ www.baby-bliss.com
Trained by Peter Walker, Sarah teaches baby massage in blocks of six classes;
£40. / HOURS *phone for appointment;* SEE ALSO *1.04 Antenatal classes; 1.06 Birth equipment.*

EAST

Arlene Dunkley-Wood
154 King's Head Hill E4 7NU ☎ (020) 8923 6452 (answerphone), (020) 8923 6452
Classes in Bethnal Green and Chingford, £10 per class. / SEE ALSO *1.04 Antenatal classes;*
2.01 Postnatal.

OUTSIDE LONDON

Essentials for Health
Church Lane Chamber, 11-15 High Street, Marlow Bucks SL7 1AU ☎ (0845) 108 0088,
01628 476 076 ⏚ www.essentialsforhealth.co.uk
Runs training International Association of Infant Massage courses for infant massage
teachers and welcomes parents of babies between three weeks and seven months for
the trainees to practice their teaching on. Classes normally costing £45 are free and
participants are provided with a free bottle of massage oil. Courses run most months.

Thilaka Perera (ICHT)
44 Chatham Ave Hayes BR2 7QD ☎ (020) 8462 2071
Qualified midwife and aromatherapist practising from home; will visit your home if
you live nearby; also offers workshops. Runs classes in Hayes and in West Wickham;
phone for details. / HOURS *Flexible daytime hours;* SEE ALSO *4.02 Health practitioners.*

READING

Baby Massage – Peter Walker (A practical guide to massage and movement for
  babies and infants; Piatkus Books; 1995; £9.99; 0-749914-71-8) – *From a leading
  name – starting with simple techniques for cleansing and nourishing the skin of
  a newborn, this book teaches gentle routines for massaging babies from the age of two
  months, helping them to cope with the sitting, crawling and standing phases of growth.A
  matching video is also available at £12.99, for example from NCT Maternity Sales.*
  / NCT Maternity Sales, *(0870) 112 1120; www.nctms.co.uk; Natural Birth Centre – (020) 7561
  9006.*

Baby Yoga – Francoise Freedman (Gentle exercises for babies, mums and dads; Gaia
  Books; 2000; £10.99; 1856751767) – *A concept akin to baby massage – ways for
  mother or father to do exercises and handle a baby, which – it is claimed – can help
  alleviate colic and sleeplessness. A Baby yoga video is available from NCT Maternity
  Sales (0870) 112 1120, www.nctms.co.uk.* / *www.gaiabooks.co.uk.*

Infant Massage – Vimla Schneider McClure (A handbook for loving parents;
  Souvenir; 1989, revised 2001; £9.99; 0285636170) – *A best-selling title now in its
  third edition, written by the author of a number of parenting books.*

[Video] **Practical Art of Baby Massage** – Peter Walker (Green Umbrella; 2001;
  £9.99) – *A step-by-step guide to a variety of routines and exercises for babies (from birth)
  and toddlers.* / *(01932) 343310, www.greenumbrella.co.uk.*

Touching – Ashley Montagu (The human significance of the skin; Harper Perennial;
  1986; £16; 0060960280) – *An examination of the importance of touching, including
  considerable discussion of infant and parent bonding through touch and massage.*

3. PLAY PROGRAMMES

There is a large and expanding choice of places providing a variety of
structured activities under one roof – often in weekly sessions – with the
explicit aim of building confidence and social skills.

The core of these programmes tends to be gym-related activities.
However unathletic the parents, most babies and toddlers revel in discovering the new things that they can achieve with their body, particularly
once they can crawl. Furthermore, this kind of play helps increase children's reliance on their own judgement; improves their ability to size up

situations and take decisions; and fosters an awareness of their capabilities and limitations.

To differing degrees, there is also usually some emphasis on music and song time.

Most classes are suited to babies from crawling age, or around six months, and a parent or carer needs to attend with the child.

Those running such classes span from one-off ventures to huge international franchises (Tumble Tots, for instance, which was started in Southampton in 1979, is now owned by a Singapore-based company and operates worldwide). Where the latter, franchise-type businesses are concerned, quality can vary noticeably from one area to another, depending on the local franchisee.

Most classes have to be booked in blocks of six to 12, but if for any reason you cannot attend you may be able to make the class up later. Some of the larger, franchised companies may allow you to attend classes at different centres.

LISTINGS

WEST

Crèchendo
Unit 1 Grange Mills, Weir Rd SW12 0NE ☎ *(020) 8772 8120* ⌁ *www.crechendo.com*
BRANCHES AT:
  Chiswick Christian Centre, Fraser St W4
  St Barnabus Church Hall, 23 Addison Rd W14
  West London Family Church, 240 Lillie Rd SW6
  Baden Powell House, Queen's Gate SW7
Well-known company running weekly classes for pre-school kids at various centres throughout London. All classes are 45 minutes, with different programmes for different age groups: Babyplay (4-8 month olds); Babyplay Plus (8-12 month olds); Toddlerplay (10 month to 2 year olds); Kidsplay (2-3 year olds); and Childsplay (3-5 year olds). Each class runs to a weekly theme with singing, story-telling, activity sessions, a well thought-out circuit for participants to climb over, plus a 'quiet corner' with puzzles and percussion items. Joining fee, £20; classes from £79 for 12 weeks (discounts if you sign up for more classes, and further siblings pay half-price). Free trial classes – all bookings are taken through the central offices.

Gymboree (Play)
☎ *Play & Music Infoline (0800) 092 0911; Retail Head Office (0116) 282 7400*
⌁ *www.gymboreeplayuk.com*
BRANCHES AT:
  Whiteleys Shopping Centre, 1st Floor W2 ☎ *(020) 7229 9294*
The play programmes actually pre-dated the creation of the well-known, eponymous international chain of kidswear outlets (both founded by Joan Barnes in California) by ten years. Its 'Play & Music' scheme runs interactive play classes for parents and children at some branches of the store. Gymbabes covers babies from birth to 6 months old, encouraging sensory stimulation and gentle play. There are six further classes for kids up to four years old which teach sports skills; approx. £145 for 12 weeks; free trial classes.

Tumbletots
Bluebird Park, Bromsgrove Rd, Hunnington, Halesowen West Midlands B62 0TT
☎ *(0121) 585 7003* ⌁ *www.tumbletots.com*
BRANCHES AT:
  Hogarth Youth Centre, Duke Rd W4 ☎ *(01932) 568263*
Claiming to be "the leading national active physical play programme for pre-school children" this business of franchises has around 50 centres in London. The weekly 45-minute classes follow a structured format including physical activities and song and rhyme sessions. The courses start with 'Gymbabes' (from 6 months to walking), with further courses from walking to school age. Annual membership of £12.50 includes personal accident insurance. Sessions are £4 a week, bookable in blocks of up to 12.

NORTH

Crèchendo
Unit I Grange Mills, Weir Rd SW12 0NE ☎ *(020) 8772 8120* 🖱 *www.crechendo.com*
BRANCHES AT:
  St Thomas More Hall, Maresfield Gardens NW3
See write-up in west.

Fit Start
Lancaster House, 6 Lancaster Rd N4 4PP ☎ *(020) 8374 7680*
Activity sessions for children from six months to three years old, divided into two age groups, a part of a comprehensive ante- and postnatal programme run by an ex-Norland nanny. Venues in Islington and Camden; classes run in terms; discounts available, free trial class. / *SEE ALSO 1.04 Antenatal classes; 2.01 Postnatal.*

Gymboree (Play)
☎ *Play & Music Infoline (0800) 092 0911; Retail Head Office (0116) 282 7400*
🖱 *www.gymboreeplayuk.com*
BRANCHES AT:
  02 Centre NW3 6LU ☎ *(020) 7794 8719*
  Business Design Centre, 52 Upper St N1 0QH ☎ *(020) 7288 6657*
  Unit 1, Bickerton House N19 5JT ☎ *(020) 7272 0979*
  St George Leisure Centre HA1 1HS
See write-up in west.

Tumbletots
Bluebird Park, Bromsgrove Rd, Hunnington, Halesowen West Midlands B62 0TT
☎ *(0121) 585 7003* 🖱 *www.tumbletots.com*
BRANCHES AT:
  Highbury Roundhouse, 71 Ronalds Rd N5 ☎ *(020) 8959 4261*
  Muswell Hill Centre, Hillfield Park N10 ☎ *(020) 8959 4261*
  United Reformed Church, Burford Centre, Fox Lane N13 ☎ *(020) 8440 0634*
  Liberal Jewish Synagogue, 28 St Johns Wood Rd NW8 ☎ *(020) 8959 4261*
  St Marks Church Hall, Abercorn Place NW8 ☎ *(020) 8959 4261*
See write-up in west.

SOUTH

Crèchendo
Unit I Grange Mills, Weir Rd SW12 0NE ☎ *(020) 8772 8120* 🖱 *www.crechendo.com*
BRANCHES AT:
  Battersea Arts Centre (rear), Lower Hall, Town Hall Rd SW11
  Putney Leisure Centre, Dryburgh Rd SW15
  Trinity United Reformed Church Hall, Mansel Rd SW19
  Queen of Peace Hall, 222 Sheen Rd TW9
See write-up in west.

Gymboree (Play)
☎ *Play & Music Infoline (0800) 092 0911; Retail Head Office (0116) 282 7400*
🖱 *www.gymboreeplayuk.com*
BRANCHES AT:
  1st Fl, Holmes Place, Battle Close, North Road SW19 ☎ *(020) 8542 4785*
  Exchange Shopping Centre SW15 1TW ☎ *(020) 8780 3831*
See write-up in west.

Tumbletots
Bluebird Park, Bromsgrove Rd, Hunnington, Halesowen West Midlands B62 0TT
☎ *(0121) 585 7003* 🖱 *www.tumbletots.com*
BRANCHES AT:
  Broomwood Methodist Church Hall, Kyrle Rd SW11 ☎ *(020) 8778 3830*
  Kitson Hall, Kitson Rd SW13 ☎ *(01342) 850001*
  Kingswood Halls, Kingswood Place SE3 ☎ *(020) 8778 3830*
  St Faith's Church Hall, Red Fort Hill SE24 ☎ *(020) 8778 3830*
See write-up in west.

4. PLAY CENTRES

Such centres usually resemble indoor adventure playgrounds for toddlers, with ball pits, climbing equipment and so on. Structured activities are not usually provided.

While slightly older children generally adore these, parents often hate them. This is not just because of the noise and crowds, but also because of the business of constant monitoring/protection required especially for younger charges, while allowing them to play. Especially if taking a younger child it is well worth aiming for a quiet time of day.

LISTINGS
CENTRAL

Seymour Leisure Centre
Seymour Place WIH 5TJ ☎ (020) 7723 8019
'The Jungle' is a drop-in zone run by the centre with ball pits, climbing equipment and so on; supervision by its staff; £2; children ages 1-11.

WEST

Bramley's Big Adventure
136 Bramley Rd W10 6TJ ☎ (020) 8960 1515 ⌐ www.bramleysbig.co.uk
Located under the Westway, this drop-in indoor activity playground comprises soft play equipment, a ball pit and a giant climbing frame; separate areas for under-fives and babies; prices start at £2.60 for one hour for under 2s and go up depending on length of session and age of child and on weekends and school holidays; the café stocks baby foods; parents must accompany children. Extra activities and workshops are put on during school holidays. Available for parties. / *HOURS Mon-Sun 10am-6.30pm.*

Brentford Leisure Centre
658 Chiswick High Rd Brentford TW8 0HJ ☎ (020) 8994 9596
The Play Centre is a supervised children's area, although parents are asked to stay; Tues-Thurs 10am-11.30am, 1.15-2.45pm, Sat and Sun 9-11.15am, £1.50 for 45 minutes.

Homefields Under 5s
Homefield Recreation Ground, Chiswick Lane W4 2QA ☎ (020) 8995 4648
Play centre with indoor and outdoor activities; children must be supervised; no charge for kids – adults £1 each. / *HOURS Tue-Thu 1pm-4pm.*

The Life Centre
15 Edge St W8 7PN ☎ (020) 7221 4602 ⌐ www.thelifecentre.com
'Soft gym' for babies; £9.50; must book in advance. / *HOURS Mon-Fri 8am-9pm, Sat & Sun 9.30am-6pm; SEE ALSO 1.04 Antenatal classes; 4.02 Health practitioners.*

Snakes & Ladders
Syon Park Brentford TW8 8JF ☎ (020) 8847 0946 ⌐ www.snakes-and-ladders.co.uk
Large, well-known facility adjoining the grounds of the Brentford stately home. There is a three-tier adventure play zone and separate toddler and intermediate areas; under twos £3; under-fives £4; over-fives £5; After 4:30 (£2, £3, £4); drop-in; parents must stay. / *HOURS Daily 10am-6pm.*

West London YMCA
25 St Mary's Rd W5 5RE ☎ (020) 8799 4800 ⌐ www.westlondonymca.org
'Tinies Tumbles' classes for one to two-year-olds, and 'Crawlers' classes for babies from eight months to a year old, from £46.20 per term (three terms a year). / *HOURS vary, open Mon-Sun.*

NORTH

The Active Birth Centre 🖃
25 Bickerton Rd N19 5JT ☎ (020) 7281 6760 ⌐ www.activebirthcentre.com
Mother and baby movement and gymnastics classes; soft gymnastics for the older baby with postnatal yoga, £10 per class. / *HOURS shop Mon-Fri 9.30am-6.30pm (Fri 4pm), Sat 10am-4pm; SEE ALSO 1.01 Where to have the baby; 1.04 Antenatal classes; 1.06 Birth equipment; 2.01 Postnatal; 2.02 Feeding; 2.03 Baby health; 3.01 Maternity wear; 3.02 Baby equipment; 4.02 Health practitioners; 4.05 Finding out more.*

Clown Town
BRANCHES AT:
222 Green Lanes N13 5UD ☎ (020) 8886 7520
Coppetts Centre, Colney Hatch Lane N12 0AQ ☎ (020) 8361 6600
These two play centres offer soft play, ball pools and slides; separate areas for 'crawlers', toddlers and for under-fives; juice café with high chairs and a baby changing area; £3.50 for two hours, (one hour at weekends/busy periods); free for under ones; drop-in or pre-book; children must be supervised. The N13 branch was previously called Monkey Business. / *HOURS Mon-Sun 10am-7pm; SEE ALSO 0 .*

Fantasy Island
Vale Farm, Watford Rd Wembley HA0 3HG ☎ *(020) 8904 9044*
🖱 *www.wherekidsplay.co.uk*
Drop-in play centre designed to encourage balancing, climbing and other physical
skills; for toddlers to children under 150cm; £3.90 for under-fives, £4.90 for 5+; parental
supervision required. / HOURS *Mon-Sun 9.30am-6.30pm.*

The Fun House
Edmonton Leisure Centre, Plevna Rd N9 0BU ☎ *(020) 8807 0712*
Soft play drop-in centre with a separate under-fives area and an in-house entertainer;
children must be supervised; £3 per session (off peak times £1.75-£2.60). / HOURS *Mon-Sun
10am-7pm.*

Hendon Leisure Centre
Marble Drive NW2 1XQ ☎ *(020) 8455 0818*
Pre-school drop-in gymnastics, for those old enough to walk (up to the age of five);
balls, bouncy areas etc; children must be supervised by a parent or carer; £2.70 per
session. / HOURS *Mon-Sun 9am-10pm (Sat 6pm).*

Moberley Sports & Education Centre
The Quadrant, 101 Kilburn Lane NW10 4AH ☎ *(020) 7641 4807*
A sensory room offers "interactive sound and light environment" plus soft play; £2 per
child. / HOURS *Mon-Fri 9am-10.30pm; Sat-Sun 10am-5.30pm.*

Play Station
2a Brabant Rd N22 6XB ☎ *(020) 8889 0001*
Drop-in play area mostly for older children but with a separate section for under-fives;
café with high chairs and a baby changing area; under twos £2.50 on weekdays, £3 at
weekends. / HOURS *Mon-Sun 10am-7pm.*

Sobell Safari
Sobell Leisure Centre, Hornsey Rd N7 7NY ☎ *(020) 7609 2166* 🖱 *www.aquaterra.org*
Soft adventure drop-in park with slides and swings; separate tiny tots section; £2.50 for
those under one metre tall, £3.50 for those over; supervised, but parents must
stay. / HOURS *Mon-Fri 9.30am-5.30pm (7.15pm-10pm for older children); Sat 9.30am-5.30pm; Sun
9.30am-9.30.*

Tropical Adventure Trail
Lee Valley Leisure Centre, Picketts Lock Lane, Edmonton N9 0AS ☎ *(020) 8345 6666*
🖱 *www.leevalleypark.org.uk*
Play area with ball ponds, slides, swings and bridges, with a separate soft play area and
ball pool for under fours; holiday activities. / HOURS *Mon, Wed & Fri 2pm-6pm, Sat & Sun
11am-4.30pm (Mon-Fri 11am-5pm in school holidays).*

Zoomaround
46 Milton Grove, Stoke Newington N16 8QY ☎ *(020) 7254 2220*
🖱 *www.zoomaround.co.uk*
Adventure play centre open 10am to 6.15pm daily with multi-level play frame with
separate zones for different ages and abilities and a toddler zone for tots; cafe with
home made cakes and fresh meals; 1-3 years £3, 4 years-plus £4 for two-hour session.
Carers must stay. / HOURS *daily 10am-6.15pm.*

SOUTH

Arches Leisure Centre
80 Trafalgar Rd SE10 9UX ☎ *(020) 8317 5020*
'Toddler's World' for children from six months to four years, a drop-in progressive
activity programme for parents and children, designed to improve social and physical
skills; also Gymtots classes, with different levels for crawling and walking (must enrol
for a term); £3.20 (siblings £1.15). / HOURS *Mon-Sun 7am-8pm; SEE ALSO 1.04 Antenatal classes;
2.01 Postnatal.*

Discovery Planet
Surrey Quays Shopping Centre, Redriff Rd SE16 ☎ *(020) 7237 2388*
🖱 *www.surreyquaysshoppingcentre.co.uk/children.html*
A two-storey complex of tunnels and slides with a ball pool; 'Totspot' parent and
toddler group 10am-noon every day, £1.99 including free drinks; '4pm Club' every day
after school, £1.99 includes free burger and chips from Burger King; both clubs
term-time only; party bookings welcomed. / HOURS *Mon-Sun 10am-6pm.*

Furzedown Family Centre
Graveney School Site, Welham Rd SW17 9BU ☎ *(020) 8672 6924*
Fully supervised playgroups, toddler groups and workshops; children under 30 months
must be accompanied. / HOURS *Mon-Fri 9.30am-3.30pm (term time only).*

Kid's Corner
232 Hither Green Lane (cnr George Lane) Lewisham SE13 6RT ☎ (020) 8852 3322
Three-level drop-in play centre in a converted cinema, for children from 12 months
old. Rope bridges, ball pools, drop and tube slides, aerial glides, scramble nets and
separate mini play area; £2.50 for under fours; parental supervision
required. / HOURS *Mon-Sun 10am-7pm.*

The Lollipop Club
*Old Deer Park (London Welsh Rugby Ground) 187 Kew Rd Richmond TW9 2AZ ☎ (020)
8332 7436*
Bouncy castle, ball pond, soft shapes, cars, rocking toys. For 90 minutes, the charge is
£3.50 (under-1s £2). / HOURS *Mon-Fri 10am-5pm (check for early closing).*

Rascals
Waterfront Leisure Centre, High St, Woolwich SE18 6DL ☎ (020) 8317 5000
'Gym Tots' gymnastics classes; £16.50 for five week course; £23.10 for seven week
course; crèche 90p per hour. / HOURS *open all week.*

Spike's Madhouse
Crystal Palace National Sports Centre SE19 2BB ☎ (020) 8778 9876
Under twos can use the soft play area while older children can choose from a vast
selection of sports equipment to play with; only open weekends and school
holidays. / HOURS *Term time Sat-Sun 10am-5pm, Holidays Mon-Sun 10am-5pm (sometimes parties have
exclusive use at weekend, phone for details)* .

The Tiger's Eye
42 Station Rd, Merton SW19 2LP ☎ (020) 8543 1655
Drop-in play area with slides, ball pools, bouncy castle, climbing equipment and
a separate play area for under-fives; £2.25 (£2 off peak and for under twos); parental
supervision required. / HOURS *Tues-Sun 10am-6.30pm; open on Monday during half term and school
holidays.*

Wimbledon Leisure Centre
Latimer Rd SW19 1EW ☎ (020) 8542 1330
'Toddlers World' classes for babies from around four months; drop in (£3.40 per
session); booking advisable; maximum 20 per class; carer must stay. / HOURS *Mon-Fri 7am-
approx 10pm; Sat 8am-5pm; Sun 8am-7pm.*

EAST

Atherton Leisure Centre
189 Romford Rd E15 4JF ☎ (020) 8536 5500
'Rascals' play area under parent supervision for under eights, including a ball pool;
£1.25 per hour. / HOURS *open all week.*

Kidsmania
28 Powell Rd E5 8DJ ☎ (020) 8533 5556 ⏱ www.kidsmania.uk
Climbing, balancing, crawling, jumping and sliding for children up to the age of 12;
£3.50 for 90 minutes' play; parental supervision required. / HOURS *Mon-Sun 10am-7pm.*

5. MUSIC (& DANCING) CLASSES

(For music tapes to play at home, see chapter 3.07 Books, music & videos.)
Babies exposed to music and songs often learn to sing before they can
talk. Indeed, all babies seem to have some innate musical ability and music
may help development in other areas, particularly language and mathe-
matics. Some researchers believe music is a catalyst for enhancing all
aspects of a child's development: physical, emotional and intellectual,
strengthening the connection between the two sides of the brain. If nothing else, singing simple songs helps a child develop speech and a sense of
rhythm.

It is apparently true that babies are born with perfect pitch (to help
with language). This is generally lost but musical stimulus might go some
way to help preserve their innate musical capacity.

Music is the kind of activity where it's easy to DIY in the home – all
you need is to know a few nursery tunes or to buy a few tapes and sing
along. However out of key, the human voice is the sound young babies
like best.

Colourstrings – one of the more serious systems of musical teaching for this age group – recommends that parents play babies and children classical music or unaccompanied or simple songs and tunes arguing that frenetic pop is too busy for small children, making them switch off to sound. (There is other research, though, that indicates that babies and toddlers respond most swiftly to music of all types with a preference for what they know, regardless of type.)

Many mothers, however, lack the confidence in their own musical abilities and prefer to rely on courses. Most music classes consist of action songs with accompaniment by a piano, guitar or sometimes a changing instrument every week. Sometimes there are instruments for babies and toddlers to play around with.

Note that music classes for young babies should be held by a woman if, as is usual, there is any singing. The lower pitch of a man's voice is such that babies cannot hear and fully react to it. A woman's voice is generally closer to their own range of around five notes.

MUSIC RESOURCES

BBC Parents' Music Room
⌂ www.bbc.co.uk/music/parents
Provides guidance for parents and teachers of children from nursery rhymes onwards, encouraging exploration of all aspects of music with the children and with material available on-line to help with this.

MES (Music Education Supplies)
101 Banstead Road South, Sutton Surrey SM2 5LH ☎ *(020) 8770 3866*
One of the best sources of musical instruments and related items, offering a vast selection of beating instruments, including both wood and metal xylophones, bar chimes, and a variety of maracas and similar. Prices start at £2.35 for a wrist bell – 15 player set £40. / HOURS Mon-Fri 9am-5pm; SEE ALSO 3.07 Books, music & videos.

READING

The Mozart Effect for Chldren – Don Campbell (Awakening your child's mind, health and creativity with music; Hodder Mobius; 2002; £10; 0-340-82091-8) – *Lots of intriguing information about music and the development of the brain. It includes a lists of suggested Mozart pieces for pregnancy, babies, infants and so on.*

LISTINGS

CENTRAL

Chamber Tots
Wigmore Hall, 36 Wigmore St W1H 0BP ☎ *Box office (020) 7935 2141, Education dept (020) 7258 8240, General (020) 7258 8200* ⌂ *www.wigmore-hall.org.uk*
Popular series of hour long midweek sessions for 2-5 year olds, 2-3 yrs 10am-11am, 3-5yrs 11.30am-12.30pm (twice a term) and 2-5 yrs 11am-12pm(three times per term); a short, 10-minute concert is followed by a workshop with instruments; book well ahead.

Monkey Music
PO Box 108, Harpenden Herts AL5 5ZG ☎ *(01582) 766464*
⌂ *www.monkeymusic.co.uk*
BRANCHES AT:
  St Peter's Church SW1 ☎ *(020) 8768 9827*
  St Michael's Church, Chester Sq SW1 ☎ *(020) 8768 9827*
Founded by Angie Davies in '92 (who runs the Chelsea classes) – a growing business run by franchisees at various venues across London. 'Heigh ho' is suitable for children from the age of six months; sessions include action songs and rhymes, musical games, music and movement, storytelling with instrumental accompaniment and the use of percussion instruments. 'Jiggety jig' is for slightly older children; new venues in Putney, Barnes and Fulham are promised as we go to press.

Music & Movement
Abbey Community Centre, 34 Great Smith St SW1 3BU ☎ *(020) 7222 0303*
Dancing, actions and singing to music, £1 for local residents, £1.50 non-members. / HOURS Phone during office hours.

WEST

Action Kids
Middlesex UB6 8AX ☎ *(07946) 707695*
BRANCHES AT:
  Priory Community Centre W3
  Chiswick Town Hall, Heathfield Terrace W4
Fun, interactive music and movement classes designed to improve co-ordination, sensory perception and motor skills: 'parachute' games, ball skills, etc using simple play equipment; children are divided into two age groups (nine to 18 months, and 18 months up to four years old). Drop-in sessions and structured classes: classes £4; drop-in £4 (Acton, Mon & Wed afternoons) and £5 (Chiswick, Wed morning); reductions for siblings; no booking necessary; call Amanda for further details.

Bea's Baby Music School
186 Casefield Rd SE27 0SZ ☎ *(020) 8670 9378* ✍ *www.babymusic.co.uk*
BRANCHES AT:
  First Step Dance Studios, 234 Lillie Rd SW6 7QA
  The Hut Community Centre, Alph Place (off Flood Street) SW3
Classes for babies from 6 months old; the aim is to boost a child's repertoire to at least 20 songs to sing at home (and one suitable for public hearing) by the age of three-and-a-half. A singer, pianist and guitarist help children to sing along to songs and nursery rhymes, with accordions, brass and wind instruments and a large selection of percussion instruments; courses are typically £40-£60 depending on the length of the term and location; cassettes available for home practice.

Blueberry Playsongs
☎ *(020) 8677 6871* ✍ *www.blueberry.clara.co.uk*
BRANCHES AT:
  Chelsea Methodist Church, 155a King's Rd SW3
  Holy Innocents Church, Paddenswick Rd W6
  Etheline Holder Hall, 5b Denbigh Rd W11
A music group for babies and children from nine months to four years old, aiming to stimulate and encourage fun with music through singing, action songs, participating in activities to develop rhythm and playing little instruments. Venues in Clapham, Putney and Chelsea.

Boogie Mites
☎ *(020) 8767 1352* ✍ *www.boogiemites.com*
BRANCHES AT:
  Brompton Library, Old Brompton Rd SW5
  Matthews Hall, Margravane Road W6
  Kings Hall, Corner of New Kings Road and Chipstead Street SW6
  Tabernacle, Powys Square W11
  Chiswick Town Hall, Heathfield Terrace W4
Original music, traditional children's songs, percussion, toys, books and costumes at Swiss Cottage, Highgate, Kensington, Notting Hill, Hammersmith, Knightsbridge and Chiswick.

Cadenza
Ealing Town Hall, Uxbridge Rd, New Broadway W5 ☎ *(020) 8567 9297*
Drop-in classes of music and movement for children under five, designed to encourage basic music skills with puppets, tapes, instruments, etc; £5 per session, £2.50 for siblings.Classes are also held at Bob's Studio, Bath Road, Chiswick and St. Francis Church Notting Hill.

Monkey Music
PO Box 108, Harpenden Herts AL5 5ZG ☎ *(01582) 766464*
✍ *www.monkeymusic.co.uk*
BRANCHES AT:
  Ashburnham Community Centre, Tetcott Rd SW10 0SH ☎ *(01582) 766464*
  Etheline Holder Hall, 5b-7 Denbigh Rd W11 ☎ *(01582) 766464*
  St Joseph's Church, Bolton Rd W4 ☎ *(020) 8847 4031*
  Mission Hall, St Dionis Rd, Parsons Green SW6 ☎ *(020) 8480 6064*
  Sst Stephen's Church, Southwell Gardens SW7 ☎ *(020) 8768 9827*
  Brompton Library, Old Brompton Road SW5 ☎ *(020) 8768 9827*
  St Joseph's Church W4 ☎ *(020) 8847 4031*
See write-up in central.

Lottie Moore
8 Hammersmith Terrace W6 9TS ☎ *(020) 8748 4823*
Rhythm, drums and nursery rhymes; morning classes on Mon and Wed (10am-10.30am) for toddlers, ages 2 to 3 (£1.30 per session).

Music & Song for Tiny Tots
Pitshanger Lane Methodist Church Hall, Pitshanger Lane W5 ☎ *(020) 8866 3813*
Barbara Young's classes were some of the first in the country for newborns and have
featured in the press, and in TV programmes on the subject. She introduces babies to
music, rhythm percussion, speech development and dance. There are classes for
children from birth to one year old, and from one to four years old. / HOURS *flexible.*

Music for Toddlers
Applegarth Studio, Augustine Rd W14 0HZ ☎ *(020) 7603 3602*
Classes for children from seven months old, accompanied by an adult; nursery rhymes,
action songs, percussion, lullabies, and singing; £10 per class, bookable in blocks or
individually (concessions available); phone for details. / HOURS *flexible; answerphone.*

Music House
Bush Hall, 310 Uxbridge Rd W12 7LJ ☎ *(020) 8932 2652*
🖑 *www.musichouseforchildren.com*
Bush Hall – a new musical venue in Shepherd's Bush – offers (as well as 200 music
teachers for older children) music & movement and music & appreciation classes for
toddlers (with the ability to play with different instruments); £5 drop-in music and
movement, £7 music appreciation. / HOURS *Mon-Fri 9.30am-6pm.*

Music Time
38 Morland Close, Hampton Middx TW12 3YY ☎ *(020) 8979 8923*
Nicola Garty runs classes in Chiswick, Grove Park and Hampton suitable for kids from
one year old – action songs, nursery rhymes, movement to music and using percussion
instruments; £40-£50 for term.

Muzsika
23 Crediton Hill NW6 1HS ☎ *(020) 7794 4848*
BRANCHES AT:
  The Kensington Leisure Centre, Walmer Road, Notting Hill W11
For children aged six months–five years, a programme of workshops (apparently based
on the teachings of various music educators) featuring singing (from blue and The
Beatles to Britten and Byrd), dancing, and play with instruments; 12-weeks £105
including a registration fee of £15.

Paint Pots
Montessori School, Chelsea Community Church, Edith Road SW10 0LB ☎ *(020) 7376
4571*
BRANCHES AT:
  Bayswater United Reform Church, Newton Rd W2 5LS
  Ashburnham Community Centre, Tetcott Road SW10 0SB
'Music and art' classes, £165 per term; must be pre-booked.

Snips
The Crypt, St John's Church, Broomfield Place W13 9LA ☎ *(020) 8840 0651*
'Music and Movement' classes on Tuesdays and Thursdays, for children from newborn
to five, £2 for 30 minutes; no need to book. / HOURS *Tue-Thu 10am-1pm; SEE ALSO 3.04 Baby
clothes; 3.06 Toys; 3.11 Hairdressers.*

Waterman's Arts Centre
40 High St Brentford TW8 0DS ☎ *(020) 8232 1020* 🖑 *www.watermans.org.uk*
Thames-side art centre which runs a regular 'Pandemonium' class with instruments
and songs (£4.50, concessions). / HOURS *daily from 12pm-9pm.*

West London YMCA
25 St Mary's Rd W5 5RE ☎ *(020) 8799 4800* 🖑 *www.westlondonymca.org*
Action Songs & Rhymes classes, from £46.20 (three terms a year). / HOURS *vary, open Mon-
Sun.*

Whippersnappers
72a Hayter Rd SW2 5AB
BRANCHES AT:
  Youth Hostel, Holland Park W8
Classes run on both a booked and drop-in basis, and are split into babies (0-15 months)
and toddlers (15 months – 3 years); workshops last for one hour and include African
drumming, singing, percussion, puppets, and "general theatricality"; primarily
term-time, but also holiday activities on different timetable (and birthday parties).

NORTH

Boogie Mites
☎ *(020) 8767 1352* ⏁ *www.boogiemites.com*

BRANCHES AT:
Swiss Cottage Community Centre, Winchester Rd NW3
Highgate Newton Community Centre, Bertram St N19
See write-up in west.

Colourstrings Music Kindergarten
☎ South London *(020) 8547 3073*, North London *(020) 8444 9435* ⏁ *www.web-marketing.co.uk/colourstrings*

BRANCHES AT:
Hornsey Parish Church, Park Rd N10 ☎ *(020) 8444 9435*
Suitable from the age of six months, this musical organisation is based on the teaching methods of two Hungarian brothers and was one of the first educational groups of its kind in the UK. Children learn about rhythm, pitch, dynamics, melody, tempo, character, form and style with nursery rhymes, percussion instruments, listening and movement. Introduction to Music classes are run for children aged from 18 months. From age two the same system teaches musical notation and inner musical hearing. There are classes on most days, for about £6 each (payable termly).

Crochets & Quavers
Our Lady of Muswell Church Hall, Colney Hatch Lane N10 ☎ *(020) 8883 2076*
Music classes for children from eight months old, £4 on Monday mornings; classes also held in Southgate on Monday afternoons, £4.

Harringay Club
50 Tottenham Lane N8 7EE ☎ *(020) 8348 2124* ⏁ *www.harringayclub.org.uk*
Music and Song, and Music and Movement classes, both suitable for children over six months' old; £3.50 non-members, £2 members (£25 membership). / HOURS Mon-Sun 9am-5pm; SEE ALSO 2.01 Postnatal.

Monkey Music
PO Box 108, Harpenden Herts AL5 5ZG ☎ *(01582) 766464*
⏁ *www.monkeymusic.co.uk*

BRANCHES AT:
Primrose Hill Community Centre, 29 Hopkinsons Place, Fitzroy Rd NW1 8TN
☎ *(01727) 768665*
Quaker Friends Meeting House, 120 Heath St NW3 1DR ☎ *(01727) 768665*
St Anne's & St Andrew's Church Hall, Salusbury Rd NW6 ☎ *(01727) 768665*
St Andrew's Church Hall, Alexandra Park Rd N10 ☎ *(020) 8883 1161*
Friends Meeting House, Church Crescent N10 ☎ *(020) 8883 1161*
St Mary's Parish Hall, 30 Hendon Lane N3 ☎ *(020) 8883 1161*
Holy Trinity Church, Granville Rd N4 ☎ *(020) 8883 1161*
Hornsey Vale Community Centre, Mayfield Rd N8 ☎ *(020) 8883 1161*
Bourne Methodist Church, The Bourne N14 6RS ☎ *(020) 8883 1161*
East Finchley Methodist Church, High Road (opposite Creighton Avenue) N2
☎ *(020) 8883 1161*
See write-up in central.

Musical Minis
80 Moss Lane, Pinner Middlesex HA5 3AU ☎ *(020) 8868 0001*
⏁ *www.musicalminis.co.uk*
From six months, introducing music and percussion using everything from jazz to classical, with instruments, puppets and learning songs; 45 minute classes (max15 per class); call the Head Office number (listed) for details of where the NW London (Hatch End, Mill Hill) and Watford branches meet. / HOURS Mon-Fri 9am-6pm.

Muzsika
23 Crediton Hill NW6 1HS ☎ *(020) 7794 4848*

BRANCHES AT:
The Liberal Jewish Synagogue, 28 St John's Wood Rd NW8
See write-up in west.

Rucksack Music Inc.
☎ *(020) 8806 9335, (07957) 608151* ⏁ *www.rucksackmusic.co.uk*

BRANCHES AT:
Lauderdale Community Arts Centre N6
St James's Church Hall, Prebend St N1
Muswell Hill Community Centre N10
Union Church, Weston Rd N8
St Mary's Catholic Church, 279 High Rd N2
Trinity Church Centre, 15 Nether St N12

Walker Hall, Christchurch Parich Centre, Waterfall Rd N14
Musical sessions for babies up to three years old, using percussion instruments, singing, clapping etc; £3.50 per child; reduced rates for siblings.

Tamar Swade
215a Chevening Rd, Queen's Park NW6 ☎ *(020) 7267 0474*
Runs 'Hopscotch' once per week for 0-2 years (there is also a class for older kids); £5, concessions.

Tick Tock Music Group (under 5s)
☎ *(020) 7359 9495*
BRANCHES AT:
St Stephen's Church Hall, 17 Canonbury Rd N1 ☎ *(020) 7359 9495*
St Mary's Neighbourhood Centre, Upper St N1 ☎ *(020) 7359 9495*
Friends Meeting House, Church Crescent N10 ☎ *(020) 8348 9946*
Hornsey Vale Community Centre, Mayfield Rd N8 ☎ *(020) 8348 9946*
Classes run by actors, musicians and singers who put on what amounts to a show for parents and children. Nursery rhymes, action songs and participation are all involved in the sessions, suitable for children as young as four months old.

Tuneful Tots
23 Brookside, East Barnet Herts EN4 8TT ☎ *(020) 8447 3795* ✇ *www.tunefultots.co.uk*
Sessions with action songs, games, movement and percussion instruments; suitable for babies from six months to five years; classes currently held in East Barnet, Enfield, Finchley, Hampstead, High Barnet and Wanstead; introductory lesson free.

Very Little People Make Music
N8/N5/N16 ☎ *(020) 8340 4512*
Drop in music and movement groups for babies and pre-school children at Crouch End, Stoke Newington and Highbury. / HOURS *flexible.*

SOUTH

Bea's Baby Music School
186 Casefield Rd SE27 0SZ ☎ *(020) 8670 9378* ✇ *www.babymusic.co.uk*
BRANCHES AT:
Putney Leisure Centre, Dryburgh Rd SW15
St Lukes Community Hall, Ramsden Rd SW12
See write-up in west.

Blueberry Playsongs
☎ *(020) 8677 6871* ✇ *www.blueberry.clara.co.uk*
BRANCHES AT:
The Contact Centre, 60 Hambalt Rd SW4
Putney Community Church, Werter Rd SW15
Queen of Peace Church, 222 Sheen Rd Richmond TW10
Holy Trinity Church, 234 The Broadway SW19
The Garage Studio, 26 Priests Bridge SW19
19-21 Station Rd SW13
See write-up in west.

Boogie Mites
☎ *(020) 8767 1352* ✇ *www.boogiemites.com*
BRANCHES AT:
Balham Library Hall, Ramsden Road SW12
Alvering Library, Allfarthing Lane SW18
Wimbledon Community Centnre, 28 St Georges Rd SW19
Southfields Library, Wimbledon Park Road SW19
See write-up in west.

Bookspread
Trident Business Centre, Bickersteth Rd SW17 9SH ☎ *(020) 8767 6377/4551*
✇ *www.bookspread.co.uk*
Baby and toddler nursery rhyme/music sessions, and 'Learning Together' for kids and mums. / HOURS *Mon-Fri 9.30am-5.30pm, Sat 9.30am-3.30pm;* SEE ALSO *3.07 Books, music & videos.*

Colourstrings Music Kindergarten
☎ *South London (020) 8547 3073, North London (020) 8444 9435* ✇ *www.web-marketing.co.uk/colourstrings*
BRANCHES AT:
St Matthias Centre, Church Rd Richmond ☎ *(020) 8948 2066*
Southlands College, 65 Wimbledon Parkside SW19 ☎ *(020) 8547 3073*

Christchurch Hall, Cottenham Park Rd, Raynes Park SW20 ☎ *(020) 8547 3073 or (020) 8444 9435*
See write-up in north.

Latchmere Leisure Centre
Burns Rd SW11 2DY ☎ *(020) 7207 8004*
Drop-in music and movement classes from three months to four years several times per week, £2.50; also school holiday activities.

Monkey Music
PO Box 108, Harpenden Herts AL5 5ZG ☎ *(01582) 766464*
⊕ *www.monkeymusic.co.uk*
BRANCHES AT:
St Luke's Church, The Avenue Richmond TW9 ☎ *(020) 8847 4031*
Ackroyd Community Centre, Ackroyd Rd SE23 ☎ *(020) 8764 5185*
St Bartholomew's Church, Westwood Hill SE26 ☎ *(020) 8764 5185*
St Barnabas Church, Calton Avenue SE21 ☎ *(020) 8764 5185*
Goose Green Community Centre, 62a East Dulwich Rd SE22 ☎ *(020) 8764 5185*
Garfield Community Centre, 64 Garfield Rd SW11 ☎ *(020) 8699 0977*
St James's Community Centre, Ouseley Rd SW12 ☎ *(020) 8699 0977*
Wilditch Community Centre, Culvert SW11 ☎ *(020) 8699 0977*
St Stephen's Parish Church, Weir Rd SW12 ☎ *(020) 8699 0977*
Holy Trinity Church, Rookery Rd SW4 ☎ *(020) 8699 0977*
The Contact Centre, 60 Hambalt Rd SW4 ☎ *(020) 8699 0977*
Putney Arts Theatre, Ravenna Rd SW15 6AW ☎ *(020) 8480 6064*
St Michael's Church Hall, Elm Bank Gardens SW13 0NX ☎ *(020) 8480 6064*
Bruce Hall, All Saints Parish Centre, Brudenell Rd SW17 ☎ *(020) 8764 5185*
Streatham Leisure Centre, 384 Streatham High St SW16 ☎ *(020) 8764 5185*
Earlsfield Library, Magdalen Rd SW18 ☎ *(020) 8764 5185*
Trinity Road Chapel, 207 Trinity Rd SW17 ☎ *(020) 8764 5185*
The Central London Golf Centre, Burntwood Lane SW17 ☎ *(020) 8764 5185*
St Oswald's Church Hall, Green Lane SW16 ☎ *(020) 8764 5185*
St Mary's Parish Hall, Church Path SW19 ☎ *(020) 8764 5185*
Holy Trinity Church, The Broadway SW19 ☎ *(020) 8764 5185*
Trinity United Reformed Church Hall, Mansel Rd SW19 ☎ *(020) 8764 5185*
Herne Hill United Church, Red Post Hill SE24 ☎ *(020) 8764 5185*
See write-up in central.

Music Makers
Holy Trinity Church, Rookery Rd SW4 ☎ *(020) 7587 1560*
Caroline Newton runs pre-school creative music groups (in Clapham and Stockwell) with singing, moving, marching and dancing to piano, flute and recorded music – percussion instruments for everyone; under-twos, £3.50; classes are 40 minutes long.

Musical Express
20 Dawlish Ave SW18 4RW ☎ *(020) 8946 6043* ⊕ *www.musicalexpress.co.uk*
Forty-minute classes for under twos, one hour for over twos in Wimbledon, Wimbledon Park, Putney and Barnes; parents or carers are actively involved; about £5.

Rucksack Music Inc.
☎ *(020) 8806 9335, (07957) 608151* ⊕ *www.rucksackmusic.co.uk*
BRANCHES AT:
Anerley Town Hall, Anerley Rd SE20
St John's CofE Church SE20
"The Nettlefold", West Norwood Library, 1 Norwood High St SE27
See write-up in north.

Tick Tock Music Group (under 5s)
☎ *(020) 7359 9495*
BRANCHES AT:
Martin Way Methodist Church, Morden Surrey SW20 ☎ *(020) 8942 7147*
United Reformed Church, New Malden Surrey KT3 ☎ *(020) 8942 7147*
See write-up in north.

Whippersnappers
72a Hayter Rd SW2 5AB
BRANCHES AT:
Brockwell Lido, Brockwell Park, Dulwich Rd SE24 0PA ☎ *(020) 7738 6633*
See write-up in west.

EAST

Rucksack Music Inc.
☎ *(020) 8806 9335, (07957) 608151* ⌂ *www.rucksackmusic.co.uk*
BRANCHES AT:
   The John Smith Children's Resource Centre, 90 Stepney Way E1
   Springfield Park Cafe, The West Room, Springfield Ppark E5
See write-up in north.

DANCE CLASSES
Most music classes incorporate some kind of movement as part of each session. Usually this is incidental, but there are classes where the aim is actually to lay the foundations for learning dance.

NORTH

Dazu
Unit 9, Claverings Industrial Estate, Centre Way, Montagu Road, Edmonton N9 0AP
☎ *(020) 8373 2718 Contact Lisa* ⌂ *www.dazu.co.uk*
Pre-school dance, songs and stories plus arts and crafts activities; Dazu welcomes children with special needs and offer concessions; otherwise prices range from £2-£5.

Harringay Club
50 Tottenham Lane N8 7EE ☎ *(020) 8348 2124* ⌂ *www.harringayclub.org.uk*
Ballet classes for toddlers and their carers; £3.50 non-members, £2 members (membership £25). / HOURS Mon-Sun 9am-5pm; SEE ALSO 2.01 Postnatal.

Ready, Steady, Go
Primrose Hill Community Centre, 29 Hopkinsons Place, Fitzroy Rd NW1 8JA ☎ *(020) 7586 5862*
A 'creative workshop' integrating dance, drama, music and storytelling; £80, per term. / HOURS wed.

SOUTH

Karen Forbes School of Dancing
St Mary's Parish Church Hall, Church Path, Merton Park SW20 ☎ *(020) 8949 7896*
Classes in Merton Park and Wimbledon, for children from 18 months old; simple movement classes for younger children – choice of ballet, modern or tap at the age of three.

6. SWIMMING CLASSES
As with gym-type activities, swimming sessions appear to improve children's general co-ordination. Fans also claim benefits relating to greater fitness and strength, while the experience of just floating is reportedly beneficial for babies with physical or behavioural difficulties.

Water safety is another important benefit. Developing a sense of ease in water means that should your child accidentally fall into a pool or river, they are less likely to panic before help arrives. Serious classes include practice that leads eventually to getting to the side and climbing out in every lesson.

Swimming unaided requires that a child has reached a certain mental and physical level. Though many courses are available for six-month olds, according to the Amateur Swimming Association it is rare for children actually to learn to swim before they are three or four years old. Practitioners of underwater swimming argue that even little babies can swim efficiently, albeit under the surface.

Most classes involve parents singing nursery rhymes at the same time as helping their offspring make swimming actions: as confidence grows, activities become more ambitious.

Operators of some courses – particularly those aimed at young babies – explicitly avoid the use of buoyancy aids. These classes encourage holding the babies briefly underwater, stimulating the automatic reflex by which they hold their breath and keep their eyes open. Unless used regularly, this reflex is lost well before a child can consciously learn to swim, and some proponents of this system believe that stimulating it has long term benefits.

The Amateur Swimming Association and the Institute of Swimming Teachers and Coaches have no problem with the use of buoyancy aids and make no special feature of under-water activities. The emphasis of mainstream coaching is to use a variety of techniques to build confidence and experience of moving in the water. (There are, however, specific doubts about floating baby seats, which are actually banned in some countries because of the danger of tipping up and drowning).

Even for babies and toddlers, courses often follow school term times. For under-twos, weekend sessions are relatively thin on the ground – a frustration for many working parents. Classes get more booked up in summer, and good ones are always heavily booked, so book ahead.

The smaller the class the better as swimming pools can get noisy even when, as is ideal, the class has exclusive use. Twelve is around the optimal maximum.

Tips

➢ Practise first in the bath.
➢ Avoid baggy swimwear which can get in the child's way, or general purpose nappies which get water-logged.
➢ Take a towel to the pool's edge to wrap up as soon as your child is out of the water.
➢ Tilt the child's head when they get out, to drain the ears.
➢ Take snacks and drinks for toddlers and for babies a bottle (or expect to breast-feed soon afterwards).
➢ If the pool is chlorinated, rinse your child's skin carefully after swimming to protect against drying, and consider using some moisturising oil or similar product afterwards.
➢ Think about a trip to the pool just to watch first.

SWIMMING COSTUMES

(See also chapter 3.04 Baby clothes for swimwear stockists.)

There is a growing range of swimming costumes available for babies which incorporate nappies. A costume which is simply tight enough around the legs to trap any debris seems a sufficient solution to some parents and teachers. See below for listings of specialist swimwear and swim nappy suppliers.

VACCINATIONS

Some pools state that they only allow babies in the water after they have had their first set of vaccinations (though the extent to which there is any serious effort to enforce such rules is a different matter all together). This is also the Amateur Swimming Association recommendation.

The Aquababies (see listings below) website states that they know of no cases of a baby contracting diptheria, whooping cough, tetanus or polio from a well-maintained, chlorinated pool. Like other experts in the field, the company also states that medical reports indicate that it is "perfectly acceptable for a baby who has not been immunised to swim in a chlorinated pool".

TAPES

[Video] **Water Babies with Sharron Davies** (£8.99) – *From Granada's This Morning, with Sharron Davies and her baby, plus other mothers and babies; tips on how to introduce infants to the water. / Granada TV, PO Box 161, Radlett, Herts WD7 8ED.*

Water Baby! – Lauren Heston & Zena Holloway (Element; 1999; £9.99; 1902618513) – *A 15-week programme of water exercises to build confidence and skills, exploring a baby's natural affinity for water.*

USEFUL CONTACTS

Amateur Swimming Association (ASA), ☎ (01509) 618 700

The national governing body for swimming and water sports. Courses and ability awards are available for babies over three months old (ideally three weeks after polio jab); the youngest category is Ducklings, in which the basics of swimming are taught – entering and exiting the water safely, going under water, blowing bubbles, kicking and using floats. Classes run for babies at Crystal Palace are £38.50 for an 11-week course.

SWIMMING KIT

Anorak Lakes Ltd

Central Buildings, Ambleside Cumbria LA22 9BS ☎ *(01539) 432235*
🖰 *www.anorakonline.co.uk*
Wet suits, Polyotter float suits and swim shoes. / HOURS Mon-Sun 9.30am-5.30pm; SEE ALSO *3.04 Baby clothes.*

Baby Flair

PO Box 3, North Cave, Brough East Yorkshire HU15 2WU ☎ *(0870) 246 1875*
🖰 *www.babyflair.co.uk*
Swimsuits for boys and girls, including with integral nappy. / SEE ALSO *3.03 Nursery decor.*

Bambino Mio

12 Staveley Way Northampton, Brixworth NN6 9EU ☎ *(01604) 883777*
🖰 *www.bambino.co.uk*
Stock swim nappies made of swimming costume fabric, with a waterproof polyester outer and leak-proof legs and waistband. / HOURS Mon-Fri 9am-5.30pm, or answerphone; SEE ALSO *3.08 Nappies.*

Bug Circus

153 Church Rd London SW13 9HR ☎ *(020) 8741 4244* 🖰 *www.kidsnclothes.co.uk*
Bambino Mio swimming nappies and Aquanappies. / HOURS Mon-Sat 10am-6pm (open Sun, Nov & Dec); SEE ALSO *3.04 Baby clothes; 3.06 Toys.*

Cotton Bottoms

7-9 Water Lane Industrial Estate, Waterlane, Storrington W Sussex RH20 3XX
☎ *(0870) 777 8899* 🖰 *www.cottonbottoms.co.uk*
Swim nappies. / HOURS Mon-Fri 9am-5.30pm; SEE ALSO *3.08 Nappies.*

Eco-Babes

17b Paradise Road, Downham Market Norfolk PE38 9HS ☎ *(01366) 387851*
🖰 *www.eco-babes.co.uk*
Swim nappies. / HOURS Mon-Sat 8.30am-6pm; SEE ALSO *3.04 Baby clothes; 3.08 Nappies.*

Flap Happy

☎ *(01494) 447000*
Distribute swimwear, including swim nappies, in bright prints and plains. / HOURS Mon-Fri 9am-5pm; SEE ALSO *3.04 Baby clothes.*

Floaties

Styrox (UK) Limited Aldershot GU12 4NL ☎ *(01252) 316626* 🖰 *www.styrox.co.uk*
Buoyancy aids from arm bands to more sophisticated inflatables for fun and to aid learning to swim; also nappies, paddling pools, beach balls and UV gear and swimming nappies; call for stockists or order direct online.

Funkidry

PO Box 246 Southampton SO32 2YL ☎ *(0870) 777 4334* 🖰 *www.funkidry.co.uk*
Designed by a keen swimmer for her own children, a flat towel with a slash and a hood in the middle and toggles down the side to turn it into a beach robe. Designs for children include a dinosaur (green, with spikes, a princess (pink with wings), duck, frog, along with plain colours. Sizes are suitable from around 18 months up to adult. Prices start around £17.50.

Incy Wincy

18 Oregon Avenue, Tilehurst Berks RG31 6RZ ☎ *(0118) 377 3581*
🖰 *www.incywincy.org*
The catalogue's heading, 'Swimming products for kids' accurately sums up the proposition – aquanappies, swim nappies, buoyancy aids, swim caps and goggles from brands such as Floaties and Kooshies. / SEE ALSO *3.04 Baby clothes.*

Kooshies
Head Office: 37 Rothschild Rd, London W4 5HJ; Warehouse PO Box 333 Gateshead NE10 8YQ ☎ *(0870) 607 0545, PHP (0870) 122 0215* ⏃ *www.phpbaby.com, www.kooshies.com*
Swim nappies. / HOURS *9am-6pm; SEE ALSO 3.08 Nappies.*

Little Dippers
PO Box 3223 Brighton BN1 3TY ☎ *(0870) 758 0302* ⏃ *www.littledippers.co.uk, www.littledippersfilms.co.uk, www.babyswimshop.co.uk*
On-line sales of Aqua nappies, flotation aids, rafts, toys, and books; also 'Waterbabies' (video or DVD) with Lauren Heston, which is based on the Little Dippers classes but starting with simple and fun exercises in the bath. Price £17.49 inc p&p for the video, £21.49 for the DVD. / HOURS *Mon-Fri 10am-4pm, Sat & Sun 10am-2pm.*

Marketing Mania Ltd
Unit 2 Aurattse, 53 Old Ridge Rd London SW12 8PP ☎ *(07002) 466466, Stockist enquiries line (08700) 706 060* ⏃ *www.goo-goo.com*
'Sposh' (known outside the UK as Ozone) swimming gear – caps, hats, suits and swim nappies. / SEE ALSO *3.04 Baby clothes; 3.05 Shoes.*

Modern Baby
Brooksby, 70 Tamworth Rd, Hertford Herts SG13 7DN ☎ *(01992) 505976*
⏃ *www.modernbaby.co.uk*
Swim nappies and tote bags. / HOURS *Office Hours & Sat; SEE ALSO 3.08 Nappies.*

PHP
Head Office: 37 Rothschild Rd, London W4 5HJ; Warehouse PO Box 333 Gateshead NE10 8YQ ☎ *Catalogue requests (0870) 607 0545, Office (0870 122 0215)*
⏃ *www.thebabycatalogue.com, www.phpbaby.com*
Wide range of Beach Club equipment which provides everything to do with swimming; swim nappies (four sizes) and rubber-soled beach shoes (suitable from three months). / HOURS *Mon-Fri 10am-5pm; SEE ALSO 3.02 Baby equipment; 3.04 Baby clothes; 3.06 Toys.*

Snuggle Naps
2 Daybrook St, Sherwood Notts NG5 2HD ☎ *(0115) 910 7220*
⏃ *www.snugglenaps.co.uk*
Swim pants and nappies. / HOURS *Mon-Fri 8.30am-4.30pm; SEE ALSO 3.02 Baby equipment; 3.08 Nappies.*

Splash About
2 impasse Desbordes, Ransanne, 16200 Foussignac, France ☎ *00 33 5 45 81 03 59*
⏃ *www.SplashAbout.net*
Produces a Warm in Water range for 0-12 years which open flat to make easy to put on and take off, with wide Velcro strips to adjust in size. Also Water Buddies buoyancy range for 1-8 years, adapted for special needs if required.

Weenees
General enquiries
☎ *(01736) 799512*
An Australian brand of disposable nappies, that also makes swim nappies; website www.eenee.com.au – available from Lollipop (details given). / SEE ALSO *3.08 Nappies.*

LISTINGS

CENTRAL

Aquababies
☎ *(020) 7702 4888* ⏃ *www.aquababiesltd.co.uk*
BRANCHES AT:
Oasis Sports Centre, Endell St WC2H 9AG
No flotation devices are used when teaching a child to swim at these classes, which run from birth to age four, and which make much of a babies' instinct as newborns to hold their breath underwater.

Swimming Nature
HQ: 35 Lonsdale Rd NW6 ☎ *(0870) 900 8002* ⏃ *www.swimmingnature.co.uk*
BRANCHES AT:
Queen Mother Sports Centre, 223 Vauxhall Bridge Rd SW1
Swimming school which provides pre-school classes and individual tuition for children from three months; they operate at the Queen Mother Sports Centre in Victoria, and in Notting Hill, Chelsea and Regent's Park. The website is a well-organised resource with information on all the pools.

WEST

Aquababies
☎ *(020) 7702 4888* ⌂ *www.aquababiesltd.co.uk*
BRANCHES AT:
  Kensington Sports Centre W11
  Gurnell Leisure Centre, Ruislip Rd East W13 0AL
  Chelsea & Westminster Hospital SW10
See write-up in central.

Brentford Leisure Centre
658 Chiswick High Rd Brentford TW8 0HJ ☎ *(020) 8994 9596*
Swimming lessons for babies from six months to five years old.

Chelsea Sports Centre
Chelsea Manor St SW3 5PL ☎ *(020) 7352 6985*
Lessons for children under five, £33 for 12 sessions. / SEE ALSO 1.04 *Antenatal classes.*

Halliwick Association of Swimming Therapy
c/o Adka Centre, Whitstable House, Silchester Rd W10 6SB ☎ *(020) 8968 7609*
⌂ *www.halliwick.org.uk*
The club promotes swimming teaching for those with special needs of all ages. Leave a message on their answerphone, write them a letter or an email to receive information about local groups.

The Holmes Place Fulham Pools
Normand Park, Lillie Rd SW6 7ST ☎ *(0870) 870 7018* ⌂ *www.holmesplace.com*
One of the largest swim schools in the UK in partnership with the ASA with classes for all age groups, bookable as 12 week courses. Also mother and baby sessions. There is a crèche for children from 3 months – £2.50/hour for non-members (max stay 2 hours).

Little Otters
c/o 4 Quarrendon St SW6 3SU ☎ *(020) 7610 6281* ⌂ *www.littleotters.com*
BRANCHES AT:
  Chelsea & Westminster Hospital SW10
  Leonard Cheshire Resource Centre W2
  Diana Princess of Wales Centre W2
Exercises and games aimed at making infants and toddlers happy and safe in and under the water; £125 for a 10-week course; classes held at Chelsea & Westminster Hospital SW10, Charing Cross Hospital £6, Leonard Cheshire Resource Centre and Diana Princess of Wales Centre W2.

New Chiswick Pool
Edensor Rd W4 2RG ☎ *(020) 8747 8811*
Ten-week parent and child swimming courses, for babies from six to 18 months old, and for toddlers from 18 months to 3 years old, £23. / HOURS *Mon, Wed, & Fri 7am-8pm, Tue & Thu noon-8pm, Sat 9am-6pm, Sun 9am-5.30pm.*

Porchester Centre
Queensway W2 5HS ☎ *(020) 7792 2919* ⌂ *www.courtneys.co.uk*
Parent and baby classes, suitable for babies from one year old; drop-in; £2.70 for parent; children up to four free. / HOURS *Mon-Fri 10am-5pm; Sat-Sun 8am-8pm.*

Swimming Nature
HQ: 35 Lonsdale Rd NW6 ☎ *(0870) 900 8002* ⌂ *www.swimmingnature.co.uk*
BRANCHES AT:
  Chelsea Sports Centre, Kings Rd SW3
  Walmer Rd W11
  Seymour Sports Centre W2
  Brondesbury Park W2
  Bayswater Sports Centre W2
See write-up in central.

NORTH

Aquababies
☎ *(020) 7702 4888* ⌂ *www.aquababiesltd.co.uk*
BRANCHES AT:
  St John's School, Friern Barnet N11
  Kentish Town Pool, Prince Of Wales Rd NW5 3LE
  Sunstone Health N16 7HR
  Clissold Leisure Centre N16 9EX
See write-up in central.

Britannia Leisure Centre

40 Hyde Rd N1 5JU ☎ (020) 7729 4485 ⏚ www.leisureconnections.co.uk
Baby swimming classes from eight weeks to three years old using the ASA ducklings, etc scheme; the pool used to be ozonated rather than chlorinated but now contains some chlorine; £35 for a ten-week course of one 30-minute lessons a week. / HOURS Mon-Fri 7am-10pm (Sat & Sun 8am-8pm).

Copthall Pools

Page St, Great North Way NW4 1PS ☎ (020) 8457 9920
Parent and baby swimming lessons, £37.20 per term (12 weeks). / SEE ALSO 1.04 Antenatal classes; 2.01 Postnatal.

Enfield Leisure Services

Leisure Services Department, Civic Centre, Silver St Enfield EN1 3XJ ☎ (020) 8379 3762
The civic centre is in charge of swimming courses in four pools in the borough; courses generally last thirteen weeks; ring for details.

Anne Herreboudt

Friern Barnet NW11 ☎ (020) 8886 0053
Sunday morning classes run by an extremely experienced (and patient) teacher, who is also a midwife (and counsellor at St John & Elizabeth).

Oakleigh Park School of Swimming

100 Oakleigh Rd North N20 9EZ ☎ (020) 8445 1911
Private pool offering lessons to small children including parent and toddler sessions. / HOURS Mon-Fri 9am-5.30pm.

Park Road Pools

Park Rd N8 8JN ☎ (020) 8341 3567
Parent and baby pre-swimming classes, for babies from six months to four years old; £22 for a course of six classes. / SEE ALSO 2.01 Postnatal.

Poolside Manor

Lyndhurst Gardens N3 1TD ☎ (020) 8349 1945 ⏚ www.poolsidemanor.com
Classes (most days) take babies from few months, divided into two groups: below and above 18 months; approximately £100 a term; also other courses for older children. / HOURS Mon-Fri 9am-9pm; Sat-Sun 9am-3pm.

Swimming Nature

HQ: 35 Lonsdale Rd NW6 ☎ (0870) 900 8002 ⏚ www.swimmingnature.co.uk
BRANCHES AT:
  Francis Holland Girls School, Park Rd NW1
  Jubilee Sports Centre NW10
See write-up in central.

SOUTH

Aquababies

☎ (020) 7702 4888 ⏚ www.aquababiesltd.co.uk
BRANCHES AT:
  Charlton Special School, Charlton Park Rd SE7 8HX
  Wolfson Centre, Copse Hill SE20 0NE
See write-up in central.

Arches Leisure Centre

80 Trafalgar Rd SE10 9UX ☎ (020) 8317 5020
Swimming for babies from four months old: must enrol for whole term; price depends on length of term (seven week term costs £30.65); child must be a member (£2-£6.20). / HOURS Mon-Sun 7am-8pm; SEE ALSO 1.04 Antenatal classes; 2.01 Postnatal.

Balham Leisure Centre

Elmfield Rd SW17 8AN ☎ (020) 8772 9577
Adult and under five pool sessions, £2.37; crèche Mon-Fri 9.30am-11.30am. / HOURS Mon-Fri 7am-10.30pm (Sat 7.30am-8.30pm, Sun 7.30am-10pm).

Dolphin Swim School

Unit 16 Boundary Business Court, 92-94 Church Rd, Mitcham Surrey CR4 3TD ☎ (020) 8640 4488
BRANCHES AT:
  Wimbledon College, Edge Hill SW19 4NS
  St Joseph's College, Beulah Hill, Upper Norwood SE19 3HL
Operate classes with ASA member teachers including parent and baby groups; teacher is always in the water with pupils; maximum five pupils per class; prices vary according to location; classes held in Mitcham, Wimbledon and Upper Norwood.

Dulwich Fusion & Leisure Centre

45 East Dulwich Rd SE22 9AN ☎ (020) 8693 1833 ⊕ www.fusion-lifestyle.com/fusion
No tuition, but weekly parent and baby pool sessions Mon 9.30am-10.30am, £2.85.

Kingfisher Leisure Centre

Fairfield Rd Kingston upon Thames KT1 2PJ ☎ (020) 8546 1042
Toddler lessons from 6 months, with 14-week Parent and Baby Splash course, £84
joinable at any point on a pro rata basis; crèche. / *HOURS vary (opens at 10am), classes mainly lunch-times and evenings.*

Latchmere Leisure Centre

Burns Rd SW11 2DY ☎ (020) 7207 8004
Parent and baby sessions twice weekly, £3.25; also ASA scheme courses for babies from
three months old (Ducklings, Turtles, etc), £60-£70 per term.

Little Dippers

*PO Box 3223 Brighton BN1 3TY ☎ (0870) 758 0302 ⊕ www.littledippers.co.uk,
www.littledippersfilms.co.uk, www.babyswimshop.co.uk*
Professional diver Lauren Heston has been teaching for ten years. Taking advantage of
the natural 'dive reflex', Lauren encourages babies to feel comfortable in and under
water, not necessarily teaching them to swim, but giving them a fighting chance if they
were to fall into water; improved mental awareness and faster development are also
reported; babies can attend from birth (preferably before they are 15 months old);
classes are held in hydrotherapy pools in Wimbledon, Richmond and Clapham, as well
as locations in Kent and Sussex (max eight per class). / *HOURS Mon-Fri 10am-4pm, Sat & Sun 10am-2pm.*

Putney Leisure Centre

Dryburgh Rd SW15 1BL ☎ (020) 8785 0388 ⊕ www.dcleisure.co.uk
Range of classes rooted in the ASA's swimming programme (Ducklings, Turtles, etc);
six-week course £36 for non-members; also shallow pool for under-fives, suitable for
babies over six months (must be inoculated).

Rascals

Waterfront Leisure Centre, High St, Woolwich SE18 6DL ☎ (020) 8317 5000
Swimming classes for babies from six months; parents must be members of the centre;
prices vary depending on length of courses. / *HOURS open all week.*

South Norwood Swimming Pool

164 Portland Rd SE25 4PT ☎ (020) 8654 6117 ⊕ www.croydon.gov.co.uk
Sessions for different age groups, in a training pool, for parents and their children.

South West Swimming School

Broadway Studios, 28 Tooting High St SW17 9DW ☎ (020) 8767 2723
BRANCHES AT:
  Battersea Technical College SW11
  Burntwood Girl's School SW17
  Henry Cavendish School SW12
  Emanual School SW11
Thirty-minute classes in for babies from four months (once they have had their jabs),
not using buoyancy aids; also children with special needs.

Splashworld Swimming Centre

Crook Log Bexleyheath, Kent DA6 8EQ ☎ (020) 8303 5781 ⊕ www.leisure-centre.com
Classes for babies from four months to five years old aim to introduce fun and
confidence in the water; £32 for a ten-week course for members (£37 for non-members;
membership £27 per year). / *HOURS Mon-Fri 9am-9pm (Mon 9.30pm), Sat & Sun 8am-7pm; SEE ALSO 1.04 Antenatal classes.*

Tooting Leisure Centre

Greaves Place SW17 0NE ☎ (020) 8333 7555 ⊕ www.kinetika.org
Classes £70 for 14 weeks course. / *HOURS Mon-Fri 7am-8.30pm (Sat 7.30am, Sun 8.30am).*

Wimbledon Leisure Centre

Latimer Rd SW19 1EW ☎ (020) 8542 1330
'Baby Splash' for inoculated babies, and 'Toddler Splash' for children over two and
carers; non members £3.65 per class. / *HOURS Mon-Fri 7am-approx 10pm; Sat 8am-5pm; Sun 8am-7pm.*

EAST

Aquababies
☎ *(020) 7702 4888* ⏁ *www.aquababiesltd.co.uk*
BRANCHES AT:
Tiller Centre, Tiller Rd E14
Ironmonger Row Baths, 1–11 Ironmonger Row EC1
See write-up in central.

Atherton Leisure Centre
189 Romford Rd E15 4JF ☎ *(020) 8536 5500*
'Aquababes' (run by a firm called Swimming Development) provides classes from five
months to three years, price £18-25 per term. / *HOURS open all week.*

Cathall Leisure Centre
Cathall Rd E11 4LA ☎ *(020) 8539 8343*
Water babies sessions led by tutor; £3.45 for adults(£2.95 for members), free for
under-fives, £1.50 over 5s. / *HOURS Mon-Fri 7am-10pm, Sat & Sun 8am-5pm.*

Newham Leisure Centre
218 Prince Regents Lane E13 8SD ☎ *(020) 7511 4477* ⏁ *www.gll.org*
The aquababies course (suitable for babies from five months) is held in a one-foot deep
baby pool; Thu, Fri and Sat lunchtimes; £21 for 10 weeks and £24.40 for 12
weeks. / *HOURS Mon-Fri 7.30am-10.30pm, Sat 9am-5.30pm, Sun 9am-10.30am.*

7. GYMNASTICS CLASSES

The word "gym" is used as a byword for "play" by many of the confi-
dence-building activity classes to be found around London. In most cases
we have listed such classes under Play Centres. This section focuses on
the few classes whose underlying intent is to start laying the groundwork
for acrobatic skills. The most reputable of these courses are those registered with British Gymnastics – the sport's statutory body. The next best
thing are courses run by good sports centres.

British Gymnastics are sensitive to any implication that its classes
might push children at too early a stage, and stress that their courses for
toddlers are unstructured. However, like some of the other classes listed,
they take place with trained coaches (sometimes but not always unsympathetic to less capable children) and often in the setting of an operating
gym. The idea is that should your child stick with the activity the move to
more formal coaching is a smooth one.

Gym classes allow babies full scope to practice their motor skills.
Moreover, starting young, when a child's centre of gravity is still close to
the ground, makes having a go relatively easy compared with later in life.
Once grown a little older, toddlers can move on to start to learn 'acrobatic' skills.

USEFUL CONTACTS
British Gymnastics, ☎ *(01952) 822395* ⏁ *www.british-gymnastics.org*

LISTINGS

NORTH

Creative Movement for Toddlers
N6 ☎ *(020) 7435 8217*
Formerly known as Baby Moves – 'Music, Movement and Rhythm' for mothers and
babies 10-20 months. Studio in Hampstead Village Wednesday, 10am-11am; 10 or 12
week course, £8 per session. Must be booked in advance.

Harringay Club
50 Tottenham Lane N8 7EE ☎ *(020) 8348 2124* ⏁ *www.harringayclub.org.uk*
Gymnastics classes for toddlers and their carers; suitable for 1-2 year olds; £3.50
non-members, £2 members (membership £25). / *HOURS Mon-Sun 9am-5pm; SEE ALSO*
2.01 Postnatal.

Swiss Cottage Sports Centre
Winchester Rd NW3 3HA ☎ *(020) 7974 6490* ✆ *www.holmesplace-camden.co.uk*
Daily drop-in gym classes for kids under five (including those aged just a few months old); children are divided into age groups for supervised sessions; £1.50; (closed for redevelopment till 2005 as we go to press). / HOURS *Mon-Fri 7am-9.30pm, Sat & Sun 9am-8pm.*

SOUTH

Tiny Tumblers
BRANCHES AT:
  Wimbledon Leisure Centre, Latimer Rd SW19 1EW ☎ *(020) 8542 1330*
Gymnastics for children from 18 months old; with soft play equipment, singing, balancing, jumping, walking along beams etc. Also Baby Bounce classes – tumbling and gymnastics courses for children from 12 months old.

TJ's Gym Club Wimbledon
Church Hall, Kohat Rd SW19 ☎ *(020) 8640 2678*
Registered with British Gymnastics (and run separately from the classes at Crystal Palace): mother and toddler or young kids' sessions (1 year-7 years); in both cases parents or carers must stay with the child. Book well ahead for these sessions which can fill up two terms in advance. A typical term's course would be £60 approximately. / HOURS *phone for details.*

TJ's Mini-Gym
Crystal Palace National Sports Centre SE19 2BH ☎ *(020) 8659 4561*
Classes (run separately from the Wimbledon classes of the same name) held daily throughout the year; for babies from 10 months to two years old, there is a pirate-themed play area with play nets, a ball pool, and scaled-down equipment like mini-trampolines; sessions last 50 minutes; classes for older children take place in a more traditional gym; lessons need to be booked (in blocks of seven or eight). Parents are needed for younger children; prices on application. / HOURS *Mon-Fri 9am-7.30pm (Sat & Sun 7pm).*

EAST

Redbridge School of Gymnastics
Pulteney Rd E18 1PU ☎ *(020) 8530 3810*
Registered with British Gymnastics: every week-day, drop-in sessions (first one £1, thereafter £3) to encourage children to run, swing, climb and jump, using lowered gym apparatus. / HOURS *Mon-Fri 10am-8pm, Sat 9am-4.30pm.*

Tiny Tumblers
BRANCHES AT:
  Newham Leisure Centre, 218 Prince Regents Lane E13 ☎ *(020) 7511 4477*
  Atherton Leisure Centre, 189 Romford Rd E15 4JF ☎ *(020) 8536 5500*
  St Mark's Church, Tollage Rd, Becton E6 ☎ *(020) 7511 4477 (council central no.)*
  Froud Centre, Manor Park, Romford Rd E12
See write-up in south.

8. PLAYGROUPS, ONE O'CLOCK CLUBS, AND DROP-IN GROUPS

There are countless drop-in playgroups and parent and toddler sessions and coffee groups across London – they operate in parks, church halls and community centres and are operated by a diverse array of organisations from local councils to the Salvation Army.

Many are free or charge a token fee only and they are an excellent place to entertain toddlers and meet other mothers.

There are so many groups and sessions that we have not attempted a comprehensive listing. No great detective work is usually required, however, to truffle them out…

Where to look:
➢ Many councils provide leaflets on facilities and activities in their area (see chapter *4.01 London boroughs* for contacts).
➢ Local publications as listed in chapter *4.05 Finding out more*.
➢ Parks.

- ➤ Playgrounds.
- ➤ Churches.
- ➤ Community centres.
- ➤ Libraries.
- ➤ NCT newsletters.
- ➤ Try asking your health visitor.

USEFUL CONTACTS

Early Learning Centre, ☎ *Customer services (01793) 443322*
🖰 www.elc.co.uk
Branches of this toyshop chain close their tills from 9.30am-11am on Tuesday mornings
for children to play with the stock. Every month a playtime session is
themed. / HOURS *Mon-Sat 9am-5pm (some stores 10am-8pm).*

Salvation Army, ☎ *(020) 7367 4856* 🖰 *www.salvationarmy.org.uk*
The size of this Christian organisation can come as something of a surprise, and it has
a huge number of halls around London (all listed with contact numbers on the
website), many of which organise play groups. / HOURS *Mon-Fri 8am-4.30pm.*

9. CITY FARMS & ZOOS

Note that pregnant women should not go near sheep during the lamb-
ing season, to avoid the risk of coming into contact with toxoplasmosis.

CENTRAL BODIES

Federation of City Farms & Community Gardens,
☎ *(0117) 923 1800* 🖰 *www.farmgarden.org.uk*
This organisation holds details on all city farms in the UK, as well as all community
gardens (open to locals, they range from small plots for a few flowers to allotments).
Call for details of the city farm nearest you. / HOURS *Mon-Fri 9am-5pm.*

CITY FARMS & ZOOS

NORTH

Freightliners Farm
Sheringham Rd N7 8PF ☎ *(020) 7609 0467* 🖰 *www.freightlinersfarm.org.uk*
Set in half a hectare, this north London city farm has cows, pigs, sheep and other farm
animals. Twice a week there is an under-fives drop-in session with activities including
modelling, weaving, jigsaws and printing (Wed pm & Thu am). / HOURS *Tues-Sun 10am-
5pm.*

Kentish Town City Farm
Cressfield Close, off Grafton Rd NW5 4BN ☎ *(020) 7916 5421*
🖰 *www.aapi/cityfarm.co.uk*
The original London city farm, all 5 hectares of it, has pony rides on Sundays. The farm
caters more for school groups but there is a weekly drop in for under 5's
(donation). / HOURS *Tue-Sun 9am-5.30pm.*

London Zoo
Regents Park NW1 4RY ☎ *(020) 7722 3333, Adoption line (020) 7449 6262*
🖰 *www.londonzoo.co.uk, www.zsl.org*
Set in a 36-acre conservation area in Regent's Park, this famous institution is home to
650 species. Lots of activities for children are run every day including feeding (by
keepers, not visitors), a new 'Adventure Reef' motion simulator, interactive displays
and animal rides. Cuddly toys and other gifts are sold in the Zoo shop, and there are
child-orientated eateries. Adults £10; three to15 year-olds £7; under-threes free.
Discounts and saver tickets available, including 'Life Watch' for friends of London Zoo
(annual child ticket, £30: one years' free access, freebies and magazines); child season
ticket £21. (Note that many of the larger animals, including the elephants, are now
housed at the Zoo's sister institution, Whipsnade.) / HOURS *Mon-Sun 10am-5.30pm; SEE ALSO*
3.10 Naming gifts.

SOUTH

Battersea Park Children's Zoo
Battersea Park SWII 4NJ ☎ (020) 8871 7540
Set within Battersea Park, this zoo was designed specifically with children in mind; animals such as otters, monkeys, meerkats and birds; includes an enclosure where children can touch the animals; the easiest access is through Chelsea Gate, next to Chelsea Bridge. / HOURS Apr-Sep 10am-5pm daily; weekends in winter 11am-3pm.

Deen City Farm & Riding School
39 Windsor Ave, Merton Abbey SWI9 2RR ☎ (020) 8545 0142
⌁ www.deencityfarm.co.uk
A five-acre site with a variety of farm animals and pony rides for all ages; call for details of any toddler activities. Also childrens parties, parent and toddler groups for under 4s: 10.15-12 on Wednesday; £2 per child and 50p per additional child. / HOURS Tue-Sun 10am-4pm, (5 April-Oct).

Surrey Docks City Farm
Rotherhithe St SE16 5EY ☎ (020) 7231 1010
This small working farm, located near the river, has a café, mini gardens, orchards and herb beds. It boasts an animal contact area for children. Individuals get in free but there is a charge for groups. / HOURS Tue-Thurs 10am-5pm, Sat & Sun 10am-1pm & 2pm-5pm.

Vauxhall City Farm
24 St Oswalds Place SE11 5JE ☎ (020) 7582 4204
A selection of livestock and ponds with plants which attract wildlife; small herb gardens and allotments worked by farm members; free admission (donation encouraged). / HOURS Closed Mon & Fri; open 10.30am-4pm.

The Wandsworth Nature Study Centre
Wandsworth Common, Dorlcote Rd SW18 3RT ☎ (020) 8871 3863, London Wildcare (020) 8773 0632
Free events throughout the year: also free activities for children on nature and wildlife on the first Sunday of every month, 2.30pm-4.30pm; (closed as we go to press, it is set to re-open later in 2004).

EAST

Brooks Farm
Skeltons Lane Park E10 5BS ☎ (020) 8539 4278
Attached to a playscheme; most suitable for children aged from 6 years old but younger children accompanied by an adult are welcome; animals include sheep, chickens, doves, cows and Shetland ponies; £1 per head for groups, free for schools in the borough. / HOURS Tue-Sun 10.30am-5.30pm (9.30am-4.30pm in winter).

East Ham Nature Reserve
Norman Rd, East Ham E6 4HN ☎ (020) 8470 4525
The reserve houses nine acres of old church yard grounds with woodland and urban animals such as foxes as well as a centre with history displays, an old classroom, a wartime kitchen and an animal display. / HOURS Tue-Fri 10am-5pm, (10am-4pm in winter) Sat & Sun 2pm-5pm (1pm-4pm in winter).

Hackney City Farm
1a Goldsmiths Row E2 8QA ☎ (020) 7729 6381 ⌁ www.hackneycityfarm.co.uk
Converted brewery and grounds; a donation allows access to the animals (there is a baby animal section too) as well as gardens, activities and a café; springtime visits are popular, when you can see the chicks and lambs. / HOURS Tue-Sun 10am-4.30pm.

Mudchute Farm
Pier St, Isle of Dogs E14 3HP ☎ (020) 7515 5901
Thirty-two acres of animals (Llamas, horses, cows, pigs, small mammals, turkeys, pond animals…) and activities (pony rides and an education centre) with a cafe and shop to boot, make up the largest urban farm in London. / HOURS 9am-5pm.

Newham City Farm
King George Ave, Custom House E16 3HR ☎ (020) 7474 4960
Established in 1977: wide collection of farm animals (including rare breeds and a shire horse); visitor centre; grazing paddocks; general tours include a chance to hold and touch some of the animals.

Plashet Zoo
Plashet Park, off Shrewsbury Rd, Forest Gate E7 ☎ (020) 8503 5994
Free zoo where the emphasis is on small, strokable animals (including chinchillas, rabbits and chipmunks): there is also a butterfly house; llamas, wallabies, pygmy goats, ponies and aviary birds. / HOURS Tue-Sun 10am-5pm (4pm in winter).

Spitalfields Farm
Weaver St E1 5HJ ☎ (020) 7247 8762 ⟨ www.spitalfieldscityfarm.org
A 1.8 acre site with a pond, gardens and animals (including donkeys and ducks);
no entry charge; special events are run in the school holidays; Sunday donkey
rides. / *HOURS Tue-Sun 10am-5pm.*

Stepping Stones Farm
Stepney Way E1 3DG ☎ (020) 7790 8204
Community farm project with full range of farm animals as well as ferrets and
chipmunks; admission is free but donations are welcome; school holiday
events. / *HOURS Tue-Sun 9.30am-6pm (open public holidays).*

10. OTHER ACTIVITIES

In this section:
➤ Large attractions.
➤ Signing classes.
➤ Film.
➤ Help with research.
➤ Miscellaneous creative activities.

Large attractions

CENTRAL

Corams Field
93 Guilford St WC1N 1DN ☎ (020) 7837 6138
Adults are admitted only if accompanied by a child at this seven-acre playground north
of Holborn, with sports and play equipment, a paddling pool, a sandpit and disabled
access. There are also organised 'drop-in' activities for under-fives, and farm
animals. / *HOURS summer 9am-8pm, winter 9am-dusk.*

SOUTH

London Aquarium
County Hall SE1 7PB ☎ (020) 7967 8000 ⟨ www.londonaquarium.co.uk
Built within what was County Hall, this intriguing building houses many aquariums,
from small tanks to the 'centrepiece' shark tank (three storeys high); child-friendly and
suitable for pushchairs. You can touch a live ray in the touchpool. Adults £8.75;
children £5.25; under threes free; family ticket £25; café and shop. / *HOURS Mon-Sat 10am-
6pm.*

Royal Botanic Gardens, Kew
Kew TW9 3AB ☎ (020) 8332 5000, Visitor info (020) 8332 5655 ⟨ www.kew.org
The aquarium under the Palm House is known as the marine display (designed to
show seaweeds, but with fish) and is great for children to watch. There are also 300
acres of gardens, and the famous glasshouses are handy when it's raining. There are
often special events, such as storytelling, during school holidays and on some
weekends; £8.50 adults, free for accompanied under 17s; Concessions £6. / *HOURS Mon-
Sun 9.30am-6pm (4.15pm in winter; 8pm on summer bank holidays).*

OUTSIDE LONDON

Legoland
WInkfield Road, Windsor Berkshire SL4 4AY ☎ (0870) 504 0404 ⟨ www.legoland.co.uk
It's not cheap (£23 – kids under three free, over three £19), but even small toddlers can
get a huge kick out of a visit to this large theme park, off junction 6 of the M4 (or take
the train to Windsor and Eton Riverside then a shuttle bus); also via Paddington to
Slough then shuttle train. / *HOURS Off Peak 10am-5pm; late 10am-6pm; Peak 10am-6pm; late 10am-
7pm.*

Signing classes

A popular actvity that has grown around interest in the idea of baby signing (discussed in the listings below).

WEST

Sing and Sign
East Sussex BN1 2NW ☎ *(01273) 550 587* ⌂ *www.singandsign.com*
BRANCHES AT:
  Ladbroke Grove W10 ☎ *(01273) 509132*
Music groups which while offering songs and musical activities, teach a range of simple baby signs; a video shows action songs and nursery rhymes teaching a range of 80-plus simple gestures derived from sign language to enable babies to communicate before they can speak.

NORTH

Sing and Sign
East Sussex BN1 2NW ☎ *(01273) 550 587* ⌂ *www.singandsign.com*
BRANCHES AT:
  Harrow, Wembley & Bushey ☎ *(020) 8950 0888*
See write-up in west.

SOUTH

Sing and Sign
East Sussex BN1 2NW ☎ *(01273) 550 587* ⌂ *www.singandsign.com*
BRANCHES AT:
  Kingston ☎ *(020) 8942 2621*
See write-up in west.

OUTSIDE LONDON

Tiny Talk
20 Artillery Terrace, Guildford Surrey GU1 4NL ☎ *(01483) 577 729, (07950) 290557*
⌂ *www.tinytalkuk.com*
Set up by a primary school teacher and teacher of the deaf who noted that infants can understand a great deal before they can talk. She also noted that signs help them to understand what people are saying and to express their feelings and needs. She created a system for use with her first child and then incorporated music for use in singing and signing classes which are operated as franchises in the UK. Classes are suitable for infants from around six to nine months until at least 12 to 18 months. Babies are reported to sign back with understanding as early as 4 to 6 weeks after starting. Classes run around the UK for parents and children. The course is also available in books, sold by Mothercare and WH Smith exclusively.

Film

More an activity for mum rather than baby...

WEST

Electric Cinema
191 Porbello Rd W10 ☎ *(020) 7908 9696* ⌂ *www.electriccinema.co.uk*
The Electric Scream, every Monday at 3pm – a screening for parents and their under 1s; tickets £5, £7.50 (footstools) and £20 (2-seater sofa).

NORTH

Phoenix Cinema
52 High Rd N2 9PJ ☎ *(020) 8444 6789* ⌂ *www.phoenixcinema.co.uk*
Once a month welcomes parents with babies up to one year for 11am screenings of recent films.

SOUTH

Clapham Picture House
76 Venn St SW4 0AT ☎ *(020) 7498 3323* ⌂ *www.picturehouses.co.uk*
Once a week (usually Thursday mornings, but call to check), this cinema holds 'The Big Scream' screenings which welcome mothers with babies and toddlers; membership £3 for two people per baby and valid until baby's first birthday. Films are a mixture of new and old releases. Changing facilities and safe area for pushchairs.

Help with research

Not perhaps the most obvious of activities, but there are a number of
units around London studying human behaviour, and participating can
make for an intriguing way of killing a couple of afternoons.

CENTRAL

Centre for the Brain & Cognitive Development
Birkbeck College, 32 Torrington Square WCIE 7JL ☎ (020) 7631 6372
⌁ www.psyc.bbk.ac.uk/cbcd or www.cbcd.bbk.ac.uk
A university research unit looking at the way babies learn, providing door-to-door
black cab service for parents and infants under 12 months old, who live within 5 miles
and are asked to visit two or three times. The parent stays with the baby at all times.
The tasks required are simple, and might include something like watching a computer
display. A play area is available for older children. / *HOURS See website.*

Child Development Research
Department of Psychology, University College London, Gower St WCIE 6BT ☎ (020)
7679 5351
Looking for babies from birth to the age of six months for studies in cognitive
development; travel expenses reimbursed in full.

NORTH

The Tavistock Clinic
120 Belsize Lane NW3 5BA ☎ (020) 7435 7111 ⌁ www.tavi-port.org
The research department of this well-known London clinic carries out research into
very specific issues relating to pregnancy and childcare. They may like to interview
mothers before and after birth, and then video them with their baby. / *HOURS Mon-Fri: 9-*
5.30pm for enquries, longer hours for appointments.; SEE ALSO 2.03 Baby health; 4.02 Health practitioners;
4.04 Miscarriage & stillbirth.

Miscellaneous creative activities

WEST

Art 4 Fun
☎ (020) 8449 6500 ⌁ www.art4fun.co.uk
BRANCHES AT:
  444 Chiswick High Rd W4 5TT ☎ (020) 8994 4100
  196 Kensington Park Rd W11 ☎ (020) 8959 7373
These drop-in paint-your-own-mug cafés can be fun for mothers with babies or
toddlers. Children are encouraged to experiment with non-toxic paints and stencils.
The finished article can be collected four days later, or posted to you. Hand and
footprints in clay are another option. More structured classes are held for different age
groups (from a few months old), using – sponging, drawing, cutting and pasting,
moulding clay and painting. Studio fee £3.95; items £2.50-£35+.

Paint Pots
Montessori School, Chelsea Community Church, Edith Road SW10 0LB ☎ (020) 7376
4571
BRANCHES AT:
  Bayswater United Reform Church, Newton Rd W2 5LS
  Ashburnham Community Centre, Tetcott Road SW10 0SB
Creative classes for toddlers, £165 per term; parents attend classes, which must be
pre-booked.

NORTH

Art 4 Fun
☎ (020) 8449 6500 ⌁ www.art4fun.co.uk
BRANCHES AT:
  172 West End Lane NW6 1SD ☎ (020) 7794 0800
  212 Fortis Green Rd N10 3DJ ☎ (020) 8444 4333
See write-up in west.

Brushstrokes
St Peter Le Poer Church Hall, Cnr Albion Avenue &Colney Hatch Lane, Muswell Hill N10
1AH ☎ (020) 8346 1486
Art sessions for children 18 months to four years with painting, play dough, stencils,
chalks, jigsaw puzzles, drawing, cutting and sticking, cooking and more, including
a story. Sessions cost £6 each. Weekly sessions, booking essential.

Crafty Kids
26A Kings Avenue, Muswell Hill N10 1PB ☎ *(020) 8374 4996, (07930) 125 214*
⌂ www.craftykidsltd.co.uk
BRANCHES AT:
  The Roundhouse, Highbury N6
  St Mary's Church, Upper Street Islington N1
  Hampstead & Primrose Hill NW3
  Hornsey Vale Community Centre N8
Sessions for under one-threes & three-five-year-olds in one class – including craft materials, themes and ideas, and protective clothing.

Crazee Kids
Jacksons Lane Community Centre, 269a Archway Rd N6 5AA ☎ *(020) 8444 5333, (07958) 510 919*
Mix of art, movement and music in various groups, starting from age 2–3.

Creative Wiz Kids
St Lukes Church, Kidderpore Ave NW3 ☎ *(020) 7794 6797*
Classes combining painting, music, singing, dancing and group play; suitable for children 1-3 years; 12-week terms (one lesson a week); classes based in Hampstead.

Messy Play
Berneys Hall, 25 The Broadway Stanmore ☎ *(020) 8959 9045*
For children 18 months to 4 years, activities including painting, chalking, sticking, colouring, water play, playdough, collage and the like. / HOURS *Mon morning; Wednesday Afternoon; classes at Stanmore.*

Sticky Fingers
Hendon and at Quaker House, Alexandra Grove N12 8HG ☎ *(020) 8458 2246*
⌂ www.stickyfingers.org.uk
Creative art classes, one for babies to toddlers and a second for toddlers to school age.

EAST

The Bull Theatre
68 High St EN5 5SJ ☎ *(020) 8449 0048*
Parent and toddler drama classes, for children from 18 months old. A move (to Finchley) was under consideration at press time. / HOURS *Tues-Sat 10am-5.30pm, Sun 1pm-5.30pm.*

CHAPTER 2.07

EDUCATION

1. **Introduction**
2. **Pre-school options**
3. **Primary education**
4. **Home-based education**
5. **Special educational needs**
6. **Round-up listings**

1. INTRODUCTION

It can seem as though the minute a baby is born you have to start looking at potential schools. You perhaps have a little longer than some parents and private schools would have you believe, but if you want the pick of the options, the sooner you start addressing the issue, the better.

This whole area can seem daunting and familiarisation can seem like an education in itself. Lists, guides, consultants and league tables can only take you so far. At the end of the day, there is no substitute for your own investigations. Among other things that means tapping into the parent grapevine, researching a shortlist of options (noting that popularity in schools, as in nurseries, is no failsafe marker of quality), then visiting establishments to make your own evaluation.

To put the timing into some perspective, children are generally expected to attend primary school from the beginning of the term after their fifth birthday, but many start sooner. This is partly because of increasing demand by parents for pre-school childcare and education, and partly because of increasing pressure by schools to have children signed up early, or risk losing their place.

While some private schools require that you get the child's name down for no more than the entitlement to an interview, state primaries do not generally want to hear from parents any sooner than the child's second birthday if you want to apply for a nursery place; or third if you are interested in entry in the 'rising fives' reception class.

WHAT ARE 'RISING FIVES'
Children who start school in the term in which they are due to become five. This is the usual starting age rather than the term after the fifth birthday.

Overview of your child's educational options

All the following types of establishments are discussed in greater depth in the appropriate section below.

OPTIONS FOR PRE-SCHOOL
(FOR TWO TO FOUR YEAR OLDS)
With pre-school establishments, distinctions are blurred, not only between pre-school and primary schools, but also between childcare and educational establishments.

The options, in rough order of being progressively more "school-like":

➢ Day nursery with educational provision – state or private (from 3 or 6 months though the educational element kicks in rather later).

➢ Pre-school – what used to be called a playgroup – or community nursery (from age 2)

➢ Nursery school – state or private (from age 2 or 3).

➢ Nursery or reception class at a primary school – state or private (perhaps from age 3, typically from age 4).

OPTIONS FOR PRIMARY SCHOOL
(FROM FIVE YEARS OLD)

Where state education is concerned there are two main types of establishment.

Types of state-run primary school:

➢ County / community school.

➢ Denominational / voluntarily-aided school.

The latter category consists largely of church-run schools, approximately one quarter of schools in the UK being jointly funded between LEAs and churches. These schools are often considered the best in a particular area, but admission policies generally favour church-going parents.

Other terms you may come across in relation to state schools include those indicating differences in the age range covered by the school: for example Infant School (ages 5–7), First School (ages 5–8/9), and Primary School (ages 5–11).

Terminologically at least, the private sector could not be more straightforward.

Types of private primary school:

➢ Pre-prep (generally covers ages 3/4–7).

OPTIONS FOR SECONDARY SCHOOL

You have to draw the line somewhere, and a full discussion of the options for secondary education is beyond the scope of this guide.

Note, however, that even at this stage it helps if you start to form in your mind a rough idea of the type of education you want to give your child. The decisions you take now will start your child on a track from which it will be increasingly difficult to break free. The more that you can hedge your bets, the better.

A classic example is a desire for a private secondary education. Although many parents wanting this for their child start with a state primary education, this strategy has pitfalls. State-run primaries are focussed on the expectations of state-run secondaries and such a school might be academically excellent but not prepare a child particularly well for the private sector.

Private pre-preps, on the other hand, often expect their pupils to be a year or even two years ahead of their state school peers academically and look to prepare children for interviews and entrances tests in private secondary schools. In addition some have strong links with specific secondary schools and focus on preparing children to meet the specific expectations of those establishments.

That said, intensive and narrow preparation has its downsides. Some teachers interviewing at private schools – noting that intensive coaching can produce 'cookie cutter' children – prefer to take those who display

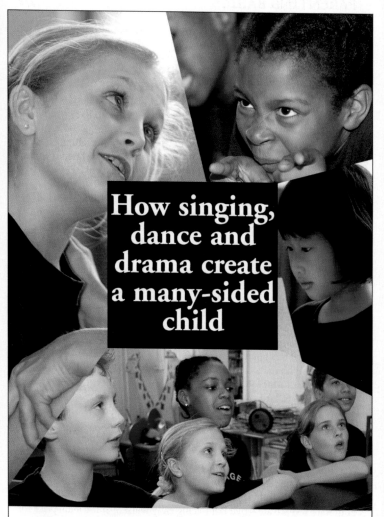

How singing, dance and drama create a many-sided child

IF YOUR CHILD is aged between 4 and 16, he or she is ready for Stagecoach. We teach the skills they need to act, sing and dance.

They will grow more confident, speak more clearly, move easily, act more naturally, become self-aware. These skills don't vanish as the curtain falls. They are learnt for life.

With over 500 schools, Stagecoach is Britain's largest part-time Theatre Arts School. Schools are open during normal term time for three hours at weekends.

For a Prospectus and for more about your local school, call us now on: **FREEPHONE 080808 78243***

STAGECOACH
THEATRE ARTS SCHOOLS

www.stagecoach.co.uk

Calls are free only within the UK

natural ability rather than merely those well-drilled at jumping through hoops.

Pre-school & primary education are increasingly inter-related

A decade or so ago, there was quite a neat distinction between where children went to be educated from the age of three to five, and where they went after the age of five.

Traditionally, children under five not staying at home attended either a playgroup (a pre-school, in more current parlance) or a nursery school. After the age of five they would move on to some form of primary or pre-prep.

Today, however, children are increasingly missing out the initial stage, and jumping straight into nursery and reception classes at primary schools – be they state-run or privately funded. Well over half the four-year olds in the UK now go to school.

There are broadly two reasons for this; the government's continuing emphasis on early years education as a form of cheap childcare for working parents, and schools' enthusiasm for the extra funding earned on nursery pupils. The government is now committed to funding a nursery place for every four-year old in the country (see Funding for pre-school education, below). The same is nearly true for three-year olds with the government aiming to meet universal provision for this age group around publication of this guide (April 2004).

This emphasis has resulted in big growth in the numbers attending nursery classes attached to primary schools, at the expense of pre-schools and playgroups, large numbers of which have closed in recent years.

Day nurseries that previously provided only childcare have noted the changes and are starting to offer educational provision as well. Meanwhile primary schools are setting up nursery and registration classes to compete for the same children.

When it comes to recruiting pupils, primaries have more clout than nurseries and indeed some parents complain that primaries 'blackmail' them into sending their children to schools early, with unsubtle hints – both state and private – that not joining early will jeopardise a full place for after the age of five.

Whether school is the best place for pre-school children to spend their time, given their limited concentration span and the poor adult to child ratios, is considered debatable by a number of observers, including many teachers.

The increase in formal teaching means that even in nursery classes children are being given less time for free play, and more energy is focussed on work-related activities. Art, for example, may not involve free drawing but instead colouring inside outlines to improve pencil control – leading to writing skills.

Recent research and comparisons with countries such as Switzerland indicate that this early start impacts adversely on children's ability to learn. In this country the Association of Teachers and Lecturers has reported that in some pupils it can trigger disruptive behaviour and even violence.

If you are concerned that your child is not yet ready for full-time school and yet have an offer of a place in a state school, the school is obliged to keep that open until three months after the fifth birthday. Of course, by that stage it may be harder on your child to join because the others in the class have already built up friendships.

General reading

(For books on play and development, and details of local London publications and newsletters, see chapter 4.05 Finding out more.)

READING

[Magazine] **Lib ED magazine** (**Libertarian Education**) (For the liberation of learning; £5.50 inc p&p for one year (three magazines)) – *Published by an organisation that promotes non-institutional learning and libertarian teaching in schools; other publications include Freedom in Education, 64-page DIY guide to the liberation of learning.* / *Lib Ed, Phoenix house, 157 Wells Rd, Bristol, BS4 2BU (www.libed.demon.co.uk).*

Primary School Planner – DofE (Stationery Office; Stationery Office, phone orders 0870 600 55 22 cheque or credit card; Bookshop, 123 Kingsway, London WC2B 6PQ tel: 020 7242 6393; £14.99; 0117026891) – *Choosing a nursery; preparing your child for the first day; entertaining activities to boost learning; (also publish School Planners covering the same issues at a secondary level).*

Ready to Learn – Martyn Rawson and Michael Rose (From Birth to School Readiness; Hawthorn Press; 2002; £9.99; 1-903458-15-3) – *A detailed look (from a Steiner perspective) by authors working in teacher training, at the way a child develops physically, mentally and emotionally. It argues that introducing intellectual stress too early risks upsetting the necessary progression.* / *www.hawthornpress.com.*

2. PRE-SCHOOL OPTIONS

For children over two years old, there are, as listed above, a range of options which offer the chance to socialise and prepare for the full experience of school. These are not childcare establishments, though in some respects they provide effectively the same service, if for limited hours.

ADULT:CHILD RATIOS

There are extraordinary differences in the staffing requirements for the youngest children in schools and those in stand-alone pre-school and nursery establishments.

Nursery classes at primary schools taking children from the age of three are permitted a ratio of 1:13. Reception classes at primary schools for four-year olds may have a ratio as high as 1:30.

By contrast, for children aged three to five, the Children's Act requires pre-schools and nurseries to maintain the much lower ratio of 1:8.

INSPECTIONS

Nurseries and pre-schools used to fall under the ambit of your local authority's Social Services department, with annual inspections. However, while local authorities retain responsibility for training in such establishments, since September 2001 OFSTED has assumed responsibility for the inspection of most aspects of childcare provision.

OFSTED therefore now performs two types of inspections for childcare establishments:

Children's Act inspections: which all establishments receive; whose subject matter is the general standards of care; and which take place annually.

Nursery Education inspections: which only certain establishments receive; where the focus is academic standards; and which typically take place every four years.

Nursery classes in schools receive education inspections from OFSTED according to the type of school. For state schools the inspection comes at least every six years (along with the rest of the school). Independent schools are inspected less frequently, unless they receive Early Years grants (which many do), in which case they are inspected at least every four years.

A. Day nurseries with education provisions

(For detailed information relating to day nurseries, see chapter 2.04 Childcare.)
Traditionally the role of day nurseries has been one chiefly of childcare rather than education. This remains their key role, but more and more are now offering their older charges some form of educational provision (in large part, due to the encouragement of government grants). Many day nurseries therefore can now offer a one-stop shop from six months old all the way through to starting primary school at age five.

B. Pre-schools (a.k.a. playgroups)

Most pre-schools are run in church halls or community rooms, for children from two-and-a-half or three-years old (usually, but not always, potty-trained) to school age. Pre-schools generally require some parental involvement and – being generally subsidised by the local authority – charge very little. A typical cost would be around £2 per morning (or £150 per child per year). Most are open almost year-round – closing for three weeks in summer is typical.

As a sector, pre-schools have been through a time of enormous change. Traditionally they opened for two–three hours, usually in the morning till about noon. Traditionally they have not been focussed on academic education, but have seen their role as fostering a child's independence and social skills. However the shift towards more early-years places in schools and nurseries hit the number of playgroups, with approximately 1,000 (of a total of 17,000) closing across the UK in 2000 and 2001.

With some government help, the sector has regrouped. Extended hours are more common, and many pre-schools now offer places for the whole day. As part of a drive to produce more consistent standards across the country, many pre-schools are accredited in a national quality assessment scheme.

As a type of institution pre-schools have some devoted advocates, who vaunt the strengths provided by their strong tradition of parent involvement, which they say allows children to feel secure in an institution whose whole self-help ethos promotes a sense of community. As more and more pre-schools are judged by similar standards to nursery schools, however, it remains to be seen whether this special ethos will survive.

WHAT TO LOOK FOR

Look for a pre-school which provides:
- A good staff-to-child ratio.
- Safe buildings and grounds.
- Happy and busy children.
- Children encouraged to listen as well as speak and to develop social skills with peers as well as adults.
- Opportunity for exercise and movement, including climbing and balancing.
- Opportunity for messy play, including with water, sand, clay and dough, cutting and sticking and painting.
- Opportunity for fine motor control and sorting, including table toys, shape and size graded toys, construction toys, matching games.
- Opportunity for the use of imagination (dressing up, for example).
- Musical play.
- A nature table.
- Floor toys.
- A settling-in process before formal attendance.

➢ A sense that your child's physical, intellectual and emotional needs will be recognised and met.
➢ Regular feedback about children and staff available, and readiness to communicate with parents.

NSPCC checklist:
➢ Is there someone in charge?
➢ Is there a health and safety policy, a leader qualified in first aid and a first aid box; and have the premises passed fire regulations?
➢ Are there children who drop out or stop going for no apparent reason?
➢ Are the staff and volunteers suitable to work with children?
➢ Is there a written code of behaviour?
➢ Is there a system for parents and carers to voice concerns?
➢ Are parents discouraged from staying to watch or become involved?
➢ Is there any favouritism shown?
➢ Is there encouragement of inappropriate physical contact?
➢ Are there any humiliating punishments?

USEFUL CONTACTS

National Playbus Association (NPA), ☎ *(0117) 916 6580*
🖰 *www.playbus.org.uk*
Umbrella organisation for Playbus organisations in England. Community organisations set up 'mobile playgrounds' in buses for children from pre-school age to 8 years old.

Playgroup Network, ☎ *(0191) 230 5520* 🖰 *www.playgroup-network.org.uk*
Works towards the formation of community groups to improve development and education with appropriate play facilities for children under five; the network can provide details of local playgroup organisations.

Pre-School Learning Alliance, ☎ *(020) 7833 0991*
🖰 *www.pre-school.org.uk*
Formerly known as the Pre-School Playgroups Association – a national educational charity and membership organisation of around 16,000 nurseries, kindergartens, and pre-schools, which cater to almost 750,000 under-fives (member bodies are usually run with the assistance of parents). The helpline is for parents seeking childcare, and the organisation can also put you in touch with local member groups. / *HOURS helpline Mon-Fri 10am-5pm; PUBLICATIONS Various publications (primarily aimed at childcarers) - call for publication list.*

READING

Longman's Parent's Guide to Pre-School Choices and Nursery Education – Elizabeth Wood & Prof Ted Wragg (Longman; 1996; £2.99; 0582299713) – *One of a series aimed at parents.*

Pre-school Education – Anne Mercer (Choosing and starting pre-school; Letts Educational; 1999; £4.99; 1857589769) – *Part of the "You and Your Child" eight-book series by educational experts, designed to offer parents jargon-free information on how to help their child at school. Other titles cover literacy, numeracy, primary education, the National Curriculum, ICT and computers, learning difficulties and successful learning.*

[Magazine] Under Five Contact – ed Ann Henderson (Pre School Learning Alliance) – *Newsletter of the Pre School Learning Alliance: topics covered include children's development; nutrition; safety; play and learning; family issues. / www.pre-school.org.uk.*

C. Nursery schools

Nursery schools are often stand-alone establishments for children up to five years old, with two or more classes. They do not offer full-time child-care because they generally run on the same holiday timetable as schools. They are more formal and educational than playgroups and therefore are a good introduction to the pattern of things in real schools.

All nursery schools are covered by the Childrens Act; therefore must be registered and, for example, all cars or minibuses used must provide children's belts or baby seats.

If your child moves from a nursery school to an attached primary school this will make the transition to school relatively easy. However, in general a child with a nursery place at such a school is not guaranteed one at the school itself.

LOCAL AUTHORITY NURSERY SCHOOLS

A local authority nursery school may be attached to a primary school and usually provides places for children aged three plus. It is important to get a child's name down quickly – say by at least the age of two.

Parents are entitled to enrol their children in a nursery school near home or work. Priority is given to places allocated by the local authority to help disadvantaged families, even on a short-term basis, for example to help a mother cope with illness, to give a child time away from bad housing conditions, or to support working single mothers. In some cases a place may be free, though if there are any charges they tend to be low.

Such schools usually offer either morning or afternoon sessions every weekday for about three hours. Sometimes there is extended provision to 6pm. These establishments are usually open only during term-time (around 36 weeks a year) and, even where they open longer, they will close for a summer holiday. Staff are qualified teachers or nursery nurses, and staff to child ratios tend to vary from 1:10 to 1:15.

Parental help and involvement is encouraged.

PRIVATE NURSERY SCHOOLS

Sometimes only for the toilet-trained (i.e. two–three year olds), private nursery schools are usually run from residential-type buildings and offer more formal pre-school teaching (some being attached to prep schools). Many are inspired by the Montessori philosophy of teaching, with children working largely individually, though sometimes in pairs and groups, choosing materials appropriate to their stage of development. They are offered the chance to watch older children and help the younger ones. Costs tend to be from £10 per morning and there may be a uniform to pay for. Many have official open days.

FINDING A NURSERY SCHOOL

Information for locating nursery schools

➤ All nurseries must be registered with the local authority, which in most cases can supply a list.

➤ Advertisements in local baby/children publications, including those of local parent support groups (see chapter *4.05 Finding out more* for local publications, and chapter *2.01 Postnatal* for support groups).

➤ There is limited information published about nursery schools. Publications like *Families* may have some details (see chapter *4.05 Finding out more*). Some school guides (see below) list the names of more prestigious establishments.

WHAT TO LOOK FOR IN A NURSERY SCHOOL

Source: National Campaign for Nursery Education

1. A ratio of ideally one to ten, at most one adult for every 13 children under the age of 5 (as recommended by the DfES).
2. Staff specially trained to work with the age group (i.e. an early years teacher and qualified nursery nurse).

3. A separate outdoor space to play away from older children (as recommended by the DfES).

4. Lavatories close to the classroom for the specific use of nursery age children.

5. Space and equipment to enable learning through playing, talking and experimenting (formal styles of learning are counterproductive if introduced too early).

6. The option of starting children part-time; and staggered admission to allow the teacher time with each child.

7. Meals eaten in small groups (large, noisy halls are overwhelming for little ones).

Also vital: kind, child-friendly staff.

D. Nursery or reception class at primary school – state/private

Conceptually, nursery classes attached to a primary school are very similar to those at a stand-alone nursery school though there may be as many as twice the number of children per adult. Attendance is not a guarantee of a place at the main school, though a significant proportion of children will usually be offered one.

Reception classes are for children under the age of five who have a place at the school. They are intended to offer a gentle introduction to the child to the environment of school.

Funding for pre-school education

Nursery vouchers – the scheme for funding nursery places introduced by the Tory government – are now a thing of the distant past. However, a similar amount of funding (£1,188 per year) remains available for the nursery education of every four-year old in the country (and an increasing number of three-year olds depending on the policy of your local authority). The claim for the grant is now made by the nursery establishment itself, rather than the parent, under arrangements called 'Early Years Development Partnerships'.

Any establishment that is registered for educational inspections with OFSTED, whether publicly or privately funded, is eligible to receive such a grant. To do so it must provide a child with five two-and-a-half hour sessions per week for three terms.

With private nurseries, parents generally pay the full fee up front and receive a rebate when the grant is received.

3. PRIMARY EDUCATION

More is at stake when deciding on a primary education than a pre-school one. This is the start of formal schooling and, hopefully, will start your child off on the right track. You will need to give some thought both to what is available and what you are looking for.

While you may be planning a more academic school career further down the line, the findings currently indicate that for some children, learning through play may be more productive at this age.

The sort of questions which you should start to be asking yourself:

➤ Would you be prepared to opt for an excellent academic school, even though it had practically no facilities for games and play?

> ➤ Where do you stand on single-sex education for this age group? (And, if you have children of differing sexes, do you want them to go to the same school?)
> ➤ How important to you are activities like music, sport, dance or art?
> ➤ Are you focused primarily on results (which may mean a competitive atmosphere), or do you like the idea of somewhere that looks more to developing a child's strengths whatever they may be.
> ➤ How important to you is religion and spirituality in the life of the school?
> ➤ What sort of approach to discipline do you expect?
> ➤ What are the hours kept by the school, and how does that meet your commitments? Is there an after-school club?

As you start to form an idea in your mind of what you are looking for, the next step is to start reviewing what schools are in your area. Your ideas will start to crystalise more once you have started to come into contact with the schools and as you start to discuss the issue with other parents.

Though subject to slightly different considerations, the steps for finding a school are broadly the same whether you are considering state-funded or privately-run options (though your shortlist of state-funded schools will be much more limited by geography, as proximity to the school is usually central to admissions policies). In both sectors, good schools are over-subscribed, but the ways they deal with the issue differ.

The process you can expect to go through:
> ➤ Work out what schools exist in your area, or – with private schools – within a manageable distance. Sources of information are listed below, but it is not such a crazy idea to pound your local streets with an A-Z and to see where parents and primary school children are heading at 8.30am.
> ➤ Contact likely-looking schools for their prospectuses. Glossy brochures have long been part of the marketing armoury of the private sector, but all state-run schools are now legally obliged to provide a booklet.
> ➤ Create a shortlist, and, if possible, arrange to visit the schools on it, ideally to include a talk with the head teacher. Enquire about the application procedure and waiting list details. Ask for any material the school publishes: for example policy documents on education, religion, and bullying, and copies of any inspection reports. Note that some private schools will not permit a visit until you have paid a deposit.
> ➤ If appropriate, make your visit, and see whether the school feels right to you. As one primary school teacher told the author, it is important that the school feels happy. Notes and a checklist of points on which you would like to base your decision may help clarify your conclusions afterwards. Once you have a revised shortlist, second visits to the remaining contenders may be a good idea.
> ➤ Aim to put your child's name down for at least three different schools.
> ➤ If there are one or two schools you are particularly keen on, start attending open days and fund-raising events such as fairs.
> ➤ Check regularly (but not too often) whether your child has a place: showing some form of continued interest in your application is an important part of the procedure. Except in the case of voluntary aided schools (generally church schools), which are usually faster in deciding on admissions, you are unlikely to know for sure until around six months before the date when your child might start.

➤ If you are applying to a state school, and no place is available, you can appeal. There is a fair chance of success: about two in five appeals at the primary level go the parents' way.

The above are guidelines only. You might find with a good state primary, for example, that visits are not welcome until the year before when your child could attend. With a private pre-prep it is more likely that visits will be encouraged at an early stage, after payment of a registration fee.

PLAYING THE OFFERS GAME

As you start to set about ranking your options and deciding which places you intend to put your child down for, give some consideration to the timing of offers that you are likely to receive.

As the school year approaches, schools set about calculating how many places they will have available (depending on how many children are leaving, how many of the applicants already have siblings at the school, and so on). Depending on how many 'slots' are available, the schools start sending out offers in the order determined by its criteria. To secure a place at fee-paying schools, it is generally necessary to return a term's pay with your acceptance.

Offers almost invariably have a time limit, so you may find yourself with an expiring offer from one school, but no communication from one you prefer.

This is particularly an issue if you are juggling offers from both private and state-run establishments. Private schools make it a priority to get offers out early. State primaries tend to do so in their own good time. Parents therefore can be forced to decide whether to accept a private offer before knowing whether a place is available at the state primary.

It is not unknown for parents to accept offers and pay fees against places which are never in fact taken up, simply as insurance in case preferred options do not come through.

ARE THESE PLACES ANY GOOD?

The parent grapevine is the most reliable source of information about schools. Even though parents with children actually at a school tend to be loath to put it down, a school's reputation tends to be pretty accurate. You do need though, to beware of plaudits or criticisms which stem from criteria different from your own.

There is also no substitute for first-hand experience. Attend as many school events as you can – open days and evenings, or perhaps better, more 'real' events such as sports fixtures or drama productions. During your visit, ask around, particularly, if you can, of children already attending the school (and, if possible, out of parental earshot).

Checklist for selecting a school:
➤ Is it a happy place?
➤ How easy is it to get to? You or someone else will be travelling there twice a day five times a week. Do you want your children (or yourself, for that matter) to start each day with a stressful school run? A local school has the advantage of local friends. A school with a wider catchment area involves time-consuming collections from play dates for example. If you have more than one child, sending them all to the same school will make life much easier, not just for the daily commute but also during holidays which – especially with private schools – may differ in dates.

- ➤ Do you like the headmaster/mistress? To what extent is he or she motivated by an enthusiasm for teaching children, and to what extent is he or she just doing a job?
- ➤ What is the physical environment like? Is there outdoor space, greenery, light, and places to be quiet?
- ➤ What is the teaching style: 'self-help' groups, or rows of listening children? Do you want a school which aims to produce culturally rounded children, sporty types, or academics?
- ➤ What are the academic expectations? Where do most of the children move on to?
- ➤ How do they rate in the league tables? This is a coarse measurement, but useful as an additional indicator, particularly if compared to previous years, which may indicate any trends. A slightly better indicator is comparing results of seven-year-olds with those achieved four years later – a measure of the difference the school is making to pupils. The Department of Education compiles these comparisons and schools should be able to show you such stats (similarly statistics comparing the school with others with a similar intake).
- ➤ How big is the school? An intake of two parallel classes of 32 might be fine for some children, but totally overwhelming for others.
- ➤ What part do religious and spiritual matters play in the life of the school – is there a religious assembly, for example?
- ➤ What is the teacher:pupil ratio?
- ➤ Is there children's work on the wall and is it genuinely creative?
- ➤ What is the policy on bullying (be sceptical of claims that there never is any). At playtime watch for children standing alone, a possible sign.
- ➤ Are there any before-/after- school care schemes?
- ➤ Are there extra-curricular activities?
- ➤ What is expected of parents? Perhaps nightly help with homework and/or regular fundraising?
- ➤ What are the other parents like and how is this going to reflect on the children?
- ➤ Are you able to assess the quality of the board of governors?
- ➤ What are the meals offered and are there any limits on food which can be brought into the school? (Some schools ban sweets, others junk food, in the interests of better concentration.)
- ➤ What is security like? Are playtimes supervised?
- ➤ Are drink and drugs at the school a concern?
- ➤ What homework is required? For younger children this equates to input from parents.
- ➤ Is there a uniform and if so is it expensive?
- ➤ Will your child be in a minority? Even well-integrated families can be surprised at the difficulties that can arise at school.
- ➤ If you have or are planning another child, what is the sibling policy? Having all your children at one school can simplify life greatly.
- ➤ Is it right for your child? Different children respond differently to different educational approaches so you need to make sure the school and child will work well together.

SCHOOL GUIDES

The Equitable Guide to Independent Schools – ed Klaus Boehm & Jenny Spalding (Bloomsbury; 2000; £17.99; 0856605557) – *Published in association with The Sunday Times – an annual round-up of over 520 private schools, with detailed listings and area-based indexes.*

The Good Schools Guide (The best-selling parents' guide to the top UK schools; Lucas Publications; £22 (£27 with online membership); 0 9532659 2 7) – *The guide that claims to tell you what the prospectus does not; subscribers can also access their online guide; you can read sample entries on the site before you invest.* / www.goodschoolsguide.co.uk.

Guide to Independent Schools 2004 – Klaus Boehm; Jenny Lees-Spalding (Trotman; 2003; £24.99; 0856608866) – *A guide to fee paying schools in the UK.*

The Independent Schools Guide – Gabbitas Educational Consultants (Kogan Page; 2002; £12.99; 0749437421) – *One of the most comprehensive UK school directories – more than 2,200 entries including a small number of nurseries; there is general information on independent education and also pieces on the curriculum, choosing a school, fees, scholarships and grants, religious affiliation of schools, single sex schools and dyslexia.*

The Independent Schools Guide 2003-04 (Kogan Page; 2003; £19.99 ; 0749439637) – *Compiled by Gabbitas Educational Consultants – a comprehensive directory to 2,200 private schools across the country.*

Independent Schools Yearbook 2003-2004 (A & C Black; 2003; £30; 0713667672) – *The official reference for five associations governing independent schools; contains details of almost 1,500 schools, and covers admissions, entrance exams, fees, scholarships, staff, governing bodies, and provisions for non-academic subjects (art, drama, music and sport).* / www.isyb.co.uk.

[Book & CD-rom] **The ISC Guide** (Independent Schools Council; 2001; free, £1.50 p&p within UK) – *Details of the 1275 independent day and boarding schools who are members of the Independent Schools Council – the body representing all the main independent schools in the country; (this effectively supersedes Choosing Your Independent School, published by ISIS – as ISCis was formerly known).* / www.iscis.uk.net, (020) 7798 1500.

The London Schools Guide   – Editor Joel Wolchover (The only guide you need to choose your child's secondary school in London; Mitchell Beazley; 2003; £12.99; 1840007834) – *A London-wide title profiling schools in all boroughs – both state and private.*

Which London School? & South East 2003/04 (John Catt Educational; 2003; £14.95; 0 901577 847) – *From the publishers of Which School? (first published in 1924 – 79th edition) this is one of a series from this specialist publisher (see www.schoolsearch.co.uk).* / John Catt Educational, Great Glemham, Saxmundham, Suffolk IP17 2DH, (01728) 663666.

INSPECTION RESULTS

Schools inspections are carried out by OFSTED (see Useful General Contacts at the end of this Section), at least every six years. A copy and summary of the most recent inspection report must be made available to anyone who asks to see it (and are to be found on the OFSTED website).

It should be remembered that OFSTED is not an independent inspectorate and is judging schools on their conformity to current government education policy. Schools working to different priorities, and particularly those deviating from the national curriculum, will be judged particularly harshly.

It is also worth bearing in mind that a Durham-based watchdog association has reported that 66% of inspectors watching the same class fail to give it the same mark. Inspection Methodology is under review, but any changes to procedures may change the goalposts, muddying historical comparisons.

Annual Performance and Assessment (PANDA) reports are not made available to the public. However, you can ask for details of results in national testing.

KEY STAGE TESTS?

Part of the terminology of education with which you need to start becoming familiar: the tests relating to the National Curriculum. Only state schools are obliged to follow this curriculum and to test children at specific points in their school career. However, private schools may mirror this framework to some degree.

Performance is measured at the following ages:

> *Key Stage 1:* at 7.
> *Key Stage 2:* at 11.
> *Key Stage 3:* at 14.
> *Key Stage 4:* at 16.

All the above ages may seem a long way in the future. However, if you have an academic secondary school in mind, it may well be that this school demands strong results at key stage two, making such performance important to you in your choice of primary school.

League tables of results show performance in the three core subjects – English, Maths and Science – showing the percentage of pupils who met the government's target level of achievement at this particular stage.

Basic league table results are published annually for example in the Evening Standard, but for a fair picture you need more detail, available to individual schools in statistics they are given by the Education Department. Among other things these show a school's results compared with those of children with similar backgrounds. Note that schools mark their own tests – a system potentially open to abuse.

State schools: the process

FIRST STEP: CONTACT YOUR LOCAL EDUCATION AUTHORITY (LEA)

Most LEAs produce brochures with much of the 'nuts and bolts' information necessary to look for schools in your area including: a list of schools; details of admissions policies; procedures for applications; and grants.

Some schools deal with their own admissions, while other schools' admissions are dealt with through the LEA.

Make sure that you don't miss closing dates for applications, especially for schools that deal with their own admissions.

Your Local Education Authority should be able to provide

➤ Help with queries on early years education from a Curriculum Adviser (Early Years).

➤ A list of LEA schools. Libraries, borough information offices, and the borough education department should all hold copies.

➤ Advice on schools admissions. Contact the borough education department

➤ Details of the procedure for applying for a place in a local authority school.

➤ Information for children with special needs.

➤ Details of before- and after- school care schemes.

CONTACT DETAILS

Barking & Dagenham, ☎ *Education (020) 8227 3022*
⌨ www.barking-dagenham.gov.uk

Barnet, ☎ *(020) 8359 4000, ⌨ www.barnet.gov.uk*

Bexley, ☎ *(020) 8303 7777, Education admissions ext 4230 & Special needs ext 4451 ⌨ www.bexley.gov.uk*

Brent, ☎ *Customer services (020) 8937 1200, Enquiries (020) 8937 1234, Children's information service (020) 8937 3001, Special education needs (020) 8937 3229 ⌨ www.brent.gov.uk*

Bromley, ☎ *(020) 8313 4160 ⌨ www.bromley.gov.uk*

Camden, ☎ *General (020) 7278 4444 Early Years (020) 7911 1603*
🖰 *www.camden.gov.uk*

Corporation of London, ☎ *(020) 7332 1750*

Croydon, ☎ *General (020) 8686 4433, Early Years (020) 8655 1299, Special Needs (020) 8656 6551, Education Department (020) 8760 5452*
🖰 *www.croydon.gov.uk*

Ealing Education Centre, ☎ *(020) 8578 6154* 🖰 *www.ealing.gov.uk*

Enfield, ☎ *(020) 8379 4453* 🖰 *www.enfield.gov.uk*

Greenwich, ☎ *(020) 8854 8888 ext 8043*

Hackney, ☎ *(020) 7354 8321, Admissions (020) 8356 7251*
🖰 *www.hackney.gov.uk*

Hammersmith & Fulham, ☎ *(020) 8748 3020* 🖰 *www.lbhf.gov.uk*

Haringey, ☎ *(020) 8489 0000* 🖰 *www.haringey.gov.uk*

Harrow, ☎ *(020) 8863 5611* 🖰 *www.harrow.gov.uk*

Hertsmere Borough Council, ☎ *(020) 8207 2277*
🖰 *www.hertsmere.gov.uk*

Hounslow, ☎ *(020) 8583 2000, Education welfare service (020) 8583 2780*
🖰 *www.hounslow.gov.uk*

Islington, ☎ *(020) 7527 5666* 🖰 *www.islington.gov.uk*

Kensington & Chelsea, ☎ *(020) 7361 3334* 🖰 *www.rbkc.gov.uk*

Kingston, ☎ *Education welfare service (020) 8547 5243, Early Years (020) 8547 6582* 🖰 *www.kingston.gov.uk*

Lambeth, ☎ *Education directorate (020) 7926 9771, One Stop Shop (020) 7926 9896* 🖰 *www.lambeth.gov.uk*

Lewisham, ☎ *(020) 8314 6200* 🖰 *www.lewisham.gov.uk*

Merton, ☎ *(020) 8545 3276* 🖰 *www.merton.gov.uk*

Newham, ☎ *(020) 8430 2000* 🖰 *www.newham.gov.uk*
/ HOURS *Mon-Fri 8am-8pm Sat 9am-1pm.*

Redbridge, ☎ *(020) 8708 3256* 🖰 *www.redbridge.gov.uk*

Richmond Education Department, ☎ *(020) 8891 7500*
🖰 *www.richmond.gov.uk*

Southwark, ☎ *Education reception (020) 7525 5001/5050*
🖰 *www.southwark.gov.uk*

Sutton, ☎ *(020) 8770 5000* 🖰 *www.sutton.gov.uk*

Sutton Childcare Information Centre, ☎ *(020) 8770 6000*
🖰 *www.childcarelink.gov.uk*

Tower Hamlets, ☎ *(020) 7364 4954, Children's information service (020) 7364 6495* 🖰 *www.towerhamlets.gov.uk*
/ HOURS *Mon-Thurs 8am-6pm, Fri 8am-5.30pm.*

Waltham Forest, ☎ *(020) 8496 3000* 🖰 *www.lbwf.gov.uk*

Wandsworth, ☎ *(020) 8871 8275, Educational psychology service (020) 8871 8744, Schools Admissions (020) 8871 7962* 🖰 *www.wandsworth.gov.uk*

Westminster, ☎ *One Stop information service (020) 7641 7777, School admissions (020) 7641 1817* 🖰 *www.westminster.gov.uk*

ADMISSION POLICIES

In theory parents choose their children's school. In practice good schools are oversubscribed, and the law has to give schools and LEAs a method of selecting which children can actually attend.

Even the theoretical choice currently offered may disappear if the current government proposal takes effect to allow groups of schools to form federations. Parents would apply to the federation, which would then decide which child goes to which school to ensure an even intake of different ranges of children. It remains to be seen if this survives the likely resultant parent outrage.

For the moment the current criteria continue to apply, the prime one being geographical. Schools define their catchment areas differently but the measurement is generally the distance on foot from your front door to the school gate. You might live close as the crow flies but be considered too far away because of an intervening railway line.

Boundaries change from year to year. If there are a large number of siblings already guaranteed places for a particular year, the catchment area for other pupils may become smaller than usual for example.

The pressure on good schools means that their official catchment areas are rather smaller than might be expected. What' more, as exact boundaries fluctuate from year to year it is quite possible that a given school may not be able to tell you whether you will be in the catchment area when it is time for your child to start.

Criteria for selecting children at oversubscribed schools:
➢ Whether you live in the school's catchment area.
➢ Whether siblings are already attending the school.
➢ Whether your child attends a linked nursery (or other) school ('feeder school').
➢ If your child has special needs – be they medical or social.
➢ The distance you live from the school and, more specifically, the travel time.
➢ With denominational schools: your religious persuasion, and whether you go to church (see church schools, below).
➢ If you live in the same borough as the school.

Schools are free to order these 'oversubscription criteria' as they wish, but they must publish the order they decide upon. 'Unofficial' criteria might include whether your application was late. A school might also give priority to those applicants who nominate it as their first choice.

If you fall outside the catchment area of your preferred school, it may be possible to get your child into it, but, for a good school, success is less likely unless you can prove some good reason why your child should attend. You do have a right to appeal but children living within the catchment area will generally get first choice.

The cost of living near a good school was estimated in 2002 as adding at least £25,000 to the cost of a home – and that's outside London. There the price of similar houses just three streets closer to a good school may jump by as much as £200,000.

WHEN TO MAKE CONTACT
Where state schools are concerned, parents seem generally to be expected to make contact when their child is about three years old. However, some state nursery and primary schools may interview children from 18 months for a place at three years, so in these cases you would need to register the child by at least 15 months. However, a nursery place does not guarantee that the child will transfer to the school.

HOW TO APPEAL
LEAs generally allocate final places around three months before a child is due to start school. Should the application for the state school of your

choice be rejected, you should receive a letter informing you of your alternative choices. It should also inform you of your right to appeal the decision.

Under the 1980 Education Act, parental choice is given strong priority by the legislation. In addition, by law, a child must be offered a school place "within reasonable travelling distance" of home.

If you feel you can make a good case as to why a particular school is better for your child than the alternative options offered, you can make an appeal. If you decide to do so, you should lodge this as quickly as possible as there are deadlines. Some are successful at the primary level, and in some cases LEAs sort out problems with parents informally before this stage is reached.

However, if your child was not offered a place because the maximum legal class size of 30 had already been reached, there are different rules of appeal. Only if it can be proved that a school did not comply with its own published admissions policy (or that an 'unreasonable' decision was reached) can an appeal be put forward.

Suggested points in drafting an appeal:

➢ Try to find out whether parents and pupils have successfully appealed vis-a-vis your chosen school in previous years.

➢ Secure a copy of the school's latest prospectus, and frame your case in relation to it: for example, matching your child's strengths against the school's good points.

➢ Visit local schools in which you are not interested so that you can articulate better why it is that a particular school best suits your child. Try to dwell on the chosen school's strengths rather than the other schools' weaknesses.

There are solicitors who specialise in the area of education law. If you make an appeal, you are likely to find that your LEA makes use of such lawyers in presenting its own case and – if you can afford the expense – it is worth considering whether you also should go down this route. This may be particularly the case if there any complicating factors – for example a special needs child.

USEFUL CONTACTS

Advisory Centre for Education Ltd (ACE), ☎ *Freephone advice line (0808) 800 5793* ⏚ *www.ace-ed.org.uk*
Free information pack about how to frame an appeal. / HOURS *Mon-Fri 2pm–5pm;* PUBLICATIONS *Free guides: Appealing for a school; Permanent and Fixed Period Exclusion.*

Department for Education & Skills (DfES), ☎ *(0870) 000 2288* ⏚ *www.dfes.gov.uk*
Formerly the Department for Education & Employment (DfEE): the website and helpline have information on appealing against a schools admission decision.

Education Law Association (ELAS), ☎ *(01303) 211570* ⏚ *www.educationlaw.org*
Although largely a training organisation for educationalists and lawyers, this company can provide names and addresses of its members – who are all specialists in education law – should you need legal advice or representation over special educational needs or an admissions appeal. / HOURS *No regular office hours.*

FAITH (CHURCH) SCHOOLS

Churches (primarily the Anglican Church, but also the Catholic Church and in a few cases other faiths) run a fair proportion of schools, especially in inner London. Such schools are often considered among the better performers.

The importance of having religious parents for admission of a particular child varies widely by school. In some cases regular attendance at a particular church is virtually a sine qua non (although most parents stop attending once the child is safely in). In other cases admission criteria are looser.

With Catholic schools, as well as the few Jewish and Muslim schools, admission tends to exclude those of other faiths. This is also true of many Church of England schools, though the church's long historical involvement in education has led to a hotch potch of different policies (for example, 98% of the pupils at one east London C of E school are Muslim). Some non-Christian parents choose to send their children to C of E schools as a higher priority is given to spirituality and moral teaching, albeit from the angle of a different religion.

USEFUL GENERAL CONTACTS

Advisory Centre for Education Ltd (ACE), ☎ *Freephone advice line (0808) 800 5793* ⌁ *www.ace-ed.org.uk*
Founded in 1960, a charitable organisation which acts as an advice centre for parents – primarily those with children already in school. ACE can help parents through appealing for a school place, trying to get extra help for a child with special educational needs or challenging an exclusion. / HOURS *Mon-Fri 2pm–5pm; PUBLICATIONS What Did You Do at School Today? Understanding your child's primary school (£5 + £1 p&p). Free guides: Tackling Bullying; Appealing for a school; Permanent and Fixed Period Exclusion.*

Campaign for State Education (CASE), ☎ *(020) 8944 8206* ⌁ *www.casenet.org.uk*
A group campaigning for the rights of all children to the best in state education (and dedicated to comprehensive – i.e. non-selective – education). Elements relating to nursery provision include working towards primary classes with less than 25 pupils (and secondary classes with less than 30 pupils). / PUBLICATIONS *CASE magazine; leaflet: Parents and Schools, and briefings (eg on Parents' Rights), free (send large SAE).*

Contact a Family, ☎ *Office (020) 7608 8700, Helpline (0808) 808 3555* ⌁ *www.cafamily.org.uk*
Advice and support for parents of children with disabilities or special needs – the local groups network offers advice on education issues. / HOURS *Helpline Mon-Fri 10am-4pm.*

Department for Education & Skills (DfES), ☎ *(0870) 000 2288* ⌁ *www.dfes.gov.uk*
Formerly the Department for Education & Employment (DfEE); the website is a valuable information source, with a 'Parents Gateway' which covers all relevant issues: choosing a school, special needs, gifted children, national curriculum tests, teacher assessment, National Childcare Strategy, admissions and appeals and almost every FAQ a parent will have. Sections for teachers and school governors may also be of interest. The helpline is useful for more particular questions.

National Campaign for Real Nursery Education (NCNE), ⌁ *www.ncne.co.uk*
The campaign, founded in 1965, now has about 600 members drawn from early-learning professionals, educationalists, governors and interested parents. The organisation exists to promote state nursery education and to support members defending existing provision. Individual membership £10, students £5. / PUBLICATIONS *Leaflets: What is Nursery Education?; The Importance of the Local Authority Nursery School; Four Year Olds in Reception Classes; When Should Your Child Start School?, all available in return for an SAE.*

National Confederation of Parent Teacher Associations (NCPTA), ☎ *(01732) 748850* ⌁ *www.ncpta.org.uk*
The largest organisation of parent teacher associations in England and Wales represents over 6 million parents and teachers; funded by membership subscriptions, it is non-sectarian and non-party political. The NCPTA promotes partnerships between pupils, parents, teachers and local education authorities, encourages parents to give help and support to their children, and ensures that parents have a say in national policy-making.

Office of Standards in Education (OFSTED), ☎ *(020) 7421 6800*
www.ofsted.gov.uk
Founded in 1992, a non-ministerial government department charged with monitoring school performance via regular inspections. Ofsted – to date – has inspected schools at least every six years (typically every 2–3 years). Private schools do not fall under the same inspection programme and though they receive a 'Registration visit' are not currently inspected in the normal course of affairs (though this situation is currently under review). All school inspections can be read on the department's website.

SchoolsNet, *www.schoolsnet.com*
A site offering information on all kinds of education issues. Primary schools can be searched for by area. Basic pupil numbers and SAT results are given (with, in some cases, more detailed profiles).

Private education

Many people believe that a private education is the best start in life that they can give a child. However paying vast amounts of money for an education is no guarantee of excellence.

In 2003 figures collected by OFSTED indicated that while one in 17 state primaries were poorly managed, the figure was one in seven among private schools. A number of the latter failed to check staff for criminal records, others failed to check pupil attendance, and overall staff turnover was reported to be too high. Religious schools in particular were criticised for failing to deliver the core curriculum. Causing particular concern were schools which are not members of the Independent Schools Council.

In assessing prospective private schools, you may wish to bear in mind the distinction between those which operate as charities, and those which operate as businesses. Most long-established private schools are charities, and all fees go to the school. However, with the ever-increasing demand for private education over recent years, more and more schools have emerged which are profit-making businesses.

Some profit-making schools are excellent, but when contemplating a profit-making school do need to ensure you are satisfied that the needs of the pupils are given due priority. This is a particular problem at prep schools judged on academic achievements. In order to continue to attract good 'raw material', they need pupils to perform well enough to get into the most highly rated secondary schools. This can result in pressure on the child, and even on parents who in effect are required to provide extra coaching.

Note that getting your child in at the primary/junior section of a respected private school does not mean that your child will not have any further barriers until 16 or 18. Most schools running both junior and senior sections aim to lose a number of juniors on entry to the senior school – sometimes as many as half.

Another issue you might want to bear in mind is fund-raising. How will you feel if the school seeks to meet its needs for equipment and so on by turning to the parents, rather than digging into its profit margin? margin or salaries for teachers?

Finally, it is also worth bearing in mind the findings of a recent report that as many as one in seven private schools are loss-making, and therefore at potential risk of closure.

Why people go private:

- Perceived better quality of teaching.
- Academically selective admissions policy.
- Less 'mixed' socially (i.e. lower proportion of 'unsuitable' playmates).
- More facilities (academic, sporting, musical…).

➤ Greater potential choice, as admission to a particular school generally has little to do with geography, and more to do with getting the child's name down in good time, the child's ability to earn a place, and the parents' ability to pay.

Fees for a pre-prep range from £700 – £2,900 per term nationally, with most London pre-preps towards the upper end of this scale. It is worth enquiring exactly what the fees include. It is not unknown to find well-reputed schools charging more than £2,000 per term, which still require parents to provide a packed lunch.

SECURING ADMISSION

There are no hard and fast rules on private pre-preps' admission procedure. A few operate a first-come, first-served list, but many different schemes exist, including interviews – yes, even at three years old – and balloting. Stories abound of schools where there are 600 waiting for 30 places.

Strong demand dictates that to secure a reasonable chance of a place it is often necessary to put children's names down frighteningly early. Even if actual entry is by selective interview the lists of potential interviewees are often closed remarkably early. If a school operates a pure list system, six months may be too late.

A fee of £20 up to a more usual £50 is generally required to register with a school. While the school will encourage you to do this, it will often refuse to give any indication of the length of the queue and/or likelihood of this resulting in the offer of a place. This approach helps fuel the suspicion that these lists are just money-making wheezes for some schools.

As most parents put their child down for several schools, to some extent the various waiting lists have names in common – when the time comes, and parents finally decide, places are freed up elsewhere. This also happens when families move from the area (reported by one educational consultant to be more common in south and west London than north London).

The quality of schools does change over time, as will your perception of what will best suit your child, and when the time comes your chosen school may no longer be quite such a desirable choice. Hedging your bets is therefore a sensible, if slightly pricey, policy.

STYLE OF EDUCATION

In London, private schools – even at primary level – tend to be extremely academic. There is a danger that this can undermine the confidence of a child who does badly in them. It is notoriously difficult to judge whether a child is going to be academic or not at the entry age (and some research indicates that pushing too early may be counter-productive, particularly in boys). Other private schools are extremely sports-orientated, but it may well be easier to judge the child's interest in this at an earlier age.

One strategy is to wait until the last year of primary school (age seven) before deciding on whether to transfer to this style of education if it seems appropriate. This should still leave time to prepare for Common Entrance (at 11, 12 or 13) or the individual exams operated by independent day schools (usually at 10). That said, even excellent state schools do not necessarily prepare children in the areas expected by private prep schools, and extra tuition may be needed in some cases for the child to pass the necessary entrance interview.

JUDGING STANDARDS

Even though there are a number of guides to private schools, the parent grapevine remains as important as ever in judging their current standards.

Inspections and regulations provide less of a safeguard, as private schools have different, less onerous requirements than those which are state run.

The Independent Schools Council Information Service (ISCIS, until recently known as ISIS) – see below – has certain standards for membership but these are generally to do with the conditions of the premises and number of lavatories rather than educational levels. Private schools, for example, do not have to use qualified teachers and may not have any explicit education policies in place.

USEFUL CONTACTS

Gabbitas Educational Consultants, ☎ (020) 7734 0161
⌂ www.gabbitas.co.uk
Advice on private schools including a free list of schools on the basis of criteria discussed. A consultation (£145 per hour) involves a description of how the private education system works and offers intensive consideration of the options which might suit your child best.

Independent Schools Council Information Service (ISCIS),
☎ (020) 7798 1560, Publication orders (020) 7798 1560
⌂ www.iscis.uk.net/southeast
Formerly known as ISIS, this membership organisation for independent schools provides information about its members to parents. The London and South East Region has 568 member schools (over half of them preparatory) and distributes over 25,000 copies of its handbook every year. The service also offers a consultation service (£135 + VAT per hour, £60 + VAT by phone or email; full placement fee £350 + VAT). The website offers a full search facility – a useful first port of call, as all details of school are listed, from academic success and extra-curricular activities to fees and girl:boy ratios (where applicable). / PUBLICATIONS For 5 free leaflets on financial and other topics see website.

4. HOME-BASED EDUCATION

There appears at the moment to be a growing dissatisfaction with conventional education. Reasons include: class sizes; a narrowing of the curriculum to meet national testing requirements; the difficulty of tailoring teaching to the needs of an individual child; and the continued division of learning into separate subjects. (This last is argued in some quarters to be out of date in a world that requires more 'multi-skilling' than ever.)

Whatever the reasons, support for home teaching is growing. There are numerous organisations keen to explain to parents that, contrary to accepted wisdom, the law does not require that you send your child to school, only that you provide what your local education authority agrees to be a suitable education.

The main problem with home schooling is the limited chances it affords for social interaction. To counter this, most home schooling families set up a group to meet at least weekly. Such an arrangement may also help with the second most pressing issue which is that of ensuring that those who are doing the teaching – usually parents – have somewhere to exchange tips. Alternatively it is a way that families can join forces to bring in external specialists in fields they themselves feel they cannot cover adequately.

READING

Natural Learning & the National Curriculum – Roland Meighan (Educational
Heretics Press (www.gn.apc.org/edheretics); 2001; £10; 1900219190) – *Author of
a number of titles on home-learning, who writes a column in Natural Parent magazine.*
/ *Natural Parent, (0800) 146054.*

USEFUL CONTACTS

Advisory Centre for Education Ltd (ACE), ☎ *Freephone advice line*
(0808) 800 5793 ✆ *www.ace-ed.org.uk*
Although primarily an advice centre for children in schools, this organisation also
produces a home education pack, including a special report produced by Education
Now; £6 plus £1 pp. / *HOURS Mon-Fri 2pm–5pm; PUBLICATIONS ACE Special Education Handbook;
Home Education Pack.*

Choice in Education (CinE), ☎ *(020) 8969 0893*
✆ *www.choiceineducation.org.uk*
A monthly newsletter, with listings for those interested in home-based education;
information includes providing legal guidelines; website includes pages for The
Otherwise Club (see also) and HesFes – the annual Home Educators Seaside Festival
(www.hesfes.co.uk).

Education Otherwise, ☎ *Recorded information line (0870) 730 0074*
✆ *www.education-otherwise.org*
The oldest and largest home-based education organisation (founded 1977), providing
a self-help organisation for interested parents. Membership £20 per
annum. / *PUBLICATIONS Free information pack (send SAE) includes a booklist.*

Free Range Education, ✆ *www.free-range-education.co.uk*
The authors of several books on home learning have put together this website which
looks at, amongst other things, legal issues of home learning.

Home Education Advisory Service, ☎ *(01707) 371854*
✆ *www.heas.org.uk*
A national charity which runs an advice line and publishes the Home Education
Handbook, plus a range of information leaflets. Subscription is £12 per annum.

The Otherwise Club, ☎ *Admin (020) 7735 7735, Help Desk (0800) 652
3145* ✆ *www.choiceineducation.co.uk/toc*
This club for families of children educated out of school meets at a community
centre (Granville Centre, Granville Road, NW6), at least one day a week (call before
arrival): it provides workshops, art classes and the opportunity for children and
parents to socialise. The club provides nothing in the way of supervision – a parent
remains to oversee the children. There is a library of books and equipment, including
microscopes and tents. Membership £150, (£100 concessions) per year per family paid
termly (some workshops extra); send an SAE or see website for more
information. / *HOURS Tues, Weds, Thurs 10am-12pm & 1pm-3pm; PUBLICATIONS A Compilation of
Selections to Help Home-Based Educators, £4 incl p&p.*

Warwick District Community, ✆ *www.warwick-district.org.uk/flexi*
A website which considers the benefits of 'flexi-time schooling', which combines
both school and home-based education (according to a contract between parents and
the local school). Information packs can be downloaded.

5. SPECIAL EDUCATIONAL NEEDS (SEN)

Special Needs in this context refers to any need which "prevents a child
from gaining maximum access to the curriculum". This may be physical,
emotional, social, sensory or intellectual, or any combination thereof.

While it is estimated that as many as one child in five may have special
educational needs at some time during their schooling, an estimated two
out of very hundred have needs so severe or complex that they require
prolonged and significant help. This group typically includes children who
are deaf, dyslexic, autistic, or with Down's syndrome.

Finding a decent education for your child can seem like a tough job
at the best of times. Discovering that she (or, actually more likely, he) has

special educational needs can turn a boring hunt into a stressful quest for the best place to bring your child on properly.

Provision is patchy and the knowledge that the right help can make a real difference to your child's development is a heavy responsibility to bear. Advice is on offer, though, both from dedicated organisations (see useful contacts below) and from charities that support particular conditions (see chapter *2.03 Baby health*) and it's well worth going looking for it.

STATEMENTING

If your child has anything more than superficial difficulties, you should have them properly assessed at the earliest opportunity. Not only does a diagnosis help ascertain what strategy will best help your child, it will be vital in securing a 'Statement' (a Statement of Educational Needs), which is a pre-requisite for council funding to help your child's education.

Some parents fear that the Statement process will stigmatise their child. But with the high expense of special needs education (at the extreme, fees at some special needs schools can be over £30,000 per annum), even wealthy parents usually end up swallowing such concerns, unless the condition is relatively minor.

Private special needs schools exist and might meet your child's needs far better than the equivalent state option, but the reverse can also be true. In any case, provision is patchy and it's largely a question of working with whatever is to hand locally. That said, a significant number of parents end up moving as a result of this.

Time is of the essence. Getting a Statement can be a long-winded process and involves reports from professionals such as educational psychologists ('ed psychs'), teachers, paediatricians, and therapists. Services which may be involved in the process include the LEA (local education authority), Education Social Work Service, the Education Psychological Service, and the Primary Learning Support Service.

Each statement is a claim on your council's already over-stretched SEN budget, so it's no surprise that they aren't handed out lightly. and because the system isn't really funded properly it tends to spin cases out. What's more, the situation is a lottery, with provision varying hugely from borough to borough.

Some parents whose children have very clear needs still have to fight, often with legal backing to secure the proper support for their child. It can be a miserable process for parents already having a tougher time than most in raising their family, (Campaigners – for example novelist and father of an autistic child, Nick Hornby – do what they can to highlight the failures of the system). It can be worth the struggle though.

You will hear story after story of – and may yourself encounter – council caseworkers dragging their feet, requiring constant chasing, not doing what they said they would and subtly varying the contents of communications, when they do finally arrive, from what was agreed verbally. Getting some expert input is a good idea, with IPSEA (seeï below) an excellent source of advice.

APPEALING THE STATEMENT

If you do not believe the Statement adequately meets the needs of your child, you have two months in which to appeal it.   •

Fighting an appeal relating to a statement typically costs about £6,000. This is a lot for most families to find, but can be a tiny fraction of the funding actually at stake. As well as legal fees, you will need to commission reports from your own team of experts and educational psychologists to support your position. It can be well worth the effort, though. Parents win at appeal in 82% of cases.

CHOOSING A SCHOOL

It is vital that whatever environment you pick for your child, it is an understanding one and one that does not judge your child's differences from the norm as being the result of mere naughtiness.

One difficulty of finding schools for special needs children is that often their needs are changing very fast age four and it can be difficult to predict how they will be performing aged five. Just finding suitable schools in your area may be no mean feat.

Remember that shooting too high relative to your child's abilities can be just as destructive as shooting too low – your child needs to be challenged, but also needs to be confident and happy.

MAINSTREAM VERSUS SPECIALIST EDUCATION

State policy nowadays is to aim for inclusion of special needs children in mainstream education. Typically a child will join a class with part- or full-time support from a learning assistant.

It is a policy that takes different parents and children different ways. Especially with children whose issues are relatively minor, it often chimes with their aims for their child to have as normal an upbringing as possible.It may be particularly useful with a condition like Down's syndrome which means learning is through copying signs.

But for parents of more profoundly affected children the on-going closure of special schools around the country can seem nothing more than a cost-cutting drive. While children with special needs can benefit from exposure to normally developing peers, mainstream inclusion can mean merely existing in a mainstream class without meaningfully taking in or participating in what's going on, and being given activities different from the surrounding children.

If you are considering some form of education in a mainstream state school, the good news is that a child with Special Needs comes very high up the priorities for criteria for a place at a school. If you can show that this is the right school for your child, they will have a hard time turning you down.

PRIVATE PROVISION

As noted above, it by no means true – even if you have the money – that the best choice for your child is a private one. However there are some excellent private schools for special needs children.

State help is available to send children to private special needs schools, but it's a bit all-or-nothing. If the council accept your case it will be just as if your child were at a state school. If they don't, however, you get nothing, and probably all external support as well.

To have the council fund a specialist private school, you have to show that your child's needs cannot be met in the state sector. Sometimes local councils are fully supportive of parents making such a case, often dependent on them having used the school in the past. If your caseworkers on the council don't agree, however, you will probably find yourself in a legal dispute with both sides drawing on their own reports from educational pyschologists to justify their position.

Some preps and pre-preps – probably with half an eye on the increasing number of diagnoses of developmental difficulties – are making themselves more receptive to special needs children. You do need to be very careful though in assessing whether their experience and level of resources will give your child the support they really need.

Note that private schools can be insincere in their treatment of parents. They want to be seen to be helpful and caring, but without necessarily wanting to tackle the issues and work created by a special needs child. Even special schools may want to take only as many seriously difficult children as they have to in order to pay the rent. As a result – especially if you are trying to aim high – you may find schools waste your time on assessments and interviews without any serious intention of taking your child, or seriously addressing their needs at all.

THERAPIES

Therapies and therapists can provide vital help with Special Needs children. Often schools will provide their own speech therapist, for example. This is not necessarily the case, though. Occupational therapy and music therapy can also have surprisingly positive effects on children's development but resources for them are quite rarely found within schools.

It's worth knowing, that their provision can be written into statements. What's needed is for you to make a reasonable case that it is one of the ways in which your child's needs should be met.

CONTACTS

Independent Panel for Special Education Advice (IPSEA), ☎ *England & Wales (0800) 0184016, Scotland (0131) 454 0082, Northern Ireland (01232) 705654; Tribunal appeals only (01394) 384711, General (01394) 380518* ⌂ *www.ipsea.org.uk*
A great resource for parents starting to weave their way through the maze of statementing and negotiating with their LEA to push for what their child needs – free independent advice; free advice on appealing to the Special Educational Needs Tribunal, including representation when needed; free second professional opinions.

Parents for Inclusion, ☎ *Admin (020) 7735 7735, Helpline (0800) 652 3145* ⌂ *www.parentsforinclusion.org*
Information, assistance and support to parents of children considered to have special educational needs, particularly for parents who would prefer their children not to go to a special school. / *HOURS Tues, Weds, Thurs 10am-12pm & 1pm-3pm.*

READING

Schools for Special Needs Guide – Gabbitas Educational Consultants (Kogan Page; £16.99; 0749440511) – *Now in its seventh edition, the guide covers how to identify the need for special education, how to make the right choice, and a listing of more than 2,000 independent, non-maintained and state-maintained special needs schools and colleges. Also mainstream schools offering provision for special needs.* / *www.gabbitas.co.uk.*

Taking Action – John Wright & David Ruebain (Appropriate education is every child's right. The essential guide to SEN law for teachers, parents, advocates and advice workers; Questions Publishing; 2002; £16.95; 1-84190-081-8) – *Produced by advice charity IPSEA, a readable guide to the education law applicable to special needs schooling. It covers your rights, how to take action, and the points you need to prove if you are to take issue with your borough's approach.*

6. ROUND-UP LISTINGS

(For information on educational resources for children with dyslexia and other special needs, see the Developmental issues section of chapter 2.03 Baby health.)

INFORMATION SOURCES

Alliance for Childhood, ☎ *(01342) 824 200* ⌂ *www.allianceforchildhood.org.uk*
A US-based "partnership of individuals and organisations committed to fostering and respecting each child's inherent right to a healthy, developmentally appropriate childhood".

British Association for Early Childhood Education
(BAECE), ☎ *(020) 7539 5400* ⏚ *www.early-education.org.uk*

Membership organisation for professionals working in education for young children.
Membership (individual), £30; concessions and group rates
available. / *PUBLICATIONS Range of books. A list and order form are available online.*

The Children's Project, ☎ *(020) 8546 8750* ⏚ *www.childrensproject.co.uk*

An organisation promoting a child-centred approach to parenting. See the website
for further information, and details of publications available.

Education Advisory Service, ☎ *(020) 8672 3185*

A service for parents explaining how education works in both the state and private
sector, starting with getting names down for schools and nursery provision. The
service points out the variable quality of both private and state schools; an hour's
consultation (£120) provides general information plus a list of appropriate schools in
your local area. It offers a service for parents of children with special needs or specific
learning difficulties, such as dyslexia or high IQ; tuition from £25 per hour.

Education Now, ☎ *(0115) 925 7261* ⏚ *www.educationnow.gn.apc.org*

Co-operative campaigning for a more flexible and diverse personalised education
system – it highlights the discovery of over 30 different learning styles. Consultancy
services for parents; conferences for parents and teachers; publications on alternative
approaches to education (including a Home Education Pack whose suppliers include
ACE) – a range of books are published by Education Now and also under its
Educational Heretics Press imprint (www.edheretics.gn.apc.org).

Families Magazines, ☎ *(020) 8696 9680* ⏚ *www.familiesmagazine.co.uk*

The publishers of a number of regional free magazines both in London (Families
SW, Families North, Families upon Thames, etc) and increasingly outside as well,
which include information on schools and schooling. It also runs the Education
Advisory Service (see also).

High/Scope UK, ☎ *(020) 8676 0220* ⏚ *www.high-scope.org.uk*

An education programme that aims to improve children's – and, in consequence,
later – lives. Based on 30 years of research, the method centres on recognising and
supporting the differences in children, on developing their self-confidence by
concentrating on their strengths and on thereby making them able to solve problems
and make decisions. Impressive social and job achievements are claimed for those
who have been schooled using the programme.

Human Scale Education, ☎ *(01275) 332516* ⏚ *www.hse.org.uk*

Campaigners for a more 'human-scale', child-centred approach in large state schools
and supporters of small (and mini) schools, and 'flexi-schooling' (combining school
with home-based education). Advice is provided to parents and teachers;
membership £25 (£15 for low income). / *PUBLICATIONS Wide range of publications for parents
and teachers – booklist online.*

Kids' Clubs Network, ☎ *(020) 7512 2100* ⏚ *www.kidsclubs.co.uk*

A national society that promotes after-school (and out-of-school) childcare services
for playworkers and parents.

Letts Educational, ☎ *(020) 8996 3333* ⏚ *www.letts-education.com*

The Letts books and electronic resources cover all ages from pre-school to A Level.
The website includes background information on the schooling system, including
pre-schools, choosing a nursery and the like.

Montessori Society (AMI) UK, ☎ *(020) 7435 7874*
⏚ *www.montessori-ami.org*

Maria Montessori, born in the late 19th century, founded a teaching approach which
has gained popularity in the UK, particularly for nursery and primary teaching. The
idea is to promote the child's natural development in socialising, exploring and
communicating and to foster a sense of independence and order to achieve
a rounded education. Children usually work individually, but together when they
want, often in groups with a span of ages. The society can send details of registered
schools offering a complete Montessori approach, and also those which incorporate
elements of the Montessori idea. Most teachers, even if Montessori-trained, tend to
break away from the official system which is often felt to be too rigid (official
Montessori schools, for example, may discourage fantasy play or stories). Note that
there is no control on use of the name – any nursery can call itself a Montessori
nursery – which led Maria to found this society in 1929 in order to protect the
integrity of her teaching. The Society can also supply information on the Montessori
approach to education, including a range of books on the subject.

National Association for Primary Education (NAPE),
☎ (01604) 647660 ⏄ www.nape.org.uk

Promoters of high-quality primary education for all children in the belief that this is the most critical phase of every child's life. The organisation also campaigns for the development of good practice and believes primary education is a partnership of all those involved – including of course parents. / *PUBLICATIONS Publications include 'What Does it Mean? A Guide to Edspeak (£2.50 + p&p), Listening for Clues (about children's thinking) (£2), Help! Advice to Parents (£2+ p&p), A Parents' Guide to Handwriting (£2 + P&P).*

S-KD Educational Consultants, ☎ (020) 8871 3057 ⏄ www.skd.co.uk

A firm of five educational consultants (including an ex-headmaster and two ex-Gabbitas people) who advise on independent schools. Having agreed a shortlist, they will contact the schools for you to obtain prospectuses and look after putting your child's name down. A typical fee for general advice and some names would be £100. / *HOURS 9am-5.30pm.*

Steiner Schools Fellowship, ☎ (01342) 822115
⏄ www.steinerwaldorf.org.uk

Rudolph Steiner (a late 19th century educator) founded a movement based on the belief that the educational process should focus on awakening the spirit rather than simply imparting information. The philosophy argues, as does recent research comparing British education with that of countries like Switzerland, that forcing academic learning too soon has a long-term and negative effect on children's ability and willingness to continue learning. As well as providing information about its methodology, the fellowship represents 26 autonomous mainstream Steiner Waldorf Schools and 56 kindergartens in the UK and Ireland, and 780 Steiner Waldorf Schools and over 1,500 kindergartens worldwide. / *PUBLICATIONS Various publications including books, journals and a monthly newsletter.*

Teacher Trading, ☎ (01420) 588 055 ⏄ www.thespanishbookshop.com

Suppliers of a range of titles about children and education, which range from the works of Chris Woodhead (one-time Chief inspector for schools), to 'Creating Kids Who Can Concentrate'; and books on home schooling.

21st Century Learning Initiative, ☎ (01225) 420290
⏄ www.21learn.org

Previously known as Education 2000 – an organisation campaigning with schools, technology-providers, communities and parents to recreate the education system in a form appropriate to the 21st century rather than the 19th. Emphasises the importance of early stimulation and cross discipline learning as more effective than single-subject lessons.

Wellspring Bookshop, ☎ (020) 7405 6101 ⏄ www.rudolfsteinerbooks.co.uk

Extensive collection of children's material – family and educational books – many relating to Rudolph Steiner's methods of teaching. / *HOURS Mon-Fri 10.30am-5.30pm Sat 12pm-5.30pm.*

EXTRA STIMULATION

Accelerated Learning Systems, ☎ (01296) 631177
⏄ www.acceleratedlearning.com

Publishers of handbooks supplied with teaching aids – systems that aim to teach parents how to stimulate their child. First FUNdamentals is a learning plan for children from birth to 18 months; FUNdamentals – a learning plan from 18 months to six years.

School of Accelerated Learning, ☎ (020) 8979 3951
⏄ www.acceleratedlearningschool.com

"How to Waken Your Child's Intelligence - How parents can make a difference for their children from birth to age six." Four-day courses led by an NLP trainer with experience in child education, promising parents a smarter, happier and more self-reliant child who can read, write and do maths by the age of four, grows up with encyclopedic knowledge, is physically excellent, can learn a foreign language and plays a musical instrument. In addition parents will learn to give the love children need without spoiling them and will parent with more success and less stress. Costs £495, with your registration fee returned if you are not satisfied.

Sing and Sign, ☎ (01273) 550 587 ⏄ www.singandsign.com

An action songs video (£12) and DVD (£18) featuring 25 Sing and Sign babies filmed at the park, on a farm and in a class setting, demonstrating a special signing system to allow babies to communicate with their parents before they can talk.

SPECIAL CASES

Hornsby International Dyslexia Centre, ☎ (020) 7223 1144

☝ www.hornsby.co.uk

The centre, founded in 1984, claims to be one of the world's largest specialist centres for dyslexia. If offers educational assessments (from age four), advice, counselling and tutoring, and has a resource centre for books and teaching.

National Association for Gifted Children, ☎ (0870) 770 3217

☝ www.nagcbritain.org.uk

Charity to help and advise individual families and professionals interested in achieving the maximum fulfilment of very able children's talents. The organisation emphasises that such talents may not be apparent in standard tests, for example if the intelligence is in ideas or seeing and doing (visual-spatial) rather than talking and listening. Help is provided to individual children and families, with clubs, newsletters, publications and counsellors (including in music and art).

National Portage Association, ☎ (01935) 471641

☝ www.portage.org.uk

A home education system for under-fives with special needs: after individual assessment a teaching programme is created, to be implemented by the parents. Trained portage home-workers visit weekly to demonstrate how to put theory into practice, and respond to any problems, and to offer guidance on the pace of development which can be expected. / HOURS Mon & Thu 9am–1pm.

Network 81, ☎ (0870) 770 3306 ☝ www.network81.co.uk

Campaigns for the education of children with special needs and seeks to inform the parents of these children about educational issues. / HOURS Mon-Fri 10am-2pm.

Support Society for Children of High Intelligence (CHI), ☎ (020) 8347 8927 ☝ www.chi-charity.org.uk

A group for children whose IQ is in the top 2%, acting particularly where it perceives the education system falls short. The society feels the greatest need for change is in primary education, where it judges that lack of suitable provision can be potentially crippling to a child's development. The organisation runs classes for children and will advise parents about how best to approach education officials. / PUBLICATIONS 'Give Them a Head Start', a DIY kit for parents to test their child's intelligence from birth to 6 years; newsletter.

CHAPTER 2.08

FINANCE

IMPORTANT!

<u>The information set out below is merely intended to provide a very general indication of some of the options available to you in planning your affairs. The publishers take no responsibility for its accuracy and completeness (or lack thereof).</u>

1. INTRODUCTION

The prospect of complete responsibility for a whole new person generally makes people focus seriously on the issue of finances.

This is small wonder when you consider the sums involved. In 2003 AXA Insurance put the price of raising a child to the age of 21 at £161,000, not including the cost of private education which would bring the figure closer to £300,000. The cost just to the age of five was estimated as £20,315. The figures can be considerably higher for a child with special needs and not included in the calculations are the costs of running a larger car, a larger house, or savings for the child.

The rules governing all aspects of finance from wills to pensions change constantly. The subject merits a book in itself (some are listed below). The following is intended only as a checklist of the chief issues and considerations to bear in mind.

Also worth addressing in advance is how, if one or other of you will be reducing or stopping work, are you going to arrange your monthly finances and spending. Different priorities are all very well when you are each spending your own money, but a lot more tricky when one of you is dependent *and* you are incurring extra expenses.

USEFUL CONTACTS

Financial Services Authority, ☎ *(020) 7066 1000* ⏏ *www.fsa.gov.uk*
The principal UK regulatory authority runs a Consumer Help section of its website which – at the 'ABC' level – offers an introduction to many financial products and concepts. / *HOURS Mon-Fri 8am-6pm.*

Society of Financial Advisers, ☎ *(020) 8989 8464* ⏏ *www.sofa.org*
"The UK's main body for the development of professional standards in the financial services industry" – can help locate a financial advisor in your area. / *HOURS Mon-Fri 8am-6pm.*

READING

The "Which?" Guide to Financing Your Child's Future – Virginia Wallis (Which? Books; 2003; £10.99 ; 0852029381)

Chartwell Guide to Investing for Children – Patrick Connolly (Chartwell; 2002) – *From a Bath-based IFA, a guide on the subject. / www.chartwell-direct.co.uk/guides.cfm; (01225) 446 556.*

Moneywise (Readers' Digest; £3.50, annual subscription £42) – *A monthly consumer magazine aobut private investment and finance. Regularly reports on suitable investments on behalf of children. / www.moneywise.co.uk.*

2. DEBTS

Short term financial fixes that might have made sense when you and your partner were both childless and in full-time employment, may not seem quite as attractive when you are trying to save for holidays, school fees...

Chances are that you can't just cut back and pay down your debts in a month or two. Now is the time, though, to avoid the natural inclination to be lazy about finance, and to make sure you are not paying over the odds on interest. Most Sunday newspapers publish the best credit card, loan and mortgage deals currently available and so long as you have a reasonable credit history it makes sense to start shopping around between providers.

If you live with a constant overdraft and don't pay down your store and credit cards each month, stop kidding yourself that these debts are short term. Think carefully about how you might consolidate them using cheaper, more appropriate borrowing. This might be a loan from a building society or if you have a reasonable amount of equity in your house, then it may make sense to increase your mortgage or opt for a mortgage that incorporates a current account.

Once you've gone to all this trouble, <u>don't do what most people do</u>. Studies show that most people who pay off their credit cards with some other form of loan, typically then rush out and re-borrow on their cards and overdraft all over again.

SAVING MONEY ON DEBT

Store cards: tend to be one of the most expensive types of borrowing. Try to transfer any long-term debts on these cards.

Credit cards: if you do nothing else, make sure you are getting the best rates on offer. Beware of sexy introductory offers (like 0% finance) that either a) evaporate if you pay late; or b) lead on to expensive rates at the end of the initial period. Again, try to pay these debts off – you're just making the bankers richer and richer.

Mortgate: lenders notoriously subsidise new customers by charging more to older ones. If you have had your mortgage for any length of time, it could really pay you to shop around and see what kind of re-mortgaging deals are available. Beware, though, anything with redemption penalties, and clauses that are going to prevent you going through the same process in two–three years time.

3. INSURANCE

If you don't have any insurance and have no great reserves of savings, then ensuring an income to raise your child in the event of an accident occurring to you or your partner should be towards the top of your list of priorities.

Life insurance: (for one or both parents.) Term assurance, known in the trade as 'drop dead' insurance, is the cheapest option. The cover lasts only until you are a certain age (say 60) and the policy will only pay out if you die, providing generally either a lump sum or a set amount per annum over a certain period. A more expensive alternative is Flexible Whole of Life Assurance. There is no set term for this and there is a surrender value that builds up over the period of the policy. You can start with a high level of cover when the children are young and reduce it later. Cover can be increased for subsequent children. Alternatively a few insurers offer family income benefit policies which pay a tax free annual income from a person's death to the end of the policy term. These are usually cheaper than lump sum policies and useful if survivors are unlikely to want to take on the responsibility of investing a large lump sum. Life insurance is a good idea for both parents, whether earning or not. It would be very expensive for example to pay for the childcare equivalent of a non-working mother. Prices vary markedly so it is worth shopping around, remembering that if both parents plan to take out a policy, two singles often work out cheaper than a joint policy for a couple. Writing the policy in trust (which should be possible on a standard form available from the insurance company) ensures that the company can pay the proceeds immediately and that the payment will be free of inheritance tax.

Critical illness cover (income protection insurance): you are five times more likely to be off work for six months or more than you are to die before the age of 60. The financial hardship is likely to be most serious if you are self-employed. You are now only eligible for state benefit relating to critical illness if you are assessed as unfit to do *any* work, not just the work you have been doing to date. To encourage people to take out their own income protection, all benefits from this type of policy (accident or illness insurance) are free from income tax. Premiums can, however, be expensive.

Mortgage protection insurance: this would repay the mortgage if you or your partner were to die. You may already have this as it is compulsory on many mortgages.

Twins insurance: offers cash if you become pregnant with twins (approximately one in 80 births in the UK and one in 50 for older mothers), to cover the extra costs of paying for two of everything. However, this is relatively expensive.

USEFUL CONTACTS

Marcus Hearn & Co
Marcus Hearn House, 65-66 Shoreditch High St London E1 6JL ☎ (020) 7739 3444
⏱ www.marcushearn.co.uk
The recommended broker for Zurich Personal Insurance, which has a twins policy. It pays a lump sum of up to £5,000 for a premium of approximately £42 per thousand, if under 29 with no history of twins; £89 per £1,000 if aged 30-34, with one instance of twins on the mothers side of the family, if paid before a first scan at 11 weeks. With ever-earlier scans you would have to get this policy as soon as possible, probably even before you get pregnant. Multiple births are more likely in women over 35 years old, those with three or more children already, and those with twins in either parent's family.

4. MAKING A WILL

The sooner you make a will the better: ideally before the birth. This is particularly important if you and your partner are not married, or if you are in a second marriage where both children and stepchildren are involved. In both such cases, were you to die without making a will ('intestate') your money might well be distributed very differently from the way you might have wished.

Making a will ensures that in the event of your death there is no lengthy delay for your survivors in receiving money from your estate. You can also stipulate exactly how your estate is to be divided. What's more, if your estate is likely to be anything in excess of £263,000 – the maximum amount that can be passed to your heirs free of inheritance tax – making a will becomes important in minimising this liability.

Even if you are in a first marriage, making a will makes matters more straightforward, particularly if you are relatively well off. If you die intestate and your net assets are less than £125,000, on your death all your wealth just passes to your spouse. However, if your net assets are greater than £125,000 your children share the balance. Even though your partner would have an interest during his or her lifetime this could mean that your spouse would lose control over decisions regarding, say, the family home.

Note that when you marry any existing will is rendered void. Also that if you should go through a divorce, any provision previously made for a husband or wife will probably be invalidated.

As well as your wishes regarding your property, a will also enables you to nominate exactly who you would like to raise your child should you and your partner die. Unless you specify your wishes about this the decision will be made by the courts. However, you may wish to include the proviso that the child should be consulted in this matter as there have been cases where a will has forced antagonistic adults and children together. You do not actually need a will to state your preferences. You can achieve the same effect with a simple letter held by a friend or relative.

Advice is that if there are children involved, especially if they are under 18 or there are children from another relationship, you should not draw up your own will without expert help. A simple will should cost £50–£100 (usually a set fee). You should check this before going ahead. A personal recommendation is the best way to find a solicitor or you can locate one through the Yellow Pages. Some charities offer free guides to writing a will (in the hope that you may wish to remember the charity while you are about it).

If you have children under 18 you might also look into the issue of setting up a trust to hold the money for them, nominating people to run those trusts – not necessarily the same people who have been nominated as their guardians. For more on trusts see below.

READING

Make Your Own Will (A step by step action pack for writing your own will; Which? Books; 1999; £10.99; 085202875X) – *Suitable for people (in England and Wales) who don't face any legal complications, a 28-page guide to writing your last will and testament, and including relevant forms.*

Wills and Probate – Paul Elmhurst (How to Make a Will and How to Administer the Estate of Someone Who Has Died, Without Employing a Solicitor; Which? Books; 2001; £10.99; 085202858X) – *Reviewing the issues surrounding the making of a will.*

USEFUL CONTACTS

The Law Society, ☎ (020) 7242 1222 ⏚ www.lawsociety.org.uk

The society maintains a website which provides detailed information regarding all areas of making a will and can provide details of solicitors with expertise in wills and trusts. / *HOURS Mon-Fri 9am-5pm.*

5. SCHOOL FEES

Few people can afford to pay the very significant costs of private education out of their disposable income alone. Figures from the Independent Schools Council for 2002/3 indicated that junior schools cost between £1,500 and £2,900 a term and between £2,000 and £4,000 a term at senior school. Boarding school prices rise to £2,000 to £4,000 for juniors, and £3,600 to £6,100 for seniors. As about 75% of the cost is spent on staff, prices rise in line with the earnings index rather than inflation, and increased NI and pension fund contributions are making further hikes more than likely.

Tax breaks on special schemes relating to school fees no longer exist in the UK: any schemes you see advertised in connection with school fees provision have no innate advantages over any of the other myriad accounts and financial instruments on the market.

School fees are relatively unusual in financial planning terms in that for a given child the sort of amounts needed and the times at which those amounts will be needed are relatively predictable. Moreover no income is needed from the investment until the time education will commence. One popular strategy is to set up a series of with-profit endowment policies maturing in sequential years (for when your child is 11, 12, 13…). This is an inflexible system, however – if you cash in your policy early, you may not get back what you paid in due to high charges in the initial years.

Alternatively there are insurance policies on which the investment of a lump sum provides an annual income for the fees, and on maturity the lump sum is returned, plus any income not already taken out (subject to capital gains tax).

Another financial instrument worth considering for school fees is zero-dividend preference shares. As with endowments, 'zeros' mature at a fixed future date and compensate for the fact that they yield no income with a guaranteed capital gain which equates to a relatively high nominal interest rate. The gain in value is – as far as the Inland Revenue is concerned – a capital gain rather than income. With careful tax planning, this distinction can be used to advantage. However, the collapse or near collapse of various 'split investment trusts' which offered zeros has undermined confidence in these instruments. If you go for these you need to look at the underlying investments carefully.

Finally, note that university is a further potential expense, currently of around £8,540 a year in London, £7,300 outside.

How to find the money (options including begging and borrowing, but avoiding theft)

➢ Savings and investments (the earlier you start the better).

➢ Remortgaging or a second mortgage.

➢ Moving to a cheaper home.

➢ Approaching grandparents (many people do).

➢ Plans run by a few schools ('Composition Fees'), whereby paying money in advance of your child attending the school secures discounted fees in due course.

➢ Education loans.

If it is important to you that your child would be able to continue at the chosen school even should you or your spouse die, you will need to consider life cover (see above), or a school fee protection plan.

USEFUL CONTACTS
Independent Schools Council Information Service (ISCIS),
☎ *(020) 7798 1560, Publication orders (020) 7798 1560*
✆ *www.iscis.uk.net/southeast*
The organisation (previously known as ISIS) has information about companies that
can give financial advice regarding planning and paying for school fees and, later,
university tuition.

6. APPROPRIATE TYPES OF INVESTMENT FOR CHILDREN TO OWN

Government Trust Funds

The government is planning to encourage investment for children with a lump sum payment of £250 for all babies born since September 2002, to be kept in an account know as a Child Trust Fund. This can be cashed in only when the child reaches 18. Friends and family can make additions to this of up to £1,000 pa tax free or lightly taxed.

It is planned that the starting sum be £250 per child or £500 for those whose parents' earnings fall into the bottom third of the country. Further government contributions are planned for the ages of five, 11 and 16, probably of £50 or £100, depending on parental income. As we go to press, exact details have yet to be announced.

Private Investments

With the exception of Child Accounts offered by Friendly Societies (which enjoy special status) products marketed for children do not necessarily confer any particular benefit. The actual position does fluctuate however and there may be the odd exception.

Child account interest is generally credited tax free but if you invest in a non-child alternative the relevant company should be able to provide you with form R85 for the Inland Revenue to allow interest to be paid without tax being deducted.

Whatever you invest in you need to consider the usual issues: rate of return, level of risk and the likely time when you will wish to withdraw the funds.

Children are unable to own stocks and shares in their own name (see Trust fund babies, below), or to own an ISA. Some fund managers will allow you to open a fund on a child's behalf, however (see Unit trusts and investment trusts held by an adult, below).

Common forms of investment for children

Friendly society plans: Friendly societies are – thanks to provisions under the Income and Capital Taxes Act – the only forms of non-government organisation able to offer tax-exempt investments for children (ISAs being limited to adults). Investment is limited to £25 a month or £300 a year per person. Policies must run for a minimum of ten years. No tax is payable on the eventual payout and all returns earned by the fund during its life are 'rolled up' on a tax-free basis. Beware of high management charges – a bugbear in this area that can strip such plans of their inherent advantages.

Children's deposit accounts: available from birth, offered by a large number of building societies and banks. Building societies tend to offer more freebies. However, as flagged above, the word 'child' or 'young' in a product title does not necessarily mean that it offers any better returns than the alternatives. A number of building societies, do, however, have a policy of offering favourable rates to children to encourage saving.

National Savings Children's Bonus Bond: The bonds run for a set period, usually five years, with a fixed tax free return. New issues are offered every year to 18 months, at varying rates of interest with possibly a bonus rate say in the fifth year. You can cash the bond in at any time, though no interest is paid if it is cashed within the first year. At the end of the five years a new fixed rate is announced and you can either leave the bond invested or cash it in. The bonds can be bought for children up to the age of 16 and held to a maximum age of 21. Investment can be anything from a minimum of £25 to £1,000 of each bond issue. Application forms are available at Post Offices.

Premium Bonds: a gamble which offers no interest payments but on which payouts of up to £1 million are a (distant) possibility. These are not investments in the traditional sense, but the chance of a single bond winning is around 1 in 15,000, so a holding of £5,000 with average luck would attract four prizes a year totalling £200 – a yield of 4%. Given their tax-free status this may not be an unattractive yield for higher rate taxpayers. The bonds can be cashed in at any time.

Unit trusts and investment trusts held by an adult on behalf of a child (their initials designated in a box on the application form): while not all fund managers allow this, for certain types of product some permit investment on a child's behalf in a designated account. If you do this it is advisable to inform the Inland Revenue in writing. You need to be able to show that you personally have not benefited from any earnings from the investment as they belong to the child.

USEFUL CONTACTS
Association of Friendly Societies
10-13 Lovat Lane London EC3R 8DT ☎ (020) 7397 9550 ✆ www.afs.org.uk
The society produces a brochure – 'Making Friends with your Friendly Society' –
detailing the types of products and financial services offered by their members.
/ HOURS *Mon-Fri 9am-5pm.*

7. TRUST FUND BABIES

Trusts used to be very tax-efficient ways of providing for children, not only in their traditional role in providing an income for someone when they come of age, but also in terms of setting aside money for school fees.

The tax advantages of trusts have gradually diminished over the past 30 years, so they have become less popular. In addition, current governments broadly consider trusts, except those where the beneficiary is a disabled child, to constitute tax avoidance.

Furthermore, a relatively recent change to the tax code now means that the transfer to a trust of any amount over £100 per annum deriving from either parent is taxed as if it was still the parent's own property (rather than the child's). This – together with the introduction of tax-free investment vehicles such as ISAs (and the now defunct PEPs) has further diminished the attractiveness of setting up a trust although they are useful as a system for administering money in the case of parents' death before a child or children reach the age of 18.

This change to the tax laws now means that the chief financial reason for parents to set up a trust for a child is avoidance of inheritance tax on the parent's death. So long as the parent dies seven years after transferring the property to the trust, inheritance tax is avoided.

Trusts may, however, still be tax-efficient ways for grandparents to provide for their grandchildren, say in contributing towards the cost of education.

Trusts are free of capital gains tax up to a specified level (£4,100 in 2004/5) so they may be useful for investments offering capital growth rather than income. In addition, if the trust is funded by and in the name of the child's grandparents, the child's own income tax and capital gains tax allowance apply.

FORMAL TRUSTS

If you have sufficient resources from savings or an inheritance you might like to set up a trust for your child as a way of providing a lump sum or income for them at some point in the future. As noted, the chief benefits of doing this (rather than making a gift, or leaving property in a will) is the avoidance of death duties, and to take advantage of potentially lower taxation rates (for parents in the higher tax brackets).

As a rule of thumb it is considered that the costs of setting up a trust are not worth undertaking unless you have more than £50,000 to invest. You will need both legal and financial advice to establish the trust, and to decide upon its investments.

There are different kinds of formal trusts. Those usually used for children are of a type known as discretionary trusts. While a standard discretionary trust is the format used in wills to avoid inheritance tax, the most usual format of trust set up for children is an Accumulation and Maintenance Settlement. This can pay out income or capital or accumulate income for up to 21 years. When the trust matures, the income could then be placed in another trust which only provides income.

Trustees (usually one or both parents plus one or two others) administer the Trust in the child's interest. The Inland Revenue likes to see a non-family member as one of the trustees.

A bare trust allows the beneficiary absolute right to the money and any income at the age of 18.

Money paid into such a trust is legally a gift to the child which means it cannot be retrieved by you at any stage and may be subject to gift tax or possibly inheritance tax should you die within seven years of setting up the trust.

Issues to consider:

➢ The age at which the child can access the money.

➢ Whether further children or grandchildren can be added as beneficiaries.

➢ Whether the income will be considered the child's and therefore benefiting from the child's tax allowance and capital gains tax allowance.

➢ Whether the money, if spent, will be treated as if it is the parents' and therefore taxed at their tax rate.

Discretionary trusts are particularly relevant in the cases of disabled children unable to earn their own living. With such children, if money is simply left in a will, the Benefits Agency will reduce benefits accordingly until the inheritance has been spent. If instead the money is placed in a discretionary trust, it does not legally belong to the child (and therefore will not be included in benefits calculations), but the trustees can make payments as and when they deem it appropriate.

8. CHILDREN'S TAX

Income tax allowance

Children are entitled to the same personal income tax allowances as adults – £4,745 in the fiscal year ending 5 April 2005 – i.e. so long as a baby's investment income is below this level no tax need be paid.

Building society and bank accounts assume that the owner of a normal account is a taxpayer and make a direct payment to the Inland Revenue on this basis ('deduction at source'). To register a child's account as non-tax-paying you will need to complete Inland Revenue form R85, available from your local tax office (see Inland Revenue in the phone book), or from building societies. Once this form is completed and accepted the child will have any interest earned on interest-bearing accounts credited to the account tax-free.

Tax paid at source by the donor on gifts of money, including on investments such as shares and unit trusts, can be reclaimed on the child's behalf using Form 232 available from any local tax office. This is worth bearing in mind on gifts for example from grandparents.

Income tax on gifts from parents

A wicked wheeze that might strike you might be to make a gift of lots of your savings to your baby to utilise her tax allowance on the interest income. Unfortunately (as noted above) the Revenue is way ahead of you – the above exemption does not apply to gifts from parents. For this reason alone, if anyone gives your child money it is worth placing it directly in an account in the child's name.

If interest earned by a child from an investment gift exceeds £100 a year, tax is paid on the whole income as if it is the parent's own. Note that this £100 limit is per parent, hence a child can earn up to £200 tax-free, which equates to a building society balance of about £4,000, assuming the investment is earning about 5%.

There are no special rules applying to gifts from grandparents.

Capital gains tax

As with adults, children have a capital gains allowance that is distinct from their income tax allowance. In the tax year ending 5 April 2005 this amounts to £8,200.

Investments such as 'zeros' – bonds which pay no interest, but which are sold at a discount to the nominal capital value – can be held by children and the extent to which they gain in value is offset against the capital gains allowance rather than the income tax allowance.

A certain amount of financial know-how is required when contemplating putting money into such a financial instrument, especially as they have fallen in and out of favour in recent times, but for the financially sophisticated they are still worth considering.

9. PARENTAL TAX

Mothers who are not working in order to look after their children will probably not be using all their tax allowance. By putting family savings into the mother's name it may be possible to shelter any income on those investments by using her tax allowance. Note though that it has been suggested that independent taxation of wives may be abolished as a method of capping maternity benefit. The position regarding this is unclear as we go to press.

If you are employed, your employer's payroll department should have details relating to this issue, or look for leaflet IR110 *A Guide for People with Savings*, from the local tax office.

In the year that a mother gives up work, a refund may be reclaimable from the Inland Revenue for tax collected on a PAYE basis using calculations that assumed a full year of work. For more details contact your tax office.

Child Tax Credit

This replaced Children's Tax Credit as well as the child elements of Working Families Tax Credit and Disabled Persons Tax Credit, Income Support and Income-based Jobseekers Allowance. It is for families where the main breadwinner earns less than £58,000 or £66,000 with a child under one year.

USEFUL CONTACTS
Inland Revenue, ☎ *CTC Helpline (0845) 300 3900, New Employers Helpline (0845) 607 0143* ⌁ *www.inlandrevenue.gov.uk*

10. STAKEHOLDER PENSIONS

If you wish and have the means to consider creating a nestegg for your child that will only be accessible later in life (aged 50), you might wish to consider contributing to a stakeholder pension in their name.

Since 6th April 2001 a parent, grandparent or other relative can make contributions into such a scheme, with payments made net of basic rate tax. If you are a tax payer, the effect of this is that you can make a £1 contribution to the fund, with it only really costing you 77p. The maximum that can be paid into a scheme in a single year is £3,600 – effective cost to the parent or grandparent £2,808.

CHAPTER 2.09

NAMING & CEREMONIES

1. **Registering the birth**
2. **Choosing a name**
3. **Announcing the birth**
4. **Ceremonies**

(For gifts and baby stationery, see chapter 3.10 Naming gifts.)

1. REGISTERING THE BIRTH

All births, including stillbirths, must be registered within 42 days at the Registry Office of the district where the child was born. If this is difficult for any reason you can go to another registry office in England or Wales which will then forward the information. Offices generally run on an appointment basis, so it is advisable to call ahead.

A short copy certificate is issued free of charge showing the baby's forenames and surname, sex, date of birth and district of birth. A full copy of the birth certificate detailing the parents is available for an extra fee. It will be more expensive if you want to obtain this at a later date.

Who needs to attend?

MARRIED PARENTS
If the parents are married, either the mother or father can register the baby.

UNMARRIED PARENTS
If the parents are not married, the father's details can only be entered in the register and/or the baby be given a different surname from the mother's, if the father attends the registration with the mother.

If the father is unable to attend, he can make a statutory declaration confirming he is the father and the mother should then produce this document for the registrar. Copies of the appropriate form for this can be obtained from any registrar.

If the mother is unable to attend the office with the father then together they can make a statutory declaration confirming the name of the father, which the father should then produce for the registrar.

If unmarried parents subsequently marry, the birth should be re-registered, apparently simply as a matter of record.

Making a correction or change

Corrections and amendments (including a change of mind regarding your child's forename) to a birth certificate may be made for the first twelve months of your baby's life. Write to the Corrections & Re-registration Section of the General Registry Office.

USEFUL CONTACTS

Family Records Centre, ☎ *(0151) 471 4800*

🖰 *www.statistics.gov.uk/registration*
This London office can also provide duplicate birth certificates: full certificate £7;
priority service £23. Available by phone, online, or just turn up. / HOURS *Mon, Wed, Fri
9am-5pm; Tue 10am-7pm; Thu 9am-7pm; Sat 9.30am-5pm.*

General Register Office, ☎ *(0151) 471 4800* 🖰 *www.statistics.gov.uk*

For corrections and amendments to a birth certificate, write to the Corrections
& Re-registration Section, Room D209 at the address in the index, or call (0151) 471
4806. Duplicate birth certificates may be obtained from PO Box 2 at the same
address, £11.50 (or £8.50 if the Office for National Statistics or ONS reference is
supplied); extra copies, £7. A priority service is available for urgently-required
certificates (£27.50, £24.50 with ONS reference). The office where you registered the
birth may be able to provide duplicates up to around three months after registration
for £7. Applications can be downloaded online.

2. CHOOSING A NAME

It's worth checking your baby's chosen name for any unfortunate meanings of the initials (e.g. WC) and unfortunate combinations (such as Master
Dwayne Pipe). Try out all possible nicknames too.

Most bookshops hold a stock of name dictionaries. Specialist books
are also available, if you are searching for a specific ethnic origin of name
– Celtic or African, for example.

A few of the more commonplace titles are listed below.

USEFUL CONTACTS

Baby Namer, 🖰 *www.babynamer.com*
A 23,000 US name database with plenty of bells and whistles.

Baby Names, 🖰 *www.babynames.com*
A US website with over 15,000 names; searches can be done by initial letter, whole
name or meaning. A name search service ($24.95 for 6 names, $34.95 for 12 names)
aims to provide a match for a host of criteria: ethnic preferences, phonetic
considerations (e.g. alliterative names), desired style (trendy, traditional, biblical) and
so on.

Baby Naming Society, ☎ *(01905) 371070*
Affiliated to the Baby Naming Society, the website www.namingceremonies.com
details the contacts for local authority celebrants available for naming
ceremonies. / HOURS *Mon-Fri 9am-5pm, or answerphone.*

Cool Baby Names, 🖰 *www.cool-baby-names.com*
A general American baby website whose introductory gimmick is access to
a database of over 50,000 names; their naming service is $16.

Popular Baby Names, 🖰 *www.popularbabynames.com*
A US site aiming to offer an ever-growing list of diverse Asian, European, African and
hard-to find ethnic names. It can be searched by meaning, gender and religion.

Your Baby's Name, 🖰 *www.yourbabysname.com*
An online baby name selection website, listing 10,000 names, with many helpful
tools to provoke thought, including a thesaurus.

DICTIONARIES OF NAMES

35,000+ Baby Names – Bruce Lansky (Meadowbrook Press; 1995; £4.95;
    088166216X)

7000 Baby Names – Hilary Spence (Classic & modern; Foulsham; 2000; £4.99;
    0572026471)

A Concise Dictionary of First Names – Patric Hanks and Flavia Hodges (OUP;
    2001; £6.99; 0198662599) – *A blockbuster volume with some 6,000 entries, including
    European, Arabic, Indian, Japanes and Chinese names. One hopes that Oxford
    scholarship is likely to mean more reliable accounts of names' meanings and history than
    is sometimes the case.*

Baby Names & Star Signs – Robert Parry (Choose a name for your baby according to the star signs; Hamlyn; 2003; £6.99; 0600603199) – *More than 2,000 name suggestions. Also a guide to the characterstics associated with the 12 astrological signs, and advice on raising children born under each sign.* / www.hamlyn.co.uk.

Baby Names Around the World – Bruce Lansky (Meadowbrook Press; 1999; £7.95; 0-881663-29-8) – *Over 50,000 names from around the world, indexed by country and ethnicity of origin; lists of the most popular names since the 1880s; advice on making up a new name and points to consider when naming your child.*

Best Baby Name Book – Louise Nicholson (Over 3,000 Names and Your New Baby's Star Sign; Harper Collins; 2002; 0007145489) – *The origins and history of names. There are also baby horoscopes, so you can predict personality traits, and choose a name to match.*

Best Baby Names – Julia Cresswell (Choose the RIGHT name for your baby; Bloomsbury; 2002; £4.99; 0747559031) – *A guide including more than 1500 options, and looking at influences on the popularity of names. Those with shared roots are gathered together in the same entry.*

Collins Pocket Reference Book of First Names – HarperCollins (HarperCollins; 1996; £6.99; 0004709411) – *Reliable histories and interpretations.*

Naming – Caroline Sherwood (Choosing a Meaningful Name; Hawthorn Press; 2000; £14.99; 1869890566) – *An overview of the whole naming business, covering what to take into account, the cultural importance of names, meanings of names, a dictionary, naming ceremonies (including DIY) and even taking a new name, in addition to the usual index.* / www.hawthornpress.com.

The New Virgin Book of Baby Names – Emily Wood (Virgin; 2000; £5.99; 0753504065)

3. ANNOUNCING THE BIRTH

A written announcement is not necessary but can add a certain weight to the occasion. You may wish to use a traditional format, or one of the many modern styles available, including those sold at most high street stationers.

Specialist suppliers may also offer a printed announcement service.

STATIONERY

Announce it!
General enquiries
☎ *(020) 8286 4044*
46 Oldfield Rd TW12 2AE
☎ *(020) 8286 4044*
Jolly designs which can be custom-lasered with your text in a variety of fonts; cheaper than printing, if not quite as smart; designs range from traditional to modern, for birth announcements and naming ceremonies; cost (including envelopes) is from £27 for 25 cards.

BabyFace Designs
61 Redwing Rise, Royston Hertfordshire SG8 7XU ☎ *(01763) 223 390*
⌂ *www.babyface-designs.com*
Mail order and web business offering birth announcements, Christening invitations, baby shower cards, matching thank-you cards and the like in a range of more and less fancy designs, in either matt or gloss; cards incorporating your photos are a speciality; prices start at £8.25 for 10; address labels can also be ordered.

Birth Announcement Service
☎ *(0800) 190190* ⌂ *www.telegramsonline.co.uk*
An 'announce the baby' service – supply details pre-birth of all those you want to send an announcement card to, then contact Telegrams Online after the birth and they will despatch in the next first class post; choice of three types of stationery – designs can be viewed on the website; £14.99 for ten addresses in the UK; extra addresses thereafter £1.10 each, including the stationery and postage.

Celebration
Racecourse Industrial Park, Mansfield Rd Derby DE21 4SX ☎ *(0845) 1308181*
Personalised stationery – gold on white & Christening invitations start at £20 for 25.
/ HOURS *Mon-Fri 9am-5pm;* SEE ALSO *3.10 Naming gifts.*

Chatterbox Cards
PO Box 142, Beckenham Kent BR3 6ZL ☎ *(020) 8650 8650*
🖰 *www.chatterboxcards.com*
Birth announcement cards: choose from 13 styles and six typefaces; proof on request;
can post within three working days of receipt of order; 25 cards cost £29.50; also
invitations and Christening cards. A brochure can be ordered online. / *HOURS Mon-Fri*
9am-5pm or 24hr answerphone.

Forget Me Not Invites
☎ *(01753) 584 990* 🖰 *www.forgetmenotinvites.co.uk*
Modern and elegant designs including for birth announcements and Christenings,
personalised and with the option of including a photograph. Prices from £23.

Hallo Baby
111 Woodside, Wimbledon London SW19 7BA ☎ *(020) 8947 1855*
🖰 *www.hallobaby.co.uk*
A choice of more than 70 birth announcements from a selection of European card
designers. These can be delivered to you in two to five working days although it is
recommended that you decide the details which don't actually have to wait till birth
in advance. A mailing service is available.

Happy Hands
7 Brockwell Park Row London SW2 2YH ☎ *(020) 8671 2020* 🖰 *www.happyhands.ws*
The same methodology used by this company to make ceramic tiles with a baby's
hand or footprints (see Portraits), can also be used to transfer the same print to birth
announcements, cards or T-shirts. / *HOURS Mon-Fri 9am-5.30pm; SEE ALSO 3.12 Portraits &*
photographs.

Heard the News
21 Fore Street, Ashton Keynes Wiltshire SN6 6NP ☎ *(01285) 869 674*
🖰 *www.haveyouheardthenews.com*
Handmade birth announcement and Christening cards, plus thank you cards.
Relatively plain graphics, with an outline pram, heart, or star, and so on.

Heritage Personalised Stationery
The Studio, Weston Patrick House, Weston Patrick Hampshire RG25 2NT ☎ *(01256)*
861738 🖰 *www.heritage-stationery.com*
Hand-printed birth announcement cards quality card in black on white or cream
with pale blue, pink or ivory bow. 3-4 working days for delivery. 50 cards
hand-ribboned with envelopes £75; 100 for £115. / *HOURS Mon-Fri am, 24hr answerphone.*

My Web Album
☎ *(01737) 841 075* 🖰 *www.mywebalbum.co.uk*
You send the photos to be scanned and this website creates a password-protected
album for friends and relatives to visit. Annual fee £10, additional pages £5.

One Fine Day
☎ *(01524) 263300* 🖰 *www.onefineday.co.uk*
A website offering artistic birth announcements, as well as other name-related
artwork. / *SEE ALSO 3.10 Naming gifts.*

4. CEREMONIES

(For suppliers of gifts relating to such ceremonies, see chapter 3.10 Naming gifts.)
Given that birth is a rite of passage for parents, grandparents and even
siblings of the new arrival, there can be a strong urge to mark this with
some kind of formal occasion. There is a variety of options, both traditional and of the DIY variety.

Baptism (or Christening)

In both Anglican and Roman Catholic churches a baptism may be held
as a stand-alone ceremony for one or a number of children, or may be
incorporated into a morning service. Which type of ceremony is used will
depend on usual practice at the local church and the parents' wishes.

Some form of donation is usually expected and if the church offers
some form of blessing certificate there may be an extra charge for this.

CHURCH OF ENGLAND

One in four children in the UK are still baptised into the Church of England. (Some priests now favour the older word baptism, over the more modern christening.)

It is a good idea to start planning in reasonably good time if you want your baby baptised while still a baby rather than a toddler. Church schedules can become booked up, so consult the local clergy sooner rather than later.

Preparation is now usual before a baptism. This may take the form of a one-off meeting to discuss the spiritual implications of the service, or can run to a series of meetings.

The church normally requires at least three godparents: two of the same sex as the child and one of the opposite sex. Parents can also be godparents (who technically speaking should be baptised and confirmed members of the church).

If you have mixed feelings about making the full baptismal promises on behalf of your child then consider the possibility of a service of Thanksgiving, which is offered by some churches. The congregation gives thanks for the birth and there is a similar service for use after adoption. This route leaves open the option of baptism at a later date.

CATHOLIC CHURCH

Having approached your priest, you will generally be invited to take part in a course of meetings to ensure parents understand fully the implications for their child of having them baptised into the Catholic faith.

Canon law proscribes the giving of names "foreign to a Christian mentality". However since 1983 there is no longer a requirement for a saint's name to be used.

It is usual to have one male and one female godparent. Both these people should technically speaking be Catholic, the participation of a non-Catholic being restricted to the role of witness to a Catholic sponsor. In practice it seems that the rules are sometimes bent in this regard. At minimum one godparent is required by the baptism ceremony and that person must be Catholic.

Jewish ceremonies

Ceremonies can take place in the synagogue or at home, and are different for boys and girls. Relatives and friends can attend the naming – one chair is traditionally left empty, for Elijah the prophet to witness the occasion. The child's *kvaterin*, (the Jewish equivalent of a godmother) and *kvater* (godfather) are symbolically involved in the ceremony.

Names are usually chosen to honour deceased members of the family, and it is usual for each child to be given a Hebrew name (by which they will be addressed when in the synagogue) as well as a secular name. The Hebrew name may be simply a translation of the secular name, or a completely different one.

The ceremony for boys, *brit milah*, or *bris*, takes place on the eighth day after the birth. Blessings and prayers accompany a naming ceremony, which is followed by the circumcision. Circumcision is carried out by the *mohel*.

Girls can be named on the eighth or fifteenth day after their birth. The ceremony is called *brit habat*, and involves just blessings, prayers and the naming ceremony. Both naming ceremonies are followed by a traditional Hebrew meal.

Many traditional rituals surround the pregnancy and birth of Jewish children: on the first Sabbath after the birth, family and friend gather to say prayers, and there may also be a 'Redemption of the Firstborn' ceremony, 30 days after the birth.

Liberal synagogues may well offer latitude on any of the elements above.

READING

The Complete Book of Hebrew Baby Names – Smadar Shir Sidi (More than 5,000 traditional and contemporary Hebrew names for your baby; HarperCollins; 1999; £10.95; 0062548506)

Hindu ceremonies

Traditions vary widely from sect to sect.

Usually, a priest prays when the baby is born (to bless the soul, wish for good health and to give thanks to God); and there may also be a naming ceremony (*namkaran*). Both ceremonies involve a fire (*havan* – usually contained in a metal pot) and may be carried out at the temple or at home.

Gifts are expected for the priest along with donations to the poor and/or the temple and/or other deserving causes. There is also generally some kind of party.

At either a year or three years old, there may be a further ceremony, unrelated to the naming called *mundan*. This involves shaving the child's head and may take place at home, or at somewhere of religious significance (for example, Haridwan, a key point on the Ganges).

USEFUL CONTACTS

Hindu Baby Names – A Kaushik (Star Publications; 1999; £4.95; 8186264574)

Muslim ceremonies

The naming of the child itself (al-Tasmiya) does not take place at any particular ceremony. A name should, however, be decided upon by the seventh day after the birth. At that time it is traditional for there to be a slaughter (Aqeequah) – two sheep for a boy and one for a girl – and there may be a meal to which guests are invited. The seventh day is also the traditional day for boys to be circumcised (al-Khitaan).

After the Aqueeqah, it is traditional to shave the baby's head (al-Halq) and for the value of the weight of the shorn hair in silver to be given to the poor.

USEFUL CONTACTS
Muslim names
⌐ *www.muslim-names.co.uk*
Listings and meanings of Muslim names, together with a bulletin board for asking questions about them.

Talk Islam
⌐ *www.talkislam.com*
One of the links from the home page leads to a comprehensive page of links on all aspects of naming. (www.muslimchild.com/index.php)

Secular ceremonies

With the decline in religious faith in the UK, a number of new parents are opting for non-religious events organised to reflect concepts of personal importance to the parents. These are relevant if you are dubious for example about promising to train your child in the practice of the relevant faith. In this event godparents tend to be renamed 'supporting adults' or 'mentors'.

It can be helpful to clarify the purpose of a secular ceremony – welcoming the child, naming her, making a public affirmation of the commitment of parents and any other adults, to her welfare, or all three.

Given that most parents do not have experience of officiating at such events a celebrant with experience of one comes in handy.

LOCAL AUTHORITY CEREMONIES

At the time of going to press, a scheme is being piloted in England that will lead to local authorities offering civil naming ceremonies, in the same way that they offer civil weddings. Brent, Barnet, Bromley and Kingston are among the London authorities in the trial scheme.

Currently, the ceremony does not have any legal status, and does not need to be attended by a registrar, although this may change if the scheme is adopted nationwide. The standard ceremony script can be added to or embellished by the parents, and the ceremony can take place in a number of specified venues.

READING

The Dead Good Book of Baby Naming Ceremonies – Jonathan How (Engineers of Imagination; 1999; £7.50; 0-952715-92-9) – *How to design and organise your own ceremony.* / Edge of Time Ltd – (07000) 780536 or www.permaculture.co.uk.

Rites and Ceremonies – Kate Gordon (Constable; 1998; £6.99; 0094787808) – *Suggested forms of words, readings and wordings for ceremonies; compares the approaches of different religions (including Celtic and pagan ones).*

USEFUL CONTACTS

Baby Naming Society, ☎ (01905) 371070

This charity (founded in 1994) helps those parents who do not wish for a religious naming or blessing to produce a pledge of continuing support for their children. The society produces a guide with a 'pick and mix' menu to help parents formulate a formal or informal event. (The society recommends more formality for larger events, where there is a danger that a sense of disorganisation may make those present feel uncomfortable.) The price of the guide (currently £40) includes a tailor-made programme for guests, a certificate for the parents and sponsors to sign and the ceremony script. The society worked with the Home Office in planning the script for the local authority naming ceremony scheme. / HOURS Mon-Fri 9am-5pm, or answerphone.

The British Humanist Association, ☎ (020) 7079 3580

⌖ www.humanism.org.uk

Founded in the 1960s (by organisations dating back to the 1890s), this registered charity is the largest British humanist organisation, and the co-founder of the European Humanist Federation. The organisation champions the rights and beliefs of the non-religious community, promotes secular education and produces humanist literature. A 36-page booklet, New Arrivals (£5 including p&p) contains ideas of prose, poetry readings and music to use at a non-religious baby naming ceremony. The association can provide a celebrant to conduct the ceremony. The fee is negotiable but might be around £80-£120. Celebrants are usually between 40 and 70 years old and there are marginally more women than men. / HOURS Mon-Fri 9am-5pm.

Civil Ceremonies Ltd, ⌖ www.civilceremonies.co.uk

The website lists details of local authorities offering naming ceremonies at approved hotels and registry offices. Alternatively send a SAE for information. An alternative URL for the site is www.namingceremonies.com.

General Assembly of Unitarian & Free Christian Churches, ☎ (020) 7240 2384 ⌖ www.unitarian.org.uk

Although they are part of the Christian tradition, ministers aim to help create a service that reflects the values and hopes of the people involved and are normally happy to incorporate elements from different faiths or to do something entirely new; often services are in the location of the parents' choice. Contact the Assembly for details of a local minister, or the telephone directory should list ministers, under 'Unitarian'. Fees are around £30 and generally include a consultation.

LifeRites, ☎ (01994) 484527 ⏚ www.liferites.org

This non-profit organisation can provide celebrants for any type of ceremony; individual spiritual beliefs are respected without judgement; cost £90 including booking fee, plus travel expenses; fee includes a planning meeting to draft and discuss the ceremony.

Stork Party, ☎ (01279) 465 048 ⏚ www.storkparty.co.uk

Supplies the material you need to run a baby shower with a party box containing all invitations and envelopes, a timing schedule, guest list planner, decoration planner, menu planner, game ideas and two prizes, a gift record (who gave what), baby toiletries, a single-use camera and so on.

Welfare State International, ☎ (01229) 581127
⏚ www.welfare-state.org

"Engineers of the imagination" is how this firm describes itself. Publishers of the Dead Good Guide to Namings and Baby Welcoming Ceremonies, it also runs courses on how to run your own celebration. It will even help create tailor-made ceremonies including food, music, ceremonial objects and "enhancing the chosen site". Phone advice is backed up by the book. Prices for a ceremony in London would start from around £200. / HOURS *Tue-Fri 10am-5pm, 24hr answerphone;* PUBLICATIONS *The Dead Good Guide to Namings & Baby Welcoming Ceremonies (£7.50 +p&p); plus similar books on other ceremonies.*

SECTION THREE

Consumer Guide

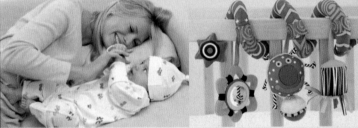

CHAPTER 3.01

MATERNITY WEAR

1. **Shopping tips**
2. **Bras & underwear**
3. **General stockists**

1. SHOPPING TIPS

For working women in particular, there is a sort of double-bind about dressing in pregnancy. If you dress to look crisp and professional, you may find the pregnancy studiously ignored, especially on public transport. If you go all frilly, and announce your condition to the world, you are less likely to be taken seriously.

Until very recently options were limited, and often very uninspired. However, things are improving, if only because of press coverage of celebrity mothers. Increasingly it's more a question of finding your own style, at what you consider a suitable price.

Options range from the traditional loose and flowing, through to the Lycra or skimpy T-shirt flaunt-the-bump look. If you want to minimise how pregnant you look, the classic advice is to go for a scoop neck/empire line/gather under the bosom (drawing attention to your cleavage), or to flaunt your extremities with attention-grabbing head and foot gear.

If you are happy to wear non-maternity clothes and don't get too big, you may need no more than larger sizes or looser fittings than you normally wear. In this case, you may be able to get more than six months' wear out of any new purchases, if only because after the birth you will remain around the size you were at six months, at least for a little while. Loose dresses, leggings and large shirts are all useful options. An alternative may be to borrow larger jeans and shirts from your partner.

Smart options of all kinds tend to be pricey. You can economise by borrowing, buying second-hand, or selling on your purchases after the birth. You can also save by buying plain basics, and dressing them up with more exotic accessories, such as waistcoats, hats and scarves, which can be used later.

Twelve weeks – when you might be feeling less nauseous and beginning to outgrow your usual garments – is about the right time to go looking for clothes. Note, however, that although pregnancy shops may have 'bumps' to help you imagine what you will look like, you can but guess.

Features worth looking for in maternity clothes:
➢ Adjustable fastenings, adjustable gathers and pleats, or very generous stretch.
➢ Natural fabrics next to your skin as the increased metabolic rate in pregnancy tends to make you warmer than usual and more prone to perspire. Your stomach, in particular, may start to itch as the skin stretches.
➢ Clothing which hangs from the shoulder, leaving the waist loose.

Shoes

With a combination of oedema and the spreading of foot joints (due to the 'relaxing' hormones), feet – on average – get half a size larger in pregnancy so you may need some new shoes. Some mothers find their feet increase permanently by a full size.

Tips

➤ To avoid backache and other related problems, it is best to avoid high heels. A low heel – no more than two inches – is recommended though some experts (who feel a slight heel helps with posture) advise against completely flat heels.

➤ Natural fabrics like leather and canvas are recommended, given expectant mothers' tendency to above-average body temperatures; similarly, sandals are a good option.

After the birth

After the birth you will want to get back into normal clothes. However, if you are breast-feeding you are likely to be limited for a while to outfits with a break in the middle (i.e. shirt and skirt, shirt and trousers, etc) so the baby can be tucked up under your top. Some suppliers offer garments with special openings. Like those which involve unbuttoning, special openings will usually mean exposing yourself to a degree, making breast-feeding more of a problem when you are out and about (not to mention making you cold in winter).

Large shawls can look elegant – if you are good at managing them – and make feeding discreet. Generously cut jackets can work in a similar way. Softer fabrics are generally better as they fold well and are also more comfortable for the baby. Longer tops can be a bit of a nuisance as you have to lift them from under your bottom before you can lift them comfortably at the front.

As milk will probably leak at least in the early days – even with breast pads – fabrics which will not show wet stains, for example dark patterns or heavily textured fabrics, are best.

USEFUL CONTACTS

Dress for Success
Unit 2, Shepperton House, 83-93 Shepperton Road London N1 3DF ☎ (020) 7288 1770 ⏚ www.dressforsuccess.org
An (international) organisation with a clever practical idea: to provide less well-off women with 'interview' suits to help them back into the workplace, and another when the hoped-for job results. (Also a good place for ex-working mothers, to off-load any no-longer needed, professional-looking outfits).

2. BRAS & UNDERWEAR

Indexes in this section refer to chapter 3.14 Shopping directory.

Underwired bras are not recommended during pregnancy as the wiring can damage the milk ducts of the breasts as they expand. This expansion may be by as much as three cup sizes by the time you have had the baby. Generally, however, women increase by two sizes in both overall bust measurement (as their ribs expand to accommodate the baby) and cup size.

Look for something with plenty of support to prevent sagging. Special pregnancy bras do exist, but a good sports bra, properly fitted, will also

work. If you find that the size of your ribs is increasing but that your cup size is relatively unchanged you can buy bra extenders.

See the listings at the end of this chapter for brands and suppliers of maternity bras and underwear.

After the birth

For the first few weeks after the birth, if you are breast-feeding, you may need to wear a bra at night to hold breast pads in place to absorb any night-time leakage. Special sleep bras are crop-top style with no catches to ensure comfort. However your normal nursing bra can do the same job. Alternatively you may prefer just to sleep on a towel.

During the day you can get by with a normal bra (or none at all if that is your style – though you might like one at first for breast pads) but a purpose-designed style does make life easier.

The experts recommend some time spent regularly without a bra to strengthen the breast and nipple skin, and to encourage any cracks to heal.

When you do want a bra the choice is:

A drop cup: with hook or press-stud on each shoulder strap. This is comfortable but difficult to do and undo discreetly. Those with just a flap folding down rather than the whole cup can be uncomfortable if the upper part is tight enough to dig in.

A zip cup bra: easier to get the whole breast out of and quite discreet. However if you are at all fleshy, you will sooner or later end up trapped in the zip.

Front-opening bras: which involve a series of hooks attaching each cup to the centre of the bra. Though fiddly, this is more supportive, and recommended for larger women.

Softer bras: sports-type styles made of something like 92% cotton, 8% spandex or Lycra, designed to expand and retract with the breast during the day, reducing the risk of mastitis. The first brand in this country was Bravado, but there are also others. Note: the stretchiness does wash out if hot washed.

Sleep bras: (see above) or one of the softer types can double up.

Tips:

➤ Two–four weeks before the due date is about the right time for buying a nursing bra. Keep the receipt in case you turn out to be a different size or end up not breast-feeding.

➤ Buy around one cup size larger than you fit at the time. (Some lines, such as Emma-Jane and Mava, offer extensions should you find you expand more than anticipated.)

➤ Allow a little extra space (say for your hand to slide into the cup) for the expansion which will occur when your milk comes in.

➤ Avoid over-tight bras which increase the chances of mastitis.

➤ Cotton is the best material.

➤ Whatever you choose, ensure that you can open and close it easily with one hand.

MEASURING YOUR BUST

If you are buying by mail order or somewhere you can't try the bra, you will need to measure yourself.

The steps:
1. Measure yourself when wearing a bra.
2. Measure around your rib cage immediately underneath your breasts.
3. Add to this figure four inches for even numbers and five inches for odd. This is your bra size.
4. The cup size is the difference between this measurement and the measurement around the fullest point of the bra (including straight across your back). 1 inch is a B cup, 2ins a C cup, 3ins a D cup, 4ins a DD cup, and 5ins an E cup.

SUPPORTIVE CLOTHING (IN PARTICULAR, TIGHTS)

Although not essential, a maternity 'body' gives your figure a smooth line and may help support the bump.

Varicose veins are a common symptom of pregnancy (as hormones encourage the valves in the veins to relax, and gravity encourages the blood to pool lower in the body – especially in the legs). Support tights may help, and are probably best if they offer only light support. The idea is to wear them constantly, removing them only just before going to bed at night.

KNICKERS

Special maternity knickers or briefs are seldom necessary and may be uncomfortable. The best policy can be to invest in a larger-than-usual size of a normal style which will also be useful after the birth. Note that a light vaginal discharge – getting heavier as time progresses – is common throughout pregnancy. Tampons are not recommended because of the danger of introducing infection, but cotton underwear will help you stay clean and dry. Tight clothes are not recommended.

Bras & underwear

Central
>   Harrods (SW1)
>   John Lewis (W1)
>   Mothercare (W1)
>   Peter Jones (SW1)
>   Rigby & Peller (W1)

West
>   Blooming Marvellous (SW6)
>   Bravissimo (W5)
>   Great Expectations (SW3)
>   Mothercare (SW6, W6)

North
>   The Active Birth Centre (N19)
>   Body Comfort (NW10)
>   John Lewis (NW4)
>   JoJo Maman Bébé (NW11)
>   Mothercare (N22, NW4)
>   Rosa (N16)

South
>   Blooming Marvellous (TW9)
>   John Lewis (KT1)
>   Mothercare (CR0, TW9)

East
>   Emma-Jane (IG3)

Mail order
>   Aphrodite
>   The Active Birth Centre
>   Blooming Marvellous
>   Body Comfort
>   Boots
>   Bravado
>   Bravissimo
>   Emma-Jane
>   Figleaves
>   JoJo Maman Bébé
>   Margaret Ann
>   Mothercare
>   Mothernature
>   NCT Maternity Sales
>   Rainbows End
>   La Redoute
>   Royce Lingerie
>   Sam-I-Am
>   Spirit of Nature

3. INDEX OF BRANDS & STOCKISTS

Suppliers in this section are divided into a number of different categories. These indexes refer to chapter 3.14 Shopping directory.

Stockists by level of expense:
➤ Cheap & cheerful.
➤ Mid-range.
➤ Luxury.

Other categories:
➤ Second-hand shops.
➤ Hire companies.

Stockists by level of expense

Cheap & cheerful

Central
Dorothy Perkins *(W1, WC1)*
Hennes (H&M) *(NW5, W1)*
Mothercare *(W1)*

West
Hennes (H&M) *(W1, W2, W8)*
Mothercare *(SW6, W6)*
Primark *(W6)*

North
Mothercare *(N22, NW4)*
Primark *(NW6)*

South
Mothercare *(CR0, TW9)*
Primark *(SE15, SE18, SW17)*

East
Primark *(E11, E6, E8)*

Mail order
Grobag
Mothercare
Tesco

Mid-range

Central
Etro *(W1)*
John Lewis *(W1)*
Long Tall Sally *(W1)*
Next *(W1, W1)*
Peter Jones *(SW1)*

West
Blooming Marvellous *(SW6)*
The Maternity Co *(W4)*
Next *(W8)*

North
John Lewis *(NW4)*
JoJo Maman Bébé *(NW11)*
Maternus *(N1)*

South
Blooming Marvellous *(TW9)*
Bump Start *(SW18)*
La Conception *(SW11)*
Funky Mama *(SW4)*
John Lewis *(KT1)*
Long Tall Sally *(CR0)*
Mums 2 Be *(SW15, SW19)*
Rosie Nieper T-shirts *(TW11)*

East
Harry Duley *(E1)*

Mail order
Bishopston Trading Co
Blooming Marvellous
Bresona
Broody Hens
Bump Start
Bumps Maternity Wear UK
Bumps to Bairns
Business Bump
Denny Andrews
Harry Duley
JoJo Maman Bébé
Just Bumps
Long Tall Sally
Mamas & Papas
The Maternity Co
Mums 2 Be
NCT Maternity Sales
Next
Rosie Nieper T-shirts
VertBaudet

Luxury

Central
   Arabella B *(W1)*
   Formes *(W1, WC2)*
   Pleats Please *(W1)*

West
   Babylist *(SW6)*
   Carla C *(W11)*
   Formes *(SW3)*
   Ghost *(W11)*
   Great Expectations *(SW3)*
   Jou Jou & Lucy *(W9)*
   9 London *(SW3)*
   Seraphine *(W8)*

North
   Formes *(NW3)*

Mail order
   Babylist
   Formes
   Ghost
   KC Collection
   Ma'Donna Maternity

Other categories

Second-hand shops

Mail order
   Budget Bumps
   Bumps to Bairns

eBay
Maternitywear Exchange

Hire companies

An excellent option for special occasions.

West
   One Night Stand *(SW3)*

South
   Mums 2 Be *(SW15, SW19)*

Mail order
   Mums 2 Be

Babylist

Babylist is a unique advisory and supply service which helps you select and source the right equipment for your baby.

During one private consultation in our London showroom we provide you with expert, independent advice tailored to your needs.

Babylist then delivers anywhere in the world, right to your door!

No pressure, no stress, just a professional and thoughtful solution to suit increasingly busy lives.

You deliver the baby, we'll deliver the rest.

Tel: 020 7371 5145
www.babylist.co.uk

CHAPTER 3.02

BABY EQUIPMENT

1. **Introduction**
2. **Car seats**
3. **Wheeled transport**
   (prams, buggies, pushchairs & travel systems)
4. **Carrying equipment**
   (slings & backpacks)
5. **Sleeping equipment**
   (cots, Moses baskets & mattresses)
6. **High chairs**
7. **Other items**
   (including safety & specialist equipment)
8. **Finding a home for outgrown gear**
9. **General stockists**

(For storage solutions, safety items – stair gates and the like – and nursery furniture, excluding cots, see chapter 3.03 Nursery decor. For all equipment relating to nappies – change bags etc – see chapter 3.08 Nappies. For feeding equipment other than high chairs, see chapter 2.02 Feeding. For travelling equipment see chapter 2.05 Travel.)

I. INTRODUCTION

A shopping spree to mark a new arrival can be fun, but babies actually needs very little in material terms to be happy and considerably less than nursery equipment lists and mother and baby magazine ads would have you believe.

If you are a new parent you represent something of a dream-customer for the retailers: you have no experience of what you are buying; are anxious to get it right, and willing to spend money to do so. So when out shopping, beware the Nothing-But-the-Best-for-My-Child syndrome, and bear in mind that market research reveals that otherwise rational adults often judge baby gear solely on price.

This may explain why average expenditure on equipment for a first baby is a hefty £2,000 in the first two years. If you follow the in-store shopping lists and/or go for the fashionable models, you could spend very considerably more. One approach is to start by calculating your budget and make certain you don't overspend, if necessary by buying second-hand.

When planning your purchases bear in mind that there is as wide a range of opinions of what constitutes useful baby equipment as there are parents. What one parent hates another may love – and they may be parents of the same child. This means that you can't judge the usefulness of an item by whether it is popular with other parents. You need to decide whether it will suit you and/or your baby's way of doing things.

Tips for buying:

➤ It can be surprisingly difficult at first to master the overwhelming variety of options and decide which items will best suit your needs. To help make your choices, try to think through on a day-by-day, hour-by-hour basis how your life is going to accommodate the new arrival.

➤ Beware contraptions. The market is full of pieces of equipment which rival a Swiss Army Penknife in number of features. Rather than buying a single (generally expensive) piece of equipment, it may well be better value in the long run to 'keep it simple stupid' and buy a larger number of less complicated, cheaper items.

➤ If you want to know more about different products, drop in on the relevant sections and chat rooms of parent web sites listed under chapter *4.05 Finding Out More*.

➤ Few of us live in enormous houses and the less gear you have cluttering up the place, the more room your baby will have to explore and play. Particularly if you have an aversion to clutter, wait until you actually need items before you buy them rather than (as usually advised) shopping in advance. You may find you don't need a particular piece of equipment at all.

➤ Consider borrowing anything you can, at least to try before you buy.

➤ Many items of baby gear – prams in particular – are hardly objects of desire. How stylish you want your kit to look is up to you. This is an area in which Continental brands often have the edge – at a price – though they may well lack durability. If you want matching items, make sure you buy them all at the same time: those you leave till next time may not be there when you come back.

➤ October, prior to the release of the new year's look, tends to be the most economical month for buying fashionable baby clobber as old pattern lines are discounted.

➤ The annual retailing cycle means stockists tend to operate on depleted stocks by late summer/early autumn. If you want a particular look and your baby is due in September/October it may be worth ordering or even buying your equipment relatively early.

➤ Even if you plan to buy mail order, if possible try out items like buggies first to make sure you can use them comfortably. This applies also to cots with drop sides.

➤ Even the largest retailers generally only stock car seats or prams in a limited selection of coverings. If you want to avoid what can be the depressing feeling of having opted for a standard choice, get hold of the manufacturer's catalogue and place a special order through a suitable retailer. You should allow up to six weeks for delivery of non-stock items.

➤ Beware scare-stories, which can emanate from the most respectable of retailers. John Lewis's staff, for example, not so long ago advised against the use of Moses baskets for newborns to sleep in at night (despite having an enormous range out on display). Reasons for this advice were mysterious – the Federation for the Study of Infant Deaths said at the time that there was no reason not to use one, for example. But as a new parent, or parent-to-be any hint of a risk is concerning.

➤ There are few truly essential items. The only thing you absolutely must have – and then only if the baby travels by car – is a car seat.

Nutkin is a small personal company run by a Norland Trained Nursery Nurse aimed at helping new and expectant mums with the new arrival, offering professional and independent advice in an ever changing environment.

Our range of services cover a complete package, from assisted shopping to safety product evaluation and nursery design.

Nutkin

CHILDCARE CONSULTANTS
Norland Diploma NVQ Level 3 NNEB

Nutkin Limited, Lawnfield House
Westmorland Road, Maidenhead
Berkshire SL6 4HB
T   01628 778856
F   01628 778859
M 07774 257 817
E   smurolo@fsmail.net

With all equipment, consider:

➤ How long it will be used for.

➤ How often it will be used.

➤ Whether another item you already have could not serve the same purpose.

➤ How easy it is to clean.

➤ How much storage space you have available.

➤ Whether adjustment or folding can be done one-handed. Little babies like to be held for a surprisingly high proportion of the day and even if they don't may be safest temporarily in your arms out of the way of marauding toddlers, pets, older children, etc.

➤ Whether it is easily used by all who may be caring for the baby. For example, how heavy it is, and whether it will suit both parents' heights.

How the listings work

Note that under the specific types of equipment set out below, only specialist retailers are listed.

In fact, most types of product can be found at the general equipment retailers, department stores and megastores listed at the end of this chapter under General stockists. Such suppliers are listed in the individual sections only if there is something particularly notable about their range in a particular category.

So for example, John Lewis is one of the largest retailers in the capital in practically all product categories, but this success is not due to a particularly specialised selection of brands or styles, so it's listed only in General stockists and not in any other section.

GENERAL INFORMATION

The Baby Products Association, ☎ *Factfile requests (01296) 660990*
The UK industry association for manufacturers of cots, buggies and so on, which (in promoting the benefits of buying new rather than used goods) aims to educate parents about the potential dangers of second-hand products. / PUBLICATIONS *Free leaflets: A child's safety is worth every penny; Car seat safety.*

British Standards Institution, ☎ *(020) 8996 9000, Customer services (020) 8996 9001* ⌕ *www.bsi-global.com*
The organisation responsible for product testing and standards development. Owners of the most famous quality mark of all – the Kitemark; they can provide details of British standards relating to products like children's car seats.

READING

The Which? Guide to Baby Products – Sian Morrissey (How and where to buy the basic essentials for your baby; Which? Books; 2002; £9.99; 0-852-02-897-0) – *Covering some of the same ground as this book, this title simiarly emphasises that you don't need everything on nursery suppliers' lists.*

2. CAR SEATS

Indexes in this section refer to chapter 3.14 Shopping directory.

From the age of one, according to the Child Accident Prevention Trust, the greatest risk to a child's life is a car accident.

By law children under one year of age must be carried in a securely restrained infant carrier (that includes the trip home from hospital), and children up to three years old should travel in an appropriate child seat. (Even above the age of three, it is not advisable to use an adult seat without some form of modification.)

Given the regular improvements in child car seats and the importance of knowing a seat is undamaged, this is one of the few areas in which it really is worth avoiding second-hand and finding a well-made, new model.

Note that babies' car seats should not be used in any circumstances where an airbag is installed. In an accident the rapid inflation of airbags is a danger in itself. (Indeed, airbags pose a serious danger for children well beyond the toddler years). Some parents get around this by disconnecting the passenger-seat bag. Some motoring organisations strongly advise against this, though, on the grounds that you may forget to re-connect them, and in any case anyone travelling in the interim will do so unprotected.

Note also that, contrary to what some people find intuitive, the determining factor in matching child and car seat is not height or age, but weight.

SAFETY

The sole purpose of a car seat is to keep your child safe, but a report by Which? in 2001 gave one model a test score of 0%. Seats for older children tested in 2002 fared a little better but still only reached average marks of around 50%. The New Programme for the Assessment of Child Seats (NPACS) is being set up with the aim of ensuring continued improvements in child seats and is hoping to offer more stringent and standardised tests.

In the absence of any global testing standard, the only clear message is that – as different models from each brand scored very differently – even the biggest brand names offer no guarantee of top quality.

DOES IT FIT?

It may seem absurdly obvious to state that a key consideration in choosing a car seat is to make sure the seat fits your particular car. However, not only are seats shaped differently, but seat belts – which are generally used to hold the car seat in place – come in various positions and lengths.

The UN has introduced the ISOFIX scheme to overcome this problem. It is proposed that child seat anchors be fitted in standardised positions on all new cars, and that seats be manufactured to slot onto these anchors.

The scheme is still in its infancy however, with only a few models of seat, and only certain makes of car which have adopted it to-date.

Until it becomes universal and regardless of manufacturers' claims, no child seat fits all cars, and some baby seats fit little over half. Four-wheel-drive models and those with bucket seats are the most problematic. Even slight modifications to the design of the same model of car manufactured in different years, may alter the suitability of a particular seat.

For all these reasons, it is not a good idea to buy a car seat from somewhere without fitters unless they (and you) recognise that you may have to take it back for a refund. Given estimates from the RAC that two-thirds of all child seats are not fitted correctly, buying from somewhere where they can demonstrate fitting is the preferred option.

Alternatively, If you are buying a new car, some models offer the option of integral child (though not newborn) seats, obviating problems of fit – albeit at a price.

PORTABILITY

Backward-facing seats (the type used for newborns) are generally fitted with carry handles. These can be a useful extra in that they allow you to carry babies in and out of cars without waking them up,. Such seats also function as a portable chair for babies while at friends', in a restaurant, etc.

Especially if you have a bad back, beware of the strain of carting these chairs around – it's one of the worst ways of carrying the baby so far as your spine is concerned. This is particularly a concern in the period after birth when a mother's joints are particularly vulnerable. Pay due attention to the weight of the seat when you buy, and try not to carry it unnecessarily.

Travel systems are the ultimate solution to the issue of portability. The idea is that the car seat doubles up as the seat of a buggy, so that you can transfer the baby from car to buggy and back with minimal disturbance. For a full description of the pros and cons of such systems, see below in Section 3, Wheeled transport.

COMFORT

Bear in mind a Which? report noting that the safest child seats were not necessarily the most comfortable. That said, consider the amount of padding on the various models you are thinking of (they differ markedly) and whether your child will be comfortable.

EASE OF USE

By definition the clips on these seats should be hard to undo, or children would master them all too quickly. However, it is worth looking for something that you personally might be able to handle while holding an uncompliant child in place. A one-pull harness (one where you don't have to adjust each strap separately) works well in this respect.

HEAD HUGGER

An optional extra which is popular for newborn babies who are dwarfed even by the smallest seats – the head hugger is a head support cushion which fits inside the car seat and stops a small baby's head from lolling to the side.

Other extras:
➢ Reclining for sleeping.
➢ Rocking facility.

➢ Storage compartments.
➢ Bottle holders.
➢ Trays (but avoid those easily removed by a child).
➢ Easy to remove, washable cover.
➢ Handles and a recline setting you can use with one hand.
➢ Guides and clips for the adult belt that hold the seat in place, that help you figure out how it should be positioned.

Car seat types

Car seats are graded by the EU, not by age but according to the maximum weight of the child.

The only seats allowed for babies up to 13kg in weight (about 12–15 months) are backward-facing ones. This arrangement protects against whiplash injuries, which – because babies' heads are heavier in relation to their bodies than those of adults – are more prone to be serious.

As babies grow beyond this weight they progress to a forward-facing seat (although most experts advise sticking with a backward-facing one for as long as possible). Although not required by UK law, there are then further EU-defined safety categories for seats for children up to the age of 11 years.

Note: a baby's legs pushing against the car seat is not a sign of needing to move to a forward-facing seat: weight is the only indicator.

Grades of car seat:

Backward-facing seat: there are two grades – for babies up to 10kg (22lbs, i.e. about 9 months old or roughly when the baby can sit unaided); and for babies up to 13kg (29lbs, i.e. about 12–15 months old). Cost, £80–£100. The former grade is an older standard, and may in due course be phased out.

Forward-facing seat: for toddlers from 9kg to 18kg (20lbs to 40lbs, i.e. from around 9 months to 4 years old. It is recommended that such models are used on the car's back seat, ideally in the middle, for maximum protection in the event of a side-on crash. There are two types of seat in this category. The first costs around £130 and has a solid metal frame inside plastic. The second is cheaper, made from moulded polystyrene and costs around £80. Being lighter, this second is convenient to move from car to car. However, because such seats use the adult belt to restrain the child some experts assert that they are not as safe as those that use a dedicated five-point harness and in particular advise against their use for a child of under 18 months.

Combination backward- and forward-facing seat: generally from birth to 18kg (40lbs) rearward to 10 or 13kg; satisfies all the above standards, so offers potential for around four years' use, though, of course, if you have a second child you will need another seat anyway. Such seats can be safer because the child can face backwards for longer. However, they can be complicated to fit, are generally heavy, and what's more some designers claim it is impossible to satisfy the specifications for all the different ages successfully in one unit.

Booster seat, often detachable from forward-facing seat: a popular option as the next-stage car seat for four year olds (sometimes three-year olds, depending on the child's weight). The reason for transfer is that the five-point harness is no longer considered strong enough to hold the child safely. This arrangement typically lasts until the child is eleven years old.

Pointers for fitting a car-seat:

➤ Check that the seat belts in your car will fit around the seat you have without tipping it up.

➤ When fitted, the seat shouldn't be able to move forwards or sideways.

➤ The buckle of the car seat belt shouldn't rest on the child seat frame as the impact of an accident could shatter it.

➤ The harness in the seat should be a five-point one for maximum safety, and should not be slack (tight enough for just two adult fingers to slip underneath) or the child could suffer whiplash. The cross belts should run along the top of the thighs, not the abdomen and a diagonal belt should rest on the child's shoulder, not neck. (The belts should be adjusted for every journey, to take account of different clothing.)

➤ If the car seat is involved in an accident, discard it. Invisible damage may rob it, in a second incident, of much of the protection it would otherwise offer.

➤ For the same reason, you should try to avoid buying a second-hand seat unless you know its history. (If you do buy a second-hand seat, ensure that you have the fitting instructions.)

Car seat brands

Bébé Confort   Maxi Cosi
Britax   Monbebe
Graco

Car seat fitting/seat belt adjusting

Autosafe   Quickfit SBS
Halfords
In-Car Safety Centre

3. WHEELED TRANSPORT (PRAMS BUGGIES, PUSHCHAIRS & TRAVEL SYSTEMS)

Indexes in this section refer to chapter 3.14 Shopping directory.

A pram or buggy is the modern symbol of parenthood and the most expensive piece of equipment you're likely to buy. Although ostensibly designed to transport the child, in practice the restraint function is at least as important to parents. A potential role as a less embarrassing version of a shopping trolley is not to be sniffed at either.

There is a bewildering range of options. For new parents who have never considered the difference between a pram, a pushchair, a two-in-one, a three-in-one, and a travel system, it can all seem rather daunting.

Retailers are keenly aware that these are expensive bits of gear and that, with encouragement, you might well buy more than one model (say a pram and a pushchair; or a pram and a baby-jogger). However, as noted above, it's worth waiting to see what you really need. If you use a sling for the first weeks or months for example, you can go direct to one of the models more suitable for an older baby, which may last you all the way through toddlerhood.

For the manufacturers, the strategy seems to be to produce ever-more complicated (and expensive) equipment which promise more and more features in a single model. Why buy a pram, a pushchair, a car seat, and a carrycot, when you could buy a unit doing all four things at once?

The answer in some cases is that the four-in-one will do four things mediocrely, rather than one thing well. It is, though, worth spending money for something lighter and more manoeuvrable (and possibly a couple of extra features you know you will find useful).

Note: many retailers only keep samples of prams and pushchairs (i.e. they don't hold stock, but order as required). Particularly if you are fussy about fabrics, you should allow six to eight weeks for delivery.

THE MOST COMMON OPTIONS

The terms two-in-one, three-in-one, and four-in-one are used in different ways by different manufacturers, and you may well find these terms used differently from the usage below.

Only those with a lie-flat option are suitable right from birth – generally up to three or four months. Some recline is desirable until at least six months or when the child can sit up, in order to protect the baby's back.

 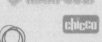

A pram: the traditional (and usually expensive) option; great for tiny babies (who can't yet hold their heads up), wonderful for those with Mary Poppins fantasies, but – given that the child is transported flat – less suited to older babies and toddlers. Romantic but also bulky and unwieldy – in use and in storage – and can be tough to transport (they don't all fold). You will probably also need a pushchair at a later stage; cost £400+.

Fixed seat pushchair (lighter models, also known as a buggy or stroller): suitable for a baby from six months up, with a canvas forward-facing seat holding the baby/toddler upright (but sometimes with the option of a slight recline position); many models feature umbrella- or flat-folding (sometimes called 'easy riders') for easy handling; particularly useful for public transport and small houses and flats. However, they generally lack the suspension of alternatives and have limited shopping storage space so you might be tempted to hang bags from the handles – a cause of distortion; cost £50+.

Adjustable seat pushchair (a fancier buggy, also known as a two-in-one): as immediately above, but the rake of the seat adjusts to allow it to go flat, and so makes it suitable for transporting young babies; later the seat can go upright. It can sometimes also be made backward-facing so allowing you to look at a younger baby as you go along. Storage for shopping is often provided. All this versatility is purchased at the expense of extra weight, and some parents of older babies still go on to buy an additional light-weight fixed seat pushchair at a later date; cost £80+.

Adjustable seat pushchair with carrycot (a fancier buggy, also known as a three-in-one): as immediately above, but the pushchair seat can be removed and a carrycot added, giving much of the appearance of a pram. Again – in theory this combination takes you from newborn to toddler, but when the toddler stage is reached you may find the lighter weight and better portability of a fixed seat pushchair impossible to ignore; cost £250+.

All terrain buggies: rugged units, generally with three large pneumatic wheels and a seat removable for washing; the juvenile equivalent of mum and dad's 4x4 – though designed for taking baby jogging and rambling, now ubiquitous as runabouts for townie babies. A Which? report however found no advantage over conventional models except on rough ground, and their size can make them inconvenient in crowded places. Neither do they fold very compactly. Good (aluminium) models are lightweight and easily folded. Cheaper (steel) models are improving, but can be heavy and difficult to manoeuvre because of oversimplified engineering. Some now incorporate a lie-flat option for newborns though this should not be used on rougher terrain. If you do want to jog with one, look for a model with handbrake and suitably positioned back axle. A swivel front wheel is vital for ease of steering; cost £150+.

All terrain buggies with carrycot (a trendier three-in-one): as immediately above, but the seat can be removed and a carrycot added. Though an expensive option, it is one which avoids the weight handicap of the traditional three-in-one solution and can offer a one-stop solution from baby to toddler; cost £350+.

Other possibilities:

Travel system: pioneered by car seat manufacturer Britax – the car-seat is at the heart of a system, and in combination with a special 'trolley' for pushing the car-seat around effectively acts as a push-chair. Potentially useful, especially if you spend lots of time in and out of the car, but it's generally outgrown by around nine months; cost £230+.

Twin buggies and pushchairs: either side-by-side or tandem, either 'buggy'-style or 'all-terrain'-style, either for twins or children of different ages. When making a selection, size and weight are a major consideration, as is manoeuvrability. Side by side are normally smaller and cheaper, tandems sturdier, but leave limited leg room for the child at the back. Check your choice will fit in the boot of your car. If you have twins (or more), TAMBA (see chapter *4.06 Support groups*) supplies a leaflet on buying appropriate pushchairs. Whatever you buy, ensure the width is less than a standard wheelchair (25-27 inches), so it should fit through most shop doors and public entrances. Though expensive, some of the three-wheel, all-terrain twin options are some of the lightest and easily folded on the market; cost £150+, all terrain £375+. (See below for specialist suppliers.)

How do I choose?

Because of the expense of buying wheels for your baby and the inconvenience of a bad choice, you need to give good thought to how you will be using your equipment, and what you want it to do. Think through your priorities to work out which model will suit your lifestyle best.

Issues to consider, and questions to ask yourself:

➤ Where you live: if you live up or down a flight of steps then you will want the lightest solution possible. Similarly, the amount of space available will affect your ability to store, say, a pram.

➤ How you travel and shop: if you go everywhere by car, you need something which can go in the boot, or some form of travel system using a car seat. If you rely on public transport you want something you can haul on and off buses and tubes. You many need space for some shopping (as bags on the handles can tip the whole thing over and distort the frame) and which easily manoeuvrable (look out for wheels that can either be locked or swivel freely).

➤ In what season will you be wheeling the baby around? In winter a young baby will need more protection than is offered by a lightweight buggy.

➤ Do you want the baby to face you or the world? If the former that rules out the traditional pushchairs and suggests a pram or some form of pram–pushchair combination.

➤ How much do you like walking and over what sort of terrain? Many new mothers find walking with their baby a prime source of exercise and an enjoyable pastime. Prams, all-terrain buggies, and some of the combinations with big wheels and a good suspension are ideal. Traditional fixed-seat pushchairs tend to have small wheels and require more effort to push. Wheels with pneumatic tyres deal with rough ground well, but can puncture. With small wheels, ones that swivel are better on pavements, but lockable ones are easier to push over rough ground.

➤ How easy is the thing to clean? How practical does it look? How well-built is it? You will use this purchase a lot – it needs to be reliable, well-designed and as good quality as you can afford.

➤ What extras, such as sunshades and rain covers etc, are included in the price.

Practical considerations specific to each model:

➤ Make sure the handles are at a comfortable height (a bad fit can lead to backache) and project far enough from the pram to leave plenty of space for your stride. Is this also the case for your partner?

➤ The more ingenious the model the more you need to check that it really does everything it claims to, and that the parts (especially clips) are both user-friendly and durable.

➤ Most pushchairs and buggies nowadays fold up to some degree. Make sure this is easily done (try it one-handed) and that the folded item fits into the boot of any car it is likely to be stored in.

➤ Footrests are valuable, including on double buggies, when children get just a little older.

Accessories which you may wish to consider:

Rain covers: ideally offer good coverage, but still allow plenty of air to circulate. They are also useful against wind. Note that carrycot covers are seldom waterproof so if your model incorporates one you may wish to consider a waterproof cover for it. Alternatively elasticated showerproof covers are cheaper and can be folded up when not in use.

Sun shades: rarely well designed. Look for one in a solid material which doesn't just filter the light. The shade should cover as much of the vehicle as possible and be adjustable. Parasols tend to be weak and don't offer much cover.

Harnesses: most prams and pushchairs incorporate these into their designs; if not you will need to buy one, ideally five-point (over both shoulders, across the waist and between the legs)

Buggy board: useful for elder siblings, these wheeled boards clip behind a buggy for a child to 'ride' on.

Foot muff/Cosytoes: only needed in the coldest weather.

Netting: against animals or insects.

Shopping trays or nets.

See below for suppliers of buggy accessories.

THE BRANDS

Most of the manufacturers below have a stab at making models in all categories.

Wheeled transport brands

Aprica America, Inc.	Jané
Bébé Confort	Kingswood
Bébécar UK	Maclaren
Britax	Mamas & Papas
Bugaboo	Monbebe
Chicco	Mountain Buggy
Cosatto	Silver Cross
Emmaljunga UK	XTS
Graco	

Buying second-hand

Check:

- ➤ That all wheels touch the ground: if not, something is bent.
- ➤ That wheels are not wobbly: worn wheel-bearings can be replaced, but at a cost.
- ➤ That any suspension is still working.
- ➤ That brakes hold firm, even when pushing quite hard: some faults are simple to repair, but failure to work at all may indicate more fundamental problems.
- ➤ That a chair folds easily: if not, the frame may be distorted.
- ➤ That the front legs of a pushchair are not bent from overloading or banging against something.
- ➤ That anti-fold locks are secure even when the buggy is shaken and that they release easily.
- ➤ That the joints of umbrella-fold models are not loose: they can trap fingers.
- ➤ For rust.
- ➤ If the handle is U-shaped that it is not bent: if it is, it may eventually snap.
- ➤ That there are no hard-to-mend tears in fabric.
- ➤ That seat adjusters all work.

➤ That any part required is still available – problematic if the item is more than five years old.

Looking after the pram

Many problems with prams and pushchairs result from a lack of proper maintenance.

To extend a pram or pushchair's life:
➤ Don't leave it folded when damp.
➤ Don't overload it, particularly with bags over the handles.
➤ Don't, to the extent you can avoid it, bump against curbs or down steps.
➤ Do oil moving parts, for example with WD40.
➤ To clean dirty fabric, cover with a strong detergent (Swarfega works well), leave for half an hour, then scrub off rinsing with boiling water.

Department stores will generally arrange for the repair of a pushchair or buggy bought from the store. John Lewis can supply a replacement one while yours is being mended. (Allow 4-6 weeks for their repair service; £50 refundable deposit required for loans.) For a list of repair services, see below.

Repair services

West
   WJ Daniel & Co *(W13)*

North
   Infantasia *(N22)*
   London Nursery
      Suppliers *(N22)*
   Soup Dragon *(N8)*

South
   Barnes Buggy Repair

   Centre *(SW19)*
   Bebeworld *(SW12)*
   Soup Dragon *(SE22)*

Mail order
   Bebeworld
   WJ Daniel & Co
   Infantasia
   Soup Dragon
   Stork Talk

Buggies for triplets

Mail order
   Baby Direct

Gordon's Production Services
Van Blanken

Buggy accessories

West
   Pixies *(W4)*

North
   Interben *(NW11)*

Mail order
   Abstract
   Baby Direct
   Bugglesnuggle Co
   Cheeky Rascals
   Pixies

Specialist buggy suppliers

Many of the largest suppliers, such as John Lewis, are listed under general stockists at the end of the chapter. This listing relates to businesses whose main business is buggy-related.

North
  Baby Munchkins *(N1, NW5)*

East
  London Prams *(E14)*

Mail order
  Baby Munchkins
  Chariots All Terrain
    Pushchairs

London Prams
Practical Pushchairs
Prams Direct
Triangles
Van Blanken

4. CARRYING EQUIPMENT (SLINGS & BACKPACKS)

Indexes in this section refer to chapter 3.14 Shopping directory.

Slings

Slings are felt by some parents to be a real day-to-day alternative (and a much cheaper one) to buying a pram. They offer great mobility for shopping and hopping on and off public transport. Their use is not restricted to travelling with the baby outside the home however: some parents swear by them for carrying newborns with them while getting on with cooking, work and other activities.

Slings are particularly useful for new babies. Not only is this when children are at their most portable and clingy, but, out-of-doors, being next to an adult's body keeps babies far warmer than if they were in a pram (especially in winter). In addition, they allow babies to observe social interaction and keep them further from car pollution than in a buggy.

One facet of slings which can be a plus or a minus – depending on your viewpoint – is that they are very effective at lulling small babies to sleep (because they recognise the rocking motions, warmth and heartbeat from being inside the womb). This can be a boon if you have a child that's difficult to settle, or it can be a problem if you have a carefully planned schedule in which sleeping and waking periods are tightly planned.

If you are planning to use a sling it is wise to start early, when the baby is still light: continued use on a regular basis builds up stamina.

From a parent's point of view, a sling needs to be designed to distribute the weight of the child as much as possible. Those which require all the weight to be borne by the shoulders will swiftly become too painful to use. For comfort you need good padding, especially over the shoulders. In addition a tie-on sling requires support round the waist, and across the back and shoulders. An over the shoulder sling needs a sufficient width of fabric to be comfortable.

More important still, the sling must be safe for the baby. A report by two US chiropractors pointed out that slings which position babies upright with legs hanging down (as in a parachute), with the main support at the base of the spine, risk a condition called spondylolisthesis, compromising the developing curves in the baby's spine. This is a widespread problem apparently in Inuit communities using this type of sling. What you need instead is support of both buttocks and thighs for the baby.

Types of sling:

Strap-on sling brands: the two big names are Baby Bjorn, and Wilkinet though the US brand Kelty which offers a design halfway between the two is also increasingly available in the UK (see chapter *3.14 Shopping directory*). Different designs suit differently shaped parents but a straw poll by the author found the Wilkinet winning for comfort and back support. Its detractors think it too much of a contraption. Do beware the large numbers of badly designed slings of this type on the market, including some of the most expensive.

Over-the-shoulder sling brands: babies can easily be slipped in and out of these comparatively simple slings which have the advantage of placing no strain on the baby's spine, though initially, at least, they seem to demand a cradling arm just to make sure the baby's safe. However, they don't suit everyone, because the baby's weight is not evenly distributed.

Good for discreet breast-feeding, they are perhaps most useful for short trips (from the car, around a shop) and for children who are beginning to walk but still require some carting about.

Flat fabric slings: the most traditional style of slings based on systems used in ethnic communities, now growing in popularity. The fabric may be woven for extra grip while some new brands offer the option of stretch jersey cotton for extra ease of use. These are reported to provide a particularly womb-like environment for a newborn, suitable even for premature infants. There are a number of positions for holding the baby but all have the advantage that the child sits on the fabric rather than dangling from it, reducing compression on the baby's spine. The full width of fabric can be used to spread the weight of the baby across the carrier's shoulders, releasing pressure from the back and distributing it across the torso. The lack of belt or buckle means there is nothing to dig into either carrier or baby. The main disadvantage is that these are only suitable for the reasonably dextrous who are also able to follow 3-D instructions. This means that like, for example the Wilkinet, there may be a short learning curve before full mastery is achieved.

West
Bill Amberg *(W2)*

Mail order
Bill Amberg
Baby Hut
The Better Baby Sling Co
Bio-Bubs (& Hugabub)
Born
Calange

The Carrying Kind
Happy Baby Co
Huggababy Natural Baby
   Products
Kari Me
Kelty Kids
Sling Easy
Storm Enterprises
Wilkinet Baby Carriers

Backpacks

Baby backpacks are rucksacks designed for carrying babies. The packs can be used, for example, when shopping, but most are primarily designed with walking and 'outdoors' pursuits in mind. They can be cumbersome in crowded places, and are relatively awkward to get on and off. Many can be stood up on the ground holding the baby, so acting as an informal babyseat (though not one to be left unattended).

Their use is restricted to older babies, who can hold their heads up. The 'passenger' is not kept as warm as in a sling but enjoys a better view than in a buggy or pram and is kept some distance from car pollution. Part of the entertainment for passengers is proximity to adult hair, ears, face and so on, which can result in some pain for the wearer.

When buying, the same rules apply as when choosing any backpack: make sure that the frame is strong but lightweight, and that it is your pelvis which takes the weight, not just your shoulders and back. Different models suit different people, depending largely on the length of the user's back and prominence of pelvis. Before purchase, everyone who may be using the backpack should give it a trial, with the baby on board dressed as for an outing. Higher prices generally correspond to more adjustability and better padding for both parent and child.

The same issues apply as with slings. The seat should support the entire bottom, not just between the legs, with feet dangling. A design with a footrest is preferable.

A rain cover, usually around £15 extra, may be a worthwhile investment. If you plan to travel in bright sun you will need to consider a shade as well (a pram shade can sometimes be used).

Sling & backpack stockists

Baby Backpacs
Bush Baby
Calange
Karrimor
macpac
Storm Enterprises
Tomy

Central
Blacks Camping Shops (W1)
Snow & Rock (WC2)

West
Blacks Camping Shops (W8)
Cotswold Essential
   Outdoor (W12)
Snow & Rock (W8)

North
Blacks Camping Shops (NW4)

Green Baby (N1)

South
Cotswold Essential
   Outdoor (KT1)

East
Blacks Camping Shops (EC2)
Cotswold Essential
   Outdoor (E1)
Snow & Rock (EC1)

Mail order
Blacks Camping Shops
Born
Cotswold Essential Outdoor
Green Baby
Holz Toys
Smilechild
Snow & Rock

Hip shelf brands

A 'hip shelf' is a relatively new option designed for toddlers who are too large to use a sling. A device fixed to the parent by a belt makes it easier to sit the child on a hip. Under the seat functions as a small hip bag.

Hippychick

5. SLEEPING EQUIPMENT (COTS, MOSES BASKETS & MATTRESSES)

(For information on cot death or sleep and related problems, see chapter 2.03 Baby health. For details about cot linen, bedding, beds for toddlers (and most nursery furniture), see chapter 3.03 Nursery decor.)

Indexes in this section refer to chapter 3.14 Shopping directory.

Where should your baby sleep?

This is one of the earliest decisions you make as a parent. It is also one of the first to raise questions which could be described as parenting decisions.

Don't expect shops to do the thinking for you. A November 2002 Secret Shopper survey by the Federation for the Study of Infant Deaths (FSID) found that over half of stores they visited undermined their cot death recommendations with inappropriate product displays and advice.

In recent years there has been more of a vogue towards babies sharing the parental bed as the argument has gained ground that it makes breast-feeding easier, and only fell out of favour in the West due to the unsanitary conditions of the industrial age.

As we go to press, a January 2004 report in the Lancet looks set to undermine this trend. It concludes that bed-sharing puts infants up to eight weeks of age at higher risk of smothering and overheating. In combination with other FSID research which shows that having the baby in the parents bedroom somewhat reduces the risk of cot death, their recommendation is now clear: babies should be in the same room as their parents, but in a separate cot (at least in the early months). Counter arguments were raised immediately. Given the statistical finessing involved, an ultimate conclusion may be difficult.

Your baby can sleep:

➢ With you in bed (now, no longer recommended under eight weeks old).

➢ In an adjacent or nearby Moses basket, cot, carrycot or crib.

➢ In one of the above, in a separate room (less recommended).

Should baby sleep in mum and dad's bed?:

➢ Experts used to divide more or less equally on whether the risk of cot death was greater with the baby sleeping separately or sleeping apart. Recent FSID research suggests the latter, but some have taken issue with the validity of that study. All agree, however, that babies should not sleep with parents who smoke, are drunk, take drugs – including sleeping pills – are ill, are overweight, or sleep in a waterbed.

➢ Those in favour of babies sleeping in a separate bed argue that it protects the baby against the parents rolling on to the child; gives the parents a better night's sleep; and accustoms the child to sleeping alone and in developing a good sleep routine.

➢ Those in favour of babies sleeping with their parents argue that this is customary around the world. They point to studies (contradicted in part in the latest Lancet study) indicating that it is safe for the child in the absence of the risk factors highlighted above. They point out that feeding a new child is easier for a breastfeeding mother

sleeping in the same bed, and argue that the baby may only be willing to sleep with the comfort of the parents' presence. This school may also believe it should be left to children to decide when they are ready to sleep alone.

Arguments for and against baby sleeping in the same room as mum and dad:

➤ The Foundation for the Study of Infant Deaths favours keeping babies in their parents' room in a cot by the side of the bed for at least the first six months as their research shows that this somewhat decreases the risk of cot death. Having said that, it is a small risk factor compared with, say, smoking near the baby or overheating the baby.

➤ Babies who sleep in the same room as their parents may not establish as regular a sleep pattern as those in their own room, as it is harder for parents to ignore cries in the night.

If you decide that your baby should sleep apart from you, you will need an appropriate bed. Serious traditionalists claim that all you need for a baby to sleep in is a deep drawer and a blanket, but more likely you will want to invest in one or more of the following…

Types of baby sleeping equipment:

Carrycots: usually these days the pram part of a pram–pushchair combination. However, if you still want to use the carrycot in its 'pram' mode, this can make it less suitable for your child to sleep in at night (for example if it has become damp out of doors). Check that any hood is easy to use and effective and make sure the carrying handles are easy to use, but can be tucked out of the way of the baby

Moses baskets: in wicker or palm (the cheaper option) are lighter than carrycots, but less suited to taking out of the house. Most come with stands, but if you feel the baby is safer with it on the floor you should make sure there are no draughts, pets or unsupervised toddlers around. Moses baskets also usually come covered with a frill of fabric and sometimes a matching quilt. (Use of a quilt is currently advised against due to issues relating to overheating and cot death.) Each Moses basket handle should be attached at two well-spaced points to avoid the basket tipping when carried. These handles should naturally fall outwards, not into the basket and on to the child. A well fitting fabric inner covering will protect the baby from any rough surfaces. Pop-up versions in fabric are marketed for use when travelling, but – though generally lacking stand – could be used at home.

Cribs: often suspended from a frame that allows the crib to swing from side to side; traditional versions do not offer the portability of Moses baskets and carrycots. Some newer fabric ones however do fold up. A brake or stop is something advised in case the baby dislikes the movement. Traditional versions are wooden, alternatives generally fabric, including hammock-style.

Cots: many parents go for one of the preceding options with their newborn, making the move to a cot when their child is outgrowing it, or can roll over (typically at three–four months). If used from birth, cots are often fitted with cot bumpers to make them seem cosier. Alternatively some cots are specifically manufactured to fit alongside the parents' bed and to open on to it (for example, for feeds).

In addition to any of the above, you will need:
➢ A mattress (usually sold separately).
➢ Sheets and blankets and/or a baby sleeping bag.

See below for pointers relating to these items.

Portable options for sleeping
Given the amount that babies sleep, it can be helpful to have options for different rooms of the house, and also for when you are out and about.

Portable options for sleeping:
Moses basket: useful around the house, but not particularly easy to carry, especially with a baby in (when they are given to tipping).

Lambskin: another largely indoor option – a comfortable and washable surface which you can carry with you to give the baby something familiar to lie on. Because of air trapped in the fleece and the moisture absorption, lambskins are said to keep the baby warm in winter and cool in summer. Note, though, that though lambskins themselves are very portable, you can't actually transport a sleeping baby on one, and there's no protection from draughts at floor-level.

Carry cots: as noted, usually these days the pram 'bit' of a pram–pushchair combination. Generally they are heavier to cart around than Moses baskets, but better-suited to outdoor use.

Travel cots: include some very well designed, relatively inexpensive and easy-to-use pieces of equipment; they are excellent for an older baby as they also double as portable play pens. Consider one with a set of wheels on the bag for extra portability. Some also feature a blind to cover the mesh sides and lessen distractions at sleep time.

Car seats, prams and buggies can be useful for short-term naps when out and about. But beware of overusing this option, as most specialists in child posture feel that the slumped position is bad for the spine.

Hanging crib: available from a growing number of suitable for use when travelling.

Lambskins

West
  Natural Mat Co *(W11)*

North
  The Active Birth Centre *(N19)*

Mail order
  The Active Birth Centre

The Carrying Kind
G L Bowron
Huggababy Natural Baby
  Products
Natural Mat Co
Sheepland

Travel cots

  Graco

Other portable sleeping equipment

The following are alternatives to the more familiar travel cots available at most larger equipment suppliers.

Mail order
  Amby UK
  Baby Hut

Baby Snug
Back to Sleep

Cots

Like prams, cots are quite major purchases, it being quite easy to spend upwards of £200.

Aside from safety, there are relatively small differences in cot-design and choosing one is largely a matter of how nice an article of furniture you wish to buy, though there are some variations in size. To the extent that there are issues, they primarily relate to the design of the sides of the cot.

➤ Not all cots come with drop sides, with many stores now selling fixed-sided cots where the base can be dropped in height as the child grows. Some people, however, swear by models with drop sides saying they are easier on the back. Look for how easily the drop-mechanism can be operated one-handed (a typical situation); some are pedal operated.

➤ Some models (known as 'cot–beds') are designed to be used when your child is older, with the sides removed to make a bed. Models which can be extended to a full-length bed can offer excellent value for money and a straightforward transition for the child. However, bear in mind that older children may not like babyish designs and this option is in any case of limited use if you are planning a short gap between children, in which case you will need either another cot or another bed.

➤ If you don't mind a fixed side cot of fixed height cot, a travel cot can be a versatile option (see Portable options for sleeping, above). Some babies actually prefer their soft sides to conventional cots.

If you want to pay a premium you can buy a cot which converts into an alternative piece of furniture – a sofa, a desk, a playhouse etc – which can make for good value in the long term.

Safety:
➢ Cots should be stable with a secure base under the mattress.
➢ Spacing between bars should be no less than 25mm and no more than 60mm (so that heads can't get stuck).
➢ There should be nothing which might help a baby climb out, i.e. no cross-struts or cut-outs (or, once the child is old enough, any toys attached).
➢ There should be no removable parts or decorations, including peelable transfers, on which the baby could choke.
➢ Any drop-side mechanism should not be releasable by the baby and once down should not drop below 250mm from the top of the drop-side to the top of the mattress.

Other points to consider:
➢ Shops mostly charge for the mattress separately.
➢ If the cot is self-assembly, how difficult will it be to assemble?
➢ If the cot includes drawers, are they on the same side as the dropside? (necessary if you want the cot against a wall).
➢ Castors may be useful.
➢ A clear plastic edge fitted to the sides of the cot as a teething rail can prevent the gnawing of woodwork

If buying second-hand:
➢ If the cot is adjustable, ask for a copy of the instructions. This is especially important if the cot is going to be handed over dismantled. (NB once assembled, some designs should not be dismantled).
➢ Check that all parts, including all screws, have been supplied and as far as possible that any working parts are in good order.
➢ Avoid a cot that is not solid enough to withstand a toddler tantrum. Movement at the joints is a bad sign.
➢ Avoid anything with cracked or damaged parts. These cannot usually be replaced and can injure a baby.
➢ Check for age and whether the cot has been repainted. If it has been, check that the paint used is non-toxic.
➢ Check the base for split slats or damaged metal springs.
➢ Buy a new mattress (generally advised for health reasons).
➢ Remove any transfers that could be chewed.

Cots

Central
   alphabeds (W1)

West
   Babylist (SW6)
   Natural Mat Co (W11)
   Pixies (W4)
   Red Studio (W4)
   Simon Horn (SW6)

North
   St John's Wood

   Interiors (NW8)

South
   Kerry Ward (SW18)

Mail order
   Babylist
   Birth & Beyond
   Community Playthings
   Lullaby Heir
   Macraft Industries
   Minor Matters

Moroccan Link   Spirit of Nature
Natural Mat Co   Storm Enterprises
Pixies   Mark Wilkinson Furniture
Patricia Sherwood
Simon Horn

Mattresses

Having bought a Moses basket or cot, you will need to buy a mattress
(they are normally sold separately). It must fit exactly (no more than 4cm
gap) to avoid the danger of the baby's head getting stuck in the gap, causing possible suffocation.

Concerns were raised a few years ago that the fire retardant chemicals
in cot mattresses may be related to cot death. A study by the Department
of Health found such fears to be groundless.

Similar concerns have also been raised about foam mattresses, or
mattresses incorporating PVC. However, it now seems that PVC-cov-
ered foam mattresses may be some of the safest around as they are so
easy to keep clean.

Mattresses come in a variety of types of construction. Some manufacturers trumpet designs that allow air to flow through them (to prevent
the build-up of moisture and associated problems), though if you are
planning to use a rubber or plastic sheet as protection it will render this
feature useless.

According to the Federation for the Study of Infant Deaths, provided
a mattress is clean, dry, firm, and well aired, there is no evidence of a link
between the type of mattress and cot death. However, the Federation
advises against the use of mattresses that are too soft.

Generally, it is suggested that mattresses should be at least 8cm thick,
especially if foam, in order to provide suitable support.

Selection of a mattress is of most concern to families with allergies.
Natural fibre and uncovered mattresses are thought to harbour dust mites
(which are linked with allergy) and as a result, covered and polyester
mattresses are generally recommended.

Types of mattress for cots and toddler beds:

Cotton: all the benefits of a natural fibre – a breathable and un-
clammy material; can only be surface cleaned however, and because
of the absorption of fluids may encourage mites; a mattress cover is
therefore useful; recommended by some, but not all, for allergies.

Wool: only available from specialists – an expensive option for those
looking for natural fibres and comfort; not easily washed so a mattress
cover is a good idea.

Polyester: often used with a breathable cover and recommended
by many suppliers for those prone to allergy.

Foam: the cheapest and least durable option; usually covered in
PVC and/or mesh, with holes at one end for ventilation; after only a
small amount of use, the material tends to settle into dips and troughs;
any liquid that reaches the interior of the mattress tends to cause mould.

Fibre: generally a latex-coated coir fibre and hair; good for comfort
and durability but coir can be a problem if allergies are an issue.

Sprung: most of the above can be combined with coiled springs,
though this is unnecessary given that a young child's weight will make
little use of these (but is great for use as a trampoline...).

Latex: primarily manufactured by Dunlopillo – durable and claimed to be hypo-allergenic and with anti-microbial properties.

Cotton/PVC: some makes have cotton on one side, PVC on the other, so you can choose which side suits best; removable panels, designed for washing, are another option.

Specialist mattress suppliers

The following suppliers specialise in mattresses made in natural fibres, or produced with hypoallergenic properties in mind. Mattresses are also sold by many (if not the majority) of the general stockists listed at the end of the chapter, some of whom can arrange for mattresses to be made to specific sizes.

Central
  alphabeds *(W1)*

West
  Natural Mat Co *(W11)*

South
  7+7 Futons & Interiors *(SW12)*

Mail order
  Beaming Baby
  Cotsafe Products
  Full Moon Futons
  Greenfibres
  Natural Mat Co
  7+7 Futons & Interiors
  Willey Winkle

6. HIGH CHAIRS

Indexes in this section refer to chapter 3.14 Shopping directory.

You won't need a high chair until your baby is five or six months old. Until then babies can't sit up by themselves and can be fed on your lap, or in a car seat or bouncy chair.

Even babies can suffer spine damage from unsuitable seating. BackCare's leaflet on pregnancy and children (see chapter *1.02 Looking after yourself*) shows that more than 35% of teenagers have permanently damaged spines and 50% of school pupils have back, hip and neck problems. It is therefore worth giving some thought to posture as you make your choice. It is advised that the seat be shorter than the baby's thighs, and the table at elbow height. What's more, there should be a distinct angle between the spine and thighs.

Most high chairs are initially used with a harness, which in some cases can double up as walking reins. Make sure these can be removed and washed.

Options include:

Chairs with integral table: particularly good for parents who want to feed their children away from the table and/or prevent tableware being seized by an over-enthusiastic toddler. Adjustable chair and table heights and a removable table are useful options, particularly if you may want the baby to join you at the adult table sometimes. The chair's table should ideally have a lip all the way round to minimise spills, and be large enough for all the child's plates and a cup and without ridges or other features to trap dirt. These chairs often fold flat for storage. If you want this feature, make sure the unit folds easily.

Old-fashioned wooden models: there are a variety of these, usually with arm rests and sometimes a table on a hinge.

'Cube' chairs: with a separate table and chair for a toddler, the chair slotting over the table to create a high chair; flexible but less useful if

you are planning a second child – unless you want them each to have their own table and chair.

Clip on: a compact fabric seat clipping onto the table edge. This arrangement is quite neat, but is only as strong as the table lip to which it is attached and for this reason ROSPA does not recommend their use. If you do opt for one, the fitting should be examined each time the table is used, and an adult chair placed underneath for safety. Look for a seat which screws rather than simply clips on, and which offers a firm but not rigid seating surface.

Designer, height-adjustable wooden chairs: a wooden chair that expands with the child, in some cases eventually to become an adult seat. The oldest design is the Tripp Trapp made by the Norwegian company Stokke, though it has inspired numerous rivals in recent years. The idea is to make sitting at table easier as children grow and to help them participate at meal times and to concentrate when working at the table (particularly useful when learning to read and write). A key feature is the improved posture they promote over most other high chairs. They are often also very easy to clean. Given that much of the point of these chairs is that they last into childhood, look for one that is really well made.

Booster (to sit on an adult chair): generally for older children, but some models are foldable and incorporate a table and restraint. Useful for when visiting friends, or restaurants without special chairs. Not all are stable, and few work with all chairs.

Fabric harness with Velcro straps or similar for attaching to adult chairs: not for day-to-day use but when visiting and travelling.

High chairs

Central
   Back 2 *(W1)*
   The Back Shop *(W1)*

West
   The Back Store *(W6)*
   Pixies *(W4)*

South
   Little Green Earthlets *(SW15)*

Mail order
   Back 2
   The Back Shop
   The Back Store
   Bibs 'n' Stuff
   The Great Little Trading Co
   Little Green Earthlets
   Macraft Industries
   Millthorne Chairs
   Pixies

7. OTHER ITEMS (INCLUDING SAFETY & SPECIALIST EQUIPMENT)

Indexes in this section refer to chapter 3.14 Shopping directory.

The list of what you might buy for your child is pretty much endless – as is the list of ways you can make-do-and-mend to avoid buying anything.

The following is a brief résumé of the most commonly-used miscellaneous 'stuff'.

Categories in this section:
➤ Monitoring equipment (Baby's room thermometer; Monitors).
➤ Bathtime equipment (Baby bath; Bathing accessories).
➤ Baby grooming.

➤ Other items (Bicycle-related items; Car accessories; Name labels).
➤ Non-baby equipment which may make life easier.

Monitoring equipment

Baby's room thermometer

Indicating ideal temperature and suitable bedclothes to use; see Section 2, Cot death in chapter *2.03 Baby health*.

Monitors and video monitors

Differences between models relate largely to power supply (mains, battery, re-chargeable) and portablity/operational distance. Some feature digital microprocessors to ensure you don't pick up noises from neighbouring children's rooms. Some allow parents to talk to the child via the parents' unit. Some plug directly into the socket, avoiding trailing flexes.

Monitors are useful for peace of mind if you have a large house, but in a small one you will hear the baby anyway. You can also use them on holiday, though few models are powerful enough to transmit through the structure of a large hotel. UK models also encounter interference in some countries.

Although there have been efforts to improve the standard of these products, it might prove better value if you are planning to use them on holiday to invest in a two-way walkie talkie system such as those sold for use on small boats. Given their status as safety equipment, these are designed to be considerably more reliable – and once the children are older will provide them with hours of entertainment.

There are also video monitors sold for keeping track of babies and toddlers at a distance, and – if this sort of idea appeals – technophiles may similarly wish to consider using a web cam.

Baby and You	Philips
Compass Watersports	Tomy
Electramax International	Voice Alert
IViewCameras	
Lindam	
Livecam	

Bathtime equipment

Baby bath

Once babies have passed the topping and tailing stage, you need a way of bathing them.

Some parents simply take their babies into the bath with them. This can be great fun, and some parents think it even improves children's confidence in water long term, but it's no solution if you don't actually want a bath yourself. And if the space around your bath is at all constricted, craning in and out holding a small baby can be both a kerfuffle and a cause of back strain.

The simplest baby bath is a small tub (a washing up bowl would be fine) that you can place wherever you like. Note, though, that when full of water these things can get heavy – also not good for your back.

At the other end of the spectrum, you can buy changing stations on casters where the top is hinged and conceals a baby bath underneath. The idea is that you wheel the whole unit to the water, fill up and wash, and then wheel it back into position when you are finished.

A third option is a unit that rests on the top of the adult bath. It makes for easy filling and emptying and means you don't have to grope around in the bottom of the bath. Its practicality is dependent on it fitting your particular bath.

In addition:

Plastic or plastic-backed apron: not necessary, but some parents like them.

Top and Tail Basin: a plastic water bowl divided into two sections for cotton wool and water, for 'topping and tailing' – you can just use separate bowls, of course.

Bath seat: at its simplest, a kind of foam rest, but more commonly a plastic seat; can be excellent for babies too young to support their own weight, but old enough to enjoy a good kick and splash by themselves. However, these can mildew unless treated with care, and the baby needs as much attention as when without one.

Non slip bathmat or attachments: for the bottom of the bath – relevant once the child can sit.

Bathing accessories

Mail order
   The Laundry

Snuggle Naps
The White Co

Baby grooming

Baby scissors: with rounded ends (for cutting a baby's startlingly sharp nails, preferably when asleep). Biting the nails is an effective alternative.

Hairbrush: for after the Kojak stage; there are soft baby ones, but spiked brushes with rounded-end bristles also work well. More useful long term are makes with different bristles for different hair types.

Other items

Bicycle-related items

If you are prepared to brave the traffic with your offspring, the following are stockists of accessories to help you do so.

Central
Evans Cycles *(SW1, W1, WC1)*

South
Evans Cycles *(KT2, SE1, SW18)*

East
Evans Cycles *(EC3, EC4)*

Mail order
Edinburgh Bicycle
Cooperative
Evans Cycles
Two Plus Two

Car accessories

Mail order
The Great Little Trading Co
The Little Star Co

Mail order
Easy2name Labels
Simply Stuck

Non-baby equipment to consider (if you don't already have them):

Washing machine and either tumble dryer or clothes drying rack.

Telephone extension or cordless phone: to make phone answering easier when feeding or attending to the baby. Alternatively, consider a telephone answering machine (which may in due course become a magnet for a toddler) or the answering services offered by your phone provider.

Low wattage light bulbs or a dimmer switch: for wherever you feed and/or change the baby at night. This will enable you to see what you are doing, while signalling that this is a quiet time and avoiding hurting the baby's eyes with a sudden bright light.

Laundry bag: in which to machine-wash breastfeeding pads and tiny baby items like bootees and socks. Otherwise they may end up blocking the waste pipe, particularly in older model machines.

Non-slip carpet underlay or grip: to avoid tripping when carrying the baby.

Muslins: useful for all kinds of situations and in particular mopping up mess; cheapest bought as fabric and hemmed.

8. FINDING A HOME FOR OUTGROWN GEAR

After all the effort it takes acquiring everything, babies grow out of their equipment, clothes and toys horribly fast. Even if you save the majority for younger siblings, or babies of relatives or friends, sooner or later you will be left with stuff on your hands that you want to be rid of.

Equipment and clothes in good condition can be sold through second-hand shops or through local newsagent windows, parent group newsletters or Loot. Toys in good condition can be offered in newsletters, or usefully donated to places like Sure-Start centres, and dentists and medical centres for their waiting rooms.

It is a rare charity shop in London, which sells baby equipment. Many take items, including buggies, and then chuck them when you've gone.

If you would like to feel that your children's things will continue to be useful, the charities listed below specialise in helping families in need and are always grateful for contributions of reasonable quality. If you have larger pieces, some local councils (see *chapter 4.01 London Boroughs*) can give details of organisations which, for example, take furniture.

USEFUL CONTACTS

Camden Family Service Unit
7 Downdey Close, Bartholomew Rd London NW5 ☎ (020) 7424 1600
Working with families with various problems, the resource centre always needs donations, but please ring before dropping things off – they may ask you to deliver direct to the family. Pushchairs, gates, monitors, cots and clothes are all welcome.

Doorstep Homeless Families Project
9a-13a Broadhurst Gardens London NW6 3QX ☎ (020) 7372 0413
All donations welcome, except large pieces of furniture. Cots, prams, pushchairs, toys, books and clothes for babies and children can all be found an owner. Adults and maternity clothes are welcome. / HOURS *7.15am-4pm (closed Wed).*

Field Lane Homeless Families Centre
Gregory House, 48 Meckenburgh Square London WC1 2NU ☎ (020) 7278 3873
⌁ *www.fieldlane.org.uk*
Children's clothes and toys in good condition are always needed. (Other items in particular shortage include men's clothes, kitchen utensils and household linen, if you are planning a big clear-out.) / HOURS *Mon-Thurs 10am-5.30pm, Fri 10am-4pm.*

Caris Haringey
107 Hampden Rd London N8 0HU ☎ (020) 8342 9080 ⌁ www.caris-uk.org
Provide goods for working, homeless families, asylum seekers and refugees. Good-quality, cleanable (and preferably educational) toys (not soft toys) are used for a mobile toy library. Books and videos in different languages and all kinds of baby equipment (in good condition) are always needed. / HOURS *Mon-Fri 9.30am-3pm.*

Prison Advice & Care Trust
254 Caledonian Rd London N1 0NG ☎ (020) 7278 3981
⌁ *www.imprisonment.org.uk*
Now merged with the Born Trust, this organisation works with the families of prisoners at four London prisons, and is particularly interested in receiving donations of clothing, pushchairs and baby bedding. / HOURS *Mon-Fri 10am-5pm.*

The Shaftesbury Resources Centre
93 Camberwell Station Rd London SE5 9JJ ☎ (020) 7737 7475
A Christian organisation helping families and individuals on or below the poverty line, providing essential household items including furniture. Baby goods, including prams, pushchairs, cots, toys and clothes are particularly welcome, and can be collected from anywhere within the M25. A good home for any surplus kit. / HOURS *Mon-Fri 9.30am-5pm.*

South London Refugee Association
UnitB 006 Trident Centre, 89 Bickersteth Rd London SW17 9HS ☎ (020) 8682 4350
Contact the refuge with details of items and they will see if they know anyone who may need them (they have no storage facilities). / HOURS *10am-5.30pm.*

Wednesday's Child
London NW3 ☎ (020) 7482 4319
A charitable trust which raises funds for projects in London that benefit children and babies who are in any way (physically, mentally, emotionally or economically) disadvantaged or deprived. Although they don't take in donations themselves, they should be able to put you in touch with local organisations who can accept your outgrown baby gear.

9. GENERAL STOCKISTS

Suppliers in this section are divided into a number of different categories. These indexes refer to chapter 3.14 Shopping directory.

Categories in this section:
➤ General stockists.
➤ Discount outlets.
➤ Second-hand suppliers.
➤ Hire companies.

General stockists

Central
- Back in Action (WC2)
- The Back Shop (W1)
- The Children's Seating Centre (WC2)
- Harrods (SW1)
- John Lewis (W1)
- Marks & Spencer (W1, W1)
- Mothercare (W1)
- Peter Jones (SW1)
- Prince Lionheart UK (W1)

West
- Baby World (SW6)
- Babylist (SW6)
- Blooming Marvellous (SW6)
- Clementine (W11)
- Cotswold Essential Outdoor (W12)
- Daisy & Tom (SW3)
- WJ Daniel & Co (W13)
- The Little Trading Co (W4)
- Marks & Spencer (W2, W8)
- Mothercare (SW6, W6)
- Woolworths (TW3, W2, W4)
- Young Smarties (W2)

North
- All Seasons (N12)
- Baby Concierge (NW4)
- Baby Munchkins (N1, NW5)
- Cheeky Kids (N18)
- Graham's Toys (HA2)
- Humla (NW3)
- Ikea (NW10)
- Infantasia (N22)
- Interben (NW11)
- John Lewis (NW4)
- JoJo Maman Bébé (NW11)
- Kindercare (WD6)
- Mini Kin (N8)
- Mothercare (N22, NW4)
- Rub a Dub Dub (N8)
- Simply Baby (HA1)
- Totland (N17)

- Woolworths (N1, NW1)

South
- Babies 'R' Us (SE15)
- Baby Nest (CR0)
- Bebeworld (SW12)
- Bentalls (KT1)
- Blooming Marvellous (TW9)
- Cotswold Essential Outdoor (KT1)
- Goldilocks (SE16)
- Ikea (CR0)
- John Lewis (KT1)
- Lilliput (SW19, SW8)
- Mothercare (CR0, TW9)
- Wear & Cheer (SE15)
- Woolworths (SW17)

East
- Cotswold Essential Outdoor (E1)
- Kiddicentre (E5)
- London Prams (E14)
- Potty People (E2)
- Victoria 2 Nursery Goods & Schoolwear (E17)

Mail order
- A Baby
- All Seasons
- Argos
- Babies 'R' Us
- Baby Boom UK
- Baby Concierge
- Baby Days
- Baby Direct
- Baby Echos (& Rad Pad)
- Baby Munchkins
- Baby World
- Babycare Direct
- Babylist
- Babys Mart
- Back in Action
- The Back Shop
- Bebeworld

Bettacare
Bickiepegs
Blooming Marvellous
Boots
Born
Cheeky Rascals
Childcare Products
The Children's Seating Centre
Cotswold Essential Outdoor
Cradle and All
Cuddlebabes
Daisy & Tom
WJ Daniel & Co
Ezee Reach
Graham's Toys
Grobag
Immaculate Contraptions
Infantasia
Interbren
Jackel International Ltd
John Lewis
JoJo Maman Bébé
Just Kidding
Kiddicare

Lilliput
Little Bugs
Little Stars
Littlewoods
London Prams
Lullabies
Lundia
Marks & Spencer
Mini Kin
Mothercare
NCT Maternity Sales
Nurserygoods.com
PHP
Pramsonline
Prince Lionheart UK
Rub a Dub Dub
Snuggle Naps
Stork Talk
Two Left Feet
Urchin
Urchins Baby World
VertBaudet
Young Ones

Discount outlets

Mail order

Discount Baby Store.co.uk

Maia Lily Loopy
Mum's Delight

Second-hand suppliers

Buying second-hand can be time-consuming, but there are some excellent bargains to be had, particularly if you are willing to turn up early at NCT equipment sales: parents often find themselves with stuff they have barely used, and sell it on practically new. Also check out local second-hand shops, as well as Loot and other local publications (particularly of parent support groups).

Some baby gear is fiendishly complicated so – as a counsel of perfection – try not to buy an item without its instructions. If the item is of a well-known brand, you might be able to get another set from the manufacturer (some of whom will also supply spare parts).

All the points made above about specific items bought new are all the more relevant when considering second-hand purchases. In general look for wear and tear and signs of lack of maintenance. This is particularly important with wheeled items.

On older items in particular, one factor to bear in mind is the possibility of paint containing lead, which is poisonous.

West

Boomerang (W14)
National Childbirth Trust
    (NCT) (W3)
Pixies (W4)

North

Simply Outgrown (N17)

South

Mum & Me (TW11)
The Rocking Horse (SW20)
Swallows & Amazons (SW12)

East

Chocolate Crocodile (E9)

Mail order
  eBay

Kiddiequipers
Pixies

Hire companies

This is a useful option if you think you are only going to need a piece of equipment for a short period, such as for a holiday or having a family to stay. It is also a good way of trying something out before buying, and many hire companies will offset initial hire charges if you choose to purchase in due course. For a month's hire of a travel cot, say, expect to pay about £35 (though you may find how firm's charge differs quite significantly from place to place).

South
  Chelsea Baby Hire *(SW19)*
  Lilliput *(SW19, SW8)*
  Mum & Me *(TW11)*

Mail order
  Lilliput
  Little Stars

CHAPTER 3.03

NURSERY DECOR

1. **Introduction**
2. **Practicalities**
3. **Safety**
4. **Specialist services & stockists**
5. **Furniture stockists**
6. **Bedding**
7. **General stockists**

1. INTRODUCTION

(For information on cots, see chapter 3.02 Baby equipment.)

Some parents really go to town on decorating their baby's space, spending more than on any other room in the house. Others limit themselves to buying the odd item. But while the look of the place is what most visitors will notice, it's the practicalities of the room layout which should be the prime concern for those who will be using it.

As with baby equipment, the average spend is high (perhaps as much as £1,800 if some articles are to be believed) so it's worth thinking about what kind of value for money that offers if the baby is going to be asleep in it or elsewhere most of the day, particularly if the items will be outgrown after two or three years.

When it comes to looks, sadly for parents inclined to restrained elegance, even the under-ones can be attracted by garish children's designs. By the time your child is toddling, bold-and-bright will be what attracts them. However, whatever their opinion on the subject, don't use anything that may make them too lively. Red walls for example increase aggression in people of all ages. For less manic behaviour try softer colours on the walls, reserving bright shades for toys and decorative highlights.

Surprisingly, few retailers specialise in nursery décor, but there are increasing numbers of manufacturers of good-looking cots and children's furniture. Some produce items designed with a dual use to extend their life — for example cots converting to small sofas, or child wardrobes that can change into cupboards with shelves, etc. This kind of options tends to be expensive but if you're happy to invest quite a lot in your child's room such pieces can offer better value for money in the long term.

If you have the budget, there are interior designers who specialise in kids' rooms. Another way to achieve a distinctive look is to commission a muralist (see listings). But again remember that something not too infantile and easily outgrown will provide best value for money.

READING

Children's Rooms – Jane Lott (Conran Octopus; 1989; £8.99; 1850292116) – *Unfancy information on planning and decorating kid's rooms.*

Children's Rooms in a Weekend – Roo Ryde (Murdoch Books; 1998; £5.99; 1853917710) – *80 pages with colour photos for ideas, mostly in bright colours but avoiding traditional designs.*

Children's Spaces – Judith Wilson and Debi Treolar (From zero to ten; Ryland Peters & Small; 2001; £18.99; 1841721204) – *A book of photographs of stylish – but real – homes with children. It covers not just children's rooms but also ideas for areas such as bathrooms, kitchens, and even the garden, where adult- and child-appeal can come together.*

Creative Spaces for Kids – Lauren Floodgate, Nikki Haslam, Gill Brewis, Karen O'Grady (innovative schemes for children of all ages, great ideas for rooms to sleep, play and elarn in; Hamlyn; 2002; £14.99; 0600605078) – *Sixteen room designs for everything from a nursery to a tenage den. It includes colour shemes, storage, colour swatches and suggestions for finishing touches, and includes plenty of DIY and hand-crafted options. / www.hamlyn.co.uk.*

Family Living – Judith Wilson with Debi Treloar (Creating the perfect family home; Ryalnd, Peters & Small; 2003; £18.99; 1-84172-405-X) – *How to create spaces which are easily adapted as children grow. The guide focusses on Activity Zones (communal areas), Peaceful Zones (bedrooms) and Practical Zones (including storage and outdoor spaces). Some fun and useful ideas.*

Great Gardens for Kids – Clare Matthews (imaginative ideas to entertain, educate and delight; Hamlyn; 2002; £16.99; 0600605167) – *A guide covering play items, play houses/spaces, furniture, plantings, party planning and Christmas decorations, with a selection of garden designs for families with children. It includes some pointers for DIY enthusiasts. / www.hamlyn.co.uk.*

Home Front: Children's Rooms – Stewart & Sally Walton (BBC Books; 1998; £7.99; 0563383895) – *Ideas from the TV programme; video also available.*

Spirit of the Nursery – Jane Alexander (Element; 2002; £6; 0007133499) – *The guide looks at ways to make a nursery feel warm and peaceful. It considers how to take into account its history and how to use colour, sound, scent and light, as well as practicalities such as storage. Also details of simple rituals and blessings for the room.*

2. PRACTICALITIES

Indexes in this section refer to chapter 3.14 Shopping directory.

Layout

At minimum, you need space for a cot and somewhere to store clothes. You may also want somewhere to change the baby and to keep nappies and associated paraphenalia. A small cot is 53cm x 117cm, while all cot beds are a standard 69cm x 140cm. After a couple of years, unless you went for a cot that converts into a bed, your toddler will graduate to a bed. You can have beds made to a size of your own specification, but this can work out expensive, especially as bespoke mattresses are usually pricey (and limited to a few types of stuffing). Most bedmakers work to the standard sizes of sprung mattresses: the smallest size is 76cm x 165cm (2'6" x 5'5") – a standard single is 90cm x 190cm (3' x 6'3").

Heating

(See also the Cot death section in chapter 2.03 Baby health.)
The best place to locate a cot is thought to be against an inside wall, but not next to a radiator, and away from direct sunlight. Positioning it like this should help protect the newborn against big changes in temperature. If the cot cannot be placed out of direct sunlight you will need reasonably thick curtains. If your baby is born in winter and you don't want to leave your central heating on all night, you may wish to invest in a portable heater. Given the link between over-heating and cot death, it is essential that whatever model you buy has a reliable thermostat.

Changing area

Not everyone goes in for tailor-made changing stations which come in a variety of formats (for example foldaway surfaces that drop down from the wall, dedicated pieces of furniture, or shelves which fit on the top of a cot). Instead, many people just have a mat on the floor, on their own bed (not ideal for your back), or on some other suitable surface.

Whatever solution you end up with must be readily accessible, at a comfortable height, and with a good-sized 'workspace'.

You will also need ready access to nappies, cotton wool, and so on. Purpose-made units often incorporate shelves, drawers or cupboards for such items, or alternatively you can use nearby shelves or fabric wall hangers.

Once a baby can roll, the lower the surface is then the safer it will be. Some stations include a harness with this in mind, but these can get rather grubby.

Light

Go for heavy curtains with black-out lining, or a black-out blind. Especially in summer this can make all the difference between a baby or toddler getting a good night's sleep and waking early. It is also vital if you want to control a baby or toddler's sleeping patterns. A low light for night-time feeds, or a dimmer, can also be useful.

Storage

Whatever storage space you have, you will find you always need more. Toy chests, although they sound like a great idea, are often too large for toddlers to find what they want in them, and there is the danger that the lid may slam shut. Ideally they should have finger-trap gaps and stay-open fittings. Open baskets or boxes may look less attractive, but are more user-friendly for small children. There is also a growing array of funky container systems on the market – see below.

Stockists

Community Playthings	JoJo Maman Bébé
The Great Little Trading Company	Knights & Daisies
	Spottiswoode Trading
The Holding Company	Step 2 (UK) Ltd

Sleep vs play

If your toddler will be spending a significant amount of time playing in the bedroom, it is useful to divide playing and sleeping areas until staying in bed at bedtime is firmly established.

Durability

As they grow, children tend to inflict damage (however unwitting) on their surroundings. It's therefore worth decorating in a style capable of taking a few knocks. Options for paint finishes include washable styles like vinyl silk emulsion (though it can attract dust), finishes such as rag rolling (to help conceal marks), or a top coat of matt varnish (to make the surface more durable). Wallpaper and borders are apt to get tatty, though one idea is to paper the top half of the wall and paint the bottom half with washable paint, dividing the two with a replaceable border. Beware patterns and designs that are swiftly outgrown.

Something adaptable will be better appreciated in time and work out cheaper.

The rest of the house

In addition to the child's bedroom you might like to start planning how to adapt your house to suit the needs of a growing toddler.

Points to consider:

➤ There will be literally heaps of toys to store, and they breed when you're not looking. If you are the kind of people who don't want to feel engulfed it is best to start thinking about this early. Large cupboards are best. Otherwise, consider allocating a dedicated play area. Giving children their own space means they should have less need to infringe on their parents'. At the end of the day, everything can then be cleared into this area.

➤ Assume that floors will come in for heavy battering and hard surfaces can take this best. If you have gone for sanded floorboards think about filling between the gaps, which toddlers see as intriguing openings for posting purposes.

➤ If on the other hand you feel that carpet or other floor covering will protect a toddler better from bumps (more of an imperative on stairs and associated landings than flat floors) there are two options. Either go for something cheap and cheerful which you can replace quickly, or go for the best quality you can afford so it can stand up to the likely beating it will endure, and in a colour or pattern which won't show stains.

➤ If you are going to buy or re-cover any soft furniture, do so in patterns which won't show stains and/or stain-proof them (though this latter does involve chemical treatments that you may prefer to avoid).

➤ Protect important surfaces, for example a good table, with a cloth or mat.

➤ Think about where to put treasured items so the baby or toddler is less likely to damage them.

➤ Add protection or remove dangerously sharp edges.

3. SAFETY

(In addition to the general ideas below, various specific suggestions for improving the safety of your home are given in chapter 3.02 Baby equipment.)

Indexes in this section refer to chapter 3.14 Shopping directory.

Newborn babies may be exhausting, but at least any damage inflicted either on themselves or on your property is generally fairly innocuous. This situation is relatively brief, however. In no time at all you need to assess the potential risks posed by your home to small people with a limited understanding of consequences.

The Child Accident Prevention Trust recommends the following as priority buys. All are particularly useful if you have two or more children who may distract you and/or push each other into trouble:

A smoke alarm per floor: available either battery-operated (the battery having to be replaced annually) or mains-operated. The best have an integral battery-operated light in case the fire cuts off the mains electricity.

A coiled kettle flex: alternatively shorten the flex on your kettle to prevent children being able to grab it.

Guards for fires and heaters: these can be floor-standing, fixed to the wall with a special clip, wall-mounted, or of a type suited to a mobile gas cylinder heater.

Safety glass or film: any glass panels below 80cm (2ft 5ins) from the ground, for example in and around doors, in room partitions, shower or bath screens, in furniture and in low level glass windows, should be replaced by safety glass. This is either laminated glass (i.e. two sheets of glass sandwiching a reinforcing plastic sheet) or toughened glass (heat-treated to shatter into small, rounded pieces). Both are available from glaziers. Alternatively, safety film, a clear plastic film, can be applied to one side of a sheet of glass to give it strength similar to safety glass. It is available from baby equipment shops and department stores in rolls about 73cm x 180cm.

Window locks: there are locks for hinged or pivoted windows which prevent them from opening more than 10cm (4ins). For other windows, burglary stop locks are effective. They should be fitted to leave no more than a 10cm gap when the window is open; keys for the locks on windows which would be needed for escape in a fire should be kept in a safe and accessible place for adults but not children. Window bars may also be useful.

A harness: these are recommended in the UK for use with any seat from which a child could fall – high chairs in particular. These are available separately from equipment suppliers.

Walking reins: these allow the new walker some independence while preventing wandering off at crucial moments: next to busy roads, in crowds, when your hands are full of a folded buggy, parcels, another child etc. Those for older walkers loop over one wrist (which may provide an insufficiently secure restraint). Some parents object that reins treat children like pets (and some children object to wearing them), but the Trust still recommends them.

Safety gates/barriers: safety gates are usually fixed to the wall with a wall fitting (cup). These are the only ones which meet British Standard strength tests. Some come with spare hinge plates so they can be used in more than one position. Some also come with extension pieces to fit wider gaps, or there are retractable fabric options. Useful places to keep them are at the bottom and top of stairs and at the door to the kitchen. Beware those with a bar at the bottom, which can cause adults to trip. If making your own gate or barrier the recommended height is at least 80cm (2ft 5ins) from the floor with bars 6–8.5cm (2.25–3.25 ins) apart, with no horizontal bars to help climbing over. Wide banisters should also be closed to crawling children. Note that not all parents go down the "gated" route, preferring to try to teach their kids from a very early age how to handle stairs. This strategy is at its weakest when there is more than one young child in the house where any jostling or mucking about on or near the stairs may cause an accident.

Front door alarm: can be fitted as part of a burglar alarm, set to make a noise every time the door is opened, offering warning of any toddler making a bid for freedom.

Also, if you have a cat:

> **Net for pram or portable cot:** cat net prevents family pets getting too close. It is coarser than, say, insect mesh, which cats can climb on.

Other items you could consider:

➤ Cooker or hob guards and/or oven-guard, though hob guards can themselves get very hot and an oven with a stay cool door is probably the safest option for the latter.

➤ A playpen (though some parents feel these are too reminiscent of a prison, and truly determined children can hurt themselves clambering out). A travel cot can double up in this capacity.

➤ Corner protectors, for example for a coffee table.

➤ Child-resistant containers.

➤ Child-resistant catches for cupboards and drawers containing dangerous items (best installed before the baby's arrival); freezer or fridge locks; washing machine and lavatory seat locks.

➤ A lockable medicine cupboard, ideally kept high up in the kitchen (which is more frequented by adults than a bathroom).

➤ Safety plugs/socket covers.

➤ Having an electrician replace your mains fuses with more sensitive trip switches (Residual Current Detectors, or RCDs. You may wish to leave out any circuits on which you work at a computer.) Alternatively an RCD socket can be installed wherever there might be particular danger.

➤ Ensuring there is a thermostat on all heaters so they do not get too hot to touch; if you are planning a new heating system there are now special low-surface-temperature radiators to aid with this. If you need a free-standing heater, the electric oil-filled varieties are the best (though pricey). Whatever you choose, the heater should never be set hot enough to burn a toddler's skin. Consider also energy-saving light bulbs that remain cool.

➤ A gas or carbon monoxide detector.

➤ Altering locks on bathroom doors to stop small children locking themselves in.

➤ Cupboard locks for all those cupboards containing breakables, spirits and other valuables.

➤ A video guard to prevent prying fingers destroying the flap mechanism and posting those proverbial jam sandwiches

➤ No-tip furniture straps to prevent shelves, for example, from tipping over.

➤ Door stops (door slam protectors) to stop fingers getting trapped between the door and hinge (or frame).

➤ Safe storage for any plastic bags.

OTHER SAFETY MEASURES

Each year 37,000 children go to hospital because of ingesting something they shouldn't have done. The vast majority of them are under 5 years old.

Before your child is mobile, consider whether you need to re-arrange the storage of anything in your home that could be harmful. As well as household and garden products this includes alcohol, perfume, mouthwash and cigarettes. Out of sight and in childproof cupboards is best. Where possible look for containers with child-resistant caps and if possible buy products with a bittering agent like Bitrex to make them unpleasant in the mouth.

You should also make sure you can secure your outside doors, especially any to the street. Walking toddlers sometimes make regular escape attempts.

You should remove any cords, for example to blinds or curtains, which a small child could get entangled around their neck.

Paints

It is important to make sure that all paints in the nursery, and preferably the whole house, are child-safe. They should be lead-free, ideally declared as non-toxic, and water- rather than solvent-based.

Anything painted with gloss paint more than 15 years ago may well contain a high proportion of lead. For this reason sanding of old paint during pregnancy or with a small baby is not recommended. (If you think your child may have chewed anything possibly containing lead you can get a hospital to do a blood test.) Note that some modern radiator paints may still include lead, though this should be well marked.

VOCs (volatile organic compounds) are a measure of the level of pollutants/irritants in the paint. A figure of below 7.9 is considered low. Generally solvent-based gloss paint are high in VOCs and best avoided when pregnant or around a baby or small child. If this kind of paint has been used, stay out of the room for several days until it dries. White spirit is also potentially harmful.

In an ideal world, you would avoid solvent-based products and stick to water-based products, including primers, varnishes and eggshells and finishes for wood like beeswax and linseed oil. One option is organic paints, but these are expensive and can be slow drying.

This index refers to chapter 3.14 Shopping directory.

Other decorating/building work

Volatile organic compounds are found in a growing number of household products as well as paint. These include plywood, particle board, wood panelling, insulation, adhesives, carpets and synthetic fabrics, along with modern cleaning materials. Benzene and formaldehyde are the main chemicals and these, together with other chemicals found in houses, mean that there is evidence that the air quality inside our homes may be worse than outdoors.

Carpets are particularly problematic, particularly if latex backed, glued to the floor and/or treated with fungicides and stain-resisting chemicals.

If you think there might be a problem with chemicals, particularly after building work, the advice is to raise the temperature to around 38C, open all windows and ensure that if you are pregnant or there are small children, they stay well out of the way. The idea is that the high temperature causes the materials to release their chemicals more quickly. You should repeat over two or three days and hope that you've avoided slow release over the months to come.

Stockists

Auro Organic Paint Supplies
Charter Design
Construction Resources
Ecomerchant Ltd
Ecos Paints

Green Building Store
International Paint
Nutshell Natural Paints
Ostermann & Scheiwe UK

Windows

Windows in those upstairs rooms where the child will eventually be spending time alone as a toddler will need some form of protection. The usual recommendation is bars – vertical ones to prevent their use as a climbing frame – and that these should be fitted even if the windows are well out of reach. Toddlers often enjoy assembling and clambering up furniture to reach their goal.

Useful contacts

The British Coatings Federation, ☎ (01372) 360660

⌘ www.coatings.org.uk

Formerly known as the Paintmakers Association, this organisation produces a leaflet with details of how to remove old lead paint safely; information is also on the website. / HOURS Mon-Fri 9am-5pm; PUBLICATIONS Free leaflet on paint removal.

Child Accident Prevention Trust (CAPT), ☎ (020) 7608 3828

⌘ www.capt.org.uk

This charity sees itself as the first port of call for parents where issues of child safety are concerned; it is committed to reducing the number of children and young people killed, disabled or seriously injured as a result of accidents. It covers all aspects of safety and organises high profile public safety campaigns, including Child Safety Week; parents can contact the trust with specific queries regarding safety equipment and accident prevention; trust can give parents advice on organising a nursery and safety equipment; factsheets are available on the website. / HOURS Mon-Fri 9am-5pm; PUBLICATIONS General safety advice and information leaflets (free, send SAE).

Nutkin, ☎ (01628) 778856, Mobile (07774) 257817

Small outfit run by a Norland Trained nanny, whose services include offering safety advice.

Royal Society for the Prevention of Accidents (RoSPA), ☎ (0121) 248 2000 ⌘ www.rospa.co.uk

Although RoSPA deals more with professionals (such as local councils) than with the general public, the organisation provides advice on car seats. There are also a variety of publications and general leaflets on child and home safety. / HOURS Mon-Fri 9am-5pm; PUBLICATIONS Free leaflet on accident prevention for first-time parents: 'They Don't Come with Instructions Do They?'; leaflets on safety and the pre-school child.

READING

How to Babyproof Your Home – Lisa Brownlie (Mainstream; 1998; £7.99; 8151589341) – Encouraging parents to see their home through the eyes of a child, room by room (including the garage); also a section on what to do if there is an accident. If you are going to use this, do so before your child is born. It includes lots of frightening and often tragic tales which are close to unreadable once you are a parent.

Safe Kids – Vivian K Fancher (A complete child safety handbook and resource guide for parents; Wiley & Sons Ltd; 1991; £11.99; 0-471529-73-7)

Safety equipment

Baby Echos (& Rad Pad)	Lindam
Baby Dan	Merriott Radiators
Baby Dux	Rabbitts
Babycare Direct	Redinap
Child Alert	Safety Zone
Clippasafe	Sui Generis
Finger Protector	Titan Forge
The Great Little Trading	Tommee Tippee
Company	Year Innovations
Kiddiproof	

In the garden

Not strictly speaking décor, but an issue of household maintenance that needs thought.

Points to consider:

➤ If possible, the garden needs to be enclosed with a gate young children can't open and fences need to be high and solid enough to prevent alternative escape routes.

➤ Toddlers and babies can drown in just inches of water. Any water feature must be of a variety that doesn't form pools, or be securely covered. Ponds can be turned into sandpits.

➤ Any equipment left out in the garden should be to BSI standards, firmly secured and checked regularly. While your own children may be familiar with how to stay safe on it, this will not be true of visitors. Equipment is best on grass. Generally bark chips are only good if there aren't any cats nearby, or they become the local litter tray (although you can get them treated to repel cats). Equipment is best within sight of the house and close enough to hear crying in case of an accident.

➤ Sandpits similarly run the risk of attracting cat litter unless covered when not in use. Note that you will need play sand – builder's sand is too abrasive.

➤ Paving may result in scrapes and bangs, but is a good all-weather surface for play, wheeled vehicles, kicking a ball etc. Conversely grass in winter can become a mud pit.

➤ Be aware of any dangerous plants (see Avoiding dangerous plants, in chapter *2.03 Baby health*).

Any garden shed – a prime storage area for dangerous items and chemicals of various kinds – needs to be kept firmly locked.

Garden designers

Garden Designs

4. SPECIALIST SERVICES & STOCKISTS

Indexes in this section refer to chapter 3.14 Shopping directory.

Listings in this section:

➤ Accessories.
➤ Art.
➤ Bedding, linen & soft furnishings.
➤ Interior designers.
➤ Muralists.
➤ Soft furnishings.
➤ Stencils & stamps.
➤ Wallpapers & fabrics.

Accessories

These can be the way to make the room feel appropriate for the age of child without spending a fortune. They can be easily swapped for something more suitable when the time comes and the relevant items stored, given away, or sold.

Central
  Boutique Descamps *(SW1)*

North
  Cuddle Pie *(N2)*
  Kappa Lambda Rugs *(NW5)*

South
  Little Wonders *(TW1)*
  Lizzies *(SW11)*
  Loophouse *(SE1)*
  7+7 Futons & Interiors *(SW12)*

Mail order
  Akta
  Carey Beckett
  Bigjigs
  Bishopston Trading Co

Boutique Descamps
Cox + Cox
Cuddle Pie
Favourite Things
Emma Jefferson
JFS
Kappa Lambda Rugs
Knightsbridge Lighting Ltd
Little Wonders
Midnight Mushroom
The Mulberry Bush Limited
The Nursery Co
Roxy Baby
7+7 Futons & Interiors
Patricia Sherwood
White Rabbit England
Zorbit Babycare

Art

  Art for Children

Interior designers

  Baby Concierge
  Colour Counsellors
  The Decor Centre
  Sara Copeland Interiors
  The Uncommon Touch

Unique Interiors
Van Blanken
Vicky Smith Interior Design &
  Decoration

Muralists

This is a job which a number of people try their hand at with a certain turnover of names. Though delightful, grand designs may be outgrown rather more swiftly than you imagine or the cost warrants. Paint effects last longer. A few specialists also decorate furniture. Styles and standards, as well as prices, are very variable.

  Bedrooms for Kids
  The Cow Jumped Over the
    Moon
  Sarah Hocombe
  Holdsworth Sign Writing

Joanna Scott Murals
Marvellous Murals
Rainbow Rooms
Cate Withacy
Wonderwalls

Soft furnishings

  ART
  Kidsfabrics

Louise Mabbs
Poppy

Stencils & stamps

A cheaper and less babyish option that can look very attractive and which is an achievable DIY goal.

  The English Stamp Company
  FuntoSee

The Stencil Library

Wallpapers & fabrics

As noted above, wallpaper is best used with caution. If you have standard-sized windows, consider ready-made curtains, or a trip to a second-hand curtain exchange.

West
Designers Guild *(SW3)*
Peter Topp Interiors *(SW6)*

South
The Uncommon Touch *(SW11)*

Mail order
Baer & Ingram
Minor Matters

5. FURNITURE STOCKISTS

Indexes in this section refer to chapter 3.14 Shopping directory.

This is a field where famously you get what you pay for (and where at all but the very top end of the market a degree of enthusiasm for flat-pack furniture assembly is essential). It may be worth shelling out a little more for items such as beds and cupboards, particularly if you are either hoping that a particular item will last the childhood of the user, or be passed on to a second child.

If you are on a limited budget, something second-hand cleaned up and repainted may well be better value than something new and cheaply made. As with toys, if you want something really durable, consider going to a specialist supplier of day nurseries and nursery schools.

Toddler beds

Central
alphabeds *(W1)*

North
St John's Wood
Interiors *(NW8)*

Mail order
Cider Woods Children's Furniture
The Fun Bed Co
The Iron Bed Co
Knights & Daisies
Lundia
Sandman Beds
Urchin

General furniture stockists

Central
The Children's Seating
Centre *(WC2)*
The Conran Shop *(W1, W1)*

West
Babylist *(SW6)*
The Back Store *(W6)*
Cheeky Monkeys *(W5, SW6, W11)*
Clementine *(W11)*
The Conran Shop *(SW3)*
Natural Mat Co *(W11)*
Red Studio *(W4)*
Seraphine *(W8)*
Simon Horn *(SW6)*

North
Cheeky Monkeys *(N1)*
Green Baby *(N1)*
Humla *(NW3)*
Sea Horse Furniture *(NW9)*
Shelfstore *(NW3)*
Soup Dragon *(N8)*
St John's Wood
Interiors *(NW8)*
Toys 'R' Us *(NW2)*
WCD (Walter Castellazzo
Design) *(N6)*

South
Cheeky Monkeys *(SE21, SW17, SW4)*
The Decor Centre *(SE9)*
The Farmyard *(TW10)*
Planet Little Kids
Furniture *(SW20)*
Soup Dragon *(SE22)*
Toys 'R' Us *(SE15)*

East
Kiddicentre *(E5)*

Potty People *(E2)*
Tom Thumb Fantasy
Designs *(E18)*

Mail order
Babylist
Babyou
The Back Store
Bexley Toys
Billie Bond
Born
Bump
Cheeky Monkeys
The Children's Cottage Co
Children's Furniture Co
The Children's Seating Centre
Giddykipper
Green Baby
Greenfibres
It's Childsplay
Steve Jones Furniture
Joshua Jones
Kantara Furniture
Knights & Daisies
Lifetime Products
Lionwitchwardrobe
The Little Chair Co
Millthorne Chairs
Minor Matters
Morley's of Bicester
Natural Mat Co
Oreka Kids
Roomers
Seraphine
Shelfstore
Simon Horn
Soup Dragon
Toys 'R' Us
Urchin
Mark Wilkinson Furniture

6. BEDDING

(For suppliers of protective bedding, see chapter 3.08 Nappies.)

There are some delightful embroidered sheets for babies. However, you can save money if you prefer by splitting old sheets into two (if this seems a bit brutal, you can make them prettier by adding an attractive border). Once your child is a little older, an interest in teddies and characters, such as Thomas the Tank Engine, will kick in (though the usual comments about out-growing designs apply).

Suggestions for bedding requirements:

➤ Three sheets to cover the mattress, ideally fitted ones for safety reasons. Flannel sheets are warmer than standard cotton.

➤ Three sheets to cover the baby. (These can easily be made from one adult sheet.)

➤ Three or four cellular blankets (the holes make it harder to smother the baby).

➤ Alternatively you can substitute a baby sleeping bag (see below) for the upper sheets and blankets.

➤ A fitted waterproof sheet (if not an integral element of the mattress).

➤ A muslin or two placed under the baby's head to absorb milk brought up after a feed if this is a baby who possets.

➤ Pillows, duvets and quilts are positively *NOT* recommended for children under 12 months, because of the danger of overheating, and in the case of pillows, suffocation.

Other possibilities:

➤ Cot bumpers – especially if you plan to use a cot from birth, padding which can be fixed to the side of a cot to stop smaller babies banging into the sides and hurting themselves. These came in for some bad press because they were believed to open up the risk of babies burrowing under them and over-heating – a risk factor in cot death. However, this was much more a serious concern when the advice was to sleep babies on their fronts rather than on their backs – as is the case now. The FSID are now 'neutral on cot bumpers'. Note that as with other cot accessories, you should remove them as soon as your toddler might use them to climb out, and they should be short enough to avoid entanglement or choking.

➤ Guardian Angels – covered foam wedges – are designed to keep babies sleeping on their side and will give more sense of security to a baby placed directly in a large cot rather than a Moses basket. They restrict natural movement, though.

Bedding

Central
Boutique Descamps *(SW1)*
Brora *(W1)*
Linen Cupboard *(W1)*

West
Brora *(SW3, W11)*
Clementine *(W11)*
Couverture *(SW3)*

Damask *(SW6)*
The Linen Merchant *(SW7)*
The Monogrammed Linen
Shop *(SW3)*
Natural Mat Co *(W11)*
Woolworths *(TW3, W2, W4)*

North
All Seasons *(N12)*

Green Baby (N1)
Rub a Dub Dub (N8)
Woolworths (N1, NW1)

South
Baby Baby (SW14)
Woolworths (SW17)

East
Dot Productions (E2)

Mail order
Abstract
All Seasons
Aztec Store
Big Hugs
Boutique Descamps
Brora
Bugglesnuggle Co
Charlotte's Cot Blankets
ClothWORKS
Couverture
Damask
Dot Productions
Farmer John Duvets
G L Bowron
Green Baby
Greenfibres
Huggababy Natural Baby

Products
Ideal Cottons
KC Collection
The Laundry
The Linen Merchant
Little Badger
Lollipop Children's Products
Katie Mawson
Melin Tregwynt
The Monogrammed Linen
    Shop
My Puku
Natural Collection
Natural Mat Co
NiNight
The Nursery Co
Otterburn Mill
Patchwork Palace
Rub a Dub Dub
Schmidt Natural Clothing
Spirit of Nature
Tyrrell Katz
The White Co
White Mischief Bed & Table
    Linen
Willey Winkle
Win Green
Zorbit Babycare

Sleeping bags

Popular on the Continent for some time, these are increasingly catching on in the UK with one manufacturer estimating that by 2004 95% of British babies will be sleeping in one. Their great advantage is that babies – who can be relied on to kick off blankets and sheets – cannot remove the bag and so do not wake up cold in the middle of the night. If you introduce a bag after your toddler has learnt to stand, do so with caution because of the potential danger of tripping.

West
Kent & Carey (SW6)

South
Kent & Carey (SW17)

Mail order
Baby Flair
Beaming Baby
Buzzness
Grobag

Kent & Carey
Kiddycare
The Little Star Co
The Nursery Co
Schmidt Natural Clothing
Sleepy Bunnies
Snug as a Bug
Snugger
Storm Enterprises
The White Co

7. GENERAL STOCKISTS

Indexes in this section refer to chapter 3.14 Shopping directory.

General stockists

Central
- Harrods *(SW1)*
- John Lewis *(W1)*
- Laura Ashley *(W1, W1)*
- Marks & Spencer *(W1, W1)*
- Mothercare *(W1)*
- Next *(W1, W1)*
- Peter Jones *(SW1)*

West
- Babylist *(SW6)*
- Blooming Marvellous *(SW6)*
- Dragons of Walton Street *(SW3)*
- The Little Trading Co *(W4)*
- Marks & Spencer *(W2, W8)*
- Mothercare *(SW6, W6)*
- Next *(W8)*
- The Nursery Window *(SW3)*
- The White House *(SW6)*

North
- All Seasons *(N12)*
- Baby Concierge *(NW4)*
- Bébécar UK *(NW7)*
- Humla *(NW3)*
- Ikea *(NW10)*
- John Lewis *(NW4)*
- London Nursery Suppliers *(N22)*
- Mothercare *(N22, NW4)*
- Nitti Gritty *(N5)*

South
- Babies 'R' Us *(SE15)*
- Bentalls *(KT1)*

- Blooming Marvellous *(TW9)*
- Chic Shack *(SW15)*
- Ikea *(CR0)*
- John Lewis *(KT1)*
- Lilliput *(SW19, SW8)*
- Mothercare *(CR0, TW9)*
- Wear & Cheer *(SE15)*

East
- Uglows *(E4)*

Mail order
- All Seasons
- Babies 'R' Us
- Baby Boom UK
- Baby Concierge
- Baby Flair
- Babycare Direct
- Babylist
- Blooming Marvellous
- Chic Shack
- Dragons of Walton Street
- John Lewis
- Laura Ashley
- Lilliput
- Littlewoods
- Mamas & Papas
- Marks & Spencer
- Mothercare
- Next
- The Nursery Window
- Tots to Teens Furniture Co.
- Wesco
- The White House
- Wigwamkids

Yes I am!

JoJo
maman
bébé

CHAPTER 3.04

BABY CLOTHES

1. **Introduction**
2. **DIY**
3. **Specialist items**
4. **General stockists**

1. INTRODUCTION

It can be fun dressing your child on the living doll principle. There are some gorgeous baby clothes available nowadays, especially as over the last few years numerous designer names have introduced baby and children's items – some of them at eye-watering prices.

Even less image-conscious baby clothes can seem expensive, especially when you consider how small they are and that they are VAT-free. Many items will last less than 12 weeks, and as babies – even tiny ones – can make an incredible mess of whatever they are wearing, lovely outfits may soon look much less so. It is therefore worth remembering that it isn't hard to make tiny babies and toddlers look cute, and you can pick up some great clothes at many budget stores.

If you are a first-time parent you may well be surprised by how many gifts of clothing you receive. It is therefore wise to shop conservatively at first. This gives you time to assess what you actually need, and also to judge your baby's size and speed of growth.

The exception to this rule is seasonal clothing, which is stocked on the same timetable as adult clothes. This can make it difficult to find a snowsuit for a January baby for example. This sort of item is therefore best bought in advance and left in the packaging until required, or returned if not in fact needed.

By six months or so the baby moves on from sleepsuits and babygrows into slightly more grown-up clothes. Leggings and cotton jerseys are a good idea. Garments that do not hamper the new-found urge to explore are ideal (dresses, for example, usually make it harder for girls trying to crawl). As they grow, it can be helpful to put toddlers in items which they can get into and out of themselves, with elasticated waists and stretchy fabrics. This is particularly important when toilet training, when dungarees, for example, become a problem.

When it comes to toddlers, good designs sell out early, even as soon as August for Christmas. There are always substitutes and you may find bargains in the sales, but the highly organised mother gets it together to shop pre-season, or even in the previous season's sales.

As with all baby-related items, don't be shy about asking friends with older children for old clobber. Many baby clothes nowadays are remarkably well made given the incredibly short period of time for which they are used, and cast-offs often have a good deal of life left in them. Most mothers are only too happy to find a good home for their old gear. (For suggestions about organisations and charities interested in used baby-related items, see chapter *3.02 Baby equipment*.)

Ease of use

Clothes may look cute on the hanger, but as well as style, consider how easy they will be to put onto a wriggling, small baby.

Some parents like nightgowns with fastenings along the bottom for use at night because it makes nappy changing easier. Stretchy sleepsuits with generous openings are not much more difficult however.

Tips when choosing:

➤ Remember these clothes are forever in the wash: check everything for washing instructions and generally avoid anything requiring hand-washing and that can't be tumble-dried (which probably also means it can't be hung over a radiator).

➤ The simplest clothes are the easiest to use and the safest.

➤ Jersey is the easiest fabric for dressing and undressing because it stretches.

➤ Cotton is a good material because it doesn't cause sweatiness (so is recommended for babies with eczema), can be machine-washed and doesn't shrink. Jersey or flannelette are more popular than woven cottons, which can feel cold on the skin when first put on.

➤ Poppers are easier than buttons, and more comfortable for a baby. They do seem prone to wear out, however.

➤ The best rompers open down the front and at least one leg to make them easy to get the baby in and out.

➤ Front-opening rather than back-opening is more convenient and can be more comfortable for the baby, given the advice about putting them to sleep on their backs.

➤ Items going over the head are a bit of a struggle with newborns who can't support their own necks; moreover babies are often afraid of having their head and face covered, even temporarily. Wide boat necks are therefore best, but look for ones that can be closed to avoid cold draughts.

➤ Buttons should be very firmly sewn on to prevent swallowing.

➤ Avoid anything with tiny buttons or nylon lace trimmings which can scratch and irritate new skin, and pom-poms and toggles near the face which could choke.

➤ Ribbons become bedraggled in the wash, come undone easily, and like any drawstring are not recommended for hoods or necklines because of the danger of strangulation.

➤ Dark colours will show posseting. Pale colours will show food stains once the baby starts eating solids. Heavy patterns will show stains less, but having everything patterned is unlikely to co-ordinate and the effect can be faintly shambolic.

➤ Socks seldom stay on babies. If it's cold enough to need covered feet it's more practical to use a garment incorporating foot coverings. This goes for both in- and outdoor wear. For a winter baby it might also be worth looking for an outer garment that covers hands as well. Once the child is walking and wearing shoes, though, you will need socks. To save valuable time sorting them post-laundry, get a few pairs the same.

➤ Rubberised soles reduce the incidence of 'Bambi-on-ice' for early walkers on smooth floors, but they are not advised once the child is really trying to walk as the adhesion makes things difficult. Bare feet are felt by experts to be better, or proper shoes.

➤ Avoid open-weave patterned fabrics, particularly in nylon and especially for newborns, as it can cut off the blood supply to fingers and toes if they become caught.

➤ Seams and labels, especially at the neck, should be soft or they may scratch and upset a baby. For maximum baby comfort check all inside finishings and if necessary remove irritating labels.

➤ Although sleeveless clothes seem a good idea for summer, when out of doors you will then need sun-protection; long sleeved clothes in cool, loose fabrics can work better.

➤ Some babies are very good at scratching themselves, and you might like to consider scratch mittens to prevent any damage. On the other hand, fingers are a newborn baby's only familiar toy and mittens deprive them of that (and can irritate them).

➤ Keep everything possible in the original packing with receipts. You can then exchange anything you get given a duplicate of, or which doesn't fit.

Items for a starter wardrobe (suggested quantity):

Cotton vests or body suits (6): the latter – being anchored at the crotch with poppers – don't ride up like vests, but may catch nappy overflow. Go for long or short sleeved or a mix, depending on season.

Babygrows (6): with feet, for winter babies.

Jumpers or cardigans (2–3)

Hat (1): a warm one for a winter baby (newborns lose most of their heat from their heads).

Jacket/All-in-one suit (1): in summer a light one should suffice. In winter a snowsuit and gloves are the ticket. To make life easier both hand and foot protection should be integral to the suit. Sometimes there is a useful option for folding back this protection when required. Without this you will need pull on bootees and gloves – both subject to falling off. Allow plenty of space for other garments underneath. Zip fastening is easiest – best down one leg, not just to the crotch. You will have to protect the baby's chin from the zip.

Socks (4 pairs): though not needed if the babygrows have feet. For best chance of staying on, go for knee length – knitted baby bootees generally fall off.

Note that the body suits and babygrows double up as sleepsuits: there is no need in the early days to make extra work and disturb the baby by 'changing for bed'.

Sizing

Sizing is as variable for baby and children's clothes as it is for adults. Before you get your eye in for baby sizes, it is wise to err on the large/older side when buying or you could find the garment grown out of almost immediately. With all the hot wash laundering that garments need to endure, there will also probably be some shrinkage, which needs to be taken into account.

As an extremely rough rule of thumb, Continental brands tend to be small; quality British and US names tend to be more generous.

Some manufacturers are now sizing by length/height rather than age.

Name tapes

Useful once your child is attending a regular playgroup or nursery if you don't want to lose large numbers of garments. Many department stores and shops offer a name label supply service.

BABY CLOTHES SIZES

Average heights for various ages

Birth	51 cm (20ins)
3 months	61cm (24ins)
6 months	66cm (26ins)
1 year	74cm (29ins)
1.5 years	80cm (31.5ins)
2 years	86cm (34 ins)

Gap sizing

Newborn			
	0-3 months	19-23ins/48-58cm	7-12lbs/3-5kg
	3-6 months	23-27ins/58-69cm	12-17lbs/5-8kg
Infant			
xs	0-3 months	19-23ins/48-58cm	7-12lbs/3-5kg
s	3-6 months	23-27ins/58-69cm	12-17lbs/5-7kg
m	6-12 months	27-29ins/69-74cm	17-22lbs/7-10kg
l	12-18 months	29-31ins/74-79cm	22-27lbs/10-12kg
xl	18-24 months	31-33ins/79-84cm	27-30lbs/12-13kg
Toddler			
2xl	24-30 months	33-36ins/84-91cm	30-33lbs/13-15kg
3xl	30-36 months	36-39ins/91-99cm	33-36lbs/15-16kg

Mothercare sizing

Tiny Baby		1.4-2.3kg/3-5lbs
Early Baby	up to 50cm	2.3-3.4kg/5-7lbs
New Baby	up to 55cm	4.5kg/10lbs
0-3 months	up to 62cm	6.5kg/14.5lbs
3-6 months	up to 69cm	8kg/17.5lbs
6-12 months	up to 76cm	10kg/22lbs
12-18 months	up to 83cm	11.5kg/25lbs

Mail order

Cash's
Easy2name Labels
The Great Little Trading Co
Namemark

Nametapes Direct
Premier Nametapes
Stuck On You

2. DIY

Indexes in this section refer to chapter 3.14 Shopping directory.

If you are a dab-hand with a pair of knitting needles, or a sewing machine – or have time to learn – it can be enormously satisfying to go beyond bootees and mittens and to create more ambitious clothes for your kids…

READING

Baby Knits – Trisha Malcolm (Editor) (The Butterwick Publishing Company; 2001; £8.95; 1573890111) – *Twenty projects for all skill levels from Vogue Knitting.*

Baby Style – Debbie Bliss (Home accessories and irresistible knitwear designs for 0-3 year olds; Ebury Press; 2000; £12.99; 0091870828) – *A collection of 25-plus designs for hand-knits from the well-known knitwear designer.*

3. SPECIALIST ITEMS

Suppliers in this section are divided into a number of different categories. These indexes refer to chapter 3.14 Shopping directory.

Categories in this section:

➢ Christening outfits.

➢ Premature baby clothing.

➢ Outdoorwear.

➢ Eco-friendly clothing.

➢ Knitwear.

➢ Sleepwear.

➢ Sun-protection clothing.

Christening outfits

West
  Babylist *(SW6)*
  The Linen Merchant *(SW7)*
  The Monogrammed Linen
     Shop *(SW3)*

North
  HeirsWears *(N16)*
  Infantasia *(N22)*

South
  Biff *(SE21)*

Mail order
  Babylist
  Christening Outfits
  Christening Stuff
  Christening UK
  Gale Classic Clothes

HeirsWears
Honfleur Christening Gowns
Infantasia
Iriss
Jacqueline Taylor Design
Susan Lawson
The Linen Merchant
Mischief Kids
The Monogrammed Linen
   Shop
My Puku
Next Door
Patricia Sherwood
Shetland Collection
Patricia Smith
Sunday Best
Thimbelina

Premature baby clothing

South
  Bebeworld *(SW12)*

Mail order
  The Baby Closet
  Bebeworld

Outdoorwear

Central
Snow & Rock *(WC2)*

West
Cotswold Essential
Outdoor *(W12)*
Snow & Rock *(W8)*
Snowdown *(W3)*

South
Cotswold Essential
Outdoor *(KT1)*

East
Cotswold Essential
Outdoor *(E1)*
Snow & Rock *(EC1)*

Mail order
Alyssa Robinson

Anorak Lakes Ltd
Baby Banz
Bugglesnuggle Co
Bush Baby
Calange
Cotswold Clothing Co
Cotswold Essential Outdoor
George Fisher
Little Trekkers
Muddy Puddles
Play Togs
Raindrops
Rrappers
Smilechild
Snow & Rock
Snowdown
Tough Customer
Young Explorers

Eco-friendly clothing

North
Green Baby *(N1)*

South
Bug Circus *(SW13)*
Little Green Earthlets *(SW15)*

Mail order
A Lot of Organics
Bao-Bab
Beaming Baby
Bio-Bubs (& Hugabub)
Born
Bug Circus
ClothWORKS
Eco-Babes

Garthenor Organic Pure
Wool
Gossypium
Green Baby
Greenfibres
Greensleeves
Little Green Earthlets
Marketing Mania Ltd
Natural Child
Natural Collection
The Nice Nappy Co
Oregano UK
People Tree
Schmidt Natural Clothing
Spirit of Nature

Knitwear

Central
Brora *(W1)*
Rachel Riley *(SW1, W1)*

West
Brora *(SW3, W11)*

South
E Sharp Minor *(SE10)*

Mail order
Aztec Store
Debbie Bliss

Brora
E Sharp Minor
Humbug
Kardigan Kiosk
Little Badger
Little SmartiPants
Little Treasures
My Puku
Rachel Riley
Rowan
Small Acorn
Fi Smith Fairisles

Sleepwear

West
Couverture *(SW3)*
The White House *(SW6)*

Mail order
Couverture
The Ellie Nappy Co
Holz Toys

Millie's Cupboard
The Nursery Co
PHP
The White Co
The White House
White Mischief Bed & Table
Linen
Wigglets

Sun-protection clothing

An increasingly popular option for protecting children from burning, believed to lead to the possibility of skin cancer in adulthood. Fabrics are categorised in a similar way to sunscreens, using the Ultraviolet Protection Factor (UPF) scale, developed by the Australian Radiation lab in co-operation with Cancer – the table is shown below. (Densely woven cotton T-shirts would fall into the maximum category.) Clothes labelled as 'prevents sunburn' must conform to British Standard 7949 which covers children's clothes.

	UPF	UVR Transmitted
High Protection	20-29	5.0–3.4%
Very High Protection	30-39	3.3–2.6%
Maximum Protection	40+	$\leq 2.5\%$

Mail order
Beach Babes & Boys
Flap Happy
The Great Little Trading Co
Incy Wincy
Kool Sun
Marketing Mania Ltd

Next Door
Ollipops
Sun-Togs
Sunhatters
Sunproof
Young Explorers

4. GENERAL STOCKISTS

Suppliers in this section are divided into a number of different categories. These indexes refer to chapter 3.14 Shopping directory.

Stockists by level of expense:
➢ Cheap & cheerful.
➢ Mid-range.
➢ Luxury.

Of their nature, these divisions are rather arbitrary in nature, and can be a general guide only. There are also two overlapping listings, by style rather than price.

Stockists by style:
➢ Funky.
➢ Traditional.

Other categories:
➢ Second-hand shops.

Note: designer labels and brands are listed in their own right *only if they have a shop* in London which stocks the label's own children's collection. So for example, neither DKNY nor Kenzo is listed, because none of their London boutiques stock the relevant kids' collection – however, both labels' children's clothes are stocked by some of the stores in the listings.

USEFUL INFORMATION

Junior Fashion, ☎ *(020) 7761 8911* ⌂ *www.juniorfashion.co.uk*
Affiliated to a magazine which has been described as "a sort of Vogue for mothers" – if you are really interested, particularly in the luxury end of the children's market – this website contains 'fashion'-related news and contacts for stockists and designers. / *HOURS Mon-Fri 9.30am-6pm.*

Stockists by level of expense

Cheap & cheerful

Central
BHS *(W1)*
The Disney Store *(WC2)*
Hennes (H&M) *(NW5, W1)*
Mothercare *(W1)*

West
Adams *(W6)*
The Children's
   Warehouse *(W3)*
Hennes (H&M) *(W1, W2, W8)*
Marco (Juveniles) Ltd *(W12)*
Mothercare *(SW6, W6)*
Primark *(W6)*
Woolworths *(TW3, W2, W4)*

North
Adams *(HA8, HA9, NW6)*
Asda *(NW9)*
Cheeky Kids *(N18)*
The Disney Store *(W1)*
KD Kids *(N22)*
Mothercare *(N22, NW4)*
Primark *(NW6)*
Woolworths *(N1, NW1)*

South
Adams *(KT1, SE15, SE16, SW17)*
Allders of Croydon *(CR9)*
Arding & Hobbs *(SW11)*
Asda *(SW11, SW15)*

Babies 'R' Us *(SE15)*
Bargains *(SW17)*
BHS *(SE16)*
Morleys of Brixton *(SW9)*
Mothercare *(CR0, TW9)*
Primark *(SE15, SE18, SW17)*
Warner Brothers Studio
   Store *(KT1)*
Woolworths *(SW17)*

East
Asda *(E14)*
BHS *(IG1)*
Bouncy Kids *(E8)*
Primark *(E11, E6, E8)*

Mail order
Arding & Hobbs
Babies 'R' Us
Baby Clothes Direct
Babycare Direct
Boots
Cheeky B Children's Clothing
The Children's Warehouse
Freemans PLC
Great Universal
Littlewoods
Mothercare
Tesco
V&A Marketing
Warner Brothers Studio Store

Mid-range

Central
Benetton *(W1)*
The English Teddy Bear
   Co *(W1, W1)*
Baby Gap *(WC1)*
Gap Kids *(W1, WC2)*
Gymboree *(W1)*
John Lewis *(W1)*

Laura Ashley *(W1, W1)*
Marks & Spencer *(W1, W1)*
Miriam Stoppard
   Lifetime *(SW1)*
Monsoon *(W1, WC2)*
Next *(W1, W1)*
Peter Jones *(SW1)*
Peter Rabbit & Friends *(WC2)*

Petit Bateau *(W1)*

West
Baby Gap *(SW3)*
Baby World *(SW6)*
Benetton *(SW3)*
Blooming Marvellous *(SW6)*
Damask *(SW6)*
WJ Daniel & Co *(W13)*
French Connection *(SW3)*
Gap Kids *(SW3, W4)*
Jokids E-Shop *(W3)*
Juniper *(W5)*
The Linen Merchant *(SW7)*
Marks & Spencer *(W2, W8)*
Miki House *(SW3)*
Monsoon *(W8)*
Next *(W8)*
Sasti *(W10)*
Trotters *(SW3, W8)*

North
Baby Concierge *(NW4)*
Baby Gap *(NW4)*
Benetton *(NW4)*
Buckle-My-Shoe *(NW4)*
Daphne & Mum *(NW11)*
Humla *(NW3)*
Infantasia *(N22)*
John Lewis *(NW4)*
JoJo Maman Bébé *(NW11)*
Monsoon *(NW3)*
Nitti Gritty *(N5)*
Purple Heart *(NW6)*
Rub a Dub Dub *(N8)*
James Selby *(N7)*
Shoe & Fashion Boutique *(N16)*
Soup Dragon *(N8)*
Trendy's *(N1)*
Trotters *(NW4)*

South
Baby Baby *(SW14)*
Baby Gap *(KT1)*
Baby Nest *(CR0)*
Bebeworld *(SW12)*
Bentalls *(KT1)*
Biff *(SE21)*
Blooming Marvellous *(TW9)*
La Conception *(SW11)*
E Sharp Minor *(SE10)*
Gap Kids *(SW15, SW19, TW9)*
Gymboree *(SW19, TW9)*
Havanas Toy Box *(SW15)*
John Lewis *(KT1)*
Lilliput *(SW19, SW8)*
Little Green Earthlets *(SW15)*

Lizzies *(SW11)*
Quackers *(SW11)*
Soup Dragon *(SE22)*
Wear & Cheer *(SE15)*

East
Khalsa Schoolwear *(E2)*
Potty People *(E2)*

Mail order
Amalaika
Aztec Store
The Baby Closet
Baby Concierge
Baby Planet
Baby World
Bébé Amour
Bebeworld
Bishopston Trading Co
Blooming Marvellous
Bumps to Bairns
ClothWORKS
Cotton Moon
Cyrillus
Damask
WJ Daniel & Co
Dribble Factory
Dromedary Trading
Dynky
E Sharp Minor
The English Teddy Bear Co
French Connection
The Great Little Trading Co
Greenfibres
Hansel & Gretel
Infantasia
John Lewis
JoJo Maman Bébé
Kardigan Kiosk
The Kids Window
Laura Ashley
Lilliput
The Linen Merchant
Little Badger
Little Green Earthlets
Little Laurels
LL Bean
Marks & Spencer
Katie Mawson
Mini Boden
Muddy Puddles
Nappy Head
Natural Collection
NCT Maternity Sales
Next
Rosie Nieper T-shirts
Over The Moon Babywear

Peter Rabbit & Friends
Picture Wear Originals
Plush Pants
Poco Ropa
Poppy
Pouch
Pumpkin Patch
Purple Heart
La Redoute
Rosa mundi
Rub a Dub Dub
Sasti

SeeSaw Children's Clothing
Shetland Collection
Patricia Smith
Fi Smith Fairisles
The Smock Shop
Soup Dragon
Spirit of Nature
Talbots
Trotters
Urchin
VertBaudet
Willy Um-Yum

Luxury

Central

Brora *(W1)*
Burberry *(SW1, W1, W1)*
Catimini *(W1)*
The Conran Shop *(W1, W1)*
Harrods *(SW1)*
Liberty *(W1)*
Oilily *(SW1)*
Petit Bateau *(W1)*
Ralph Lauren *(W1)*
Rachel Riley *(SW1, W1)*
Selfridges *(W1)*
Tartine et Chocolat *(W1)*
Versace Jeans Couture *(W1)*
Young England *(SW1)*

West

Babylist *(SW6)*
Bon-Bleu *(W3)*
Brora *(SW3, W11)*
Caramel *(SW3)*
Clementine *(W11)*
The Conran Shop *(SW3)*
Daisy & Tom *(SW3)*
Joanna's Tent *(SW3)*
Kiddy Boom *(W2)*
Paul Smith *(W11)*
Pearlfisher *(W11)*
Petit Bateau *(SW3, W4)*
Pollyanna *(SW6)*
Tots in the Terrace *(W4)*
What Katy Did *(W8)*
Patrizia Wigan *(SW3)*

North

American Collections *(N16)*
Diverse Kids *(N1)*
Early Clothing *(N10)*
Kiddi Chic *(N16)*
Look Who's Walking *(NW3)*
Maternus *(N1)*
Petit Bateau *(NW3)*
Thoe Tho *(N10)*

Tiddlywinks *(NW8)*

South

Barney's Children's
   Store *(SW19)*
Bunny London *(SE1)*
Catimini *(KT1, TW9)*
IANA *(SW15)*
Membery's *(SW13)*
Mon Choisie *(SW16)*
Peppermint *(SE17)*
Petit Bateau *(TW9)*

East

Childsplay *(IG1)*
Jakss *(E3)*

Mail order

Babylist
Brora
Bunny London
Catimini
Childsplay
Daisy & Tom
Fat Face
Finetica Child
Greensleeves
Hickory
KC Collection
Little Treasures
Mischief Kids
Oilily
Paul Smith
Pelirocco
Rachel Riley
Silk Story
Small Acorn
Tartine et Chocolat
Thimbelina
Tiddly Pomme
Young England
Zaki-do-dah

Stockists by style

Funky

Central
Oilily *(SW1)*

West
What Katy Did *(W8)*

North
Leila *(N8)*
Notsobig *(N6)*
Cecilie Telle *(-)*
Torkidz *(N19)*

South
Bunny London *(SE1)*
E Sharp Minor *(SE10)*
Havanas Toy Box *(SW15)*

Mail order
The Baby Closet

Baby Planet
Bishopston Trading Co
Bunny London
Cinnamon Kids
E Sharp Minor
Flap Happy
Happy Baby Co
Rosie Nieper T-shirts
Notsobig
Oilily
Petra Boase
Snuglo
Su Su Ma Ma World Wear
Cecilie Telle
Torkidz
Tyrrell Katz
Wotwu

Traditional

This category is of particular concern to the sizeable number of parents, particularly those of girls, who feel that kids are encouraged to grow up too quickly nowadays. There is a trend – particularly among designer labels and the cheaper ranges that ape them – for the entire collection above the newborn stage to be the same – from toddler to teen. Doubtless this is more convenient for the producers, but the results can seem a bit tacky and/or inappropriate.

Central
 BonPoint *(SW1, W1)*
 Laura Ashley *(W1, W1)*
 Rachel Riley *(SW1, W1)*
 Young England *(SW1)*

West
 BonPoint *(W11)*
 Babylist *(SW6)*
 Kent & Carey *(SW6)*
 The Monogrammed Linen
  Shop *(SW3)*
 Swann's Way *(SW10)*
 Patrizia Wigan *(SW3)*

North
 Adam & Eve *(NW11)*

South
 The Farmyard *(TW10)*
 Fig *(SE5)*
 Kent & Carey *(SW17)*

Pied Piper *(SW15)*

Mail order
 Babylist
 Dromedary Trading
 Emma Henley
 Fig
 Gale Classic Clothes
 Gigglycat
 Ideal Cottons
 Iriss
 Kent & Carey
 Laura Ashley
 Little Laurels
 Little Treasures
 The Monogrammed Linen
  Shop
 Rachel Riley
 The Smock Shop
 Startsmart
 Tati
 Young England

Other categories

Second-hand shops

Some second-hand children's clothes shops are more inspiring than others, but all of them may have items which for one or another reason are completely unused. As stock turns over fairly fast it may also be worth return visits.

Some NCT areas organise regular sales for their members. This can make it worthwhile joining before the baby is born. If there is little organised in your particular area, try to find out about neighbouring ones. Another option is dealers in second-hand clothes who sell by visiting playgroups, and the like.

And if you are looking to economise, don't forget the markets.

West
 Boomerang *(W14)*
 The Little Trading Co *(W4)*
 Pixies *(W4)*
 Snips *(W13)*

North
 Rainbow *(N6)*

South
 Mum & Me *(TW11)*
 The Rocking Horse *(SW20)*
 Swallows & Amazons *(SW12)*

East
 Chocolate Crocodile *(E9)*

Mail order
 Bumps to Bairns

Buy Baby Clothes   Milliemoos
Dapper Nippers   Pixies
eBay

CHAPTER 3.05

SHOES

1. **Shopping tips**
2. **Footwear options**
3. **General stockists**

1. SHOPPING TIPS

Indexes in this section refer to chapter 3.14 Shopping directory.

A proper fit

Well-fitting shoes are an important element in ensuring the healthy development of your child's feet.

Babies' feet are largely made up of cartilage that has not yet started hardening into bone. Such bones as develop at this age are short and spaced widely apart. Poorly-fitting shoes – and even overly-constricting socks or all-in-one suits – can permanently distort feet which are so soft and pliable.

Because of this flexibility and because the nerve endings in children's feet are deep in soft tissue, the child will not necessarily complain of discomfort or pain until long after any damage has been done. In fact, podiatrists reckon that over half of adult foot problems relate to poorly-fitting shoes in childhood.

During the researching of this guide a manager for one large, well-reputed brand admitted that his firm currently believes that parents rank fashion in children's shoes well ahead of a proper fit. Guess which aspect of shoe-design his firm is making a priority?

Shoes vs bare feet

There is some debate about the correct time to start children in shoes. The issues of protecting and supporting the feet need to be balanced against the danger of unduly constricting them. Likewise providing children with socks or shoes with soles that grip needs to be weighed against the danger that these may cause children to trip. Broadly speaking, there are two schools of thought.

SHOES AS SOON AS WALKING STARTS

The first school (broadly that followed on the Continent) argues that as soon as children are spending time on their feet they need support and should have shoes.

The idea is that a good shoe will place the foot in a correct position and prevent it from taking up any other, so reducing the likelihood of structural anomalies. The Continental style of baby ankle boots aims to do this.

It is also argued that, if stiffened, shoes will help with balance. Start-rite shoes for example offer inside-support at the back of the shoe in addition to the shoe itself, to help keep the foot upright.

The pro-shoe argument continues that the right shoes can help correct the bad positioning of problem feet. Club feet are one example, flat feet are another (though these second can be difficult to spot in children under the age of two), as is pronating (the tendency to walk on the inside edges of the feet). Apparently all children pronate to some degree at some stage, but nearly all cases correct as muscles develop.

BARE FEET, EXCEPT WHEN SHOES ARE NEEDED

The opposing view is that walking barefoot is the healthiest option because it exercises muscles that aren't used when walking in shoes, and because fresh air is good for the skin.

The barefoot camp argues that children should use shoes for the same reason as adults: to protect their feet from rough ground and to a lesser extent to keep them warm.

Even once the child has started walking more than a few steps at a time, some experts argue in favour of leaving the baby shoeless for six weeks to enable them to become aware of the sensations underfoot and to increase their feet's flexibility and grip.

Even some shoe fitters are in the barefoot camp, believing that the vast majority of baby feet are healthy, and that shoes won't make them any healthier.

Shoes versus trainers

Once children are walking confidently a new issue arises. Some commentators argue that trainers are ideal for children, allowing the foot plenty of flexibility. Others, pointing to the fact that walking regularly places more pressure on the foot, argue that the support provided by standard shoes is now more important than in babyhood. One idea from a physio supporting the second argument is to limit the wearing of trainers to one day in four.

Pointers on foot care:

➤ Socks that are too small can be equally, or even more, harmful than poorly-fitting shoes and should be checked regularly for shrinkage. Wool or cotton are better fibres than nylon or acrylic, which because they stretch and recoil, can end up cramping soft feet. Socks that are too large can bunch up causing pressure points once walking.

➤ Tightly-fitting bedcovers at the foot of the cot can similarly cause problems. Bedwear should be loose and light.

➤ Keep feet clean and cut toenails straight across (but not too short) to avoid them becoming in-grown.

➤ Allow children to walk when ready, but don't force them.

➤ Remember that children are unlikely to complain about ill-fitting footwear because they don't feel much discomfort.

Foot disorders

Sometimes, even with the best footwear some babies' and children's feet may develop problems because of tight or loose muscle groups, or genetic factors that influence the development of the bones and nails. (Note that flat-footedness, though common, is generally grown out of by the age of three years, as are bow legs or knock knees by five years, so should not be considered a big deal in under-twos.)

If you think your child is one of the rare ones with a problem, before selecting shoes you should get expert podiatric advice, as genuine foot problems can affect knees, hips and the back. The Society of Chiropodists and Podiatrists advise that "the earlier problems are detected, the earlier they can be treated, and it is not unusual to treat children as young as one or two years of age". The organisation advises in particular to watch for "toeing in or out", which may be signalled by tripping.

Your GP can refer you to a special podiatry centre or specialist state registered chiropodist. You don't actually need a referral, however, and it may be more convenient to go direct if you can find details of a suitable clinic or practitioner (your health visitor may be able to help with this).

Specialists can offer help with curly toes or flat feet for example, as well as offering gait or weight distribution analysis. Children are entitled to free NHS treatment for such care, if referred by a GP.

USEFUL CONTACTS
Children's Foot Health Register (CFHR), ☎ *(01295) 738726*
⌂ www.shoe-shop.org.uk
The register is published annually, and contains listings of over 600 children's shoe shops in the UK; all shops listed have fully-trained staff for fitting shoes, and stock up to four width fittings and half-sizes. The website has shoe tips for new parents and facts on foot care for babies.

The Society of Chiropodists & Podiatrists, ☎ *(020) 7234 8620*
⌂ www.feetforlife.org
The professional body for chiropodists and podiatrists, representing 92% of state-registered practitioners. Advice on children's foot health promotes walking barefoot. Details of local members are available (not all childrens' specialists – there are no specific qualifications in paediatric podiatry). / PUBLICATIONS *Leaflet Foot Health: Children's Feet.*

Buying

Tips when buying:
➢ Shoes should be new if at all possible, as used shoes will be distorted to the shape of the previous wearer's feet.
➢ Fitting should be done by a trained shoe fitter who should be asked to measure both feet for length and girth as both vary from foot to foot. (Clarks and Start-rite fitters should measure the child's foot on a stool when the child is seated, giving a half-weight length – the most appropriate for a good fit.)
➢ Shoes should be up to 2cm longer than the longest toe and wide enough to allow the toes to lie flat on the inner sole of the shoe (i.e. new shoes should allow growing spaces around the toes, and should be neither too loose nor too tight).
➢ Because feet grow in spurts it is important to have shoes checked every six to eight weeks for a toddler and every three to four months when older. The better shops are happy to do this for you even if you don't positively plan to buy shoes that visit.
➢ Baby shoes should be flexible at the front, firm at the back, wide at the front and slim at the back. The perfect design has a straight inside edge, round toes and low heels. The best styles are those with fully adjustable laces, buckles or Velcro fastenings to hold the heel snugly in position. If the heel slips off when the child stands on tiptoe, the shoe doesn't fit properly.
➢ A fastening over the instep (laces or bar) stops the foot slipping forward and damaging the toes (which is where most foot troubles start).

➤ Shoes in half sizes and different widths allow both the distance across the foot (width) and the depth of the foot (girth) to be taken into account. (The shape of the sole of the foot alone is not an adequate measure of the suitability.) Such finer fittings help protect the child's feet, particularly by offering control round the ankle, which reduces the movement of the foot in the shoe. Start-Rite offers up to six width fittings. Chain stores and mail order catalogues generally sell shoes with only one width fitting (a middle fitting of E to F), suitable for about a third of all children properly.

➤ Shoes with leather uppers are best, as the material is flexible and can mould to the foot's shape. It can also absorb sweat easily and allow the foot to breathe. Linings should ideally also be in leather or another natural material like cotton. Soles should be non-slip.

➤ Additional features to look for include cushioned ankle support, lightweight, flexible soles, close-cut soles to prevent tripping, and if possible leather dyed right through to offer some visual defence against the inevitable scuffs.

➤ Older children's shoes tend to be more tapered than those for toddlers. Consequently even if you find a shoe of an older age group which fits, you should nonetheless stick to the shape of shoe for the appropriate age group.

➤ If you can't afford the best, buy cheap shoes you can afford to throw away as soon as they are worn out. (An expensive pair for best is a false investment, as it is soon outgrown.)

➤ Ill-fitting shoes will not last as well as those which fit properly and may not work out as cheap as they seem in the long run.

SHOE SIZES

In the UK, shoe sizes for children run from 1–13, before the numbering starts again for adult sizes. In Continental sizing, size 24 is equivalent to UK size 6.

Very few brands start at size 1 because it is rare that a child is walking with such small feet (Start-rite, for example, start at size 2). It is relatively common, though, to find bootees and soft boots to fit smaller feet.

The average shoes size for a one-year old is 4.5, and for a two-year old 6.5.

Approximate shoe sizes at different ages:

3–6 months	0	–	2
6–12 months	2	–	3.5
12–18 months	3.5	–	5
18–24 months	5	–	6.5

DIY CHECK FOR A PROPER FIT

You can check if your child's shoes are the appropriate length using the following steps. Of prime importance, however, is that the fit of the ankle is such as to prevent the shoe shifting around on the foot.

1. Take two narrow strips of cardboard and make your child stand on them in bare feet.
2. Measure the overall length of the foot by marking behind the heel, and at the longest toe.
3. Cut the strips using these two marks and insert the strip into the shoe.

DIFFERENT SCALES FOR FOOT SIZE

Source: Start-Rite

4. With the front end of the cardboard touching the front end of the shoe, the gap at the back will show how much space there is left for the foot.

Foot growth gauges

Mail order
Malthouse Foot Growth Measure

2. FOOTWEAR OPTIONS

Indexes in this section refer to chapter 3.14 Shopping directory.

PADDERS
Resemble big socks made from a fabric such as cord, with elasticated ankles. They may have semi-grip soles. If not, children tend to slip in them on smooth floors but they are useful foot coverings for non-walkers and smarter than just socks. Generally laundered like socks, to minimise stray singletons, get extras in the same design and fabric.

SOFT PRAM SHOES
Such shoes are soft and light and some mothers regard them as little more than foot warmers. They provide some protection from hard floors, however, and – in good weather – some makes are suitable for outdoor use. The sole is almost always very flexible to allow movement, but the back may be stiffened. As more of a fashion item, they are expensive – some cost up to £50 – especially considering how fast babies grow out of them. They may come with a suede or similar sole, for a better grip when learning to walk.

TRADITIONAL QUALITY SHOES
These come in a range of width fittings and generally offer good ankle support. The biggest names are Start-Rite and Clarks.

SHOES WITH WIDE, MOULDED SOLES
Principally from well-reputed brand Birkenstock, for somewhat older children (the smallest size fits the average two and a half-year-old). These come in limited width fittings but the Birkenstock sole offers five supports and as most of the models are sandals, the issue of width is less important.

FASHION SHOES
The rest. Fashion shoes differ in width from brand to brand but individual styles are practically always made only in just one width (all styles of DMs, for example, are F). An experienced fitter is, therefore, even more important in achieving a proper fit, but is less common in stockists of this kind of footwear.

CANVAS SHOES AND JELLY SANDALS
Both tend to be sold in summer and are useful beach and holiday options, though they offer little support for feet.

Shoe makers

The main brands

Baby Pure
Birkenstock
Bobux
Boots
Clarks
Daisy Roots
Ede and Nia
Jester Boots

Kiwi Slippers
Naturino
Prada
Shoozies
Squeakyfeet
Star Child
Start-rite
Timberland

Bespoke shoes

Green Shoes

Handmade Shoe Co.

3. GENERAL STOCKISTS

Indexes in this section refer to chapter 3.14 Shopping directory.

Suppliers

Central

Birkenstock *(WC2)*
Gucci *(SW1, W1)*
Harrods *(SW1)*
John Lewis *(W1)*
Peter Jones *(SW1)*
Rachel Riley *(SW1, W1)*
Selfridges *(W1)*

West

Chiswick Shoes *(W4)*
Daisy & Tom *(SW3)*
Footsies *(SW7)*
Gillingham & Co *(SW6)*
Pieton Shoes *(W2)*
Pollyanna *(SW6)*
Russell & Bromley (Feet First) *(W5)*
Sasti *(W10)*
Stepping Out *(W5)*
Trotters *(SW3, W8)*

North

Bowleys *(HA7)*
Brians Children's Shoes *(HA7, NW11)*
Buckle-My-Shoe *(NW4)*
Early Clothing *(N10)*
Instep *(EN4, NW11, NW8)*
John Lewis *(NW4)*
Kiddie Shoes *(N16)*
Look Who's Walking *(NW3)*
Notsobig *(N6)*
Preston Shoes *(HA3)*
Rub a Dub Dub *(N8)*
Russell & Bromley (Feet First) *(NW4)*

Shoe & Fashion Boutique *(N16)*
Trendy's *(N1)*
Trotters *(NW4)*

South

John Barnett Shoes *(SE22)*
Bentalls *(KT1)*
Bowleys *(TW9)*
Elys of Wimbledon *(SW19)*
Footsies *(SW19)*
Havanas Toy Box *(SW15)*
Instep *(SW13, SW17)*
John Lewis *(KT1)*
Johnsons Shoes *(SW14, TW11)*
Little Willies *(SW4)*
Merlin Shoes *(SE19)*
Pares Footwear *(SE3)*
Pied Piper *(SW15)*
The Shoe Station *(TW9)*
Start-rite *(SW19)*
David Thomas *(SE21)*
James Webster *(SW9)*

Mail order

Birkenstock
Born
Daisy & Tom
Freemans PLC
Gillingham & Co
Hippychick
Inch Blue
John Lewis
Marketing Mania Ltd
Mischief Kids
Notsobig
Ollipops
Poco Ropa

Rachel Riley
Rub a Dub Dub
Russell & Bromley (Feet First)

Sasti
Smilechild
Trotters

Cheeky Monkeys

Cheeky Monkeys toy shops are renowned across London for their fabulous array of children's gift items. Now, the company has launched a stylish new website:

http://www.cheekymonkeys.com

For the first time, customers can buy great Cheeky Monkeys gift items from the comfort of their own home.

The attractive and easy-to-use website has been getting rave reviews from users since it launched in November '03. There's also been a lot of interest in the cheekymonkeys.com Birthday Book – a ground-breaking service which reminds you when important birthdays are coming up and recommends appropriate gifts.

CHAPTER 3.06

TOYS

1. **Introduction**
2. **Safety**
3. **Specialist items**
4. **General stockists**

I. INTRODUCTION

Indexes in this section refer to chapter 3.14 Shopping directory.

(For lots of reading suggestions about how to play with young children, not necessarily involving toys, see the introduction of chapter 2.06 Baby & toddler activities.)

Young babies need little in the way of toys. Human faces and voices intrigue them most, so the easiest way of entertaining little ones is to keep them around you and other people.

Few parents, however, can devote 100% of their day to entertaining their children, and even comparatively young babies get bored. After a couple of months the search is on for items to keep your child busy while you get on with things.

There are exceptions but, on the whole, full-blown toys to play with unaccompanied don't really come into their own until the child is at least two years old – though there is significant variation between children and some reach this stage much later. Before this time it's more a question of finding things which offer an element of entertainment – usually movement or noise. Items like puppets, Noah's Arks and model farms are more useful as props with which adults can entertain the child.

Although some adults have an instinctive idea of the kind of activities that will keep children amused, many people find useful inspiration in books which help understand how their youngsters' minds work and the kind of things and activities that they are likely to respond to. Some of these give age related guidelines but it's more useful to match toys to what a child can do – focus, grasp, sit, move, etc…

Pointers:

➢ You will probably be given some toys when the baby arrives so – as with clothes – it can be sensible to wait and see what other people give you before buying too many yourself – particularly soft toys. Some parents end up with so many that they start giving them away before the end of the first year.

➢ All children are different and toys played with enthusiastically by one sibling may be studiously ignored by another. Watching what your child responds to and buying accordingly gives the best, though not a failsafe, chance of success.

➢ Beware toys pounced on with enthusiasm at another child's house. Borrowing from a toy library – see below – will give a truer idea of the real level of enthusiasm.

➢ It can be worth removing things which appear of little interest so they can be discovered afresh at a later stage, when they sometimes prove a surprise hit.

➢ Bear in mind research showing that too many toys actually impairs development. It seems that being left with one or two good items allows children to focus their concentration much more easily. Indeed, Tracey Hogg in the Baby Whisperer argues that if your baby has difficulty settling this is particularly relevant. She believes a baby should have no more than one or two toys in a cot.

➢ As always with babies, a few key items will cater to all needs.

➢ Think carefully before buying toys which require batteries. They're forever running out and replacing them is an extra job you don't need. Consider investing now rather than in a few years' time in rechargeable batteries and a charger.

➢ If you're planning more children try, as far as possible, to avoid toys with small parts. You spend a lot of time with siblings ensuring their playthings stay separate.

➢ Shop cheaply at school fairs and jumble sales (checking your purchases for safety).

TOY LIBRARIES

An excellent way of testing a type of toy, or varying your child's playthings at little (and sometimes no) expense.

Hounslow Toy Library, ☎ (020) 8569 5451

Exclusively for children with disabilities – 3,000 toys, books and videos (many of them specialised) are available. / HOURS Wed 9.30am-12.30pm, Thu 1.30pm-5pm.

National Association of Toy & Leisure Libraries (Play Matters), ☎ (020) 7255 4600 ⊕ www.natll.org.uk

The HQ for children's toy and leisure libraries (the latter including special needs equipment for adults and children). Its campaign, Play Matters, stresses the importance of play for children and encourages provisions to aid this, particularly through toy libraries – of which there are over 1000 in the UK. Call for details of your nearest facility, or use the response form on the website. / HOURS 10am-1pm, 2pm-5pm; PUBLICATIONS leaflets and books on starting a toy library; Good Toy Guide.

Toy options

NEWBORN

Initially a baby's limited abilities mean that you need to focus on sound and vision. Any noise is likely to produce some kind of reaction, though something rhythmic or melodious might be preferable from your point of view. In terms of images, faces offer endless fascination but otherwise, because the baby's sight is not yet fully developed, it is better at discerning contrasts (black from white) than colours. Some of items on the market look more like maths problems than baby products, but many small babies react to them with surprising enthusiasm. Something with a little movement is likely to attract even more attention.

Suggestions

A mobile: either in black and white or with bright, primary colours and a curved design of some kind. Around 20cm from the baby is an ideal distance for newborn sight. Note: mobiles designed to hang over the cot have a limited life-span as they have to be removed when children are old enough to grab and pull themselves up.

Funky lights: an attractive and easy way of creating what can be a source of fascination from the youngest of babies through to toddlers.

Musical toys: 'wind-up' may describe both the usual operating method and their common effect on parents, but babies often love them and find them soothing.

A rattle: wrist and ankle rattles can be used for very small babies, although some newborns find them irritating.

BY ABOUT THREE OR FOUR MONTHS

Your child will be starting to grip objects, though not many babies can either sit unsupported or turn themselves over at this stage, and so are restricted to what they can look and swat at.

Suggestions

A rattle or similar to manipulate: ideally brightly-coloured – those with varying textures and sounds offer more interest.

A 'baby gym': that is, a frame under which the baby can lie or sit and play with different dangling objects – sometimes incorporating an 'activity mat'. These start to be outgrown as soon as the child is on the move, but in the meantime you can add variety by hanging alternative and home-made items.

A baby nest or playmat: the first allows the baby to be propped up; typically both areas with different textures, flaps and noises.

Bath toys: (though the water itself provides plenty of entertainment), rubber ducks, wind-up toys, sponges and so on.

Soft toys: although most furry ones are not recommended for babies under one because of the danger that they may chew and swallow the fur. Smaller toys are easier for a baby to hold, and a gentle noise adds interest. However, these seem of less interest to many boys.

BY ABOUT SIX MONTHS

By this point, babies are usually becoming more dextrous, able to move objects, and potentially mobile. Once a child is crawling, for a short while toys may be eclipsed by the pleasures of exploration.

Suggestions

Toy mirrors: some are specifically designed for use in a cot, although newborns are too young to appreciate mirrors; however by 6–8 months the sight of their own features can be a source of fascination.

Wooden building blocks: initially enjoyed for simple handling but gradually used for construction.

Small toys with wheels: cars, trucks etc, to push around.

Slotting toys: designed to encourage placing items in small holes.

FROM AROUND A YEAR

Your child is possibly learning to walk, and toys encouraging this – both ride on and pushing toys – are likely to prove popular. Toys requiring defined actions may also be of interest and indeed will reinforce the actions – though these may require adult guidance, at least at first.

Suggestions

Toys to manipulate: e.g. items with levers to turn that open flaps, button to press to propel vehicles; boards with holes to hammer pegs through.

Bead maze: though quite pricey, larger models will get a lot of use and be enjoyed well beyond toddlerhood.

Simple musical instruments: like rattles/maracas, rain sticks, bells, simple xylophones and drums.

Items with lids: to open and shut.

A wooden baby walker trolley: after being used as a walking aid these double up as boats, scooters, prams and more.

Stacking toys: rings, cups and the like, cups with the advantage that they can be used as containers for putting in, taking out.

A building product: such as Duplo or Stickle Bricks.

Pull or push along toys: generally on wheels and with some extra movement created when in motion (clacking of a crocodile, flapping of a duck's feet, etc.)

Balls: soft ones are good; also balls that are small enough to be gripped by small hands (but not small enough to be swallowed).

Simple puzzles: those with shapes and knobs on pieces for small hands to pick them up with are best at first.

FROM AROUND 18 MONTHS

As the understanding of cause and effect increases, along with mobility, fine motor control and, with any luck, concentration, the range of possible toys increases.

Suggestions

A simple train set: classically Brio or Thomas the Tank Engine.

Something to ride on: a low rocker or wheeled item.

Tricycle: often with steering stick attachment.

Musical toys: requiring slightly more defined movements such as xylophones, triangles, tambourines and drums.

Playdough: with supervision. If your child is determined to eat it, rather than use a commercial product make your own with flour and water.

Chunky crayons and paper to scribble on: (and protective covering for what lies underneath). The increasing variety of screen scribblers with stylus pen allow for drawing with no mess.

Shape sorters: though some children short circuit these by simply removing the lid.

More puzzles: for example with parts making up a single image, rather than the style mentioned above.

From now on your child's tastes will become increasingly evident. In particular some will gravitate to items supporting imaginative and make believe play, while others focus more on practical items.

DIY first toys

Once your child can sit unsupported the possibilities for play start to open up.

In addition to purpose-made toys you can entertain children for hours with household objects with different textures, weights, smells, appearances and sounds. Paper especially can keep them happy for an age. A nice idea is to combine items like these in a discovery box.

Avoid items with sharp parts or elements small enough to stick in the throat or swallow. It is also wise not to make playthings of items such as toothbrushes which will shortly have to be used for a real purpose; similarly anything which it is useful for the child to learn to leave alone, such as keys.

Potential play-things:

➤ Large pebbles.

➤ Raffia matting.
➤ Pumice stone.
➤ A loofah.
➤ Lemons, oranges, apples etc.
➤ A napkin ring.
➤ Pieces of non-splintering wood.
➤ Non-breakable egg cup.
➤ Small non-breakable boxes.
➤ Wooden spoon.
➤ Metal spoons.
➤ Tins with rounded edges.
➤ Lemon squeezer.
➤ Plastic funnel.
➤ Tea strainer.
➤ Garlic squeezer.
➤ Leather purse.
➤ Darning mushroom or egg.
➤ Small cloth bags containing scents for drawers.
➤ Tennis ball.
➤ Piece of velvet fabric.
➤ Notebook with spiral rings.
➤ Greaseproof paper.
➤ Unbreakable containers – filled with rice or beans for noise.

USEFUL CONTACTS
British Toymakers Guild, ☎ (01225) 442440
🖰 www.toymakersguild.co.uk
Founded in 1955, a group of craft toymakers recognised by the Crafts Council who
promote "real toys". The guild publishes an annual directory of members and
associates (retailers), nationwide (£3.50) whose emphasis is on "traditional
contemporary" toys (not just reproductions).

The National Toy Council, ☎ British Toy & Hobby Association (020) 7701
7271 🖰 www.btha.co.uk/toycouncil.html
Run by the British Toy & Hobby Association (see also), the NTC produces leaflets of
interest to parents such as: Toy Safety; Advertising and Your Child; Toys for Boys
and Girls; Aggressive Toys and Play; Games.

Toy Tips, 🖰 www.toytips.com
A US web site, mainly designed to provide parents with unbiased information about
toys and children's products which are considered to "build skills an enhance a child's
personal development'.

Pre-school brands

Brio	Pin Toys
Chicco	Plan Toys
Fisher-Price	Playmobil (UK)
Galt Educational	Sevi
Lamaze International	Step 2 (UK) Ltd
Leap Frog Toys (UK) Ltd	Tomy
Lego	TP Activity Toys
Lego Rebuilders	V-Tech Electronics
Little Tikes	Wonderworld
Mamas & Papas	WOW Toys
Manhattan Toy Co	
Mattel UK/Fisher-Price	
Orchard Toys	

2. SAFETY

The biggest general danger posed by toys to babies and toddlers is that of choking, explaining why numerous toys with small parts are marked as suitable only for ages three and above.

Toys for children under the age of three must pass the Choke Hazard Test. If parts of the toy are capable of slipping down a test tube designed to reflect the size of a toddler's gullet, it will fail and be labelled for age 3+. Some retailers sell such a tube to enable you to test small items and toys for yourself. The inner tube of a loo roll is approximately the same size.

Other pointers on keeping children safe with toys:

➢ Review overall sturdiness – the strength of seams, for example, should be checked with a view to the battering the item is likely to endure.

➢ Check toys regularly and repair broken ones (or keep them out of reach until they are mended or thrown out). Broken items can, for example, cause cuts. If you can insert a fingernail under a removable part (a teddy bear's eye, for example), it may over time become loose enough to be pulled off, so should be checked regularly.

➢ Toys hung along a string should be taken out of cots once – or preferably before – babies can get on to hands and knees (around five months or more) to avoid any risk of strangulation.

➢ Activity centres should be removed from cots as soon as a baby can start to stand to remove the temptation to use the toy as an aid to climbing out.

➢ Noisy toys such as cap guns should be avoided for young children as they can damage hearing. Similarly they should never be fired near a young child's head. The Health and Safety Executive also advises that permanent hearing damage can result from slightly quieter but continuously noisy toys used for 15 minutes or more.

➢ When changing batteries, all batteries should be changed in one go: mixing charged and uncharged batteries can result in dangerously high temperatures.

➢ Garden toys should be fixed over grass or soil, not paving or concrete; paddling pools should be emptied and deflated when adults are not available to supervise (toddlers can drown in collected rainwater).

➢ There have been concerns over chemicals used in PVC teethers but in the UK there has been a voluntary agreement to take these off sale. However, you might like to beware imports.

The following marks give some indication as to safety:

CE mark: indicates that the toy meets the essential safety requirements of the EU. However, strictly speaking this is not actually a safety mark, but one of enforced conformity to EU rules aimed at assisting the free movement of goods within the EU.

Lion Mark: a consumer symbol of safety and quality backed by a code of practice operated and licensed by the British Toy & Hobby Association (BTHA – see listings). The mark can only be used by members of this association, and toys with this logo have been made to at least the relevant EU standard.

Lion Mark Approved Retailer: another scheme run by the BTHA in conjunction with the British Association of Toy Retailers (BATR) which focuses on shops rather than products: everything sold in a shop bearing this sign will comply with current EU legislation (but will not all necessarily have a Lion Mark). In addition, all staff must be briefed on toy safety matters. 75% of the toy trade are members of the scheme.

Age labelling: similar to a road sign – a circle with a diagonal slash, featuring an unhappy child's face and an age range (e.g. 0-3) –the toy should not be given to children under the age shown (nor should they be allowed to play with it). Details of the specific hazard are given underneath the pictogram, e.g. 'choking hazard'. This mark forms part of the EU legislation that will replace the manufacturer's discretionary warning (e.g. 'not suitable for children under 3 years').

'Under supervision': this phrase appears on toys that conform to required EU safety standards but expect some form of adult involvement – for example bath toys.

National Toy Council suggestions for safely selecting toys

0-1 YEAR OLDS

Avoid:
➢ Sit-in baby walkers.
➢ Trundle trucks.
➢ Motorised toys.
➢ Hairy and furry toys.

Go for:
➢ Push-along toys.
➢ Toys with smooth fabric covers.
➢ Solid plastic toys.

1-3 YEAR OLDS

Avoid:
➢ Little toys or little pieces including thin, breakable crayons and pencils.
➢ Toys you can bite (such as foam balls).

Go for:
➢ Large toys and drawing materials that can't be swallowed or stuffed in ears or up noses.
➢ Tough toys that can be chewed.

USEFUL CONTACTS

British Association of Toy Retailers (BATR), ☎ *(01494) 474762*
⌁ www.batr.co.uk
Founded in 1950, the BATR represents more than 75% of the toy trade, and acts as watchdog and political pressure group to ensure fair play for retailers. In association with the British Toy & Hobby Association, the BATR launched the Lion Mark Retailer Scheme – when a shop carries the Lion Mark it means that all products sold meet the Toy Safety Standard.

British Toy & Hobby Association (BTHA), ☎ *(020) 7701 7271*
🖑 *www.btha.co.uk*
Trade Association that represents 95% of the UK toy market. The Lion Mark is
a symbol of safety and quality backed by a code of practice operated by the BTHA.
Of more interest to consumers is the leafleting service operated by the National Toy
Council (part of BTHA), see also.

3. SPECIALIST ITEMS

*Suppliers in this section are divided into a number of different categories. These
indexes refer to chapter 3.14 Shopping directory.*

Categories in this section:
➢ Art supplies.
➢ Character toys.
➢ Comforters.
➢ Cuddly toys.
➢ Dressing-up clothes & toys.
➢ Pre-school toys.
➢ Educational toys.
➢ Outdoor & activity toys.
➢ Toys for children with special needs.
➢ Toys repairs.
➢ Traditional & wooden toys.

Art supplies

Homecrafts Direct

Character toys

Central
The Disney Store *(WC2)*
Paddington Bear Shop *(W1)*
Peter Rabbit & Friends *(WC2)*
The Tintin Shop *(WC2)*

North
The Disney Store *(W1)*

South
Warner Brothers Studio
Store *(KT1)*

Mail order
Amazon
Emma Jefferson
Peter Rabbit & Friends
Shop4Toys
The Tintin Shop
Warner Brothers Studio Store

Comforters
Beddy Bears
Comfort Blankets
Cuski International
Nature's Hug
Swingolino

Cuddly toys

Central
The English Teddy Bear
Co *(W1, W1)*
Hamleys *(W1)*
Harrods *(SW1)*

Mail order
The Door Mouse
The English Teddy Bear Co
Greenfibres
Hamleys
Schmidt Natural Clothing

Dressing-up clothes & toys

West
Cheeky Monkeys (SW6, W5, W11)
The Children's Book Centre (W8)

North
Cheeky Monkeys (N1)

South
Cheeky Monkeys (SE21, SW17, SW4)

Little Green Earthlets (SW15)

Mail order
Charlie Crow
Cheeky Monkeys
The Children's Book Centre
The Hill Toy Co
Hopscotch Dressing-Up Clothes Ltd
Little Green Earthlets

Pre-school toys

Central
Mothercare (W1)

West
Blooming Marvellous (SW6)
Early Learning Centre (SW3, W5, W6)
Mothercare (SW6, W6)

North
Early Learning Centre (NW4)
Mothercare (N22, NW4)

South
Babies 'R' Us (SE15)
Bebeworld (SW12)
Blooming Marvellous (TW9)
Early Learning Centre (KT1, SE13, SE9, SW15, SW19, TW9)
Lilliput (SW19, SW8)

Little Green Earthlets (SW15)
Mothercare (CR0, TW9)

East
Krucial Kids (MK45)

Mail order
Babies 'R' Us
Babycare Direct
Bebeworld
Blooming Marvellous
Early Learning Centre
Krucial Kids
Lilliput
Little Green Earthlets
Mothercare
NCT Maternity Sales
Tesco
VertBaudet

Educational toys

Central
Miriam Stoppard Lifetime (SW1)

North
Playgear (N14)
Teaching Trends (N2)
Word Play (N8)

South
Childhood Discoveries (KT6)
Quackers (SW11)

Mail order
Bright Minds

Childhood Discoveries
Dickory Dock Designs
Formative Fun
JFS
Lanka Kade
Let's Learn
Lifetime Education
Mindstretchers
Owls Educational Direct
PHP
Storysack
Teaching Trends
VIPonline.co.uk

Outdoor & activity toys

Though your child may be too young for a large climbing frame, most under-twos are already developing an interest in equipment that they can clamber about on.

Modular designs have a lot to be said for them as they can be adapted for the relevant age and you may still get use out of them as part of an expanded system when your children are older.

If you opt for a swing you will need at least 6.4m of swing space; pure climbing frames and slides require less.

These are expensive bits of kit, but value for money if they last. To make sure they will, make sure any purchases you make are manufactured from quality materials that have been properly treated to endure weathering.

West
Snap Dragon *(W4)*

North
All Seasons *(N12)*

East
T Ditchfield *(E10)*

Mail order
The Active Toy Co
Advanced Play Systems
All Seasons
Backyard Escapes
Childlife
The Children's Cottage Co
Cider Woods Children's Furniture

Dunster House
Happy Landings
Home Front
Norfolk Leisure Co
Rainbow Play Systems Inc
Sovereign
Step 2 (UK) Ltd
Super Tramp Trampolines
The Outdoor Toy Co.
Tiny Set Toys
Toytime
TP Activity Toys
TreeTops Play Equipment
Wicken Toys Limited
Wicksteed Leisure Ltd
Win Green

Toys for children with special needs

See also Toy libraries and Educational Toys, above.

Mail order
Magic Planet

Toy repairs

Dolls' Hospital   Maureen Palmer

Traditional & wooden toys

Central
Wellspring Bookshop *(WC1)*

North
Applepie Toys *(N1)*
Kristin Baybars *(NW3)*
Fagin Toys *(N10)*
F Frederick Beck *(N1)*
Humla *(NW3)*
JoJo Maman Bébé *(NW11)*
Never Never Land *(N10)*
Nitti Gritty *(N5)*
Soup Dragon *(N8)*

South
Artemidorus *(SE24)*
The Farmyard *(TW10)*
Havanas Toy Box *(SW15)*

Little Wonders *(TW1)*
Soup Dragon *(SE22)*

Mail order
Babyou
Bexley Toys
Bigjigs
Born
Community Playthings
Croglin Toys
Direct to Your Door
Escor Toys
Fiesta Crafts
Found
GyGy
Holz Toys
It's Childsplay
Jigsaw Tree

JoJo Maman Bébé
Knock on Wood
Letterbox
Linn Jigsaws
Little Timbers
Little Wonders
Lollipop Children's Products
The Mulberry Bush Limited
Mummy Can I Have
Myriad
Never Never Land

Next Door
Ollipops
Orange Tree Toys
David Plagerson
Rocking Rhinos
Skipper Ltd
Smilechild
Soup Dragon
Toys for Children
Woolgar's Wooden and
   Traditional Toys

4. GENERAL STOCKISTS

Suppliers in this section are divided into a number of different categories. These indexes refer to chapter 3.14 Shopping directory.

Categories in this section:
➤ General stockists.
➤ Own-brand stockists.
➤ Nursery suppliers.
➤ Second-hand stockists.

General stockists

There are lots of big toy brands and large toy retailers are the best bets for mass-market items, both in terms of selection and price.

However, the relative importance of branded toys tends to be greater for older children than it is for babies and toddlers.

It can be great fun shopping for toys, but beware that parents as well as children are susceptible to the 'Wonderland' effect created by large well-stocked stores. If you are counting the pennies, it's worth shopping in smaller outlets that put less emphasis on razzamatazz, or from alternatives on the internet.

Central
The Conran Shop *(W1, W1)*
Hamleys *(W1)*
Harrods *(SW1)*
John Lewis *(W1)*
Peter Jones *(SW1)*
Selfridges *(W1)*
WH Smith *(SW1)*
Wilton Cycles & Radios *(SW1)*

West
Baby World *(SW6)*
Cheeky Monkeys *(SW6, W5, W11)*
The Children's Book
   Centre *(W8)*
The Conran Shop *(SW3)*
Daisy & Tom *(SW3)*
WJ Daniel & Co *(W13)*
Patrick's Toys & Models *(SW6)*
Paul Smith *(W11)*
Snap Dragon *(W4)*

Stepping Out *(W5)*
¡tridias! *(SW7)*
Trotters *(SW3, W8)*
WH Smith *(W11, W6)*

North
Asda *(NW9)*
Cheeky Monkeys *(N1)*
F Frederick Beck *(N1)*
Graham's Toys *(HA2)*
Happy Returns *(NW3)*
JJ Toys *(NW8)*
John Lewis *(NW4)*
Kindercare *(WD6)*
Pearson Toymaster *(N22)*
James Selby *(N7)*
Toy Wonderland *(NW3)*
Toys 'R' Us *(NW2)*
Trotters *(NW4)*
Susan Wainwright *(NW3)*

South

Allders of Croydon (CR9)
Arding & Hobbs (SW11)
Art Stationers & Village Toy
    Shop (SE21)
Asda (SW11, SW15)
Barney's Children's
    Store (SW19)
Bentalls (KT1)
Bug Circus (SW13)
Cheeky Monkeys (SE21, SW17,
    SW4)
Domat Designs (SW15)
Elys of Wimbledon (SW19)
Goldilocks (SE16)
John Lewis (KT1)
Lizzies (SW11)
Membery's (SW13)
Moonlighting (SW19)
QT Toys (SW11)
Second Impressions (SE3)
Smiths Bros Tooting (SW17)
Toys 'R' Us (SE15)
Toystop (SW11, SW14, SW15)
¡tridias! (TW9)

East

Asda (E14)
T Ditchfield (E10)
Rossi's (E4)

Mail order

Amazon
Arbon & Watts

Arding & Hobbs
Argos
Baby World
Bébé Amour
Bishopston Trading Co
Bug Circus
Cheeky Monkeys
The Children's Book Centre
Daisy & Tom
WJ Daniel & Co
The Entertainer
Graham's Toys
The Great Little Trading Co
Hamleys
Hawkin's Bazaar
The Hill Toy Co
Immaculate Contraptions
John Lewis
Letterbox
Little Laurels
Midnight Mushroom
Paul Smith
Small Folk
Spottiswoode Trading
Toycentre
Toys 'R' Us
Toytime
¡tridias!
Trotters
Urchin
Youth Sport Trust/Davies The
    Sports People

Own-brand stockists

For very young babies, some of the best options are own brand items
produced by supermarkets and other large retailers. Boots is particularly good for this.

Boots
Ikea
Woolworths

Nursery suppliers

Especially if you have a number of children – or if you are looking to
push the boat out on a toy – it may be worth considering these sorts of
suppliers. They are normally more expensive, as the items they provide
are designed to withstand much more battering than they would in a
home.

Active Learning
Eduzone
Kit for Kids

NES Arnold
SBS (Step by Step)
Wesco

Second-hand stockists

In addition to the following school fairs and jumble sales are good places to find toys for little more than pennies – though you will need to check them for safety.

West
    Boomerang *(W14)*
    The Little Trading Co *(W4)*
    Pixies *(W4)*
    Snips *(W13)*

North
    Kristin Baybars *(NW3)*
    Rainbow *(N6)*
    Simply Outgrown *(N17)*

South
    Mum & Me *(TW11)*

    The Rocking Horse *(SW20)*
    Swallows & Amazons *(SW12)*

East
    Chocolate Crocodile *(E9)*

Mail order
    eBay
    Pixies
    Toytime

CHAPTER 3.07

BOOKS, MUSIC & VIDEOS

1. **Books**
2. **Music**
3. **DVDs & Videos**

1. BOOKS

Indexes in this section refer to chapter 3.14 Shopping directory.

From around three months, a baby can focus briefly on simple pictures in a book and will enjoy the pages turning and a voice talking about them. Although this is probably best not forced, early exposure to books appears to make it easier for children to learn to read. Books don't have to be purpose-designed. Catalogues, photo albums and even cards attached by ribbons tied through holes are all fun for small children, as are scrapbooks.

When it comes to buying printed storybooks, look for those with good rhythm and rhyme, action, movement, repetition, and which aren't too long. A good children's book, like a poem, should bear very many re-readings, and the best mark of that is if it has been around for a good few years. Avoid books you will quickly tire of. (For example, buy TV and film spin-off titles with care, as if you find them dull your tedium will be infectious.)

For unsupervised use look for fabric or board books.

The listings below give details of London's specialist children's book shops as well as smaller, local book shops and the branches of the big chains that have particularly good children's sections.

BOOK CLUBS

Book clubs may offer books at as much as 50% below the cover price and are worth considering if you buy a lot of books.

Take care, though, that you have carefully researched the range on offer. In many clubs, most titles are no more than £2 cheaper which means you have to buy a few to make a saving, especially if you take into account the cost of postage and packing.

Above all, make sure you understand the rules of the club. Many have contracts that are Byzantine in their complexity and may include harsh rules you don't understand. A classic example are clauses which – in the event of, say, a late payment by you – allow the club to bill you at full price for all books you had previously bought at a discounted rate (i.e. reversing the special deal that caused you to sign up in the first place). Another notorious problem is the right for the club to send you (unwanted) substitute books for orders you've made where the club is out-of-stock.

Given how cheap books are nowadays in supermarkets, increasing price-competition in bookshops and the advent of cheap catalogue and online stores, really question whether the benefits any particular club offers you are worth the commitment.

READING

Babies Need Books – Dorothy Butler (Sharing the joy of books with children from birth to six; Heinemann; 1995; $15.95; 0-435081-44-6) – *Suggestions from a grandmother and teacher of good titles for different ages.*

Books to Grow By – Robert Keeshan & Kyle Corkum (Fairview Press; 1996; £13.99; 0-925190-83-7) – *American title suggesting recreational and educational titles for children up to the age of 8.*

Children's Picture Books – Checker Bee Publishing (A reader's checklist and reference guide; Checker Bee Publishing; 1999; $4.95; 1-585980-00-5) – *American book with suggestions for pre-school titles.*

The Rough Guide to Children's Books – Nicholas Tucker (Rough Guides; February 2002; £6.99; 1-858287-87-1) – *Subdivided by age (0-5) and subject matter, this guide lists the best children's books available, recommends titles and notes any educational value.*

Waterstone's Guide to Children's Books – ed Neil Johnstone (Waterstone's Booksellers; 1999; £2.99; 1-902603-06-0) – *An excellent starter's list of children's books for a range of ages. Illustrations from the books and profiles of authors help you recognise what you might be looking for.*

Book shops

Central
Borders *(W1, WC2)*
Dorling Kindersley *(WC2)*
Hamleys *(W1)*
Harrods *(SW1)*
Hatchards *(W1)*
John Lewis *(W1)*
Peter Jones *(SW1)*
Peter Rabbit & Friends *(WC2)*
Selfridges *(W1)*
Waterstones *(W1)*
WH Smith *(SW1)*

West
Bookends *(SW7)*
Books etc. *(W2)*
The Children's Book Centre *(W8)*
Children's Book Co *(W5)*
Daisy & Tom *(SW3)*
Early Learning Centre *(SW3, W5, W6)*
French Bookshop *(SW7)*
The Golden Treasury *(SW6)*
John Sandoe Books *(SW3)*
Nomad Books *(SW6)*
The Pitshanger Bookshop *(W5)*
WH Smith *(W11, W6)*

North
Bookworm *(NW11)*
Children's Bookshop *(N10)*
Children's Bookshop (Middx) *(HA5)*
Early Learning Centre *(NW4)*
John Lewis *(NW4)*

Letterbox Library *(N16)*
Owl Bookshop *(NW5)*
Regent Bookshop *(NW1)*
Willesden Bookshop *(NW10)*
Word Play *(N8)*

South
Arcade Bookshop *(SE9)*
Beckett's Bookshop *(SW17)*
The Bolingbroke Bookshop *(SW11)*
Bookseller Crow on the Hill *(SE19)*
Bookspread *(SW17)*
Dulwich Books *(SE21)*
The Dulwich Bookshop *(SE21)*
Early Learning Centre *(KT1, SE13, SE9, SW15, SW19, TW9)*
John Lewis *(KT1)*
Lion & Unicorn Bookshop *(TW9)*
Soma Books *(SE11)*

East
Chocolate Crocodile *(E9)*
Newham Bookshop *(E13)*

Mail order
Amazon
Arcade Bookshop
Barefoot Books
Beckett's Bookshop
Book People Ltd
Bookseller Crow on the Hill
The Children's Book Centre
Children's Book Co
The Children's Bookcase

Children's Bookshop
Daisy & Tom
Dulwich Books
Early Learning Centre
Floris Books
French Bookshop
Golden Treasury
Hamleys
Hatchards
John Lewis
Letterbox Library
Lion & Unicorn Bookshop

Newham Bookshop
Owl Bookshop
Peter Rabbit & Friends
Teacher Trading
Waterstones
Willesden Bookshop

Book clubs

Books for Children
Bookstart
Discovery
Puffin Book Club
Red House Books
Young Book Trust

2. MUSIC

(For details of music classes for babies and toddlers, see chapter 2.06 Baby & toddler activities.)

Indexes in this section refer to chapter 3.14 Shopping directory.

Some specialist bookshops also sell children's music tapes, but rarely with any particular expertise. For bearable tapes, the best bet is to go straight to the better producers.

In addition to music specifically for children, it has been reported recently that listening to works by certain baroque and classical composers boost the thought processes of both adults and children, improving abstract reasoning and reading ability. The benefits of listening to Mozart have been particularly highlighted; and Bach and Vivaldi also receive some mention. Some recordings of these composers' works are marketed as particularly suitable for babies, but renditions can be teeth-grindingly saccharine. Cheap and cheerful round-ups for example from Classic FM or complete works (for example from the well-known budget label Naxos) are usually better buys.

Music tape suppliers

Acoustics
Baby Whisperer
ellipsis arts
Nicola Hadley
Headstarter
Knock on Wood
MES (Music Education
    Supplies)

Moonbeam Music
Peony Records
Playsongs Publications
Quality Children's Music

RECOMMENDED RECORDINGS
The author has a particular aversion to crass music tapes aimed at babies and toddlers. The following are, in her humble opinion, some of the better recordings around.

[Tape] **Lively Time Playsongs & Sleepy Time Playsongs** (Playsong Publications; £4.99) – *Two selections of new and traditional songs with acoustic arrangements; the suppliers also sells others including CDs of counting songs. Books to accompany the tapes are planned.* / www.playsongs.co.uk, (01799) 599054.

The Lullaby Treasury – M Polee et al (Floris Books; £8.99; 0-863152-58-9) – *Cradle songs from around the world.*

Mama's Lullabys (ellipsis; Approx £15, less in small independent record stores) – *US world music recordings sung by some of the best performers in each country.* / UK dist Harmonia Mundi, 4 Vyner Street, London E2 9DQ (020) 8709 9500 info@harmoniamundi.com Can supply direct but recommend ordering thorugh your local supplier. .

[Tape] **Playsongs** (Action songs and rhymes for babies and toddlers; Playsong Publications; £7.99) – *Comes complete with a book of words and actions.* / www.playsongs.co.uk, (01799) 599054.

[Tape] **Riggidy Jig** – *Two entertaining tapes of modern nursery rhymes, traditional songs (e.g. "I do like to be beside the seaside"), and folk songs from other countries to a pleasant, acoustic accompaniment; £6.95 per tape.* / 47 Davenant Road, London N19 3NW – (020) 7281 5340.

[Tape] **Someone Special** (Playsong Publications; £6.99) – *Lap games, dances, action songs and lullabies with booklet, ideal for babies.* / www.playsongs.co.uk, (01799) 599054.

[CD-Rom] **They Sang and Were Glad** (Julia Plaut; £7.99) – *Nursery rhymes and action songs (all actions included on sleeve notes) performed using traditional instruments and with original arrangements; appealing to children but should not drive parents crazy.* / -.

3. VIDEOS & DVD

Indexes in this section refer to chapter 3.14 Shopping directory.

Whatever your views on over-feeding children with television, there is no doubting that videos are a great way of keeping kids occupied. This is true even from an early age, if you choose the right one.

From the age of about six months, Teletubbies is the main option (but one family reported a swimming video as a surprise hit). From two years there starts to be a plethora of choice – Tweenies, Thomas the Tank Engine, Bob the Builder, Postman Pat…as well as the more overtly educational specialist products for example from suppliers listed.

The listing relates only to specialist suppliers – all well-known current releases are available at larger supermarkets and on the high street.

Suppliers

Babies Love Babies
Baby Einstein
Babydelix Films
CNL

CHAPTER 3.08

NAPPIES

1. **Disposables vs reusables**
2. **Reusable nappies**
3. **Disposable nappies**
4. **Nappy changing equipment**
5. **Potty training**

(For stockists of swim nappies, see chapter 2.06 Baby & toddler activities.)

1. DISPOSABLES VS REUSABLES

Disposable nappies have been manufactured in the UK since 1949. However, it was only with the arrival of reasonably effective models in the '70s that they started to offer a genuine alternative to traditional fabric versions.

Popularity increased as designs improved. Today, disposables account for about 85% of all nappy changes, most of them either Pampers or Huggies, produced respectively by Procter & Gamble and Kimberley-Clark. There is, however, a growth once again in the use of reusable nappies, which are worn by an estimated 25–30% of babies, and account for about 15% of the market.

The resurgence of interest in reusables owes much to increasing environmental awareness. However, improving design has also been a factor, as has the fact that they are considerably cheaper than disposables.

If cost is not an issue, but the desire to be eco-friendly is, an emerging option is environmentally-friendly disposables (made, for example, with bio-degradable plastic and/or unbleached paper pulp). These nappies are beginning to break down the equation reusable=green, disposable=non-green. For the time being, though, cost remains higher than for alternatives, and green credentials vary significantly from make to make.

Whichever type of nappy you opt for:
➢ Bear in mind that not all nappies fit or suit all babies. You may have to try two or more brands before you find one that your child does not leak from, which you find easy to fit, and which your baby seems to find comfortable.
➢ Don't stock up too much on the newborn size until you know the baby's weight. Even then buy cautiously as babies quickly move into the next size up. Fabric nappies tend to allow a little more latitude for this.
➢ Note, however, that nappies which are too large are prone to leak.

Advantages of disposable nappies:

Convenience of use: disposable nappies are easier and more pleasant to handle than fabric ones. Disposable nappies may be more absorbent, in which case the baby may need to be changed less often (but see the comments on nappy rash below).

Constantly changing design: manufacturers of disposables are constantly seeking to refine their product and have usefully introduced leg cuffs to prevent leakage, tapes which stick even when covered in cream, and stretchy waistbands. (Other ideas such as nappies with different areas of absorbency for girls and boys have been quietly dropped.) Note, however, that designs of cloth nappies are also improving all the time. The elastication is now soft on baby legs, they too come with cuffs to prevent leakage, stretchy waistbands, and reliable fixings – and most brands are washable at high temperatures.

No need for washing: in contrast, fabric nappies create about two extra loads of laundry per week, about double that in the case of a newborn. (An alternative is a nappy-laundering service, though this destroys many of the economies relating to the use of reusables).

Disadvantages of disposable nappies:

Price: they are considerably more expensive than self-laundered fabric nappies (see below).

Nappy rash: the superior absorbency of disposables creates a tendency to skip changes. Nappy rash is not solely caused by wetness, but also by the effect of urine decaying into ammonia, (as well as by faeces in contact with the skin). Absorbency alone does not prevent this, one reason why the Advertising Standards Authority ruled that disposable manufacturers can't claim that nappy rash is less likely with their products. In fact, some studies show that babies wearing disposables get nappy rash more often than those wearing professionally laundered nappies.

Green issues: standard disposables are very environmentally unfriendly, contributing significantly to landfill waste. (The Women's Environmental Network estimates that disposables account for about 4% of domestic waste, at a national cost of £40m a year. In addition, much of the material in disposables takes generations to break down, with some plastics lasting indefinitely.) If all the claims of the green lobby are to be believed, the manufacture of disposable nappies is five times more energy intensive than that of cotton ones; gives rise to more toxic by-products, poses health-risks to workers in the manufacturing plants, and may raise animal-testing issues. Eco-friendly disposables are considerably less damaging to the environment than conventional disposables, but can still not be considered totally green. Local councils, aware of the costs of getting rid of disposables, sometimes offer a rates rebate to parents who use reusables, or a free trial of a nappy washing and collection service.

Health issues: there are some reports that the gels used in standard disposables can create allergic reactions or 'dry burns'. What's more, there are one or two concerns about the safety of standard disposables. The American Pediatric Association has withdrawn at least one brand from its recommended list because of reports of chemicals entering the baby's genitals, and in May 2000 the toxin TBT was found in some brands in research carried out for Greenpeace. There is a nebulous fear that some syndrome such as Toxic Shock with tampons will emerge. Standard disposables are highly flammable, and very dangerous for children if they chew them. Reusable nappies, particularly when wet, are breathable and cooler next to a baby's bottom than the plastic and paper, of disposables. Particularly if there is a family history of eczema and psoriasis, you may feel happier having cotton next to your baby's skin. Research at Kiel in Germany in 2000 also suggested the higher tem-

Sam-I-Am offer a wide range of cloth nappies and accessories to suit you, your baby and your lifestyle.

We have a large selection of organic natural fabrics, including cottons and silk. Also available are things for Mum, bath time and now we can help with accessories for potty training.

Lots to see in our nappy department including nappies from Tots Bots, Popolino and SnuggleNaps.

At Sam-I-Am we pride ourselves in our personal service, prompt delivery, feel free to telephone or email with your questions.

Visit www.sam-I-am.co.uk or call 01522 778926 for a brochure.

peratures inside the plastic of standard disposables may keep boys' testicles too hot to develop normally, leading to infertility.

Convenience: with disposables, you constantly have to re-stock on bulky items.

The price trade-off

It is recommended that you change babies six times per day, which adds up to needing about 2,190 nappies per year, or more than 5,000 between birth and potty training (assuming that occurs aged two and a half).

Factors to bear in mind

➤ If you launder fabric nappies separately, over the 30 months you use them washing costs will total in the order of £100.

➤ Self-laundered fabric nappies are particularly cheap if you use the same nappies on a second child.

➤ Fabric nappies require an initial financial outlay approximately equivalent to the cost of 10 weeks of disposables.

Nappy rash

See chapter 3.09 Lotions & potions for brands of nappy and barrier creams.
Huggies research indicates that as many as 57% of babies get nappy rash every two to three weeks and the condition apparently accounts for 20% of all dermatology consultations in the UK.

Causes are not clear although research at Bristol University revealed that wetness alone is not the culprit. As well as infrequent nappy changes and associated problems mentioned above, diarrhoea may also be linked,

Nappy	Approx. cost over 30 months (inc. washing)
Terry Towelling (terries)	£250
Cotton Nappies & overpants	£350
All in Ones	£500-850
Laundry Service Fabric Nappies	£850-1100
Disposables	£850
Ultra Disposables	£1200

as may diet – particularly the early introduction of foods which the baby is not ready for.

According to the authors of Cosmetics Unmasked (published by HarperCollins), a trial by a Danish government body has implicated moist baby wipes in causing nappy rash. They further assert that the cocktail of chemicals wipes contain are also associated with conditions such as eczema.

You can avoid chemicals with some of the newer brands of wipes (see Eco-friendly and gel-free disposables pg 531) which are generally alcohol-free and may contain Aloe Vera. Alternatively you can create a washable alternative with a soft cloth, a little camomile tea, vegetable oil and drop or two of anti-bacterial lavender oil.

Use of good nappy and barrier creams can make all the difference to preventing or clearing nappy rash. For brands see chapter *3.09 Lotions & Potions (pg. 535).* Another less conventional idea is a mulberry silk nappy liner as the gum in the silk is thought to have a healing and anti-bacterial effect.

2. REUSABLE NAPPIES

Indexes in this section refer to chapter 3.14 Shopping directory.

Cloth nappies are only available on a limited basis in shops: for example, Boots, Mothercare and John Lewis branches stock one or two brands each and some independent chemists offer them. Baby shops with a more alternative slant generally offer a wider range.

Most are bought by mail order, usually with trial packs available. It can be a good idea to try a variety of styles – say five – to see which suit best. Suppliers offering a range of brands generally make a point of also supplying plenty of information to help parents make an appropriate choice.

There are a variety of systems. The most common involves a liner; an absorbent fabric inner; and a waterproof outer. The main alternative is an 'all-in-one' system combining the latter two elements. In whichever style, design is becoming ever more refined and the traditional problems of poor fit and leakage are being overcome, though all require three washes before becoming fully absorbent – with effectiveness then depending on the type of fabric used – see table pg 529.

Learning to fit them correctly is vital if you are going to use them successfully. Most suppliers are happy to advise on this, but the key point is to ensure they are snug around the thighs, which in turn requires a snug fit at the waist. This grows progressively easier as the baby grows and pads out.

LINERS

Disposable liners cost around £4 for 100, and 'catch' the solid waste (hopefully). Most sold retail are made of polypropylene, which should not be disposed of in lavatories. Paper liners are biodegradable and can simply be flushed away, making them considerably simpler to use.

Reusable nappy suppliers may also sell washable liners. Washable polyester ones are designed to allow the urine through and keep it away from the baby's skin. Raw silk liners are recommended for nappy rash or sensitive skin (see Nappy Rash opposite).

Most suppliers also offer extra-absorbency inserts in a similar fabric to the basic nappy, which may prove useful at nights and on long trips. Alternatively if you use small muslins or terries for a newborn, these can be reused as inserts later once the child has grown.

HOW MANY DO YOU NEED?

If you feel happy washing the nappies with your underwear (at 60°C) you will need about 16 nappies, though if you launder daily you might get away with less. If you plan to wash dedicated nappy loads you will need more – up to 24. You will need around four overpants for each growth stage.

With newborns you will have to wash more often or buy more as they may need changing eight or even 12 times a day.

TYPES OF REUSABLE NAPPY

Many designs of nappy will adapt to fit different sizes of baby, thus saving on the initial investment. Overwraps are less adjustable so you will probably need to buy bigger ones as the baby grows.

You can boost absorbency in all cases by inserting extra pads. Some systems are specifically designed for this but it is easy to mix and match, with pre-folds and muslin sheets particularly flexible.

Traditional terry and muslin squares worn under waterproof pants: muslin is soft for a newborn's skin, while terry is very long-lasting. Both types of fabric can be readjusted to fit a growing child, but the fabric has to be folded in a certain manner to fit the baby, or they are close to useless. This is not always easy and you would be wise to learn how to do this before the baby arrives. There are Illustrations on www.thenappylady.co.uk and one experienced user reports that you make a complete hash at first but after a day or so become very adept. Nappi Nippa clips – available direct from the supplier (see below) – are safer than the proverbial safety pin (though this usually sticks into the adult not the baby). Average cost is £2 each, making them the cheapest option. Waterproof pants are around £4 each.

Cloth nappies with ties (wraparounds) worn under waterproof pants: similar to the above – easier to fit, but most, being muslin, wear less well; cost £2.50 each (plus waterproof pants as above).

All-in-ones: fitted cloth nappies with an integral waterproof shell and generally Velcro closings. These offer a high level of convenience for a reusable but there are drawbacks. They are not ideal for the first months as the baby will be moving swiftly through the sizes (though some brands do offer a one-size-fits-all option). They may be prone to leaking, (though extra absorbency liners are available). They are more likely to be damaged by chemical nappy soaking solutions and hot washes. The outers don't wear well, the nappies cannot be laundered as hot as the inners of two-piece systems, and all-in-ones are relatively slow to dry. They are also among the more expensive options at around £7.50 each.

Shaped cloth nappies, worn under waterproof pants: fitted cotton nappies, similar to disposables, generally in terry towelling with optional additional strip for extra absorbency, generally with snap fit fastenings and worn under an outer with Velcro and/or snap fit fastenings. The inners offer a particularly good fit and separate washing means greater durability.

Waterproof pants with fitted pads: absorbent fabric pads to fit breathable waterproof pants with Velcro or popper closings. Some designs have pads that slot into a pocket, others are attached to the outer by poppers, others have pads which are shaped simply to slip into place, and yet others use the inners commonly used by most nappy-laundry companies – a rectangle divided into three sections. This style is as easy to fit as an all-in-one, but washes better and dries faster. The degree of padding used can be adjusted, and there is an option with the choice of disposable rather than reusable pads.

Trainer pants: for potty-training older children. These can be more effective in promoting potty-training than disposable pull-ups because children can feel when they are wet.

Further issues:

➢ Is the nappy size adjustable for growth – generally with poppers or buttons – so you can use the same set from birth to toddlerdom, and on more than one child at a time if you have two in nappies.

➢ Velcro fastenings are easier, but their functionality suffers after too much hot washing. They can be replaced but snap fastenings may anyway be better proof against a toddler determined to remove a nappy.

TWO ALTERNATIVES FOR OUTER LAYERS

Conventional outer pants for the above types of nappy are made of plastic, nylon, or fabric coated in those or similar materials. However, there is a growing range of alternatives which, while waterproof, allow air to circulate, helping prevent skin problems. These are recommended if you will be using the nappy in tropical climates, or your baby suffers repeated nappy rash.

In all cases wraps which incorporate gussets at the legs are particularly useful in protecting against leaks or wicking of moisture from the nappy underneath onto clothes.

Lanolin-impregnated, natural wool outers: at first sight an option only for the seriously committed eco-warrior, particularly the knitted variety, but there are some more elegant options, for example imported from Sweden. The lanolin neutralises the urine and, unlike plastic covers, unless soiled, these outers only need washing around once a fortnight. Perhaps more importantly, because wool can absorb a third of its own weight in water without feeling wet, they keep things dry both inside and out, and are less likely to leak than waterproof layers. If in doubt drop water on to the surface to see that it is not absorbed. Suppliers sell lanolin for a monthly soak to renew effectiveness. One of the most expensive options and best hand washed, but long-lasting and very breathable.

Fluffies or fleece: manmade alternatives, cool in summer and warm in winter; because of the air circulation, good at preventing nappy rash.

Breathable fabric wrappers: coated with polyurethane, sometimes combined with nylon, generally shaped with Velcro fastenings. Hard-wearing and machine washable, but around double the price of plasticised fabric.

Plasticised fabric: shaped with Velcro fastenings. May become hard after two or three months of laundering and may develop small holes.

Nylon: cheap and last several months, but not breathable.

All the above need to be treated more delicately than nappies, washing at 40°C and in the case of wool or fleece, in soap alone to protect their waterproof properties.

ABSORBENCY

See table on page 528.

You don't want to be changing nappies every five minutes so absorbency is an important issue, and one mainly down to the fabric used. Fabrics, though, do have other advantages and disadvantages to be taken into consideration as well.

Absorbency is a function of the weave of the fabric, its weight, and what it is made of. For example, stretch terry (which has about 15% of polyester added to the cotton) is less absorbent than standard terry (which contain only 3-7% polyester and then, generally, not in the sections of the nappy which do most of the absorbing.) Because of its weave, flanelette is weight for weight the most absorbent material but it tends to be used in less bulky nappies so the nappies themselves are not. Hemp weight for weight is more absorbent than cotton but is generally used in a hemp-cotton mix to create a softer fleece style fabric.

NOTES FOR TABLES ON PAGES 528 AND 529

Fit: all depends on the shape of your baby with the key area being the size of the thighs. Chubby thighs make for a tighter fit round the legs and less likelihood of leaks. Particularly if your child is leaner it is important that the nappy can be adjusted appropriately. Bulky nappies are not good for this. If a nappy leaks you can try fitting it tighter, but if it leaks again, you need a different nappy.

Ease of drying: whether you line or machine dry, thicker nappies and particularly all-in-ones with their integral plastic layer, take more time and effort to dry. Something which splits into component parts, whether attached or detached, will dry faster and the thinner the fabric, the faster again. Faster drying means you need fewer nappies.

Ease of fitting: the easiest reusables mirror the design of disposables – an all-in-one shaped design with easy fixings at either side. This is of particular relevance if you have a wriggly baby, or if anyone who changes the baby is not particularly deft in this department. However, given the major advantages of keeping the inner, absorbent section of the nappy and the outer, waterproof one, separate, two shaped pieces are what most experts advise.

Durability: plastic and fastenings of the Velcro type do not respond well to repeated and hot washing, and still less to harsh sanitation. The Velcro can be replaced but plastic poppers are more difficult. If integral waterproof layers start to break up, the nappy has reached the end of its life – another argument in favour of keeping any plastic layer separate from the nappy itself.

Bulkiness: the silhouette of babies has changed since disposables became widespread, making them look more slimline. Some reusable nappies return them to a more old-fashioned look, which does not appeal to some parents.

Nappy laundering services

These services deliver an agreed number of nappies each week, usually 50 for newborn babies, 30–40 for babies of 12lbs upwards and gradually decreasing numbers thereafter. Used nappies are collected and taken to be washed to a standard laid down by the Department of Health. The cost of such services is around £10 per week.

Such services normally insist that you will use nappies hired by the service. In addition, any nappy laundering service will sell you nappies. For those not put off by the idea, used nappies from one of these services are a bargain.

The tables below use a scale from * (lowest) to **** (heighest).

	Absorbency	Bulk	Drying
Flanelette	***	**	**
Muslin (unfolded)	**	***	***
Muslin (prefolds)	**	**	**
Terry towelling	***	*	**
Stretch terry towelling	***	*	**
Hemp	****	**	**

	Terries	Muslins	Wraparounds	Shaped Nappies (generally muslin)	Outers plus attached inner pads	All-in-ones
Snugness of Fit	*	**	***	***	***	*
Ease of drying	**	***	***	**	**	*
Ease of Fitting	*	*	**	**	***	***
Durability	***	***	**	**	**	*
Bulkiness	*	***	***	** depending on fabric used	**	**

Almost all companies use pre-folded cotton nappies designed to with-stand vigorous laundering. Such nappies are generally made up of three panels sewn together: the central one made of six–eight layers, the outer panels four layers each. Waterproof fabric-feel wrappers are sold sepa-rately and home laundered.

Services may also supply deodorised, lockable travel bins, which can, for example, be useful to take into hospital.

Nappy laundering services seem to be constantly changing in terms of their owners and the geographical areas they cover.

Home washing

Unless you use a nappy laundering service, the main practical issue with reusable nappies is storing the dirty ones before laundering them. This is best done in a pail of cleansing solution.

Conventional bleach is not recommended for nappies as it may cause a reaction on the baby's skin and can damage Velcro fastenings and the waterproofing. Nappy cleansing solutions such as Milton and Napisan are safer but can still cause adverse effects. Ecover oxygen-based bleach how-ever is suitable and more effective the hotter the wash. However, none of these substances is absolutely essential to hygiene so long as the nappies are hot washed (at 60°C or more).

In hard water areas, water softener powder or less detergent in the wash can help keep the nappies softer.

In eco-terms, home laundering uses 2.5 times as much water as a nappy laundering service. In financial terms it works out considerably cheaper.

Suggested alternative soaking liquids for half to three-quarters of a nine-litre bucket of water (the solution should be changed every two or three days):

➤ 4–6 tablespoons of vinegar, preferably white.

➤ 2 tablespoons borax (take care – it's toxic); borax is a germicide so detergent is not required in the wash.

➤ 2 tablespoons sodium bicarbonate.

➤ 2 tablespoons nappy sanitising powder; an environmentally friendly alternative, available from chemists, health food shops or most mail order suppliers of reusable nappies.

➤ Dettol.

➤ Tea tree oil.

A plastic bin holding about 20 litres (4.5 gallons) may be more convenient than a conventional 9 litre (2 gallons) nappy bucket for soaking. Beer fermentation buckets are another alternative. A nappy mesh is sometimes used for easy transfer of the nappies into the washing machine. Keeping a pair of rubber gloves handy is also a good idea.

Tips when laundering nappies:

➤ Biological detergents and products containing perfumes or whiteners should be avoided in case of skin irritation (see chapter *3.09 Lotions & potions* for stockists of non-biological washing powders).

➤ Note: if you have soaked the nappy first in a sanitising solution, so long as you have removed any solids, further laundering is not absolutely essential to hygiene.

➤ Ironing is not necessary, but is a further sanitising process.

➤ Biotex or a similar stain-removing product can be used on stubborn marks.

➤ Half to 3/4 cup vinegar on the last rinse cycle will help keep the nappies soft (but check with the manufacturer to make sure this will not damage the fabric). Note that fabric softeners can coat the nappy surface with a waxy lining, so reducing absorbency.

➤ Drying in the sun will deodorise, sanitise and naturally bleach the nappies. This will take around 8 hours, depending on the material.

USEFUL CONTACTS

Nappy Information Service, ⌖ www.nappyinformationservice.co.uk
The Absorbent Hygiene Products Manufactures Association (AHPMA) is the body representing the UK's main disposable nappy manufacturers Kimberly-Clark, Procter & Gamble UK and SCA Hygiene Products; their website looks at the advantages of disposables over reusables.

Nappy Nights, ☎ (020) 8568 4913
This west London volunteer-run campaign offers new parents a chance to inspect around 20 types of the reusable nappies on the market, by hosting twice-monthly meetings (£3); call to book ahead; they also provide information on issues like costs, health and environmental impact.

National Association of Nappy Services (NANS),
☎ (0121) 693 4949 ⌖ www.changeanappy.co.uk
The association promotes the use of washable nappies, and aims to raise awareness of the environmental issues surrounding disposables. Call or use the website to find your nearest nappy service. Nappy services deliver, collect and launder easy-to-use cotton nappies. Services are available in most areas of the country at a cost of around £10 a week – which works out (at the most) comparable to using disposables. / HOURS Mon-Fri 9.30am-5pm.

The Real Nappy Association, ☎ (01983) 401959 ⌖ www.realnappy.com; www.wen.org.uk
Started by two mothers concerned about the health and environmental issues relating to disposable nappies, this organisation links real nappy manufacturers, the National Association of Nappy Companies and environmental groups. It is a central source of information, advice and practical support on all nappy-related issues. Send a large SAE with two stamps for a copy of the information pack, details of the membership scheme and regular information about any new suppliers or products.

Women's Environmental Network (WEN), ☎ (020) 7481 9004
⌂ www.wen.org.uk
Campaigning charity providing independent advice on environmental issues, including on types of reusable nappy, nappy suppliers and washing services (send A4 SAE (41p) or see website for information). / PUBLICATIONS Leaflets: *Pregnancy; Parenting and the Environment; Chlorine: Pollution and the Parents of Tomorrow.*

Reusable nappies – brands & single-brand stockists

Baby Hut
Bio-Bubs (& Hugabub)
Boots
Bumkins
Buzzness
ClothWORKS
Cotton Bottoms
Cotton Tails
Cushy Tushies
Ella's House
The Ellie Nappy Company
Kooshies
Linco Care
Modern Baby
Nappysaurus
Natural Collection
Nature's Baby
The Nice Nappy Company
Sam-I-Am
Schmidt Natural Clothing
Snazzy Pants
Snuggle Naps
Spirit of Nature
Tots Bots
Yummies
Zorbit Babycare

North
Green Baby *(N1)*
Rub a Dub Dub *(N8)*

South
Lilliput *(SW19, SW8)*
Little Green Earthlets *(SW15)*

Mail order
Bambino Mio
Born
Cotton Bottoms
Cuddlebabes
Eco-Babes
Green Baby
Kittykins
Lilliput
Little Green Earthlets
Lollipop Children's Products
Natural Child
Number One for Nappies
Plush Pants
Rub a Dub Dub
Smilechild
Twinkleontheweb

Reusable nappy accessories

Nappi Nippas

3. DISPOSABLE NAPPIES

Indexes in this section refer to chapter 3.14 Shopping directory.

Conventional disposables

As well as being on sale in supermarkets and chemists, there are one or two home-delivery services (though companies in this business tend to come and go). Your local independent chemist may also deliver in bulk.

Especially for newborns when you are changing the baby very regularly, own brand nappies are considerably cheaper than the heavily advertised alternatives. Some own-brand options lack the quality of the big two brands, however – in terms of convenient fastenings, or seemingly with a greater tendency to cause nappy rash – so it is worth experimenting with smaller packs before stocking up in any quantity.

Eco-friendly & gel-free disposables

Though 'green' disposables are sold in some mainstream supermarkets, these brands are generally not the most eco-friendly. As well as the suppliers given below, it's worth looking for brands of eco-friendly disposable nappies stocked in many organic and wholefood shops listed in chapter *2.02 Feeding*.

Included in the listings are gel-free disposable nappies. These are generally made of cotton and are not particularly eco-friendly. Their benefit is they avoid the chemicals that ordinary disposables bring into contact with your baby's skin.

Eco-friendly & gel-free disposable nappy brands

Moltex Oko
Nature Boy & Girl (Naty)
Tushies
Weenees

Eco-friendly & gel-free disposable nappy suppliers

West
The Natural Baby Co *(PO33)*

North
Green Baby *(N1)*
Mini Kin *(N8)*
Rub a Dub Dub *(N8)*

Mail order
Beaming Baby
Cuddlebabes
Eco-Babes
Green & Organic
Green Baby
Lollipop Children's Products
Mini Kin
The Natural Baby Co
Natural Collection
Nature Botts
Rub a Dub Dub
Spirit of Nature
Tairua Limited

4. NAPPY CHANGING EQUIPMENT

For all types of nappy, equipment you may need:

Changing mat: the standard model is padded plastic, cheap, comfortable and wipeable, though not durable. The feature to look for is a raised edge all the way round to catch baby pee. A towel on top is more comfortable than cold plastic on bare skin and also helps soak up any liquid. However, the towel alone might be adequate unless the surface underneath is particularly fragile. There are inflatable mats designed to prevent babies from rolling off. When out and about, a foldable mat can be handy and some parents use these mats all the time. An alternative is a sheet of plastic-backed towelling sold by some suppliers as a travel change mat, which doubles as a mattress protector and can be laundered regularly.

Nappy changing bag: these offer an integral changing mat, and pockets for nappies, wipes, bottles and other paraphernalia, which can be particularly useful if you are going to use the bag to carry your own things as well. It is perfectly possible to use a normal bag, or, for example a sports bag with waterproof compartment. Originally most nappy changing bags were in lightweight, pretty and pale baby fabrics which show the dirt and lacked much sense of style. There is, however, a burgeoning range of more elegant and indeed fashionable options which may also survive their daily bashing better. Many mothers however simply use a bag they own already, or buy a large, multi-purpose bag they like the look of. Whichever you choose, avoid too many compartments, in which everything will get lost.

Nappy sacks: perfumed plastic bags – old carrier bags are perfectly adequate if not as (synthetically) sweet smelling. Alternatively there are now some bio-degradable options, available in some supermarkets.

Bucket or bin for used nappies: there are competing brands but broadly for disposables the idea is to seal around three days' worth of used nappies into a long sausage of plastic. But beware the price of the 'cassettes' of replacement bags. For fabric nappies, a bin such as is used for beer-making is a more practical size than the traditional bucket (unless, that is, you will have to carry it to the washing machine).

Change bags, mats and other accessories

West
Bill Amberg *(W2)*
Nina Campbell *(SW3)*

Mail order
Bill Amberg
Caboodles

Cuddlebabes
Grobag
Kelty Kids
Snuggle Naps
Storm Enterprises
Willy Um-Yum
ZPM

Disposable nappy bins

Sangeric

5. POTTY TRAINING

Indexes in this section refer to chapter 3.14 Shopping directory.

This somewhat dreaded rite of passage for parents does at least hold out the (eventual) prospect of some degree of self-sufficiency on the part of your offspring.

Advice on when to start has changed a great deal since our parents day, when potty training one-year olds was the norm. Starting too early is currently widely believed to risk psychological difficulties in later life, and a softly, softly approach is strongly promoted. An alternative approach inspired by practices for example in Africa, argues that there is a natural window of awareness at around eight months. In the developed world however, it is not uncommon these days for children to reach the age of three in nappies.

As with everything, different children start at very different times, sometimes depending on the time of year, with summer weather a major advantage. Toddlers aren't the most co-operative creatures however, and this is an area where you want co-operation. If your child is showing zero interest, the time probably isn't right.

According to a top paediatrician at Great Ormond Street, the level of emotional maturity required to start toilet training is reached at the same time as that required for pretend play. If you child is becoming interested in the latter, it's a good time to make a start.

For this purpose you will probably need a potty. Something very simple will do perfectly well but if you want to go to town there are a variety of alternatives now including potty chairs, toilet seat adapters, musical potties and travel potties. Patterned items look fun but paler ones allow you to judge from the colour of liquid whether the child is drinking enough. Vital for boys is to make sure the front is high enough to catch any inadvertent upward flow.

Another useful item is a stool to help your toddler climb up onto an adult loo, and to be able to reach taps to start learning a hand-washing routine.

Note too that if you have not yet invested in mattress protection, now is probably the time to do so.

You may wish to try trainer pants as sold by the nappy brands and companies, but these don't always work for children who need the trigger of feeling wet.

READING

Diaper Free! – Ingrid Bauer (The gentle wisdom of natural infant hygiene; Natural Wisdom Press; 2001; US$16.95; 0968751903) – *A look at how people without nappies potty train their babies from just months old. / US title available from www.amazon.com.*

Infant Potty Training – Laurie Boucke (With or Without Diapers - The Natural Way; Colin White & Laurie Boucke; £13; 1888580259) – *A US title on potty training at around four or five months, adopting the approach used in no-nappy countries. The authors admit that total training is unlikely before 24 months. .*

[Video] **Lootime** – Sally Farmiloe (Farmingham Productions; 2000; £9.99) – *A 20-minute video for toddlers, to help them understand the drill; it is in short, repetitive bursts to appeal to the age group's attention span with musical songs for every point made; older children show younger children what to do. It has been endorsed by a professor at Queen Charlotte's. / Farmingham Productions, 3 St Andrews Road, London W14 9SX; tel: (020) 7381 5735 with £1.50 p&p.*

NCT Potty Training – Heather Welford (Thorsons; 2002; £6.99; 0-00-713606-4) – *A look at different methods to help decide on the one for you. / NCT Maternity Sales, (0870) 112 1120; www.nctms.co.uk.*

Potty Training in One Week – Gina Ford (Your One-stop guide to successful potty training; Vermilion; 2003; £5.99; 0091887569) – *Another title from the doyenne of parental control. She says it's pointless starting the process until the child can follow simple instructions; can pull pants up and down; can point to different parts of the body; and can concentrate on a toy, book or video for 5-10 minutes (none of this is likely before 18 months). She advises starting at the weekend and picking a quiet week. / www.randomhouse.co.uk.*

Practical Parenting - Potty Training – Jane Gilbert (Making the transition to dry days and nights; Hamlyn; 2003; £5.99; 0600606678) – *How to recognise the signs that your child is ready to move out of nappies. The guide includes tips on problems such as bedwetting, and comes complete with checklists, charts, case studies and Q&As. / www.hamlyn.co.uk.*

Potties & accessories

Bibs 'n' Stuff	Weeman
Family Seat	Bibs 'n' Stuff
Natural Wisdom	McCabe (UK)
Urchin	NYA Plastic & Rubber
V&A Marketing	Industry

CHAPTER 3.09

LOTIONS & POTIONS

1. **Introduction**
2. **Product Safey**
3. **Index of brands & stockists**

(For products aimed at alleviating eczema, colic or teething, see chapter 2.03 Baby health. For information on practitioners of aromatherapy, herbalism and massage as ways of reducing the stress of labour and helping with postnatal difficulties, see chapter 4.02 Complementary medicine & Health practitioners. For information on nipple creams, see chapter 2.02 Feeding.)

1. INTRODUCTION

There is a wealth of well-advertised products designed for use on babies. The mass market is dominated by Johnson & Johnson and the own-brand equivalents from supermarket and chemist chains.

However, following the growth of interest in organic foods, there is a growing awareness of what substances are being used on the outside of the body as well as within. The focus of this chapter is some of the issues this raises, and details of the more elusive brands that offer an alternative to the mainstream products.

2. PRODUCT SAFETY

The current situation on bodycare products is similar to that on foods many years ago. There is some regulation, but little control over label claims, limited requirements over stating ingredients, no effective policing, and limited public concern, at least in the UK. The public's view is slightly different in the US where there has been a boom in books on the subject, in part because of worries about potential carcinogens, whether as intended ingredients or contaminants.

Samuel Epstein, a leading US campaigner in this field, reports for example that an American survey in 1993 found the toxic and carcinogenic 1,4 dioxane in 27 out of 30 children's shampoos and bath products tested.

According to the MD of one of the leading alternative US brands, the main reason problematic ingredients are permitted is that they were passed for use back in 1948 when it was believed that the skin functioned as a barrier. Once authorised, it is said, it is difficult to overcome the inertia of acceptance. And given that many of the ingredients are cheap petroleum by-products, there is limited industry impetus to find alternatives.

It is now clear that the skin is nothing like as impermeable as was once thought. (If you want to check, Peter Walker memorably suggests rubbing garlic on a baby's foot before smelling it on the breath 20 minutes later.) There is particular concern about products used when the skin is warm and the pores more open – such as in the bath.

The issue of safety is most pressing with products to be used on babies or young children because their thinner skins, and the higher relative surface area of a their skin proportionate to their weight, means minors absorb relatively more of a given substance than an adult. Furthermore, their immature systems are less capable of excreting any toxins which might build up. For these reasons particular care needs to be taken over what you put on a child's skin, particularly with products not specifically designed for babies.

Once ingredients are absorbed by the body, if they can't be broken down, they may be excreted, potentially via the skin, one possible explanation for eczema, or failing that, stored in organs and fatty tissue, eventually building to levels where they can cause problems.

READING

A Consumer's Dictionary of Cosmetic Ingredients – Ruth Winter, MS (Complete Information About More Than 6,000 of the Harmful and Desrable Ingredients Found in Toiletries and Cosmetics; Three Rivers Press; 1999; $16; 0-609-80367-0) – *Now in its 7th edition, an A-Z of ingredients and their status in the US. Entries indicate where your should look out for particular ingredients, their potential side effects, and whether the industry's own Cosmetics Ingredients Review considers them safe. The author notes that a 1980 study by the US National Research Council and National Toxicology Program found there was no toxicity information available for over half of cosmetic ingredients. / Stocked by Neals Yard Remedies.*

Cosmetics Unmasked – Dr Stephen & Gina Antczak (Your family guide to safe cosmetics and allergy-free toiletries; Harper Collins; 2001; £9.99; 0-007105-68-1) – *Not a scaremongering book, but a useful resource of information about the ingredients in cosmetics and toiletries (particularly those from big-name companies).*

Legislation

EU law on cosmetics (which covers all bodycare products) requires that those designed for use on children contain at least fifty times fewer microbes than is normally permitted. This means that they usually contain more preservatives than those designed for adults.

The EU does not consider baby skin to be any more sensitive than that of adults because there is no scientific evidence on the subject. It does note that the increased surface area to weight ratio of minors means that their exposure to chemicals applied to the skin is two or three times greater than that of adults. The Commission reports that this difference is taken into account in the risk assessment process.

In general, laws on bath products and shampoos – products which are considered to be washed off the skin – are less stringent than those applying to products such as lotions or barrier creams which are left on.

Where ingredients are banned, effective enforcement can be hampered by trade secret laws, which means that implementation of any regulations is largely dependent on self-regulation by manufacturers. The DTI has the right to demand that a given manufacturer defends any implied claim made on packaging – e.g. that a product said to be for babies is safe for them. However, there is significant disagreement about what is and is not safe.

There is no requirement that the manufacturers demonstrate that the ingredients are safe – still less that they are safe in combination. Some researchers are pointing out that the effect of cocktails of ingredients may be very different from their effect independently.

When it comes to the functional ingredients in bodycare products, one of the "hot potato" issues is whether or not there is be a difference between substances which occur naturally, and the same materials created synthetically. Opinions differ so widely it is difficult to do more than flag this as a potential concern.

Chemical preservatives, and more natural alternatives

Although some mainstream suppliers argue that they have to introduce rather harsh ingredients as preservatives to ensure their products are safe, some sceptics argue that part of the reason for this is that these products contain so much – cheap – water, in which bacteria can thrive. The term acqua near the top of the ingredients list indicates this, ingredients being listed in order of quantity.

Some natural extracts (such as herbs and flowers, proteins and vitamins) may carry a risk of microbial infection because they too make good nutrition for the microbes. Because of this a product containing these substances may also be full of preservatives.

The aim of any preservative is to kill cells or alter the way they reproduce. It is hypothesized that, when used on the skin, (and in the body if they penetrate) this could affect the cells of the user as well as those in the product.

For this reason if no other, where products use preservatives it is safest to go for those with ingredients the human body can handle. In particular food grade preservatives such as sodium benzoate, Vitamin E or Aloe Vera (also called Aloe barbadensis) are suggested, along with certain essential oils such as rosemary. These are more expensive than the more usual choices. These can generally be used providing there are not too many microbe nutrients in the product and the user accepts a shorter shelf life than that of standard cosmetics.

Some products should not require preservatives at all. These include powders, and those principally made up of oil. Products supplied in tubes should need less preservative than those in pots because there are no fingers dipping into them, introducing germs.

It is, incidentally, always best to use all products quickly as the longer you keep them, the more likely it is that they will decay to produce potentially harmful chemicals.

The products

PRODUCTS FOR PREGNANCY

The main bodycare product sold for pregnancy is for reducing stretchmarks. A variety of oils and creams containing variously vitamins and different oils are reported helpful in their prevention. It is not clear whether they work but they will moisturise the skin. Products for sore feet may also be helpful but most other items are of the pampering variety, with names suggesting, soothing, calm and reassurance.

Although there does not appear to be any research on the subject, it would be logical to assume that anything problematic might be equally or more so during pregnancy and when breastfeeding. It is known for example that chemicals including fragrances, which accumulate in fatty tissue, can be passed to children through breastmilk. For this reason products with minimal chemicals are probably advisable, and this is not always true of dedicated ranges, particularly those from the US.

MASSAGE OILS AND LOTIONS

If you are planning to try baby massage, expert Peter Walker advises the use of vegetable-based products over mineral-based ones. The main ingredient (butalyated hydroxytoluene) is believed by some researchers to be carcinogenic and it has been reported to have an adverse effect on the reproductive organs of animals. It is also reported a potential cause of contact dermatitis.

Note however that just because a product is vegetable-based doesn't mean it is suitable for small children. Where aromatherapy essential oils are concerned, they are not recommended for children under three months old, except for lavender and chamomile.

Lotions are also sometimes marketed for massage and moisturising of babies. However, while oil-based products do not require preservatives, lotions often do because of their being water based, and/or the inclusion of emulsifiers and other additives.

If concerned about the potential of an allergy trigger from use of nut oils, note that suppliers (for example, Weleda) refine their oils to medicine grade, removing the proteins that can trigger anaphylaxis.

SOAPS, SHAMPOOS AND WASHING

Newborns don't need much in the way of cleaning, nor in most cases does their skin need much in the way of moisturising. Indeed, some experts consider it best to avoid washing them too much, so that their skin does not become dry (if it does a good quality massage oil will help). Until the child is mobile and able to get themselves dirty, topping and tailing is nowadays considered by many experts all that is required for good hygiene.

If you want to wash your baby, plain water will do the trick, with lavender or chamomile essential oil if you like the smell. If you want to use a soap, shampoo or bubble bath, the main issue is the detergent/foaming agent used.

Soaps are made from vegetable oils, (sometimes organic) treated generally with caustics (alkalines) like sodium or potassium hydroxide, to create the saponification – i.e. ability to lather. The mix is then left to stand for about three weeks to revert to a less alkaline, and ideally neutral ph value.

Handmade soap are generally high in glycerine – the mildest type of soap – which is harvested out of most commercial soaps. (Clear soaps have added alcohol plus a glycerine and sugar mix.)

Soaps are not the same as detergents which are generally more chemical and less biodegradable and which are found in some 'soap' bars. Most liquid washes on the market for example include sodium lauryl sulphate or other members of the family (see Ingredients to Watch Out For). Alternatives are more expensive but are available from some of the companies listed here.

TALCUM POWDER

There seem to be an increasing number of sources suggesting that talcum powder should be avoided for babies. The Safe Shopper's Bible for example maintains that even cosmetic grade talc is carcinogenic. In addition, powder can also cause irritation in the creases of a baby's skin, tend to dry it, and combine with substances found in sweat to block the sweat ducts, or as one ex-supplier puts it 'inhibit natural skin function in an immature skin'. As powder can get into a baby's airways, with cases of death reported in the US, if you do choose to use powder, it is always best to be sparing.

There is also concern about the aluminium content of some powders used as anti-perspirants, but this should not be included in a product for babies.

NAPPY CHANGING

Health visitors often counsel against the use of wipes, in part because they can encourage thrush. Studies have also raised concerns that mois-turised wipes cause nappy rash, possibly because the alcohol breaks down the skin's natural barriers. The fragrances included are also potentially a cause for concern, (see below). Lukewarm water and cotton wool or soft tissues are the safest route, in the case of newborns at any rate.

Supermarket shelves groaning with wipes attest to their convenience. If you do use these, the ideal is to keep this to a minimum and mop up any surplus cleaner left on the skin with plain tissues. Alternatively stockists of reusable and eco-friendly disposable nappies may also stock more eco-friendly wipes with ingredients like essential oils, which are likely to prove less problematic. (For details see chapter *3.08 Nappies*.)

Oily calamine, zinc and castor oil barrier creams are widely used as preventives against nappy rash. There are concerns about their use, but not on a par with the more serious concerns mentioned in this chapter. Some allergy specialists see them as possible irritants or causes of eczema. Some homeopaths counsel against using zinc-based products, though practically all nappy rash treatments feature some zinc. The peanut (arachis oil) in some products causes worry to some parents though a randomised double blind crossover challenge study on peanut oil in people allergic to peanuts found that the oil did not cause any reaction. However, Weleda for example has noted the potential for concern and has changed its formulation to almond.

The alternative is to make your own with essential oils – initially say almond oil with lavender and chamomile, but further ideas are given in the titles on aromatherapy for children listed in chapter *4.02 Complementary medicine & Health practitioners*.

INGREDIENTS TO WATCH OUT FOR

If you can bring yourself to read labels the following items are considered cause for concern by some commentators, though by no means all:

Propylene glycol (PG): a wetting/moisture carrying agent and solvent used for example in haircare products, some face moisturisers, body lotions and toothpaste. Also the main ingredient in antifreeze and brake fluid. Among other things it apparently increases the permeability of the skin, making it easier for other ingredients to be absorbed. Where used industrially the handlers apparently use heavy protection gear and shower immediately if it comes into contact with the skin because it has been judged systemic, potentially leading to kidney and liver damage, as well as skin problems.

Sodium lauryl sulphate (SLS): used in toothpaste (even some 'natural' brands) and shampoos; also often used as an engine degreaser and for cleaning garage floors. It has been linked amongst other things to cataract formation. Some reports indicate that it may have a degenerative effect on cell membrane and tests have shown that it may slow down hair growth. Other studies have also suggested that SLS prevents children's' eyes from developing properly, possibly by denaturing proteins in the eye and inhibiting correct structural formation. There are also reports that the protein denaturing properties have been linked to immune system impairment in the skin. However, the Journal of the American College of Toxicology found SLS safe for use in products which have brief contact with the skin or hair and are rinsed off afterwards. Various alternatives with bafflingly similar names are considered less problematic by some (but naturally by no means all) commentators – sodium laureth sulphate, ammonium laureth sulfate, sodium lauroyl lactylate… Some of these make less foam/lather which gives most users the impression of less cleansing – not in fact the case. Some suppliers argue that at least as important as the ingredient, is the proportion which is used, but the fact that alternatives are expensive may well explain why they are not more common.

DEA (diethanolamine), TEA (triethanolamine), MEA (monoethanolomine): used as a solvent, emulsifier and detergent, found in foaming products like shampoos, soaps and bubble baths, to thicken and clean. They react with nitrites to form carcinogenic nitrosamines, DEA and MEA being considered the most dangerous in this respect. There is some evidence of them being carcinogenic and that when absorbed through the skin may accumulate, for example, in the brain.

Synthetic paraben preservatives (Alkyl hydroxy benzoates): i.e. methylparaben, ethylparaben, butylparaben and propylparaben, found in an estimated 90+% of all cosmetic and bodycare products. Synthetic methyl, ethyl and propyl parabens kill all bacteria and halt enzyme activity, ensuring that creams don't go rancid and mouldy. They have reportedly been found in cancerous tumours, particularly in breast tissue. While some commentators argue that the problem is the way they halt enzyme activity both on the skin, and in the body when absorbed, upsetting the body's normal processes, others focus on the way the ingredients mimic oestrogen. It has been suggested that parabens absorbed through the skin of pregnant women may act as an alien female hormone, resulting in later fertility problems for any male baby subject to them.

Phenylmercuric acetate: a preservative found for example in soap-free cleansers and antiseptic sprays. It is also referred to as mercurochrome, merthiolate, sodium ethylmercurithiosalicylate, thimerosalate, thiomersosal, merzonin, mertogan and more. It is used as a preservative as well as a fungicide, herbicide and to avoid slime in swimming pools.

Petroleum based products: while the US's CIR panel rates these ingredients as safe cosmetic ingredients, The Dictionary of Cosmetic Ingredients comments, "many petroleum products are reported to be cancer-causing ingredients. Others, presumably those used on food, are inert." It is reported that the thinner the oil the higher the levels of volatile hydrocarbons, including carcinogenic ones. One commonly used material is Petrolatum, also known as mineral oil jelly, liquid Vaseline, paraffinum liquidum and baby oil, which some reports say can cause photosensitivity, making skin more prone to damage from the sun. There is much debate over the idea that the oil clogs pores.

Isopropyl alcohol: isopropanol is used in shampoo as well as paint thinner and antifreeze. Methanol is found in antifreeze as well as cosmetics. Others are butanol, ethanol and the terms propyl, methyl, butyl, benzene, toluene, xylene, and styrene also indicate membership of the family. The potential problem is neurological damage because of attraction to the lipid layer surrounding the cells and nerves where the chemical apparently interferes with the messenger proteins that send information to the cells.

Fragrances: 95% of these are made from synthetics with as many as 600 or more raw materials and chemicals in each formulation, though there is no requirement to reveal these. Apparently 80% of these have never been tested for toxicity although on a list of around 3,000 almost a third are recognised as toxic by the US National Institute of Occupational Safety and Health. The US FDA notes that adverse reactions to fragrances are increasing, involving the immune system and neurotoxic reactions. Although there are stern warnings about the dangers of individual aromatherapy oils, their less complex composition is felt by some, including the authors of the Safe Shoppers Guide, to be less likely to cause this kind of problem and these and herb extracts are useful alternatives as perfumes. A particular issue is phalates, which are found in synthetic fragrances. The EU has just banned phalates although they are still permitted in the US. In tests by WEN (Women's Environmental Network) it was discovered that even where a producer believes they have been eliminated, they may be found to have contaminated raw ingredients and found their way into the end product. Phalates can harm reproductive capacity and foetal development, and in one US study women aged 20 to 40 appeared to receive the highest exposure: up to 20 times the average.

'Natural' products: it is estimated that 60% of lanolin (excluding that which is organically produced) is contaminated with organochlorine pesticides. Plant extracts which will retain elements of any pesticides and herbicides used in their cultivation can similarly be problematic. If you choose to eat organic food and use bodycare products containing herbs and essential oils, you may want to consider buying only organically certified ranges.

How to choose a safe product

If you are seriously concerned with this issue, invest in one of the books detailed under Reading. You don't stand much chance of making head or tail of things without one because as Samuel Epstein comments 'the list of names you see on the back are absolutely meaningless to 99.9% of toxicologists and chemists. You have to have highly specialised expertise to be able to evaluate cosmetic labels.' Even the term 'plant-based' is no guarantee of safety, a potential toxin from a plant source is still a potential toxin.

He notes that in addition to problematic ingredients, there is the problem of harmless ingredients which can break down to free carcinogens or interact with others to produce carcinogens, and finally, there may be contamination by carcinogens.

Although EC legislation requires that all ingredients should be detailed on labels using their official names as stipulated by INCI (International Nomenclature of Cosmetic Ingredients), this does not appear to be adhered to by all suppliers. The aim of the rule is to prevent manufacturers from hiding the exact nature of their ingredients. However, the system has the disadvantage that ingredients which are natural also sound like dubious chemicals. Green People cites Decyl Glucoside, a foaming agent derived from corn, and cetearyl alcohol, not alcohol at all but an emulsifier in the form of fatty waxes derived from plant oils.

Given the difficulties of interpreting the ingredients list, the rough rule of thumb seems to be to go for items with the fewest ingredients, and fragrance free except for scents from herbal or essential oil ingredients. The words 'natural', 'pure', 'hypoallergenic', 'plant-based', 'organic' (unless certified by a reputable organisation), 'green', 'healing', 'earth-friendly' and the like have no firm or reliable meaning and cannot be taken as a marker of quality. There could be less than 1% of the 'natural' ingredients advertised in anything which uses the word on the label.

However reputable the manufacturer, contamination in the supply, processing and packaging can never be ruled out. Plastics are a particular source of concern as they can leach chemicals such as phalates. Reputable suppliers ensure that at least the plastic in which their products are supplied will not do this and ideally use inert material such as glass.

A supplier who is transparent about ingredients and happy to discuss the product and the role of the different ingredients, including any herbs or essential oils, is the ideal. Most of those listed here provide a lot of information on their web sites and in their catalogues. Ultimately, though, how confident you feel about the safety of these products is a question of trust.

FURTHER INFORMATION
Friends of the Earth, ☎ *Information service (0808) 800 1111, HQ (020) 7490 1555* ⏚ *www.foe.co.uk/safer_chemicals*
The group produces a Parents' Guide to Safer Chemicals in a fold-out set of cards, produced in association with the NCT. Copies are available from the Information Team. The guide includes a section on toiletries, plus information on other chemicals to watch out for.

3. BRANDS (AND STOCKISTS)

I have obtained lists of ingredients from all the brands included here. To the best of my knowledge they are among the safest around. I have noted the occasional use of ingredients which might be considered less desirable in ranges which I feel are otherwise good. In addition to those mentioned here, see also suppliers listed under Aromatherapy in chapter *4.02 Complementary medicine & Health practitoners*, a number of which offer not only the oils on their own but also mixtures appropriate for use in pregnancy or with babies.

(As well as brands, the listing below also includes one or two of the better stockists.)

Barefoot Botanicals
282 St Paul's Rd London N1 2LH ☎ *(0870) 220 2273* ⏚ *www.barefootuk.com*
Products include head lice lotions, natural first aid spray called Kiss It Better with witch hazel, aloe vera, calendula, St John's Wort, yarrow, nettles, echinacea and comfrey, propolis and lavender, eczema and psoriasis cream, suitable from three months. The Rosa Fina range is designed to tone and firm and is reported to prevent stretchmarks for example; the SOS range is for dry skin; Skin Rescue Cream is suggested for babies from three months.

Dr Hauschka Skin Care
Elysia Natural Skin Care, Unit 27, Stockwood Business Park, Stockwood, Redditch Worcs B96 6SX ☎ *(01386) 792622* ⏚ *www.drhauschka.co.uk (skin care only)*
Organically-produced skincare (and sun protection) products in the Dr Hauschka range, one of the few found free of phalates in tests by WEN. Elysia also stock a limited number of products from the Lindos Baby Care range which is free of artificial additives, preservatives and colourants. / *HOURS Mon-Fri 9am-5:30pm; SEE ALSO 2.05 Travel.*

Farmacia
169 Drury Lane London WC2B 5QA ☎ *(020) 7404 8808* ⏚ *www.farmacia123.com*
Friendly, central London 'integrated health centre': complementary health clinic, pharmacy and shop. Products stocked include Lavera baby products, Baby Bee, Dr Hauschka, Burt's Bees, and Jurlique organic products, pregnancy-safe nail polishes and many more; also an own-brand range of aromatherapy oils, beauty products and herbal remedies. / *HOURS Mon-Fri 9am-7pm, Sat 10.30am-5.30pm; SEE ALSO 4.02 Health practitioners.*

Forever Living Products
Independent Distributor: 68 Badminton Rd London SW12 8BL ☎ *(020) 8626 9540 (24 hours)*
The world's largest grower and distributor of aloe vera products, marketed

worldwide by a network of direct marketing agents; the range extends from health drinks to personal care products (and can be excellent for – amongst other things – burns, sore skin and eczema). Free catalogue; 60-day money back guarantee. One or two products contain methylparabens. / HOURS 24hr answerphone; SEE ALSO 2.05 Travel.

Green Baby

345 Upper St London N1 0PD ☎ *(020) 7359 7037* ⌂ *www.greenbabyco.com*
Environmentally-friendly toiletries and massage oils. / HOURS Mon-Sat 10am-5pm; SEE ALSO *3.02 Baby equipment; 3.03 Nursery decor; 3.04 Baby clothes; 3.08 Nappies; 3.10 Naming gifts.*

Green People Company

Brighton Rd, Handcross West Sussex RH17 6BZ ☎ *(01444) 401444*
⌂ *www.greenpeople.co.uk; www.organicbabies.com*
Founded by a mother with a nursing background, knowledge of herbal medicine, and 11 years' experience in the pharmaceutical industry. The company is committed to good environmental practice and where possible uses organically-grown herbs and plants, and in all cases avoids petrochemicals, animal derivatives, synthetic additives, artificial perfumes or colours. The brochure gives full details of ingredients. The Happy Kids range includes talc-free baby powder, lotion (moisturiser), baby oil, nappy balm, baby milk bath and more, including sunscreen for older babies.

Greenfibres

99 High St Totnes TQ9 5PF ☎ *(01803) 868001* ⌂ *www.greenfibres.com*
Sells Tautropfen (dewdrop) Demeter certified bodycare products imported from Germany from the first certified biodynamic manufacturer of skin and hair care products worldwide. All ingredients used are derived from organic agriculture and approximately 90% are Demeter certified; processing is by sun-infusion, believed to transfer the active plant ingredients to the oil; there is a baby oil with calendula, chamomile and lavender, children's oil with chamomile, lavender, olive oil, St John's Wort, fennel and caraway, plus a baby cream with calendula, lavender and

chamomile and beeswax, as well as base oil, recommended for nappy rash. / *HOURS Mon-Sat 10am-5pm; mail order Mon-Fri 10am-5.30pm, or answerphone; SEE ALSO 3.02 Baby equipment; 3.03 Nursery decor; 3.04 Baby clothes; 3.06 Toys.*

House of Mistry
*15-17 South End Road, Hampstead Heath London NW3 2PT ☎ (020) 7794 0848
⁂ www.mistry.co.uk*
A range produced by an Indian chemist who has lived in London for 30 years, including shampoos and soaps (many using Neem oil), a product reported anti-bacterial, an anti-viral, a fungicide, an insect repellent and a treatment of head lice. Other products include a range of organic baby products, most with calendula.

Jurlique
The Naturopathic Health & Beauty Co Ltd, Willow Tree Marina, West Quay Drive, Yeading Middlesex UB4 9TB ☎ (0870) 770 0980 ⁂ www.jurlique.com.au
Founded by a biochemist and naturopath, a babycare range prompted by his daughter's pregnancy. It includes washing, massage and barrier products for the baby, plus products for foot and leg care, for massage during labour, and for cracked nipples. The company grows its plant ingredients in Australia with organic certification, though some of the formulations would not be accepted as organic under UK Soil Association standards; ingredients include sodium lauryl sulphate (in concentrations of under 10%), but in some products, for example baby shampoo and body wash, substitutes sodium lauroyl sarcosinate. / *HOURS Mon-Fri 9am-5pm; SEE ALSO 4.02 Health practitioners.*

La Spiezia Organic Care
The Barn Workshop, Rosuick Farm, St Martin, Helston Cornwall TR12 6DZ ☎ (01326) 231 600 ⁂ www.spieziaorganics.com
One of the purest ranges on the market (and all Soil Association accredited). It includes a baby cream with olive oil, beeswax, wheatgerm oil, camomile, lavender and St John's Wort, for dry skin and nappy rash, and baby oil with almond oil, olive oil, camomile and lavender for soothing the skin all over. The adult range should be suitable in pregnancy and includes an anti-stretchmark cream, foot balm, skin care and bath oils.

Lavera
*PO Box 7466, Castle Douglas Dumfries & Galloway DG7 2YD ☎ (01557) 814 941
⁂ www.lavera.co.uk*
A German brand, the baby products containing only vegetable oils and extracts from organic agriculture; products include baby and child almond cream, shampoo, bath oil and skin oil; also toothpaste, all containing natural plant oils; stocked by Farmacia and the Organic Pharmacy.

Living Nature
Gardeners Business Park Sherfield English Lane, Plaitford Hants SO51 6EJ ☎ (01794) 323 222 ⁂ www.livingnature.com
A range which guarantees no herbicide or pesticide residues, no artificial preservatives or foaming agents and is made from wildcrafted plants of New Zealand; good for babies – calendula oil, lavender baby massage balm, manuka oil and honey gel (designed to soothe the skin including nappy rash, grazes and cuts), soothing evening primrose and honey gel (to nourish the skin, recommended for eczema); also head lice products, honey soap (suitable for babies), an eczema relief pack, and products for treating thrush and candida; also sunscreens with titanium dioxide. Beautiful Belly Oil is designed for use in pregnancy; commended by WEN for absence of phalates in products. The Beautiful Baby Pack costs £24.50. / *SEE ALSO 4.02 Health practitioners.*

Liz Earle
PO Box 50, Ryde Isle Of Wight PO33 2YD ☎ (01983) 813 913, Customer care (01983) 813 999 ⁂ www.lizearle.com
A range using food grade preservatives at the lowest levels felt safe, and planning some preservative free products. In pregnancy recommends the Daily Skin Smoother with Vitamin E for stretchmarks; for babies Orange Flower Botanical Body Wash as a mild cleanser because the foaming agent is plant derived; for mobile babies, Sunshade SPF 15 and 24 made from pure titanium dioxide ground into small particles to avoid the usual white cream look, zinc oxide, again powdered, and plant based melanin, plus green tea, pomegranate, vitamin E as antioxidants.

Mother Earth
*Birkrow Farm Cottage, Blawith, Nr Ulverston Cumbria LA12 8EG ☎ (01229) 885 266
⁂ www.motherearth.co.uk*
A range of products including chamomile and oat soothing bodywash in a muslin bag (to be hung on the taps for the water to run through and ease itchy skin), baby

& kids massage oil, tangerine children's oil, and lavender and calendula cream. Also soaps (one called Dewdrop recommended for kids with skin problems) made in small batches from natural ingredients with no artificial preservatives.

Neal's Yard Remedies

General enquiries
☎ (0845) 262 3145
15 Neals Yard WC2H 9DP
☎ (020) 7379 7222
9 Elgin Crescent W11 2JA
☎ (020) 7727 3998
Chelsea Farmers Market, Sydney St SW3 6NR
☎ (020) 7351 6380
68 Chalk Farm Rd NW1 8AN
☎ (020) 7284 2039
15 King St TW9 1ND
☎ (020) 8948 9248
32 Blackheath Village SE3 9SY
☎ (020) 8318 6655
6 Northcote Rd SW11 1NT
☎ (020) 7223 7141

A range of babycare products. While some are Soil Association accredited, others would appear to contain ingredients which would make such accreditation unattainable. / *HOURS mostly Mon-Fri 9.30am-5.30pm, Sun noon-4pm; SEE ALSO 2.06 Baby & toddler activities; 4.02 Health practitioners.*

NHR Organic Oils UK

5 College Terrace Brighton BN2 0EE ☎ (0845) 3108066 ⟳ *www.nhr.kz*
Organic bodycare products, including children's marigold shampoo, moisturising lotion (apricot kernel oil, vegetable glycerin, African shea nut butter, cetylic alcohol, palm oil and chamomile), and marigold soap (just coconut oil and marigold extract). Also children's toothpaste and sun tan lotion for children with plant-based sunscreen. / *SEE ALSO 4.02 Health practitioners.*

Organic Soap Company

23 Farquar Road, Upper Norwood London SE19 1SS ☎ (020) 8488 2469
Soaps manufactured with coconut, palm and olive oil, plus calendula, sesame and hemp seed oils, and some with cocoa butter; various herbs and spices are variously used. The baby soap has none of the extras but is 'superfatted' with almond oil.

The Organic Pharmacy

396 Kings Rd London SW10 0LN ☎ (020) 7351 2232
⟳ *www.TheOrganicPharmacy.com*
A complementary pharmacy run by the mother of two small children. It offers a range of skin and beauty products prepared by homeopathic pharmacists without artificial preservatives, mineral oils or petrochemical derivatives, artificial colours or fragrances. The range includes massage baby oil, bath oil, nappy balm and milk bath, plus a stretchmark oil for pregnancy. In addition stock ranges from Living Nature, Paul Penders, Aubrey Organics (including a baby and Kids range), Beauty and the bees (including skin cream for mother and products for babies), plus the Lavera and Logona ranges (see also). / *SEE ALSO 4.02 Health practitioners.*

Verde

General enquiries
☎ *Mail order & advice line (020) 7720 1100, Office (020) 7720 1122*
3 Princes Close, Old Town SW4 0LQ
☎ *Mail order & advice line (020) 7720 1100, Office (020) 7720 1122*
15 Flask Walk NW3 3HG
☎ (020) 7431 3314
75 Northcote Rd SW11 6PJ
☎ (020) 7223 2095

Products with only food grade preservatives where necessary, ie in gels and creams; relevant products are chamomile baby body balm with myrrh, chamomile, lavender and calendula, reported anti-fungal and anti-viral and antiseptic, or baby soothing nourishing cream with calendula, geranium and sandalwood, useful for skin problems; also stretchmark oil with wheatgerm, almond, apricot, Moroccan rose and neroli oils, jojoba, avocado and vitamin E, benzoin, sandalwood and geranium to feed the skin, and ease itching. Also does a lice repellant spray. / *HOURS Mon-Sat 10am-6pm (SW11 opens at 9.30am), Sun noon-6pm (NW3 only); SEE ALSO 2.03 Baby health; 4.02 Health practitioners.*

Catherine Walker
65 Sydney Street, London SW3, and 46 Fulham Rd London SW6 ☎ (020) 7352 4626
A "completely natural" skin care range produced by the dress designer who has recovered from cancer. It includes Centella Refining and Toning Body Lotion (wounded tigers are said to heal themselves by rolling in Centalla Asiatica), orange flower serum for the face, White Tea Day Moisturiser with olive and sunflower oils plus extract of white tea buds (apparently a source of antioxidant polyphenols), and Lemon Balm Mild Cleansing Gel.

Weleda
Heanor Rd, Ilkeston Derbyshire DE7 8DR ☎ (0115) 944 8200 ⌂ www.weleda.co.uk
Producers of calendula babycare products, from baby lotion and baby oil to soap and nappy change cream (which, in the author's experience, is the very best barrier cream). The range does not include any synthetic substances (fragrances, colouring, preservatives, mineral oil derivatives) and is fragranced with pure essential oils; although using plants and herbs for example grown to exacting Demeter standards, the organisation believes it would be misleading to call is range organic because, to ensure purity, ingredients like lanolin and vegetable and nut oils, are refined to medical grade. / *HOURS Mon-Fri: 9am-5pm ; SEE ALSO 2.03 Baby health; 4.02 Health practitioners.*

Washing powders

Big brand biological washing powders and fabric conditioners use some very powerful detergents and other chemicals. There is widespread concern that use of these powders on a baby's clothes can provoke skin reactions, so many parents opt for more gentle powders.

There are some big-name non-biological brands – Fairy non-biological for example – with more specialist names including Dreft, Surcare or the environmentally-friendly Ecover.

Alternatively there are organic suppliers: Jurilique produces Gentle; and ACDO (available from Astley Dye & Chemical Co Ltd) is a clothes detergent for sensitive skins, but it is designed for use with soft water (and therefore requires the addition of a water softener in London).

WASHING POWDERS
Acdo Co
Imperial Works, Mallison St, Astley Bridge, BL1 8PP ☎ (01204) 600500 ⌂ www.acdo.co.uk
A non-biological, enzyme-free washing powder made from pure vegetable oils; available by mail order; prices from £19 for 4 x 1-kilogram boxes.

Jurlique
The Naturopathic Health & Beauty Co Ltd, Willow Tree Marina, West Quay Drive, Yeading Middlesex UB4 9TB ☎ (0870) 770 0980 ⌂ www.jurlique.com.au
The Gentle Fabric Wash is a natural alternative for washing baby clothes, £13 for 500ml.

CHAPTER 3.10

NAMING GIFTS

Indexes in this section refer to chapter 3.14 Shopping directory.

It is of course traditional to greet the arrival of a new baby with gifts. Many – probably the majority – of the suppliers listed in the shopping directory offer something suitable. The suppliers listed below are those whose ranges are particularly targeted, with an emphasis on personalised and pricier items.

Alternatively, and refraining here from naming any particular names, big sports clubs generally sell a range of children's items for newborns upwards, including in some cases even bottles. Perhaps more useful for a genuine fan though is to get the child's name down for club membership.

Index of stockists

Central
Asprey *(W1)*
Brora *(W1)*
The Illustration Cupboard *(W1)*
Kit Heath *(WC2)*
Mason Pearson Bros *(W1)*
Peter Rabbit & Friends *(WC2)*
Salvatore Ferragamo *(W1)*
Tartine et Chocolat *(W1)*
Tiffany & Co *(W1)*

West
Babylist *(SW6)*
Brora *(SW3, W11)*
Couverture *(SW3)*
Natural Mat Co *(W11)*
Nina Campbell *(SW3)*

North
Baby Concierge *(NW4)*
Cuddle Pie *(N2)*
Green Baby *(N1)*
London Zoo *(NW1)*
Mayfair Embroidery *(NW1)*
Mini Kin *(N8)*
Purple Heart *(NW6)*

South
Art for Children *(SW8)*
Artemidorus *(SE24)*
La Conception *(SW11)*

Mail order
Asprey
Astrokidz
Babies Island

Babies Wishworld
Baby Babble
Baby Concierge
Baby Gem
Baby Treasures
Babylist
Bearing Gifts
Billie Bond
Bonne Nuit
Born Gifted
Boxtot
Braybrook & Britten
Brora
Cameron Gift Co
Celebration
Charlotte's Cot Blankets
Couverture
Cuddle Pie
Cuddlies Direct
Enfant
Equinox
Gigglycat
Glevum Bears
Green Baby
Heirlooms UK
International Star Registry
International Tree Foundation
Kit Heath
Letterbox
Life Memories Box Co
Little Badger
Little Laurels
London Zoo
Made By Marian
Mason Pearson Bros
Mavis Klein

Mayfair Embroidery
Melting Hearts
Mini Kin
Nappy Cakes UK
The National Forest Co
Natural Mat Co
Natures Cocoons
Nursery Times
One Fine Day
Peter Rabbit & Friends
Petra Boase
Plate, Rattle & Bowl
Purple Heart

Roomers
Scrumptious Design
Silk Story
Silver Editions
Stork Express
Tales from the Earth
Tartine et Chocolat
Tiffany & Co
Toys for Children
The Woodland Trust
Yorkshire Dales Millenium
   Trust

CHAPTER 3.11

HAIRDRESSERS

Indexes in this section refer to chapter 3.14 Shopping directory.

It can come as something of an emotional wrench to trim those burgeoning curls, but eventually the sublime begins to approach the ridiculous and it's time for your toddler's first haircut.

You may be willing to grab a pair of scissors and to have a go yourself, or your own regular hairdresser may be willing to cut your toddler's hair. There is some art in lopping the locks from a wriggling, uncooperative child, however, and enough specialists exist to suggest that a fair number of parents feel it is worth the investment. Many of these try to make an event out of a first haircut, providing a certificate or a lock of hair.

A few toddlers absolutely loathe having their hair cut. Some parents press on with what can be an upsetting experience (and quite a dangerous one for all involved). The answer for other parents is to give up on the professionals and to adopt Delilah's strategy with Samson.

Hairdressers

Central
  Harrods *(SW1)*

West
  Beauty Tree *(SW6)*
  Cosmos Hair & Beauty
    Salon *(W4)*
  Daisy & Tom *(SW3)*
  Hairloom *(SW6)*
  Headways *(W4)*
  The Little Trading Co *(W4)*
  Patricia *(W4)*
  Snips *(W13)*
  Tops *(W4)*
  Trotters *(SW3, W8)*

North
  Mini Kin *(N8)*
  Trotters *(NW4)*

South
  Angela Conway *(SW4)*
  Headmaster *(SW19)*
  Little Willies *(SW4)*
  SW4 *(SW4)*
  Swallows & Amazons *(SW12)*

Mail order
  Daisy & Tom
  Mini Kin
  Trotters

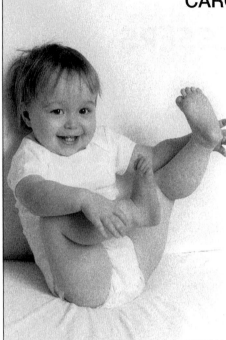

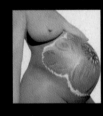
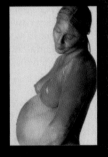

CHAPTER 3.12

PORTRAITS & PHOTOGRAPHS

1. **Photographers**
2. **Artists**
3. **Taking your own photos**
4. **Castings & imprints**

Forgetting what your baby looked like just a month, let alone six months ago appears to be a universal problem: they change so quickly.

Pictures and videos are the obvious way to immortalise the different stages of your baby's life and growth into childhood. Not everyone is content with their own efforts, however, in which case it may be time to call in the professionals…

1. PHOTOGRAPHERS

The cost of premises means high street portrait studios are dying out, though some survive. If you haven't seen one you like near you, the Yellow Pages and Thomsons Directory have listings under Photographers General. These generally include details of photographers who have transferred their studios to home, plus those who work on location. Alternatively you could contact one of the professional organisations:

Before picking a photographer it is a good idea to ring at least three to get more of an idea of whether they are suitable for what you want. They may have a card of sample shots, sample pictures on a web site, or may be willing to arrange an appointment to view their portfolio.

USEFUL CONTACTS

Babyweb
⌁ www.babyweb.co.uk
This company offers website space that enables friends and relatives to see pictures or movie clips of your children; the set-up charge of £50 includes up to 12 pictures, with an additional 12 pictures costing a further £50. Your site can be set up within a week (contact them on info@babyweb.co.uk).

The British Institute of Professional Photography (BIPP)
Fox Talbot House, Amwell End, Ware Herts SG12 9HN ☎ *(01920) 4640111*
⌁ www.bipp.com
Professional photographic qualifying association offering a list of local photographers by phone, post and on the website. / HOURS *Mon-Fri 9am-5.30pm.*

The Master Photographers Association
Hallmark House, 1 Chancery Lane, Darlington Co Durham DL1 5QP ☎ *(01325) 356555* ⌁ *www.mpauk.com*
An association of professional photographers with around 80 members in London, most of whom operate the Cherubs programme. This scheme offers a no-sitting-fee discount deal on a series of photographs of your child, taken at 4, 8 and 12 months. Call for a list of local members. / HOURS *Mon-fri 9am-5pm.*

The Society of Wedding & Portrait Photographers
6 Bath Street Rhyl Denbigh LL18 3EB ☎ *(01745) 356935* ⌁ *www.swpp.co.uk*
Professional trade body – the website includes links to members. / HOURS *Mon-Fri 9am-5pm.*

MAKING A BOOKING

When arranging a sitting you should discuss in advance:

➢ How much experience the photographer has of working with children the age of yours and if they operate any age limits. Some won't deal with under-5s because of the extra work. It can be a good idea to look for someone with children of their own.

➢ Whether the session will take place at home, in the studio or on location – say a local park. If at home, will any specific set-up be required and do they include discussion time and/or an inspection visit in the price.

➢ When and how long the session will be.

➢ What style of shot you would like (an example, say from a magazine, might be useful).

➢ Whether the shots will be in black and white or colour.

➢ Whether the photographs will be posed or action shots.

➢ What happens if the baby is unhappy (will the photographer wait or return).

➢ What the child should wear.

➢ Whether they will require a toy.

➢ Who will be expected to handle the baby.

➢ A copy of the photographer's terms and conditions for you to read at leisure before going ahead.

The photographers listed below are either specialists in child and family photography or offer a particular style of photography which may appeal to parents. They cover all London unless otherwise indicated.

Experienced photographers recommend only organising sittings in the morning and avoiding times when the baby is likely to be hungry or up to three days after vaccinations as these are times that children are likely to be grizzly.

Pricing is subject to no general rules and may include some of the following: sitting; film, contacts and prints (often pricier for colour, especially if the black and white is hand printed); a studio session (usually more expensive); home (usually cheaper); or on location. You should check if there are separate charges for any of the above.

Particularly at the cheaper end of the market, photographers often offer special deals. An example would be a 'granny pack' of four 7ins x 5ins prints. It is worth asking what is currently available. Photographers customarily retain the negatives.

(Note that group photography sessions normally involve the photographer offering a percentage fee either to the organising establishment or group. This is sometimes treated as a method of fund-raising for charity.)

SPECIALIST PHOTOGRAPHERS

Alice Auster-Rhodes
☎ (07798) 867 994
Black and white and colour photography from a Royal College of Art MA, who has worked in the V&A and at Saatchi Collection. Offers a contemporary, classic portraiture or creative documentary style, shot at home or in a studio.

Michael Bassett Photography
Unit S5 Shakespeare Business Centre, 10 Leamington Ave, Bromley Kenton BR1 5BL
☎ (020) 8860 9391   ✎ www.michaelbassett.co.uk
Mainly black and white – some colour and sepia work – in your home or on location. Prices from £180 + prints.

Bibby
London SW15 1BN ☎ *(020) 8788 7702*
Children and families, action and posed, black and white and colour, shots in your home, studio or on location.

Beverley Byrd Photography
14 Clarendon Gardens London W9 1AY ☎ *(020) 7286 5071*
Colour or black and white, on location or at your home; babies from six months up.
/ HOURS 24hr answerphone.

Candice Photography
The Studio, 1 Sunnyhill Rd London SW16 2UG ☎ *(020) 7787 9396*
⌁ www.candice.co.uk
Photographers who aim to catch children's personality in relaxed images. They expect to spend time getting to know the child and will photograph in your house, garden or a local park; black and white or colour; the website has a gallery of pictures. */ HOURS 24hr answerphone.*

Ann Charles Photography
Professional Photography Dept, PO Box 9755 London SW16 2ZE ☎ *(020) 8769 2950,*
mobile (07860) 407803 ⌁ www.acp-photos.co.uk
Photographic sessions for groups of 25 to 100, run by a team of two, allowing up to 15 minutes per child. Range of colour and B&W packages. Also home-sittings: £150 for 36 prints (6ins x 4ins).

David Chesner Studios
230 Golders Green Rd London NW11 9AT ☎ *(020) 8905 5665*
Thirty year-old business specialising in families and children (and weddings) – operates from the studio. */ HOURS Mon-Thu 10am-5pm, Sun by appointment.*

Pauline Cutler
7 Plum Lane, Plumstead London SE18 3AF ☎ *(020) 8854 1606*
🖰 *www.hollyblue.co.uk/PaulineCutler; www.paulinecutler.co.uk*
Sittings at the photographer's home, clients home or on location – relaxed or formal poses. Lots of fun pictures with children, families and pregnant women; black and white or colour. / *HOURS 24hr answerphone.*

Elaine Morris
☎ *(01273) 203932, (07905) 746 717*
Children's photographer offering documentary-style shots in colour and b&w.

Embody
☎ *07803 121923* 🖰 *www.embody.org.uk*
Why wait till your child is born to celebrate their presence – make-up artist and freelance body painter Julia Laderman specialises in transforming women's bumps into works of art; judging by the testimonials on her website, it's quite relaxing and empowering too.

Ewe & Us Studio
34 Darby Crescent, Lower Sunbury Middlesex TW16 5LA ☎ *(01932) 785533*
Relaxed family photographic business specialising in children; studio or clients home; very child-friendly – lots of toys; black and white or colour. / *HOURS Mon-Fri 9.30am-6pm.*

Robin Farquhar-Thomson
Battersea Park London ☎ *(020) 7622 3630* 🖰 *www.robinft.co.uk*
'Unique style' of photography; sittings done in your home; b&w prints on exhibition quality paper; samples of work on website.

Desi Fontaine Studios
60-62 Archway St London SW13 0AR ☎ *(020) 8878 4348* 🖰 *www.desifontaine.co.uk*
Portraiture from award-winning female photographer of babies, mothers and babies, pregnancy shoots and complete families, in the studio or on location in London. Make-up artist available. / *HOURS by appointment.*

Richard Greenly Photography
8-9 Charnham Lane, Hungerford Berks RG17 0EY ☎ *(01488) 685256*
Natural and informal photographs, largely black and white, in your home. Hand-colouring and framing available. Also offers Christmas cards, montage prints, etc. Prices on application. / *HOURS Mon-Fri 8.30am-5pm.*

Heather Ruddy
22 Palliser Road, Barons Court London W14 9EE ☎ *(0781) 386 5958*
Intimate photographs which are shot close up, to produce a "tonally landscaped image", printed slightly larger than life, hand printed on museum quality paper and hand mounted and signed with the child's name and date. Frames are sanded, dyed and waxed by hand.

Cato James
Belsize Park ☎ *(020) 7916 9461*
Studio, b&w portrait photography.

James Bignell
☎ *(01737) 559 588*
Natural portraits, in b&w or colour.

Jim Stagg
Mulberry House, Winterlane West Hanney OX12 0LF ☎ *(01235) 867 500*
B&w photography in a variety of styles. / *HOURS by appointment.*

Jojo
☎ *(07932) 023 221* 🖰 *www.jojoandco.com*
London-based photographer willing to travel across the UK, offering natural, hand-finished b&w portraits – no posed or studio shots.

Kate Magson
120 St Stephens Ave London W12 8JD ☎ *Kate (07941) 688 012, Cliff (07956) 897 302* 🖰 *www.kiddipics.com*
Natural photography of children, b&w, studio, at home or in the location of your choice.

Richard Kerber
1454 High Rd London N20 9BS ☎ *(020) 8445 4105*
🖰 *www.richardkerberphotography.co.uk, www.babycherubs.com*
Studio-based portraitist with variety of styles. Frequent special offers for baby portraits.

Majken Kruse

Wimbledon London SW19 ☎ *(020) 8944 7975* ⏎ *www.majkens.co.uk*
Female photographer who specialises in photographing children in colour or black and white; prefers natural light; sample work can be viewed on the website.

Lupe Cunha Photography

The Studio Herts EN7 5NJ ☎ *(07071) 225351* ⏎ *www.lupecunha.com*
Woman photographer, offering studio (in Finchley), location and home photographs (the last with studio lighting) of children and families, black and white and colour, with images different from the norm (including digital portraits). £100-£250 price range. / HOURS *Tue-Sat 11am-4pm.*

Marten Collins

R & R House, North Bridge Road, Berkhamstead Herts HP4 1EH ☎ *(01442) 871 010*
⏎ *www.martencollins.co.uk*
Fine art photography, including b&w and home sittings.

Mary Dunkin

☎ *(020) 8969 8043* ⏎ *www.marydunkinphotogrpahy.co.uk*
B&w family photographs.

Mark Mather

London SW4 ☎ *(020) 7622 0796* ⏎ *www.markmather.com*
Professional portrait photographer offering largely black and white shots, either in your home or his studio.

Momins Photography

112 Goodmayes Road, Goodmayes Ilford Essex IG3 9UZ ☎ *(020) 8586 1414*
⏎ *www.mominsphotography.co.uk*
Colour and b&w work, including fantasy portraits (your child as a fairy or as pearl in a shell), plus family portraits; photo sessions including one photo £25; package including six photos £60.

Paper Wings

☎ *(0795) 233 7389* ⏎ *www.paperwings.co.uk*
Digitally-created portraits with your child's image (dressed, say, as a fairy, pixie or flower babe) is placed into an appropriately-themed 'magic' background. / HOURS *by appointment.*

Roberta Ross Studios

28 Mill Street, St Osyth Clacton-on-the-Sea CO16 8EJ ☎ *(01255) 822202*
Studio shots in colour, black and white or sepia from a baby specialist of 20 years standing.

Sam Worwood

☎ *(020) 7254 2900, mobile (07767) 872525* ⏎ *www.samworwood.co.uk*
Working mainly in b&w; the basic charge of £150 covers a shoot at your home, three to four rolls of film presented as contact sheets and an 8"x10" print.

Sarah Doll-Steinberg

☎ *(020) 7722 6976, (07956) 910 297*
Action shots in b&w.

SK Photography

295 Willow Rd, Enfield Middlesex EN1 3BX ☎ *(020) 8367 2233*
⏎ *www.skphotography.co.uk*
Studio, customers home or on location; black and white or colour – examples on website; also nursery groups.

Helen Venables

6 Orchard Cottages, Eaton Road, Tarporley Cheshire CW6 0BP ☎ *(01829) 732512*
⏎ *www.helenvenables.com*
Cheshire-based photographer who commutes to London as necessary. Candid, naturally-lit portraits in black and white or colour in the location of your choice.

Venture

Premier Park, Road One, Winsford Cheshire CW7 3PH ☎ *(01606) 558854*
⏎ *www.thisisventure.co.uk*
"Forget portrait photography. Venture is new. Venture is different. Venture is vibrant, spontaneous images that capture the spirit of life." That's what it says on the website of this national chain of galleries (10 in London) where 'Lifestyle' images in both b&w and colour are manipulated using the latest digital techniques.

Vibeke Dahl Photography
18 Beechwood Ave, Kew Richmond TW9 4DE ☎ *(020) 8876 8113*
📧 *www.dahlphotography.com*
Black and white specialist in studio shots against plain background; will advise on
clothes and on series aimed at capturing different facets of the child; children must be
able to sit up. / HOURS *by appointment.*

Carolyn Weller
London N6 ☎ *(020) 7272 5545* 📧 *www.carolynweller.com*
Predominantly black and white; takes 'studio' to parents home; works mostly in
central and north London.

2. ARTISTS

Commissioning your child's portraits might seem a bit much, but a good
picture can be a lovely keepsake, and the prices charged by some artists
compare well with those of some of the fancier photographers.

Few portraitists will deal with really small children except by photograph, however. If you find that the idea appeals, you might prefer to
wait until your baby is a little older, in order to get the full benefit of the
exercise.

Commissioning

➢ If you want to seek out a rising star, try visiting the annual
summer/autumn show at the National Portrait Gallery (or, to a
lesser extent, the Summer Exhibition at the Royal Academy).

➢ You could contact one of the London art schools where students
might charge £150 for a life-size drawing of a baby and £400 for an
oil, including materials – to help eke out the grant. Some schools
no longer consider figurative drawing or painting important but
those worth approaching are listed below.

➢ If your budget is £20-£40 you could try checking out the street portraitists who do brisk business in the three summer months on
Leicester Square and sometimes outside the National Portrait
Gallery. Though a number can offer no more than a likeness, you
can find skilled people working there who might be interested in a
commission. These may be people interested in experimental art,
working to fund their activities, seasonal visitors from either the
old Eastern Bloc or even parts of Asia, looking to earn better money
than available at home, or sometimes talented artists whose traditional style is out of fashion with art colleges and who are therefore
still struggling for recognition.

USEFUL CONTACTS

Federation of British Artists
17 Carlton House Terrace London SW1Y 5BD ☎ *(020) 7930 6844*
📧 *www.mallgalleries.org.uk*
Child portraits can be commissioned from some of the federation's 40 or so
members. Potential clients can view reference material in the Mall Galleries portrait
commissions room by appointment or material can be sent on loan if necessary.
Prices are from £1,000 for a pencil portrait, from £3,500 for an oil.

The Heatherly School of Fine Art
Upcerne Rd London SW10 0SH ☎ *(020) 7351 4190* 📧 *www.heatherleys.org*
The school can give contact with students who may take commissions. For price
estimates and further details refer to office. / HOURS *Mon-Fri 9.30am-5pm.*

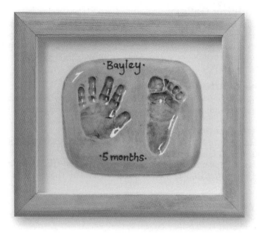

The National Portrait Gallery

St Martin's Place London WC2H 0HE ☎ *(020) 7306 0055 ext 257*
☞ *www.npg.org.uk*

The Heinz Archive & Library's Public Study Room holds a list of over 1,000 artists in their Living Artists files (including many BP award-winners and entrants), with photographs of their work. The list of 'copyists' may also be an interesting place to look for portraitists. Negotiations are made with the artist (or their representative) direct – prices may range from £100 and a couple of pints of Guinness to several thousand pounds. / *HOURS Mon-Fri 10am-5pm.*

The National Portraiture Association

59-60 Fitzjames Ave London W14 0RR ☎ *(020) 7602 0892* ☞ *www.natportrait.com*

Two services are offered by this association, useful to anyone wanting to commission a portrait, but with no idea where to start. The phone advisory service can answer questions, from what to wear to how much it will cost, and can recommend artists, both from its members and non-members. In addition, the website allows you to view past portraits, and gives details of artists and prices. All payments are made through the association, with full refunds if you are not satisfied. Prices for pastel and watercolour portraits start at £195 (for head and shoulders); oils are more expensive (from £495). / *HOURS Telephone advisory service – am only.*

New Academy Gallery

34 Windmill St London W1 2JR ☎ *(020) 7323 4700* ☞ *www.curwengallery.com*

Commissions quite a lot of portraits, including family groups and siblings (and also bronze busts of children): the gallery discusses styles and budget, and shortlists two or three people on their books. / *HOURS Mon-Fri 10am-6pm (Thu 8pm), Sat 11am-5pm, closed bank holidays.*

The New Grafton Gallery

49 Church Rd London SW13 9HH ☎ *(020) 8748 8850* ☞ *www.newgrafton.com*

Gallery in Barnes with a number of commissioning portrait artists on its books.

The Royal Academy Schools

Burlington House, Piccadilly London W1J 0BD ☎ *(020) 7300 8000, Infoline (020) 7300 5760* ☞ *www.royalacademy.org.uk*

The school can put parents in contact with former students specialising in portraiture; ask for the Schools Administrator. / *HOURS Mon-Thurs 10am-6pm, Fri 10am-10pm.*

The Royal Society of Portrait Painters

Federation of British Artists, 17 Carlton House Terrace London SW1Y 5BD ☎ *(020) 7930 6844* ☞ *www.mallgalleries.org.uk*

At the Federation's galleries there is a portrait commissions room with works by the group's 40 artists available to view, and the society operates a commission service free of charge (ask for the Commissions Officer). Prices range from £500 for a pencil portrait and from £1000 for a 16in x 20in oil. Not all portraitists will paint children; some will work from a photograph. / *HOURS gallery 10am-5pm; by appointment only.*

3. TAKING YOUR OWN PHOTOS

If you would prefer to try your hand at taking your own pictures – perhaps monthly, to retain a record of your child's development – you might like to invest in a book on the subject. Note that you may need to be quite snap-happy to get a really good shot (many keen photographers are happy to get a single good shot from a whole roll of film). But even being quite liberal with how much film you use, your costs will still work out considerably less than that of employing someone.

USEFUL CONTACTS

I'm Online

☎ *(0870) 241 9039* ☞ *www.imonline.uk.com*

For £75 a web scrapbook set up using your photos, text, handprints, videos, soundclips, newspaper cuttings and so on. A username and password is provided for you, and you can give access to others by providing their e-mail addresses. A guestbook allows family and friends to leave comments.

Monkey Sites
London SW4 ☎ *(020) 7498 2516* ⏁ *www.monkeysites.co.uk*
Step-by-step instructions for parents wanting to build a website announcing a birth.
Price, including hosting the site, is £5 for members.

Portraitshop
20 Tidlock House, Erebus Drive London SE28 0GD ☎ *(020) 8331 0579*
⏁ *www.portraitshop.net*
Andy Warhol-style pop art portraits from your snaps on surfaces ranging from
organzas and silks to vinyls or canvas (but more usually on standard photographic
paper). Prices start at £35.

READING

Creative Techniques of Photographing Children – Vik Orenstein (Writer's Digest
  Books; 2001; £19.99; 1582970289) – *A specialist title.*

How to Photograph Children – Lisa Jane and Rick Staudt (Secrets for Capturing
  Childhood's Magic Moments; Abbeville Press; 2001; £16.95; 0789206528) –
  Written by two photographers, an illustrated publication whose aim is just as stated.

Photographing Your Children – John Hedgecoe (How to get great photographs
  every time; Collins and Brown; 2000; £14.99; 1855858096)

4. CASTINGS & IMPRINTS

A cast or print of your baby's hands or feet is a way to remember how
small they once were. There are people who make a business out of
this. Alternatively, you can DIY at the burgeoning number of ceramics
cafés, see chapter *2.06 Baby & toddler activities*.

USEFUL CONTACTS

Art 4 Fun
General enquiries
☎ *(020) 8449 6500*

☎ *(020) 8449 6500*
196 Kensington Park Rd W11
☎ *(020) 8959 7373*
444 Chiswick High Rd W4 5TT
☎ *(020) 8994 4100*
172 West End Lane NW6 1SD
☎ *(020) 7794 0800*
212 Fortis Green Rd N10 3DJ
☎ *(020) 8444 4333*
These cafés offer a DIY option for those wanting to create prints in ceramic from
their child's hand or feet. / *HOURS Mon-Sun 10am-10pm; SEE ALSO 2.06 Baby & toddler activities.*

Cast in Time
Studios in Peterborough and Merton Abbey Mills London SW19 ☎ *(01733) 564366*
Castings in solid and plated sterling silver, solid bronze and stone cast (see ad).

Fingers & Toes
45 Green Way, Newton Longville Milton Keynes MK17 0AP ☎ *(01908) 367 365*
⏁ *www.fingersandtoesuk.biz*
Create a mould of children's hands and feet and cast these in bronze or in the
material known as stone. DIY kits and shoe-bronzing is also available.

First Impressions
263 Nether St London N3 1PD ☎ *(020) 8346 8666* ⏁ *www.firstimpressions.org.uk*
Artist Judy Wiseman casts babies' feet (or a mother's or sibling's hands holding the
babies' hands) in glass, solid bronze or silver; the moulds can be taken in the home.
Almost anything can be cast, from a pregnant tummy to a cat's paw. / *HOURS by
appointment.*

Gilian Wood Ceramics
London W4 ☎ *(020) 8995 3638, Mobile (07931) 884673*
Imprints of children's hands and feet in clay (from six weeks old), available as a wall
plaque, paperweight or box-framed. Home visits are available.

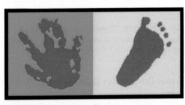

Cast In Time ™

Tasteful, Artistic, Sculptured, Life Casting Designs™

**A gift so special and a love so strong,
a hand to hold when we walk along.
The hugs the kisses, the sweet little smiles,
are part of the bonding between parent and child.
Here's a reminder for all to see,
of a loving you and a sweet little me.**

*Castings undertaken by appointment only at our studio
in Peterborough, or at
Merton Abbey Mills, Wimbledon, London.*

*For bookings or further information on any of our
services or prices, please contact us on:
01733 564 366*

*Your finished sculptures can be created in
Solid & Plated Sterling Silver, Solid Bronze and Stone Cast.*

HappyHands
7 Brockwell Park Row London SW2 2YH ☎ (020) 8671 2020 ⌂ www.happyhands.ws
Hand and foot prints on ceramic tiles; parents take a print using a kit supplied by the company and return it for transfer to a ceramic tile in your choice of colour; basic item with frame £25; also mugs. / *HOURS Mon-Fri 9am-5.30pm; SEE ALSO 2.09 Naming & ceremonies.*

Matthew Harvey
62 Lamcresse Court, De Beauvoir Town London N1 5TG ☎ (020) 7241 4811
Portraits in cement or bronze from photographs and short sittings; can also do oil paintings. / *HOURS 24hr answerphone.*

Image Casting
5 Bushnell Rd London SW17 8QJ ☎ (020) 8673 4029 ⌂ www.imagecasting.co.uk
Hands, feet, busts or faces in resins or metal; prices for babies start from: framed hands and feet £275, framed feet from £175; also paper weights and bronze casts. / *HOURS Mon to Fri 9.30am-6.30pm.*

Imprints
1 Brierley Rd, Balham London SW12 9LY ☎ (020) 8772 0070 ⌂ www.imprints.org
Ceramic children's hand and foot prints, mounted in a hand-finished frame; a hand or foot from £45, two hands or feet from £55. All work is done (including booking and payment) through branches of John Lewis (in the Nursery Department; see the website for your nearest branch). Sample work and price information can be found on the website. / *HOURS Mon-Fri 9am-6pm.*

Little Impressions
7 Bulkington Avenue, Worthing West Sussex BN14 7HH ☎ (01903) 230515 ⌂ www.little-impressions.com
Impressions of hands or feet in plaster, mounted, and framed in oak.

Samantha McEwan
London ☎ (020) 7602 4302
Footprints are pressed (in the home) onto a pale blue oil paint ink pad then placed into the centre of a stretched canvas – the finished product (£200) is about 12ins square; within the first three months is recommended – the tinier the footprint the more impact the final result; similar idea with the thumbprints of all the children in the family. / *HOURS 24hr answerphone.*

Sarah Page Sculpture
Unit 37, Townmead Business Centre, William Morris Way London SW6 2SZ ☎ (020) 7223 8399 ⌂ www.sarahpagesculpture.co.uk
Casting of hands and feet. Polished plaster is from £85, solid bronze from £275, Sterling silver from £600, and lead crystal glass from £350 for a newborn's feet. Plated shoes start from £85 for copper and £95 for silver. Home visits are available, however there is free parking at the Fulham studio. (Work is on display at Lilliput Nursery Stores – see also.)

The Body Cast Studio
38 Radwell Road, Milton Ernest, Bedford Bedfordshire MK44 1SH ☎ (01234) 823 569 ⌂ www.thebodycaststudio.co.uk
Mail order hands and feet home casting kit contains all materials needed to cast and display a baby's hand and foot, or child's single hand using non toxic/allergenic material; £40.

Twinkle Toe Fairy
Home Form, Shipton George, Bridport Dorset DT6 4NA ☎ (01308) 898659 ⌂ www.twinkletoe-fairy.co.uk
Kits to make own framed casts of baby feet, including a keepsafe box.

Unique Sculptures
47 Summerhill, Hedworth JARROW NE32 4RP ☎ (0191) 536 4820 ⌂ www.uniquesculptures.netfirms.com/
Any small object can be copper-plated, and then finished in bright copper or antiqued bronze. Possibilities include baby shoes, baby bottles, dummies, …. All pieces can be supplied on mahogany bases with or without picture frames.

Wrightson & Platt
Unit 42, Broccoli Close, 96 Endwell Rd London SE4 2PD ☎ (020) 7639 9085 ⌂ www.wrightsonandplatt.com
Casts of hands or feet in silver, bronze or glass; a pair of bronze feet from £380, glass from £380 and solid silver from £725 (exclusive of VAT); impressions are taken at your home (travel included within the M25). / *HOURS 24hr brochure request line.*

blue kangaroo

Family Restaurant • Play Centre

WHO ARE YOU, BLUE KANGAROO?

For good food and great atmosphere for you and your kids bounce down to this unique new family restaurant and adventure play centre.

WHAT CAN WE DO, BLUE KANGAROO?

THREE FAB PLAY AREAS

(1) 0-1yr olds - try our brightly coloured soft shapes for some tumbling fun

(2) 2-3yr olds - adventurous slides, nets and activities makes it great fun for your toddler

(3) 4-7yr olds - crawl your way through a maze of seriously fun & challenging slides, nets, tunnels and ladders - plus ball pond!

WHAT CAN WE CHEW, BLUE KANGAROO?

Unwind in our coffee bar downstairs in the play area, providing healthy and nutritious breakfast, lunch and teatime menus for you and your little ones. Or relax in our restaurant whilst keeping an eye on your kids on the big screen specially linked to the play area downstairs and choose a delicious meal made with high quality ingredients!

WE DELIVER EXHAUSTED & HAPPY KIDS TO REFRESHED & RELAXED PARENTS!

WHERE CAN WE SEE YOU BLUE KANGAROO?

555 Kings Road | London SW6 2EB

Nearest Tube: Fulham Broadway | Parking: Pay & Display in surrounding streets
Tel: 020 7371 7622 | Fax: 020 7371 7637
Party Booking Line: 07979 000 832 Evening Venue Hire: 020 7371 7622
E-mail: info@thebluekangaroo.co.uk Web: www.thebluekangaroo.co.uk

Blue Kangaroo is open every day from 9.30am to 8.30pm (excluding Christmas Day and New Year's Day).

Please remember your little ones are your responsibility at all times.

CHAPTER 3.13

BABY-FRIENDLY RESTAURANTS

1. **Introduction**
2. **Listings**

1. INTRODUCTION

The pleasurable activity of eating out often becomes rather less so with the arrival of children. It's easy to choke on your food when seized with anxiety about how other customers are reacting to your child – especially if said child is being a mite 'difficult'.

The British – famously not a nation of child-lovers – are slowly changing their spots when it comes to children in public. Be prepared, though that unless you play utterly safe (restricting your excursions to McDonalds and the like) you won't get far before you encounter some form of mixed reception: a grudging welcome from staff; neighbours who on your arrival request to move to the other side of the room; and service so rapid that the management's motivation appears to be to get you out ASAP. And this is when your child is being good.

Restaurants *are* becoming more kid-friendly, however, and it's worth persevering. If your first experience is awful, try again. There are restaurants that will take a screaming child from you, and cart them off to be entertained by the staff while you enjoy your meal. You just might not have found them yet.

Parents who take their children out from an early age often believe they reap the benefits when their offspring are aged four or five and know how to handle themselves in public. Even very young toddlers can enjoy the experience of being out-and-about, and while eating out with children is not the relaxing experience that it is *à deux*, parents eating as a family can still feel they have some vestiges of a life.

In some ways, eating out is easiest with a very small baby ... so long as they don't wake up. Time your meal to coincide with a sleep, and you can attempt a visit to many places which would be too 'civilised' for a toddler. Even if it can be a little like dining with a time bomb, and may necessitate emergency feeds in a backroom or the car (or the dining room itself, if the staff have the right attitude), you may think it's worth a go. The couple who apparently dined at The Ivy with their child asleep in a carrycot in the cloakroom should inspire us all.

As your child grows older, however, you can probably count on them being awake. The question becomes: "which restaurants are best suited to everyone having as enjoyable a time as possible?" The listings below focus on restaurants that are avowedly child-friendly, while the following offer general pointers:

Go by nationality: Italians are legendarily friendly to children, leading to a sense of betrayal whenever you encounter a less than overwhelmingly enthusiastic welcome (by no means uncommon). Nevertheless, the general rule holds true that some nationalities of restaurant tend to be friendlier than others. Italians, Indians, Chinese and Thai places in particular seem to 'get' the whole kid thing.

Go trendy: 'in yer face' joints often wilfully deviate from what they doubtless see as the stuffy approach of more traditional places: if there are complaints over kids are more prone to side with the parents than those doing the complaining.

Go for places which cater somewhat for children: although possession of a high chair is not an absolute guarantee of infinite tolerance for the tantrums of little precious, it does at least show a degree of willing; even better, kids' menus, specific kids' entertainment and other facilities.

Go for places in parks: whatever the standard of décor, the quality of the food can be surprisingly OK and they are venues naturally suited to kids.

Go for Sunday lunch: restaurateurs and non-parent customers alike recognise that Sunday lunch is a time for families, and that unless children are shockingly behaved they should be encouraged and welcomed.

Go more suburban: restaurants outside the West End are better suited to children because a higher proportion of the customers have kids and the expectation is of a degree of child-friendliness. Think Richmond/Crouch End, rather than Soho/St James's.

Go somewhere themed: the food won't be anything to write home about, but if the theming is well done it may entertain you as well as your child/children.

Go for food on arrival: the joy of anticipation is a concept unknown to kids. Get some/any kind of food to the table fast (even if that means taking it with you). There is always a danger that your child will eat so much bread that your carefully ordered dishes are a waste of money, but that's infinitely better than howling in the meantime.

Go somewhere noisy: any wails will be drowned out.

Go early: places are emptier so there are few other people to irritate, and the kitchen is not so busy so food arrives quicker.

Go prepared: sitting at a table can be a pretty dull experience for under-10s, never mind under-twos. Anticipate this by taking favourite toys, books and games to keep your child occupied. If your child is misbehaving out of boredom in a situation of your own making, you only have yourself to blame.

Above all, go for it

Who says poker-faced child-haters should call the shots when it comes to children eating out?

Few parents would deny that if you have chosen a restaurant where people go for tranquillity and you introduce a child who is being noisy and disruptive it is your responsibility to prevent your child from running amok. The answer is probably not to choose such places.

In less exalted establishments, however, don't always be too apologetic. Is it entirely reasonable for others to feel that children should be seen and not heard? If your child is being a little louder than an adult would be, be sensitive, but don't be abject in your desire to keep another table happy. Parents form a very significant proportion of restaurant-going consumers. Yes, restaurateurs should be expected to worry about keeping all their customers happy, but that includes you too.

Finally, don't be too quick to judge the mood of those around you. It is not unknown for parents to go through a meal desperately worried about the attitude of an adjacent table, to find that on departure what you have perceived to be stony faces crack into doting smiles amidst much cooing directed at your infant.

READING

Harden's London Restaurants – Richard & Peter Harden (Harden's Limited; Annual; £9.99; 1873721587) – *Over 1000 independent restaurant reviews, based on contributions from over 5,000 restaurant-goers. Listings, updated annually, include restaurants with high chairs, children's menus, weekend entertainments and those willing to prepare small portions for children.*

2. LISTINGS

Unless otherwise stated, restaurants listed here are open for lunch and dinner (L & D) every day.

CENTRAL

Abeno
47 Museum St WC1 ☎ (020) 7405 3211
If you're looking for something different (or somewhere to lunch near the British Museum) consider this very friendly Japanese okonomi-yaki – a sort of omelette – restaurant, which is happy to provide children's portions.

Bank
1 Kingsway WC2 ☎ (020) 7234 3344 ⏥ www.bankrestaurants.com
This smart modern British brasserie on the fringe of Covent Garden is spacious and busy enough to swallow up all but the most disruptive families. Sunday brunch is kids' special time, when attractions include a play area, crayons and colouring books. (It's worth asking for the kid's meal, £7.25, at any time, though it only actually appears on the menu at weekends.) 1 ⏥ www.bankrestaurants.com

Chuen Cheng Ku
17 Wardour St W1 ☎ (020) 7437 1398
Best known for its lunchtime dim sum, served from passing trolleys, this Chinatown landmark has highchairs, and welcomes children "at any time".

Giraffe
BRANCHES AT:
VARIOUS
A fast-growing chain of bright and quirky child-friendly cafés, serving healthy, global-style food and juices; ideal for quick snacks or brunch.

Hard Rock Café
150 Old Park Lane W1 ☎ (020) 7629 0382 ⏥ www.hardrock.com
Adults will do well to hear each other, so children's din passes pretty much unnoticed at this famous West End shrine to hamburgers and loud music. Kids form quite a large part of the trade, so they're well catered for, with weekend attractions including magicians.

The Ivy
1 West St WC2 H 9NE ☎ (020) 7836 4751
If you can get a booking – ah!, there's the rub – London's most popular restaurant is perfectly pleased to welcome junior customers. So for a special event, try for a slot at this Theatreland stalwart: weekend (adult) set lunches,in particular, are reasonably priced, and kiddie portions are available at reduced prices.

Pizza On The Park
11 Knightsbridge SW1 ☎ (020) 7235 5273
For a calming place to conclude (or kick off) a trip to Knightsbridge or Hyde Park, you could do very much worse than this large and airy pizzeria (a PizzaExpress in disguise). Crayons and balloons are available at the weekend.

PizzaExpress
⏥ www.pizzaexpress.co.uk
BRANCHES AT:
30 Coptic St WC1 1NS ☎ (020) 7636 3232
154 Victoria St SW1 0HW ☎ (020) 7828 1477

21-22 Barrett St W1 1BD ☎ *(020) 7629 1001*
80-81 St Martins Lane WC2 4AA ☎ *(020) 7836 8001*

London's longest-established major chain is immensely popular with families, and most branches are well-equipped for children. Plain dough balls (not advertised on the menu) can be served to toddlers.

Planet Hollywood

13 Coventry St W1 ☎ *(020) 7287 1000* ⌁ *www.planethollywood.com*

Almost by definition, this large West End theme-restaurant attracts a fairly juvenile crowd, so the good news is that – with its baby-changing facilities, for example – it's pretty well equipped to deal with all ages. They claim to serve over 2000 children a week; kids' menu £7.95.

La Porte des Indes

32 Bryanston St W1 H 7AE ☎ *(020) 7224 0055* ⌁ *www.la-porte-des-indes.com*

This palatial Indian restaurant near Marble Arch gets quite a family following. Though the menu doesn't say so, they're quite happy to do 'English' food (chicken 'n' chips, and the like) on request. A going-home balloon and cartoons at the weekends are further inducements sometimes on offer. / *HOURS closed Sat L.*

Porters

17 Henrietta St WC2 E 8QH ☎ *(020) 7836 6466* ⌁ *www.porters.uk.com*

This spacious, long-established English brasserie isn't in the culinary vanguard, but makes a useful stop-off for families in the vicinity of Covent Garden, complete with baby-changing facilities and a children's menu (£4.95).

The Ritz

150 Piccadilly W1 ☎ *(020) 7493 8181* ⌁ *www.theritzlondon.com*

For a bit of a 'do', why not consider Sunday lunch (or indeed any other meal) at what many people think of as London's most attractive (if certainly not best) dining room? A child-friendly menu (£20) is always available.

Smollensky's

⌁ *www.smollenskys.co.uk*
105 Strand WC2 R 0AA ☎ *(020) 7497 2101* ⌁ *www.smollenskys.co.uk*

On the fringe of Covent Garden, this American diner has long been famous for the efforts it makes to attract the weekend kiddie market, with entertainers and a play area on tap all afternoon. Possibly the largest draw is the more-or-less total absence of non-parents!

Strada

⌁ *www.strada.co.uk*
BRANCHES AT:
15-16 New Burlington St W1S 3BJ ☎ *(020) 7287 5967*
6 Gt Queen St WC2 ☎ *(020) 7405 6295*

This pizza (and more) chain manages to be quite a success all round, not least with families. It's a touch more sophisticated than your average multiple, but still bustly enough that junior's indiscretions are unlikely to be closely observed.

Zafferano

16 Lowndes St SW1 ☎ *(020) 7235 5800*

Children are "absolutely welcomed" at what remains one of London's very hottest Italian – if you can get a booking! Weekends are most popular times with families.

WEST

Big Easy

334 King's Rd SW3 ☎ *(020) 7352 4071*

This American-style diner in Chelsea has long attracted a good following, even though its prices are far from bargain-basement. The kids' menu is £4.95, and includes a soft drink. As the bar is a key part of the attraction in the evenings, families may prefer to visit at other times.

Blue Elephant

4-6 Fulham Broadway SW6 1AA ☎ *(020) 7385 6595* ⌁ *www.blueelephant.com*

If you want to take the children for a special Sunday outing, one strong contender is the lunchtime buffet (£22, under-11s half price) on offer at this spectacularly designed Thai restaurant in Fulham. Clowns, cartoons and the like are usually organised to keep the younger ones amused. / *HOURS closed Sat L.*

Blue Kangaroo

555 King's Rd SW6 2EB ☎ *(020) 7371 7622* ☜ *www.thebluekangaroo.co.uk*

Never mind being kid-friendly – how many restaurants do you know with an indoor adventure playground in the basement… This café (near the Christopher Wray light emporium) serves decent food and coffee for such a kid-oriented place and provide an experience a notch well above that of a typical play centre (even in the more raucous downstairs).

Bonchurch Brasserie

349 Portobello Rd W10 5SA ☎ *(020) 8968 5828*

This nice relaxed North Kensington corner bistro is an ideal, relaxed take-the-kids sort of place, even if, technically speaking, it doesn't offer much in the way of facilities. / HOURS *closed Sun D.*

Chiswick House (Burlington Café)

Burlington Lane W4 ☎ *(020) 8742 7336*

Tailor-made for families, this simple café in the grounds of Chiswick House is always packed inside and out with families at the weekend, especially in summer. It serves simple, well-done snacks (panini, fry-ups and so on) and good coffee. You can BYO, too.

Da Mario

15 Gloucester Rd SW7 4PP ☎ *(020) 7584 9078* ☜ *www.damario.co.uk*

This long-established pizzeria is a warm and cosy place. It's an ideal destination after a walk in Kensington Gardens, and a popular family destination in its own right for the local burghers.

Famiglia

7 Langton St SW10 ☎ *(020) 7351 0761*

The large garden is the best feature of this fashionable and not inexpensive Chelsea trattoria, which welcomes children at most times (especially in the early-evening). Simple pasta dishes can be prepared.

Julies

135 Portland Rd W11 ☎ *(020) 7229 8331* ☜ *www.juliesrestaurant.com*

A crèche takes the strain off Sunday lunchtime parent-visitors to this romantic basement restaurant of long standing, near Holland Park.

King's Road Café

208 King's Rd SW3 5XP ☎ *(020) 7351 6645*

If you're cruising Chelsea with your buggy, it's striking how few congenial places there are to eat (and not just for families) on the King's Road. This makes it all the more worth venturing into Habitat, whose first-floor Mediterranean (and cakes) restaurant is something of an airy refuge. / HOURS *L only.*

Mandalay

444 Edgware Rd W2 1EG ☎ *(020) 7258 3696*

Service which is excellent for adults too makes it worth seeking out this Burmese café, which offers small portions to kick-start your child's awareness of ethnic cuisines: this one combines elements of Chinese and Indian. This may be a modest place, but its popularity is such that it's best to book. / HOURS *closed Sun.*

Mandarin Kitchen

14-16 Queensway W2 ☎ *(020) 7727 9012*

If you have a passion for seafood, and wish to indulge it in surroundings where none of your child's antics are likely to be noticed, you could not do much better than this top-quality – but chaotic – Bayswater Chinese. It's said to be London's largest consumer of lobsters.

PizzaExpress

☜ *www.pizzaexpress.co.uk*
BRANCHES AT:
23 Bond St W5 ☎ *(020) 8567 7690*
895 Fulham Rd SW6 5HU ☎ *(020) 7731 3117*
35 Earls Court Rd W8 6ED ☎ *(020) 7937 0761*
6-7 Beauchamp Place SW3 1NG ☎ *(020) 7589 2355*
246 Old Brompton Rd SW5 0DE ☎ *(020) 7373 4712*
363 Fulham Rd SW10 9TN ☎ *(020) 7352 5300*
26 Porchester Rd W2 6ES ☎ *(020) 7229 7784*
137 Notting Hill Gate W11 3LB ☎ *(020) 7229 6000*
7 Rockley Rd W14 0DJ ☎ *(020) 8749 8582*
252 Chiswick High Rd W4 1PD ☎ *(020) 8747 0193*
See write-up in central.

Raouls Café
13 Clifton Rd W9 ☎ *(020) 7289 7313*
Quite a trendy rendezvous down Maida Vale way, this pâtisserie-cum-brasserie is
a useful all-day destination, particularly handy as a relaxed destination at weekends.

Riccardo's
126 Fulham Rd SW3 6HU ☎ *(020) 7370 6656*
Tapas-style Italian dishes – all dishes effectively come in children's portions – help
make this welcoming Chelsea destination very popular. Bambini are most in in
evidence at the weekends. / HOURS *D only.*

The River Café
Thames Whf, Rainville Rd W6 9HA ☎ *(020) 7381 8824*
Probably the most 'pukka' restaurant in town to make a feature of encouraging kids,
especially at the weekends. This world-famous Italian is hardly known for its bargain
pricing of course, but if you want to family celebration with top-quality cooking, this
is one of the top places. / HOURS *closed Sun D.*

Le Shop
329 King's Rd SW3 5ES ☎ *(020) 7352 3891* ⏏ *www.leshop-chelsea.co.uk*
A rather superior Chelsea crêperie – one of the few in town of any note – which has
long been a popular 'treat' destination for children (and their parents).

Sticky Fingers
1a Phillimore Gdns W8 7QG ☎ *(020) 7938 5338*
This long-established American diner in Kensington – now under the same
ownership as Maxwell's burger restaurants – has always been known for its
child-friendly formula. Weekends offer face-painting as an attraction, and a kids'
menu (much more expensive than it used to be, at £7.25) is always available.

Strada
⏏ *www.strada.co.uk*
BRANCHES AT:
  175 New King's Rd SW6 4SW ☎ *(020) 7731 6404*
See write-up in central.

Texas Lone Star
154 Gloucester Rd SW7 ☎ *(020) 7370 5625*
Crayons and balloons, and a set menu for £4.75, are the sort of attraction which
recommend this rather battered but modestly-priced South Kensington Tex/Mex
cantina to families for lunch and dinner, and every day of the week.

NORTH

Banners
21 Park Rd N8 ☎ *(020) 8348 2930*
The famously relaxed atmosphere is the special strength of this Crouch End
bar/diner, and makes it very popular with kids too – "we only have four highchairs",
says the management, "so please bring your own if you can". Special menus, offering
the likes of fishfingers and chips for a couple of pounds, are available for kids until
7.30pm.

Don Pepe
99 Frampton St NW8 ☎ *(020) 7262 3834*
The oldest and one of the most authentic-feeling tapas bars in town, this St John's
Wood fixture has none of the hang-ups about children eating out which still afflict
some Anglo-Saxon establishments. As the manager says, "children are our future
customers". / HOURS *closed Sun.*

The Engineer
65 Gloucester Ave NW1 ☎ *(020) 7722 0950* ⏏ *www.the-engineer.com*
Kids are actively encouraged at this trendy and ever-popular Primrose Hill
gastropub, especially at weekends when balloons and crayons are distributed. On
nice days, make sure you arrive early if you want to bag a seat in the large garden.

Frederick's
106 Camden Pas N1 8EG ☎ *(020) 7359 2888* ⏏ *www.fredericks.co.uk*
Children are welcome at any time at this smart and well-established Islington
restaurant, whose rear conservatory is large enough to accommodate families
without attracting too much attention. Saturday lunchtime, when a children's menu
(£5.95) is available, is particularly popular. / HOURS *closed Sun.*

Giraffe

BRANCHES AT:

29-31 Essex Rd N1 3PS ☎ (020) 7359 5999
46 Rosslyn Hill NW3 1NH ☎ (020) 7435 0343

See write-up in central.

Kenwood House (Brewhouse)

Hampstead Lane NW3 7JR ☎ (020) 8341 5384

The cafeteria at Kenwood House has a large outside area, and is an ideal destination after a walk on Hampstead Heath. At weekends and during school holidays, child-friendly dishes are available.

Manna

4 Erskine Rd NW3 3AJ ☎ (020) 7722 8028 ⌐ www.manna-veg.com

Presumably in an effort to inveigle converts to non-meat-eating, Primrose Hill's venerable vegetarian offers small portions for potential adherents to the creed. / HOURS *closed weekday L.*

PizzaExpress

⌐ *www.pizzaexpress.co.uk*
BRANCHES AT:

94-98 Chaseside N14 ☎ (020) 8886 3300
92-94 The Broadway NW7 ☎ (020) 8959 3898
227 Finchley Rd NW3 ☎ (020) 7794 5100
94 Golders Green Rd NW11 ☎ (020) 8455 9556
820 High Rd N12 ☎ (020) 8445 7714
319 West End Lane NW6 1RP ☎ (020) 7431 8229
290 Muswell Hill N10 ☎ (020) 8883 5845
701 Green Lanes N21 ☎ (020) 8364 2992
12 Crouch End Hill N8 ☎ (020) 8347 6090
1264 High Rd N20 ☎ (020) 8446 8800
30 Highgate High St N6 5JG ☎ (020) 8341 3434
187 Kentish Town Rd NW1 2AE ☎ (020) 7267 0101
39-39a Abbey Rd NW8 0AA ☎ (020) 7624 5577
335 Upper St N1 0PB ☎ (020) 7226 9542

See write-up in central.

Porchetta Pizzeria

BRANCHES AT:

141-142 Upper St N1 1QY ☎ (020) 7288 2488
147 Stroud Green Rd N4 3PZ ☎ (020) 7281 2892

Famous for their sheer value, these popular and ever-bustling pizzerias are the sort of places where your children are most unlikely to be noticed, never mind heard.

Regent's Park Café

Rose Garden Buffet, Inner Circle, Regent's Park NW1 4NU ☎ (020) 7935 5729

There's a large cafeteria at the heart of Regent's Park's Rose Garden, with a playground (occasionally closed for private functions) at the rear. A children's menu is available.

Smollensky's

⌐ *www.smollenskys.co.uk*
BRANCHES AT:

O2 Centre, 255 Finchley Rd NW3 6LU ☎ (020) 7431 5007

See write-up in central.

Strada

⌐ *www.strada.co.uk*
BRANCHES AT:

105 Upper St N1 1QN ☎ (020) 7704 9902

See write-up in central.

Troika

101 Regent's Park Rd NW1 8UR ☎ (020) 7483 3765

If you're looking for a cool place to hang out with the kids, this Russian tearoom on Primrose Hill fits the bill nicely. Open all day, the place offers something for all the family, with junior appetites catered for with smaller portions.

Vegia Zena
17 Princess Rd NW1 8JR ☎ *(020) 7483 0192*

For a weekday lunch trip which offers something for parents as well as the kids, it's worth checking out the reasonably-priced menu at this interesting Primrose Hill Italian, where smaller portions are available for the kids.

SOUTH

Babur Brasserie
119 Brockley Rise, Forest Hill SE23 ☎ *(020) 8291 2400*

This high-quality Forest Hill Indian could teach other restaurants a lot when it comes to attracting families – children can join a free 'birthday club' and will receive a birthday card from the staff. Children dining at the restaurant on their birthday receive a small gift. / HOURS *closed Fri L.*

Boiled Egg & Soldiers
63 Northcote Rd SW11 ☎ *(020) 7223 4894*

They say that the little bit of Wandsworth around this accommodating café has the highest density of pre-school children in Europe. That's possibly untrue, but when the local nannies descend on it, you can certainly believe it. Nursery fare is the house speciality (with cooked breakfasts for the grown-ups). / HOURS *not open for D.*

Le Bouchon Bordelais
5-9 Battersea Rise SW11 1HG ☎ *(020) 7738 0307* ✆ *www.thebouchon.co.uk*

A Gallic brasserie in Battersea with a strong local following, especially amongst parents at weekend lunchtimes, when there is a crèche.

Bread & Roses
68 Clapham Manor St SW4 ☎ *(020) 7498 1779*

This Clapham boozer is very baby- and child-friendly: it has a conservatory supplied with toys and games, and runs regular community and family events.

Café Portugal
5a & 6a Victoria House, South Lambeth Rd SW8 1QX ☎ *(020) 7587 1962*
✆ *www.outworld.ision.co.uk/cafe*

It's not exactly the Algarve, but this simple and inexpensive Vauxhall café (which becomes a restaurant by night) offers something slightly different on the culinary front in a relaxing and child-friendly environment. The menu is quite extensive, and small portions are available.

Canyon
Riverside Twickenham TW10 6UJ ☎ *(020) 8948 2944* ✆ *www.canyonfood.co.uk*

It's the spectacular riverside setting which is the greatest strength of this American restaurant in Richmond – an ideal sunny weekend destination when families form a large proportion of the brunching clientèle. For junior, a special menu is available.

Chez Bruce
2 Bellevue Rd SW17 7EG ☎ *(020) 8672 0114*

One of the few quality non-smoking restaurants, this hugely-popular Wandsworth Common-sider is very happy to accommodate families with children and small babies at lunchtimes; evenings can get quite packed, so are less suitable. If you warn them in advance, they will place you (with a suitable or high chair) at a table where the baby will not be knocked or disturbed. Small portions are available. / HOURS *closed Sun D.*

The Depot
Mortlake High St SW14 8SN ☎ *(020) 8878 9462*

Make sure you book before a weekend visit to this classic sunny lunchtime destination. This Barnes brasserie benefits from a great location, on a bend of the river, and a very relaxed and child-friendly atmosphere.

don Fernando's
27f The Quadrant Richmond TW9 ☎ *(020) 8948 6447* ✆ *www.donfernando.co.uk*

Lively and atmospheric tapas bar next to Richmond BR station with inexpensive, good-value dishes. It makes a natural venue for a family meal.

Film Café
South Bank SE1 8XD ☎ *(020) 7928 5362*

If you're looking to eat somewhere near the London Eye, what tends to strike you is the depressing 'chaininess' of all the options. It's worth a short stroll, then, to this busy cultural centre café. The food is nothing special, but there's a wide range of inexpensive fare, and on a nice day you can sit outside.

The Light House
75-77 Ridgway SW19 4ST ☎ (020) 8944 6338
One of the few decent restaurants in Wimbledon! Its spacious surroundings are quite family-friendly and simple dishes are available on request.

Ma Goa
244 Upper Richmond Rd SW15 6TG ☎ (020) 8780 1767 ⌂ www.magoa.co.uk
If you're looking to introduce your children to the delights of subcontinental dining, you don't want to start too fiery, so this Goan bistro in Putney would be ideal. You can start them off with kiddie portions too. / HOURS D only, closed Mon.

Murano
3 Hill St Twickenham TW1 ☎ (020) 8948 8330
A kids' play area adds to the Sunday lunching attractions of this Richmond Italian, handily located in the centre of the town. A special menu for children is also available.

Newton's
33 Abbeville Rd SW4 ☎ (020) 8673 0977
It's not aiming for any culinary highs, but this Clapham brasserie is a relaxed spot for lunch with the kids, and it's especially popular at weekends. Kid's menu: £3.95 for a main course and a drink.

The Pepper Tree
19 Clapham Common Southside SW4 ☎ (020) 7622 1758
If spice is to hold no fear for your children, start 'em young at this ever-popular Thai refectory in Clapham: kids' portions are available. It's a fun, informal place – adults sit at benches – and you may have to queue.

PizzaExpress
⌂ www.pizzaexpress.co.uk
BRANCHES AT:
70 Westow Hill SE19 ☎ (020) 8670 1786
64 Tranquil Vale SE3 ☎ (020) 8318 2595
4 Church St SE10 ☎ (020) 8853 2770
14 Barnes High St SW13 ☎ (020) 8878 1184
316 Kennington Rd SE11 4LD ☎ (020) 7820 3177
305 Up Richmond Rd W SW14 6SS ☎ (020) 8878 6833
84 High St SW19 ☎ (020) 8946 6027
539 Old York Rd SW18 1TG ☎ (020) 8877 9812
144 Upper Richmond Rd SW15 2RP ☎ (020) 8789 1948
230 Lavender Hill SW11 1LE ☎ (020) 7223 5677
198 Trinity Rd SW17 ☎ (020) 8762 0200
43 Abbeville Rd SW4 9JX ☎ (020) 8673 8878
34 Streatham High Rd SW16 ☎ (020) 8769 0202
Cardomom Bldg, Shad Thames SE1 2YR ☎ (020) 7403 8484
94 The Village SE21 ☎ (020) 8693 9333
See write-up in central.

Ransome's Dock
35 Parkgate Rd SW11 4NP ☎ (020) 7223 1611 ⌂ www.ransomesdock.co.uk
Dependable cooking is set off by a tip-top wine list at this hidden-away, but popular, Battersea spot. It's a relaxed and child-friendly place, too, with children's portions available at modest cost, so it really does offer something for all the family. / HOURS closed Sun D.

Sarkhel's
199 Replingham Rd SW18 ☎ (020) 8870 1483
When you're with children, staff attitude is key, and they don't come much more accommodating than at this Southfields spot. Not the least attraction is some of the best reasonably-priced Indian cooking in town. / HOURS closed Mon.

Sonny's
94 Church Rd SW13 ☎ (020) 8748 0393
This ever-popular Barnes restaurant has long offered standards above the 'suburban' norm. It prides itself as a child-friendly destination, and there's a special menu (£5.50) always available. / HOURS closed Sun D.

The Stepping Stone
123 Queenstown Rd SW8 ☎ (020) 7622 0555
Baby-changing facilities are among the attractions which make this relaxed Battersea restaurant (not far from Chelsea Bridge) a popular lunching destination for all the family. Children's portions are available, as are toys and crayons. / *HOURS closed Sat L & Sun D.*

Strada
⁀ www.strada.co.uk
BRANCHES AT:
  11-13 Battersea Rise SW11 1HG ☎ (020) 7801 0794
See write-up in central.

The Sun & Doves
61 Coldharbour Lane SE5 ☎ (020) 7733 1525 ⁀ www.sundoves.com
Camberwell not being overly blessed with decent eating places, it's particularly worth knowing about this pleasant, updated pub. It has a friendly attitude, serves good food (available in half portions) and a large garden.

Tate Modern
Sumner St SE1 ☎ (020) 7401 5020 ⁀ www.tate.org.uk
There are two dining options at the Bankside art gallery: on level seven – with amazing views of St Paul's and the river – there's a relatively formal restaurant; and on the second level, a café serves food all day. Both have high chairs and entertainments for children, and are completely non-smoking. / *HOURS L only.*

Tentazioni
2 Mill St SE1 2BF ☎ (020) 7237 1100 ⁀ www.tentazionirestaurant.co.uk
If you're sightseeing down Tower Bridge way, there are a lot of quite expensive dining opportunities. For family dining it's worth seeking out this small Italian, which is distinguished by above-average food and service. Small portions are available for the children. / *HOURS closed Mon L, Sat L & Sun.*

3 Monkeys
136-140 Herne Hill SE24 9QH ☎ (020) 7738 5500 ⁀ www.3monkeysrestaurant.com
South London being not exactly flush with destination restaurants, it's especially worth considering a Sunday lunchtime excursion to this fashionable Herne Hill Indian. And on weekdays, families who arrive between 6pm and 7.30pm get a kid's plate free (one per adult). / *HOURS D only (Sun open L&D).*

White Cross
Water Lane Richmond TW9 ☎ (020) 8940 6844 ⁀ www.youngs.co.uk
This large, prominently-situated Richmond tavern is one of the nicest in the metropolis, especially in the summer when families can take advantage of the large garden overlooking the Thames. Indoors, there's an attractive upstairs room to which children are admitted. / *HOURS L only.*

EAST

Frocks
95 Lauriston Rd E9 7HJ ☎ (020) 8986 3161
Weekend breakfasts are a big deal at this popular English bistro in the East End, which, by its nature, is a very informal event where kiddie mischief in unlikely to raise an eyebrow. A visit here is an ideal complement to one to Victoria Park. / *HOURS closed Mon & Sun D.*

PizzaExpress
⁀ www.pizzaexpress.co.uk
BRANCHES AT:
  76 High Rd E18 ☎ (020) 8924 4488
  45 Old Church Rd E4 ☎ (020) 8529 7866
  Salway Rd E15 ☎ (020) 8534 1700
  78-80 Wapping Lane E1 ☎ (020) 7481 8436
  2nd Floor, Cabot Place East E14 4QT ☎ (020) 7513 0513
  26 Cowcross St EC1 6DQ ☎ (020) 7490 8025
  7-9 St Bride St EC4 4AS ☎ (020) 7583 5126
  125 London Wall EC2 5AS ☎ (020) 7600 8880
  Leadenhall Market EC3 1LR ☎ (020) 7621 0022
See write-up in central.

Strada

🖰 www.strada.co.uk

BRANCHES AT:
  70 Exmouth Market EC1 ☎ *(020) 7278 0800*
See write-up in central.

CHAPTER 3.14

SHOPPING DIRECTORY

A Baby 🖼
Evertown Farm, Evertown, Canonbie,
Dumfriesshire DG14 0TJ ☎ (01387) 371614
🖰 www.ababy.co.uk/
Online retailer with a small-medium sized
selection covering most bases.
Baby equipment – **Stockists:** buggies and car
seats are mainly from the Graco range, plus
Alu-Rax all-terrain strollers (and a number of
other major brands).

A Lot of Organics
Absolute Web Solutions, Douglas House, 33
Douglas Road, Caversham, Reading
RG4 5BH ☎ (0118) 375 9375
🖰 www.alotoforganics.co.uk
Baby clothes – **Eco-friendly clothing:** a search
engine designed to help consumers find
organic, ethical, eco-friendly, vegetarian and
special diet produce in the UK.

Abacus Baby Hire & Party Hire
Long Lodge, Nightingale Ave, West Horsley,
Surrey KT24 6PA ☎ (01483) 285142
🖰 www.babyhire.co.uk
Baby equipment – **Hire:** hire of travel cots, car
seats, high chairs, buggies. Also items for
parties: small tables and chairs, tunnels, ball
ponds and junior trampolines. / *Hours: flexible.*

Abstract 🖼
35 North Road, Brighton, Sussex BN1 1YB
☎ (01273) 693 737 🖰 www.abstractuk.com
Baby equipment – **Buggy accessories:** a
website retailer of fleece products, including
blankets.
Nursery decor – **Bedding:** fleece specialists
who sell attractive patchwork baby blankets.

Acoustics 🖼
PO Box 350, Reading RG6 7DQ ☎ (0118)
926 8615 🖰 www.acousticsrecords.co.uk
Books, music & videos – **Music tapes:**
musicians Hilary James and Simon Mayor have
worked for Play School, Listening Corner and
BBC Radio for Schools. Their tapes (folk
tradition with a Western touch), offer good,
original material which bear re-hearing.
Musical Mystery Tour Vols 1-5, £8
each. / *Hours: Mon-Fri 9am-5pm; online catalogue;
Delivery: p&p £1 per CD, £1.50 per book or video
(max £6).*

The Active Birth Centre 🖼
25 Bickerton Rd, London N19 5JT ☎ (020)
7281 6760 🖰 www.activebirthcentre.com
Run by Janet Balaskas, a well known name in
Active Birth circles, the centre's chief activity is
teaching active birth preparation for labour and
the training of active birth teachers. In addition
the centre offers a comprehensive range of

workshops, courses and talks by childbirth and
childcare luminaries (including water birth
guru Dr Michel Odent). It also provides a base
from which some complementary therapists
practice. All classes must be pre-booked –
no drop-ins.
Maternity wear – **Bras and underwear:**
suppliers of Active Birth nursing bra.
Baby equipment – **Lambskins:** lambskins,
slings and miscellaneous other items. / *Hours:
shop Mon-Fri 9.30am-6.30pm (Fri 4pm), Sat 10am-
4pm; Delivery: p&p £4.50.*

Active Learning 🖼
28 Hartley Business Centre, Hucknall Rd,
Nottingham NG5 1FD ☎ (0115) 960 6111
🖰 www.activelearning-uk.com
Toys – **Nursery suppliers:** a wide selection of
high quality play mats, modular soft play
systems, portable ball pools, soft gym items,
toddler climbing frames, bag seating, playrings
and the like. An unfolding cube with Velcro,
toggles, buckles etc is about £40.

The Active Toy Company 🖼
Langley Farm, World's End, Beedon,
Newbury, Berks RG20 8SD ☎ (01635)
248683 🖰 www.activetoy.co.uk
A farmhouse one hour from west London
where the majority of things in stock are on
show so children can play before you pay.
Toys – **Outdoor items & active toys:** major
outlet of TP and Little Tikes outdoor
equipment, especially traditional wooden
designs, with some exclusives: wooden/steel
climbing frames, swings and slides. Also
trampolines and paddling pools. / *Hours: Mon-
Sun 9.30am-4.30pm; free catalogue; Delivery: p&p
extra; no Amex.*

Adam & Eve
5 The Market Place, London NW11 6LB
☎ (020) 8455 8645
Baby clothes – **Traditional:** cute, if expensive
outfits – exclusive designs at the upper end of
the market, all in Continental styles. / *Hours:
Mon-Sat 9.30am-5.30pm, Sun 10am-1pm.*

Adams
CENTRAL CONTACT DETAILS
☎ (0500) 330040,
Customer care (024) 7635 1000
🖰 www.adams.co.uk
BRANCHES:
*(Only selected branches are listed –
call the enquiry line for other outlets.)*
48-49 King's Mall, King St W6 0QB
☎ (020) 8741 3820
Unit 8 Broadwalk Centre, Edgware HA8 7BD
☎ (020) 8951 3761
431-433 High Rd HA9 7AB
☎ (020) 8795 4102
70-72 Kilburn High Rd NW6 4HF

☎ (020) 7624 0972
Unit F5 Bentalls Shopping Centre KT1 1TP
☎ (020) 8541 0928
65-67 Rye Lane SE15 5EX
☎ (020) 7277 9678
Unit 17 Redriff Rd, Surrey Quays Shopping
Centre SE16 7LL
☎ (020) 7252 3208
61-63 Tooting High St SW17 0SP
☎ (020) 8682 2432
Large well-known chain; over 50% of shops
have play areas.
<u>Baby clothes</u> – **Cheap & cheerful:** modern
styling at the casual/sporty end of the market
in bright, cheerful colours; good co-ordinating
ranges; lots of extras including play shoes,
socks, underwear, swimwear and nightwear;
girl's cotton T-shirt £10, cotton dress or jumper
£13. / *Hours: mostly Mon-Sat 9am-5.30pm.*

Advanced Play Systems ⌂
10 Ham Road, Wallborough, Swindon,
Wiltshire SN4 0DF ☎ (01793) 485 200
⏁ www.advancedplay.co.uk
<u>Toys</u> – **Outdoor items & active toys:**
ready-built and DIY products, such as
a modern Wendy House, a dark green 'survival
pod', an 'explorer' tank or even a play kitchen,
in designer style (if at designer prices). Items
are built to order in birch plywood and high
performance paint and with 'finger-friendly'
doors. / *free catalogue or online; Delivery: p&p
extra.*

Akta ⌂
☎ (020) 7625 7770 ⏁ www.akta.co.uk
Toys, equipment and designer furniture for
children.
<u>Nursery decor</u> – **Accessories:** children's
lighting and accessories, plus seating.

All Seasons ⌂
654-656 High Rd, North Finchley N12 0NL
☎ (020) 8445 6314
⏁ www.allseasonslondon.co.uk
"North London's premier nursery store" is the
claim at this store, which says that 80% of its
customers come on word-of-mouth
recommendation. You can also order online at
their website www.1stopbabyshop.co.uk.
<u>Baby equipment</u> – **Stockists:** brands include
Jané, Sauthon, Mamas & Papas (main stockist),
Chicco, Dutailier, Stokke, Baby Bjorn, Grobags
and Heather Spencer.
<u>Nursery decor</u> – **Bedding:** various bedroom
displays featuring – amongst other brands –
Clair de Lune – **General stockists:** wardrobes,
beds and cots from Mamas & Papas, Sauthon
and Heather Spencer designs.
<u>Toys</u> – **Outdoor items & active toys:**
battery-powered jeeps and bikes and rocking
horses for children from 6 months old. / *Hours:
Mon-Fri 9.30am-5pm, Sat 9.30am-5.30pm.*

Allders of Croydon
2 North End, Croydon CR9 1SB ☎ (020)
8681 2577 ⏁ www.allders.com
<u>Baby clothes</u> – **Cheap & cheerful:** large
department, with clothes for girls and boys,
from newborns to pre-teens.
<u>Toys</u> – **General stockists:** good general toy
department, with plenty for younger children
and all major brand names. TP Activity Toys

stockist. / *Hours: Mon-Fri 9.30am-6pm (Thu 9pm),
Sat 9am-6pm, Sun 11am-5pm.*

alphabeds
92 Tottenham Court Rd, London W1T 4TL
☎ (020) 7636 6840 ⏁ www.alphabeds.co.uk
Well-regarded bed emporium with an
emphasis on eco-friendly manufacture and
organic materials, whose attachment to a mill
allows for a fair number of customisation
options.
<u>Baby equipment</u> – **Cots:** wooden cot-bed and
organic mattress (£280); options include
under-cot storage box £50, ball-ended legs,
different foot and headboard designs, a wide
range of woods, stains and colours,
and a conversion kit to a full length bed.
– **Specialist mattress suppliers:** the firm
claims to be the only maker offering a full
choice of all natural materials with no added
fire retardant chemicals. Organic options are
also available (in which regard, the company
has been working with the Soil Association and
the British Wool Marketing Board), with
Welsh wool, latex, coir and cotton covers.
<u>Nursery decor</u> – **Beds:** range of child-sized
designs, all in natural materials. / *Hours: Mon-
Weds 10am-6pm, Thu 10am-7pm, Fri-Sat 10am-6pm,
Sun 11am-5pm.*

Alyssa Robinson ⌂
☎ (01536) 771687
<u>Baby clothes</u> – **Outdoorwear:** range of
made-to-order children's jackets, trousers and
snowsuits, including a lightweight nylon
snowsuit, jacket and trouser set that can
compress to fit in a pocket and all-in-one
waterproof trousers welded to wellingtons; all
rainwear has reflective strips; choice of 20
colours; prices £20-£35. / *Hours: Mon-Fri 9.30am-
5pm; free catalogue; no credit cards.*

Amalaika ⌂
Sandpiper Fibbards Rd, Brockenhurst
Hampshire SO42 7RD ☎ (01590) 623273
⏁ www.amalaika.com
<u>Baby clothes</u> – **Mid-range:** sister company to
Milliemoos, offering new designer wear for
children at heavily discounted prices. Currently
specialising in French designer wear and Oilily,
but also some British designer outfits. The
majority of our outfits are 'one-offs', with the
site updated daily and new stock added at least
three times a week.

Amazon ⌂
Accounts Department, Bestobell Rd, Slough,
Berks SL1 4SZ ☎ (0800) 279 6620
⏁ www.amazon.co.uk
The world's leading e-tailer now incorporates
'Toys and kids!' as one of the key areas on its
site. If you are looking for an out-of-print title,
the site's 'zShops' section is an excellent place
to look.
<u>Toys</u> – **General stockists:** the non-character
section of the site is as yet relatively restricted
and majors in items from mass market names
such as Lego, Fisher-Price and Tomy;
the Lamaze brand is the exception.
– **Character toys:** as you might expect, given
its expertise with books, DVDs and so on,
character-branded items are the strongest area
of the site and available in many ways, shapes
and forms.

Books, music & videos – **Bookshops:** the UK sites' comprehensive childrens' section is divided into four age groups under 12 and categorised by subject or character (e.g. Pingu). Reader reviews and editor's recommendations can be e-mailed to you on a regular basis. Audio cassettes, videos and DVDs are also stocked in depth. / *Hours: 24hrs; Delivery: p&p £2.16 + 59p per book.*

Bill Amberg ⌂
10 Chepstow Rd, London W2 5BD ☎ (020) 7727 3560 ⌂ www.billamberg.com
By Royal Appointment to Posh and Becks, this luxury leather designer is – amongst other things – known for his glamorous baby accessories.
Baby equipment – **Slings:** sheepskin papoose worn at the front of the body, in black, cream, pink or blue.
Nappies – **Change bags:** the 'magazine' design bag is his best known item, complete with mat and interior pockets. / *Hours: Mon-Sat 10am-6pm, Sun 10am-7pm.*

Amby UK ⌂
1B Cloonmore Ave, Orpington, Kent BR6 9LN ☎ (0845) 603 1589
⌂ www.naturesnest.co.uk
Baby equipment – **Portable sleeping equipment:** the Natures Nest (£149) is an Australian invention – a baby sleeping pod suspended by a spring from a metal frame, marketed as the natural transition from the womb to the world outside. It is suitable for use to 12 months. It is easily erected and packed, and, at 9kg, suitable for use as a travel cot. / *online catalogue.*

American Collections
41 Oldhill St, London N16 6LR ☎ (020) 8806 0702
Baby clothes – **Luxury:** designer baby and children's wear (age newborn to 15 years) shop, mostly American clothes; no shoes. / *Hours: Mon-Thu 10am-6pm, Fri 10.30am-2pm, Sun 10.30am-4pm, Closed Sat.*

Anorak Lakes Ltd ⌂
Central Buildings, Ambleside, Cumbria LA22 9BS ☎ (01539) 432235
⌂ www.anorakonline.co.uk
Founded in 1935, this outdoor clothing shop and mail order business has knowledgable staff, and stocks numerous quality brands; it aims to provide "Everything for a winter or summer holiday."
Baby clothes – **Outdoorwear:** a selection of sun and winter outfits for babies and toddlers; waterproof jackets, 'breathables', wet suits; Polyotter float suits and swim shoes; outdoor footwear, snow boots, walking boots, aqua shoes. / *Hours: Mon-Sun 9.30am-5.30pm; online catalogue; Delivery: p&p £3.95 (free over £50).*

Aphrodite ⌂
St Michaels Works, 141 Blandford Road, Hamworthy, Poole Dorset BH15 4AT
☎ (01202) 668 596
⌂ www.aphrodite-designs.com
Maternity wear – **Bras and underwear:** online vendor of maternity swimsuits designed to look good and feel comfortable. The range features some attractive patterns and some

items with separate tops and bottoms. Prices up to £35.

Applepie Toys
113 Shepherdess Walk, London N1 7QA
☎ (020) 8807 9777
⌂ www.spottydogtoys.com
Toys – **Traditional toys:** distributors of award-winning pull-along wooden toys that turn their heads and wag tails as they move.

Aprica America, Inc. ⌂
17101 S. Central Ave, Unit 1G, Carson, California USA 90746 ☎ +1 310 639 6387
⌂ www.apricausa.com
Baby equipment – **Wheeled Transport-brands:** good quality baby equipment from the US, principally buggies (strollers); makers of the Flash Prestige buggy, said to be a celeb' favourite. / *Hours: Mon-Fri 8.30am-12pm, 1pm-4.30pm.*

Arabella B
24 Berkeley Square, London W1J 6EJ
☎ (020) 7408 1688, (0870) 112 3688
⌂ www.arabellab.com
Maternity wear – **Luxury:** fashion maternity wear for all occasions – from denim jeans and jacket, to little black dresses, to work and exercise outfits. Each piece is designed to fit well, with hidden room for growth as the baby develops. Zips, stretch and draping fabrics are all used. Some, such as gabardine tailored jacket (£195), are designed for continued use after the baby is born.

Arbon & Watts ⌂
39 Sherrard St, Melton Mowbray, Leics LE13 1XH ☎ (08700) 129090
⌂ www.mailorderexpress.com
The website is one of the UK's best of its type.
Toys – **General stockists:** with two toy shops in the Midlands, this family-run company (established 1946) claims to have 17,000 different products in stock at any one time – including Brio, Corolle French dolls, Manhattan Toy Co, John Crane / Plan & Pin Toys, Tomy, Barbie, V-Tech and Playmobil. They will attempt to find any item produced by the major toy brands and deliver it ASAP; gift wrapping available, £3. / *Hours: Mon-Fri 8.30am-6pm, Sat 9am-5pm; free catalogue; Delivery: p&p (£6.99 for 48 hours; £3.99 standard); no Amex.*

Arcade Bookshop ⌂
3-4 The Arcade, Eltham, London SE9 1BE
☎ (020) 8850 7803
Books, music & videos – **Bookshops:** what was once a small bargain outlet has grown into a predominantly children's bookshop, specialising in fiction books for older children and an extensive range of bargain books including children's picture books. They hold regular author events and readings for all ages, and provide a newsletter for parents. / *Hours: Mon-Sat 9am-5.30pm; no Switch.*

Arding & Hobbs ⌂
315 Lavender Hill, London SW11 1QL
☎ (020) 7801 2100 ⌂ www.allders.co.uk
Baby clothes – **Cheap & cheerful:** children's wear includes smart clothes, underwear and premature baby outfits. Some designer clothes (including Donna Karen, Calvin Klein and

Diesel).

Toys – General stockists: good general range of all the popular brands, including Lego and Playmobil. / *Hours: Mon-Weds 10am-7pm, Thu-Fri 10am-8pm, Sat 9.30am-6pm, Sun 11am-5pm; Delivery: orders below £100 charge £4.*

Argos 🖰

CENTRAL CONTACT DETAILS

☎ (0870) 600 3030, Direct home shopping (0870) 600 2020

🖰 www.argos.co.uk

BRANCHES:

(Branches throughout London –
call the enquiry line for your nearest outlet.)

Toys and equipment account for about 5% of the stock of this nationwide catalogue shopping chain, which has about 40 branches in Greater London (call for your nearest branch – also listed at the rear of the catalogue). With their Stock Enquiry & Reservation service (on-line and on 0870 600 1010) you can ensure that the item you want is in stock, and reserve it ahead of time. For items such as vacuum cleaner bags they operate a free mail order service – call the Spares & Accessories line (0870 600 4040).

Baby equipment – Stockists: cots, prams, safety-gates from the likes of Britax, Maclaren, Cosatto, Mamas and Papas, and Graco.

Toys – General stockists: most big-name brands are stocked: Fisher-Price, Playskool, Tomy, Lego and Little Tikes. / *Hours: hours vary; free brochure; Delivery: p&p £3.95 (free over £125).*

ART 🖰

72 Poplar Avenue, Hove, East Sussex BN3 8PS ☎ (01273) 770 877

🖰 www.artrugs.co.uk

Nursery decor – Soft furnishings: individually designed hand-tufted carpets and wall-hangings in New Zealand wool in 360 colours. The standard designs, which can be in a variety of textures and finishes, include a range specifically for children. They can also use original artwork as a design, or match any fabric or wallpaper; (also trade as "Cachet Carpets at www.cachetcarpets.com). / *Hours: flexible; free catalogue or online; no Amex.*

Art for Children

Unit 72, Abbey Business Centre, Ingate Place, London SW8 3NS ☎ (020) 7498 5921

Antique and limited edition prints chosen to suit kids' bedrooms or playrooms.

Nursery decor – Art.

Naming gifts – Naming gifts.

Art Stationers & Village Toy Shop

31 Dulwich Village, London SE21 7BN

☎ (020) 8693 5938

Toys – General stockists: at the back of an art stationery outlet, this toy shop specialises in educational toys and craft kits; brands include Ambi, Galt, Lego, Playmobil, Wow, John Crane and Roila. / *Hours: Mon-Sat 9am-5.30pm; no Amex.*

Artemidorus

27b Half Moon Lane, London SE24 9JU

☎ (020) 7737 7747

As well as those items listed below, there's a small range of other items – T-shirts, pyjamas, Daisy Roots shoes and Swedish baby towels.

Toys – Traditional toys: handmade, traditional toys and British craft items: carved animals, farmyards, skittles, mobiles, hobby horses and toy boxes all to order; also soft animals and board games.

Naming gifts – Naming gifts: all the very traditional British toys sold here would be suitable to give as naming gifts, especially the wooden rattles (from £20) which can be plain or with silver bands, and may be personalised. / *Hours: Tues-Fri 10.30am-7pm, Sat 10.30am-6pm.*

Asda

CENTRAL CONTACT DETAILS

☎ (0113) 243 5435

🖰 www.asda.co.uk

BRANCHES:

(Only selected branches are listed –
call the enquiry line for other outlets.)

Capital Park Industrial Estate, Edgware Rd NW9 0AS

☎ (020) 8200 4833

204 Lavender Hill SW11

☎ (020) 7223 0101

31 Roehampton Vale SW15 3DT

☎ (020) 8780 2780

151 East Ferry Rd E14 3BT

☎ (020) 7987 2614

All of the branches of this large nationwide supermarket chain (now owned by Walmart) have baby changing facilities, but not all stock toys or the full range of clothes; only the best branches for kids' things are listed.

Baby clothes – Cheap & cheerful: own-brand George clothing, most in complete outfits for babies 0-18 months; good-value clothes for older children, modern machine washable fabrics include soft jersey or fleece, and colours range from acid brights to strong pastels.

Toys – General stockists: general range of the big names including Lego, Barbie, and Crayola, at competitive prices. / *Hours: mostly 8am-10pm; no Amex.*

Asprey 🖰

167 New Bond St, London W1S 4AR

☎ (020) 7493 6767 🖰 www.asprey.com

Naming gifts – Naming gifts: this famous jeweller offer a variety of suitable silverware, much of which can be engraved with a name or message (at extra cost): cups and spoons with a rabbit motif, spinning tops, Humpty Dumpty egg cups, an alphabet plate and even silver yo-yos; prices start at around £60. / *Hours: Mon-Sat 10am-6pm; free catalogue.*

Astrokidz 🖰

50D Pemberton Gardens, London N19 5ZD

☎ (020) 7281 0935 🖰 www.astrokidz.com

Naming gifts – Naming gifts: astrological profiles for children (£20).

Auro Organic Paint Supplies 🖰

Unit 2 Pamphillions Farm, Saffron Walden, Essex CB11 3JT ☎ (01799) 543077

🖰 www.auroorganic.co.uk

Nursery decor – Paints: environmentally-friendly finishes for wood, cork and plaster surfaces; no petrochemicals used (and they declare all ingredients). / *Hours: Mon-Fri 9am-5pm; free catalogue or online; Delivery: p&p £5 for under £50; no Amex.*

Autosafe
London NW6 ☎ (020) 7372 3141
⌕ www.auto-safe.co.uk
Baby equipment – **Car seat fitting/seat belt adjusting:** operating on a call out basis (usually via a garage – but you can call direct), this firm supplies and fits seat belts for any age and will provide free advice on any aspect of car safety over the phone; also, if you had a problem with a car baby seat, for example, they can come and show you how to fit it correctly; call out charge £20, anywhere within M25. / *Hours: Mon-Sat 9am-6pm.*

Aztec Store ⌑
Unit 212b, The Business Centre, 3-9 Broomhill Rd, London SW18 4JQ ☎ (020) 8877 9954 ⌕ www.aztecstore.com
Nursery decor – **Bedding:** hand-knitted cotton baby blankets and cushions, from £25.
Baby clothes – **Mid-range.** – **Knitwear:** hand-knitted and hand-embroidered cotton clothes and furnishings: jumpers, hats and long-sleeved T-shirts; jumper £30; embroidered T-shirt £12. / *Hours: Mon-Fri 9.30am-5.30pm.*

Babies 'R' Us ⌑
Old Kent Rd (junction with Asylum Rd), London SE15 INJ ☎ (020) 7732 7322, Store finder (08000) 388889
⌕ www.babiesrus.co.uk, www.discounttoys.co.uk
The sister company of Toys 'R' Us; branches can also be found, for example, near Lakeside and Brent Cross shopping centres. Operates a baby gift list service similar to a wedding list, the list compiled using a form featuring sections such as For Mum, Travel and Bathtime; also sells for example a small selection of books; although not the most fashionable range, it includes some attractive items.
Baby equipment – **Stockists:** a comprehensive range of items large (cots, car seats, buggies, baby carriers) and small (safety items and monitors).
Nursery decor – **General stockists:** co-ordinating own-brand ranges of nursery accessories, equipment, bedding and furniture.
Baby clothes – **Cheap & cheerful:** branded and own-brand clothing for newborns; plain colours and cottons; gift sets.
Toys – **Pre-school specialists:** cot toys and items for newborns – the range for older children is stocked at Toys 'R' Us. / *Hours: Mon-Fri 9am-8pm, Sat 9am-7pm, Sun 11am-5pm; online catalogue or print 75p; Delivery: p&p £3.90.*

Babies Island ⌑
PO Box 7824, Epping, Essex CM16 4WB
☎ (08702) 012435
⌕ www.babiesisland.co.uk
Naming gifts – **Naming gifts:** a one-stop shop offering an assortment of products and gifts for babies, mums and dads. Gift registry, gift vouchers with a no-quibble returns policy.

Babies Love Babies ⌑
7 Belsize Park Gardens, London NW3 4LB
☎ (020) 7483 0644
⌕ www.babieslovebabies.com
Books, music & videos – **Videos:** dVD (£15) and Video (£13) to aid understanding your baby's development through play from a firm whose mission statement is "to inform and prepare parents and to stimulate, educate and entertain babies".

Babies Wishworld ⌑
Unit 7, Canal Terrace, Worksop, Nottinghamshire S80 2DF ☎ (0870) 350 1230 ⌕ www.babieswishworld.co.uk
Naming gifts – **Naming gifts:** an on-line 'wedding list'-type service for parents of newborns and children of up to two, including both luxury and practical items.

Baby and You ⌑
108 George Lane, South Woodford, London E18 IAD ☎ (020) 8532 9595
⌕ www.babyandyou.com
Part of the same group as Babycare Tens.
Baby equipment – **Monitors-brand:** stockists of the Core brand – a £30 pound monitor, range 100m, incorporating thermometer.

Baby Babble ⌑ Q
33b Park Rd, Bushey WD23 3EE ☎ (020) 8386 7046 ⌕ www.babybabble.co.uk
Naming gifts – **Naming gifts:** a baby gifts specialist offering a baby shower service, free internet birth announcements and baby lists (gift registry). Simple items with a bit of extra styling – like muslins with a label reading 'oops!' Also fleece and cotton blankets, T-shirts, soft toys, designer bottles and dummies, Aromakids lotions, Tomy slings and photo albums. / *Hours: Mon-Fri 9am-5.30pm.*

Baby Baby
193 Sheen Lane, East Sheen, London SW14 8LE ☎ (020) 8876 3153
Nursery decor – **Bedding:** fleece pram blankets with handles either plain or with applique; plus plain Swedish-style bedding in 100% cotton including waffle blankets.
Baby clothes – **Mid-range:** simple, Scandinavian-style accessories including tops, hats and slippers. / *Hours: Mon-Fri 9am-5pm; free brochure; Delivery: p&p extra.*

Baby Backpacs ⌑
CENTRAL CONTACT DETAILS
☎ (01872) 270 213
⌕ www.babybackpacs.co.uk
Penrose Outdoors, Town Quay, Truro TR1 2HJ
☎ (01872) 270 213
Baby equipment – **Slings- Backpack:** specialist online retailer of carriers and accessories from such brands as Kelty Kids, Dales, Karrimor, Vaude, Bushbaby and Hippychick. / *UK only; no Amex.*

Baby Banz ⌑
Sunproof Limited, Unit I Monks Dairy Workshops, Isle Brewers, Taunton, Somerset TA3 6QL ☎ (01460) 281229
⌕ www.babybanz.co.uk
Australian designed UV protective products for

babies and children.

<u>Baby clothes</u> – **Outdoorwear:** sunglasses for 0-3 years with elasticated strap, £10. Buy direct or phone for a list of stockists.

Baby Bjorn

2 The Old Stables, Shredding Green Farm, Langley Park Rd, Iver SL0 9QS ☎ (0870) 1200 543 ᐧ᠐ www.babybjorn.com
Swedish company which, though best known for its sling, produces a small range of well-designed products for children under three.

<u>Baby equipment</u> – **High chairs:** range includes a Baby Sitter suitable for use up to around two years old with a toy bar for young babies and restraint system. Also a safety seat to attach to a dining chair and a booster seat suitable for a child who doesn't need the safety bar.
– **Slings:** widely stocked – the clips are easier to use than on other models; possibly less comfortable than the Wilkinet, as the straps are less well padded and there is no support for the lower back (so the shoulders take more strain); suitable for use for babies from 8lbs/3.5kg–33lbs/10kg. The standard model now has a trendy black leather alternative.

<u>Nappies</u> – **Change bags:** the Diaper Bag is semi-solid, so remains upright even when the two zipped compartments are opened; incorporates a changing pad and thermal bottle holder. The Backpack also holds a changing pad, is lightweight and has pockets that can be accessed without removing the pack.

Baby Boom UK 🖭

St.Martin's Walk, Dorking, Surrey RH4 1UT ☎ (01306) 887575
ᐧ᠐ www.baby-boom.co.uk/
Established 1996, this 2,500 sq ft Surrey showroom aims to meet "…all your baby needs"; it runs a very comprehensive, well organised website (and also organises personal shopping by appointment).

<u>Baby equipment</u> – **Stockists:** many major brands are stocked including Mamas & Papas, Bébé Confort, Britax, Maclaren, Maxi Cosi, Mutsy, Baby Bjorn and Clippasafe.

<u>Nursery decor</u> – **General stockists:** a good array of furniture and other items, from Eurobaby, just4kidz, Dutailier and Mamas & Papas nursery collection.

The Baby Closet 🖭

41a Broomwood Rd, London SW11 6HU ☎ (020) 7924 4457
ᐧ᠐ www.thebabycloset.co.uk
<u>Baby clothes</u> – **Mid-range:** simply laid-out online store that's the work of an ex-fashion buyer and sells items from a selection of quality but lesser-known ranges including No Added Sugar, Lili Gaufrette, Bob & Blossom and Album di Famiglia; she promises 24-hour despatch. – **Funky.** – **Premature deliveries.**

Baby Clothes Direct 🖭

Unit 32, Vulcan House, Vulcan Rd, Leics LE5 3EF ☎ (0116) 253 2297
ᐧ᠐ www.babyclothesdirect.co.uk
<u>Baby clothes</u> – **Cheap & cheerful:** packs of nightwear, romper suits and outdoor wear from £4; also bibs and gift sets. / *no Amex & no Switch.*

Baby Concierge 🖭

3 Hollyview Close, London NW4 3SZ ☎ (020) 8202 4060
ᐧ᠐ www.babyconcierge.co.uk
A 'personalised baby shopping service' that offers guidance and assistance across the whole range of baby equipment and nursery decor. Their pricing aims to be "the same as regular high street stores such as John Lewis". Private consultations take place in the London showroom. After the meeting a CD Rom featuring images of all the items discussed is sent to the client to help finalise decisions and involve others in the decision-making. The order is then delivered in bulk on a suitable date.

<u>Baby equipment</u> – **Stockists:** all major brands are sourced, as well as less well-known names; clients can see products up close and take larger, wheeled goods for a 'test drive'.

<u>Nursery decor</u> – **General stockists:** wide selection of furniture. – **Interior designers:** complete design service, including bespoke murals.

<u>Baby clothes</u> – **Mid-range:** the focus is on baby items from 0-3 months; brands include Petit Bateau, Melting Hearts, Daniela Besso and Bonne Nuit.

<u>Naming gifts</u> – **Naming gifts:** a mail order baby gift service (and baby gift list service) whose catalogue includes toys, funky changing mats, gift box sets, sleeping bags, blankets, personalised wooden gifts and designer nappy bags. There is no charge to set up a gift list if it is combined with a consultation, otherwise there is a £35 administration charge which includes delivery.

Baby Dan

5 Duke St, Southport PR8 1SE ☎ (01704) 547021 ᐧ᠐ www.babydan.com
Danish manufacturers of baby equipment. Call for details of stockists.

<u>Baby equipment</u> – **High chairs:** a variant on the Tripp Trapp.

<u>Nursery decor</u> – **Safety items:** a selection of safety gates and other home safety products. / *Hours: Mon-Fri 9am-5pm.*

Baby Days 🖭

84 High Street, Reigate, Surrey OH2 9AP ☎ (01737) 241126 ᐧ᠐ www.babydays-e.com/
<u>Baby equipment</u> – **Stockists:** a comprehensive online service from a clearly organised website, offering every sort of baby item from many top brand names. Or you can visit the shop, five minutes from the M25.

Baby Direct 🖭

92-96 New Roadside, Horsforth, Leeds LS18 4QB ☎ (0113) 225 0505
ᐧ᠐ www.baby-direct.com
Mainly suppliers to nurseries and local authorities but also to the general public.

<u>Baby equipment</u> – **Stockists:** general stockists of all baby equipment "all you've got to do is produce the baby!". Wide range of buggies including three wheelers. – **Buggies for twins and triplets:** stockists of a triplet buggy.
– **Buggy accessories:** useful source of accessories for buggies and advice on which ones will fit your particular buggy; specialists in

more unusual products. / *Hours: Mon-Sat 10am-*
pm; Sun 11am-4pm.

Baby Dux 🖼

Greenway, Warrington, Cheshire WA1 3EF
☎ (01925) 817 892 🔗 www.babydux.com
Nursery decor – Safety items: a website
offering 'innovative safety products for babies
and toddlers', including musical changing mats
and a safety bath frame.

Baby Echos (& Rad Pad) 🖼

Alison Brazendale, 349 Hungerford Road,
Crewe, Cheshire CW1 5EZ ☎ (01270) 255
201 🔗 www.babyechos.co.uk
A website offering innovative gadgets and
devices to help parents and to protect children.
Baby equipment – Stockists: items include the
'Fuss No More' (to distract babies while
dressing), and the memorably-named 'Vomit
Proof Vest' (to protect parents from their
offspring).
Nursery decor – Safety items: suppliers of the
'Rad pad' – a decorative protective cowling for
radiators. / *Delivery: p&p £3.50.*

Baby Einstein 🖼

The Walt Disney Company, 3 Queen
Caroline St, London W6 9PE ☎ (020) 8222
1571 🔗 www.babyeinstein.co.uk
Books, music & videos – Videos: videos,
DVDs, books, music CDs and toys aiming to
look at "real world objects, music, art,
language, science, poetry and nature in playful
and enriching ways". Baby Bach is a video for
birth to 3 years – a "whimsical award-winning
introduction to classical music for your little
one".

Baby Flair 🖼

PO Box 3, North Cave, Brough, East
Yorkshire HU15 2WU ☎ (0870) 246 1875
🔗 www.babyflair.co.uk
"For unique babies with original parents" is
this website's strapline, which includes made to
order nursery products.
Nursery decor – General stockists: cream
waffle, chambray and chocolate nursery sets
including sheets, cot bumpers, baby rockers
and more. **– Sleeping Bags:** baby fleece
sleeping bags in a range of (quite subdued)
colours.

Baby Gap

CENTRAL CONTACT DETAILS
☎ Customer services (01788) 866222; Head
office (01788) 818300
🔗 www.gap.com
BRANCHES:
40 Brompton Rd SW3 1ER
☎ (020) 7581 0321
Unit W24-25 Brent Cross NW4 3BA
☎ (020) 8202 9339
Unit F2 Bentalls Shopping Centre KT1 1TP
☎ (020) 8974 8073
376-384 Oxford St WC1 1JY
☎ (020) 7408 4500
Though all Gap Kids stores (see also) stock
much of the Baby Gap range, there are also
dedicated Baby Gap stores.
Baby clothes – Mid-range: well co-ordinated
casual clothes which are fashion-aware,
without making kids look like fashion victims;

bright colours, pastels and patterns appear in
denim, jersey and other classic 'Gap fabrics'.
Bib, £5.50; sleeveless body suit, £7.50;
embroidered denim pinafore, £240.

Baby Gem 🖼

Highway Farm, Downside, Cobham, Surrey
KT11 3JZ ☎ (01932) 863999
🔗 www.babygem.com
Though this luxury catalogue and website has
some 'neat' items – particularly toys – that you
might want for your own kids, the thrust of the
business is gifts. All items can be gift-wrapped
(with a hand-written note) for £3.99.
Naming gifts – Naming gifts: many gifts can
be personalised, and range from silver items
(Christening mug, £105) to nursery furniture
(chair, £80; stool, £55; rocking sheep, £225).
Baby toiletries, sleep sets, toys and clothes are
also available. / *free catalogue; Delivery: p&p £4.50.*

Baby Hut 🖼

PO Box 3401, Brighton BN1 3WE ☎ (01273)
245 864 🔗 www.babyhut.net
Distributors of a small range of baby goods,
majoring in slings. The website gives you
details of retailers, or you can order direct.
**Baby equipment – Portable sleeping
equipment:** suppliers of a range of hammocks
in different styles – from those meant as
alternatives to cribs and cots to play items.
– Slings: brands include Babylonia, Didymos
sling, Tie Sling, Carrier Cloth and Hug-a-bub.
Also Tri-Cotti and Tricot-Slen – the first of
these consists of two cylindrical shafts in which
you can carry the baby in four different
positions. The second is a long, wrapping cloth
with offers a further two possible positions.
Both allow the baby to be carried both curled
up in the foetal position, and in an upright
'kangaroo' position, so weight is not carried by
the baby's spine; broad straps distribute the
baby's weight over a wide area of the carrier's
body. **– Slings:** the strongest area of the range
– a number of up-and-coming types including
Tricotti, Babylonia, Didymos sling, Tie sling,
Carrier Cloth and Hug-a-bub.
**Nappies – Reusable stockists - brands
& singles:** washable cotton nappies. / *Hours: 24
hour answerphone.*

Baby Munchkins 🖼

🔗 www.babymunchkins.com
186 Hoxton St N1 HL5
☎ (020) 7684 5994
91 Kentish Town Rd NW5 5LH
North London duo of stores, also with an
extensive website that will deliver within
London.
Baby equipment – Stockists: an intelligently
chosen, if not huge range. **– Buggy suppliers:**
the website claims to showcase the largest
range of all-terrain pushchairs in the
country. / *Hours: Mon-Sat 10am-6pm; London.*

Baby Nest

230 London Rd, Croydon, Surrey CR0 2TF
☎ (020) 8667 9363 🔗 www.baby-nest.com
This Croydon store offers expectant parents
a payment plan – leave a 20% deposit and pay
off the costs of your goods in instalments. Full
payment must have been made before
collection.

Baby equipment – Stockists: stockists of all forms of baby equipment: furniture, car seats, buggies, mobiles, sterilisers. They claim to be able to "beat any price in London".
Baby clothes – Mid-range: range of clothes, including some for premature babies and formal occasions. / *Hours: Mon-Sat 9.30am-5.30pm; no Amex.*

Baby Planet 🖥
60 Melbourne Rd, Clacton-on-Sea, Essex CO15 3HZ ☎ (01255) 470314
🖱 www.baby-planet.co.uk
Mail order business, with a stall on Portobello Market every Saturday.
Baby clothes – Mid-range. – Funky: tie-dyed clothes in differing basic shades: T-shirts, bibs, hats, trainer pants, joggers, hooded sweatshirts, and vests; sleepsuits (in cotton or terry) for newborns £10.50. / *Hours: Mon-Fri 9.30am-5.30pm; online catalogue; Delivery: p&p free in England; Secure website, No Amex.*

Baby Pure 🖥
20 Midland Road, Thrapston, Northants
☎ Orderline (01832) 736784
🖱 www.babypure.co.uk
Shoes – Brands: cute, modern fabric shoes for pre or new walkers. Website includes details of stockists or can order on line.

Baby Snug 🖥
Small Start, 5 Elmsdale, Wightwick, Wolverhampton WV6 8ED ☎ (01902) 765 683 🖱 www.small-start.co.uk
Baby equipment – Portable sleeping equipment: cribs designed as an alternative to Moses baskets – a solid wood folding frame fabric bed, washable at high temperatures. The company reports that the bed (£145) follows FSID recommendations to give firm support. You can choose between a wipe-clean pvc mattress and a washable, breathable alternative. The cribs come complete with matching nappy bag, mattress and covered hardboard base for firmness.

Baby Treasures 🖥
670 Bradford Rd, Huddersfield HD2 2JY
☎ (01484) 519 494
🖱 www.babytreasures.co.uk
Naming gifts – Naming gifts: a large range of baby gifts, from the contemporary to the traditional. Personalisation is available.

Baby Whisperer 🖥
🖱 www.babywhisperer.com
Books, music & videos – Music tapes: a website linked to the author of the successful eponymous book, selling for example A Child's Gift of Lullabies and a range of videos, DVDs and CDs on related subjects.

Baby World 🖥
239 Munster Rd, London SW6 6BT ☎ (020) 7385 0059 🖱 www.babyworldlondon.co.uk
An "Aladdin's cave of children's goods" – most types of everything are included at this store in deepest Fulham, though the place is sufficiently densely stocked and jumbled that you may have to work to find what you are after.
Baby equipment – Stockists: claim to stock the largest range in London of specialist

equipment, including 12 types of 3-wheel all-terrain joggers, car seats and cots. Also carry nursery furniture.
Baby clothes – Mid-range: mainly French designs.
Toys – General stockists: stock most major brands, including Tomy & Chicco as well as wooden toys, soft toys, and books. / *Hours: Mon-Fri 10am-6pm, Sat 10am-5.30pm; Delivery: free in London (otherwise p&p extra).*

Babycare Direct 🖥
Craigearn, Kemnay, Aberdeenshire AB51 5LN ☎ (0870) 442 2580
🖱 www.babycare-direct.co.uk
Three-year-old online shop with a reasonable selection of goods in each category.
Baby equipment – Stockists: wide range of goods from a variety of manufacturers: prams, cots, car seats; equipment and accessories for bathing, changing, travelling and feeding; also safety items.
Nursery decor – General stockists: "Everything to decorate a child's bedroom", from curtains and bedding to character stickers and doorknobs. – **Safety items:** fire, stair and bed guards; safety locks; harnesses and baby monitors.
Baby clothes – Cheap & cheerful: competitively priced basics for babies: vests, bibs and rompers; Christening robes and shawls.
Toys – Pre-school specialists: good range for young children, from activity playmats to soft character toys, rattles and mobiles. / *Hours: Mon-Fri 10am-4pm; 300-page online catalogue; Delivery: p&p £4.00.*

Babydelix Films 🖥
☎ (07092) 199 789
Books, music & videos – Videos: a series of videos/DVDs (for about £12–£16) designed for babies, using classical music plus images of animals and animations to "boost creativity, concentration, musical and kinetic sense, and an affinity to nature".

Babylist 🖥
The Broomhouse, 50 Sulivan Rd, London SW6 3DX ☎ (020) 7371 5145
🖱 www.babylist.co.uk
"You deliver the baby – we deliver the rest". This advisory and supply service (similar to wedding list companies) aims to take the pressure and stress out of selecting and sourcing baby equipment. During one private consultation in their London showroom Babylist offers independent advice tailored to your needs. The firm then delivers to your door.
Maternity wear – Luxury: high quality range drawn from a selection of brands.
Baby equipment – Stockists: all major brands can be sourced for all the key items including prams, car seats and feeding equipment. – **Cots:** selection including natural oak cots.
Nursery decor – Furniture: quality furniture handmade in England – changing units, wardrobes and toy boxes. – **General stockists:** the showroom showcases a number of collection of fabrics, wallpapers and so on.
Baby clothes – Luxury: carefully selected range including Dimples, Marketing Mania and Petit Bateau. – **Traditional.** – **Christening**

gowns: from £95.
Naming gifts – **Naming gifts:** gift service
available for registered clients, with a number
of quality items to choose from. / *Hours: by
appointment; Delivery: p&p depending on weight and
destination (free for registered clients' full lists within
M25); no Amex.*

Babyou 🎴
19 Wychwood Rd, Rice, Great Missenden
HP16 0HB ☎ (01494) 868 383
🖰 www.babyou.com
On-line retailer majoring in wooden toys and
furniture; also the Baby Bjorn range of slings
and accessories.
Nursery decor – **Furniture:** an interesting
selection of quality items – changing stations,
beds and other furniture – in cheerful, modern,
styles with hand-painted decoration.
Toys – **Traditional toys:** a nice selection of
wooden items – from smaller toys through to
rocking horses. / *Hours: 24 hours; international.*

Babys Mart 🎴
4 River Terrace, Keynsham, Bristol
BS31 1HE ☎ (0870) 7878 978
🖰 www.babys-mart.co.uk/
Baby equipment – **Stockists:** comprehensive
website offering all types of equipment and
many of the leading brands.

Back 2 🎴
28 Wigmore St, London W1H 9DF ☎ (0800)
374604, (020) 7935 0351
🖰 www.back2.co.uk
Formerly known as Anatomia, a specialist
retailer stocking products aimed at alleviating
back problems.
Baby equipment – **High chairs:** stockists of
Tripp Trapp chairs. / *Hours: Mon-Fri 9am-5.30pm,
Sat 10am-6pm, Sun noon-5pm; free catalogue;
Delivery: p&p £5 (small products)-£20 (chairs, etc).*

Back in Action 🎴
11 Whitcomb St, London WC2H 7HA
☎ (020) 7930 8309
🖰 www.backinaction.co.uk
Mini chain operating in London with a couple
of Home Counties outlets; orders may also be
placed via the website. (The London store is
co-branded as the Children's Seating Centre).
Baby equipment – **Stockists:** in addition to
the Stokke Tripp Trapp and cot, stockists of
the Stokke Sleepi Care (a changing unit that
transforms into a writing desk), and the Sleepi
Campus (a play centre that doubles up as a bed
and matting – it can also double up as a toy
theatre or play area). / *Hours: Mon-Fri 9.30am-
5pm.*

The Back Shop 🎴
14 New Cavendish St, London W1G 8UW
☎ (020) 7935 9120
🖰 www.thebackshop.co.uk
Specialists in equipment designed to protect
the back.
Baby equipment – **Stockists:** the Zipper
all-terrain pushchair can be used by skaters.
- **High chairs:** range includes the Tripp Trapp
chair. / *Hours: Mon-Fri 10am-5.30pm, Sat 10.30am-
5pm; free catalogue.*

The Back Store 🎴
330 King St, London W6 0RR ☎ (020) 8741
5022 🖰 www.thebackstore.co.uk
Specialist retailers of ergonomically-designed
furniture.
Baby equipment – **High chairs:** stockists of
Tripp Trapp and offer high chairs.
Nursery decor – **Furniture:** range of
height-adjustable children's tables, desks and
chairs designed for school and home
use. / *Hours: Mon-Fri 9am-5pm, Sat 10am-4pm; free
catalogue; Delivery: p&p extra (eg chair £15).*

Back to Sleep 🎴
68 Pritchett Tower, Arthur Street, Small
Heath, Birmingham B10 0NY ☎ (0871) 700
0089 🖰 www.mimiproducts.com
Baby equipment – **Portable sleeping
equipment:** a baby hammock based on
traditional eastern designs, suitable from birth.
Soft-sided, it gives a baby the sense of security
with the potential to swing to soothe. The
frame folds flat when not in use and the
hammock itself is washable. Weighing around
3.8kg and stored in a compact pack, it will also
function as a travel cot. About £70, including
postage and packing.

Backyard Escapes 🎴
72 High Street, Horsell, Woking, Surrey
GU21 452 ☎ (01483) 771 161
🖰 www.plumproducts.com
Toys – **Outdoor items & active toys:**
produced in Canada by one of North America's
largest suppliers of modular wooden play
centres, and supplied flat pack for home
assembly. The recommended minimum units
cost £500. / *Hours: Mon-Fri 9am-5.30pm; Delivery:
includes p&p; no Amex.*

Baer & Ingram 🎴
Dragon Works, Leigh on Mendip, Radstock
BA3 5QZ ☎ (01373) 813800
🖰 www.baer-ingram.co.uk
The Fulham store no longer exists: the
business now is mail order only from near
Bath.
Nursery decor – **Wallpaper & fabrics:** fabrics
and wallpapers: patterns include Daisy Check
(pink, yellow, or blue wallpaper), Wallace
& Gromit (wallpaper and boards in 5 colours),
and the Village & Fanfare and Country Living
collections. / *free catalogue.*

Bambino Mio 🎴
12 Staveley Way, Northampton, Brixworth
NN6 9EU ☎ (01604) 883777
🖰 www.bambino.co.uk
Nappies – **Reusable stockists - multiple
brands:** all products pertaining to washable
nappies: nappies, covers, liners, etc. Various
brands of nappy covers are stocked (for
example, MioSoft), including ones with snap
fastenings for babies who have learnt to undo
Velcro, and the MioLite (made from
quick-drying polyester fabric that is light and
waterproof); also layered woven cotton inners
which are meant to be less bulky and more
absorbent than terry towelling; trial packs
available from £9.95. / *Hours: Mon-Fri 9am-
5.30pm, or answerphone; free catalogue; Delivery:
p&p included (minimum order £6); no Amex.*

Bao-Bab ⌂
210 Parkers House, 48 Regent St, Cambridge
CB2 1FD ☎ (01223) 894 158
⌂ www.bao-bab.co.uk
Launching April 2003
<u>Baby clothes</u> – **Eco-friendly clothing:** an
ethical clothing company for children (from
newborn to five years old), offering clothes in
organic cottons and hemps, coloured with
natural dyes including tumeric, logwood and
indigo. The owners claim that the organic
fabrics are particularly good for children with
eczema. The garments are even made in
a house run on eco principles, so shouldn't be
contaminated by cigarette smoke, perfumes or
household sprays.

Barefoot Books ⌂
124 Walcot St, Bath BA1 5BG ☎ (01225)
322400 ⌂ www.barefootbooks.com
<u>Books, music & videos</u> – **Bookshops:**
publisher of children's books with striking
illustrations, and a 'folk and fable' flavour with
a modern twist, plus CDs and stationery;
the 'Teachers Tent' has books for home
educators; also sold by agents – call for your
nearest supplier. / *Hours: Mon-Fri 8.30am-6pm.*

Bargains
89 Mitcham Rd, London SW17 9PD ☎ (020)
8767 6566
<u>Baby clothes</u> – **Cheap & cheerful:** full range
of children's clothing at modest prices. / *Hours:
Mon-Wed 9.30am-6pm, Thu-Sat 9.30am-6pm, Sun
10am-5pm; for orders £100+ within 10 mile radius.*

Barnes Buggy Repair Centre
100-106 Haydons Rd, London SW19 1AW
☎ (020) 8543 0505, 07946 870 958
<u>Baby equipment</u> – **Buggy & pram repairs:**
service, safety inspections and repairs of prams
and pushchairs; main service agent for
Maclaren, Bébé Confort, Britax, Bebecar and
Beebop; will also repair Mamas & Papas, Maxi,
Cosi and Jané. / *Hours: by appointment.*

John Barnett Shoes
137 Lordship Lane, London SE22 8HX
☎ (020) 8693 5145
<u>Shoes</u> – **Suppliers:** suppliers of branded shoes,
including Clarks, GBB and Kickers; Clarks
shoes are fitted. / *Hours: Mon-Sat 9.30am-5.30pm;
no Amex.*

Barney's Children's Store
6 Church Rd, London SW19 5DL ☎ (020)
8944 2915
Mainly clothes stockists, with some toys, gifts
and books. A toy box and videos help keep kids
occupied, and there is also a garden.
<u>Baby clothes</u> – **Luxury:** designer clothing
(Petit Bateau, IKKS, Kookai, Oxbow, Les
Robes, O'Neill, Quiksilver, Guess, Charavia,
Kenzo, Replay) – not traditional but a lot of
special occasion wear (girls party dresses
£35-£100), and some trendier casual clothes.
Also Christening gifts and a good range of
accessories (children's jewellery, hair slides
etc).
<u>Toys</u> – **General stockists:** mobiles and soft
toys: makes include Jellycat and Gund
(wooden toys). Range increases near
Christmas. / *Hours: Mon-Sat 10am-6pm, Sun noon-
5pm; no Amex.*

Kristin Baybars Q
7 Mansfield Rd, London NW3 2JD ☎ (020)
7267 0934
<u>Toys</u> – **Traditional toys:** mostly 'classical' toys
including second-hand items that aren't being
made any more, doll's houses, miniatures,
glove puppets and handmade products; many
items are based on simple scientific principles,
such as spinning tops, gyroscopes,
kaleidoscopes and flicker books.
– **Second-hand shops.** / *Hours: Tue-Sat 11am-
6pm; no credit cards.*

Beach Babes & Boys ⌂
48 Cranley Gardens, London N10 3AL
☎ (020) 8352 0359
⌂ www.beachbabesandboys.com
<u>Baby clothes</u> – **Sun-protection clothing:** sun
protection suits, made in the UK, from Lycra in
a variety of colours; also 'Kooshies', shoes, hats
with flaps, sunglasses and beach robes. / *free
catalogue.*

Beaming Baby ⌂
Unit 1, Place Barton Farm, Moreleigh,
Totnes, Devon TQ9 7JN ☎ (0800) 0345 672
⌂ www.beamingbaby.com
Mail order and internet business with a small
number of items in disparate areas – all of an
eco-friendly variety and towards the upper end
of the quality range; as well as the categories
listed, there is also a selection of lotions and
potions, gifts and small toys.
<u>Baby equipment</u> – **Specialist mattress
suppliers:** a number of natural fibre mattresses
in varying sizes.
<u>Nursery decor</u> – **Sleeping Bags:** undyed,
unbleached naturally-coloured merino wool:
0-9 months, 9-24 months.
<u>Baby clothes</u> – **Eco-friendly clothing:** organic
cotton towelling sleepsuit £5, towelling sleepsuit £9.99,
baby dress £13.
<u>Nappies</u> – **Suppliers-Eco friendly
disposables:** suppliers of Tushies nappies and
wipes; also various bathtime products.
MALTEX make and other towelling. / *Hours:
Mon-Fri 9am-5pm; free and on Web; Delivery: p&p
£3.95.*

Bearing Gifts ⌂
27 Crossland Crescent, Peebles H45 8LF
☎ (01721) 722 567 ⌂ www.bearing-gifts.com
<u>Naming gifts</u> – **Naming gifts:** babygift
delivery service on the web, specialising in
imported designer items including nursery
items, toys, outfits and gift sets.

Beautiful Mammas ⌂
4 West Road, off Lesbourne Road, Reigate,
Surrey RH2 7JT ☎ (01737) 246 888
⌂ www.beautifulmammas.com
Surrey shop, plus website with online ordering.
<u>Maternity wear</u> – **Mid-range:** a website
retailer of business, smart/casual and occasion
wear, and underwear. / *mammas.*

Beauty Tree
394 Lillie Rd, London SW6 ☎ (020) 7385
3611
<u>Hairdressers</u> – **Hairdressers:** basic children's
haircuts £6.50 (up to five years old), £10.50 (up
to 10 years old). / *Hours: Tue-Fri 9am-8pm, Sat
9am-5pm (no children on Sat).*

Bébé Amour 🖃
Bébé Amour, P.O.Box 426, High Wycombe,
Bucks HP10 8RN ☎ (0870) 420 4893
🖰 www.bebeamour.co.uk
Mail order baby essentials and gifts with five
sections (clothes, toys, home, mum and gifts)
of which the first has the greatest selection.
__Baby clothes__ – __Mid-range:__ a number of
attractive fleeces in varying sizes, £18.99
matching raincoats (£21.99) and wellies
(£12.99); denim hand-knit jumper £35; assorted
other items.
__Toys__ – __General stockists:__ the range is on the
traditional side, and offers a reasonable
selection of smaller items; Noah's Ark with
animals £24.99. / _Hours: 9am-5.30pm; free
catalogue; Delivery: p&p £3.95; no Amex._

Bébé Confort
🖰 www.bebeconfort.com/UK/
Quality French make.
__Baby equipment__ – __Wheeled
Transport-brands:__ the strength of this brand is
their pram-pushchair combination styles, also
an all-terrain three-wheeler; call for brochures
and a list of stockists. – __Car seat brands:__
makers of car seats and travel cots.

Bébécar UK
Bébécar House, Mill Hill Industrial Estate,
Flower Lane, London NW7 2HU ☎ (020)
8201 0505 🖰 www.bebecar.co.uk
The brand's main showroom – call for lists of
local stockists and agents.
__Baby equipment__ – __Wheeled
Transport-brands:__ as well as the standard
range of pushchairs, some models come with
optional large air tyres.
__Nursery decor__ – __General stockists:__ décor,
furnishings, furniture and bedroom furniture;
changing stations, playpens, drawers,
cupboards and cots, including
cot-beds. / _Hours: Mon-Fri 9am-5.30pm._

Bebeworld 🖃
191 Balham High Rd, London SW12 9BE
☎ (020) 8675 8871 🖰 www.bebeworld.co.uk
Small but well-stocked shop offering
"everything for baby".
__Baby equipment__ – __Stockists:__ prams,
pushchairs, three wheelers, cots, highchairs,
nursery furniture and car seats from brands
including Mamas & Papas, Bébé Confort,
Britax, Maclaren, Cosatto, Jané and
Emmaljunga; also Tripp Trapp chairs and
sleepi cots. – __Buggy & pram repairs:__ repairs
service for all makes.
__Baby clothes__ – __Mid-range:__ small range of
clothes for children under two; babygrows
(£4-5). – __Premature deliveries.__
__Toys__ – __Pre-school specialists:__ brands include
Galt and Tomy; lots of wooden toys. / _Hours:
Mon-Sat 9.30am-5.30pm (Wed 1.30pm); free
catalogue._

Carey Beckett 🖃
Hurstcroft, 32 Market St, Fordham,
Cambridgeshire CB7 5LQ ☎ (01638)
720323, mobile (077861) 95555
__Nursery decor__ – __Accessories:__ hand-painted
presents for children customised with names or
initials, for example Mason Pearson hair
brushes, with hand mirrors and matching

tooth mugs; pictures include ribbons and
flowers, teddies, trains or tractors; endeavour
to despatch within 24 hours of order. / _Hours:
Mon-Fri 10am-4pm, or answerphone; no credit cards._

Beckett's Bookshop 🖃
6 Bellevue Rd, London SW17 7EG ☎ (020)
8672 4413
__Books, music & videos__ – __Bookshops:__
one-third of this local bookshop is devoted to
children's titles. Fiction and non-fiction books,
as well as a few educational and curriculum
titles are available, and there's a good selection
of picture and board books for the under-twos,
and a basket of toys for kids to play
with. / _Hours: Mon-Sat 9.30am-5.30pm, Sun 10am-
5pm; Delivery: p&p extra._

Beddy Bears 🖃
11 Wheatley Court, Glasgow T32 7JP
☎ (0797) 425 3396
__Toys__ – __Comforters:__ children's teddy shaped
hot water bottles filled with treated wheat
which can be heated in a microwave. They are
scented with lavender, to encourage sleep.

Bedrooms for Kids 🖃
Unit 2 Gordon St, Birkenhead, Wirral
CH41 2JQ ☎ (0151) 650 2401
🖰 www.friezeframe.com;
www.bedroomsforkids.com
__Nursery decor__ – __Murals and other
Decorating:__ mural DIY kits for nurseries and
children's bedrooms. Designs include
underwater world, dolphins, jungle,
old-fashioned steam train, woodland scene,
teddy bears picnic, dinosaurs, space (suitable
for slightly older kids), Formula One and
clowns. Co-ordinating fabric for six of the
designs is available for making pillowcases,
duvets and curtains. Call for list of your nearest
outlet (including Homebase and Fads – they
may not hold stock but should be able to loan
you a promotional video or design book) or
you can buy direct. / _Hours: Mon-Fri 9am-5.30pm;
Sat 9am-5pm; view online; Delivery: p&p included._

Benetton
CENTRAL CONTACT DETAILS
☎ (020) 7495 5482
🖰 www.benetton.com
BRANCHES:
_(Only selected branches are listed –
call the enquiry line for other outlets.)_
255-259 Regent St W1R 7AD
☎ (020) 7647 4200
23-27 Brompton Rd SW3
☎ (020) 7591 0925
Unit 16, Brent Cross Shopping Centre NW4
☎ (020) 8203 9056
Unit L084, Bluewater Shopping Centre
☎ (020) 8563 9685
The flagship Oxford Circus store (listed as
Regent St) is the biggest stockist of Benetton's
'Zero Tondo' (0-12) range in the world.
__Baby clothes__ – __Mid-range:__
remorselessly-promoted brand of bright,
colourful, well-made, fun clothing with
continental styling; natural fabrics dominate;
dresses around £14. / _Hours: Regent St, Mon-Sat
10am-7pm (Thu 8pm)._

Bentalls

25 Clarence St, Kingston upon Thames KT1
☎ (020) 8546 1001
(There isn't a branch in Ealing any more.)
Baby equipment – **Stockists:** cots, bedding
and pushchairs (including Mamas & Papas and
Maclaren).
Nursery decor – **General stockists:** bedding,
wallpaper and curtains.
Baby clothes – **Mid-range.**
Shoes – **Suppliers:** shoes from Buckle my
Shoe.
Toys – **General stockists:** small departments
in both stores: Lego, Playmobil, Barbie, Little
Tikes, Brio and Fisher-Price.

Bettacare 🖳

Bettacare House, 9-10 Faygate Business
Centre, Faygate, West Sussex RH12 4DN
☎ (01293) 851896 ∽ www.bettacare.co.uk
Manufacturer and supplier of nursery products,
by mail order, or contact them for details of
your nearest stockist.
Baby equipment – **Stockists:** bouncing
cradles; safety equipment, such as safety gates,
car seats, bath supports and
head-huggers. / *Hours: Mon-Fri 8.30am-5pm; free
catalogue; Delivery: p&p £1.75 (for orders up to £10),
£3.50 (£10–£60), free for orders over £60; no Amex.*

The Better Baby Sling Company 🖳

47 Brighton Rd, Watford, Herts WD24 5HN
☎ (01923) 444442
∽ www.betterbabysling.co.uk
Baby equipment – **Slings:** sling available in
Blackwatch tartan or navy blue in washable
fabric; one size only (up to 42 inch chest);
£34.95 includes postage and packaging; enables
you to carry a baby, apparently even twins, in
a variety of positions, including for
breast-feeding. / *Hours: Mon-Sat 9.30am-3pm; free
catalogue; Delivery: p&p included.*

Bexley Toys 🖳

The Cottage, Rattlesden Rd, Drinkstone,
Bury St Edmunds, Suffolk IP30 9TL
☎ (01449) 736408
Nursery decor – **Furniture:** chairs in a variety
of shapes – cats, pigs and rooster.
Toys – **Traditional toys:** around 25
hand-crafted toys including a Noah's Ark
which dismantles like a 3-D jigsaw, push-along
wooden ducks or penguins, puzzles and cot
mobiles. / *Hours: 24hr answerphone; free leaflet;
Delivery: p&p extra.*

BHS

CENTRAL CONTACT DETAILS
☎ Head office (020) 7262 3288
∽ www.bhs.co.uk
BRANCHES:
*(Only selected branches are listed –
call the enquiry line for other outlets.)*
252–258 Oxford St W1N 9DC
☎ (020) 7629 2011
Unit 68–48 Surrey Quays Shopping Centre,
Redriff SE16 1LL
☎ (020) 7237 3156
129-133 High Rd, Ilford IG1 1DE
☎ (020) 8478 5208
Baby clothes – **Cheap & cheerful:** bright
fashion-led collection of children's clothing in

good-quality fabrics; also shoes, accessories an
swimwear; check shirt, £7; embroidered
trousers, £16. / *Hours: mostly Mon-Sat 9.30am-
6pm.*

Bibs 'n' Stuff 🖳

26 Bonehurst Road, Salfords Industrial
Estate, Near Redhill, Surrey RH1 5EW
☎ (01923) 774924 ∽ www.bibsandstuff.com
Online equipment suppliers who pride
themselves "on supplying unique products tha
are… practical but also very different from
anything else you can buy elsewhere." The site
has four areas: feeding, toiletting, bedtime and
bathtime.
Baby equipment – **High chairs:** stockists of
'The Svan' – a Swedish-designed adjustable
wooden chair that can be used from about six
months–adult; children can be raised to the
same level of the table and – unlike the Tripp
Trapp – you can also initially use it as
a traditional high chair with the addition of
a clip-on tray; about £100, tray and safety bar
for young babies about £20 each.
Nappies – **Potty training:** the Rymax
FamilySeat is a single unit that looks like
a traditional wooden loo seat, but also
incorporates a smaller child-seat; £30.
– **Protective bedding:** sheet and mattress
protector – £15.

Bicester Village

50 Pingle Drive, Bicester, Oxfordshire
OX26 6WD ☎ (01869) 323200
∽ www.bicestervillage.com
Discount shopping village at Junction 9 of the
M40.
Baby clothes – **Luxury:** around 90
end-of-season clothing outlets, including
designer labels such as Ralph Lauren, Cerruti,
Descamps, Jaeger, Petit Bateau, Clarks Shoes
and Paul Smith; play area. / *Hours: Mon-Sun
10am-6pm; Sat 10am-7pm.*

Bickiepegs 🖳

5 Blackburn Industrial Estate, Kinellar,
Aberdeen AB2 0RX ☎ (01224) 790626
∽ www.bickiepegs.co.uk
Manufacturers of hard teething biscuits (sold in
all leading chemists), who also offer useful
baby items by mail order.
Baby equipment – **Stockists:** items available
by mail order include: American and
Norwegian toothbrushes; a bath thermometer;
the Doidy Cup – a sloping cup that makes
drinking easier; the Infa-dent toothbrush which
fits on a finger which can be used to massage
gums while teething, and to brush first teeth;
and fluoride-free toothpaste. / *Hours: Mon-Sat
9am-6pm; free catalogue.*

Biff

43 Dulwich Village, London SE21 7BN
☎ (020) 8299 0911
Baby clothes – **Mid-range:** many clothes for
the older child and baby to six years old; makes
include Petit Bateau, Jean Bourget, Lili
Gaufrette, Weekend a La Mer and Catamini.
The range spans socks at £1.75 to dresses for
over £100. Also Bobux leather baby shoes,
beach shoes, Flap Happy sun protection hat
and swimwear. – **Christening gowns:** silk
Christening robes by Collins and Hall some

ver £100. / *Hours: Mon-Fri 9.30am-5.30pm, Sat 10am-6pm; Delivery: p&p extra; no Amex.*

Big Hugs
5 Litchfield Grove, Finchley, London N3 2JL
☎ (020) 8343 0286 ◌ www.thebighugs.com
Nursery decor – Bedding: snazzy kids' duvet covers, flat sheets, valances and quilts in 100% cotton – lots of big designs with bears, ballet dancers and nursery rhyme characters.

Bigjigs
Imsfield, Canterbury Rd, Ottinge, Elham, Kent CT4 6XH ☎ (01303) 863900
◌ www.woodentoysonline.co.uk
Nursery decor – Accessories: wooden nursery items including coat hooks, door plaques and eight charts.
Toys – Traditional toys: traditionally-styled wooden toys, lorries, cars and trains; bright wooden jigsaws with an educational slant from very simple to 200 pieces). / *free catalogue; Visa, Mastercard, Switch.*

Bio-Bubs (& Hugabub)
2 Charminster Rd, London SE9 4BT
☎ (07929) 354 057 ◌ www.bio-bubs.co.uk, www.hugabub.com
Baby equipment – Slings: bio-Bubs™ is also the main UK distributor of the hug-a-bub® baby carrier from Byron Bay, Australia.
Baby clothes – Eco-friendly clothing: babygrows, bodysuits and sleepwear made from 100% organic cotton, dyed using environmentally responsible dyes and with nickel-free fastenings.
Nappies – Reusable stockists - brands & singles: a "Unique Complete Washable Nappies Starter Kit".

Birkenstock
CENTRAL CONTACT DETAILS
☎ Mail order (0800) 132194, Customer Services (020) 7603 2644
◌ www.birkenstock.co.uk
BRANCHES:
HQ: 1 Addison Bridge Place W14 8XP
☎ Mail order (0800) 132194, Customer Services (020) 7603 2644
70 Neal St WC2H 9PA
☎ (020) 7240 2762
Shoes – Brands: a Continental brand of adult and children's shoes – wide sandals and clogs for kids from Continental size 24 (the equivalent of a UK 6) in wide and narrow widths, in waterproofed leather or Birkoflaw leather look). One design comes with extra footbeds in the next size up, extending the life of the shoe. The mail order service provides you with a sheet on which to draw the outline of the foot, to ensure a correct fit. – **Suppliers:** the Covent Garden shop just stocks their own brand – other stockists in London include the Natural Shoe Company (not listed). / *Hours: Mon-Fri 10am-6pm, Sat 10am-6.30pm, Sun noon-5.30pm; free brochure.*

Birth & Beyond
8 Butts Close, Aynho, Oxfordshire
OX17 3AE ☎ (01869) 811099, (0870) 905 7878 ◌ www.birthandbeyond.co.uk
Baby equipment – Cots: suppliers of the Bettersleep, an innovative hammock-style bed on a frame; suitable until a baby is 12 months old (or 12kg, or until a baby can kneel/stand/sit). Designed in Australia to promote calm in colicky or unsettled babies, the idea is that newborns feel continuously cuddled (as in the womb) and can be easily rocked. It is used in maternity units, nurseries and hospitals for babies with respiratory conditions; expert endorsements claim it encourages development. Foldable and lightweight (around 9kg), it can be used in the home and as a travel cot; cost from £195 or rent from £25 a month (minimum three months) with an option to buy (deducting rental to date); organic cotton version (from £250), sheets and mattress covers also available. / *Hours: Mon-Fri 9.30am-6pm (Sat 1pm); online catalogue; Delivery: p&p £10 (next day delivery); no credit cards.*

Bishopston Trading Company
193 Gloucester Rd, Bishopston, Bristol
BS7 8BG ☎ (0117) 924 5598
◌ www.bishopstontrading.co.uk
Workers' co-op set up in 1985 to create employment in a south Indian village – a business combining mail order with five shops in the west of England. Designs are made exclusively for the company from hand-woven cotton or other natural fibres; four catalogues a year.
Maternity wear – Mid-range: the company no longer produces a specific maternity range but a lot of their ethnic-inspired clothing suits pregnancy.
Nursery decor – Accessories: children's cotton duvet covers, sheets and so on, in a range of simple but attractive embroidered and appliqued designs. Baby mats and cots also available.
Baby clothes – Mid-range. – Funky: unusual garments made from hand loom organic cotton. Reversible rompers £13.90. Appliqued baby jackets £15.90.
Toys – General stockists: fabric baby letter cubes £2.95; dolls clothes set/Indian dolls £5-£12. / *Hours: Mon-Sat 9.30am-5.30pm; free catalogue with swatch card of colours.; Delivery: p&p £3.20; no Amex.*

Blacks Camping Shops
CENTRAL CONTACT DETAILS
☎ (01604) 441111
◌ www.blacks.co.uk
BRANCHES:
(Only selected branches are listed – call the enquiry line for other outlets.)
53 Rathbone Place W1
☎ (020) 7636 6645
176 Kensington High St W8 7RG
☎ (020) 7361 0060
Mall 4, Brent Cross NW4 3FP
☎ (020) 8203 9895
10-11 Holborn EC2N 2LE
☎ (020) 7404 5681
L61 Lower Thames Walk, Bluewater Shopping Centre DA9 9SJ
☎ (01332) 624288
Any equipment that you have seen in one of their shops can be supplied by the mail order side of the business, by next day delivery.
Baby equipment – Stockists - slings & backpacks: stockists of Karrimor papooses

(with special waterproof covers and sun shades) and baby carriers. / *Hours: hours vary; free catalogue (which does not include baby gear); Delivery: p&p extra (max £5).*

Debbie Bliss ☎
☎ (01535) 664222
🖱 www.debbiebliss.freeserve.co.uk
Well-known knitwear designer whose books include 'Debbie Bliss Baby Style'.
Baby clothes – Knitwear: primarily a mail order company for those who are keen to knit their own clothes: kits, yarns and books are stocked; designs range from traditional to modern, with some toys and cushions. Some ready-made items are available – contact for details. Saturday knitting workshops can help you improve your technique. / *online catalogue; no Amex.*

Blooming Marvellous ☎
CENTRAL CONTACT DETAILS
☎ Customer services (0870) 751 8966, Catalogue requests (0870) 751 8944, Order line (0870) 751 8977
🖱 bloomingmarvellous.co.uk
BRANCHES:
725 Fulham Rd SW6 5UL
☎ (020) 7371 0500
12c Eton Street TW9 1EE
☎ (020) 8948 1010
23 Oakdene Parade, Cobham KT11 2LR
☎ (01932) 864343
U071 Upper Thames Walk, Bluewater Shopping Centre D9 5AR
☎ (01322) 427823
"The UK's leading maternity wear company" – this 21-year old firm is still to a large extent a catalogue company (four per year), though they now also have ten shops (only the two London branches are listed) and a sophisticated website. The Fulham Road branch is their flagship store, but all outlets carry the whole range in the catalogue. Maternity wear remains the lynchpin of the range.
Maternity wear – Mid-range: the biggest range of maternity wear in the country, with items to suit all ages from teenagers to executives in the mid-price range. The range majors in very wearable mix and match basics, though it does run to more designer looks: cotton T-shirt, £15; cotton button front sweatshirt, £27; most dresses are around £40. Also a good variety of nightwear and swimwear. **– Bras and underwear:** drop and zip cup nursing and pregnancy bras, plus maternity tights and knickers.
Baby equipment – Stockists: a large range of baby clobber, including bottle warmers, storage gear, bedding, swimming gear, lots of travel-related products (including travel cots and anti-tip stroller weights), feeding and bathing equipment and more.
Nursery decor – General stockists: the range covers most of the bases, including a selection of nursery furniture.
Baby clothes – Mid-range: a wide range up to aged two, for example kids' basics bright cotton jersey separates – T-shirt, £7; tracksuit bottoms, £11; hooded fleece cardigan, £15. In summer, selection includes beach shoes, some swimwear and hats and sun protection gear.
Toys – Pre-school specialists: a selection of

first toys including Gymini gym, playnest, Skwish rattle, and more. / *Hours: mail order Mon–Sun 8am-8pm, 24hr answerphone other times; all stores open Mon–Sun (times vary).; free catalogue; Delivery: p&p £3.95; no Amex.*

Bobux ☎
Marketing Mania Ltd, Unit 15 Hackford Walk, 119-123 Hackford Rd, London SW9 0QT ☎ Order line (07002) 466466
🖱 www.goo-goo.com
A quality brand available via mail order and at many retailers.
Shoes – Brands: "The shoes that stay on" are designed in New Zealand, handmade in soft leather with flexible non-skid safety soles, with an ankle elastic system making them easy to slip on. The firm was the first to produce this type of style. Shoe sizes range from 2-6.5 (size chart included in catalogue). Wide variety of colours, including a pastel girl's range, and star or teddy motifs, £15.50; designs range from classic to contemporary. 'Sole Mania' durable and washable suede shoes are also available for children over two. / *Hours: 24hr answerphone; free catalogue; Delivery: p&p included; no Amex.*

Body Comfort ☎
77 Hardinge Rd, London NW10 3PN
☎ (020) 8459 2910
🖱 www.maternitybras.co.uk
Maternity wear – Bras and underwear: antenatal teachers Julie Krausz and George Rogerson run this mail order company; stockists of Bravado maternity and nursing bras in a range of colours, £20.95; also washable breast pads, £11.25 for 10.

The Bolingbroke Bookshop
147 Northcote Rd, London SW11 6QB
☎ (020) 7223 9344
Books, music & videos – Bookshops: this general bookshop stocks over 2000 childrens titles, and is particularly strong on books for under-fives. There are toys for kids to play with, and a good range of family healthcare books. / *Hours: Mon-Sat 9.30am-6pm, Sun 11am-4pm.*

Bon-Bleu
Unit 2, Kendal Court, Kendal Avenue, London W3 0RU ☎ (020) 8992 5611
🖱 www.bon-bleu.com
Baby clothes – Luxury: "Fashionable and practical clothes", from 0-14 years. The website gives details of retail stockists.

Billie Bond ☎
Warners Farm, Howe St, Great Waltham, Essex CM3 1BL ☎ (01245) 360164
🖱 www.billiebond.com
Nursery decor – Furniture: hand-stencilled solid pine nursery furniture made to order. Specialise in bespoke childrens beds, including bunk and cabin beds.
Naming gifts – Naming gifts: traditional wooden gifts and toys, all of which can be personalised, e.g. four-legged stools with name and date of birth, from £40. / *Hours: 24hr answerphone; gift brochure, free; furniture brochure, £2.50 (refundable against first order); Delivery: p&p £4.50 under £75.*

Bonne Nuit 🖼
7 Galveston Rd, London SW15 2RZ ☎ (020)
8871 1472 🖱 www.bonne-nuit.co.uk
Mail order specialists in French-made baby
sleeping bags; other 'bedtime' items have been
added to the range – bathrobes, hooded
towels, slippers, laundry bags.
Naming gifts – **Naming gifts:** a number of gift
packages from £40-£100. / *Delivery: p&p £3 (free
over £50).*

BonPoint
CENTRAL CONTACT DETAILS
☎ (020) 7584 8826
🖱 www.bonpoint.fr
17 Victoria Grove W8 5RW
☎ (020) 7584 8826
35b Sloane St SW1X 9LP
197 Westbourne Gr W11 2SE
38 Old Bond St W1
Worldwide French chain (whose Kensington
branch previously traded as Anthea Moore
Ede).
Baby clothes – **Traditional:** high quality
traditional clothes at the upper end of the price
scale. / *Hours: Mon-Fri 9am-5pm, Sat 10am-1pm;
closed for lunch hour; other shops Mon-Fri 10am-6pm.*

Book People Ltd 🖼
Parc Menai, Bangor LL57 4FB ☎ Customer
Enquiries (0870) 607 7780, Orderline (0870)
607 7740 🖱 www.thebookpeople.co.uk
Books, music & videos – **Bookshops:** not
really a bookshop, nor a bookclub – more
a sort of phenomenon: The Book People have
grown explosively over the years supplying
books through reps in offices. More lately the
same deep discount range has become
available mail order and online – you can bag
great savings, even sometimes on the biggest
names and always with a selection of kids titles.

Bookends
25-28 Thurloe Place, London SW7 2HQ
☎ (020) 7589 2285
Books, music & videos – **Bookshops:** this
bookshop, located close to the South
Kensington museums, specialises in books on
papercrafts, but also has a wide general range
of books for under-twos, as well as more
unusual books, lots of activity packs and audio
cassettes. / *Hours: Mon-Fri 9am-6.30pm, Sat 10am-
5pm, Sun 2pm-6pm.*

Books etc.
Unit F, Whiteleys Of Bayswater, Queensway,
London W2 4YQ ☎ (020) 7229 3865
🖱 www.booketc.co.uk
Books, music & videos – **Bookshops:** now
part of Borders UK, all branches of Books etc.
stock a number of children's titles and are
generally child-friendly. The listed branch (at
Whiteleys) has one of the best children's areas,
with a café and branch of Paperchase in-store.
The branches at Wimbledon, Croydon and
Finchley Road O2 Centre are also good for
children. / *Hours: Mon-Sat 10am-10pm,
Sun12.30pm-6pm.*

Books for Children 🖼
Greater London House, Hampstead Rd,
London NW1 7TZ ☎ (020) 7760 6500
🖱 www.booksforchildren.co.uk
Books, music & videos – **Book clubs:** online
children's bookshop – one of a series of the
Books Direct book clubs; over 100 titles for
children of all ages.

Bookseller Crow on the Hill 🖼
50 Westow St, Crystal Palace, London
SE19 3AF ☎ (020) 8771 8831
🖱 www.booksellercrow.com
Books, music & videos – **Bookshops:**
extensive child's section for a smallish shop
whose owner writes book reviews for Families
Southeast; range includes board books, buggy
buddies, large range of picture books for young
children and extensive book range for
beginning readers; play area. / *Hours: Mon-Fri
9am-7.30pm, Sat 9am-6.30pm, Sun 11am-5pm; no
Amex.*

Bookspread
Trident Business Centre, Bickersteth Rd,
London SW17 9SH ☎ (020) 8767 6377/4551
🖱 www.bookspread.co.uk
Books, music & videos – **Bookshops:** a
bookshop in the same building as the
Children's Discovery Centre (a charity which
organises children's events) which also runs
mobile bookshops for schools and a schools
advisory service. It is largely aimed at primary
school-age children, but there are also titles for
pre-schoolers. / *Hours: Mon-Fri 9.30am-5.30pm,
Sat 9.30am-3.30pm.*

Bookstart
45 Easthill, London SW18 2QZ ☎ (020) 8516
2977 🖱 www.bookstart.co.uk

Books, music & videos – **Book clubs:** a
scheme available in certain boroughs only,
providing a pack of two or three starter books
for families with a baby. It is generally run in
conjunction with local libraries, encouraging
parents to take out membership for children. If
you don't get any books at the baby's 8-month
check, ask your health visitor if there is
anywhere you can apply for them.

Bookworm
1177 Finchley Rd, London NW11 0AA
☎ (020) 8201 9811
Books, music & videos – **Bookshops:** this
north London store exclusively stocks titles for
children of all ages. They run a reading club
('Storytime', with readings twice a week), hold
events and competitions and publish a regular
newsletter, and there's a play area for
children. / *Hours: Mon-Sat 9.30am-5.30pm, Sun
10am-1.30pm; no Amex.*

Boomerang Q
69 Blythe Rd, London W14 0HP ☎ (020)
7610 5232 🖱 www.boomerangonline.co.uk
New and nearly-new store.
Baby equipment – **Second-hand:** prams,
wooden playpens, buggies, cots, highchairs, etc.
Baby clothes – **Second-hand shops:** variety of
second-hand items and leather booties.
Toys – **Second-hand shops:** specialise in new
wooden toys and second hand toys. / *Hours:
Mon-Sat 10am-6pm (closed Sun).*

Boots 📖

CENTRAL CONTACT DETAILS

☎ Customer services (08450) 708090

🖰 www.boots.com

BRANCHES:

(Branches throughout London –
call the enquiry line for your nearest outlet.)
Though its competitors are breathing down its
neck, the UK's biggest chemists still has a wide
range to offer parents. Many London branches
do not stock their maternity/childrens' range
of clothes, equipment and toys, but all are
available through the 'Mother & Baby at
home' catalogue (Brent Cross and Kensington
High St are the only branches that stock the
full range of both baby and maternity items).

<u>Maternity wear</u> – **Bras and underwear:**
catalogue only: small pure cotton range of
good basics with some more stylish extras,
such as: palazzo pants, £16; sleeveless A-line
dress, £20; also nightwear, swimwear, lingerie
and tights.

<u>Baby equipment</u> – **Stockists:** all stores have
items such as feeding equipment and safety
devices. Cots, car seats and pushchairs are only
available from the catalogue.

<u>Baby clothes</u> – **Cheap & cheerful:** available in
some branches and the catalogue: co-ordinated
garments at mid-range prices in a variety of
bright and modern styles that are very good on
child-scale details (nothing clumsy); lots of
matching accessories; lovely 'newborn' range
in white, sleepsuits two-pack, £12; in 250 stores
across the UK the range merits a stand-alone
boutique area.

<u>Shoes</u> – **Brands:** a range of own-brand tiny soft
shoes and bootees: sizes 00-3.

<u>Toys</u> – **Own brand:** all own-brand; fun,
colourful and original selection which tends to
the educational without being dull such as
a 'learn-to-dress clown', 'animal piano', or the
excellent, award-winning 'Musical Octopull'.

<u>Nappies</u> – **Reusable stockists - brands**
& singles: two-in-one waterproof overpants
with washable absorbent pad in soft terry,
reportedly more absorbent than standard. The
overpant includes soft elastication and
a leakage barrier. / *free 'Mother & Baby at home'*
catalogue (not available in shops).

Borders

🖰 www.borders.com

BRANCHES:

120 Charing Cross Rd WC2H 0JR
☎ (020) 7379 8877
203-207 Oxford St W1R 1AH
☎ (020) 7292 1600

<u>Books, music & videos</u> – **Bookshops:** giant
American book superstore chain which also
owns the home-grown Books etc. chain
(concentrated in London). Its branches have
large children's departments with good
selections for under-twos. / *Hours: Mon-Sat*
8.30am-11pm, Sun noon-6pm.

Born 📖

64 Gloucester Rd, Bishopston, Bristol
BS7 8BH ☎ (0117) 924 5080

🖰 www.borndirect.com

The company (formerly called First-Born)
specialises in reusable nappies, but also stocks
a wide range of products for mother and baby;
the range (they claim "the largest selection of

natural and practical products for parents and
their baby") includes many
environmentally-friendly and less commonly
available products.

<u>Baby equipment</u> – **Stockists:** off-road
pushchairs and buggies, including
three-wheelers and the Bugaboo Frog.
– **Slings:** stockists of the Hugababy, Wilkinet
and Hippychick child seat. – **Stockists - slings**
& backpacks: backpacks from LittleLife and
Bush Baby.

<u>Nursery decor</u> – **Furniture:** as well as a range
of nursery furniture, this company stocks
Stokke's cot and the firm's Tripp Trapp high
chair.

<u>Baby clothes</u> – **Eco-friendly clothing:** range
of clothing including outdoor wear, underwear
and sleepwear; mostly in organic cotton and
wool.

<u>Shoes</u> – **Suppliers:** soft leather shoes and
padders.

<u>Toys</u> – **Traditional toys:** primarily nifty
stackable wooden items and mobiles.

<u>Nappies</u> – **Reusable stockists - multiple**
brands: wide range of washable and reusable
nappies; lots of different brand names; nappy
accessories also stocked, including trainer
pants. / *Hours: Mon-Sat 9.30am-5.30pm; online*
catalogue; no Amex.

Born Gifted 📖

Unit 414 Solent Business Centre, Millbrook
Road West, Southampton SO15 0HW
☎ (023) 8078 3338 🖰 www.borngifted.co.uk
Luxury baby gifts and nursery accessories.

<u>Naming gifts</u> – **Naming gifts:** on-the-web
baby gifts listings, wedding-style. There's
a decent selection of 'topdrawer' gifts,
including 'heirloom' toys such as £100 bears,
and a £300 Noah's Ark.

Bouncy Kids

26 Kingsland Shopping Centre, London E8
☎ (020) 7254 2420

<u>Baby clothes</u> – **Cheap & cheerful:** clothing.

Boutique Descamps 📖

197 Sloane St, London SW1X 9QX ☎ (020)
7235 6957 🖰 www.descamps.com
General linen and towelling store where stock
largely showcases the Petit Descamps range of
nursery linen (also found at John Lewis, House
of Fraser, etc), towels and bathrobes; also soft
toys.

<u>Nursery decor</u> – **Accessories:** towelling bath
robes and other nursery products. – **Bedding:**
nursery bedding ranges include sheets,
pillowcases, cot bumpers and duvet covers;
plain white or different colours. / *Hours: Mon-*
Sat 10am-6.30pm (Wed 7.30pm); free brochure;
Delivery: p&p extra.

Bowleys

CENTRAL CONTACT DETAILS

☎ (01932) 226688

BRANCHES:

34 Church Rd, Stanmore HA7 4AL
☎ (020) 8954 6381
72-73 George St TW9 1HE
☎ (020) 8940 1564

<u>Shoes</u> – **Suppliers:** part of Johnsons Shoes (see
also).

Boxtot 🖃
Suite 6, Silk House, Park Green, Macclesfield
SK11 7QJ ☎ (01625) 430085
🖰 www.boxtot.com
Naming gifts – Naming gifts: handmade gift
boxes with treats for a new baby; also
Christening presents. / Delivery: £3.95; no Amex.

Bravado 🖃
☎ (020) 7738 9121
🖰 www.bravadodesigns.com
Maternity wear – Bras and underwear: a
Canadian brand of specialist maternity lingerie.
Maternity and nursing bras are 95% cotton and
5% spandex for breathability and stretch;
the extremely comfortable and practical sports
bra cut looks less armour-plated than
traditional styles; black, coloured and patterned
styles as well as white. Three styles of
matching, specially-designed knickers and
washable breast pads are also available.
Contact them for a list of retail and mail order
stockists.

Bravissimo 🖃
28 High St, London W5 5DB ☎ Shop (020)
8282 4797, Mail order (0700) 244 2727
🖰 www.bravissimo.com
Maternity wear – Bras and underwear:
formerly a mail-order-only service, this
company specialises in providing lingerie for
"big-boobed women", from all bra
manufacturers. Cup sizes D-J, back sizes 30-40.
A selection of swimwear (cup sizes D-G) and
some nursing bras are also available. The shop
in Ealing stocks the full catalogue
range. / Hours: shop Mon-Sat 10am–5.45pm; free
catalogue.

Braybrook & Britten 🖃
12 Park Parade, Gunnersbury Avenue,
London W3 9BD ☎ (020) 8993 7334
🖰 www.braybrook.com
Naming gifts – Naming gifts: 'Silversmiths by
post' (and over the web), offering a range of
attractive Christening cups and beakers,
around £125. Engraving from £16.50 for 10
letters. Also range of other children's gift items
from a silver baby comb to a teddy tooth box.

Bresona 🖃
Birchfield House, Strathallan Rd, Onchan, Isle
of Man IM3 1NN ☎ (01624) 670380
🖰 www.9monthsplus.com
Maternity wear – Mid-range:
traditionally-styled 'dual purpose' clothing
(suitable for maternity and breast-feeding);
particularly tops (£16-£45) and dresses with
opening slits; bras, sportswear and swimming
costumes; specialist clothes for breast-feeding;
they claim to have the largest range of clothes
available on the Internet; also pillows and baby
wraps. / Hours: 24hr mail order; free catalogue;
Delivery: p&p £2.99; no Switch.

Brian's Children's Shoes
BRANCHES:
68 The Broadway, Stanmore HA7 4DU
☎ (020) 8954 3712
2 Hallswelle Parade NW11 0DL
☎ (020) 8455 7001
Small North London chain of quality
shoe-fitters, with – they claim –
the "highest-trained fitting specialists in the
country".
Shoes – Suppliers: a wide range incorporating
everything from Start-rite to fashion shoes –
brands include Nike, Elefanten, Ricosta,
Babybotte, Kickers, Pod and their own-brand
Italian shoes. / Hours: Mon-Sat 9.15am-5.30pm
(NW11 closed Thu & open Sun 10.30am-1pm); no
Amex.

Bright Minds 🖃
Braysdown Yard, Peasedown St. John, Bath
BA2 8LL ☎ (0870) 4422 144
🖰 www.brightminds.co.uk
Toys – Educational: catalogue aimed
primarily at stimulating older children; also has
items including early alphabet
materials. / Hours: Mon-Fri 8.30am-8.30pm; no
Amex.

Brio
Messenger Close, Loughborough, Leics
LE11 5SP ☎ (01509) 231874
🖰 www.brio.co.uk
Toys – Brand: well-known brand of
hard-wearing wooden, plastic and character
toys. Perhaps best-known for its wooden and
battery-operated train sets (though note that
the former star seller, Thomas the Tank
Engine is no longer part of the firm's stable of
products). Brio Soft toys are suitable from birth
up. The website holds a list of Brio 'Gold Star'
stockists; the company warrants all
manufacturing defects for as long as you own
the toy.

Britax
1 Churchill Way West, Andover, Hampshire
SP10 3UW ☎ (01264) 386034
🖰 www.britax.co.uk
Part of an industrial group which also
manufactures airline seats.
Baby equipment – Wheeled
Transport-brands: pioneers of the 'travel
system' – infant car seats which can fit on
a special pushchair chassis; brand names
include Ultra, Solo and the Italian Collection
(Classicale and Practicale). – Car seat brands:
the UK's leading brand of car seat (the
best-seller is the Rock-A-Tot). Can advise on
which of the seats is suitable for a given car,
discuss safety aspects of products and the
suitability of a particular product for a child's
age or weight; other model names include
Babysure (birth-one year); Club Class Extra
(birth-four years); Renaissance, Eclipse,
Freeway (nine months-four years); Cruiser plus
(nine months-six years); seats for older children
and booster seats also available. / Hours: Mon-
Thu 8.30am-5pm, Fri 8.30am-4pm.

Broody Hens 🖃
69 Wandsworth Common West Side,
London SW18 2ED ☎ (07787) 502 175,
(07850) 140 939 🖰 www.broodyhens.co.uk
Mail order supplier; the catalogue's online,
but you order by 'phone or fax.
Maternity wear – Mid-range: clothing
designed to be close to what you might wear
normally, but taking into account your
expanding waistline. A small but well chosen
range in natural fabrics with individual touches
and including trousers, T-shirts, fleeces and

dresses; cotton and Elastane dress £30. / online catalogue.

Brora 🏠

CENTRAL CONTACT DETAILS
☎ (020) 7736 9944
🖰 www.brora.co.uk
BRANCHES:
81 Marylebone High St W1U 4QJ
☎ (020) 7224 5040
344 King's Rd SW3 5UR
☎ (020) 7352 6397
66-68 Ledbury Rd W11 2AJ
☎ (020) 7229 1515

Nursery decor – **Bedding:** pram and cot blankets, from £20 in lambswool, £100 in cashmere.

Baby clothes – **Luxury:** 'The Baby Collection': cashmere cardigans from £34, matching trousers, bonnets and Inca-style hats and mittens. Also childrens clothes: cashmere cardigan £85. – **Knitwear.**

Naming gifts – **Naming gifts:** cashmere clothes, cot blankets and many more gifts suitable for Christenings or namings: can be gift-wrapped and delivered. / free catalogue.

Buckle-My-Shoe

Brent Cross Shopping Centre, London NW4 3FP ☎ (020) 8202 4423
🖰 www.bucklemyshoe.co.uk
Baby clothes – **Mid-range.**
Shoes – **Suppliers:** attractive, if not inexpensive designs; different styles offer different width fittings but each particular style comes in just that one width.

Budget Bumps 🏠 Q

9 The Rowans, Riplingham Fields, Gainsborough, Lincs DN21 1WH ☎ (0845) 226 2673
🖰 www.budget-bumps.com/Budget_Bumpsx.html
Maternity wear – **Second-hand shops:** "Good-as-new" maternity and nursing clothing, to buy online. They sometimes buy, too; (also a few new items such as the Belly Bra.)

Buffalo Systems

Unit 3, The Old Dairy, Broadfield Rd, Sheffield S8 0QX ☎ (0114) 258 0611
🖰 www.buffalosystems.co.uk
"For the professional and committed outdoor person for use in the very worst weather". No direct sales – contact them or see the website for local stockists.
Baby clothes – **Outdoorwear:** a high quality all-in-one baby suit (the 'Baby Buffalo') is around £40. / Hours: Mon-Fri 9am-5pm.

Bug Circus 🏠

153 Church Rd, London SW13 9HR ☎ (020) 8741 4244 🖰 www.kidsnclothes.co.uk
Baby clothes – **Eco-friendly clothing:** all natural-fibre clothing plus an organic range, including cotton pyjamas; brands include: Pampolina, Peter Rabbit and Babar; Kaloo babywear; 'Shoo b' shoes and clothing; Abeko (Swedish) rainwear; also handmade felt hats and hand-knits.
Toys – **General stockists:** a good range of animal toys and items including Jellycat,

and Manhattan soft toys; pocket money items; also doll's houses. / Hours: Mon-Sat 10am-6pm (open Sun, Nov & Dec).

Bugaboo

The Coda Centre, Unit 24/8, 189 Munster Rd, London SW6 6AW ☎ (0800) 587 3265
🖰 www.bugaboo.nl
Baby equipment – **Wheeled Transport-brands:** manufacturers of the "Frog" – a particularly nifty, easily manoeuvrable (and fashionable) all-terrain buggy whose passengers can face forwards or backwards; the website can provide stockists.

Bugglesnuggle Company 🏠

Clockhouse, Latch End Industrial, Middle Aston, Oxon OX25 5QL ☎ (01869) 340 694
🖰 www.buggysnuggle.com
From its buggy blanket origins, the range and its trademark designs now covers full-sized blankets and clothing.
Baby equipment – **Buggy accessories:** snuggles in eye-catching fleece and fake fur designs (giraffe, cow print, stars & stripes, ...) to fit any buggy.
Nursery decor – **Bedding:** fleece blankets (from cot size) and throws in the same designs as the buggy blankets.
Baby clothes – **Outdoorwear:** pull on fleece tops in the patterned fleeces, plus matching quirky hats.

Bumkins

🖰 www.bumkins.com
Nappies – **Reusable stockists - brands & singles:** a US brand of reusable nappies – available either as all-in-ones or as a two-piece system – which claims to be hardwearing and highly waterproof. The shaped all-in-ones have a coated polyester outer-coating with 100% cotton flannelette liner and come in three sizes (plus two larger ones for bed-wetters). The two-piece system comprises a shaped polyester waterproof cover with T-shaped flannel nappy. Check for UK retailers on the website.

Bump 🏠

London ☎ (020) 7249 7000
🖰 www.bumpstuff.com
Nursery decor – **Furniture:** ready-to-paint MDF children's beds, bunks and furniture. They are delivered flat-pack, but can be pre-painted any Dulux colour. / Hours: Mon-Fri 9am-6pm; free catalogue or online; Delivery: p&p depends on weight; no Amex.

Bump Start 🏠

119 Revelstoke Rd, London SW18 5NN
☎ (020) 8879 3467 🖰 www.bumpstart.co.uk
Maternity wear – **Mid-range:** clothing that aims to be usable after pregnancy; options are divided into wardrobe essentials (but not dungarees or leggings), casual wear and a smart/evening collection; pure natural fabrics are rare, though often this is to achieve a particular look, e.g. PVC trousers, £50; if you organise a party of 5+, they will come to SW6 and most of SW11-SW20 addresses at a cost of £5 per head. / Hours: shop Mon-Sat 10am-5.30pm (Thu 8.30pm), Sun 10am-4pm; free catalogue; no Amex.

Bumps Maternity Wear UK ⌂

19 Frederick Street, Sunderland, Tyne and Wear SR1 1LT ☎ (0191) 5653232
⁷ www.bumpsmaternity.com
Sunderland-based store, with an online ordering facility.

<u>Maternity wear</u> – **Mid-range:** a website retailer, offering an attractive selection of essentially classic maternity wear, including dresses, pinafores, jackets and coats, knitwear, tops, skirts, trousers and jeans, plus underwear, swimwear and nightwear.

Bumps to Bairns ⌂ Q

⁷ www.bumps2bairns.co.uk/
A Scottish-based online vendor of second-hand (and some new) mother and babywear.

<u>Maternity wear</u> – **Mid-range.** – **Second-hand shops.**

<u>Baby clothes</u> – **Mid-range.** – **Second-hand shops.**

Bunny London ⌂

Unit 1.22, 22 Oxo Tower Wharf, Bargehouse St, London SE1 9PH ☎ (020) 7928 6269 ⁷ www.bunnylondon.com
Boutique run by ex-make up artist Deborah Bunn, whose publicity makes no small mention of its popularity with Madonna and Lourdes (not to mention Jamie Oliver, Davina McCall and Brooke Shields).

<u>Baby clothes</u> – **Luxury:** very funky girls clothes; including one-offs, whose trademark is a mix-and-match approach using floral patterns and trimmings such as brocade; typical dress £70, coat £120. – **Funky.** / Hours: Mon-Sat 11am-6pm, or by arrangement; Delivery: p&p approx £5; no Amex.

Burberry

CENTRAL CONTACT DETAILS
☎ (020) 2968 0000
⁷ www.burberry.com
BRANCHES:
21-23 New Bond St W1S 2RE
☎ (020) 7839 5222
165 Regent St W1B 4PH
☎ (020) 7734 4060
3 Brompton Rd SW1X 9PB
☎ (020) 7839 7222

The famous English luxury brand now has an infant collection. The widest selection is in their own stores, though parts of the range can be found elsewhere.

<u>Baby clothes</u> – **Luxury:** even kidlets can now wear the check; popular items include babygrows (£35), a tartan girl's shirt (£29), or mini-duffle coat in pink, white or blue (£200).

Bush Babes

Herts Pram and Nursery Centre, The Maltings, Watton Road, Ware, Herts SG12 0AA ☎ (01920) 484555
⁷ www.bushbabes.co.uk

<u>Baby equipment</u> – **Stockists:** "One of the largest pram and nursery stores in the South East," with, for example, more than 100 prams on display. The website (which does not have online ordering) gives you a good taste of what you can expect.

<u>Nursery decor</u> – **General stockists:** fifteen room sets showcasing different ranges of bedding and furniture are on display.

<u>Baby clothes</u> – **Mid-range.** / Hours: Mon-Sat 9.30am-5pm, Thurs 9.30am-7pm, Sun 10am-4pm; no Amex.

Bush Baby ⌂

PO Box 61, Stockport, Cheshire SK3 0AP ☎ (0161) 474 7097 ⁷ www.bush-baby.com
Mail order business offering a range of products for parents who want to get out and about with their child in tow.

<u>Baby equipment</u> – **Slings- Backpack:** 'Premier' child carrier, one of the best options currently available, with an entirely adjustable and well-padded harness, rain cover, sun cover and canopy with UV-resistant accessories. Stocked at Snow & Rock, Outdoors, John Lewis or can supply direct. Prices upon application or in catalogue.

<u>Baby clothes</u> – **Outdoorwear:** outdoor clothing, including the 'Hot Tot' range combining windproof and waterproof outer with a furry lining; from £37. An all-in-one Splashsuit for toddlers is in machine washable waterproof coated nylon big enough to fit over bulky clothing with a diagonal zip from top to bottom and details like elastic loops to fit under wellies. / Hours: Mon-Fri 9am-5pm; free catalogue; Delivery: p&p (free on child carriers) ; no Amex.

Business Bump ⌂

Bean Hill House, Church Lane, Shearsby, Leicestershire LE17 6PG ☎ (0870) 240 5476
⁷ www.businessbump.co.uk

<u>Maternity wear</u> – **Mid-range:** an online maternity wear merchant, specialising in formal outfits and classic 'office' clothes in natural fabrics, but with a fashionable twist. A linen shirt for example costs £55.

Buy Baby Clothes ⌂ Q

⁷ www.buybabyclothes.co.uk

<u>Baby clothes</u> – **Mid-range:** online auctions of clothes from Next, GAP, Osh Kosh, M&S. Gymboree and so on, for 0-3 years. Items are labelled as Brand New, As New, or Nearly New. – **Second-hand shops.**

Buzzness ⌂

7 Woodpecker Close, Brackley, Northamptonshire NN13 6QH ☎ (01280) 841 262 ⁷ www.thebuzzness.co.uk
Mail order company with "a carefully selected range of washable cloth nappies, wraps and related baby products."

<u>Nursery decor</u> – **Sleeping Bags:** sleeping bags from 6 months to three years, plus baby sleepgowns from 0-3 months, in organic cotton jersey with elastic gathering at hem (to allow for easy nappy changes) and cuffs which can be folded over to make integral scratch mittens.

<u>Nappies</u> – **Reusable stockists - brands & singles:** a wide range of cloth nappies in various styles; also accessories including washable wipes, flushable one-way liners, nappy bag, washing net and more. / no Amex.

Caboodles ⌂

20 Priory Rd, Faversham, Kent ME13 7EJ ☎ (01795) 590664
⁷ www.caboodlebags.co.uk

<u>Nappies</u> – **Change bags:** superior nappy bags, combining practical features with designer

style; range of colours and decorations from plain navy to elephants, zebras, koalas and elephants. Caboodle bag/organiser £20; car seat cosy £20; active bag £25. / *Hours: 9am-5pm or 24hr answerphone; free catalogue; Delivery: p&p extra; no Amex & no Switch.*

Calange 🏠

PO Box 61, Stockport, Cheshire SK3 0AP
☎ (0161) 474 7097 ⏱ www.bush-baby.com
Outdoorwear make, allied with the Bush Baby brand of slings and backpacks. The website gives full details, including of retailers both on-and offline.

Baby equipment – **Slings:** in 2003, introduced one of the latest wave of slings which aim to combine the ergonomics of backpack design with papoose-style carrying (US brand Kelty has produced something similar.) This machine-washable harness features a deep padded waist belt and shoulder straps and adjustable system, the pouch having a padded head and back rest attached to the harness by two buckles. The child, however, carries most of its weight on its crotch. – **Slings- Backpack:** suppliers of some of the better-quality backpacks on the market.

Baby clothes – **Outdoorwear:** for toddlers and children as well as adults, kit that's designed to be practical but with a slightly offbeat look (shades of surfer gear). Toddler fleece £20.

Cameron Gift Company 🏠

Byron House, 21/23 Rectory Road, West Bridgford, Nottingham NG2 6BE ☎ (0115) 923 4818 ⏱ www.camerongiftcompany.com/
Naming gifts – **Naming gifts:** a website offering traditional Christening and similar gifts, including some antique items. The selection includes a wide range of silver items, a selection of bears and photo frames.

Caramel

291 Brompton Rd, London SW3 2DY
☎ (020) 7589 7001
Baby clothes – **Luxury:** mainly own-brand collection babywear, but other ranges include Diesel and Marni. Ages 3months-18 months and children 2-10 years. / *Hours: Mon-Sat 10am-6.30pm, Sun 12pm-5pm.*

Carla C

302 Westbourne Grove, Notting Hill, London W11 2PS ☎ (020) 7243 3950
⏱ www.carla-c.com
A Swedish company with many shops internationally, and now in London; also online ordering.

Maternity wear – **Luxury:** designer maternitywear – all fabrics are selected for breathability and ease of washing, but are elasticated. The range includes wedding dresses and the shops receive new designs approximately every two weeks. Special sizes can also be made. Prices are around £65 per garment.

The Carrying Kind 🏠

2 Hayes Hill Cottages, Crooked Mile, Holyfield Nr Waltham Abbey EN9 2EH
☎ (01992) 651 717 ⏱ www.the carryingkind.com
A range of items to support attachment parenting, including books on breastfeeding

and co-sleeping, plus for example Diaper Free about caring for babies without nappies. Also some children's books about breastfeeding and babies being carried in different cultures around the world.

Maternity wear – **Bras and underwear:** bravado bras all with sports style back, adjustable straps and popper fasteners; £21.50.
Baby equipment – **Lambskins:** undyed and unbleached machine-washable British lambskins for babies: shorn (easy-care) or silky unshorn; about £40. – **Slings:** probably the widest range of baby slings in the UK including Huggababy, Wilkinet, Perraja, Rebozo, Hug-a-bub, Baby Bunder, Tonga, Lifter, Maya Pouch, New Native and Tricotti. The website evangelises the whole concept of devices for carrying children, and contains much useful information about the range offered (which includes many ethnic options and work in different ways). No online ordering, but you can request a catalogue; prices £17.50 to about £50. / *Delivery: from £1.25; no Amex.*

Cash's 🏠

Torrington Avenue, Coventry CV4 9UZ
☎ (02476) 466466, Orderline (02476) 422228 ⏱ www.jjcash.co.uk
Baby clothes – **Nametapes:** the traditional tapes, with coloured names woven on white; available through many outlets, including Marks & Spencer, Woolworths, BHS, Clarks Shoes, Mothercare and the John Lewis Partnership, and also direct. / *Hours: Mon-Thurs 8.30am-4.30pm, Fri 8.30am-3.30pm; can order online or by catalogue; Delivery: p&p included.*

Catimini 🏠

⏱ www.catimini.com
BRANCHES:
52 South Molton St W1Y 1HF
☎ (020) 7629 8099
38 High St KT1 1HL
☎ (020) 8541 4635
3 Paradise Road TW9 1RX
☎ (020) 8605 3880
75 Upper Thames Walk, Bluewater Shopping Centre, Dartford DA9 9SZ
☎ (01322) 624765
French designer firm – originally just a mail order business, but now with three London shops. The mail order business is based at the Kingston shop. Two English catalogues per annum. They no longer do the La Mama range of maternity wear.

Baby clothes – **Luxury:** 'Continental' styling with a funky edge, and not the cheapest (it gets relatively more expensive the older they get), using a lot of natural fabrics. The range includes tights, socks, hats and bags (but no nightwear or underwear as French safety regulations are not as strict as English ones). / *Hours: Mon-Sat 9am-5.30pm; free catalogue; Delivery: p&p £2 (orders up to £50), £3.50 (up to £150), £5 (orders over £150); no Amex.*

Celebration 🏠

Racecourse Industrial Park, Mansfield Rd, Derby DE21 4SX ☎ (0845) 1308181
Naming gifts – **Naming gifts:** personalised photo albums and engraved photo frames. / *Hours: Mon-Fri 9am-5pm; free catalogue; Delivery: p&p extra; no Amex.*

Chariots All Terrain Pushchairs 🖼
Orchard Farm, Spreyton, Devon EX17 5AS
☎ (01363) 881110 🖰 www.pushchairs.co.uk
<u>Baby equipment</u> – **Buggy suppliers:** stockists
of mountain buggy and baby jogger buggies
and accessories (including carry cots to convert
pushchairs for newborns); various packages
may mean quite major accessories are included
in the basic price; staff can advise on the most
suitable model for your needs; the range
includes the Montaine double buggy. / *Hours:
9am-9pm.*

Charlie Crow 🖼
Unit 2 Crabtree Close, Fenton, Stoke-on-
Trent ST4 2SW ☎ (01782) 417133
🖰 www.charliecrow.co.uk
<u>Toys</u> – **Dressing up toys:** 70+ designs, priced
typically at £10-£35. / *free catalogue; Delivery: p&p
£2 (express £5).*

Charlotte's Cot Blankets 🖼
11 Heigham Rd, Norwich NR2 3AT
☎ (01603) 627448
🖰 www.charlottecotblankets.com
<u>Nursery decor</u> – **Bedding:** hand-made cot
blankets with patterns of flowers and ducks;
available in wool or cotton mix in a variety of
colours, £50.
<u>Naming gifts</u> – **Naming gifts:** 'Modern
heirloom' cot blankets that can be personalised
with the baby's name and date of birth as
a naming gift; hand-knitted in a choice of
materials and colours, from £50. / *Hours: 24hr
answerphone; free catalogue; Delivery: p&p £3.80 per
blanket; no credit cards.*

Charter Design 🖼
1 Church Rd, Roberttown, W Yorks
WF15 7LS ☎ (01924) 413813
Mail order business – can provide a list of other
firms who stock the company's products.
<u>Nursery decor</u> – **Paints:** lead-free colour paints
from the US, based on milk (Williamsburg
Buttermilk Paint – some recipes date from
1775); mainly matt and low sheen finishes; also
a lead-free range of oil-based paints (Old
Village). / *Hours: Mon-Fri 9am-5.30pm; free colour
charts; Delivery: p&p minimum £6.50.*

Cheeky B Children's Clothing 🖼
148 Manor Rd North, Thomas Ditton,
Surrey KT7 0BM ☎ (020) 8398 5595
🖰 www.cheekyb.co.uk
<u>Baby clothes</u> – **Cheap & cheerful:** online
retailer of its own "traditional range with
a fashion twist". / *Hours: Mon-Fri 9am-5pm; on the
web or design sheet; Delivery: first order free; no Amex.*

Cheeky Kids
175 Fore St, London N18 2XB ☎ (020) 8807
5898
North London store describing itself as "a mini
Mothercare".
<u>Baby equipment</u> – **Stockists.**
<u>Baby clothes</u> – **Cheap & cheerful.** / *Hours:
Mon-Sat 9.30am-6pm.*

Cheeky Monkeys 🖼
🖰 www.cheekymonkeys.com
BRANCHES:
94 New King's Rd SW6 4UL
☎ (020) 7731 3031
202 Kensington Park Rd W11 1NR
☎ (020) 7792 9022
38 Cross St N1 2BG
☎ (020) 7288 1948
1 Bellevue Rd SW17 7EG
☎ (020) 8672 2025
4 Croxted Rd SE21 8SW
☎ (020) 8655 7168
24 Abbeville Rd SW4 9NH
☎ (020) 8673 5215
Mid-sized chain (W11 is the original) selling
mainly children's toys and gifts – stock differs
somewhat between outlets. You can now also
buy from their easily searchable website.
<u>Nursery decor</u> – **Furniture:** handmade
furniture.
<u>Toys</u> – **General stockists:** unusual wooden
toys and gifts (including the Manhattan range
of soft toys). Also party accessories, as well as
stationery, cards and books. – **Dressing up
toys:** large range. / *Hours: Mon-Fri 9.30am-
5.30pm, Sat-Sun 10am-5.30pm (W11 closed Sun).*

Cheeky Rascals 🖼
1 Stone Barn, The Brows, Farnham Road,
Liss, Hampshire GU33 6JG ☎ (0870) 873
2600 🖰 www.cheekyrascals.co.uk
<u>Baby equipment</u> – **Stockists:** mail order
company with a small range of useful,
generally imported items: products include the
Kiddieguard stairgate, £55; also sleepsuits,
changing bags, chair boosters, baby baths and
bath seats, Tip-MeNot weights for buggies and
a variety of child safety items. – **Buggy
accessories:** stockists of the KiddyBoard and
BuggyBoard – platforms that attach to the axle
of a pushchair or buggy so a toddler can ride
on it, £45. / *Hours: 9am-6pm, or answerphone; free
catalogue; Delivery: p&p extra.*

Chelsea Baby Hire 🖼
31 Osborne House, 414 Wimbledon Park
Rd, London SW19 6PW ☎ (020) 8789 9673
🖰 www.chelseababyhire.com
<u>Baby equipment</u> – **Hire:** offers cots, high
chairs, car seats, playpens, pushchairs, buggies,
Z-beds and travel cots. A cot for a month costs
£100 (delivered and collected). There is
a discount for hiring more than one item at
a time. / *Hours: Mon-Sat 9am-5pm.*

Chic Shack 🖼
77 Lower Richmond Road, Putney, London
SW15 1ET ☎ (020) 8785 7777
🖰 www.chicshack.net
Most of the items in the catalogue are on show
in the shop.
<u>Nursery decor</u> – **General stockists:** painted
furniture and accessories inspired by French
and Swedish 18th century designs, plus fabrics
and other accessories. Most is painted white
and suitable for a child's bedroom. Some items
are specifically child-sized and there are a few
cots and cribs, including one in iron. Items can
be made to measure if required.

Chicco
Prospect Close, Kirkby, Ashfield, Notts
NG17 7LF ☎ (01623) 750870
🖰 www.chicco.com
Classic Continental general equipment brand
with a strong emphasis on the 'look'; it can
supply lists of local suppliers and free product
catalogues and has a good website (though
many lines are not available in the UK).
Baby equipment – **Wheeled**
Transport-brands: highchairs, travel beds,
baby walkers, wheeled goods of all types,
bouncing chairs.
Toys – **Brand.** / no credit cards.

Child Alert
PO Box 29961, London SW6 6EZ ☎ (020)
7384 1311 🖰 www.childalert.co.uk
Nursery decor – **Safety items:** for a fee of
£150, a Child Alert childproofing expert will
conduct a survey of your home, and will sell
and fit the recommended items. The
organisation focuses on items that are
"purposeful, smart and as unobtrusive as
possible". / Hours: Mon-Fri 9am-5pm, 24-hr Web
site.

Childcare Products 🖰
PO Box 84, Marple Delivery Office, Marple,
Stockport SK6 5YX ☎ (0161) 427 8598
🖰 www.childcareproducts.co.uk
Baby equipment – **Stockists:** equipment for
travelling with babies and children: car seats;
reusable travel bottle warmers; play mats; hot
water bottle 'animals'. / Hours: Mon-Fri 8.30am-
5pm; free catalogue or online.

Childhood Discoveries 🖰
23 Victorian Rd, Surbiton, Surrey KT6 4JZ
☎ (020) 8390 2168
🖰 www.educational-toys.co.uk
Toys – **Educational:** a shop offering a basic
selection of good toys with brands including
Lamaze and Plan Toys. You can also order
online.

Childlife 🖰
Parsonage Farm, Childrey, Nr Wantage,
Oxon OX12 9PH ☎ (01235) 751717
🖰 www.socialclimbers.com
'The original wooden play system since 1945',
a range of modular play equipment.
Toys – **Outdoor items & active toys:** the only
UK distributor of a range made in New
England since 1945 with a range of hard cedar
modular equipment, prefinished and partially
assembled. The multi-coat enamel finish makes
it splinter free. Also available are attractive and
sturdy wagons and tricycles suitable from one
year up, and garden cottages in Cape Cod
style. Prices for play frames start around £800,
and wagons from £49. / Hours: Mon-Fri 9am-5pm;
free catalogue; no Amex.

The Children's Book
Centre 🖰
237 Kensington High St, London W8 6SA
☎ (020) 7937 7497
🖰 www.childrensbookcentre.co.uk
With its prominent location on the High
Street, this two-floor store has books on the
ground floor, and a selection of toys in the
basement.

Toys – **General stockists:** the toy department
stocks book tie-in toys from brands such as
Lego and Mattel (Barbie) as well as outdoor
toys, kites, bat and ball games. – **Dressing up**
toys: selection of fancy dress outfits from
pirates to princesses.
Books, music & videos – **Bookshops:**
specialist bookshop, categorised by age,
starting with a selection for one to five years;
frequent in-store promotions, and author visits.
They also stock a selection of cassettes and
multimedia tools. The website allows books to
be searched by age from babies up. After your
first 10 purchases from the site you
automatically become a member of the
Privilege Club, entitling you to 10%
discount. / Hours: Mon-Sat 9.30am-6.30pm (Tue
6pm, Thu 7pm) Sun noon-6pm; Delivery: p&p extra,
min packing cost; no Diner's card.

Children's Book Company 🖰
11 The Green, London W5 5DA ☎ (020)
8567 4324
🖰 www.childrensbookcompany.com
A relatively new (1999) bookshop, which has
also invested heavily in its online presence.
The range encompasses family-related topics
on illness, divorce, disability, etc.
Books, music & videos – **Bookshops:** the
website includes book reviews, lists of
award-winning titles, a chat room, and advice,
plus supply of any British children's book
currently in print (delivered in three days).
There's a 10% online discount and shoppers
can build up loyalty points for further
discounts. The shop features low-level
furniture and has monthly author events and
character visits and a weekly storytime
session. / Hours: Mon-Sat 9.30am-5.30pm; no Amex.

The Children's Bookcase 🖰
Greyhound House, 23-24 George Street,
Richmond, Surrey TW9 1HY ☎ (020) 8948
0097 🖰 www.thechildrensbookcase.com
Books, music & videos – **Bookshops:** a
website which is a good place to find
old-fashioned books, which you can search for
by age and type. It offers detailed reviews too.

Children's Bookshop 🖰
29 Fortis Green Rd, London N10 3HP
☎ (020) 8444 5500
Books, music & videos – **Bookshops:** this
small, specialist store caters for all age ranges,
but has a good range of board and picture
books for under-twos. Events and story
readings are organised, and a regular
newsletter is published. There's a good section
for parents on dealing with difficult issues such
as disability. / Hours: Mon-Sat 9.15am-5.45pm, Sun
11am-4pm; Delivery: p&p extra.

Children's Bookshop (Middx)
1 Red Lion Parade, Bridge St, Pinner,
Middlesex HA5 3JD ☎ (020) 8866 9116
Books, music & videos – **Bookshops:**
"Whatever you need, you'll find it here" – this
specialist bookshop offers an exhaustive range
of books for children of all ages, including
a wide selection of educational titles,
and a good choice for the under twos including
bath, cloth and board books. Regular activities,
reading schemes, author visits and promotions

are run, and there's also a play area. / *Hours: Mon-Sat 9.15am-5.30pm, Sun 10am-4pm.*

The Children's Cottage Company 🖃

The Sanctuary, Shobrooke, Crediton, Devon EX17 1BG ☎ (01363) 772061
🖰 www.play-houses.com

Nursery decor – **Furniture:** scaled-down furniture to fit Wendy houses; cupboards, stools, tables and chair sets, picket fences and beds.

Toys – **Outdoor items & active toys:** some of the world's best Wendy houses – weatherproofed and triple-coat painted in two colours with stable doors and three windows. Fantasy designs include castles, Queen Anne, Tudor Cottage and thatched cottages; various roofing options and external finishes available. Also play systems – climbing frames with cargo nets, walkways, ladders, swings and slides – and summer houses. Furniture and accessories also available. / *Hours: Mon-Fri 9am-5pm; free catalogue.*

Children's Furniture Company 🖃

PO Box 31681, London SW2 5EZ ☎ (020) 7737 7303
🖰 www.thechildrensfurniturecompany.com

A range designed by Charles Codrington, member of the Worshipful Company of Furniture makers and Furniture Guild award winner, (a man who reckons good furtniture has a civilising influence on children).

Nursery decor – **Furniture:** beds are full-sized to last, and the bunk beds will turn into singles. A sleepover bed can be added underneath; there is also a wardrobe and toystore. All items are in beech and can be supplied painted. Mattresses with springs or fabric and cotton wadding, are available. / *Hours: Mon-Fri 9am-5.30pm; free catalogue or online; Delivery: smaller items £10 per item; no Amex.*

The Children's Seating Centre 🖃

11 Whitcomb St, London WC2H 7HA
☎ (020) 7930 8308
🖰 www.backinaction.co.uk

Sharing premises with Back in Action, this is one of three outlets concentrating on seating that prevents back problems in children, from newborns upwards; also campaigns for better seating in schools. Fact sheets and mailing lists for further information about products, and leaflets from the National Back Pain Association are all available here.

Baby equipment – **Stockists:** adjustable chairs (including Tripp Trapp and variations on this model) that bring children up to the correct height for any given table, from £100; posture packs (seat wedge and desk slope to promote good posture); buggies; cots, cradles and pillows.

Nursery decor – **Furniture:** furniture and accessories that are ergonomically designed for children from five months upwards; ergonomic analysis of children's rooms. / *Hours: Mon-Fri 9.30am-5pm ; free catalogue or online; Delivery: p&p depends, £5 up to £20.*

The Children's Warehouse 🖃

Unit 4, 44 Colville Rd, London W3 8BL
☎ (020) 8752 1166
🖰 www.childrens-warehouse.com

Mail order business.

Baby clothes – **Cheap & cheerful:** a large and comprehensive range of practical clothes for children, without logos, primarily in pure cotton. They have an attractive catalogue of fun, fresh styles with good colour choice. Range includes swimwear, 100 percent cotton nightwear, wet weather clothes and accessories. / *Hours: 24 hours a day 364 days a year (closed Christmas Day); free catalogue or online; Delivery: p&p £3; no Amex.*

Childsplay 🖃

11-13 Clements Rd, Ilford IG1 1BA ☎ (020) 8514 5007 🖰 www.childsplay.co.uk

The largest independent childrenswear store in the country.

Baby clothes – **Luxury:** the focus is on designer labels: DKNY, Kenzo, Trusardi, Diesel, Elle, Burberry, Versace and so on. Every item is designer, with average items around £35. / *Hours: Mon-Sat 9.30am-6pm.*

Chiswick Shoes

1 Devonshire Rd, London W4 2EU ☎ (020) 8987 0525

Shoes – **Suppliers:** small traditional independent store, just off the High Road, stocking – amongst other brands – StartRite, Buckle My Shoe, Ricosta, and Elefanten. / *Hours: Mon-Sat 9.30am-5.30pm; no Amex.*

Chocolate Crocodile ℚ

39 Morpeth Rd, Victoria Park, Hackney, London E9 7LD ☎ (020) 8985 3330

Baby equipment – **Second-hand:** wide range including prams, pushchairs, swinging cribs, buggy boards and Baby Bjorn carriers. New and used equipment.

Baby clothes – **Second-hand shops:** mostly items for under 8s.

Toys – **Second-hand shops:** including large items and new wooden toys.

Books, music & videos – **Bookshops:** second-hand and new. / *Hours: Mon-Sat 11am-5pm.*

Christening Outfits 🖃

35 Derwent Cr, Kettering NN16 8UH
☎ (01536) 515 401
🖰 www.christeningoutfits.co.uk

Baby clothes – **Christening gowns:** a website offering a wide range of clothing suitable for Christenings. You can call to discuss your requirements if you prefer a rather more personal approach.

Christening Stuff 🖃

☎ (01202) 249855
🖰 www.christeningstuff.co.uk/

Baby clothes – **Christening gowns:** christening clothing for girls and boys, from £30 in poly-cotton and £100-plus for embroidered silk. Also more multi-purpose 'special occasion' wear, new baby and Christening gifts (including silver items), and alternatives like soft toys.

Christening UK

59 Bridge Street Row, Chester CH1 1NW
☎ (01244) 347 424
🖰 www.christening.uk.com
Baby clothes – Christening gowns: specialists
in high-quality Christening gowns, outfits and
accessories, plus a few general special occasion
outfits as well. Age 0-3 years. They claim to
have the only dedicated Christening room in
the UK, but a website service (with worldwide
delivery) is also available. / *Hours: Mon-Sat
10am-5pm; from manufacturers; Delivery: p&p extra.*

Cider Woods Children's Furniture

36 Station Rd, Taunton TA1 1NL ☎ (01823)
322466 🖰 www.ciderwoods.co.uk/
A firm which claims to offer the largest
selection of children's furniture in the UK (and
says it won't be beaten on price either). If
you're in the West Country, you can visit the
firm's showroom, but they deliver to 90% of
the UK. Most items can be viewed (but not
ordered) online.
Nursery decor – Beds: as well as items for
older children, it has a good range of cots and
smaller beds, including some with fancy
themes (diggers, Formula One cars etc).
– Furniture: wardrobes, baby-changing units
and other related items.
Toys – Outdoor items & active toys: a good
range of options.

Cinnamon Kids

1 Hambrook Hill Cottages, West Ashling
Road, Hambrook, West Sussex PO18 8UF
☎ (01243) 573 674
Baby clothes – Funky: modern classic clothes
in natural fibres including cotton fleece, jersey,
cord, merino and cotton/cashmere, for
children to eight years. / *free brochure.*

Clair de Lune

Shentonfield Road, Wythenshawe,
Manchester M22 4RW ☎ (0161) 491 9801
🖰 www.clair-de-lune.co.uk
Manufacturers of baby bedding, blankets and
nursery accessories for over 60 years; don't
supply direct, call for stockists.
Nursery decor – Accessories: co-ordinated
collections; items include Moses baskets (and
stands), lampshades, cot bumpers, nappy tidies
and curtains; matching bedding also available.
– Bedding: a wide range of both patterned and
plain baby bedding collections, from pram sets
and quilts to blankets. / *Hours: Mon-Fri 8.30am-
5pm.*

Clarks

CENTRAL CONTACT DETAILS
☎ (01458) 443131, Foot Health Department
(0800) 616427
🖰 www.clarks.com
BRANCHES:
*(Only selected branches are listed –
call the enquiry line for other outlets.)*
476 Oxford St W1
☎ (020) 7629 9609
Brent Cross NW4 4FH
☎ (020) 8202 6423
79 Clarence St KT1 1RV
☎ (020) 8546 0388
37 High St, West Wickham BR4 0LR
☎ (020) 8777 0472
170 High Rd SW16 1BJ
☎ (020) 8769 4308
6 The Mall E15
☎ (020) 8534 7118
107-109 High St, Bromley BR1 1JQ
☎ (020) 8460 3937
142 Central Rd, Worcester Park KT4 8HH
☎ (020) 8337 0900
120-121 Whitgift Centre, Croydon CR0 1UT
☎ (020) 8688 6666
Dominant children's (and adult) shoe brand
with stores on most high streets, and whose
empire includes K Shoe Shops (and also names
such as Peter Lord and Milwards). Those shops
with a good range of children's shoes tend to
be towards the outskirts of town – stores with
a particularly good range are listed.
Shoes – Brands: styling has become a higher
priority for the brand, though the range's
hallmark wide selection of sizes and widths
remains. / *Hours: mostly 9am-5.30pm.*

Clementine

73 Ledbury Rd, London W11 3AG ☎ (020)
7243 6331
Baby equipment – Stockists: stockists of
Emmaljunga buggies and Bugaboo.
Nursery decor – Bedding: a range of bed linen
can be found downstairs. **– Furniture:** stokke
furniture.
Baby clothes – Luxury: mostly Petit Bateau
but occasional other items, for example Ureka
Kids. / *Hours: Mon-Sat 10am-6pm, Sun 12pm-5pm.*

Clippasafe

Lanthwaite Road, Clifton, Nottingham
NG11 8LD ☎ (0115) 921 1899
🖰 www.clippasafe.co.uk
Nursery decor – Safety items: manufacturers
of child safety products including harnesses
conforming to British Standard 6684, wrist link
and dining chair harnesses, plus home safety
products and safety nets for cots, prams and
strollers. / *Hours: Mon-Fri 8.30am-4.30pm; free
catalogue or online; Delivery: p&p £2.50; no Amex.*

ClothWORKS

Clothworks, PO Box 3233, Bradford on
Avon BA15 2WB ☎ (01225) 309218
🖰 www.clothworks.co.uk
A small mail order catalogue specialising in
organically-produced items; it has an attractive
website, but you still order by phone or mail.
Nursery decor – Bedding: organic cotton bed
linen in children and adult sizes: pillowcases
from £7.
**Baby clothes – Mid-range. – Eco-friendly
clothing:** clothing for children in fabrics with
organic certification: some knitwear, pyjamas,
and jackets; organic cotton jersey trousers, £22;
also fabrics (jersey, waffle, linen, terry
towelling and chambray) by the metre.
**Nappies – Reusable stockists - brands
& singles:** terry nappies, with buttons or ties;
both in 100% organic cotton; nappy outer £6
each, padded insert £2.50; all fully machine
washable. / *Hours: 24hr answerphone; free
catalogue; Delivery: £1.25 up to £25, £3.50 up to £60,
then free; no credit cards.*

CNL 🖂

EM House, Littlemead, Cranleigh, Surrey
GU6 8TT ☎ (0870) 727 4159
Books, music & videos – **Videos:** no big name
titles, but a range of videos aimed at babies and
up, from £5. / *Hours: 24hrs; free lists of titles.*

Colour Counsellors

3 Dovedale Studios, 465 Battersea Park Rd,
London SW11 4LR ☎ (020) 7978 5023
⌁ www.colourcounsellors.co.uk
Nursery decor – **Interior designers:** a
nationally-franchised network of interior
designers. Everything proceeds from an initial
consultation, the price of which varies by
'counsellor' and location. / *Hours: Mon-Fri
9.30am-5.30pm; no credit cards.*

Comfort Blankets 🖂

135 Willersley Avenue, Sidcup, Kent DA15
9EP 9EP ☎ (020) 8302 6510
⌁ www.comfortblankets.co.uk
Toys – **Comforters:** fleece blankets edged and
backed in soft satin in small sizes for babies to
hold, as well as larger versions (to cover them
up). Fabrics include funky patterns designed to
offer visual stimulation, such as Dalmatian
spots. / *online catalogue; Delivery: p&p £1.50; orders
over £22 is £2.50.*

Community Playthings 🖂

Robertsbridge, East Sussex TN32 5DR
☎ (0800) 387457
⌁ www.communityproducts.co.uk
An organisation run by an international
religious community which produces high
quality and attractively simple, unpainted,
wooden equipment (some of it for the
disabled), much of it made in the UK. Much of
the equipment is of a quality suitable for use in
schools.
Baby equipment – **Cots:** wooden cots and
cribs.
Nursery decor – **Storage:** maple changing
units, cupboards, boxes and shelves. Hinges
and castors in different combinations make
storage items suitable for housing children's
toys and equipment.
Toys – **Traditional toys:** one of the loveliest
ranges of items for children on the market
including wooden blocks, wheeled vehicles and
play furniture as well as building bricks. A new
range includes a wide range of different shapes
in exactly half the traditional sizes but large
enough to be safe for children of 1 year
up. / *Hours: Mon-Fri 9am-5pm; free brochure;
Delivery: p&p included; Visa, Mastercard or Switch.*

Compass Watersports 🖂

Ridout Yard, Great Cheverell, Devizes, Wilts
SN10 5XZ ☎ (01380)) 813 100
⌁ www.compass24.com
Mail order service for sailors.
Baby equipment – **Monitors-brand:** the
walkie-talkies used on boats (8 Alan
456/PMR446 Walkie-Talkie) are more reliable
than most baby monitors, will work outside
the UK, offer eight channels and voice
activation mode, and with a range of up to
6km are functional over a much greater
distance. A set costs £120 and a charging unit
£18. / *free catalogue; Delivery: p&p £4.95; no Amex.*

La Conception

46 Webbs Rd, London SW11 6SF ☎ (020)
7228 7498
Maternity wear – **Mid-range:** maternity wear
from Italy, France and the US, focussed on
funky casual and evening wear.
Baby clothes – **Mid-range.**
Naming gifts – **Naming gifts.**

The Conran Shop

⌁ www.conran.com
BRANCHES:
55-57 Marylebone High St W1M 3AE
☎ (020) 7723 2223
12 Conduit St W1S 2XQ
☎ (020) 7399 0710
Michelin House, 81 Fulham Rd SW3 6RD
☎ (020) 7589 7401
The kid's departments at this well-known trio
of style stores are not large, but contain
a number of interesting items; toys
predominate; some areas of the range are
priced more competitively than others.
Nursery decor – **Furniture:** children's canvas
cabin wardrobes.
Baby clothes – **Luxury:** small, upper middle
market selection – jumpers, dresses, hats.
Toys – **General stockists:** soft and wooden
toys; ranges include Brio and Babar; good
mobiles. / *Hours: Mon-Fri 10am-6pm (Wed & Thu
7pm), Sat 10am-6.30pm, Sun noon-6pm.*

Construction Resources 🖂

16 Great Guildford St, London SE1 0HS
☎ (020) 7450 2211
⌁ www.constructionresources.com
Suppliers of sustainable building products
mainly to the building trade but whose large
showroom welcomes members of the public.
Nursery decor – **Paints:** non-toxic paints;
natural flooring including timbers and natural
carpets; clay plasters and finishes that – it is
claimed – help absorb internal pollution and
improve air quality. / *Hours: Mon-Fri 10am-6pm
(Wed 8pm); online catalogue; Delivery: p&p depends
on weight; no credit cards.*

Angela Conway

London SW4 ☎ (01883) 347967
Hairdressers – **Hairdressers:** day and evening
appointments covering south of the river from
East Dulwich to Putney; only does children
when adult has an appointment as well. Prices:
age six and under £8; adult cut – ladies £38,
men £20. / *Hours: by appointment.*

Cosatto

Lakeside View, Bentinck St, Farmworth,
Bolton BL4 7EP ☎ (0870) 050 5900,
Catalogue request (08000) 852628
⌁ www.cosatto.com
"...because we care" is the slogan of this large
equipment manufacturers with a good
reputation for quality. No mail order supply,
but the company can provide lists of local
stockists and sends out free catalogues.
Baby equipment – **Wheeled
Transport-brands:** pushchairs, 'shoppers',
convertible travel systems, all-terrain buggies
and carrycot prams; matching accessories are
available. / *free brochure.*

Cosmos Hair & Beauty Salon

265 Chiswick High Rd, London W4 4PU
☎ (020) 8995 9071

<u>Hairdressers</u> – **Hairdressers:** haircuts for boys and girls, from babies upwards; Mon-Fri only; £10 for under 12s.

Cotsafe Products 📬

WHWL Wrights House, Manchester Road, Eaton, Cheshire CW12 2CE ☎ (01260) 280716

<u>Baby equipment</u> – **Specialist mattress suppliers:** baby mattresses, including cot and crib mattresses, made with polyester fibres and breathable polypropylene covers; all machine washable, hypoallergenic, free of fire retardants and designed so that vomit will soak away (reducing the risk of choking). The cover is microporous polypropylene, chosen for breathability but sufficiently water-resistant for minor soiling to be wiped off. Can be made to measure. / *Hours: Mon-Fri 9am-7pm; free catalogue; Delivery: p&p included.*

Cotswold Clothing Company 📬

The Granary, Lower Farm, Hempton Rd, Duns Tew, Oxfordshire OX25 6JX
☎ (01869) 337770

<u>Baby clothes</u> – **Outdoorwear:** family business selling exclusive lines produced by the company in its own workshop, sold by mail order. "Practical country clothing" including waterproof cotton and corduroy all-in-ones for toddlers and fully-lined polar fleeces, from toddler to adult; corduroy high waist trousers, £36; pure cotton pyjamas and nightshirts £20. / *Hours: Mon-Fri 9am-3pm, or answerphone; free catalogue; Delivery: p&p £5.00; no Amex.*

Cotswold Essential Outdoor 📬

CENTRAL CONTACT DETAILS
☎ (01666) 575575, Mail order (01285) 643434, Store (01285) 863930
🖲 www.cotswold-outdoor.co.uk
BRANCHES:
Gateway Visitor Centre, A419 Spine Rd, East Junction, South Cerney GL7 5TL
☎ (01666) 575575, Mail order (01285) 643434, Store (01285) 863930
42-46 Uxbridge Rd W12 8ND
☎ (020) 8743 2976
72-76 Clarence St KT1 1NW
☎ (020) 8549 9500
Leyden St E1 7LL
☎ (020) 7655 4660

Hiking, camping and climbing specialist with a few quality items for children.

<u>Baby equipment</u> – **Stockists:** stockists of 'Zipper', a 3-wheel buggy made by Baby Jogger. – **Stockists - slings & backpacks:** baby carriers (front and back): brands include macpac and Karrimor, the latter including the Possum model which has extensive storage space, a sunshade and a rain cover.

<u>Baby clothes</u> – **Outdoorwear:** 'Country clothes' with an emphasis on practicality and waterproof rainwear; also summer microfibre clothes, T-shirts, trousers, shorts, hats and nightwear. / *Hours: 24hr answerphone; free catalogue; no Amex.*

Cotton Bottoms 📬

7-9 Water Lane Industrial Estate, Waterlane, Storrington, W Sussex RH20 3XX ☎ (0870) 777 8899 🖲 www.cottonbottoms.co.uk

Primarily a supplier of reusable nappies

<u>Nappies</u> – **Reusable stockists - brands & singles:** reusable cotton nappy systems; outer wrap is cotton, breathable, and waterproof; inner nappy is layered cotton; biodegradable liner is completely flushable – solid waste goes down the WC and not into the rubbish. Prices: wraps, £9.95 each; six nappies, £12; roll of 200 liners, £4.95. – **Reusable stockists - multiple brands:** claiming to be the largest nappy supply company in the UK, offering a choice of reusable cotton nappy systems; weekly supply schemes from £8 per week; nappy sizes from premature through to large; discount rates for twins (or more) or two children of different ages; training pants, swim nappies, Velcro pants and a laundry service also available. / *Hours: Mon-Fri 9am-5.30pm; free catalogue; Delivery: p&p extra; London & South East only; no Amex.*

Cotton Moon 📬

Freepost PO Box 280, London SE3 8DR
☎ (020) 8305 0012
🖲 www.cottonmoon.com

The emphasis here is on pure cotton products. Among other things, they are the mail order suppliers of the Motley Crew's children's range of T-shirts and sweatshirts.

<u>Baby clothes</u> – **Mid-range:** baby clothes in 100% cotton: rompers, from £12; pyjamas. The 'Motley Crew' range of printed T-shirts, sweatshirts, and shorts have storybook themes (pirates, dragons, space, magic) at prices from £10. / *Hours: Mon-Fri 10am-6pm; free catalogue; Delivery: p&p £3 (free over £100); no Amex.*

Cotton Tails 📬

Oxford ☎ (01865) 744977
🖲 www.cotton-tails.co.uk

<u>Nappies</u> – **Reusable stockists - brands & singles:** suppliers of Canadian Mother-Ease nappies (100% cotton terry towelling with poppers) and Air-Rika wraps; Grobags; Bumbo baby seats; Moltex nappies; also nappy buckets, feeding cushions and occasionally other baby-related goods; online advice on soaking and washing nappies.

Couverture 📬

310 Kings Rd, London SW3 5UH ☎ (020) 7795 1200 🖲 www.couverture.co.uk

Chelsea boutique specialising in luxury home accessories. It does mail order, but only via their catalogue (not from the website).

<u>Nursery decor</u> – **Bedding:** tastefully-embroidered bed linen and soft toys with embroidery, all in cotton; pillowcases include a pocket for the tooth fairy; duvet cover £79; pillowcase £19.

<u>Baby clothes</u> – **Sleepwear:** kids pyjamas in poplin, from £35; nightdress £29.

<u>Naming gifts</u> – **Naming gifts:** accessories such as baby shoes and cot blankets; occasional ranges include items such as vintage rattles and toys. / *Hours: Mon-Sat 10am-6pm; 2 free catalogues; Delivery: p&p up to £4.95.*

The Cow Jumped Over the Moon
18 Onslow Gardens, London N10 3JU
☎ (020) 8883 0888, mobile (07966) 233535
<u>Nursery decor</u> – **Murals and other Decorating:** children's murals and painted furniture, tailored and customised to suit different budgets and requirements.

Cox + Cox 🈂
Willowbeck, Water Lane, Drayton St Leonards, Oxfordshire OX10 7BE ☎ (0870) 442 4787 🖰 www.coxandcox.co.uk
<u>Nursery decor</u> – **Accessories:** "For creative living" – inventive collections of decorative accessories and gifts for all ages (window decorations, stamps, stencils and laser transfers, plus basics like lighting, hooks and handles); also some small furniture. / *Hours: Mon-Fri 9.30am-5.30pm; free catalogue; Delivery: p&p £4.95; free over £60.*

Cradle and All 🈂
3, Station Chambers, Station Road, Biggleswade, Bedfordshire ST18 8AH
☎ (01767) 600601
🖰 www.cradleandall.co.uk/
<u>Baby equipment</u> – **Stockists:** a comprehensive and easy-to-use online baby store, offering a good range of more standard items from a number of well-known brands.

Croglin Toys 🈂
Croglin, Nr Carlisle, Cumbria CA4 9RX
☎ (01768) 896 475
Fifteen-year-old Lake District shop with mail order business.
<u>Toys</u> – **Traditional toys:** original wooden toys in British hardwoods and pine such as a boxed set of wooden dolphins, whirligigs, farmyard animals, spinning tops, cube bells for babies and tumblers and farmyard buildings with matching accessories. / *Hours: Mon-Fri 9.30am-4.30pm; Easter to Mid-December; free catalogue.*

Cuddle Pie 🈂
4 Rowan Walk, London N2 0QJ ☎ (020) 8455 6991 🖰 www.cuddlepie.co.uk
<u>Nursery decor</u> – **Accessories:** importers of a range of Spanish baby items, many themed with a teddy bear motif; hangers; picture frames; height charts; lampshades and musical toys; call stockists or mail order.
<u>Naming gifts</u> – **Naming gifts:** a Spanish range of teddy-bear-themed gifts; soft and musical toys; blankets; rattles; nursery accessories; and other items ideal for gifts or the nursery. / *Hours: Mon-Fri 9.30am-5pm; online catalogue; Delivery: p&p extra.*

Cuddlebabes 🈂
22 The Stray, South Cave, East Yorkshire HU15 2AL ☎ (01430) 425257
🖰 www.cuddlebabes.co.uk
This site primarily focuses on nappies (both sale and information), but sells a few other items.
<u>Baby equipment</u> – **Stockists:** a selection of slings, including Wilkinet, Huggababy, Kari-Me and Tri Cotti.
<u>Nappies</u> – **Reusable stockists - multiple brands:** "Cloth nappy choices for all with help and advice on choosing the most cost-effective and appropriate" – helpful catalogue and good one-stop shop for various brands including Popolino, Daisy Diapers, Mother-ease, Disana, and Sandys (a two-size nappy in stretch cotton terry fastened with poppers); trial set available; silk liners, flushable liners, washable wipes and trainer pants also sold. – **Suppliers-Eco friendly disposables:** suppliers of Moltex Oko eco-friendly disposables. – **Change bags:** waterproof nappy bags that will hold two or three used washable nappies. / *Hours: usually Mon-Sat 9am-6pm; free brochure; no Amex.*

Cuddlies Direct 🈂
International House, Ethorpe Crescent, Gerrards Cross, Bucks SL9 8QR ☎ (01753) 891914, (01753) 888369
🖰 www.cuddliesdirect.co.uk
A mail order gift service particularly useful as an alternative naming gift.
<u>Naming gifts</u> – **Naming gifts:** mail order cuddly toys, including the well-known Manhattan Toy Company range, sent gift-wrapped; small, £17; large, £25. / *Hours: Mon-Fri 9am-5.30pm; Delivery: p&p £2.99.*

Cushy Tushies 🈂
☎ (0845) 644 3490
🖰 www.elvika-nappies.co.uk
Web site usefully details councils offering a subsidy for parents using reusables.
<u>Nappies</u> – **Reusable stockists - brands & singles:** "Independent and impartial advice on all nappy brands available" – that's the sweeping claim of this "independent nappy consultant". The website offers a lot of information, but you can't actually order online.

Cuski International
Unit 8, Ash Road North, Wrexham Industrial Estate, Wrexham, Clwyd LL13 9JP ☎ (0845) 166 2906 🖰 www.cuski.co.uk
<u>Toys</u> – **Comforters:** a soft, roughly doll-shaped toy to be used as a comforter; the idea is that the mother sleep with it before the birth so the baby recognises the smell.

Cyrillus 🈂
PO Box 351, Bedford MK41 9XZ ☎ (0870) 241 0242 🖰 www.cyrillus.co.uk
French catalogue company with a reputation for Continental stylishness.
<u>Baby clothes</u> – **Mid-range:** like the adult range, quality clothing for babies and children, with classic French styling. / *Hours: Mon-Sat 8am-7pm; free catalogue or online; Delivery: p&p £3.95.*

Daisy & Tom 🈂
181 King's Rd, London SW3 5EB ☎ (020) 7352 5000 🖰 www.daisyandtom.com
Over its first four years the first branch of Tim Waterstone's budding national chain of quality child department stores has gone through a number of evolutions. Most notably out has gone the café and in a wide selection of nursery equipment. A website is another recent introduction. New stores are planned nationwide, one of which may be a second London shop.
<u>Baby equipment</u> – **Stockists:** the equipment department carries a selection of widespread appeal, but with the focus at the luxury end of

the market; buggy brands stocked include Mamas & Papas, Maclaren and Silver Cross, but the range makes a feature of high quality, less well-known Continental brands including Keolstra, Gesslein and Emmaljunga.

Baby clothes – Luxury: the store's own-brand includes a number of well-priced items, but in general the emphasis is on the upper end of the market with brands such as Baby Dior, Petit Bateau, Kenzo, Elle, Timberland, Baby Graziella, and Burberry.

Shoes – Suppliers: wide choice with the main emphasis on Start-rite and Clarks, with D&Ts own-brand focussing on slippers, summer shoes, buckle shoes; also shoes from Babybotte, Buckle My Shoe, KangaROOS, Mod 8 and Pom d'Api and an array of funky bootees and padders.

Toys – General stockists: an excellent selection of pre-school branded items, including by Brio, Galt, Lamaze, Sevi, Playmobil, Plan, Pin and V-Tech.

Books, music & videos – Bookshops: as you might expect given its founder, this specialist children's store has a good-sized book department with a well chosen selection; individual sections of interest for pre-schoolers include books for babies, books for toddlers, and nursery rhymes. A daily story reading at 4.30pm (and 11.30am at weekends) is a popular event.

Hairdressers – Hairdressers: children's cuts from £12; first haircut (includes photo) £13.50. / Hours: Mon-Sat 10am-6pm (Wed 7pm), Sun noon-6pm; free catalogue.

Daisy Roots ⌂
The White House, Northampton Road, Brixworth, Northampton NN6 9BU
☎ (01604) 880 017 ⌂ www.daisy-roots.com
Shoes – Brands: soft leather pull-on baby bootees and padders, with non-skid soles; 13 colours in 45 different designs, including bows, frogs, stars, moons, tartan, leopard skin and Dalmatian print; six sizes, from £15. Also 'Happy Flannelies' – new range of bathtime products. / Hours: Mon-Fri 9am-5.30pm; free catalogue; Delivery: p&p included; no Amex.

Damask ⌂
CENTRAL CONTACT DETAILS
☎ (020) 7731 3470
⌂ www.damask.co.uk
BRANCHES:
3-4 Broxholme House, New King's Rd (nr Harwood Rd) SW6 4AA
☎ (020) 7731 3553
Although they supply other retailers, the brand has just a single standalone shop (and concessions in House of Fraser stores).
Nursery decor – Bedding: appliquéd nursery quilts (£115), laundry bags, bed and bath linen.
Baby clothes – Mid-range: delightful embroidered traditional childrens night clothing, plus bibs and Christening gowns. All in pure cotton with flame retardant finish; nightgowns from £35. / Hours: Mon-Sat 10am-6pm (Thu 7pm); catalogue £2.50; Delivery: p&p £3 (£6 for orders over £100).

WJ Daniel & Co ⌂
96-122 Uxbridge Rd, London W13 8RF
☎ (020) 8567 6789, (020) 8579 1234
⌂ www.daniel-nursery.co.uk;
www.danielstores.com
Especially where equipment is concerned it's worth a visit (though they do deliver) to this unprepossessing Ealing store (with another branch in Windsor) which is apparently the largest independent nursery supplier in the UK; large car park.
Baby equipment – Stockists: claiming the ability to supply 400 prams and cots and with a wide array of showroom stock; prams – a good range of the all the main brands are on display; cots – the showroom stock includes Cosatto and Mamas & Papas (about 10-20 styles); wide range of other items such as changing stations, cribs and baths. – **Buggy & pram repairs:** minor repairs can be done on the premises.
Baby clothes – Mid-range: selected designer names; name tape kit available in haberdashery. – **Premature deliveries.**
Toys – General stockists: the toy range, though still not quite as extensive as that for equipment, continues to grow in scale (including quality names like Galt, Lego, Fisher-Price and Playmobil). / Hours: Mon-Sat 9am-5.30pm; Delivery: free delivery over £100; no Diner's Card.

Daphne & Mum
7 Belmont Parade, 838 Finchley Rd, London NW11 6XP ☎ (020) 8458 7095
Baby clothes – Mid-range: small shop with a comparatively wide range of items; caters to all tastes and pockets with Continental and English garments and a designer made-to-measure service as well as hair accessories; boys and girls clothing ranges from socks at £1 to a dress at £200. / Hours: Mon-Wed 9.30am-6pm, Thu 9.30am-7pm, Fri 9am-6pm, Sun 10.30am-4pm; Delivery: p&p extra; no Amex.

Dapper Nippers ⌂ Q
14 Glenester Close, Hoddesdon EN11 9LS
☎ (07905) 929922
⌂ www.dappernippers.com
Baby clothes – Second-hand shops: a family-run business, specialising in personally-selected, second-hand, well-cared-for, mostly designer clothes, chosen for being a little different from the norm.

The Decor Centre
82 Green Lane, London SE9 2AP ☎ (020) 8859 4735
Nursery decor – Furniture: painted 'Chartley' furniture and some nursery accessories.
– **Interior designers:** interior design consultancy, which incorporates a service for making quilts, curtains, etc. / Hours: Tue-Fri 10am-5pm, Sat 9.30am-5pm; no Amex.

Denny Andrews ⌂
Clock House, Coleshill, nr Swindon, Wilts SN6 7PT ☎ (01793) 762476
⌂ www.dennyandrews.co.uk
Ethnic-style clothing business.
Maternity wear – Mid-range: lots of loose cotton clothing suitable for maternity wear, including nightwear and trousers with

elasticated or drawstring waists. Range
includes kaftans, kimonos, waistcoats, dresses,
simple shaped shirts and jackets. Some silk
items available; cotton nightgown £35. / *Hours:
by appointment, Office hours answerphone; free
catalogue; Delivery: p&p extra.*

Designers Guild
267-277 King's Rd, London SW3 5EN
☎ (020) 7893 7400
🖰 www.designersguild.com
The Chelsea showroom of this widely-stocked
fabric and wallpaper brand (adjacent to the
eponymous store stocking household items
and 'lifestyle products', which keeps different
opening hours).
Nursery decor – **Wallpaper & fabrics:**
children's ranges of fabric, wallpaper, bed
linen, rucksacks, hats, rugs, towels and bath
robes; curtain making service; new designs
every season, with many colourful
contemporary styles. / *Hours: Mon-Sat 10am-
6pm, Sun noon-5pm.*

Dickory Dock Designs 🖃
Bridgemills, Huddersfield Road, Holmfirth,
West Yorkshire HD9 3TW ☎ (01484) 689
619 🖰 www.dickorydockdesigns.co.uk
Toys – **Educational:** manufacturers and
suppliers of fabric wall hangings for story
boards and other educational purposes, plus
other items including hand puppets and
animals and some wooden toys; six nursery
rhymes wall hanging, £45. / *Hours: Mon-Sat
10am-4pm; closed Sun; educational catalogue available
only; Anywhere.*

Direct to Your Door 🖃
Ellerbeck Court, Stokesley Idustrial Estate,
Stokesley, North Yorkshire TS9 5PT
☎ (01642) 714882, (0800) 137880
🖰 www.directtoyourdoor.co.uk
Toys – **Traditional toys:** an online vendor
which claims it may offer the widest choice of
wooden trains in the world, plus ranges such as
Sylvanian families, dolls and dolls' clothes, Plan
Toys, Pin Toys, die-cast cars and
garages. / *Hours: Mon-Fri 9am-5pm, Sat 10am-1pm;
free catalogue; Delivery: p&p extra.*

Discount Baby Store.co.uk 🖃
Unit A13, Maritime Park, Criterion Way,
Pembroke Dock, Pembrokeshire SA72 6UL
☎ (0870) 991 4047
🖰 www.discountbabystore.co.uk
Website business which claims that "if you
have seen any product cheaper anywhere else,
please e-mail us and we will beat the price".
Baby equipment – **Discount Outlets:** a wide
range of discounted equipment of all types
from brands including Cosatto, Graco,
Kingswood and Maxi Cosi. / *Delivery: p&p
included.*

Discovery 🖃
Guild House, Farnsby St, Swindon SN99 1BY
☎ Customer Service (01793) 548135, Direct
line (0870) 165 0299
🖰 www.booksforchildren.co.uk
Books, music & videos – **Book clubs:** book
club for children; buy six books at the (very
low) introductory prices, then six books a year
at the 'normal' discounted level.

The Disney Store
CENTRAL CONTACT DETAILS
☎ (020) 8222 1000
🖰 www.disney.co.uk
BRANCHES:
*(Only selected branches are listed –
call the enquiry line for other outlets.)*
91 The Piazza WC2E 8HD
☎ (020) 7836 5037
360-366 Oxford St W1N 9HA
☎ (020) 7491 9136
You either love or hate the
technicolour-in-your-face charm of the stores;
reasonable-quality branded clothing and toys.
Baby clothes – **Cheap & cheerful:** all the
familiar cartoon characters on an array of items
from bibs to T-shirts and sportswear.
Toys – **Character toys:** lots of smaller items
which are of dependable quality and perhaps
not as pricey as might be expected.

T Ditchfield
792 High Rd, London E10 6AE ☎ (020) 8539
2821 🖰 www.ditchfields.co.uk
Toys – **General stockists:** the "widest range of
toys in East London", they claim, with all the
big names: Lego, Meccano, Hornby,
Fisher-Price, Mattel. – **Outdoor items
& active toys:** a number of items including
slides. / *Hours: Mon-Sat 9.15am-5.30pm (Thu 5pm).*

Diverse Kids
46 Cross St, London N1 ☎ (020) 7226 6863
🖰 www.diverseclothing.com
Baby clothes – **Luxury:** part of Islington's high
fashion Diverse chain, triggered by the birth of
a grandchild of the original owners and run by
their daughter (a fashion graduate of
St Martin's). Brands – mirroring the
womenswear branch – include Antik Batik,
Maharishi, Diesel, Paul Smith and Quincy.

Dolls' Hospital
The Purbeck Toy and Musical Box Museum,
Arne, nr Wareham, Dorset BH20 5BJ
☎ (01929) 552018
Toys – **Repairs:** specialists in repairing antique
dolls and tin toys plus musical boxes of all
types. / *Hours: Apr-June, Sept 11am-5pm (closed
Mon), Jul-Aug 10am-5.30pm (open Mondays);
Delivery: p&p extra (recorded).*

Domat Designs
3 Lacy Rd, London SW15 1NH ☎ (020) 8788
5715 🖰 www.domas.co.uk
Traditional toy shop.
Toys – **General stockists:** good range of toys
and soft toys; many 'classics' including Beatrix
Potter; brands include Galt, Lego, Orchard and
a good range of Brio. / *Hours: Mon-Sat 9.30am-
5.30pm; no Amex or Diners Card.*

Donaldson
🖰 www.donaldson.be
Baby clothes – **Luxury:** a luxury Disney brand
(the name barely mentioned), offering more
tasteful than usual clothes embroidered with
Walt Disney characters or related patterns;
boutiques and concessions across Europe,
and now also at Harrods (they no longer have
a dedicated store).

The Door Mouse 🐾
7 Hunter St, Paisley PA1 1DN ☎ (0141) 887 9916 🖰 www.bearsbysuequinn.co.uk
<u>Toys</u> – **Cuddly toys:** superior cuddly toys – squirrels, rabbits and bears – complete with outfits. Customised items can be made. / *Hours: by appointment; free leaflet; Delivery: p&p extra; no Amex & no Switch.*

Dorling Kindersley
80 Strand, London WC2R OLR ☎ (020) 7010 3000 🖰 www.dk.com
<u>Books, music & videos</u> – **Bookshops:** distinctive brand of reference and picture books; all age ranges are well catered for, including toddlers, as well as titles on pregnancy, baby health and parenting; games and multimedia products also stocked. / *Hours: Mon-Fri 10am-6pm.*

Dorothy Perkins
CENTRAL CONTACT DETAILS
☎ (0800) 731 8285
🖰 www.dorothyperkins.co.uk
BRANCHES:
(Only selected branches are listed – call the enquiry line for other outlets.)
187-189 Oxford St W1R 1AJ
☎ (020) 7494 3769
118-132 New Oxford St WC1A 1HN
☎ (020) 7255 2116
<u>Maternity wear</u> – **Cheap & cheerful:** unfussy and practical clothes suitable for work and leisure. The Oxford Street branch has one of the best maternity selections.

Dot Productions 🐾
103 Redchurch St, London E2 7DL ☎ (020) 7252 2123 🖰 www.dotproductions.co.uk
<u>Nursery decor</u> – **Bedding:** vibrantly-coloured soft furnishings – bed linens and cot sets, cushions, curtains – including Moses basket (£160 to order; prices can vary); also a small range of own-style kids T-shirts. / *Hours: showroom open by appointment Mon-Sun; online catalogue; Delivery: p&p extra.*

Dragons of Walton Street 🐾
23 Walton St, London SW3 2HX ☎ (020) 7589 3795
🖰 www.dragonsofwaltonstreet.com
Well-known Chelsea boutique specialising primarily in hand-painted furniture (not just for children); also offer a complete interior design service.
<u>Nursery decor</u> – **General stockists:** beds, wardrobes, tables, chairs (some upholstered, from £150), co-ordinated fabrics, wallpapers and borders. Prices range from £30 to over £1,000. / *Hours: Mon-Fri 9.30am-5.30pm, Sat 10am-5pm; catalogue £3.50 or online; Delivery: p&p extra.*

Dribble Factory 🐾
24 Snowy Fielder Waye, Isleworth, Middx TW7 6AQ ☎ (020) 8758 2601
🖰 www.dribblefactory.com
<u>Baby clothes</u> – **Mid-range:** t-shirts with logos like 'Part-time Angel', 'Property left here entirely at owners risk', and 'Danger of Flooding'. Sizes from newborn to 18 months, price £13.

Dromedary Trading 🐾
Estate Office, Healey Hall, Riding Mill NE44 6BH ☎ (01434) 673961
<u>Baby clothes</u> – **Mid-range.** – **Traditional:** mail order business supplying "traditional with a twist" clothing predominantly in cord and moleskin; crop trousers £15, toggle fleece £22, girl's 'yum yum' dress in cotton with velvet ribbons £26.

Dulwich Books 🐾
6 Croxted Rd, London SE21 8SW ☎ (020) 8670 9842
<u>Books, music & videos</u> – **Bookshops:** this general bookshop is well known for its childrens section; picture books, CDs and cassettes are a particular speciality, and there's a play area. / *Hours: Mon-Sat 9.30am-5.30pm; no Amex.*

The Dulwich Bookshop
1d Calton Avenue, London SE21 7DE
☎ (020) 8693 2808
<u>Books, music & videos</u> – **Bookshops:** ex Nibbie-winner (the Oscars of the book trade – Independent Bookseller of the Year) which has a good children's selection (and whose manger contributes regular reviews for NCT publications).

Dunster House 🐾
Caxton Rd, Elms Farm Estate, Bedford MK41 0EB ☎ (01234) 272 445
🖰 www.dhleisureandgarden.com
<u>Toys</u> – **Outdoor items & active toys:** a wide range of play and garden products (climbing frames, swings, towers and sandpits), well displayed on an easy-to-use website. / *Hours: Mon-Fri 9am-6pm, Sat 9am-4pm; free catalogue; no Amex.*

Dutailier
Unit 26, Perivale Industrial Park, Horsenden Lane South, Greenford, Middlesex UB6 7RJ ☎ (020) 8810 8818 🖰 www.dutailier.co.uk
<u>Nursery decor</u> – **Furniture:** manufacturers of the Glider Rocker, the luxury rocking chair and foot rest stocked by some larger equipment retailers. It comes in four wood finishes with a number of fabrics. Some models incorporate a reclining feature. (Call for stockists.) / *Hours: Mon-Thur 8.30am-5pm; Fri 8.30am-4.30pm.*

Dynky 🐾
JEM House, Littlemead, Cranleigh, Surrey GU6 8TT ☎ (0870) 727 4144
🖰 www.dynky.com
<u>Baby clothes</u> – **Mid-range:** quirky but practical garments from birth to six years. Some have lots of detailing, but there is also the occasional more classic item; long-sleeved T-shirts £13, jeans £19.

E Sharp Minor 🐾
6 Earlswood St, London SE10 9ES ☎ (020) 8858 6648 🖰 www.esharpminor.co.uk
Shop and mail order business.
<u>Baby clothes</u> – **Mid-range:** mainly cotton for 0-4 years. – **Funky.** – **Knitwear:** "Funky shapes and luscious colours" is the promise from this company, who make knitted items, from hats to knitted dresses (£15-£60). All clothes are machine washable and suitable for most children with eczema. / *Hours: shop & mail*

order enquiries Tue-Sat 10am-4pm; online catalogue; Delivery: p&p extra; no Amex.

Early Clothing
79-85 Fortis Green Rd, London N10 3HR
☎ (020) 8444 9309

<u>Baby clothes</u> – **Luxury:** designer names including Petit Bateau, Oilily, Pamporina, Timberland, Balu, Kenzo, DKNY, Jean Bourget and Catimini; ranges from socks at £3.95 to items from £100.

<u>Shoes</u> – **Suppliers:** brands include Start-rite, KangaROOS, O'Neill, Timberland, Naturino, Ricosta and Mod8. / *Hours: Mon-Sat 9.30am-5.30pm.*

Early Learning Centre ⌨
CENTRAL CONTACT DETAILS
☎ Customer services (01793) 443322
🖰 www.elc.co.uk
BRANCHES:
(Only selected branches are listed – call the enquiry line for other outlets.)
Customer Services & Mail Order, South Marston Park SN3 4TJ
☎ Customer services (01793) 443322
Unit 8 The Broadway Centre W5 2NP
☎ (020) 8567 7076
Unit 7 Kings Mall, King St W6 0TZ
☎ (020) 8741 2469
36 Kings Rd SW3 4HD
☎ (020) 7581 5764
Brent Cross Shopping Centre NW4 9FE
☎ (020) 8202 6948
The Bentalls Centre, Kingston KT1 1TR
☎ (020) 8549 2918
Unit 8 Putney Exchange, High St SW15 1TN
☎ (020) 8780 1074
Unit 111 Centre Court Shopping Centre, 4 Queen's Rd SW19 1YE
☎ (020) 8944 0355
Unit 7 St Mary's Place, High St SE9 1DO
☎ (020) 8294 1057
110 High St SE13 4TJ
☎ (020) 8318 3930
9 The Quadrant TW9 1BP
☎ (020) 8948 8632

This well-known specialist retailer (200+ branches nationwide) is the UK's only toy chain, that targets pre-schoolers. All branches are very child-friendly, with toys and games, and some hold holiday events and activities. There is a comprehensive mail order catalogue which promises to "match any price anywhere".

<u>Toys</u> – **Pre-school specialists:** the range focuses on stimulating, traditional toys: fun art and craft items, farm and train sets (their own brand), water and garden toys (e.g. junior microscope, £6; play food, £4); they also now stock some computer software; one of the first retailers to operate a 'no guns' policy, which it continues to do. A range of ELC toys is also available in selected Sainsbury's.

<u>Books, music & videos</u> – **Bookshops:** all branches of this specialist chain stock at least 50 children's titles – the biggest ranges being in the larger, out-of-town stores. The ELC has one of the best selections for under-twos, with numerous pop-up, pre-reading and 'activity' books. Books are also listed on the ELC website, categorised by price, subject, brand and age range. The site allows for searches by

age, type of toy and budget. / *Hours: Mon-Sat 9am-5pm (some stores 10am-8pm); free catalogue; Delivery: p&p £2.95 (free for orders over £60).*

Easy2name Labels ⌨
2 Malthouse Cottages, Ecchinswell, Newbury, Berks RG20 4UA ☎ (01635) 298326 🖰 www.easy2name.com

<u>Baby equipment</u> – **Name labels:** name stickers are dishwasher and microwave-proof for baby bottles, beakers and other equipment; 50 small labels £7, 100 for £10; sample accompanies leaflet.

<u>Baby clothes</u> – **Nametapes:** iron-on name tapes, stickers and transfers; prices as above. / *Hours: Mon-Fri 9.30am-5.30pm; Free catalogue as well as samples; also available online; Delivery: p&p £1.*

eBay ⌨ Q
🖰 www.ebay.co.uk
Even many wealthy people are addicted to picking up bargains on this online auction website – one of the most successful operators in cyberspace. If you're a budget-conscious parent, it's well worth keeping a good eye on what's on offer.

<u>Maternity wear</u> – **Second-hand shops.**
<u>Baby equipment</u> – **Second-hand.**
<u>Baby clothes</u> – **Second-hand shops.**
<u>Toys</u> – **Second-hand shops.**

Eco-Babes ⌨
17b Paradise Road, Downham Market, Norfolk PE38 9HS ☎ (01366) 387851
🖰 www.eco-babes.co.uk
An eco-friendly company offering an impressive range of 'green' nappies, accessories, clothes, toiletries and household products; the catalogue offers a useful breakdown of the benefits of the various reusable nappy systems.

<u>Baby clothes</u> – **Eco-friendly clothing:** unbleached organic cotton jersey products: sleepsuit £12; baby bodysuit £5; bib £2.75; also adult underwear.

<u>Nappies</u> – **Reusable stockists - multiple brands:** a wide range of ecologically-sound nappies at decent prices; brands include Kooshies; Tots Bots; Popolino from Austria; Mother-Ease (from Canada); Bumhuggers; Snuggle Nap; also traditional terries with modern wraps; all liners and accessories also available. A variety of eco-nappy kits available from £4 per week (minimum of two weeks) to help you decide which is the right nappy for you. Also swim nappies, trainer pants and accessories such as sanitisers, washing powders, nappy bags, Nappi Nippas, mats and soaking buckets. – **Suppliers-Eco friendly disposables:** brands stocked include Moltex Oko and Tushies. / *Hours: Mon-Sat 8.30am-6pm; Delivery: p&p £2.99 ; no Amex.*

Ecomerchant Ltd ⌨
Head Hill Road, Goodnestone, Faversham, Kent ME13 9BU ☎ (01795) 530130
🖰 www.ecomerchant.co.uk
<u>Nursery decor</u> – **Paints:** stockists of Livos natural paints, a range which uses only natural ingredients, and natural oils; can provide colour charts and other literature on application; sample pots available. / *Hours: Mon-Fri 8am-5pm, Sat 9am-4pm.*

Ecos Paints ⌂

Unit 34 Heysham Business Park, Middleton Rd, Heysham, Lancashire LA3 3PP ☎ (01524) 852371 ⌨ www.ecospaints.com

<u>Nursery decor</u> – **Paints:** stockists of ECOS (environment-conscious, odourless, solvent-free) paints and varnishes – they say, the only completely solvent-free range in the world, suited to asthmatics, allergy sufferers and babies; there are 84 co-ordinated colours; also environmentally-friendly paint strippers and algicides; brochures include hand-painted colour cards for accurate colour matching (£8); sample pots £2.50. / *Hours: Mon-Fri 9am-5pm; brochure with colour charts or online; Delivery: p&p £7 up to 4, 5 litre tins.*

Ede and Nia ⌂

☎ (020) 7602 8229 ⌨ www.edeandnia.co.uk

<u>Shoes</u> – **Brands:** cute first shoes, in felt.

Edinburgh Bicycle Cooperative ⌂

8 Alvanley Terrace, Edinburgh EH9 1DU ☎ (0131) 331 5010
⌨ www.edinburghbicycle.com

One of the largest cycling shops in the UK (run as a workers co-operative) produces what they claim is the UK's most comprehensive bicycle catalogue.

<u>Baby equipment</u> – **Bicycle-related items:** seats to carry your child on the back or front of your bike (£75-£100) as well as trailers, helmets, reflective and protective items, storm outfits and cold-weather gear. / *online catalogue; Delivery: p&p £3 (small items), £7.50 (bikes & trailers).*

Eduzone ⌂

29 Friern Barnet Rd, London N11 1NE ☎ (0845) 644 5556 ⌨ www.eduzone.co.uk

<u>Toys</u> – **Nursery suppliers:** an early-years catalogue supplier whose range includes items like Brio and similar train sets, dolls houses and a good selection of musical instruments. There is an intelligent toddler section, and also one strong on multi-cultural items. / *Hours: Mon-Fri 11am-5pm; free brochure; Delivery: p&p extra.*

Electramax International ⌂

The Seedbed Centre, Units D10-D11, Davidson Way, Romford, Essex RM7 0AZ ☎ (01708) 714 200
⌨ www.electramaxinternational.com

<u>Baby equipment</u> – **Monitors-brand:** a supplier which describes itself as a Baby Monitor Warehouse, offering options for a range of budgets including video wireless colour and black and white monitors and digital monitors with talk back, night lights, visual sound lights and up to 30 sub-channels. The website gives lots of information, though you can't actually order online.

Ella's House ⌂

Old Post Office, Bower, Wick, Caithness KW1 4TL ☎ (01955) 641 358
⌨ www.ellashouse.com

<u>Nappies</u> – **Reusable stockists - brands & singles:** a company offering nappies and pads made to order in high quality hemp, cotton and polyester fleece. / *Hours: Mon-Fri 8am-6pm.*

The Ellie Nappy Company ⌂

PO Box 16, Ellesmere Port, Cheshire CH66 2HA ☎ (0151) 200 5012
⌨ www.elliepants.co.uk

<u>Baby clothes</u> – **Sleepwear:** organic cotton pyjamas, £16.

<u>Nappies</u> – **Reusable stockists - brands & singles:** award-winning Ellie's 'Super Nappies', £30 for 12; night-time nappies, £38 for 12; boosters, £19 for 12. Good absorbency, washable to 95 degrees; also pants with poppers (washable to 60 degrees) which are usable with other nappies. Seven sizes from newborn to over 25kg: £6 single item or £5.50 each for 3 or more. Woollen pants £16 each. / *Hours: Mon-Fri 8am-8pm, Sat 8am-1pm; 24hr answerphone; free catalogue; Delivery: p&p included; no Amex.*

ellipsis arts ⌂

Germany ☎ +49 221 500 859-0
⌨ www.qrious.de

<u>Books, music & videos</u> – **Music tapes:** a range of pleasant world music, including CDs with Celtic, Latin American, African and Asian songs; available from most music shops or it is possible to buy direct.

Elys of Wimbledon

16 St Georges Rd, London SW19 4DP ☎ (020) 8946 9191, (020) 8946 5954

<u>Shoes</u> – **Suppliers:** stockists of Clarks ranges.

<u>Toys</u> – **General stockists:** good general toy section including all the well-known brands such as Fisher-Price, Lego, Tomy, Galt, Waddingtons and Chicco. / *Hours: Mon-Fri 9.30am-6pm, Sat 9am-6pm, Sun 11am-5pm.*

Emma Henley ⌂

38 Holcombe Lane, Bathampton, Bath BA2 6UL ☎ (01225) 466 835

<u>Baby clothes</u> – **Traditional:** clothes and accessories with handmade buttons and appliqué motifs; mixture of formal and casual items; fleeces; traditional designs including sailor suits and flowery dresses; to see the full range call for details of upcoming fairs and details of stockists. / *free price lists with postcard (& fabric samples on request); no credit cards.*

Emma-Jane ⌂

PO Box 65, Ilford, Essex IG3 8RT ☎ (020) 8599 3004 ⌨ www.emma-jane.com

<u>Maternity wear</u> – **Bras and underwear:** leading manufacturer of zip and drop cup bras with the biggest size range in the UK – all products are recommended by the Royal College of Midwives; also swimwear, tights, support belt (one design), sleep bras and nightshirts; average bra price £17 (extensions are available separately). / *Hours: Mon-Thu 9am-5pm, Fri 9am-2pm; free catalogue & lists of stockists; Delivery: p&p £2; no Amex.*

Emmaljunga UK

⌨ www.emmaljunga.co.uk

70-year-old Swedish pram and buggy manufacturer with a typically Scandinavian emphasis on safety and a reputation for high-quality products – a kind of Swedish Silver Cross; see website for stockists.

<u>Baby equipment</u> – **Wheeled Transport-brands:** models from rugged pushchair to pram-pushchair; also nifty-looking

models for twins or close-in-age siblings, and an interesting toddler seat option whereby you practically stack your children on top of one another.

Enfant ⊞ Q
Crown House, Old Mill St, Stoke-on-Trent ST4 2RP ☎ (01782) 845 870
⊙ www.repeatrepeat.co.uk
<u>Naming gifts</u> – **Naming gifts:** traditional gifts, but sometimes with a modern twist, including bone china nurseryware, bone china moneyboxes, photo albums, Christening spoons and egg and cup sets.

The English Stamp Company ⊞
Worth Matravers, Dorset BH19 3JP
☎ (01929) 439117 ⊙ www.englishstamp.com
<u>Nursery decor</u> – **Stencils & stamps:** attractive unfussy stamps for walls, furniture and fabric; designs include wild and farm animals, a rocking horse, and 'adult' patterns such as suns and stars; also custom stamps (designs, logos, or even children's hand and feet prints) and Christmas theme kits (including paint) as gifts. Phone for details of retail outlets. / *Hours: Mon-Fri 9am-5pm, or answerphone; free catalogue or online; Delivery: p&p £1.95.*

The English Teddy Bear Company ⊞
CENTRAL CONTACT DETAILS
☎ Direct sales (01225) 338655, Head office (0870) 333 2455
⊙ www.theenglishteddybearcompany.co.uk
BRANCHES:
42 Piccadilly W1V 9AJ
☎ (020) 7491 2091
153 Regent St W1R 7FD
☎ (020) 7287 3273
Headquartered in Bath, this company has shops around the UK (including three in London) as well as its mail order business. Their motto is "excellent quality with affordable prices".
<u>Baby clothes</u> – **Mid-range:** teddy bear T-shirts and sweatshirts (for kids as well as adults) in pure unbleached cotton; all designs are done in-house.
<u>Toys</u> – **Cuddly toys:** a comprehensive range of bears from £2-£400 including limited editions (though these are aimed almost exclusively at adults) and from other brands such as Ty (Beanie Babies). / *Hours: Mon-Fri 10am-6pm (may vary); Delivery: p&p £3.95; no Amex.*

The Entertainer ⊞
Broughton Business Park, Bell Lane, Little Chalfont, Amersham HP6 6GL ☎ (0870)905 5100 ⊙ www.thetoyshop.com
<u>Toys</u> – **General stockists:** mail order service for Lego, TP, Hasbro, Mattel and other major manufacturers (run by a group which incorporates 36 toy shops throughout England). / *Hours: Mon-Fri 9am-5.30pm; free catalogue.*

Equinox ⊞
78 Neal St, London WC2H 9PA ☎ (020) 7497 1001 ⊙ www.equinoxastrology.com
<u>Naming gifts</u> – **Naming gifts:** astrological chart and interpretation (£18), drawn up by

consultant astrologer Robert Currey (who also holds a degree in psychology and philosophy).

Escor Toys ⊞
Elliott Rd, West Howe, Bournemouth BH11 8JP ☎ (01202) 591081
⊙ www.escortoys.com
<u>Toys</u> – **Traditional toys:** award-winning, traditional wooden toys mainly for pre-schoolers. They include pull-along, counting, and construction items, and pure playthings such as merry-go-rounds. / *Hours: Mon-Thu 9am-5pm, Fri 9am-1pm; free catalogue & lists of stockists; Delivery: p&p included; no Amex.*

Etro
14, Old Bond St, London W1 ☎ (020) 7495 5767
<u>Maternity wear</u> – **Mid-range:** smart kaftans suitable for use in pregnancy.

EuroBaby
12 Victory Close, Woolsbridge Industrial Park, Three Legged Cross, Wimborne, Dorset BH21 6SX ☎ (01202) 820821
All products are sold through stockists (no mail order or brochures); call for a list of retailers.
<u>Baby equipment</u> – **Cots.**
<u>Nursery decor</u> – **Furniture:** furniture, dressers and wardrobes. / *Hours: Mon-Fri 9am-5pm.*

Evans Cycles ⊞
CENTRAL CONTACT DETAILS
☎ (0870) 600 0908
⊙ www.evanscycles.com
BRANCHES:
178 High Holborn WC1V 7AA
☎ (020) 7836 5585
51-52 Rathbone Place W1T 1JP
☎ (020) 7580 4107
320-320b Vauxhall Bridge Road SW1V 1AA
☎ (020) 7976 6298
111-115 Waterloo Rd SE1 8UL
☎ (020) 7928 2208
77-81 The Cut SE1 8LL
☎ (020) 7928 4785
127-129 Wandsworth High St SW18 4JB
☎ (020) 8877 1878
48 Richmond Rd KT2 5EE
☎ (020) 8549 2559
5 Cullum Street, (off Fenchurch St) EC3M 7JJ
☎ (020) 7283 6750
1 Farringdon Street, London EC4M 7LD
☎ (020) 7248 2349
One of the biggest cycle retailers in town also maintains a mail order business and on-line shop.
<u>Baby equipment</u> – **Bicycle-related items:** a range of trailers (3-4 choices), seats (4-5 items), carriers, helmets and so on. / *Hours: Mon-Sat 9am-6pm, Sun 11am-4pm; free brochure; Delivery: 2-3 days £2.50, £7 next day.*

Ezee-Reach ⊞
Unit 36, Burners Lane, Kiln Farm, Milton Keynes, Bucks MK11 3HB ☎ (01908) 565 001 ⊙ www.ezee-reach.com
<u>Baby equipment</u> – **Stockists:** suppliers of a number of ingenious devices for babies and toddlers including stay-put cutlery (attached to the table by flexible coil and suction pad), a window pouch for use in the car, and a trolley buffer for use, for example, in the

supermarket. Also a sunshade which attaches directly to car windows.

Fagin Toys
84 Fortis Green Rd, London N10 3HN
☎ (020) 8444 0282
<u>Toys</u> – **Traditional toys:** the emphasis is on the more traditional toys, dolls and games – brands include Galt and Brio. / *Hours: Mon-Fri 9am-5.30pm, Sat Sun 10am-3pm; no Amex.*

Family Seat 🗔
Bibs & Stuff, 26 Bonehurst Road, Salfords Industrial Estate, Nr Redhill, Surrey RH1 5EW ☎ (01480) 350 645, (020) 8962 8118 🗠 www.familyseat.com
<u>Nappies</u> – **Potty training:** produces a lavatory seat (from £30) with two seats, one normal adult-sized and another, hinged above the adult one, child-sized. Stockists are listed on the website, and include outlets like John Lewis, Mothercare and Blooming Marvellous.

Farmer John Duvets 🗔
Gaer Farm, Cwmyoy, Abergavenny, Monmouthshire NP7 7NE ☎ (01873) 890345
<u>Nursery decor</u> – **Bedding:** traditional farmhouse quilts (with cotton casings), filled with hand-washed wool from local sheep; only suitable for children over one year old; available in cot and single bed sizes; also adult sizes up to king size. / *Hours: Mon-Fri 9am-5pm, or answerphone; free catalogue; Delivery: p&p £3-£6.50; no credit cards.*

The Farmyard
54 Friars Stile Rd, Richmond TW10 6NQ
☎ (020) 8332 0038
Primarily a children's gift and toy shop that aims to stock slightly different items.
<u>Nursery decor</u> – **Furniture:** hand-painted; desks, tables, toy boxes and bookends.
<u>Baby clothes</u> – **Traditional:** range of Damask nightwear; plus a range of somewhat unusual baby clothes including hand embroidered items.
<u>Toys</u> – **Traditional toys:** primarily wooden and educational items including puzzles, dolls houses and furniture, rockers and pull-along toys; Skipper Yachts and Brio. / *Hours: Mon-Sat 9.30am-5.30pm; no Amex.*

Fat Face 🗔
PO Box 1, Havant, Hampshire PO9 2UA
☎ (0870) 6000 090 🗠 www.fatface.co.uk
<u>Baby clothes</u> – **Luxury:** ski- and surf-bum fashion range, suitable from six months onwards; surfer T-shirts (from £12.50), track suit trousers, sweats and even dresses.

Favourite Things 🗔
19 Woodlands Ave, West Byfleet, Surrey KT14 6AT ☎ (01932) 355603
🗠 www.afavouritething.co.uk
<u>Nursery decor</u> – **Accessories:** fabric nursery accessories including appliquéd quilts and playmats in bright or sampler designs (from £40 to £199); other items include wooden accessories, fleece blankets, mobiles, lamps, pyjama cases, fabric houses, and early learning books; also Emma Jefferson wooden height charts, skittles, trinket boxes and miniature chests of drawers. / *Hours: office hours; answerphone; free catalogue; Delivery: p&p £3.50; no Amex.*

Fiesta Crafts 🗔
2nd Floor, Tower House, Skillion Commercial Centre, Lee Valley Trading Estate, Edmonton, London N18 3HR ☎ (020) 8803 7508 🗠 www.fiesta-crafts.co.uk
Mail order business, formerly known as Skills for Kids.
<u>Toys</u> – **Traditional toys:** the catalogue includes over 80 items, including numerous handmade educational and fun toys such as wall hangings, activity books, playhouses, mobiles, height charts, play mats and washable soft toys. / *Hours: Mon-Fri 9am-5pm; free catalogue; Delivery: p&p included.*

Fig 🗔
37 Grove Park, London SE5 8LG ☎ (020) 7884 1312
<u>Baby clothes</u> – **Traditional:** traditional English nightwear including pyjamas and nighties in brushed cotton (with fleece dressing gowns to match). From 12 months.

Figleaves 🗔
7 Finchley Industrial Centre, 879 High Rd, London N12 8RA ☎ (020) 4999 002
🗠 www.figleaves.com
<u>Maternity wear</u> – **Bras and underwear:** one of the most successful dot com retailers in the country – the site offers practically every brand, size and type of lingerie, including a good range of maternity, nursing and support bras; free delivery and returns in the UK. / *online & mail order catalogue; Delivery: p&p free returns.*

Finetica Child 🗔
88 East Main Street #428, Mendham, NJ, USA 07945 ☎ +1 973 543 0053
🗠 www.fineticachild.com
<u>Baby clothes</u> – **Luxury:** US business with comprehensive online catalogue of kid's clothing.

Finger Protector 🗔
Innovation House, 385 Chepstow Avenue, Hornchurch, Essex RM12 6AU ☎ (01708) 855 777, Customer care (07071) 22 28 55
🗠 www.fingerprotector.co.uk
<u>Nursery decor</u> – **Safety items:** from a British inventor whose child caught her finger in a door, a product which fits between the door and frame and keeps intrusive digits out of the way as the door closes; cost £13.95. / *Hours: Mon-Fri 9am-5pm; online catalogue; Delivery: p&p £10; no Amex.*

Fisher-Price
☎ Consumer helpline (01628) 500303
🗠 www.fisher-price.com
<u>Toys</u> – **Brand:** major toy brand; hard-wearing moulded plastic toys for all ages that extend to items such as activity centres and mobiles. You can view the products online or call the consumer helpline. / *Hours: Mon-Fri 9am-5pm; no credit cards.*

Flap Happy 🗔
☎ (01494) 447000
Own Merry Berries and distribute Lollipop brand.

Baby clothes – **Funky:** hair accessories, sunglasses and bags from Lollipop; cotton strawberry hats and cardigans from Merry Berries. – **Sun-protection clothing:** hats and swimwear, in bright prints and plains. / *Hours: Mon-Fri 9am-5pm.*

Floris Books 🖼

Scottish Book Source, 15 Harrison Gardens, Edinburgh EH11 1SH ☎ Floris Books (0131) 337 2372, Orders (0870) 240 2182
🖰 www.florisbooks.co.uk
Books, music & videos – Bookshops: children's and parenting books: small range of picture books, unusual European titles. Also books of songs and a 'Little Folk' nursery songs tape, £6.

Footsies

CENTRAL CONTACT DETAILS
☎ (020) 8947 3677
BRANCHES:
27 Bute St SW7
☎ (020) 7589 4787
15 High St SW19
☎ (020) 8947 3677
Small, two-branch chain.
Shoes – Suppliers: some shoes are under the shops own label; stock European makes such as Buckle My Shoe and GBB. / *Hours: SW7 Mon-Sat 10am-6pm; SW19 Mon-Sat noon-6pm.*

Formative Fun 🖼

Education House, Hornpark Business Centre, Broad Windsor Rd, Bearminster, Dorset DT8 3PT ☎ (01308) 868999
🖰 www.formative-fun.com
Ten-year-old business run by an ex-teacher, comprising mail order and franchise outlets, none of which are in London.
Toys – Educational: "Toys with an educational slant" is the company's proposition and though the mail order catalogue does not carry the whole range, it has a useful selection of items from interesting mobiles, rattles and baby gyms to tapes, Brio items and sorting boards; playgym £35, Skwish rattle £5. Many items are intended to help overcome learning difficulties, such as left hand/right hand confusion. / *Hours: Mon-Fri 9am-5pm; free catalogue; Delivery: p&p extra; no Amex.*

Formes 🖼

CENTRAL CONTACT DETAILS
☎ (020) 8689 2288, Catalogue requests (020) 8689 1133
🖰 www.formes.com
BRANCHES:
33 Brook St W1 1AJ
☎ (020) 7493 2783
28 Henrietta St WC2E 8NA
☎ (020) 7240 4777
313 Brompton Rd SW3 2DY
☎ (020) 7584 3337
66 Rosslyn Hill NW3
☎ (020) 7431 7770
7 Police Street M2 7LQ
☎ (0161) 832 6277
International chain, based in France, with four stores in London and a mail order business. Exclusively maternity wear, all clothes are designed by Daniel Boudon for "women who don't want to change their style while pregnant".
Maternity wear – Luxury: one of the most stylish, fashion-conscious maternity selections around – everything from smart working clothes to holiday and evening wear including trouser suits, smart short dresses and skirts, casual clothing, swim suits, tights, scarves and tummy bands, in good fabrics such as linen. Skirts from £35; Madras dress, £70; trouser suit, £120; suit, £200. Some items can easily be worn post-pregnancy. / *Hours: mostly 9am-6pm (Thu 6.30pm); free catalogue.*

Found 🖼

Great Thurlow, Haverhill, Suffolk CB9 7LF
☎ (0870) 1668131 🖰 www.foundat.co.uk
Toys – Traditional toys: mail order gift collection, including slightly nostalgic toys, one of which is a charming bear gift set in its own suitcase with clothes to dress it in, £50; prices are not the lowest and the range is quite limited but good quality (china tea set £20; tool box £20), free wrapping included. / *Hours: 24hrs; catalogue £3.50 or free online; Delivery: £4.95.*

F Frederick Beck

22-26 Camden Passage, London N1 8ED
☎ (020) 7226 3403
Toys – General stockists: not just a toyshop (their range includes antiques and electrical goods), they sell traditional quality toys from makes such as Brio, Meccano, Scalextrix, and Hornby, as well as soft toys and smaller 'pocket-money' toys. – Traditional toys.
/ *Hours: Mon-Sat 9am-5.30pm.*

Freemans PLC 🖼

PO Box 1761, Sheffield S96 5FS ☎ (0800) 900 200 🖰 www.freemans.co.uk
Home shopping catalogue company.
Baby clothes – Cheap & cheerful: brands include Adidas, Puma, Reebok, Freemans own brand and Adams; Paper Bears newborn set (sleepsuit, hat, bib, etc), £12.50.
Shoes – Suppliers: brands include Timberland and Kickers. / *Hours: 24hrs; free catalogue; Delivery: p&p included.*

French Bookshop 🖼

28 Bute St, London SW7 3EX ☎ (020) 7584 2840 🖰 www.frenchbookshop.com
Books, music & videos – Bookshops: much as the name suggests, this bookshop specialises in French language titles. Educational and school texts are stocked, but there is a good selection of picture, cartoon and basic word books for younger Francophiles, along with videos, games and cassettes. / *Hours: Mon-Fri 8.15am-6pm, Sat 10am-5pm; Delivery: p&p extra (minimum order £5).*

French Connection 🖼

140-144 King's Rd, London SW3 7UU
☎ (020) 7225 3302 🖰 www.fcuk.com
The only branch of this nationwide chain which sells children's clothes.
Baby clothes – Mid-range: a designer range of everything from outerwear to knitwear from a T-shirt at £15 to a jacket at £45. Mail order catalogue has a small range of children's clothing. / *Hours: Mon-Tue 10am-6.30pm, Wed-Fri 10am-7pm, Sun noon-6pm (11.30am for browsing); free brochure; Delivery: p&p £2.50.*

Full Moon Futons ⌂
20 Bulmershe Rd, Reading, Berks RG1 5RJ
☎ (0118) 926 5648
⌁ www.geocities.com/fullmoonfutons
**Baby equipment – Specialist mattress
suppliers:** standard size and made-to-measure
cot, crib and Moses basket mattresses; made
from pure cotton with unbleached cotton
covers (conforming to all British Standards
safety requirements). Futons double up as
travel mattresses/day beds as they can be
rolled up and stored; adult beds and futons also
available; standard cot mattress £69 + £20
delivery. / Hours: Mon-Sat 10am-6pm, 24hr
answerphone; free leaflet.

The Fun Bed Company ⌂
Unit 1 Greysmere Mews, Beacon Hill Rd,
Beacon Hill, Surrey GU26 6NR ☎ (01428)
607878 ⌁ www.funbeds.co.uk
Nursery decor – Beds: a range of painted
wooden children's beds shaped as cars,
Thomas the Tank Engine, boats, little princess
four posters, fire engine, etc; from
£260. / Hours: office hours; answerphone; free
catalogue; Delivery: from £19.

Funky Mama
1 Macauly Court, Macaulay Rd, London
SW4 0QA ☎ (020) 7622 7564
⌁ www.funkymama.co.uk
Maternity wear – Mid-range: t-shirts
(£16–£32) including halter neck, v-neck, with
spaghetti straps and slashed back, carrying
logos like 'It Started with a Kiss'. Also stretchy
dresses, with some halter neck in pretty,
stretch fabrics, and skirts.

FuntoSee ⌂
14 Compton Place Road, Eastbourne, East
Sussex BN20 8AB ☎ (01323) 416 472
⌁ www.funtoseeworld.net
Nursery decor – Stencils & stamps:
removable jumbo cartoon-style vinyl wall
stickers for decorating babies' and children's
rooms. Themes include Undersea Adventure,
Funky Flowers, or Outer Space, with both
a pack of up to 96 designs, plus a separate but
linked height chart. Prices are around £50 per
pack.

G L Bowron ⌂
41 High Street, Chipping Sodbury, Brstol
BS37 6BA ☎ (0800) 212 198
⌁ www.bowron.com
Large multinational sheepskin brand. They will
deal directly with the public, though their
website – which showcases their extensive
range – has no ordering facility.
Baby equipment – Lambskins.
Nursery decor – Bedding: lambskin duvets
(also skins like travel rugs for pushchairs and
buggies).

Gale Classic Clothes ⌂
Dill House, 69 Priory St, Corsham, Wilts
SN13 0AS ☎ (01249) 712241
Baby clothes – Traditional: all items made to
order; traditional gowns, matinee jackets and
smocked children's clothes, plus layette in pure
cotton or wool-cotton mix; two-piece romper
suits from £55. – **Christening gowns:** all styles
of Christening gown: designs can be either

smocked from shoulder to high waist or with
a tucked bodice. Coats, carrying cape, bonnet
and cap, bibs, bootees and petticoats also
available to match; from £100. / Hours: Mon-Fri
2pm-6pm, or answerphone; free catalogue, SAE
requested; Delivery: p&p £1.95 per item (max £5.85);
no credit cards.

Galt Educational ⌂
Johnsonbrook Rd, Hyde, Cheshire
SK14 4QT ☎ Customer service (0870) 242
4477 ⌁ www.galt.co.uk
Over 150 years old – a respected brand with
a strong emphasis on educational items.
Toys – Brand: a fair selection of baby items
including their 'Play Nest' and 'Activity Cat';
for toddlers, simple jigsaws, items for
imaginative and creative play (finger painting
and so on), blocks and other construction
toys. / Hours: Mon-Fri 8.30am-5pm; free catalogue;
UK.

Gap Kids
CENTRAL CONTACT DETAILS
☎ (0800) 427789, Head office (01788)
818300
⌁ www.gap.com
BRANCHES:
376-384 Oxford St W1C 1JY
☎ (01788) 866222
260 Chiswick High Rd W4
☎ (020) 8995 3255
145 Brompton Rd SW3 1PQ
☎ (020) 7225 1112
38 George St TW9 1HY
☎ (020) 8332 7080
Putney Exchange SW15
☎ (020) 8780 0733
Wimbledon Centre Court Shopping Centre,
Queens Rd SW19
☎ (020) 8947 9074
122 King's Road SW3 4TR
☎ (020) 7823 7272
121-123 Longacre WC2E 9PA
☎ (020) 7836 6646
All Gap Kids stores stock the Baby Gap range.
In addition there are a few dedicated Baby Gap
stores (see also). Many shops have a permanent
sale rail that is worth checking out.
Baby clothes – Mid-range: stylish American
casuals which successfully manage to be
fashion-conscious but avoid the 'mini-adult'
look. The selection of sweatshirts, T-shirts,
shorts and so on are very well proportioned
with many cotton clothes in strong colours;
great accessories include hats and sunglasses,
T-shirts from £10 and a denim jacket for
£20. / Hours: hours vary.

Garden Designs
34 Highworth Rd, London N11 2SH ☎ (020)
8368 1403, (07899) 026 080
Nursery decor – Gardens: two mothers, both
qualified as garden designers and one as
a horticulturalist, who specialise in family
gardens; will design, plant and maintain it also;
a design costs from £450; work mostly in north
London.

Garthenor Organic Pure
Wool ⌂
Llanio Road, Tregaron, Ceredigion
SY25 6UR ☎ (01570) 493 347

🖰 www.organicpurewool.co.uk
Baby clothes – Eco-friendly clothing: wool
garments for babies and children (and also
adults), and also yarn in undyed yarn from
British sheep (including rare breeds).

George Fisher 🖰
2 Borrowdale Road, Keswick, Cumbria
CA12 5DA ☎ (017687) 72 178
🖰 www.georgefisher.co.uk
Baby clothes – Outdoorwear: function first,
fashion second, that's the style of this Keswick
shop (which offers equipment to hire,
including for children) which sells some of the
best children's outdoor gear around, including
the waterproof fleece-lined Bushbaby Hot Tot
suit; if you don't want to drive to the Lakes,
you can shop online. / *Hours: Winter: Mon-Sat
9am-5.30pm, Sun 10.30am-4.30pm; Summer: Mon-Sat
9am-6pm, Sun 10.30am-4.30pm; can order from Web
or by phone; Delivery: p&p free in mainland UK.*

Ghost 🖰
36 Ledbury Rd, London W11 2AB ☎ (020)
7229 1057 🖰 www.ghost.co.uk
Maternity wear – Luxury: a label well-known
for its fluid, classic garments; the website lists
stockists, and includes a mail order section of
basics (tops, jackets, trousers, skirts and
dresses) which, as one fashion writer has
pointed out, are "a great way to stay chic while
pregnant". / *Hours: Mon-Fri 10.30am-6.30pm; Sat
10am-6pm; online catalogue; Delivery: p&p £5.*

Giddy Kipper 🖰
Unit 20, The Old Malthouse, Springfield
Road, Grantham, Lincolnshire NG31 7BG
☎ (01476) 594 646, Workshop (07718) 106
374 🖰 www.fishcraftdesign.co.uk/
Nursery decor – Furniture: formerly trading
as Fish Craft & Design – handmade,
hand-painted chunky funky furniture and
accessories. A Tiddlers range includes name
plaques, creepy crawlies mirrors and cabinets,
farm animals and large toy boxes.

Gigglycat 🖰
2nd Floor, 43 Conduit St, London W1S 2YJ
☎ (07748) 702 366 🖰 www.gigglycat.com
Catalogue and on-line retailer.
Baby clothes – Traditional: traditional
hand-smocked and embroidered clothing with
rompers (3-12 months) and dresses for 3
months-4 years (though it may be possible to
have other sizes made to order). Prices are
from £36 to £56.
Naming gifts – Naming gifts: gifts Unusual,
handmade items like books, hand puppets,
mobiles, tooth fairy storage cushions (details
not available currently on the website).

Gillingham & Co 🖰
365 Fulham Palace Rd, London SW6 6TA
☎ (020) 7736 5757
🖰 www.gillinghamshoes.com
Shoes – Suppliers: all staff here are trained
shoe fitters; brands include Start-rite, Clarks,
Birkenstock summer range and a few
Continental styles. / *Hours: Mon-Sat 9.30am-6pm;
Delivery: p&p min £4.50 p&p.*

Glevum Bears 🖰
6A Osier Close, Gloucester GL4 6SP
☎ (01452) 521 672
Naming gifts – Naming gifts: manufacturer of
collector's item teddy bears (all one-offs) – not
suitable for children under 12 but suitable as
decorative presents.

Global Nursery Products
4 Nicholas Court, Nicholas St Mews,
Chester CH1 2QS ☎ (01244) 348869
🖰 www.globalnurseryproducts.com
Manufacturer and distributor of baby items.
Baby equipment – Cots: manufacturer of the
original 'Bedside Cot' (which adjusts to
multiple heights and sits alongside the parents'
bed); also wide range of pushchairs, highchairs,
cribs and changing bags.

Golden Treasury 🖰
CENTRAL CONTACT DETAILS
☎ (020) 8333 0167
🖰 www.thegoldentreasury.co.uk
29 Replingham Rd SW18 5LT
☎ (020) 8333 0167
97 Wandsworth Bridge Rd SW6 2TD
☎ (020) 7384 1821
In addition to the Southfields original, the firm
has recently taken over Fulham's "Books for
Children."
Books, music & videos – Bookshops:
whereas the Southfields original caters to
younger children, the Fulham store has books
for all ages of children (with a comprehensive
parent/teacher resource section). Both shops
are very child-friendly. / *Hours: Mon-Fri 9.30am-
6pm, Sat 9.30am-5.30pm; Delivery: p&p extra; no
Amex.*

Goldilocks
214 Jamaica Rd, London SE16 4BD ☎ (020)
7231 8550
Good general children's store in an
underprovided area. Flexible payment systems
available.
Baby equipment – Stockists: prams, cots,
Moses baskets, high chairs and car seats; brands
include Pegasus, Baby Jogger, Kidabout, Silver
Cross, Mamas & Papas, Cosatto and Bébé
Confort.
Toys – General stockists: general stock of soft
toys, jigsaws, games and big name
brands. / *Hours: Mon-Sat 10am-5.30pm .*

Gordon's Production Services 🖰
58 Cavendish Rd, Salford, Manchester
M7 4NQ ☎ (0161) 740 9979
🖰 www.lotsofbabies.com
**Baby equipment – Buggies for twins and
triplets:** specialists in equipment for triplets
(lightweight buggies, with one removable seat
to convert to a twin buggy) and quads
(tandem-style, pushchair); accessories available
for all models; also a twin buggy designed for
disabled children, suitable for children up to
the age of eight years old. / *Hours: Mon-Fri
9.30am-5.30pm; free catalogue.*

Gossypium 🖰
Abinger Place, Lewes BN7 2QA ☎ (0800)
085 65 49 (01273) 488221
🖰 www.gossypium.co.uk

Baby clothes – Eco-friendly clothing: an ethical supplier of organic cotton garments, offering attractive, quite plain eco-friendly clothing, including for children and babies. Designs include a kimono-style babygrow.

Graco

Rubbermaid UK & Ireland, First Floor, 900 Pavilion Drive, Northampton NN4 0YR ☎ Stockists (0870) 9090 510, Customer service (0870) 909 0501 ⌂ www.graco.co.uk
Large international brand originating in Taiwan; as well as the equipment items listed, the company also makes baby swings and 'entertainment centres'.

Baby equipment – Wheeled Transport-brands: pushchairs (LiteRider, and the ultra-lightweight aluminium SportRider), including double pushchairs, and travel systems with 'lift and lock' technology; travel systems come with an AutoBaby rearward-facing infant car seat. – **Car seat brands:** the options include Autobaby (rear-facing; for newborns-9 months), Next Step (front-facing; for 9 months up to around 7 years) and Contours booster seats. – **Travel cots:** makers of the UK's best-selling lightweight travel cot.

Graham's Toys ⌂

178-182 Alexandra Ave, South Harrow HA2 9BN ☎ (020) 8423 0666
⌂ www.londontoycompany.co.uk
Not just a toy shop – around half of the store is devoted to baby equipment.

Baby equipment – Stockists: the big names in cots, prams, high-chairs and sterilising equipment plus a buggy repair workshop.
Toys – General stockists: claims to be stockists of "just about everything from every toy company you can think of". / *Hours: Mon-Fri 9am-5.30pm, Sat 9am-6pm, Sun 10am-3pm; free catalogue; Delivery: p&p extra for next day delivery.*

Great Expectations

78 Fulham Rd, London SW3 6HH ☎ (020) 7584 2451
⌂ www.greatexpectationsmaternity.co.uk
Maternity wear – Luxury: one of the best places for smart clothes for the working woman and evening wear – classic, simple items which allow you to create your own look. The shop has its own label, and stock also includes clothes from France, Italy and America; skirts, £50-£60; jackets £160-£250; dresses from £70; evening dresses from £100; also maternity swimwear and underwear. A lot of clothes can be worn after pregnancy. – **Bras and underwear:** maternity and nursing bras with matching pants; underwear. / *Hours: Mon-Sat 10am-6pm (Wed 7pm), open Sun in December.*

The Great Little Trading Company ⌂

1 Broad Plain, Bristol BS2 0JP ☎ (0870) 850 6000 ⌂ www.gltc.co.uk
"Practical products for parents", with over 200 items, many exclusive (not to be confused with Turnham Green's Little Trading Company). The range spans too many categories for a comprehensive listing the following examples showcase what's on offer.
Baby equipment – Car accessories: food and

bottle warmers that work from a car cigarette lighter are handy for long journeys, £9. – **High chairs:** the Safe Seat (a fabric harness with Velcro straps for attaching to adult chairs) is useful when visiting or travelling, £14.99.
Nursery decor – Safety items: lots of child-proof safety equipment such as smoke alarms, lockable medicine cabinets and food containers. – **Storage:** nursery storage items for toys and clothes including crates on wheels for under-bed storage, low-level hangers as well as shelves, duvets, seats etc.
Baby clothes – Mid-range: small range of outerwear from nylon rainsuits, rain ponchos and all-in-one fleecy zip-up jackets.
– **Nametapes:** vendors of the Fabrimarker, a personalised self-inking stamp which leaves a permanent mark on all fabric surfaces (including trainer linings). – **Sun-protection clothing:** protective sun gear and swim nappies.
Toys – General stockists: play tunnels, outdoor Wendy houses and play frames, fabric stacking rings, clocks, face paints, activity books, educational software and stickers. / *Hours: Mon-Fri 9am-5.30pm; 24hr answerphone; free catalogue; Delivery: p&p £3.95 (free over £75); no Amex.*

Great Universal ⌂

CENTRAL CONTACT DETAILS
☎ (0870) 907 0870
⌂ www.greatuniversal.co.uk
GUS Home Shopping Ltd, Universal House, Devonshire St M60 6EL
☎ (0870) 907 0870
Large mail order business incorporating a big, high street-style website with a largish range of kid and baby clothes and items for the nursery.
Baby clothes – Cheap & cheerful. / *Hours: enquiry line Mon-Fri 8am-10pm (Sat 9pm), Sun 9am-8pm; free catalogue.*

Green & Organic ⌂

Unit 2, Blacknest Industrial Estate, Blacknest Rd, Blacknest, nr Alton, Hampshire GU34 4PX ☎ (0871) 425 2405
⌂ www.greenandorganic.co.uk
A company formed from the merger of Greenacres Organic and The Organic Food Company.

Nappies – Suppliers-Eco friendly disposables: stock a range of products including Tushies gel-free disposable nappies. / *Hours: office Mon-Fri 9am-5pm, shop Wed-Fri 10am-4pm; free catalogue; no Amex.*

Green Baby ⌂

345 Upper St, London N1 0PD ☎ (020) 7359 7037 ⌂ www.greenbabyco.com
Comprehensive baby shop and mail order from a Canadian mother keen to encourage the use of eco-friendly products, especially nappies. (Website statistics claim that 70% of Canadian babies use reusable nappies, as opposed to 5% of UK babies.)
Baby equipment – Stockists - slings & backpacks: the Baby Trekker, with five different carrying positions; Huggababy side sling; organic cotton sling.
Nursery decor – Bedding: natural bedding, duvets and sheets: also organic wool blankets and sheepskins. – **Furniture:** natural wood changing table and cot beds.

Baby clothes – Eco-friendly clothing: clothes for newborns and fashion items for older kids. Organic and unbleached cotton products, including sleepsuits, and Fair Trade products.
Nappies – Reusable stockists - multiple brands: washable nappies and nappy laundry products; brands include Bambino Mio, Bummi, Ellie Pant, Imse Vimse, Kooshies and Mother-Ease; organic cotton terry and pre-fold nappies available; also wraps including the simple and effective Bumpy woollen overpants, and trainer pants. **– Suppliers-Eco friendly disposables:** stockists of Tushies disposable nappies.
Naming gifts – Naming gifts: aromatherapy starter kits for mother and baby; amber teething necklaces; sustainable wood products and push toys; good presents for eco-friendly parents. / *Hours: Mon-Sat 10am-5pm.*

Green Building Store 🖅
11 Huddersfield Rd, Meltham, Holmfirth, Yorkshire HD9 4NJ ☎ (01484) 854898
🖰 www.greenbuildingstore.co.uk
Nursery decor – Paints: run by Environmental Construction Products; various eco-friendly building supplies, including a Natural Paint Collection, based on 'natural raw materials'; range of colours – colour charts and sample pots available. / *Hours: Mon-Fri 9am-5pm; free catalogue or online; Delivery: p&p £5.25 or £8.95; no Amex.*

Green Shoes 🖅
69 High St, Totnes, Devon TQ9 5PB
☎ (01803) 864997 🖰 www.greenshoes.co.uk
Shoes – Bespoke shoes: shoes, sandals and boots tailored to the foot shape of the individual and made from breathable vegan material; all infant shoes fasten with a buckle, laces or Velcro and leave a thumb's width of growing room around the toes. Re-soling and stretching is available to increase shoes by one size. Seven designs in up to three colours for children, from £34; sizes start at 4 for toddlers; extra wide or slim fittings and adult shoes also available. / *Hours: Mon-Sat 9.30am-5pm; free catalogue; Delivery: p&p £4-£6.*

Greenfibres 🖅
99 High St, Totnes TQ9 5PF ☎ (01803) 868001 🖰 www.greenfibres.com
Organically-produced fabrics and clothing by mail order are central to this catalogue business, though the styles are not only for hippies.
Baby equipment – Specialist mattress suppliers: organic mattresses made from untreated wool, with an organic latex centre and organic cotton covers; child and adult sizes available.
Nursery decor – Bedding: organic household linen including children's duvets; also fabrics by the metre, including organic cotton, linen, hemp, silk and knitting wool; dyed and undyed materials; organic cotton sheets in standard sizes, or tailor-made; towels in cotton and linen. **– Furniture:** an intelligently designed cot with three height settings, and which can be converted into a child's bed.
Baby clothes – Mid-range. – Eco-friendly clothing: more elegant than many organic ranges – most items are undyed and made to

a high standard: striped dress, £16; skater top, £25; cotton baby hat, £4; long johns, £6.10.
Toys – Cuddly toys: stuffed toys made from organic cotton and spelt (like bean bag filling). / *Hours: Mon-Sat 10am-5pm; mail order Mon-Fri 10am-5.30pm, or answerphone; free catalogue; Delivery: p&p £3.50 (free over £60).*

Greensleeves 🖅
61 Oakwood Rd, London NW11 6RJ
☎ (020) 8458 1559
🖰 www.greensleevesclothing.com
Baby clothes – Luxury. – Eco-friendly clothing: "The most stylish organic clothing available": Swiss organic wool garments, undyed cotton basics, plus a range of socks and tights; some coloured and stripey sleepsuits; cotton-velour babygrow, £25; range of gift boxes available.

Grobag 🖅
Fusion House, Union Rd, Kingsbridge, Devon TQ7 1EF ☎ (01548) 854 444
🖰 www.grobag.com
Well-known sleeping bag supplier.
Maternity wear – Cheap & cheerful: why not stick with the trousers you know and love? The Belly Belt, developed in Australia, allows you to extend them.
Baby equipment – Stockists: apart from the sleeping bags, the catalogue and site offers a range of other items such as the Baby Nomad wrap to keep a baby warm when travelling, feeding items like flexible baby spoons and the South African Bumbo baby sitter, an alternative to bouncy chairs.
Nursery decor – Sleeping Bags: 100% cotton in five sizes with different patterns; and in summer and winter weights ranging from 0.5 to 2.5 togs (with a towelling option); prices from £18 for the smallest, up to £30; also nightwear, hooded bathrobes and towels. (Also sells the Baby Be Safe cot sheet, invented in the US, with 14-inch end pockets secured over the mattress using thick elastic and Velcro so it can only be removed by an adult lifting the mattress and opening the pockets. The cotton sheets costs £9.
Nappies – Change bags: a wide range of carefully designed and sporty-looking changing bags (including Red Castle Sport brand) in a variety of sizes but all with an outside pocket which opens right down and contains a detachable changing mat. They are designed for life after babyhood, being suitable, for example, for carrying a laptop. / *Hours: Mon-Fri 9am-7pm, Sat 10am-1pm; free catalogue or online; Delivery: p&p £3.50 (free over £75); no Amex.*

Gucci
🖰 www.gucci.com
BRANCHES:
34 Old Bond St W1
☎ (020) 7629 2716
18 Sloane St SW1
☎ (020) 7235 6707
Shoes – Suppliers: now you can get the look for your child early in life – if that's what you want – with baby bootees designed to ape the adult loafers (from £100).

GyGy ⊞
Unit D3, Rosehill Industrial Estate, Ternhill,
Shropshire TF9 2JU ☎ (01630) 638978
⊓ www.gygy.co.uk
Well-established French brand of rocking
horse. Call for stockists.
Toys – Traditional toys: as well as full-sized
models (for £300-£400), the range includes
a number of cute smaller options (for £60-£70)
such as a baby-sized horse or rocking swan, or
push-and-ride donkey. / *free catalogue.*

Gymboree
CENTRAL CONTACT DETAILS
☎ Retail Head Office (0116) 282 7400, Play &
Music Infoline (0800) 092 0911
⊓ www.gymboree.com,
www.gymboreeplayuk.com
BRANCHES:
198 Regent St W1R 5DF
☎ (020) 7494 1110
53 George St TW9 1HJ
☎ (020) 8940 9450
120 Centre Courts Shopping Centre SW19
8YE
☎ (020) 8879 3001
LO63 Bluewater Shopping Centre, Hedge
Place Road DA9 9BA
☎ (01322) 624912
31 The Glades, Borough of Bromley BR1
3EA
☎ (020) 8460 0109
An American shopping experience tailored to
the English market; of the 25 or so stores in the
UK, those in the London area are listed. All
shops have activities and play areas for kids.
Baby clothes – Mid-range: unusually well
co-ordinated and stylish range of quality,
colourful clothes designed not to fade in the
wash. They're not cheap but they do
a 'Matchmatics' service designed to persuade
you to buy more garments for not too much
more money which will give you nine outfits
from six items. Staff are very cheerful and
helpful. / *Hours: hours vary.*

Nicola Hadley ⊞
47 Davenant Rd, London N19 3NW ☎ (020)
7281 5340
Books, music & videos – Music tapes: two
excellent tapes from music teacher Nicola
Hadley; musical settings are intelligent and
varied, with multi-cultural songs from many
lands; £8. / *Delivery: p&p included.*

Hairloom
111 Munster Rd, London SW6 ☎ (020) 7736
5923
Hairdressers – Hairdressers: £6.95 in week,
£8.25 on Sat; toys; free lollipop with haircut,
children 0-13. / *Hours: Mon-Wed 9am-6pm, Thu
10am-5pm, Fri 9am-7pm, Sat 8.30am-6pm.*

Halfords
CENTRAL CONTACT DETAILS
☎ (08457) 626625
⊓ www.halfords.com
BRANCHES:
*(Branches throughout London –
call the enquiry line for your nearest outlet.)*
National chain of car accessory and
maintenance superstores.
**Baby equipment – Car seat fitting/seat belt
adjusting:** larger shops stock the full range of
car seats (around 50 styles) and seat-belt kits;
car seat brands include Britax, Klippan, Chicco,
Concord and Mamas & Papas; equipment is
grouped by age – group 1 (0-15 months),
to group 3 (6-11 years).

Hamleys ⊞
188-196 Regent St, London W1B 5BT
☎ Shop (0870) 3332455, Delivery/Mail Order
(0870) 333 2450 ⊓ www.hamleys.com
As well as the famous Regent Street store,
there are mini-outlets in Terminals 2 & 4 at
Heathrow.
Toys – General stockists: the world's largest
toyshop stocks more than 45,000 toys, games
and gifts over seven floors. Cuddly toys aside,
the emphasis is on well-known branded goods
with few out-of-the-ordinary items. – **Cuddly
toys:** the ground floor has a vast selection of
cuddly toys, including own-brand items.
Books, music & videos – Bookshops: the
second floor of this world-famous toy store
stocks a reasonable selection of children's
books arranged by age. The focus is on toy and
TV or film-related titles. Author visits and
events are held occasionally. / *Hours: Mon-Fri
10am-8pm, Sat 9.30am-8pm, Sun noon-6pm; free
catalogue; Delivery: 3-5 days £6.99; next day £9.99.*

Hansel & Gretel ⊞
Buckthorns, Upper Largo, Fife KY8 6EA
☎ (01333) 360219
⊓ www.hansel-and-gretel.co.uk
Baby clothes – Mid-range: a one-woman-band
mail order company, with twice-yearly
(summer and winter) collections. Smart casual
wear in fairly classic designs in 100% cotton;
a good selection of cotton tights; typical prices:
pinafore dress, £22; summer shorts, £12; skirts,
£16; full catalogue also on website. / *Hours: 24hr
answerphone; free catalogue or online; Delivery: p&p
£3.50 (free over £100); no Amex.*

Happy Baby Company ⊞
16a Ballyman Rd, Bray, Co Wicklow, Ireland
☎ +353 12826590
⊓ www.happybabysling.com
Baby equipment – Slings: formerly called
Suantrai Slings (Irish for 'lullaby'),
the company sells simple slings which enable
you to carry a baby in up six positions;
available in a variety of 100% cottons and sizes;
custom models available using your own fabric
or for larger figures.
Baby clothes – Funky: hand tie-dyed clothing
includes babygrows, T-shirts, socks, tights,
leggings and hats; wide range of colours, with
a custom service available. / *free catalogue;
Delivery: p&p extra.*

Happy Landings ⊞
Unit 5, Homeground, Buckingham Industrial
Park, Buckinghamshire MK18 1UH
☎ (01280) 822 949
⊓ www.HappyLandingsUK.com
Toys – Outdoor items & active toys:
moulded rubber tiles, nursery play mats (with
A-Z, 0-9 and animals), and a playhouse (which
can be extended). Also moulded rubber
products such as stepping posts and
mushrooms. / *Hours: Mon-Fri 9am-5pm; free
catalogue; no credit cards.*

Happy Returns
36 Rosslyn Hill, London NW3 1NH ☎ (020) 7435 2431

<u>Toys</u> – **General stockists:** local toy shop stocking all the well-known brands. / *Hours: Mon-Fri 9.30am-5.30pm, Sat 10am-6pm, Sun noon-5.30pm; no Amex.*

Harrods
87-135 Brompton Rd, London SW1X 7XL ☎ (020) 7730 1234 ⏱ www.harrods.co.uk

As with shopping for many things, if you are relatively cost insensitive, Harrods offers a great selection. Particular strengths are the children's shoe department, and – of course – toys (and books).

<u>Maternity wear</u> – **Bras and underwear:** stocks nursing bras by Berlei and Wacoal.

<u>Baby equipment</u> – **Stockists:** a small department covers all the bases, but with a limited range.

<u>Nursery decor</u> – **General stockists:** small departments on the 4th and 2nd floors – if you have deep pockets they have one or two funky, unusual items.

<u>Baby clothes</u> – **Luxury:** a huge variety of designer brands with names such as Catimini, Babar, Jean Bourget, Peter Rabbit, Marese, Dior, Armani, Tommy Hilfiger and Ralph Lauren, plus one of the UK's largest Petit Bateau concessions.

<u>Shoes</u> – **Suppliers:** instep have taken over the running of the shoe department at the store (as they have taken over all Start-Rite's concessions – previously one of their largest London outlets); they do sell other brands include D&G, Missouri, Moschino, Pinco Pallino, Simonetta, and Todd's.

<u>Toys</u> – **General stockists:** child heaven on the fourth floor – hugely well stocked with all the latest stuff; also good for large items; there is even a special toy enquiry line: (020) 7225 5848. – **Cuddly toys:** only Hamleys vies with the soft toys room here for such a huge array.

<u>Books, music & videos</u> – **Bookshops:** children's books at Harrods are stocked on the fourth floor, adjacent to the toy department (rather than in the main book department run by Waterstones on the second floor). With over 10,000 titles it is one of the best in town.

<u>Hairdressers</u> – **Hairdressers:** certificate for first cut with lock of hair; videos offer distraction; £20 for first cut (plus £12 if you want the diploma). / *Hours: Mon-Sat 10am-7pm; no Switch.*

Harry Duley 📷
Studio 29, 1-13 Adler St, London E1 1EE ☎ (020) 7377 0181 ⏱ www.harryduley.co.uk

<u>Maternity wear</u> – **Mid-range:** good basics with-a-slight-twist: tops, trousers, tunics and dresses in stretchy fabrics. The company can make up the outfit you choose in a range of colours; trousers, £65.

Hatchards 📷
187 Piccadilly, London W1J 9LE ☎ (020) 7439 9921 ⏱ www.hatchards.co.uk

<u>Books, music & videos</u> – **Bookshops:** children's books are on the third floor of this historic bookshop (founded in 1797, and now a part of the Waterstones chain). A good range of titles includes hardbacks, classics and boxed

gift sets, many picture books and modern fiction titles. Some toys are available to play with. / *Hours: Mon-Sat 9.30am-6.30, Tues 10am-6.30pm, Sun 12pm-6pm; free catalogue; Delivery: p&p £3.50 (free over £35).*

Havanas Toy Box
Unit 36 Putney Exchange, Putney High St, London SW15 1TW ☎ (020) 8780 3722

<u>Baby clothes</u> – **Mid-range.** – **Funky:** handmade clothes including little dresses, woolly hats and jumpers; girl fairy dress for 2-8 years(£25), jumpers (£30).

<u>Shoes</u> – **Suppliers:** brands stocked include Bobux.

<u>Toys</u> – **Traditional toys:** well-stocked toy shop: primarily soft and wooden items; the main brands include Ty and Kaloo. / *Hours: Mon-Sat 9am-6pm, Sun 11am-5pm.*

Hawkin's Bazaar 📷
St Margaret, Harleston, Norfolk IP20 0HN ☎ (0870) 429 4000 ⏱ www.hawkin.co.uk

<u>Toys</u> – **General stockists:** a fascinating collection of stocking fillers, silly tricks, gimmicks, and revived Victoriana (and also educational and science-based toys used in schools) – mostly for older children (and parents) but a number suitable for toddlers – from under £1 to £150. / *Hours: Mon-Fri 9am-5pm, Sat 9am-1pm; answerphone; free catalogue; Delivery: p&p £2.95 (free on orders over £30, plus 10% discount on orders over £100); no Amex.*

Headmaster
32-34 Ridgeway, London SW19 ☎ (020) 8946 1855, Head office (020) 8241 2299 ⏱ www.hmhair.co.uk

Chain of hairdressers in south-west London and the outer suburbs including Kingston, Weybridge, New Malden, Putney, Raynes Park, Richmond, Croydon & Fulham. Call the head office for details of your nearest branch.

<u>Hairdressers</u> – **Hairdressers:** open late and Sundays; same-day appointments available at weekends; under-tens £10. / *Hours: Mon-Fri 9am-9pm (Sat-Sun 6pm), weekends call on day of for appointment; no Amex.*

Headstarter 📷
214 Boardwalk Place, Canary Wharf, London E14 5SQ ☎ (020) 7517 7801 ⏱ www.headstarter.com

<u>Books, music & videos</u> – **Music tapes:** cDs for babies, produced by a Dutch musician (and father). They offer a blend of music and sound designed to stimulate the baby's brain, instilling calm and provoking a positive response. There are four CDs, three of original compositions and one of Baby Classics (like Ave Maria and the Brahms Lullaby) given similar treatment. Each costs £12.95 inc p&p. You can listen to samples on the website.

Headways
7 Chiswick Terrace, Acton Lane, London W4 5LY ☎ (020) 8995 9107

<u>Hairdressers</u> – **Hairdressers:** toys and books to play with; prefer children to come earlier in the week; ages 0-6, £8.50; 6-12, £10.50. / *Hours: Tue, Wed, Fri 9am-6pm, Thu 10am-8pm, Sat 8.30am-5.30pm.*

Heirlooms UK ⌂
Pilot Associates, 23 Spencer Rd, London
SW18 2SP ☎ (020) 7738 1868
🖑 www.heirlooms.uk.com
<u>Naming gifts</u> – **Naming gifts:** a company set
up by a Goldsmiths College graduate, with
textile expertise, offering personalised
embroidered silk cushions which can include
images (such as an owl for wisdom) as well as
names or other text. Picture cushions (using
conventional photographs to turn into
embroidered images), and star sign cushions
are also available, as are Christening shawls
(£95). Picture cushions are £110 for 45cm
square.

HeirsWears ⌂
2 Arbor Court, Queen Elizabeth Walk,
London N16 0QU ☎ (020) 8809 7160
<u>Baby clothes</u> – **Christening gowns:**
traditional, handmade Christening outfits in
silk, satin, Nottingham lace, etc; will make to
your design; also shoes, caps, bonnets and
bootees; dresses from £50. / *Hours: 24hr
answerphone (on 020 number); 'semi-brochure' plus
photos; no credit cards.*

Hennes (H&M)
CENTRAL CONTACT DETAILS
☎ (020) 7323 2211
🖑 www.hm.com
BRANCHES:
*(Only selected branches are listed –
call the enquiry line for other outlets.)*
174 Oxford St W1N 0EE
Units 7-8 Brent Cross Shopping Centre
NW5 3FP
☎ (020) 8202 5440
481-483 Oxford St W1C 2QD
☎ (020) 7493 8557
103-111 Kensington High St W8
☎ (020) 7368 3920
Whiteleys W2
☎ (020) 7313 7500
International Swedish chain of fashion shops
with a 'Kids' range and a 'Mama' range of
maternity wear – not all shops in the London
area stock both ranges.
<u>Maternity wear</u> – **Cheap & cheerful:** a wide
selection of high fashion maternity wear (for
once one that doesn't assume pregnant women
lose their fashion sense) at competitive prices;
trousers £20-25; shirts £20; heavy knit tunics
£30; on the whole, helpful and knowledgeable
assistants. The Big is Beautiful (BiB) section of
larger-size clothes may also come in useful for
pregnancy wear.
<u>Baby clothes</u> – **Cheap & cheerful:** good
selection of trendy clothes for kids: chinos £10;
cotton jumper with US flag £12; flower dress
£8. / *Hours: Mon-Sat 10am-7pm (Thu 8pm), Sun
noon-5pm.*

Hickory ⌂
c/o RSB Associates, Highthorn Farm, Wide
Lane, Wymeswold, Leics LE12 6SE ☎ (01509)
881300 🖑 www.babyclothing.co.uk
<u>Baby clothes</u> – **Luxury:** modern designer
childrenswear, primarily for babies and
younger children; co-ordinated leisure wear for
boys and girls; from T-shirts to jackets,
accessories, hats and shoes; order from website
or call for a list of stockists. / *Hours: Mon-Fri*

*9am-5.30pm; online-only mail order; free lists of
stockists.*

The Hill Toy Company ⌂
Unit 1, The Tavern, Lower Green, Highan,
Bury St. Edmund, Suffolk IP28 6NL
☎ (08706) 071248 🖑 www.hilltoy.co.uk
<u>Toys</u> – **General stockists:** activity toys
(including kits), construction toys, wooden
toys such as forts, farms and garages; also dolls,
teddies and puzzles. – **Dressing up toys:** mail
order company specialising in dressing-up
clothes; also party gifts. / *Hours: Mon-Fri 9am-
5.30pm, Sat 10am-5pm; free catalogue; no Amex.*

Hippychick ⌂
1 Roberts Drive, Taunton Road, Bridgwater,
Somerset TA6 6BH ☎ (01278) 434 440
🖑 www.hippychick.com
A Somerset-based mail order company selling
children's products; as well as the own-brand
Hip Seat, they are suppliers of Aromakids
aromatherapy oils for children.
<u>Baby equipment</u> – **Slings- Hip shelves:**
makers of the Child Hip Seat:
a machine-washable fabric belt that fits round
the adult with a seat for the child to sit on
(facing in or out); incorporates inner pockets;
endorsed by osteopaths, the hip seat ensures
correct weight distribution, so the spine is not
strained; one size fits all; four colours; suitable
for use from six months to three years; £35.
<u>Shoes</u> – **Suppliers:** suppliers of 'Shoo b' soft
leather padder shoes, with non-slip soles and
elasticated ankles; range of colours and
designs. / *Hours: Mon-Fri 9am-6pm; free leaflet;
Delivery: p&p £2.95 for Hip Seat; no Amex.*

Sarah Hocombe
Studio 3 Cornwell House, 21 Clerkenwell
Green, London EC1R 0DX ☎ (020) 7251
6631, (07958) 942295
<u>Nursery decor</u> – **Murals and other
Decorating:** muralist who feels that some
nursery murals can be outgrown rather quickly
– her designs include trompe l'oeil effects,
inventive stencilling or traditional figures; £200
per day – allow 3-4 days for an average-sized
room (more time for original designs). / *Hours:
Mon-Fri 8.30am-2.30pm; other times by appointment.*

The Holding Company ⌂
241-245 Kings Rd, London SW3 5EL ☎ (020)
7352 1600 🖑 www.theholdingcompany.co.uk
<u>Nursery decor</u> – **Storage:** just the place to
introduce your children to the lifelong benefits
of organisation; children's storage options
include bedroom shelving and a variety of
boxes, bags and toy carts, all sturdily made and
attractively decorated. / *Hours: Mon-Sat 10am-
6pm, Wed & Sat until 7pm; Sun 12pm-6pm; free
catalogue or online; Delivery: p&p £4.95.*

Holdsworth Sign Writing
22 Meadowcourt Rd, London SE3 9DY
☎ (020) 8852 7625
<u>Nursery decor</u> – **Murals and other
Decorating:** murals in any design from
picture-book scenes to cartoon characters from
a sign writer who works for restaurants and
pubs. / *Hours: Mon-Sat 9am-5.30pm; no Amex.*

Holz Toys 🏠

The Creamery, Lostwithiel, Cornwall
PL22 0HD ☎ (0845) 130 8697
🖥 www.holz-toys.co.uk

<u>Baby equipment</u> – **Stockists - slings
& backpacks:** a German brand of sling
(Diddymos): in woven fabric, usable in six
different ways (based on traditional fabric
slings).

<u>Baby clothes</u> – **Sleepwear:** bodies and
sleepsuits in Egyptian cotton.

<u>Toys</u> – **Traditional toys:** handmade in
Germany, a high-quality range of toys
including rattles, construction toys, arks,
stacking toys, blocks and rocking horses, with
lots for slightly older children. / *Hours: Mon-Fri
8.30am-5.30pm, Sat/Sun answerphone; free catalogue;
Delivery: £4.50.*

Home Front 🏠

PO Box 76, Guildford, Surrey GU2 9GH
☎ (01483) 894 200
🖥 www.home-front.co.uk

Natural wood play systems.

<u>Toys</u> – **Outdoor items & active toys:** natural
timber play systems in Redwood and Southern
Yellow Pine. Design is modular, can include
swings, slides, monkey bars and so on, plus
trampolines.

Homecrafts Direct 🏠

PO Box 38, Leicester LE1 9BU ☎ (0845) 458
4531 🖥 www.homecrafts.co.uk

<u>Toys</u> – **Art supplies:** art supplies, from online
and offline catalogues. It's one of the most
comprehensive sources there is – everything
from children's paints (as well as felt and so on)
to fine oils. / *Hours: Mon-Thurs 8.45am-4.45pm, Fri
8.45am-4.15pm; catalogue £3.95; Delivery: p&p £2.95-
4.95.*

Honfleur Christening Gowns 🏠

☎ (01424) 752732 🖥 www.honfleur.co.uk/

<u>Baby clothes</u> – **Christening gowns:**
particularly lush traditional Christening gowns,
rompers and accessories, in silk, satin and
cotton. Also silver Christening items. The
website offers worldwide delivery.

Hopscotch Dressing-Up Clothes Ltd 🏠

Rangefield Court, Farnham Trading Estate,
Farnham, Surrey GU9 9NP ☎ (01252) 717
768 🖥 www.hopscotchdressingup.co.uk

<u>Toys</u> – **Dressing up toys:** wide range of
dressing-up clothes, costumes and accessories;
animal hats and hoods; nativity range; prices
from £3 for a sequinned tiara, to £35 for a full
pirate captain's outfit; sold mail order and
through selected stockists – call for list of
retailers. Usually despatched within 24
hours. / *free catalogue; Delivery: £4-£6.*

Huggababy Natural Baby Products 🏠

19-21 The Prya Center, Talg LD3 0DS
☎ (01874) 711629 🖥 www.huggababy.co.uk

<u>Baby equipment</u> – **Lambskins:** undyed,
unbleached British sheepskins. – **Slings:**
quality baby carriers sold via mail order – quite
expensive but made of durable, double
thickness cotton designed to last more than
one child; also safety harness for extra security;
money-back guarantee; four adult sizes and
colours (navy, green, black and red); also
organic cotton sling.

<u>Nursery decor</u> – **Bedding:** cot blankets and
sleeping bags made from Welsh wool; also
a 'cradle cushion' – multi-purpose cushion for
use by pregnant women and babies,
£37. / *Hours: hours vary (24hr answerphone); free
catalogue; Delivery: p&p included.*

Humbug 🏠

31 Montague Road, Datchet, Berkshire
SL4 9DT ☎ (01753) 594 665

<u>Baby clothes</u> – **Knitwear:** children and adult
designer knitwear, made in England, in cotton
and wool. Designs include large teddy bears,
repeat fruit patterns, and flags on white or
navy background.

Humla

13 Flask Walk, London NW3 1HJ ☎ (020)
7794 8449

Shop based in Hampstead: selling clothes and
toys as well as interior design goods and
furniture.

<u>Baby equipment</u> – **Stockists:** cots and high
chairs stocked.

<u>Nursery decor</u> – **Furniture:** stocks a range of
nursery furniture. – **General stockists:**
complete interiors service: wallpaper, paint,
curtains and bed linen.

<u>Baby clothes</u> – **Mid-range:** designer wear at
the middle-upper end of market, which
includes a range made for the shop itself (all
made in England); knitted, Continental and
traditional styles in bright colours; dresses,
£14-£40, hats and soft pre-walking shoes.

<u>Toys</u> – **Traditional toys:** wide range of the
more traditional end of the toy market, from
Brio to tricycles and rocking horses; specialise
in wooden toys. / *Hours: Mon-Sat 10am-6pm, Sun
noon-6pm.*

IANA

CENTRAL CONTACT DETAILS
☎ (020) 7352 0060
🖥 www.iana.it
186 King's Rd SW3
☎ (020) 7352 0060
Putney Exchange SW15
☎ (020) 8789 2022

<u>Baby clothes</u> – **Luxury:** local outposts of
Italy's largest chain of baby and childrenswear
shops. The look varies from season to season,
but can usually be described as 'fresh
traditional'.

Ideal Cottons 🏠

72a Madeira St, Edinburgh EH6 4AU
☎ (0131) 553 4191
🖥 www.idealcottons.com

Run by the same person as Snug as a Bug (see
sleeping bags).

<u>Nursery decor</u> – **Bedding:** playmats (£70), bed
covers, washbags finished with a variety of
motifs, and embroidered duvet covers.

<u>Baby clothes</u> – **Traditional:** dresses, romper
suits, pyjamas, nighties, dressing gowns and
dungarees in very soft cotton, hand-smocked
and/or with embroidered or appliqued motifs.
Smock dresses from £28. / *Hours: Mon-Fri 10am-
5pm or answerphone; Small free catalogue; Delivery:
p&p min £2; no Amex.*

Ikea

CENTRAL CONTACT DETAILS
☎ (0845) 355 1141
🖰 www.ikea.co.uk
BRANCHES:
2 Drury Way, North Circular Rd NW10
OTH
The Old Power Station, Valley Park, Purley
Way CR0 4UZ
Lakeside Retail Park, Heron Way, West
Thurrock RM20 3WJ
This huge Scandinavian furniture business
makes a good effort for young families with
play areas, in-store pushchairs, supervised play
rooms and a free video cinema.
Baby equipment – Stockists: limited selection
of cots, all cheap, cheerful and basic; high
chairs; wide variety of goods such as safety and
bathing items.
Nursery decor – General stockists: excellent
selection of funky nursery items to spice up
a toddler's room; wardrobes, chairs, soft
furnishings, bedding, mirrors, rugs,
storage … you name it.
Toys – Own brand: an eclectic selection of
own-brand toys: early music toys, cute furry
animals; wooden stacking, hammering and
sorting toys are particularly good value; also
some outdoor and educational items. / *Hours:
Mon-Fri 10am-8pm (Sat 6pm), Sun 11am-5pm; no
Amex.*

The Illustration Cupboard

401 Langham House, 302 Regent St, London
W1B 3HH ☎ (020) 7610 5481
🖰 www.illustrationcupboard.com
Naming gifts – Naming gifts: specialists in
contemporary picture book art (mainly
children's books) – original artworks and some
limited editions can be bought as Christening
gifts; works, by around 80 illustrators (names
include Anthony Browne, Babette Cole,
Shirley Hughes, Satoshi Kitamura and Jane
Ray) can be viewed by appointment; prices
from £100 to £2,000; a biannual newsletter can
update interested buyers on new stock. / *Hours:
by appointment.*

Immaculate Contraptions 🖾

103-105 Broadwater Street East,
Broadwater, Worthing, West Sussex
BN14 9AW ☎ (01903) 216 566
🖰 www.icbaby.com
Baby equipment – Stockists: an online retailer
providing a wide range of goods, from larger
items such as prams, cots and car seats to
accessories.
Toys – General stockists: quite a range – from
mobiles to rocking horses.

In-Car Safety Centre

Unit 5, The Auto Centre, Stacey Bushes,
Milton Keynes MK12 6HS ☎ (01908) 220909
Established for over 20 years, what claims to be
the only specialist centre of its type in the UK
(exclusively focused on car safety). With its
nursing room and crèche, it's an hour's drive
from the start of the M1.
Baby equipment – Car seat fitting/seat belt
adjusting: they advise on car seats to fit your
car, suit your child and be safe. Ill-fitting seats
are adapted with a special 'fitting kit'. An
extensive showroom holds more than 30 seats

in stock for babies and toddlers; also booster
cushions and seats, seat belts and special needs
seats; the main brands stocked are Britax,
Maxi-Cosi, Concord, Klippan. / *Hours: Mon-Fri
9.30am-5.30pm, Sat 9.30am-4pm; no Amex.*

Inch Blue 🖾

PO Box 100, Caerphilly CF83 1YX ☎ (029)
2086 5863 🖰 www.inch-blue.com
Shoes – Suppliers: soft leather baby boots with
suede soles, handmade in the UK. Sizes up to
four years. You can order a catalogue by phone
or through the website. / *free catalogue.*

Incy Wincy 🖾

18 Oregon Avenue, Tilehurst, Berks
RG31 6RZ ☎ (0118) 377 3581
🖰 www.incywincy.org
Baby clothes – Sun-protection clothing: this
comprehensive catalogue sells floatsuits with
UV protection and Stingray rompers (SPF 50)
and caps and wetsuits for babies.

Infantasia 🖾

Unit 103 Shopping City, High Rd, London
N22 6YA ☎ (020) 8889 1494
🖰 www.infantasia.co.uk
27-year-old north London store; it maintains an
extensive website, but you can't order online;
the store runs its own credit scheme.
Baby equipment – Stockists: cots, cribs,
pushchairs and baby baths. – **Buggy & pram
repairs:** authorised Maclaren repair agent.
Baby clothes – Mid-range: premature babies
to four years old. – **Christening gowns:**
starting from £20–£100. / *Hours: Mon-Fri 10am-
6pm, Sat 9.30am-6.30pm, Sun 11am-5pm; Delivery:
p&p extra.*

Instep

🖰 www.instepshoes.co.uk
BRANCHES:
117 Golders Green Rd NW11
☎ (020) 8458 3911
267 East Barnet Rd EN4 8SX
☎ (020) 8440 9860
45 High St NW8 7NJ
☎ (020) 7722 7634
80 Church Rd SW13
☎ (020) 8741 4114
11 Bellevue Rd SW17
☎ (020) 8767 3395
Well-established and growing chain of shoe
shops with experienced fitters and good range
of stock; the chain has assumed control of
many of Start-Rite's own shops,
and concessions, including the shoe
department at Harrods.
Shoes – Suppliers: every branch stocks a range
of Start-rite styles as well as lots of Continental
styles and 'fashion' shoes: Kickers, Nike and
Salamander. / *Hours: Mon-Sat 9.30am-5.30pm.*

Interben 🖾

St. Albans House, St. Albans Lane, London
NW11 7QE ☎ (020) 8731 9666
🖰 www.interben.net
Baby equipment – Stockists: a firm which
aims to import goods not readily otherwise
available in the UK, all of which are listed on
the website. The site does not offer full online
ordering, but you can print off an order form
to post or fax. – **Buggy accessories:** importers

of a stand and sit buggy trailers, behind a standard buggy, for a toddler.

International Paint

Plascon International Ltd, Brewery House, High St, Twyford, Winchester SO21 1RG ☎ (01962) 711177 ⁌ www.plascon.co.uk
<u>Nursery decor</u> – **Paints:** range of paint products certified as safe to use on children's toys and furniture, and tough enough to withstand knocks and scrapes: 'Child Safe Paint' (only available in white); 'Japlac' primer undercoat and high-gloss enamel (12 colours/finishes including clear, gold and silver); and quick-drying wood and MDF primers; further information available on request; stocked by major outlets including B&Q; the website is a useful source of information on issues such as lead in paint. / *Hours: Mon-Fri 9am-5pm.*

International Star Registry ⊞

23-28 Penn St, London N1 5DL ☎ (020) 7684 4444
⁌ www.international-star-registry.org
<u>Naming gifts</u> – **Naming gifts:** register a real star with the name of the recipient – an unusual and ever-lasting gift; you get a commemorative gift pack that includes a certificate, chart and an explanatory booklet. / *Hours: Mon-Fri 9.30am-5pm.*

International Tree Foundation ⊞

Sandy Lane, Crawley Down, West Sussex RH10 4HS ☎ (0870) 7744269
⁌ www.internationaltreefoundation.org
<u>Naming gifts</u> – **Naming gifts:** an alternative to the 'big name' tree foundations; one of their properties is a wood with native tree species related to homeopathy such as oak, beech and hawthorn, and underplantings of homeopathically related plants like Aconite. Can also plant overseas – fruit trees in the grounds of a school in India, for example. Single tree with dedicatory card £12.50; clump of 3-5 trees with certificate £35. / *no Amex.*

Iriss ⊞

66 Chapel St, Penzance, Cornwall TR18 4AD ☎ (01736) 366568 ⁌ www.iriss.co.uk
<u>Baby clothes</u> – **Traditional:** small collection of traditional baby clothes mostly with beautifully detailed flower and animal embroidery; traditional hand-knits (Arran and Guernsey styles) in white or bright 'Rowan' cotton; accessories include hats, bootees, bibs, and bags. – **Christening clothes:** hand-knitted shawl in 'winter white' wool, £89. / *Hours: 24hr answerphone; Delivery: p&p £2.60.*

The Iron Bed Company ⊞

Funtington Park, Funtington, Chichester, West Sussex PO18 8UE ☎ Head office (01243) 578888 ⁌ www.ironbed.co.uk
<u>Nursery decor</u> – **Beds:** the full range of iron beds includes designs for children (head and tail boards with sunflowers; also plain single beds) in a chip-resistant finish; also supply headboards to fit standard divans. / *free catalogue or online; Delivery: p&p £39 includes assembly.*

It's Childsplay ⊞

Treworthal Barn, Treworthal, Crantock, Nr Newquay, Cornwall TR8 5PJ ☎ (01637) 830896 ⁌ www.itschildsplay.co.uk
<u>Nursery decor</u> – **Furniture:** plain and painted 'cottage style' pine furniture – infant chairs, armchairs, rockers, tables, settees, desks and toy boxes: chair from £28, settee from £65.
<u>Toys</u> – **Traditional toys:** from push-along toys and spinning tops to much more imaginative items such as a large play cooker or sink (about £80). / *free brochure; Delivery: p&p extra; Not by phone.*

IViewCameras ⊞

107 Lavender Walk, London SW11 1JS ☎ (0870) 744 2298
⁌ www.babyviewcam.co.uk
<u>Baby equipment</u> – **Monitors-brand:** a vendor which sells a range of video, audio and breathing baby monitors, and whose website offers helpful advice in the field. Products include the Philips Baby Cam which has night vision and can be attached to a specified channel on the TV, allowing parents to switch across to make a check during viewing. Prices start at around £100.

The Jack Horner Cot Company

PO Box 1448, Rugby, Warwickshire CV23 8ZE ☎ (01788) 891890
⁌ www.jack-horner.co.uk
Cots and cot beds; available by mail order from Nursery to Leisure (see also).
<u>Baby equipment</u> – **Cots:** the range includes corner cots (£215) with adjustable bases (mattress at extra cost, in coir or foam). These latter are popular with parents whose baby sleeps in their room, and those with twins or triplets (you can put different cots in different corners).
<u>Nursery decor</u> – **Furniture:** complete matching room sets, including cots (and cot beds), wardrobes, chests of drawers, chests and bedside tables; also a space-saving corner changer (£135); range of styles and designs.

Jackel International Ltd ⊞

Dudley Lane, Cramlington, Northumberland NE23 7RH ☎ (0191) 250 1864, Helpline (0500) 979899
Owners of the Tommee Tippee, Maws and Sangenic brands.
<u>Baby equipment</u> – **Stockists:** all the firm's products are widely stocked. Call for local stockists. / *Hours: Mon-Fri 9am-5pm (Fri 2.30pm); free catalogue; Delivery: p&p extra; no Amex & no Switch.*

Jacqueline Taylor Design ⊞

11 Park Lane Court, Manchester M7 4LP ☎ (0161) 278 8979
⁌ www.designerchristeninggowns.com/
<u>Baby clothes</u> – **Christening gowns:** made to measure satin and silk christening gowns, suits and rompers; also accessories and gifts; see their website for details.

Jakss

463 & 469 Roman Rd, London E3 5LX ☎ (020) 8981 9454
A family business a quarter of a century old –

the Islington branch is much the larger of the two of this small branch of retailers (the E3 branch is actually two shops a couple of doors away from one another).

Baby clothes – **Luxury:** one of the best selections of designer children's wear in the capital including: D&G, DKNY, Diesel, Catamini, Cakewalk, Kenzo and Chipie; shoes from Oilily and others.

Jané

107A Shore Rd, Belfast BT15 3PL ☎ (028) 9077 0779 ⌁ www.johnstonprams.co.uk
The Ireland and UK distributor for a Spanish manufacturer of baby equipment, best known in the UK for their pushchairs.

Baby equipment – **Wheeled Transport-brands:** the range includes prams, pushchairs, travel systems and buggies for twins; many fabric designs, from classic to funky. In 2003/4 the brand reported that it was particularly proud of its Carrera C buggy, claimed to be the most compact umbrella folding buggy available. Other products include 3-wheelers with extra light alloy chassis and another, available in tandem version, with 360° front wheel rotation to give extra manoeuvrability. – **High chairs:** a range of high chairs including folding, cube and table-mounted. / *Hours: 9.30am-5.30pm.*

Emma Jefferson ⌁

16 Cross Bank, Great Easton, Leics LE16 8SR ☎ (01536) 772074
⌁ www.emmajefferson.co.uk
Nursery decor – **Accessories:** themed bedroom accessories for boys and girls – height charts, table lamps, wall hooks, shelves and so on; also trinket boxes and decorative doorknobs for cupboards.

Toys – **Character toys:** character skittles, chest sets, and money boxes. / *Hours: Mon-Fri 9am-5pm; free catalogue; Visa & Mastercard.*

Jester Boots

13 Lewis Road, Chichester PO19 7LZ ☎ (01243) 790009, mobile (07930 339195)
⌁ www.jesterboots.co.uk
Shoes – **Brands:** in 26 colours of canvas and 8 of fleece to create your own colour scheme, hand-made machine-washable shoes in four sizes from birth to toddler; see the website for full details.

JFS ⌁

43 Hutton Close, Crowther, Washington NE38 0AH ☎ (0191) 419 0086
⌁ www.jfs2000.co.uk
Nursery decor – **Accessories:** in addition to tiles in a variety of colours and patterns, offers firm but soft children's stools and tables (set £29) which pack flat for storage.

Toys – **Educational:** suppliers of Fun Tiles, which pass the Child Critical Fall Height test so they can be used on the floor where it acts as a noise absorber. Note that officially the items are not recommended for under-3s but this is only if unattended. The products are made of a recyclable form of plastic (which earns a green label in Germany) and are suitable for use under all kinds of active toys. They are available in ABCs, numbers, maths signs and the like. There is also Hopscotch and 10-pin bowling, plus a rocking horse, building blocks,

construction sets and an interlocking growth chart. Box of alphabet tiles £21.50. / *Hours: Mon-Fri 8.30am-5pm; online catalogue.*

Jigsaw Tree ⌁

Jigsaw Tree House, 19 Blackstitch Lane, Webheath, Redditch, Worcs B97 5TE ☎ (01527) 545 545 ⌁ www.jigsawtree.co.uk
Toys – **Traditional toys:** a range of award-winning jigsaws for children and adults.

JJ Toys

138 St John's Wood High St, London NW8 7SE ☎ (020) 7722 4855
Toys – **General stockists:** local shop with a good selection, with all sorts of toys, games, and ball games from infant to adult: Meccano, Lego, character items (such as Batman, Spiderman, Star Wars) and soft toys; a second shop in Gerrards Cross, Howard Marshall, does a good range of large outdoor items. / *Hours: Mon-Sat 10am-6pm.*

Joanna Scott Murals

☎ (0795) 793 2476
⌁ www.joanna-scott.co.uk
Nursery decor – **Furniture:** "Fine art furniture", intricately painted by hand. – **Murals and other Decorating:** fine art mural projects and interior design themed rooms for children and adults, on themes ranging all the way from Alice in Wonderland to funky airbrush style – see the website for examples. She only undertakes work she is happy is consistent with her approach! Also Murals to Go – readymade self-adhesive trompe l'oeils and decorative murals as limited editions.

Joanna's Tent

289b King's Rd, London SW3 5EW ☎ (020) 7352 1151
Baby clothes – **Luxury:** full range of good quality designer clothing (and also hats and shoes, depending on the season). / *Hours: Mon-Sat 10am-6pm (Wed 7pm).*

John Lewis ⌁

CENTRAL CONTACT DETAILS
☎ (08456) 049049
⌁ www.johnlewis.co.uk
BRANCHES:
279-306 Oxford St W1A 1EX
☎ (020) 7629 7711
Peter Jones, Sloane Square SW1W 8EL
☎ (020) 7730 3434
Brent Cross Shopping Centre NW4
☎ (020) 8202 6535
Wood St KT1 1TG
☎ (020) 8547 3000
For some people, the default choice when shopping for practically all household items (their "never knowingly undersold" leit-motif helps), and the partnership's stores are well adapted to accommodate parents with feeding and changing areas in all but the smallest branches (including, facilities accessible to fathers as well as to mothers) and also a range of leaflets on cots, car seats, shoe-fitting and so on. If there is an area where the range is weak it is in clothes for mothers-to-be and for babies.

Maternity wear – **Mid-range:** most of the range is their own 'Two-plus-one' brand – a full range of garments of good quality, if not particularly fashion conscious; also a selection of Vida Vita and Blooming occasional-wear. – **Bras and underwear:** the ideal place to shop, as they have trained fitters and a wide range of zip and drop-cup styles.

Baby equipment – Stockists: practically everything you could want or need – a prime area where the stores' range and trained staff come into their own. You can make an appointment with a nursery advisor for impartial advice on different products and brands, with demos of how to use the different pieces of equipment.

Nursery decor – General stockists: the range covers all the bases, if not always in as much depth as in equipment.

Baby clothes – Mid-range.

Shoes – Suppliers: very well-stocked shoe departments where brands include Start-rite, Clarks, Elephantine, Buckle My Shoe, and the stores' own brand JFB; first shoes, casual and smart shoes, slippers and boots. Not all fitters are equally good however.

Toys – General stockists: a reasonable range from traditional games and puzzles to the latest 'craze' items, with a good selection of soft toys; the department is considerably larger pre-Christmas.

Books, music & videos – Bookshops: children's books can be found in the fourth floor book department (board and picture books) and the toy and nursery departments on the fourth floor (activity and bath books) of the Oxford Street store. The selection is not enormous but is well chosen. / *Hours: hours vary; no Amex.*

John Sandoe Books

10 Blacklands Terrace, London SW3 2SR
☎ (020) 7589 9473 ⏾ www.johnsandoe.com
Books, music & videos – Bookshops: this small, independent bookseller, just off Sloane Square, has a basement full of children's books, including plenty of picture and activity books for the under-twos, and a range of titles on pregnancy and baby health. / *Hours: Mon-Sat 9.30am-5.30pm (Wed 7.30pm).*

Johnsons Shoes

CENTRAL CONTACT DETAILS
☎ (01932) 226688
⏾ www.johnsons-shoes.co.uk
BRANCHES:
Unit 11, Shepperton Business Park, Govett Ave, Shepperton TW17 8BA
☎ (01932) 226688
413 Upper Richmond Rd SW14
☎ (020) 8876 5789
60 Broad St TW11
☎ (020) 8977 4447
Incorporating Bowleys, this small chain is that increasingly very rare commodity – a family-owned group (established in 1952) of retail shoe shops.

Shoes – Suppliers: stockists of Start-rite, Clarks, Elefanten (a German make), Dr Martens and Kickers; shoes fitted by qualified fitters. They run a 'loyalty card' scheme for kids: when the child has bought ten pairs of leather shoes the 11th pair is free.

JoJo Maman Bébé 🛏

3 Ashbourne Parade, 1259 Finchley Rd, London NW11 0AD ☎ Shop (020) 8731 8961, Mail order (0870) 241 0560
⏾ www.jojomamanbebe.co.uk
Quality, British-owned maternity mail order company – the address is their first shop.
Maternity wear – Mid-range: among the more elegant options available – a limited selection covering the whole range of office wear, evening wear, swimwear and underwear; also feeding shirts with slits and bras; long viscose evening dress, around £40, shaped sarong skirt £25; suit: navy gabardine jacket £50, navy trousers £30. – **Bras and underwear:** the Bravado range of bras; other maternity underwear and tights; and the Reenie support belt.

Baby equipment – Stockists: not a huge selection, but a well-chosen range of smaller items covering most aspects of child care, and with some interesting products: for example, useful travel items – inflatable change mats and baths, seat belt adjusters, car tidies and bottle warmers.

Nursery decor – Storage: offers a range of storage options including cabinets on castors in different configurations with rigid nylon fabric pullout drawers in a choice of colours. Also hanging storage, under-bed storage and various fabric bags and sacks. Toy Tidy Sacks £35.

Baby clothes – Mid-range: there is a definite Continental flavour to this small range of stylish basics, with some more original items. Their 'First Clothes' range is for small babies: funky sleepsuit £10.

Toys – Traditional toys: small interesting range, including traditional wooden toys, first books, and story song tapes. / *Hours: 24hr catalogue line; shop Mon-Sat 9.30am-5.30pm, Sun 10am-4pm; free brochure; Delivery: p&p £3.95; no Amex.*

Jokids E-Shop

35 Brunel Rd, London W3 7XR ☎ (020) 8740 1100 ⏾ www.jokids.com/
Baby clothes – Mid-range: baby and children's basics and fashion clothing and accessories for 0-10 years; includes Jeffrey Ohrenstein hand-smocked dresses.

Steve Jones Furniture 🗄

3f-3g Lion Works, Pool Rd, Newtown, Powys, Mid Wales SY16 3AG ☎ (01686) 625454, mobile (07801) 842821
⏾ www.lifetime-furniture.co.uk
Nursery decor – Furniture: cabinets – marketed under the name Lifetime Products – with specialist marquetry and certificates of uniqueness to your child; also other items of furniture can be produced and customised to order.

Joshua Jones 🗄

Whitemill Farm, Sturminster Marshall, Wimbourne, Dorset BH21 4BX ☎ (01258) 858470 ⏾ www.joshua-jones.co.uk
Nursery decor – Furniture: claiming to offer "the very best children's furniture"; traditional wardrobes, chests of drawers, shelves, toy boxes, and dressing tables are individually made and painted to order, using hardwoods (including American oak); a standard range of

painted furniture is also available; a child's bed starts from £395+VAT; call for a brochure. / *Hours: 9am-5.30pm; no Amex & no Switch.*

Jou Jou & Lucy
32 Clifton Rd, London W9 1ST ☎ (020) 7289 0866
<u>Maternity wear</u> – **Luxury:** european designer wear for 0-8s with names such as Petit Bateau, Tartine, Baby Graziella, Simonetta, Trussardi, Benlingo and Mafrat. / *Hours: Mon-Sat 10am-6pm, Sun 12pm-4pm; Delivery: p&p extra; no Amex.*

Juniper
88 Pitshanger Lane, London W5 1QX
☎ (020) 8998 0144
<u>Baby clothes</u> – **Mid-range:** clothing and accessories using a lot of natural fibres, many from the UK; brightly coloured items for under-twos. / *Hours: Mon-Fri 9am-5.30pm, Sat 9.30am-5.30pm; no Amex.*

Just Bumps
CENTRAL CONTACT DETAILS
☎ (01622) 683 988
🖰 www.justbumps.co.uk
53 Union St ME14 1ED
☎ (01622) 683 988
<u>Maternity wear</u> – **Mid-range:** attractive maternity wear with an ethnic (eastern-influenced), modern slant (from a designer called Nicola Wallace); also do a made-to-measure service. / *Hours: Mon-Sat 10am-5pm; online catalogue; Delivery: p&p extra; no Amex.*

Just Kidding
CENTRAL CONTACT DETAILS
☎ (0121) 622 3100 & (0121) 624 0700
🖰 www.just-kidding.com/
Stone Yard, Digbeth B12 0LX
☎ (0121) 622 3100 & (0121) 624 0700
This Birmingham Warehouse outlet (estd 1990) claims to be one of the largest equipment retailers in the UK. You can order quite a number of items via the site – they call you back to confirm.
<u>Baby equipment</u> – **Stockists:** a wide range of equipment, including many of the top brand names. (Their Birmingham warehouse outlet stocks up to 30 furniture ranges). / *Hours: Mon-Sat (closed Weds) 10am-5pm, Sun 11am-4pm.*

Kantara Furniture
Bishopswood Leigh, Ross on Wye, Hereford HR9 5QX ☎ (01594) 860328
<u>Nursery decor</u> – **Furniture:** a business operating mail order (also sells at fairs and at their workshop by appointment); quality children's shelves with Palladian detailing or built as brightly-coloured bi-planes and tri-planes, from £75 to £115. / *Hours: 24hr answerphone; free leaflet; Delivery: p&p £12; no credit cards over the phone.*

Kappa Lambda Rugs
Unit 8 Regis Rd, London NW5 3EW ☎ (020) 7485 8822 🖰 www.kappa-lambda.co.uk
Primarily a warehouse that supplies retailers but it can send direct to the public and will give advice over phone.
<u>Nursery decor</u> – **Accessories:** a delightful, small range of hand-tufted modern rugs for

children, in bright colours with animals, stripes and polka dots; cheerful and uncutesy. / *Hours: Mon-Fri 9am-5pm; Delivery: p&p £10.*

Kardigan Kiosk
41 Cotswold Drive, Coventry CV3 6EZ
☎ (02476) 411776, (07974) 569068
🖰 www.kardigankiosk.co.uk
<u>Baby clothes</u> – **Mid-range.** – **Knitwear:** handmade cardigans and jerseys in colourful patterns with embroidery and appliqué (rainbows, fish, animals) £24-£30; no brochure – ring to discuss what you are looking for, or look at the website. / *Hours: Mon-Fri 9am-5pm or 24hr answerphone; no Amex & no Switch.*

Kari Me
15 Mentmore Rd, St Albans AL1 2BG
☎ (0870) 199 6970 🖰 www.kari-me.com
<u>Baby equipment</u> – **Slings:** a carrier in soft, stretchable (but mainly cotton) fabric in a variety of colours, suitable from birth to 3-4 years (and tested for weights of up to 15kg). The fabric is drip dry so particularly suitable for use when travelling. The website includes links to published articles on 'baby wearing'. Price is £37.95.

Karrimor
Petre Rd, Clayton-Le-Moors, Accrington, Lancashire BB5 5JZ ☎ (01254) 893000
🖰 www.karrimor.com
<u>Baby equipment</u> – **Slings- Backpack:** well-known backpack brand that also makes baby carriers and papooses; from £40-£100; call for a list of suppliers. / *Hours: Mon-Fri 10am-5pm.*

KC Collection
PO Box 342, Farnham, Surrey GU9 9XF
☎ (01252) 715 818
🖰 www.kccollection.co.uk
Specialist in lamb and sheepskin articles, most sold at shows or mail order. (The website does not offer an online purchasing facility.)
<u>Maternity wear</u> – **Luxury:** italian lambskin gilets and jackets suitable for pregnancy. Visit the website for a catalogue, and for a list of shows at which their collection will be presented.
<u>Nursery decor</u> – **Bedding:** lambskin cot throws.
<u>Baby clothes</u> – **Luxury:** lambskin jackets, boots, bonnets, mittens. / *Hours: Mon-Sat 9am-5pm; Delivery: p&p approx £6.*

KD Kids
150 High Rd, London N22 6EB ☎ (020) 8881 3320
<u>Baby clothes</u> – **Cheap & cheerful:** wide selection of children's clothes, from vests at 99p to party dresses for £20. / *Hours: Mon-Sat 9.30am-6pm; no Amex & no Switch.*

Kelty Kids
Man O' Leisure, Unit 8, South Farm, South Farm Rd, Budleigh Salterton, Devon EX9 7AZ ☎ (01395) 443789
🖰 www.kelty.com
Distributors of a number of interesting US-made items; contact for details of stockists. The US web site shows the different models.
<u>Baby equipment</u> – **Slings:** distributors of a quality US range of soft carriers and backpacks (designed to distribute the baby's

weight to the carrier's waist and hips). The Kangaroo (£55) – the fancier of the two soft carriers – is for babies up to 28lbs and is made to fit parents of all shapes and sizes. The baby can face in or out and fits in a pouch that's detachable from the main harness. It has a zip out hood and a variety of zip off storage sacks and pockets but the baby carries most of the weight on its crotch. There are six back carriers suited to toddlers up to 60lbs, highly adjustable in terms of their 'suspensions' and with a number of patented features (e.g. no-pinch hinges). A mid-range option is the Euro Trek (£140). Call for stockists.

<u>Nappies</u> – **Change bags:** accessories for the slings distributed by the same company (see also), including a number of 'Diaper Pack' backpacks (Diaper DayPack and Super Diaper Daypack with upgraded suspension); also a Diaper Duffel bag designed to sit under the backpack and a cooler bag with insulating liner and bottle holders. / *Hours: Mon-Fri 9.30am-5.30pm; free brochure; no credit cards.*

Kent & Carey 🖘
CENTRAL CONTACT DETAILS
☎ Mail order (020) 7924 5479
🖱 www.sleepycozy.com
BRANCHES:
154 Wandsworth Bridge Rd SW6 2UH
☎ (020) 7736 5554, (020) 7751 9828
30 Bellevue Rd SW17 2EF
☎ (020) 8682 2282
Small chain incorporating two London shops. As well as the items listed below the company sells nursery accessories, including cover-up bibs with sleeves, hooded towels, and changing mats. (Note: online ordering is restricted to the sleepycozy sleeping bags only).
<u>Nursery decor</u> – **Sleeping Bags:** the Sleepycozy sleeping bag, suitable for babies from three months to two years old, £30.
<u>Baby clothes</u> – **Traditional:** range includes nightwear and beach wear: romper suit £25; hand-smocked dress from £25, pinafore dresses from £25. / *no Amex.*

Kerry Ward
Wandsworth, London SW18 ☎ (020) 7350 1022
<u>Baby equipment</u> – **Cots:** as well as 19th-century French furniture, Ms Ward sells from her shop Victorian and early-20th-century children's sleigh beds and cots in pine. Each is slightly different and painted off-white and or cream, or comes in a natural waxed finish. The beds come as flat packs and generally cost £395. / *Hours: 24 hour answerphone.*

Khalsa Schoolwear
388 Bethnal Green Rd, London E2 0AH
☎ (020) 7729 3286
<u>Baby clothes</u> – **Mid-range:** clothes and uniforms for toddlers and above: Reebok, Adidas, Ellesse, Joe Bloggs, Levis, Ton sur Ton, Timberland and Osh Kosh; school stockists. / *Hours: Mon-Thu 9am-5.30pm, Fri & Sat 9am-6pm; no Amex.*

Kiddi Chic
19 Amhurst Parade, Amhurst Park, London N16 5AA ☎ (020) 8880 1500
<u>Baby clothes</u> – **Luxury:** designer labels such as Marese, Catimini and Borgese; middle to upper price range. / *Hours: Mon-Thu 10am-5.30pm, Fri 10am-12pm, (closed Sat) Sun 10am-2pm.*

Kiddicare 🖘
1182 Lincoln Road, Werrington, Peterborough PE4 6LA
🖱 www.kiddicare.com
Attached to a 15,000 square feet megastore in Peterborough.
<u>Baby equipment</u> – **Stockists:** this website retailer, offers a very wide range of baby equipment.

Kiddicentre
147 Clapton Common, London E5 9AE
☎ (020) 8809 4251
One of the better-quality smaller stockists.
<u>Baby equipment</u> – **Stockists:** high-quality pram brands including Emmaljunga (from Sweden); also Maclaren, Mamas & Papas, Chicco and Cosatto; also cots and changing stations.
<u>Nursery decor</u> – **Furniture:** nursery furniture. / *Hours: Mon-Thu 9.30am-5.30pm, Fri 9.30am-2.30pm (closed Sat), Sun 10.30am-2pm; no Amex.*

Kiddie Shoes
8 Amhurst Parade, London N16 5AA
☎ (020) 8809 5059
<u>Shoes</u> – **Suppliers:** brands stocked include Start-rite, Elefanten, Ricosta, Buckle My Shoe, Richter and Italian shoes. / *Hours: Mon-Thu 10am-6pm, Fri 11am-1pm (closed Sat), Sun 10am-2pm.*

Kiddiequipers 🖘 Q
The Business Exchange, Rockingham Road, Kettering, Northants NN16 8JX ☎ (01536) 526464 🖱 www.kiddiequipers.co.uk/
"Discount Nursery Necessities" sold online.
<u>Baby equipment</u> – **Second-hand:** though billing itself as a discount site, there's no huge emphasis on end-of-line items – the aim is just to price competitively; many items are from Hauck and Graco.

Kiddiproof
c/o Beldray Ltd, PO Box 20, Beldray Rd, Bilston, West Midlands WV14 7NF
☎ Customer services (01902) 406243, switchboard (01902) 353500
🖱 www.beldray.co.uk
Call for stockists if you are looking for a particular item from the range of this leading brand of safety equipment – the website showcases all their various products.
<u>Nursery decor</u> – **Safety items:** most conceivable items; they claim to be Europe's biggest manufacturer of safety gates. / *Hours: Mon-Thurs 8.45am-5pm; Fri 8.45am-3pm; no Amex.*

Kiddy Boom
36 Edgware Road, London W2 2EH ☎ (020) 7724 8544 🖱 www.kiddyboom.com
<u>Baby clothes</u> – **Luxury:** designer children's wear shop; much of the range is for older children, but there are some items and gift sets for babies. / *Hours: daily 10am-7pm.*

Kiddycare 🖘
Easter Lawrenceton Farmhouse, Forres IV36 2RL ☎ (0870) 046 5542
🖱 www.kiddycarebabybags.com

Also stockists of Baby Bjorn 'smocks' ie cover-up bibs.

Nursery decor – Sleeping Bags: available with elasticated waist, zip round base or, for older children, with a zip front. Some bags are 100% cotton and suitable for children aged from birth to six years (3 sizes). Also available are a small range of slippers and toys. / *Hours: Mon-Fri 9am-5pm, or answerphone; free catalogue; Delivery: p&p £3 (free over £50).*

The Kids Window 🖾
Unit 5 Brook Lane Business Centre, Brook Lane North, Brentford TW8 OPP ☎ (0800) 542 5093 🕾 www.thekidswindow.co.uk
Though the same firm runs stores outside London (trading as Scallywags), it is their mail order service that is of interest to Londoners.

Baby clothes – Mid-range: aims to give same day despatch of designer clothes from names such as Sucre d'Orge, Sarah Louise, Marèse, Trois Pommes, Gillian Joy Christening wear and Inch Blue; many items are discounted and there is a 'Sale' section on the site. / *Hours: 24hr telephone ordering; online catalogue; Delivery: p&p free on 2day delivery for orders over £50; £2.99 on orders under £50; Next day delivery £5; no Amex.*

Kidsfabrics 🖾
Dryslwyn House, 25 Llandeilo Road Upper Brynaman, Ammanford, Carmarthenshire SA18 1BA ☎ (01269) 825 796
🕾 www.kidsfabrics.co.uk/
Nursery decor – Soft furnishings: a range of 100% cotton children's novelty furnishing fabrics, sold by the metre or in ready-cut kits. The site offers information on sewing curtains, duvet covers and pillowcases, plus a quantity calculator.

Kindercare
116 & 130 Shenley Rd, Borehamwood WD6 1EF ☎ (020) 8953 2002
Baby equipment – Stockists: "Find a lower price within 14 days of purchase in a different store and we will refund the difference" – stockists of all the major pram and buggy brands including three-wheeled buggies; also highchairs, car seats and booster seats.
Toys – General stockists: wide range of toys stocked in the shop at number 130, with all the major brands, including Tomy and Lego. / *Hours: Mon-Sat 9.30am-5.30pm; no Amex.*

Kingswood
Units 5&6 Satellite Business Park, Blackswarth Rd, St George, Bristol BS5 8AU
🕾 www.kingswood-collection.co.uk
UK equipment brand, whose aim is the creation of fashion-led items at affordable prices. The website details their wide range of products and lists stockists.
Baby equipment – Wheeled Transport-brands: still strongest in pushchairs – the best-seller is the Buzz Around three-wheeler with full accessories at £160 (which also comes in a twin version); much emphasis is placed on numerous accessories for the different models. – **Cots:** a number of moderately-priced options.

Kit for Kids 🖾
45 High Street, Sevenoaks, Kent TN13 1JF ☎ (0870) 417 3000, (01732) 455 000
🕾 www.kitforkids.com
Toys – Nursery suppliers: manufacturers and suppliers of inflatables, educational products and soft play items. They supply the well-known Tumbletots play programme. / *Hours: Mon-Fri 9am-5.30pm; free brochure; Delivery: p&p extra.*

Kit Heath 🖾
31 James Street, Covent Garden, London WC2E 8PA ☎ (020) 7379 6661, 01271 329123 🕾 www.kitheath.com
Naming gifts – Naming gifts: a silver jewellery designer who offers a 'baby' range, including charms, alphabet pendants, bracelets and chains.

Kittykins 🖾
Southerly, Church Road, Heveningham, Suffolk IP19 0EA ☎ (01986) 798939
🕾 www.kittykins.co.uk
Nappies – Reusable stockists - multiple brands: motherease, Tots Bots, Nature Babies and other cloth nappies and accessories. The website includes useful ratings for each item including breathability, adjustability, ease of care and comfort.

Kiwi Slippers 🖾
St Margaret, Harleston, Norfolk IP20 0TB ☎ (01986) 783333 🕾 www.kiwislippers.com
Shoes – Brands: makers of sheepskin slippers with a couple of models for newborns; basic version £8.95, with tightening toggle to make removal by the wearer more difficult, £13.95. / *Hours: Mon-Fri 9am-5pm or 24hr answerphone; no Amex.*

Knights & Daisies 🖾
Unit 2, 4 Hawkins Lane, Gt Northern Business Park, Burton-on-Trent DE14 1PT ☎ (01283) 566676
🕾 www.knightsanddaisies.co.uk
Furniture makers; buy direct or call for a list of stockists.
Nursery decor – Beds: with sizes from 4', in a variety of styles – from 'normal' beds with a twist (e.g. angled sides, etc) to beds themed as pirate ships, diggers and so on; generally from £300. – **Furniture:** bookcases and shelf units; drawers from £300; wardrobes from £350. – **Storage:** funky storage boxes designed as dice or building blocks; also traditional toyboxes. / *Hours: Mon-Fri 9am-5pm; free catalogue or online; Delivery: 50-100 miles £25, 100-180 miles £35; no Amex.*

Knightsbridge Lighting Ltd 🖾
Unit 9 Station Rd Trading Estate, Attleborough, Norfolk NR17 2NP ☎ (01953) 455100 🕾 www.lightingforall.com
Nursery decor – Accessories: hanging nursery lights in a variety of designs and materials including carved pine: aeroplanes, rag dolls and clowns; cascade water lights ('Water Garden' and 'Magic Castle'). Also pottery bedside lights in Noah's Ark and tortoise designs, with matching money boxes, from £20. / *Hours: Mon-Fri 9am-5.30pm; free catalogue or online; Delivery: p&p extra, approx £6 (free locally); no Amex.*

Knock on Wood ⌂

Mail order: Glasshouses Mill, Glasshouses,
Harrogate, North Yorkshire HG3 5QH
☎ (01423) 712712
⌂ www.knockonwood.co.uk

<u>Toys</u> – **Traditional toys:** suppliers of
instruments for world music, a good source of
wind chimes (good for soothing babies) and
multiple percussion items including a number
specifically for children.

<u>Books, music & videos</u> – **Music tapes:** world
music specialist. African, Cuban and Brazilian
lullaby CDs, plus books and CDs of songs for
children. / *Hours: Mon-Sat 9.30am-5pm (mail order
Mon-Fri only); free catalogue; Delivery: p&p free over
£200; no Amex.*

Kool Sun ⌂

Smeatonside, Priorsfield Road, Godalming,
Surrey GU7 ISL ☎ (01483) 417 753
⌂ www.koolsun.com

<u>Baby clothes</u> – **Sun-protection clothing:**
launched in 2003, sun protection clothing from
6 months-12 years which, instead of the usual
nylon/lycra fabrics (which can be hot and
clammy), uses stretch polycotton and polyester
alternatives. They also try to offer designs
which look a little different from the norm. All
fabrics have been tested to Australian safety
standards and are guaranteed to block 98% of
the sun's IVA and UVB rays. / *Hours: 24 hours;
online catalogue; Delivery: p&p extra; no Amex.*

Kooshies ⌂

31-33 Park Royal Rd, London NW10 7LQ
☎ (0870) 607 0545, PHP (0870) 122 0215
⌂ www.phpbaby.com, www.kooshies.com
The parent company PHP (see also) also
produces other baby equipment.

<u>Nappies</u> – **Reusable stockists - brands
& singles:** three types of washable nappies: the
'Classic' is a two-piece nappy with eight layers
of cotton flannelette, a hidden waterproof layer
(and a patented flap for quick drying and
insertion of a booster liner to increase
absorbency); estimated to last 180 washings
each; available in two sizes – infant (£7.50 each,
£36 for ten) and toddler (£9 each, £45 for ten);
waterproof wraps, £5. The 'Ultra' has five
layers of cotton and two inner 'soaker' pads of
polyester and rayon for greater absorbency,
and an internal flap (adjustable for boys and
girls); no wrap needed; estimated to last 120
washings; two sizes – infant (£8 each, £39.50
for five) and toddler (£9.50 each, £47.50 for
five). The 'Diaper Basic' nappies are good for
holidays; two sizes – infant and toddler (£5
each, £25 for five); waterproof wrap £2.99.
Other nappy products include booster liners
(£9 for ten), nappies for premature babies,
swim nappies and trainer pants. / *Hours: 9am-
5pm; free catalogue; Delivery: p&p £2.95.*

Krucial Kids ⌂

Unit 11, Enterprise Way, Flitwick,
Bedfordshire MK45 5BW ☎ (01525) 722 740
⌂ www.krucialkids.com
Business combining showroom and mail order
catalogue.

<u>Toys</u> – **Pre-school specialists:** development
toys for babies supplied to retailers and via mail
order; including the Educo range of
multi-coloured maze wires with removable

wooden beads on a wooden base. / *Hours: Mon-
Fri 9am-5.30pm; free catalogue; Delivery: p&p £1.95-
£3.95.*

Lamaze International

Century House, Station Way, Cheam, Surrey
SM3 8SW ⌂ www.lamaze.com;
www.flairplc.co.uk
The well-known American natural childbirth
and early parenting organisation.

<u>Toys</u> – **Brand:** developed in conjunction with
leading child development specialists, 'Infant
Development System' toys are fun, well-made,
stimulating, semi-educational products; all toys
have a lifetime guarantee; the 'stage 1'
playthings, cot toys and playmats for babies
from birth and up are excellent, with
geometric shapes, sounds, contrasting textures
and strong colours to help young eyes to focus.
Also toys designed for babies from 3 months,
from 6 months and from 12 months; tub toys;
books; and cuddly toys. Stockists include Daisy
& Tom, Hamleys, Harrods, Mothercare,
Selfridges and Lilliput.

Lanka Kade ⌂

Unit 1, Southfolds Road, Oakley Hay, Corby
NN18 9EU ☎ (01536) 461 188
⌂ www.lankakade.co.uk
'Fair trade toys with a difference'.

<u>Toys</u> – **Educational:** an attractive range of
painted wooden toys including mobiles, wall
hooks, Noah's Ark, block puzzles, letters and
numbers, and the like. Also multi-cultural soft
dolls using Sri Lankan handloom cotton
fabrics. A Fairtrade supplier, which hopes to
introduce full online ordering soon. / *Hours:
Mon-Fri 9am-5pm; free catalogue; Delivery: p&p £4
for orders under £30.*

The Laundry ⌂

PO Box 22007, London SW2 1WU ☎ (020)
7274 3838 ⌂ www.thelaundry.co.uk

<u>Baby equipment</u> – **Bathing:** luxury accessories
include a hooded towel in cream edged in
spotty fabric, bath mitts and bibs.

<u>Nursery decor</u> – **Bedding:** '40s-style bed linen
in pure cotton; also laundry bags and
padded/painted coat hangers for children;
prices from £19 for a pillowcase. / *Hours: 9am-
5pm, 24hr answerphone; free catalogue; Delivery: p&p
£4; no Amex.*

Laura Ashley ⌂

CENTRAL CONTACT DETAILS
☎ Customer service (0870) 562 2116
⌂ www.laura-ashley.com
BRANCHES:
*(Only selected branches are listed –
call the enquiry line for other outlets.)*
449-451 Oxford St W1 IDA
☎ (020) 7355 1363
256–258 Regent St W1R 5DA
☎ (020) 7437 9760
Mail order: PO Box 19, Newtown SY16 1LX
☎ (0800) 868100
Only the range of nursery decor is available by
mail order.

<u>Nursery decor</u> – **General stockists:** an
extensive range of wallpaper, borders, curtains
and bed linen, mostly with traditional themes,
some aimed specifically at children – ballet,
flowers, farms and sailors.

<u>Baby clothes</u> – **Mid-range.** – **Traditional:**

lots of pretty, flowered cottons, chambrays and jersey fabrics, but not, perhaps, with the strongly individual style they once had; at their best with modern classics combining good styling, nice muted colours and close attention to detail. / *Hours: hours vary; free brochure; Delivery: p&p £4.25.*

Susan Lawson 🖃

7 River View Close, Holme Lacey, Hereford HR2 6NZ ☎ (01432) 870977
🖰 www.susanlawson.co.uk
<u>Baby clothes</u> – **Christening gowns:** "Designer handmade Christening and special occasion wear" by mail order; gowns from £55-£195, romper suits from £80. / *Delivery: p&p £5.*

Leap Frog Toys (UK) Ltd

106 Oxford Rd, Uxbridge UX8 1NA
☎ (0800) 169 5435 🖰 www.leapfrog.com
<u>Toys</u> – **Brand:** makers of the 'Leap Pad' – electronic interactive books suitable for nine months upwards, sold strongly (and not unjustifiably) on their educational qualities.

Lego 🖃

Lego Europe North, Capital Point, 33 Bath Rd, Slough SL1 3UF ☎ Consumer service number (0845) 708 0070, Shop at Home (00800) 5346 1111 🖰 www.lego.com
<u>Toys</u> – **Brand:** manufacturers of Lego Explore, an infant and pre-school range superceding Duplo, the well-known under-fives version of the famous plastic construction system; colourful and easy to handle. Details of the full range can be found on the website which offers a 'shop at home' facility. / *Hours: 9am-5.30pm; online catalogue; no Amex & no Switch.*

Lego Rebuilders Q

🖰 www.lego-rebuilders.com
<u>Toys</u> – **Brand:** not the manufacturers but a good source of second-hand Duplo and Lego (including discontinued items). The website includes various links to other sites about and selling Lego.

Leila

25 Topsfield Parade, Crouch End, London N8 8TP ☎ (020) 8340 4640
<u>Baby clothes</u> – **Funky:** in a women's clothes shop, an attractive selection of unusual garments, largely for girls but some boys'. Good quality across the market range, sized from newborn to teens. Labels include Albetta, Rutsou and Rene Dehry. / *Hours: Mon-Sat 10am-6pm, Sun 12pm-5pm; no Amex.*

Let's Learn 🖃

11 Wykeham Rd, London NW4 2TB
☎ (020) 8203 8888
🖰 www.letslearntoys.com
<u>Toys</u> – **Educational:** a small catalogue of educational items (all in non-toxic, non-allergenic, soft materials) developed with child therapists and safety experts to stimulate creativity, imagination and co-ordination; Clics range of construction toys for 4 years and up; large variety of playmats (over 39 different ranges; including, alphabet, street map, snakes and ladders, hopscotch); building blocks; soft bowling set; giant dominoes; cubes of stacking blocks; all £15-£20. / *Hours: Mon-Fri 9.30am-5pm or 24hr answerphone; free brochure; no credit cards.*

Letterbox 🖃

Tregony Business Park, Tregony, Truro, Cornwall TR2 5TL ☎ (0870) 6007878
🖰 www.letterbox.co.uk
<u>Toys</u> – **General stockists:** a good choice (over 350 ideas) of imaginative presents, many of which can be personalised with names, birth dates or messages; Soft Noah's Ark £19.99; named hairband £7.99; named lunch box £9.99. – **Traditional toys:** the range (aimed not just at kids) includes a number of traditional wood and hand-painted toys (soldier train, £6; ballerina bookends, £14.99).
<u>Naming gifts</u> – **Naming gifts:** wide range of traditional items and toys that can be personalised with a child's name and date of birth. / *Hours: Mon-Fri 9am-5.30pm; free catalogue; Delivery: p&p £2.35 (orders up to £20), £3.95 (£20–£120), free on orders over £120.*

Letterbox Library 🖃

71-73 Allen Rd, London N16 8RY ☎ (020) 7503 4801 🖰 www.letterboxlibrary.com
<u>Books, music & videos</u> – **Bookshops:** the shop belonging to the mail-order-only Children's Book Co-operative, stocks the same multicultural, non-sexist, enjoyable and fun titles as the mail order side of the business; 'issues' books on subjects such as handicapped children and divorce are a feature. There are a number of titles for under-twos, lots for older children and a visitors' area with toys and games. A one-off membership of £5 entitles you to discounts on most books. / *free quarterly catalogue; Delivery: p&p £1.99 (orders up to £10), £2.99 (£10-£25), £3.99 (£25-£75), £4.50 (£75-£100), free for orders over £150.*

Liberty

Regent St, London W1B 5AH ☎ (020) 77434 1234 🖰 www.liberty.co.uk
<u>Baby clothes</u> – **Luxury:** a dedicated department sells attractive garments from baby to eight years including babygrows, rompers, T-shirts, jumpers, shirts/blouses, trousers and dresses, in plain plus relatively sober Liberty patterns (stripes, geometrics and flowers), creating a modern designer feel; shirt £32.

Life Memories Box Company 🖃

Keepsake Corner, 9 Glebe Close, Wigston, Leicestershire LE18 3LU ☎ (0116) 288 7781
🖰 www.lifememoriesbox.co.uk
<u>Naming gifts</u> – **Naming gifts:** boxes specially designed to store key items from the staging posts of a baby's life as it progresses through childhood.

Lifetime Education 🖃

PO Box 72, Ratford, Notts DN22 7WG
☎ (01777) 869 044
<u>Toys</u> – **Educational:** a good selection of soft play equipment including the Playring – an ingenious system for entertaining children (especially babies) – it comes with loops, squeaks, rustles and bells (£120). Also supply room dividers and floor mats. / *Hours: Mon-Fri 9am-5pm; free catalogue; Delivery: p&p extra; no credit cards.*

Lifetime Products ⌂
☎ (01686) 625454, mobile (07801) 842821
🖰 www.lifetimefurniture.co.uk
<u>Nursery decor</u> – **Furniture:** see Steve Jones Furniture.

Lilliput ⌂
CENTRAL CONTACT DETAILS
☎ (0800) 783 0886
🖰 www.lilliput.com
BRANCHES:
100 Haydons Rd SW19 1AW
☎ (020) 8542 3542, Buggy repairs (020) 8543 0505
255-259 Queenstown Rd SW8 3NP
☎ (020) 7720 5554
Small south-west London chain with notable expertise in the area of baby equipment. The sizeable Battersea branch (limited car parking) claims to be "the biggest dedicated children's equipment shop in London". The shops offer the convenience of shopping out of hours (by appointment) and promise that they will not be beaten on price.
<u>Baby equipment</u> – **Stockists:** stock includes car seats (Maxi Cosi, Britax), cots (Stokke, Classic Baby and Kidsmill; also travel cots), prams (Baby Confort, Jané, Maclaren) and several styles of three-wheeled pushchairs. Buggy repairs are done at the Wimbledon Branch (020 8543 0505); will check your car seat is fitted correctly; will order anything they don't have in stock. – **Hire:** will consider renting any item: the hire brochure includes prices for car seats, baby swings, cots and prams; rental is credited against the purchase price if you decide to buy.
<u>Nursery decor</u> – **General stockists:** wallpapers, borders, curtains and furniture spanning a wide price range, including nursing chairs and Tripp Trapp chairs; mattress fitting service.
<u>Baby clothes</u> – **Mid-range:** a smallish range in the medium to upper end of the style and price markets; labels include Raindrops, Koolsun, Noukie and Flap Happy.
<u>Toys</u> – **Pre-school specialists:** the range includes old-fashioned wooden toys (including Brio), cuddly toys and jigsaw puzzles.
<u>Nappies</u> – **Reusable stockists - multiple brands:** stockists of reusable nappies, and brands such as Mio Bambino. / *Hours: Mon-Fri 9.30am-5.30pm (Battersea Wed 7pm), Sat 9am-6pm, Battesea Sun 11-4; Delivery: p&p free for orders over £100; no Amex.*

Linco Care ⌂
Linco House, Manchester Rd, Carrington M31 4BX ☎ (0161) 777 9229
🖰 www.calypsosun.com
<u>Nappies</u> – **Reusable stockists - brands & singles:** 'Dimples' brand – reusable pads and pants with polycotton padding in Dry-Tex (washable at 90°C) and nylon waterproof outer (washable at 40°C); newborn, small, medium and large sizes; starter pack from £6. / *Hours: 9am-5.30pm; free leaflet; Delivery: p&p 75p per item; no credit cards.*

Lindam
Hornbeam Square West, Hornbeam Park, Harrogate, North Yorkshire HG2 8PA
☎ Customer care (01423) 855 833

🖰 www.lindam.co.uk
British baby equipment brand; call the helpline for stockists; all products are shown on the website; they do not sell mail order, but can provide parts and spares.
<u>Baby equipment</u> – **Monitors-brand:** three models from a basic plug-in one to a rechargeable digital number.
<u>Nursery decor</u> – **Safety items:** one of the best-known safety gate brands. / *Hours: 9am-5pm; no Amex.*

Linen Cupboard
21 Great Castle St, London W1G 0HY
☎ (020) 7629 4062
<u>Nursery decor</u> – **Bedding:** a throwback to another time, surviving just behind Oxford Street, sells all kinds of household linens, including cot bedding.

The Linen Merchant ⌂
11 Montpelier St, London SW7 1EX ☎ (020) 7584 3654 🖰 www.thelinenmerchant.com
As well as the ranges listed, this Knightsbridge boutique also stocks rattles, bibs, changing bags, mats and so on; items can be made to order.
<u>Nursery decor</u> – **Bedding:** traditional good-quality cotton bedding, linens and towels with charming embroidered images such as rabbits, alphabet, soldiers and racing cars in bright colours and pastels; a good gift section (will wrap and send); also bumper sets and quilts.
<u>Baby clothes</u> – **Mid-range:** baby bodysuits for 0-1 year. – **Christening gowns:** robes are held in stock or can be made to order. / *Hours: Mon-Sat 9.30am-6pm (open Sun in Dec); online catalogue; Delivery: p&p extra depending on order; no Amex.*

Linn Jigsaws ⌂
Hillside House, Jacob's Knoll, Burleigh, Stroud, Gloucestershire GL5 2PR ☎ (01453) 885482 🖰 www.linnjigsaws.co.uk
This 25-year-old firm do mail order and attend craft fairs (call for the location and dates of one near you).
<u>Toys</u> – **Traditional toys:** attractive handmade wooden jigsaws (about 50 designs) and wooden tray puzzles in bright primary colours; designs include a pre-nursery range with farmyard animals, trains and zoo animals; also alphabet and number sets. / *free catalogue; no credit cards.*

Lion & Unicorn Bookshop ⌂
19 King St, Richmond, Surrey TW9 1ND
☎ (020) 8940 0483
🖰 www.lionunicornbooks.co.uk
<u>Books, music & videos</u> – **Bookshops:** this tiny ("prize-winning") specialist children's retailer is crammed with books (and tapes) for all ages, including hundreds of picture and board books for younger ages; events and a regular newsletter ('The Roar') encourage children to get involved. / *Hours: Mon-Fri 9.30am-5.30pm, Sat 9am-6pm, Sun 12pm-5pm; Delivery: p&p £1+.*

Lionwitchwardrobe ⌂
PO Box 26470, London SE10 8YB ☎ (020) 8265 8449 🖰 www.lionwitchwardrobe.co.uk
<u>Nursery decor</u> – **Furniture:** children's furniture in contemporary, clean styles (calmer than the usual bright 'plastic' styles); the core

collection includes a children's bed (prices from £800), wardrobe, cot-bed and changer. Wardrobe drawers include details like a groove to stop fingers getting trapped. Call for a list of stockists, or you can buy direct, / *free catalogue or online; Delivery: p&p extra; no Amex.*

Little Badger ✉

Studio 2.06, Oxo Tower Wharf, Bargehouse St, London SE1 9PH ☎ Orderline (020) 7620 2422, (020) 7620 1992
♲ www.littlebadger.com

<u>Nursery decor</u> – **Bedding:** embroidered chequered cot blankets in knitted cotton, £89 (can be personalised, £5 extra).

<u>Baby clothes</u> – **Mid-range. – Knitwear:** knitwear, all hand-knitted or hand-framed; stripey sailor jumpers, matching scarf and hat sets, rucksacks, hats and a denim pram coat; also T-shirts printed with pirates, little devils, hearts, stars or stripes; prices from £16 for a T-shirt, knitwear from £35.

<u>Naming gifts</u> – **Naming gifts:** the company's best-seller is a delightful chequered cot blanket embroidered with hearts and the child's name or date of birth in knitted cotton, £89 (£94 personalised). / *Hours: Mon-Fri 9.30am-5.30pm, or answerphone; free catalogue; Delivery: p&p £4, gift box £5.*

Little Bugs ✉

Fenwood House, Pilcorn Street, Wedmore, Somerset BS28 4AP ☎ (01934) 710 340
♲ www.littlebugs.co.uk

<u>Baby equipment</u> – **Stockists:** a website offering "new and innovative nursery, pregnancy and baby products", and particularly strong in gift items, health products and toys.

The Little Chair Company ✉

Little Humphreys, Lested Lane, Chart Sutton, Maidstone, Kent ME17 3RZ ☎ (01622) 843 312

<u>Nursery decor</u> – **Furniture:** catalogue suppliers of chairs for children, hand-painted (not stencilled) to order. Also toyboxes, tables and other furniture. / *free brochure; Delivery: £7.50 for chair; £15 for larger items.*

Little Green Earthlets ✉

CENTRAL CONTACT DETAILS
☎ (01825) 873301
♲ www.earthlets.co.uk
BRANCHES:
Mail order: Units 1-3 Stream Farm, Chiddingly, Lewes BN8 6HG
☎ (01825) 873301
163 Lower Richmond Rd SW15 1HH
☎ (020) 8780 3075

Mail order supplier (also with a shop in Putney) selling a changing variety of disparate but well-chosen items, often with an eco-friendly bias.

<u>Baby equipment</u> – **High chairs:** tripp Trapp high chair, £109 (also other items by Stokke, including the Sleepicot and Xplory buggy).

<u>Baby clothes</u> – **Mid-range. – Eco-friendly clothing:** a mid-sized range of simple vests, T-shirts, dressing gowns, cardies, trousers and briefs.

<u>Toys</u> – **Pre-school specialists:** a small range of toys, including lots to do with magnets.
– **Dressing up toys:** fair selection including angel, animal, dragon and soldiers outfits.

Nappies – **Reusable stockists - multiple brands:** seven types of reusable nappies; UK distributors for Canadian Mother-ease in knitted cotton terry towelling (to be wrapped round an inner terry towelling layer), size adjusted by poppers; typical price £8.50.

Little Laurels ✉

171-172 High Street, Lewes, East Sussex BN7 1YE ☎ (01273) 470 248
♲ www.littlelaurels.co.uk

Online business attached to a shop, which – among other items – sells baby and children's clothes.

<u>Baby clothes</u> – **Mid-range:** classic clothes with a contemporary twist, for babies and children.
– **Traditional:** made in-house – largely natural fabrics and fleeces, including dresses (about £40), rompers and waistcoats.

<u>Toys</u> – **General stockists:** small range of attractive toys.

<u>Naming gifts</u> – **Naming gifts.** / *Hours: Mon-Sat 9am-5pm; online catalogue; Delivery: p&p £4.*

Little SmartiPants ✉

Brimpsfield House, Brimpsfield, Gloucestershire GL4 8LD ☎ (01452) 863 384 ♲ www.littlesmartipants.com

Selling largely through fairs in London, the Cotswolds and sometimes slightly further afield, and sales hosted in your home.

<u>Baby clothes</u> – **Knitwear:** children's clothing and accessories from 0-8 years old, with a classical traditional range from 0-2 years (and 'cooler' items for the 3 and ups); as well as a classic layette and babywear, numerous Continental brands are stocked including Barbar, Arc en Ciel, Il Gufo, Mollie and Bienvenue Sur Terre.

The Little Star Company ✉

☎ (01737) 371221

Small mail-order business.

<u>Baby equipment</u> – **Car accessories:** the CosyBag sleeping bag for babies to wear in their car seat, £30; it unzips via a front panel for easy access and has three slots in the back for the harness.

<u>Nursery decor</u> – **Sleeping Bags:** baby sleeping bags with fitted top and zippered bag below – main product is in a 'teddy' cotton fleece with a tog rating of 1.9; baby bag from birth to six-nine months, with soft flannel inside has a tog rating 1.1 (equivalent to one blanket); also do lightweight summer bags in larger sizes and warmer bags with polyester filling with tog rating 2.6; prices from £23. / *Hours: hours vary, 24hr answerphone; no credit cards.*

Little Stars ✉

8 Anselm Rd, Pinner, Middlesex HA5 4LJ
☎ (020) 8621 4378, (020) 8537 0980
♲ www.littlestars.co.uk

Run by two mums with six kids under the age of seven – better known for hire, but about half their business is sales.

<u>Baby equipment</u> – **Stockists:** though their website includes a range of merchandise, they will supply any item available from wholesalers. – **Hire:** the whole gamut of baby equipment (from monitors to pushchairs) can be hired for a minimum of three days (Christmas one week). / *Hours: Mon-Fri 9am-6pm, 24hr answerphone; free brochure.*

Little Tikes

900 Pavilion Drive, Northants NN4 7RG
☎ (0800) 521558 🖰 www.littletikes.com
<u>Nursery decor</u> – **Furniture:** play chests and
beds, for example in the shape of a racing car
or Noah's Ark; small chairs and tables, easels
and even children's computer desks. The new
'anti-monster' design has no space underneath.
<u>Toys</u> – **Brand:** started in the 1970s in Ohio,
the company is perhaps best known for its little
moulded plastic cars, but does a wide range of
other moulded plastic products, from climbing
frames to rattles. – **Outdoor items & active
toys:** as well as the well-known ride-on wagons
and cars, this company makes large items such
as playframes and slides which can fold up,
swings for toddlers, a sandbox (with cover) and
play kitchens. / *Hours: 8.30am-4.45pm.*

Little Timbers 🖰

8 Bridge Meadow, Denton,
Northamptonshire NN7 1DA ☎ (01604) 899
356
<u>Toys</u> – **Traditional toys:** mail order suppliers
of brightly coloured wooden toys from
alphabet letters to Noah's Arks. Also bouncy
animals on a spring for over-2s.

The Little Trading Company 🖰

7 Bedford Corner, The Avenue, London
W4 1LD ☎ (020) 8742 3152
"Everything you need when you have a baby"
– most stock is second-hand, with some new
items (not related to the Great Little Trading
Company, also listed).
<u>Baby equipment</u> – **Stockists:** cots, prams,
cribs (including some antiques) and
three-wheeler buggies.
<u>Nursery decor</u> – **General stockists:** linens,
cots, cribs, furniture and high chairs from
many of the well-known makers.
<u>Baby clothes</u> – **Second-hand shops:** a wide
selection from well-known, quality brands.
<u>Toys</u> – **Second-hand shops:** no soft toys
(except new or in very good second-hand
condition); brands such as Galt and Early
Learning Centre; dressing up clothes.
<u>Hairdressers</u> – **Hairdressers:** haircuts are
available Wednesdays and Fridays from 2pm
and Saturday from 9.30am by appointment,
£9.50; lock of hair and certificate for first
cuts. / *Hours: Mon-Fri 9am-5pm, Sat 9am-4.30pm;
no credit cards.*

Little Treasures 🖰

10 Braemar Crescent, Leigh on Sea, Essex
SS9 3RL ☎ (01702) 559005
🖰 www.littletreasures.co.uk
<u>Baby clothes</u> – **Luxury.** – **Traditional:** a
range mixing classic and contemporary styles;
girls Liberty smocked dress £80;
complementary wool and cotton knitwear;
a comprehensive range of nightwear ('Pajama
Party'). – **Knitwear:** a variety of pullovers and
cardigans, from about £35 up to £90 for
cashmere. / *Hours: Mon-Fri 10am-6pm, Sat 10am-
1pm; free catalogue; Delivery: p&p £4.*

Little Trekkers 🖰

Unit 9, Springfield Mill, Denby Dale,
Huddersfield HD8 8TH ☎ (01484) 868321
🖰 www.littletrekkers.co.uk/

Run by a family, a very professional-looking
website (and now also a shop) for active
families.
<u>Baby clothes</u> – **Outdoorwear:** they aim to
offer what they believe to be the best outdoor
(as well as camping and so on) gear for kids;
plus baby day bags, water bottles, child carriers
and so on. The site also includes extensive
information on buying a backpack.

Little Willies

16 The Pavement, Clapham Common,
London SW4 0HY ☎ (020) 7498 7899
<u>Shoes</u> – **Suppliers:** stockists of brands like
Pom d'Api, Natrino, Asta, Daisy Roots,
Country Kids and more.
<u>Hairdressers</u> – **Hairdressers:** real barbers'
chairs (but with baby seats) lend an added air of
authenticity. / *Hours: Mon-Fri 11am-5.30pm, Sat
10am-5pm.*

Little Wonders 🖰

🖰 www.littlewonders.co.uk
BRANCHES:
3 York St TW1 3JZ
☎ (020) 8255 6114
12 Angel Gate, Guildford GU1 4AE
☎ (01483) 577648
Home counties chain of three shops, which
also supplies via the web.
<u>Nursery decor</u> – **Accessories:** small range –
mats, chairs, table, junior coat stand.
<u>Toys</u> – **Traditional toys:** range mainly consists
of educational items and doll's houses.

Littlewoods 🖰

CENTRAL CONTACT DETAILS
☎ (08457) 888222
🖰 www.littlewoodsonline.com
BRANCHES:
*(Branches throughout London –
call the enquiry line for your nearest outlet.)*
<u>Baby equipment</u> – **Stockists:** the website
includes a wide range, from strollers and car
seats to cots.
<u>Nursery decor</u> – **General stockists:** furniture,
safety items and accessories.
<u>Baby clothes</u> – **Cheap & cheerful.** / *free
catalogue; Delivery: p&p included (minimum order
£6); no Amex.*

Livecam 🖰

Unit 18, Mossedge Industrial Estate,
Linwood, Renfrewshire, Scotland PA3 3HR
☎ (01505) 324336, Customer care (01505)
321418 🖰 www.teddycam.co.uk
<u>Baby equipment</u> – **Monitors-brand:** a
teddybear with miniature video camera in the
nose and miniature microphone under his fur,
which transmits to a receiver which can be
attached to a standard television.

Lizzies

143 Northcote Rd, London SW11 6PX
☎ (020) 7738 2973
<u>Nursery decor</u> – **Accessories:** colourful wall
hangings, and hand-painted photo frames.
<u>Baby clothes</u> – **Mid-range:** including
American-made clothing of especially soft
fabrics (Cotton Caboodle and Merry Berries);
unusual items such as bloomers and sun hats;
all-cotton fireproof nightwear; wide range of
fleece wear.
<u>Toys</u> – **General stockists:** unusual gifts, toys

and books; brands include Jellycat and Maisy. / *Hours: Mon-Sat 10am-6pm; no Amex.*

LL Bean 🛒
Casco St, Freeport, Maine, ME 04033, USA
🖰 www.llbean.com
Baby clothes – Mid-range: the New England preppie favourite leisurewear catalogue now also offers a small quantity of items for children and babies. / *Hours: 24hrs; online catalogue; Delivery: p&p, airmail & duty payable from US; no Switch.*

Lollipop Children's Products 🛒
Bosigran Farm, Pendeen, Penzance, Cornwall TR2U 8YX ☎ (01736) 799512
🖰 www.teamlollipop.co.uk
Children's company selling mail order and via a network of consultants. They have ambitions to supply all baby products, but nappies are currently the strongest area.
Nursery decor – Bedding: colourful fleece blankets, mattress protectors, lambskins and sleeping bags.
Toys – Traditional toys: stockists of colourful wooden toys.
Nappies – Reusable stockists - multiple brands: suppliers of many of the larger reusable nappy brands, including Kooshies, Mother-ease, Earthwise; terry nappies, muslin squares and pre-folds; organic brands also available. Manufacture own washable stuffable fleece nappies. **– Suppliers-Eco friendly disposables:** sole UK distributor of Weenees, as well as other disposable brands. / *Hours: Mon-Fri 9am-5pm; free brochure; Delivery: £3.95; no Amex.*

London Nursery Suppliers
Hardy Passage, off Berner's Rd, London N22 6NZ ☎ (020) 8889 3003
Baby equipment – Buggy & pram repairs: repair service for all sorts of buggies, prams and pushchairs.
Nursery decor – General stockists: wide range of nursery equipment, from cribs to blankets, bedding and wheeled goods. / *Hours: Mon-Fri 8.30am-5.30pm, Sat 8.30am-1pm; no Amex.*

London Prams 🛒
175 / 179 East India Dock Road, Chrisp Street Shopping Centre, London E14 0EA
☎ (020) 7537 4117
🖰 www.londonprams.co.uk
Despite the name, the motto is "everything your baby needs" at this 2,000 square feet showroom, on the A13 just outside Canary Wharf. You can also buy via the website (though stock seems to be more limited than in the store).
Baby equipment – Stockists. – Buggy suppliers: mamas & Papas, Maclaren, Emmaljunga, Chicco, and Silver Cross.

London Zoo 🛒
Regents Park, London NW1 4RY ☎ (020) 7722 3333, Adoption line (020) 7449 6262
🖰 www.londonzoo.co.uk, www.zsl.org
Naming gifts – Naming gifts: an alternative present idea and a good cause – adopt an animal at the zoo. You receive an adoption certificate, a photograph of the animal species, a badge, car sticker and one free ticket to the Zoo for every adoption (or shared adoption of larger animals), a one year's magazine subscription and the adopter's name is listed on a board at the Zoo; a whole animal can be adopted for a minimum of £25, or in units of £35 for any animal over £70. / *Hours: Mon-Sun 10am-5.30pm; no Switch.*

Long Tall Sally 🛒
CENTRAL CONTACT DETAILS
☎ Mail order (020) 8649 9009
🖰 www.longtallsally.co.uk
BRANCHES:
21 Chiltern St W1U 7PH
☎ (020) 7487 3370
Unit 1 Peterwood Park, Peterwood Way CR0 4UG
☎ (020) 8649 6009
A reasonable-sized chain (26 stores around the country) of specialist clothes stores aimed at tall women, with mail order operating out of the Croydon branch.
Maternity wear – Mid-range: the maternity selection has been cut back in their stores and catalogue of late, but they still do a small selection of jeans and trousers for £40. / *Hours: Mon-Sat 9am-5.30pm, Sat 10am-4pm; free quarterly catalogue; Delivery: p&p £2 (orders up to £30), £3 (orders over £30).*

Look Who's Walking
78 Heath St, London NW3 1DN ☎ (020) 7433 3855
The company also has a store at 166a High Road, Loughton, Essex IG21 1DN (020) 8508 7472.
Baby clothes – Luxury: brands include Oilily, Elle, Paul Smith, Diesel, DKNY, Moschino, Versace.
Shoes – Suppliers: brands include Buckle My Shoe, Start-rite, Simonetta and many Continental designs. / *Hours: Mon-Sat 10am-5.30pm, Sun noon-6pm.*

Loophouse
88 Southwark Bridge Rd, London SE1 0EX
☎ (020) 7207 7619 🖰 www.loophouse.com
Nursery decor – Accessories: range of funky rugs for children; designs include cats, cows, the alphabet and a clock; four sizes (can be made to different sizes to order); alphabet rug (2m x 2m), £400. / *Hours: by appointment only; no credit cards.*

Lullabies 🛒
10 St Johns Hill, Shrewsbury SY1 1JD
☎ (01743) 233 233 🖰 www.lullabys.co.uk
Baby equipment – Stockists: an online nursery retailer whose range includes a number of quality brands such as Stokke's Tripp Trapp chairs, Bugaboo strollers and Dutailer glider chairs; as well as an extensive selection of nursery furniture and décor in a number of distinct styles.

Lullaby Heir 🛒
Mervyn Davis, Llandyssil, Montgomery, Powys SY15 6LX ☎ (01686) 668 765
Baby equipment – Cots: handmade swing cribs in oak with a ply base. A brass plate can be supplied to record the baby's name and date of birth. The crib can be supplied fully assembled, or part-assembled to facilitate storage when not in use. / *leaflet.*

Lundia 🖰
39 Goodramgate, York YO1 7LS ☎ (01904)
637442 🖰 www.lundia.co.uk
Shop and mail order business.
Baby equipment – **Stockists:** stockists of the
Stokke Tripp Trapp chair and cot.
Nursery decor – **Beds:** stockists of the Flexa,
a full-size, first bed that can take side rails and
can be raised to turn into a cabin bed or high
sleeper; also the Stompa range (similar to Flexa
– Scandinavian design). / *Hours: Mon-Sat 9.30am-
5pm; free catalogue or online; Delivery: free up to 50
miles; no Amex.*

Ma'Donna Maternity 🖰
Morley's Place, High Street, Sawston,
Cambridge CB2 4TG ☎ (01223) 830 100
🖰 www.ma-donna.co.uk
Maternity wear – **Luxury:** uK and imported
designer maternity wear, being the exclusive
UK retailers for US brands Japanese Weekend,
Meet Me in Miami, and Duet.

Louise Mabbs
Balham, London SW12 ☎ (020) 7801 0313
Nursery decor – **Soft furnishings:**
made-to-measure quilts, cushions and wall
hangings (many with an optical illusion theme)
for children and adults; patchwork quilting or
appliqué; will undertake most type of
commission. / *Hours: 24hr answerphone, studio
visits by appointment; no credit cards.*

Alex MacDonald
Pembrokeshire ☎ (01834) 842491, (07900)
582 110 🖰 www.alexmacdonald.co.uk
Nursery decor – **Furniture:** slightly
retro/Scandinavian tables and chairs in
moulded ply and melamine. See the website
for stockists. / *Hours: flexible.*

Maclaren
Station Works, Long Buckby, Northampton
NN6 7PF ☎ (01327) 842662
The seminal British buggy invented by Owen
Maclaren, an aircraft designer, in 1965.
Baby equipment – **Wheeled
Transport-brands:** hallmarks of the brand are
manoeuvrability, lightness, strength and
reliability; call for a brochure or to find your
nearest outlet; can supply replacement parts
for all Maclaren models. / *Hours: Mon-Fri
8.30am-5pm (Fri 3.30pm).*

macpac
PO Box 8399, Christchurch 8002, New
Zealand ☎ +64 3 338 1106
🖰 www.macpac.co.nz
Baby equipment – **Slings- Backpack:** a New
Zealand brand of outdoor clothing and
equipment; their child carrier is at the Rolls
Royce end of the market, available from
trekking shops – the website lists all the UK
retailers.

Macraft Industries 🖰
Riverside Business Park, Unit 3, Ferry Rd,
Southrey, Lincs LN3 5TA ☎ (01526) 398815
Baby equipment – **Cots:** large range of
wooden cots that can be folded and stored
when not in use; sizes standard and mini; from
£77–£150 + VAT; mattresses under £20 + VAT.
– **High chairs:** folding wooden high chairs
with a variety of seat colours, from

£48. / *Hours: Mon-Fri 9am-4.30pm; free brochure;
Delivery: p&p £10 (free on orders over £275); no credit
cards.*

Handmade Shoe Co. 🖰
64 Colston St, Bristol BS1 5AZ ☎ (0117)
9214247
Shoes – **Bespoke shoes:** made-to-measure
shoes come in eight styles for children and
a good range of colours; available by post from
the Bristol shop after customer supplies an
outline of the child's feet; the shoes allow for
some growth but can also be returned for
a new insole and sole to extend the whole shoe
by one size; shoes take up to three weeks to
make. / *Hours: Mon-Sat 10am-6pm; free catalogue;
Delivery: p&p £5 for kid's shoes; no Amex.*

Made By Marian 🖰
Old Chapel House, Grove Road, Ingham,
Norwich NR12 9ST ☎ (01692) 580 628
🖰 www.madebymarian.com
Fabric gift items for the family.
Naming gifts – **Naming gifts:** personalised
items – bath towels, shoe and swimming bags,
appliquéd fleeces, duvet covers, pillow covers,
big bibs; prices range from £6.50–£67;
gift-wrapping £3.50 per item. / *free catalogue;
Delivery: p&p £3.*

Magic Planet 🖰
5-7 Severnside Business Park, Severn Rd,
Stourport on Severn, Worcs DY13 9HT
☎ (01299) 827820 🖰 www.magic-planet.biz
Toys – **Special needs:** 'Fun & Achievement'
catalogue with books, toys and equipment
(such as bikes) for children (and adults) with
special needs. / *Hours: Mon-Fri 8.30am-5pm or
answerphone; free catalogue; Delivery: p&p extra
(10% of order amount or £6.95).*

Maia Lily Loopy 🖰
10 Christchurch Close, Arbury, Nuneaton,
Warwickshire CV10 7GD
🖰 www.maialilyloopy.co.uk/
Baby equipment – **Discount Outlets:** new but
reduced-price items, (end of line, overmakes
and over-stockings). The firm specialises in
baby essentials (blankets, bibs etc), but covers
a variety of items for 0-5s, including feeding,
travel, safety, bed and bath items, toys and
clothing. / *Hours: visits by appointment.*

Malthouse Foot Growth Measure 🖰
Ridge Lane, Kings Stag, Sturminster Newton
DT10 2DE ☎ (01258) 818080
🖰 www.malthouse-hunter.com
Mail order business; the website includes some
information on how to select shoes.
Shoes – **Foot growth gauges:** gauges (of the
types used by assistants in shoe shops with
a foot plate and strap) to enable you to check
on the growth of your kid's feet at home, price
£17.85; units can be calibrated UK-style, or
with US or European measurements. / *Delivery:
p&p included; no Amex.*

Mamas & Papas 🖰
Head Office: Colne Bridge Rd, Huddersfield
HD5 0RH ☎ Catalogue requests (01484)
438226, Store info (0870) 830 7700
🖰 www.mamasandpapas.co.uk
Large Italian brand of fashion-led products for

both mother and baby. Check the website or call for details of stockists (which include John Lewis) or superstores (nearest to London are Staines and Romford).

Maternity wear – Mid-range: stylish clothes and nightwear; mock leather trousers £35, fleece pyjamas £40; also support and nursing bras.

Baby equipment – Wheeled Transport-brands: well-known cot and pushchair brand with an emphasis on fashion: many different styles and fabric/colour combinations available; three-in-ones, travel systems and pushchairs.

Nursery decor – General stockists: best known for their pushchairs, this company also make large collections of nursery decorations and furniture.

Toys – Brand: educational and stimulating toys. / *Hours: Mon-Fri 8am-6pm, Sat 9am-5pm; free catalogue (can be mailed); Delivery: non furniture delivery 5-7 working days; furniture 2-3 weeks. ; no Amex or Solo.*

Manhattan Toy Co 🖭
The Loft, 204 Durnsford Rd, London SW19 8DR ☎ (0800) 731 2857, Mail order (08700) 129090 🖰 www.manhattantoy.com
Toys – Brand: well-designed soft toys including hand and finger puppets; one of the best options is the striking Whoozit which is tactile, soft and emits sounds. / *Hours: Mon-Fri 9am-5.30pm; free catalogue; Delivery: P&P extra under £150.*

Marco (Juveniles) Ltd
168 Shepherds Bush Market, London W12 8DF ☎ (020) 8743 6843
Primarily a child and babywear shop, with some equipment.
Baby clothes – Cheap & cheerful: the selection includes Christening clothes and ranges from socks and bootees at 50p to a communion dress for £80. / *Hours: Mon-Sat 9.30am-5.30pm (Thu noon); no Amex & no Switch.*

Margaret Ann 🖭
Milestone Cottage, Tytherington, Warminster, Wilts BA12 7AE ☎ (01985) 840520 🖰 www.margaretann.co.uk
Maternity wear – Bras and underwear: bra specialists; visits by appointment only; brands include Anita and Royce; made-to-measure service also available. / *Hours: Tue-Fri 10am-5pm, Sat 10am-2pm; online catalogue; Delivery: p&p £3.*

Marketing Mania Ltd 🖭
Unit 2 Aurattse, 53 Old Ridge Rd, London SW12 8PP ☎ (07002) 466466, Stockist enquiries line (08700) 706 060
🖰 www.goo-goo.com
Baby mail order catalogue with a number of focused, rather eclectic ranges of baby wear.
Baby clothes – Eco-friendly clothing: mini Mania wool and brushed cotton underwear – vests and bodies in either material for about £7 or £8. **– Sun-protection clothing:** 'Sposh' (known outside the UK as Ozone) nylon/Lycra and polycotton/Lycra sun protection gear (UVF 50+) caps, hats, suits and swim nappies. **Shoes – Suppliers:** comprehensive range of Bobux shoes (0-2 years) and Sole Mania (water repellent, washable suede shoes, 2-5 years).

Marks & Spencer 🖭
CENTRAL CONTACT DETAILS
☎ (0845) 302 1234
🖰 www.marksandspencer.com
BRANCHES:
(Only selected branches are listed – call the enquiry line for other outlets.)
458 Oxford St WIN 0AP
☎ (020) 7935 7954
173 Oxford St W1R 1TA
☎ (020) 7437 7722
113 Kensington High St W8
☎ (020) 7937 3711
258 Edgware Rd W2 1DU
☎ (020) 7723 5554
Only the largest stores are listed here and only the flagship Marble Arch store (458 Oxford St) holds the full range. There is also a mail order service for larger items.
Baby equipment – Stockists: travellers, carriers, all-terrain three-wheelers and other nursery equipment are stocked, in association with brands including Graco and Britax.
Nursery decor – General stockists: co-ordinating range of bed linen, curtains, rugs, wallpapers, borders and lampshades in nice bright designs that are jolly without being overpowering. The small but thorough range of furniture includes several different styles of bed (including bunks), work stations, chests, wardrobes and bookcases, all in pale beech veneer.
Baby clothes – Mid-range: all branches stock baby and children's clothes, the range depending on the size of the store. The quality is good – styling can be hit-and-miss, but with some well-designed pieces. As a general rule the younger the age group, the more successful the clothes. / *Hours: mail order Mon-Sun 8am-11pm; free catalogue; Delivery: p&p £3.50 (free for furniture and orders over £200); no credit cards.*

Howard Marshall
5 Station Rd, Gerrards Cross, Bucks SL9 8ES ☎ (01753) 882952
Toys – Outdoor items & active toys: sibling store to JJ Toys, St John's Wood High Street, with a good range of large outdoor items including TP Outdoor toys, swings, paddling pools, prams and bikes. / *Hours: Mon-Sat 9am-5.30pm.*

Marvellous Murals
44 High Street, Milton Regis, Sittingbourne, Kenton ME10 2AD ☎ (01795) 553584
🖰 www.marvellousmurals.co.uk
Nursery decor – Murals and other Decorating: hand-painted – anything from nursery designs to trompe l'oeil, individually designed to order. / *Hours: Mon-Fri 9am-5pm; answerphone; no credit cards.*

Mason Pearson Bros 🖭
37, Old Bond St, London W1X 4HL ☎ (020) 7491 2613 🖰 www.masonpearson.com
Naming gifts – Naming gifts: manufacturers of the rubber-cushion hairbrush – designed in 1885 and modernised in the 1920s! Not the cheapest on the market but probably the best. The 'Child' brush is designed to enable a child to become accustomed to the activity of brushing (although a standard pocket sized or junior brush would also be suitable, with boar

bristle recommended for fine to normal hair and boar and nylon for thicker hair). Available at good independent chemists, and Harrods, Fortnum & Mason, Selfridges and John Lewis.

The Maternity Co 🖃
42 Chiswick Lane, London W4 2JQ ☎ (020) 8995 4455 🖱 www.thematernityco.com
Maternity wear – Mid-range: this shop was set up by two new mothers frustrated at trying to find fashionable maternity wear; leading European designs; classic styles for professionals and trendy styles for all types of occasions; also accessories, tights, underwear, swimwear and gymwear. / *Hours: Mon-Sat 10am-5.30pm; online catalogue; Delivery: p&p £4.*

Maternitywear Exchange 🖃 Q
Wyevern, Cores End Road, Bourne End, Buckinghamshire SL8 5HR ☎ (01628) 851 187 🖱 www.maternityexchange.co.uk
Maternity wear – Second-hand shops: new and nearly new maternity clothes at up to 80% off recommended retail prices. Up to 5,000 garments are in stock at any one time, and the site allows searching by size, brand, type of garment, extra length, and more. The range includes nightwear and swimwear. Prices generally £10-£50. / *Hours: by appointment; all garments online; Delivery: p&p depends on weight.*

Maternus
54 Cross St, London N1 ☎ (020) 7359 5791 🖱 www.maternus.co.uk
Relocated from Dulwich Village.
Maternity wear – Mid-range: aiming for a younger look, with brands including 40 Weeks (a designer range), Fragile, Noppies, Vida Vita and Sara (all of them at 'high street' prices); the range covers casual wear, office wear, and evening wear (this last also for hire).
Baby clothes – Luxury: newborn items – expensive but cute.

Mattel UK/Fisher-Price
Vanwall Businesss Park, Vanwall Rd, Maidenhead, Berks SL6 4UB ☎ General enquiries (01628) 500303, Fisher-Price line (01628) 500302 🖱 www.mattel.com, www.fisher-price.com
Toys – Brand: one of the toy giants with names like Matchbox, Barbie and Scrabble under its umbrella; more relevant for younger kids are Disney items (including soft toy characters like Winnie the Pooh), and the extensive Fisher-Price brand (see also). Their 'Infants and Pre-School' range includes brands such as Sesame Street. / *Hours: Mon-Fri 9am-5pm.*

Mavis Klein 🖃
46 Eton Place, Eton College Rd, London NW3 2BU ☎ (020) 7483 2603
Naming gifts – Naming gifts: in-depth horoscope analysis of character and talents to enable parents to achieve a child's full potential. Mavis Klein is an author, a psychotherapist and an astrologer. / *Hours: by appt.*

Katie Mawson 🖃
9 Arthur, Penrith, Cumbria CA11 7TU ☎ (01768) 210494 🖱 www.katiemawson.com
Nursery decor – Bedding: knitted, felted or fleece cot blankets.
Baby clothes – Mid-range: charming modern selection of colourful clothing and knitwear for kids: designed to be comfortable and fun as well as practical and long-lasting; long-sleeved T-shirts, fleeces, dresses, and hats; all handmade in England; machine washable (except knitted lambswool). / *Hours: 24hr answerphone; free catalogue; Delivery: p&p £3.*

Maxi Cosi
Dorel Juvenile Group UK, Hertsmere House, Shenley Road, Borehamwood, Hertfordshire WD6 1TE ☎ (020) 8236 0707 🖱 www.maxi-cosi.com
Baby equipment – Car seat brands: manufacturers of car seats and children's safety products; no catalogues, but call for details of local stockists.

Mayfair Embroidery 🖃
5th Floor, Goodyear House, 52-56 Osnaburgh St., London NW1 3ND ☎ (020) 7388 4994
Naming gifts – Naming gifts: same-day personalisation of items (such as linens, towels and clothing), using type of any size; up to 1 inch characters £5 for up to five letters, then 70p per letter); 2 inch characters £9 for up to 5 letters, then £1.20 per letter. / *Hours: Mon-Fri 9am-5pm; Delivery: p&p extra.*

McCabe (UK) 🖃
13 East Green, Anstruther, Fife KY10 3AA ☎ (01333) 312260 🖱 www.dogdays.ndirect.co.uk/Wet-n-Dry/
Nappies – Protective bedding: the Wet'n'Dry blanket is an aid to night-time toilet training – a waterproof blanket made of absorbent cotton enclosing a waterproof but breathable polyurethane membrane designed to cover the 'danger area' of the bed, and which can be lifted off, leaving dry bedding; sanitised, but can be washed at 95°C and tumble-dried; £5 (also two larger sizes at £16 and £20). / *Hours: 24hr answerphone; free catalogue; Delivery: p&p included; no credit cards.*

Megabloks
Hampton House, Monument Business Park, Chargrove, Oxford OX44 7RW ☎ (01865) 893 240 🖱 www.megabloks.com
Toys – Educational: chunky plastic building blocks in lighter-weight plastic than the alternative (Lego), and therefore somewhat cheaper. / *Hours: Mon-Fri 9am-5.30pm.*

Melin Tregwynt 🖃
Castle Morris, Haverfordwest, Pembrokeshire SA62 5UX ☎ (01348) 891644 🖱 www.melintregwynt.co.uk
Nursery decor – Bedding: pram and cot blankets in pure new wool; traditional styling in beautiful rich colours, from brights to darks to pastels, plaids, stripes, checks and plains; cot-size, £38; pram-size, £22; co-ordinating woollen cushions and throws also available from £28. / *Hours: Mon-Fri 8.30am-5pm; free*

catalogue; Delivery: p&p £3 (orders up to £30); £4 (£30-£55); £6.50 (£55+); next day delivery £8.

Melting Hearts 🖴
77 Grandison Rd, London SW11 6LT
☎ (020) 7640 2794
🖱 www.meltinghearts.co.uk
<u>Naming gifts</u> – **Naming gifts:** gifts aimed at mothers more than the baby: for example, trimmed muslin squares and matching clothing and accessories, gift wrapped.

Membery's
1 Church Rd, London SW13 9HE ☎ (020) 8876 2910
Barnes store where some of the stock is designed by owner Sally Membery who also supplies other stores, including Harrods.
<u>Baby clothes</u> – **Luxury:** clothes for all occasions, but with some special occasion wear, such as traditional party dresses and pinafores; also Christening, bridesmaid and page boy outfits. Also some casual rompers. Brands stocked include Petit Bateau, Marese, Kenzo, Catamini; IKKS; Berlingot and Osh Kosh; dresses from £24, romper suit £17; accessories from Ikks and others.
<u>Toys</u> – **General stockists:** toys include rattles, teddy bears, soft toys and mobiles. / Hours: Mon-Sat 10am-5.30pm.

Merlin Shoes
44 Westow St, London SE19 3AH ☎ (020) 8771 5194
<u>Shoes</u> – **Suppliers:** children's shoe specialist; brands include Start-rite, Salamander, Ecco, Rhino, Sketchers, Birkenstock and Hi-Tech. / Hours: Mon-Sat 9.30am-5.30pm.

Merriott Radiators 🖴
Davis Rd, Clonmel, Co Tipperary, Ireland
☎ (01942) 262466
🖱 www.merriottradiators.com
<u>Nursery decor</u> – **Safety items:** manufacturers of low surface temperature radiators designed for use in places like nurseries and kindergartens. The rounded edges are designed for increased safety and easy cleaning. A variety of lengths and heights is available plus three depths. Radiators are generally custom-made. Contact the sales office for further details; although based in Ireland, the phone number is for Leigh, where the Customer Service office used to be. / Hours: Mon-Fri 9am-5pm; no invoice before delivery .

MES (Music Education Supplies) 🖴
101 Banstead Road South, Sutton, Surrey SM2 5LH ☎ (020) 8770 3866
<u>Books, music & videos</u> – **Music tapes:** a good selection of music tapes and CDs, including most of the A&C Black range, which are of good quality and designed for use in nurseries and schools. Also the Playsong range, and baby titles like Babies Make Music! and Rainbow Music for Babies and Tots. / Hours: Mon-Fri 9am-5pm; free colour; Delivery: £5 under £200; no credit cards.

Midnight Mushroom 🖴
123a Gloucester Terrace, London W2 3HB
☎ (020) 7724 7311
🖱 www.midnightmushroom.co.uk

<u>Nursery decor</u> – **Accessories:** design and produce highly decorative, child-safe mushroom-shaped night lights for continuous unattended use; suitable for all ages in a range of colours, £27.30; also money boxes and wall-mountable lights in the same designs; also marine lighthouses designs available.
<u>Toys</u> – **General stockists:** money boxes, hand-crafted wooden bookends, and a children's book continuing the theme of mushrooms and rabbits. / Hours: 24hr answerphone, visits by appointment; free information sheet; Delivery: p&p extra.

Miki House
107 Walton St, London SW3 3HP ☎ (020) 7838 0006 🖱 www.mikihouse.co.uk
Owned by the same company as Young England (see also); mainly Japanese items with an emphasis on the 'Hello Kitty' genre.
<u>Baby clothes</u> – **Mid-range:** a Japanese brand of colourful children's clothes is stocked here; also accessories and some ski gear. / Hours: Mon-Sat 10am-5.30pm (Sat 6pm).

Millie's Cupboard 🖴
PO Box 138, Wantage OX12 0XT
☎ (01235) 868422
<u>Baby clothes</u> – **Sleepwear:** traditional children's nightclothes and accessories (the former with smocking or embroidery).

Milliemoos 🖴 Q
Sandpiper Fibbards Rd, Brockenhurst SO42 7RD ☎ (01590) 623273
🖱 www.milliemoos.com
<u>Baby clothes</u> – **Second-hand shops:** new and nearly new discount designer and brand name European kids clothes (including Oilily), Osh Kosh, international labels, Christening wear and baby equipment. The site's a bit impenetrable, but offers a good selection of secondhand items, searchable, for example, by season.

Millthorne Chairs 🖴
10 Fore St, Hartland, Nr Bideford, North Devon EX39 6BD ☎ (01237) 441590
Mail order business with Devon showroom, making a range of chairs and stools for adults as well as children in a choice of beech and elm, or ash and elm; larger items can be made to measure.
<u>Baby equipment</u> – **High chairs:** sturdy high chairs with or without trays.
<u>Nursery decor</u> – **Furniture:** traditional Windsor chairs with painted decorations in a water-resistant oil finish; a wide range of decorative back designs including birds, animals or initials is available; prices range from £12- £400. / Hours: Mon-Sat 8.30am-6pm; free catalogue; no credit cards.

Mindstretchers 🖴
The Warehouse, Rossie Place, Auchterarder, Perthshire PH3 1AJ ☎ (01764) 664 409
🖱 www.mindstretchers.co.uk
Originally an educational consultancy, now designs, produces and sources a range of resources to motivate and inspire children and adults to learn, focusing on a multi-sensory environment.
<u>Toys</u> – **Educational:** categories in the brochure include Play Naturally – The

Younger Years, with items like rattles, Lamaze toys, and a turning wheeled toy for walking children to push. Under the Gathering and Transporting section is a charming collection of containers, and under Singing and Sound-making some fun instruments, including the plastic tube Boomwhackers. / *free catalogue; Delivery: p&p £8; no credit cards.*

Mini Boden 🔲

Customer Service Dept, Boden Central, Meridian West, Meridian Business Park, Leicester LE19 1PX ☎ (0845) 677 5000
🔸 www.boden.co.uk
The junior operation of the extremely popular Boden mail order catalogue business.
Baby clothes – Mid-range: large range of 100% natural fabrics designed to endure hard washing and tumble drying; all baby clothes have press studs under the crotch, baby T-shirts and sweatshirts have extra wide neck openings; romper suits 12-24 months, £14; crawlers £10; baggy trousers for six months £16; hooded sweatshirts around £15.

Mini Kin 🔲

22 Broadway Parade, Crouch End, London N8 9DE ☎ (020) 8341 6898
🔸 www.mini-kin.com
Crouch End shop which operates a baby list for those hoping for specific gifts for the new arrival.
Baby equipment – Stockists: a range of designer and off beat items is available, from Bug-a-Boo and high chairs to potties.
Nappies – Suppliers-Eco friendly disposables: stockists of Moltex Oko.
Naming gifts – Naming gifts: a range of interesting options including illustrations from the Illustration Cupboard as well as more practical items.
Hairdressers – Hairdressers: aiming to be a 'kinder' salon of hair, skin and body therapy for children, haircuts £12; decor is on a jungle theme; products include 'nit' treatments, silver baby's first curl holders, little hairbrush sets, a range of toiletries and cosmetics (Earth Friendly Baby, Aromakids) plus Christies children's towels, bathrobes and similar. / *Hours: Mon-Sat 9.30am-5.30pm, Sun 11am-5pm; no Amex.*

Minor Matters 🔲

54 St Marys Row, Mosely Village, Birmingham B13 8JG ☎ (0121) 449 3553
🔸 www.minormatters.co.uk
Midlands-based online retailer of designer furniture and equipment: ranges are primarily Baby Jou, Stokke, Saplings and Teutonia.
Baby equipment – Cots.
Nursery decor – Furniture: the ranges they cover include a number of less usual, high quality items. **– Wallpaper & fabrics:** stockists of dutch brand Bébé Jou: wallpapers, blinds, fabric, furniture and accessories.

Miriam Stoppard Lifetime

Greencoat House, Francis St, London SW1P 1DH ☎ (020) 7630 1400
🔸 www.miriamstoppard.com
Now a brand rather than just a doctor or even plain old author. The website publicises a range of products, some available exclusively though specified outlets, some produced in conjunction with well-known manufacturers such as Tomy.
Baby clothes – Mid-range: baby Clothing Layette, available exclusively at Debenhams.
Toys – Educational: a range of first toys – a rattle, "discovery ball" and activity centre for instance. / *Hours: Mon-Fri 9am-6pm.*

Mischief Kids 🔲

22 Market St, Leigh, Lancashire WN7 1DS ☎ (01942) 679530
🔸 www.mischiefkids.co.uk, www.christening-clothes.com
Shop in the north west which sells mail order via its website.
Baby clothes – Luxury: labels including Moschino, Quicksilver, Miniman and Marese; items for newborns upwards; prices start from £15–£20 for a designer T-shirt, and there are also seasonal sales. **– Christening gowns:** christening robes, shawls, shoes, hats, bibs and socks; all made in England; all items (except the socks) in pure silk; accessories trimmed to match; prices from about £90.
Shoes – Suppliers: a range of leather pre-walkers; silk and velvet shoes for Christenings; also Doc Martens, Moschino and Naturino. / *Hours: Mon-Sat 9.30am-5pm; online catalogue.*

Modern Baby 🔲

Brooksby, 70 Tamworth Rd, Hertford, Herts SG13 7DN ☎ (01992) 505976
🔸 www.modernbaby.co.uk
Nappies – Reusable stockists - brands & singles: shaped cotton or pre-fold nappies; sizes from newborn up; starter packs £25 (for five nappies, two covers and 25 biodegradable liners); also swim nappies, nappy liners and tote bags. / *free brochure; No Amex & no Diners.*

Moltex Oko

🔸 www.moltex.de
Nappies – Eco-friendly disposables brands: a German nappy brand made of recycled, unbleached cellulose with mainstream levels of absorbency and features including Velcro style fastenings, cotton-like inner and textile style outer, leg cuffs and 'fluid repellant' breathable sides; it contains a small proportion of absorbent gels but not TBT and the nappies are recommended in Germany for babies with eczema; the website is in German – UK suppliers include Spirit of Newborn, Natural Baby Company, Eco-babes and Cuddlebabes.

Mon Choisie

131 Streatham High Rd, London SW16 1HJ ☎ (020) 8664 6874
Baby clothes – Luxury: designer clothing; shoes from Buckle My Shoe; dresses £10-£200. / *Hours: Mon-Sat 9.30am-6pm (Fri 7pm).*

Monbebe

🔸 www.monbebe.co.uk
Italian baby equipment manufacturer, best-known in the UK for its car seats.
Baby equipment – Wheeled Transport-brands: buggies, prams, carrycots, pushchairs and joggers, in a variety of styles, combinations and colours. **– Car seat brands:** available in a number of styles. **– Buggy accessories:** matching sun canopies, rain covers, foot muffs and change bags.

<u>Nursery decor</u> – **Furniture:** change units with shelves, removable baths and changing mats. / *Hours: Mon-Fri 8.30am-5.30pm (Fri 4.30pm).*

The Monogrammed Linen Shop 🖻

168 Walton St, London SW3 2JL ☎ (020) 7589 4033 🖰 www.monogrammedlinen shop.co.uk

<u>Nursery decor</u> – **Bedding:** cot linen embroidered to your specification (the shop has standard patterns such as stars, penguins, bears or ducks) in addition to monogramming; other items include children's towels, bathrobes, slippers, baby blankets and shawls.

<u>Baby clothes</u> – **Traditional:** traditional styles in natural fibres, many hand-smocked; knitwear in wool, cotton and cashmere.

– **Christening gowns:** wide range of gowns, accessories and other items; gowns from £99; also rompers that are suitable for Christenings. / *Hours: Mon-Sat 10am-6pm ; free catalogue or online; Delivery: p&p £8.50.*

Monsoon

CENTRAL CONTACT DETAILS
☎ (020) 7313 3000
🖰 www.monsoon.co.uk
BRANCHES:
(Only selected branches are listed – call the enquiry line for other outlets.)
264 Oxford St W1 9DD
☎ (020) 7499 2578
5–6 James St WC2 8BH
☎ (020) 7379 3623
5 Barkers Arcade, Kensington High St W8 4EP
☎ (020) 7376 0366
1a Hampstead High St NW3 1PR
☎ (020) 7435 1726

This well-known high street chain does not have a specific maternity range but many of their clothes are suitable for pregnancy. All the shops stock children's clothes.

<u>Baby clothes</u> – **Mid-range:** predominantly cotton clothing with the brand's very distinctive look; dresses from about, £20. / *Hours: Mon-Sun 10am-8pm.*

Moonbeam Music 🖻

The Old Repeater Station, Libberton, South Lanarkshire ML11 8LX ☎ (01555) 841168
🖰 www.mrboom.co.uk

<u>Books, music & videos</u> – **Music tapes:** 'Mr Boom', a Scottish musician (aka Andy Monroe), does shows for children (can do them in London) and produces four entertaining tapes with his own songs and music, including 'Singalong with Mr Boom', £6 each. / *Delivery: p&p included.*

Moonlighting

11 Leopold Rd, London SW19 7BB ☎ (020) 8947 3932

<u>Toys</u> – **General stockists:** mobiles and soft toys (from Russ), books and toys with a difference, fillers for party bags and stationery (for kids and adults); modern rather than traditional styles. / *Hours: Mon-Sat 9.30am-6pm.*

Morley's of Bicester 🖻

Furniture for Early Years, Arkwright Rd, Bicester, Oxfordshire OX26 4UU ☎ (01869) 320 320 🖰 www.morleys.co.uk

<u>Nursery decor</u> – **Furniture:** truly sturdy furniture and storage, in a range of styles, suitable for children over 18 months old; specialists in nursery and classroom furniture.

Morleys of Brixton

472-488 Brixton Rd, London SW9 8EH ☎ (020) 7274 6246

Brixton's central department store.

<u>Baby clothes</u> – **Cheap & cheerful:** adams concession withing the shop; with their own-label clothing. / *Hours: Mon-Fri 9.30am-6pm, Sat 9am-6pm.*

Moroccan Link 🖻

5 Bingley Road, Bradford, West Yorkshire BD9 6HR ☎ (01274) 547973
🖰 www.moroccanlink.com

<u>Baby equipment</u> – **Cots:** an importer of Moses baskets, wooden cots and cribs, plus associated handicrafts. The product range can be inspected on the website.

Mothercare 🖻

CENTRAL CONTACT DETAILS
☎ Order line (08453) 304030, (01923) 210210, Catalogue request line (01923) 206139
🖰 www.mothercare.com
BRANCHES:
(Only selected branches are listed – call the enquiry line for other outlets.)
461 Oxford St W1R 1DB
☎ (020) 7629 6621
316 North End Rd SW6 1NE
☎ (020) 7381 6387
26 King's Mall Shopping Centre W6 0PZ
☎ (020) 8600 2860
Brent Cross Shopping Centre NW4 3FD
☎ (020) 8202 5377
38 High Rd N22 6BX
☎ (020) 8888 6920
77-78 Whitgift Square CR0 1UR
☎ (020) 8686 2785
Unit A1, Retail Park, Mortlake Rd TW9 4DU
☎ (020) 8878 3758

With over 250 branches nationwide (30 or so of which are in London), most mothers end up in one of the stores sooner or later. Moreover the chain is widely credited with 'getting its act together' more of late and bringing its range and 'offering' into the 21st century. The mail order catalogue (Mothercare Direct) has a number of useful checklists and the chain has its own account card and 'Nursery Plan' to help you spread costs. The selection in the catalogue is often greater than that in the stores. The website offers general parenting advice and interactive guides to choosing pushchairs and car seats, and is one of the bigger online baby outlets in the UK.

<u>Maternity wear</u> – **Cheap & cheerful:** an acceptable but not particularly stylish range, about half in natural fabrics; roll neck cotton jumper £20, denim skirt £28; also underwear and nightwear. – **Bras and underwear:** a comprehensive range of maternity underwear including at least ten varieties of nursing and support bras.

Baby equipment – Stockists: one of the chain's better points – among a wide variety of branded and own-brand items anything you want is probably here: cots, bedding (in natural and manmade fibres), feeding and bathing equipment and a good variety of safety harnesses and locks.
Nursery decor – General stockists: co-ordinated items including bedding, paint, friezes and ready-pasted wallpaper, plus a good range of mobiles.
Baby clothes – Cheap & cheerful: all own-brand clothing in a range of styles: a reasonable proportion are made from cotton and natural fibres; also items for premature babies; baby suit £12, twill dungarees £11.
Toys – Pre-school specialists: the emphasis is on the big names such as Fisher-Price, Tomy, Chicco and Little Tikes but the company also makes own-brand indoor and outdoor items. / Hours: mostly Mon-Sat 9am-5.30pm, Sun 11am-5pm; catalogue £1; Delivery: p&p £4.

Mothernature ⌨
Acorn House, Brixham Ave, Cheadle Hulme, Cheshire SK8 6JG ☎ (0161) 485 7359
⌂ www.mothernaturebras.co.uk
A company which used to stock a range of breast-feeding equipment, but has in recent years focused just on underwear.
Maternity wear – Bras and underwear: this company claims to offer 'one of the most comprehensive ranges of maternity underwear available in the UK but also does swimwear, sleep bras and maternity belts and supports; bras sizes: 32-46 inches up to cup J; brands include Berlei, Emma Jané, Royce, Bravado and Anita at an average price of £20; helpful service and fitting advice. / Hours: Mon-Fri 9am-5pm; free catalogue; Delivery: p&p extra; no Amex.

Mountain Buggy ⌨
Mill Farm, Fairmile, Ottery St. Mary, Devon EX11 1LS ☎ (0140) 4815555
⌂ www.mountainbuggy.co.uk
Baby equipment – Wheeled
Transport-brands: top of the range all-terrain prams and pushchairs by mail order (or call for details of stockists). The most expensive but probably best one weighs just 8kg and is designed for easy manoeuvrability; it has pneumatic tyres, a two-position zip hammock and a removable washable pocket. The 'Mountain Terrain' can be adapted for children with special needs. Accessories include car seat clip attachment, clip-on carrycot, sleeping bag, shade extender, UV shade cloth, pvc storm cover, handlebar extensions and a travel bag (£396). There is also a double buggy ('The Double') which includes a sun hood and storage basket (£545), and a swivel-wheeled buggy ('The Urban', £439). / Hours: 24hr answerphone; free catalogue; Delivery: p&p included.

Mozzee
☎ (020) 7278 3636 ⌂ www.mozzee.co.uk
Baby equipment – High chairs: designers of a luxury, funky, '60s-pod-style high chair. See the website or call for stockists.

Muddy Puddles ⌨
Hingston Farm, Bigbury, Kingsbridge, Devon TQ7 4BE ☎ (01548) 810477
⌂ www.muddypuddles.co.uk
Baby clothes – Mid-range: range of clothing for active children including sweatshirts, T-shirts and romper suits. – Outdoorwear: brightly-coloured children's waterproofs designed to withstand a reasonable amount of dirt; double-stitched taped seams, hood, protected zip and elasticated ankles and wrists. Range includes all-in-ones up to 3 years (£22.50), trousers, jackets, bibs & braces, Sou'Wester hats, wellies, gloves and waterproof duffel bags with wet and dry sections. / Hours: 24hr orderline; Customer Service Mon-Fri 9am-5pm; free catalogue or online; Delivery: p&p £3.

The Mulberry Bush Limited ⌨
Newbridge Lodge, Billingshurst Rd, Broadbridge Heath, Horshaw, West Sussex RH12 3LN ☎ (01403) 754400
⌂ www.mulberrybush.co.uk
Nursery decor – Accessories: wide range of nursery items, including height measures (£25), storage hangers, pegs, small chests, mats, snuggle sacks and novelty umbrellas.
Toys – Traditional toys: a wide range of well-designed, distinctive, mostly wooden toys ranging from a pull-along ladybird at £4 to a farm at £75; the focus is on smaller items – other examples include soft toys, puzzles, mobiles and doll's houses. / Hours: Mon-Fri 9am-6pm; free catalogue; Delivery: p&p £2.50 (orders up to £12); Visa, Mastercard, Switch, debit &cheque.

Mum & Me ♀
61 High St, Teddington TW11 8HA ☎ (020) 8255 0073
Baby equipment – Second-hand: lots of good quality, well-known makes of equipment. – Hire: rental service: car seats, cots, high chairs, buggies and travel cots.
Baby clothes – Second-hand shops: well-known labels, including a number of designer items.
Toys – Second-hand shops: games, toys, books and videos of all description; suitable for all ages. / Hours: Mon-Fri 9.30am-4pm (Sat 5.30pm).

Mum's Delight ⌨
Mill Barn, Mill St, Necton, Swaffham, Norfolk PE37 8EN ☎ (01760) 723178
⌂ www.mumsdelight.co.uk
Baby equipment – Discount Outlets: formerly known as Baby Pages, a mail order company offering competitive prices on prams and pushchairs, cots, and accessories from well-known names. Clothing for children up to the age of four is sold on site, but not by mail order. / Hours: Mon-Sat 10am-5pm.

Mummy Can I Have ⌨
93 Clare Road, Maidenhead, Berkshire SL6 4DN ☎ Customer Services (01628) 626 162, Order Line (0870) 420 3044
⌂ www.mummycanihave.co.uk
Toys – Traditional toys: an attractive selection of largely European toys in natural materials from brands including Vilac, haba and Erzi – wooden books, puzzles, pull- and

pushalongs, rattles, stacking toys, and ride-on items. / *Hours: 24 hour orderline, Customer Services 9.30am-6pm, Mon-Fri.*

Mums 2 Be ⌂

CENTRAL CONTACT DETAILS
☎ (020) 8332 6506
⌂ www.mums-2-be.co.uk
3 Mortlake Terrace, Mortlake Rd TW9 3DT
☎ (020) 8332 6506
157 Lower Richmond Rd SW15 1HH
☎ (020) 8789 0329
Wimbledon SW19

Until 2004 this name was just associated with a single shop in Kew. At that time the firm took over the two 'Bumpsadaisy' shops in Putney and Wimbledon.
<u>Maternity wear</u> – **Mid-range:** all kinds of maternity clothing including leisure, business and swimwear, a bra fitting service and a made-to-measure and alteration service for converting non-maternity clothes into maternity clothes and vice versa; skirts £35-£60. – **Hire:** hire of evening and formal maternity garments from £60. / *Hours: Mon-Sat 10am-5.30pm; Delivery: p&p extra; restricted service; no Amex.*

My Puku ⌂

PO Box 46831, London SW11 1YJ ☎ (020) 7585 0792 ⌂ www.mypuku.com
<u>Nursery decor</u> – **Bedding:** satin-bound blankets either patterned or classic air cell.
<u>Baby clothes</u> – **Christening gowns:** fine 'heirloom' shawls, available round or square. – **Knitwear:** baby wraps, matinee cardigans, jumpers, leggings, beanies and booties all in New Zealand merino wool (which is particularly durable as well as soft). Also sun hats, long- and short-sleeved T-shirts, leggings and sun dresses in 95% eco-friendly New Zealand cotton. Jumpers are around £30-£37. / *Hours: Mon-Fri 9am-5pm; flexible; answerphone; online catalogue; Delivery: p&p usually £4.*

Myriad ⌂

The Buckman Building, 43 Southampton Rd, Ringwood, Hampshire BH24 1HE ☎ (01725) 517085 ⌂ www.myriadonline.co.uk
<u>Toys</u> – **Traditional toys:** colour-washed, handmade wooden items from distinctive rattles to farmyard or nativity figures – 15-piece shepherd set £75 (individual figures typically £8-£12); (for slightly older kids craft materials, books and musical instruments; brands include Ostheimer and Spiel and Holz educational brands from Germany). / *Hours: 9am-noon or 24hr answerphone; free catalogue; Delivery: p&p £4.50.*

Namemark ⌂

PO Box 1792, Christchurch, Dorset BH23 4YR
<u>Baby clothes</u> – **Nametapes:** self-adhesive 'WhoShoe' name labels for the inside of shoes and trainers; £5 for 20 labels. (Recommended by Instep.) / *Delivery: p&p included.*

Nametapes Direct ⌂

Permark House, 4 Lavender Gardens, Harrow Weald, Middx. HA3 6DD ☎ (020) 8954 6333 ⌂ www.nametapesdirect.com

<u>Baby clothes</u> – **Nametapes:** iron-on and woven nametapes.

Nappi Nippas ⌂

PO Box 35, Penzance TR18 4YE ☎ (01736) 351263
<u>Nappies</u> – **Non-disposable accessories:** two of the best products of their type: Nappi Nippas are a safe alternative to pins for fastening terry nappies and consist of a T-shaped, three-way clip that stretches and grips onto the front of the nappy; fit any nappy and any size baby; £3.50 for three; money back if not satisfied (also on sale in John Lewis). Nappi Nikkas are soft cotton blend pull-up pants with a waterproof lining in five sizes from newborn to extra large and cost £6.50. (Also sell Nippa Clippas, nail clippers for babies and infants, £5.95). / *free catalogue; Delivery: p&p 75p; no credit cards.*

Nappy Cakes UK ⌂

Knights House, 142A Knights Hill, West Norwood, London SE27 0SR ☎ (07957) 556 316 ⌂ www.nappycakesuk.com
<u>Naming gifts</u> – **Naming gifts:** a concept imported from the US – a tiered wedding cake style baby gift made up of quality nappies and items like bibs, comb & brush set, teddies, teething rings, rattles, soothers, booties and bottles, in different colours, sizes and themes.

Nappy Head ⌂

Icknield House, 3 Icknield Road, Luton, Bedfordshire LU3 2NY ☎ (01582) 513 630 ⌂ www.nappyhead.co.uk
<u>Baby clothes</u> – **Mid-range:** rather funnier than average, wisecrack logo T-shirts, bibs and so on, size 0-24 months.

Nappysaurus ⌂

8 Anston Close, Lower Earley, Reading RG6 4AQ ☎ (0118) 9549549 ⌂ www.nappysaurus.com
<u>Nappies</u> – **Reusable stockists - brands & singles:** fleece wraps for use with cloth nappies, and the materials to make your own if you prefer, from a business run by a work-at-home mum.

The National Forest Company ⌂

Enterprise Glade, Bath Lane, Moira, Swadlincote, Derbyshire DE12 6BD ☎ (01283) 551211 ⌂ www.nationalforest.org
<u>Naming gifts</u> – **Naming gifts:** allows you to sponsor a tree, attend the tree planting (in the autumn) or even plant it. You may also be able to choose the tree though they are not usually individually dedicated. Each tree costs £25 a year (minimum five years) to adopt, or you can plant a tree for a one-off payment of £25; the adopter also gets a personalised certificate and magazine. / *Hours: Mon-Thu 9am-5.30pm, Fri 9am-5pm; no credit cards.*

The Natural Baby Company ⌂

PO Box 76, Ryde PO33 3XH ☎ (01983) 810925 ⌂ www.naturalbabycompany.com
<u>Nappies</u> – **Suppliers-Eco friendly disposables:** deliveries of eco-friendly

disposables; unbleached Moltex or gel-free Tushies, plus Tushies baby wipes. A pack of 40 small Tushies is £8.30+ £3.50 delivery, or £33 for 160 (delivery free within London); Moltex Mini £10 for 58 or £37.50 for a box of 232; free sample nappy with brochure. / *Hours: 9.30am-5pm, 24hr answerphone; free brochure; Delivery: £3.50.*

Natural Child 🖃
Lower Stanley Farm, Gretton, Cheltenham GL54 5HQ ☎ (01242) 620445
🖰 www.naturalchild.co.uk
Mail-order suppliers of eco-friendly mother and baby items.
Baby clothes – Eco-friendly clothing: one or two basics (e.g. sleepsuits).
Nappies – Reusable stockists - multiple brands.

Natural Collection 🖃
9a Monmouth Place, Bath BA1 2DQ
☎ (01225) 40 40 20, Orderline (0870) 331 333, Customer service (0870) 331 3335
🖰 www.naturalcollection.com
Mail order business where the focus is on eco-friendly, chemical-free products.
Nursery decor – Bedding: organic cot sheets in unbleached cotton, from £8.
Baby clothes – Mid-range. – Eco-friendly clothing: organic cotton pyjamas, babygrows, socks and tights all in 'natural' colours; prices from £3.50 for a hat; for ages 0-5.
Nappies – Reusable stockists - brands & singles: "Traditional terry nappies with modern features" – Velcro tabs, flushable liners and elasticated legs to "ensure minimum leakage"; pure brushed unbleached cotton nappies, cotton nappy inserts, waterproof overpants, paper liners; 'Nappy Fresh' a hypoallergenic, enzyme and chlorine-free sanitiser) and cleansing wipes, £4.50 (box of 60). – **Suppliers-Eco friendly disposables:** stockists of Moltex Oko nappies; from £9.50 for 18 mini size (four sizes available). / *Hours: daily 9am-8pm; free catalogue or online; Delivery: p&p £3.95 for order up to £100; Free for over £100 in UK; no Amex.*

Natural Mat Company 🖃
99 Talbot Rd, London W11 2AT ☎ (020) 7985 0474 🖰 www.naturalmat.com
Originally solely a website retailer, now with a shop in Notting Hill.
Baby equipment – Cots: one of the most intelligently designed and best-looking cots on the market – at a price. It comes in either black American Walnut (with Canadian maple) or solid pine, and can be converted to a child's bed and in due course to a desk. Prices from £1,750. Also handmade willow cribs with a domed hood and a folding wooden stand.
– **Lambskins:** extra-large American lambskin fleece trimmed to 3/4", or medium-sized Australian 1" deep fleece; both machine-washable. – **Specialist mattress suppliers:** range of handcrafted infant mattresses made in Devon from renewable resources: The Coco mat (lightweight, tufted in mite-resistant lambswool, wrapped around a coir – to absorb moisture – core); The Latex mat – for older babies (the latex sandwiched between two layers of coir, finished in the lambswool); and The Mohair mat (Chinese

horsetail hair sandwiched between coir, with mohair tufting). The matresses are covered in unbleached cotton herringbone ticking and are naturally fire retardant; three standard sizes or made to measure, with prices from £65 for a coco crib mat.
Nursery decor – Bedding: the range includes unbleached Scandinavian waffle blankets, unbleached Welsh lambswool blankets and bedclothes in combed cotton percale and pure linen; fitted linen cot sheet £43, merino wool blanket £43. – **Furniture:** modern, functional and stylish range of contemporary nursery items – as well as cots and cot beds, changing units and cupboards.
Naming gifts – Naming gifts: linen can be embroidered in pink, blue or brown, at £1.50 per letter; for £4.50 will gift wrap orders. / *Hours: Mon-Fri 9am-6pm, Sat 10am-4pm; free catalogue; Delivery: £4.50 under £50, £9.50 over £50; cots by separate quote.*

Natural Wisdom 🖃
🖰 www.natural-wisdom.com
Nappies – Potty training: a website which can be "your comprehensive resource for natural infant hygiene, also known as Elimination Communication". It also sells the (American) author's book on the subject.

Nature Botts 🖃
60 Bath Rd, Swindon SN1 4AY ☎ (0845) 226 2186 🖰 www.naturebotts.co.uk
Nappies – Suppliers-Eco friendly disposables: stockists of Moltex Öko nappies, plus Moltex baby wipes and other supplies, unperfumed nappy sacks and organic cotton wool (free from chlorine) available in balls, pleats and cotton buds.

Nature Boy & Girl (Naty)
Gamla Värmdövägen 10, 131 37 Nacka, Sweden ☎ +46 8 644 9696 🖰 www.naty.com
Nappies – Eco-friendly disposables brands: 70% of the nappy is biodegradable, compostable cellulose and non-plastics (GM-free cornstarch and maize products), the other 30% the usual non-biodegradable 'super-absorbent'; normal nappies are around 70% non-biodegradable so this is greener than mainstream alternatives but not as green as its most zealous competitors. Four sizes (4kg-25kg), from £5.65. The firm also makes 100% biodegradable nappy sacks. Stocked by Sainsbury's, Tesco and Waitrose.

Nature's Baby 🖃
PO Box 2995, London NW2 1DW ☎ (020) 8905 5661
Nappies – Reusable stockists - brands & singles: sole UK suppliers of the Bumpkins brand – available either as all-in-ones or as a two-piece system – which claims to be hardwearing and highly waterproof. The shaped all-in-ones have a coated polyester outer-coating with 100% cotton flannelette liner and come in three sizes (plus two larger ones for bed-wetters). The two-piece system comprises a shaped polyester waterproof cover with T-shaped flannel nappy. Extra absorbency inserts are available with biodegradable paper liners. A two-piece sample pack is £12.50 for a nappy cover and two nappies, a one-piece

pack in white costs £7.50 + £1p&p (designs cost £1 extra).

Nature's Hug 🐾

PO Box 1259, London SW1V 4BR ☎ (0800) 161 3713, (020) 7233 6805
🖳 www.natureshug.co.uk
<u>Toys</u> – **Comforters:** blankets for use in cot, pushchair or car in 100% cotton filled with buckwheat, resulting in a "hugging" sensation for the baby. It can also be heated in a microwave (or briefly in a conventional oven), warming the baby for about an hour.

Natures Cocoons 🐾

17 Rodborough Avenue, Stroud GL5 3RR
☎ (0845) 458 9550
🖳 www.naturescocoons.co.uk
<u>Naming gifts</u> – **Naming gifts:** alternative hampers containing flower remedies, homeopathy, aromatherapy, organic foods and natural bodycare items, plus information on how to use them.

Naturino

64 High St, Reigate, Surrey RH2 9AY
☎ (01737) 221011 🖳 www.naturino.com
Showcase store for the Naturino brand in the UK.
<u>Shoes</u> – **Brands:** italian brand which claims that wearing its shoes is "like walking on sand", and which – on its website – makes quite a feature of the feet-friendliness of its products. / *Hours: Mon-Sat 9am-5.30pm.*

NCT Maternity Sales 🐾

239 Shawbridge St, Glasgow G43 1QN
☎ (0870) 112 1120, Breatfeeding helpline (0870) 444 8708 🖳 www.nctms.co.uk
The direct sales branch of the NCT, where products for the catalogue have in some cases been designed or commissioned specifically for the NCT (Mava is the brand name). Also an intelligent selection of books on parenting, breast-feeding, etc. The idea is to include useful items not easily found elsewhere so the range on offer changes as innovations are picked up by mainstream shops.
<u>Maternity wear</u> – **Mid-range:** two items adapted for breast-feeding mothers – a fleece top and a rugby shirt; also swimwear and nightwear; designer wear from Sweden.
– **Bras and underwear:** 'Mava' drop cup or zip bras (the Mava 3 is the best-seller), not the prettiest range but recommended for comfort, is available in white, ivory and black. A fitting and guidance service is available from 200 agents throughout the country (call for details); also Mava knickers and bra accessories (extenders).
<u>Baby equipment</u> – **Stockists:** a variety of small accessories and equipment such as medicine dispensers, cat nets, room thermometers and wash bags, plus bathing, feeding, changing and travel items. – **Second-hand:** details of NCT Nearly new sales are listed on the main NCT website's news page.
<u>Baby clothes</u> – **Mid-range:** long traditional cotton gowns and waterproof splash suits for toddlers, designed to last.
<u>Toys</u> – **Pre-school specialists:** small range of smaller items: rattles, mobiles, jigsaws; stimulating black and white toys and colourful

wooden toys. / *Hours: Mon-Fri 9am-5pm; Helpline 8am-10pm; free catalogue; Delivery: p&p extra; No Amex & No Solo.*

NES Arnold 🐾

Novara House, Excelsior Rd, Ashby Park, Ashby De La Zouche, Leics LE65 1NG
☎ (0845) 120 4525 🖳 www.nesarnold.co.uk
<u>Toys</u> – **Nursery suppliers:** mail order company selling educational and rehabilitation items, including musical instruments and children's furniture; a limited range is also available from website. / *Hours: Mon-Fri 8.15am-5pm; free catalogue; Delivery: £6.95.*

Never Never Land 🐾

3 Midhurst Parade, London N10 3EJ ☎ (020) 8883 3997
<u>Toys</u> – **Traditional toys:** a tiny shop with some attractive, old-fashioned toys. / *Hours: closed Mon, Thu, Sun - other days 10am-5pm; free catalogue; Delivery: p&p extra.*

Newham Bookshop 🐾

745-747 Barking Rd, London E13 9ER
☎ (020) 8552 9993
<u>Books, music & videos</u> – **Bookshops:** there are separate bookshops for adults and children within the centre, which has strong links with local schools, and organises regular readings and author visits. Books for children of all ages are stocked, and there are titles for parents on childcare, education and children's health. / *Hours: Tue-Fri 9.30am-5pm, Sat 10am-5pm; Delivery: p&p approx £3.50.*

Next 🐾

CENTRAL CONTACT DETAILS
☎ (0845) 600 7000, Head office (0845) 4567777
🖳 www.next.co.uk
BRANCHES:
(Only selected branches are listed – call the enquiry line for other outlets.)
Marble Arch, 526-28 Oxford St W1N 9HH
☎ (020) 7355 4929
327-329 Oxford St W1R 1HA
☎ (020) 7409 2746
50-54 Kensington High St W8
☎ (020) 7938 4211
Next Directory: PO 4000 S97 3ET
☎ (0845) 600 7333
About half of this high street chain's London stores carry children's clothing, but the stock of maternity and nursery decor items is generally more limited. Practically all of the stock available in the stores is also available through the well-run catalogue and online Next Directory (where there is a greater emphasis on items like cots, beds and high chairs).
<u>Maternity wear</u> – **Mid-range:** not the most exciting range but reasonably fashionable. A small selection in a variety of fabrics, mainly classic maternity wear in dark shades such as big shirts, jumpers, trousers and dresses and also trousers and skirts with expandable panels.
<u>Nursery decor</u> – **General stockists:** co-ordinating ranges of contemporary designs which tend towards bright colours and big patterns; bedding, curtains, wallpaper, lighting paint, cushions, borders, stencils with baby ranges.
<u>Baby clothes</u> – **Mid-range:** a collection with seasonal ups and downs but generally lots of

right colours and pastels; typically includes good trendy basics such as mini fleeces and dungarees that are quite sporty; jersey features heavily as do pretty prints, dresses and cardigans; most garments are pure cotton; cute accessories include hats, socks and shoes. / *Hours: mostly Mon-Sat 10am-7pm (Thu 8pm), Sun noon-6pm; catalogue £3.50; Delivery: p&p £2.50.*

Next Door 🖃
10 West St, Chipping Norton, Oxfordshire OX7 5AA ☎ (0845) 458 9292
A mail order catalogue business attached to a Cotswold shop.
<u>Baby clothes</u> – **Christening gowns:** silk Christening suits and dresses, plus accessories, made in England by Christine Anne; prices from £72. – **Sun-protection clothing.**
<u>Toys</u> – **Traditional toys:** "Wood and Toys for Children" – bead frames, cot toys and pull-and-push-alongs and more.

The Nice Nappy Company 🖃
1 New Moorsite, Westfield, East Sussex TN35 4QP ☎ (07941) 412003
🖳 www.nicenappy.co.uk
<u>Baby clothes</u> – **Eco-friendly clothing:** organic and hemp clothing from basics to snowsuits and batik dresses; unfortunately no pictures on the site.
<u>Nappies</u> – **Reusable stockists - brands & singles:** a website offering Bumkins nappies, hemp, shaped and prefold nappies, a small selection of nappies and covers made by a Work At Home Mother, and the Happy Pant. Also Polar Babies Velcro in recycled fleece.

Rosie Nieper T-shirts 🖃
3 Princes Works, Princes Rd, Teddington TW11 0RW ☎ (020) 8255 9926
🖳 www.roseinieper.com
<u>Maternity wear</u> – **Mid-range:** humorous maternity T-shirts, such as: "Pregnant" and "Does my bump look big in this?".
<u>Baby clothes</u> – **Mid-range.** – **Funky:** printed T-shirts with humorous quotations and pictures. Baby T-shirts, children's T-shirts with themes (ballet, ponies, dogs, cartoons "happy", "cute", "naughty" etc.) £10; other products include 'Bang on the door' products and kids sweatshirts £15. / *Hours: 24hr answerphone; free catalogue or online; Delivery: p&p £2.50; no Amex.*

Nina Campbell
9 Walton St, London SW3 2JD ☎ (020) 7225 1011 🖳 www.ninacampbell.com
<u>Nappies</u> – **Change bags:** the range includes smart nappy (£35) and weekend (£65) bags.
<u>Naming gifts</u> – **Naming gifts:** this famous designer doesn't do any children's fabrics, but her Chelsea shop does sell baby gifts like cute enamel mugs, night lights, bootees and bibs. / *Hours: Mon-Sat 10am-6pm.*

9 London
4A Beaufort Gardens, Knightsbridge, London SW3 1PU ☎ (020) 7838 0703
By appointment only. Launched by two friends who met while modelling, and claiming to boast clients like Elle Macpherson, Liz Hurley, Kate Moss, Claudia Schiffer, and Sharleen Spiteri.
<u>Maternity wear</u> – **Luxury:** a shop for mothers who want to remain glamorous while pregnant. The idea is to pick items from current designer ranges (for example Marc Jacobs, Diane von Furstenberg, Alex Gore Browne cashmere and Maria Grachvogel) which can be worn when pregnant. There are even jeans from Earl, Jo's and Juicy for example. Also the likes of the Elle Macpherson's maternity bras.

NiNight 🖃
2 Lawrence Close, Burnham on Sea, Somerset TA8 1JT ☎ (01278) 794555 (24hr answermachine) 🖳 www.ninight.co.uk/
<u>Nursery decor</u> – **Bedding:** a good selection of children's single duvet covers. Alongside a wide range of UK TV/video characters and football team designs there are some very attractive, subtler embroidered and appliqued options (including for boys).

Nippers Q
🖳 www.nippers.co.uk
BRANCHES:
Waffrons Farm, Woodstock Lane South, Chessington KT9 1UF
☎ (020) 8398 3114
Coddimoor Farm, Whaddon, Nr Milton Keynes MK17 0LR
☎ (01908) 504506
Chalkpit Farm, School Lane, Bekesbourne CT4 5EU
☎ (01227) 832008
Whites Farm, Bures Rd, White Colne, Colchester CO6 2QF
☎ (01787) 228000
Leyhill Farm, Bridge St, Whaddon, Royston SG8 5SQ
☎ (01223) 207071
Baby equipment supplier which often uses farm buildings for its showrooms: there are five outlets within reasonable reach of London, of eight nationwide; new goods, discontinued items, seconds and second-hand wares are stocked at keen prices. All branches have lots of play areas (not to mention the odd duck or pig). Sometimes there are open days featuring a specific manufacturer.
<u>Baby equipment</u> – **Stockists:** a comprehensive range from many of the top makes; you can test car seats in your own car.
<u>Toys</u> – **General stockists:** a good selection of indoor and outdoor toys. / *Hours: mostly Tue-Sun 10am-4pm (some branches closed Sun & Wed); no Amex.*

Nitti Gritty
223 Blackstock Rd, London N5 2LL ☎ (020) 7690 1341
Children's clothing and gift shop.
<u>Nursery decor</u> – **General stockists:** wooden furniture, rugs, cushions, wooden gifts and sleep sacks.
<u>Baby clothes</u> – **Mid-range:** soft shoes, knitted hats and T-shirts.
<u>Toys</u> – **Traditional toys:** dolls, dressing-up clothes and traditional wooden gifts. / *Hours: Tues-Thurs 10.30am-5.30pm, Fri 11.30am-6pm, Sat 10am-5pm; no credit cards.*

Nomad Books

781 Fulham Rd, London SW6 5HA ☎ (020)
7736 4000 ⊕ www.nomadbooks.co.uk
<u>Books, music & videos</u> – **Bookshops:** this
general bookshop has a floor devoted to travel
including titles on travelling with babies and
children; there are also large children's and
parenting sections. / *Hours: Mon-Fri 9am-8pm, Sat
10am-6pm, Sun 11am-5pm.*

Norfolk Leisure Company ⌂

Setchey, King's Lynn, Norfolk PE33 0BE
☎ (01553) 811 717
⊕ www.norfolkleisure.sagesite.co.uk
<u>Toys</u> – **Outdoor items & active toys:** sells
Woodlawn Playcentres. / *free catalogue; Delivery:
p&p included.*

Notsobig ⌂

31a Highgate High St, London N6 5JT
☎ (020) 8340 4455
A tiny ground floor and basement shop.
<u>Baby clothes</u> – **Funky:** an offbeat range with
many imports from LA and New York, plus
Petit Bateau, Essential, Cacheral and Woolrich;
examples have included Maharishi shirts with
embroidered dragons (£80).
<u>Shoes</u> – **Suppliers:** small selection, including
Birkenstock sandals. / *Hours: Mon-Fri 9.30am-
6pm, Sat 10am-6pm; Sun 11am-5pm; no Amex.*

Number One for Nappies ⌂

271 Holdbrook Court, Holdbrook South,
Waltham Cross EN8 7SL ☎ (01992) 713665
⊕ www.numberonefornappies.co.uk
<u>Nappies</u> – **Reusable stockists - multiple
brands:** nappy laundering and supply service;
cotton nappies delivered and collected weekly;
from £8.50 per week; nappy bin provided;
member of NANS; wraps and liners
extra. / *London only.*

The Nursery Company ⌂

5 Cloncurry St, London SW6 6DR ☎ Order
line (020) 8878 5167
⊕ www.nurserycompany.co.uk
'Linens and sleepwear' in simple, very
traditional designs.
<u>Nursery decor</u> – **Accessories:** covered hangers
(pale blue or pink £6), £10 a pair; cot tidies,
lined baskets. – **Bedding:** cot quilts, bumpers
and blankets. – **Sleeping Bags:** baby sleeping
bags (£33-£39) in various weights and sizes.
<u>Baby clothes</u> – **Sleepwear:** checked cotton
pyjamas, nightgowns in pure cotton, fleecy
dressing gowns: from £25.

Nursery Times ⌂

Ilfrecombe Gdns, Whitley Bay, Tyne & Wear
NE26 3ND ☎ (0191) 289 89 89
⊕ www.nursery-times.com
<u>Naming gifts</u> – **Naming gifts:** a website
offering an attractive selection of baby and
Christening gifts, teddies and soft toys, dolls
houses and accessories – cherry wood rattle or
wooden letters box, each about £20.

The Nursery Window ⌂

83 Walton St, London SW3 2HP ☎ (020)
7581 3358 ⊕ www.nurserywindow.co.uk
<u>Nursery decor</u> – **General stockists:** fabric and
wallpaper for babies and children's rooms plus
a wide range of matching accessories and soft
furnishings. Exclusively own-range fabrics that

include a selection of designs for a variety of
ages – from pastels to primary colours.
Accessories include layette baskets, cot
bumpers, quilts, cot linen and more. A Moses
basket, mattress and cover costs £130. / *Hours:
Mon-Sat 10am-5.30pm; free catalogue or online;
Delivery: p&p £6.50 .*

Nurserygoods.com ⌂

The Paddocks, Marston Lane, East Farndon,
Market Harborough LE16 9SL ☎ (01858)
469162 ⊕ www.nurserygoods.com
<u>Baby equipment</u> – **Stockists:** a website whose
comprehensive range is well indicated by its
name, selling toys, pushchairs, cots, prams,
bedding, mattresses, highchairs, travel cots,
moses baskets, nursery furniture, strollers,
buggies and more.

Nutkin

Lawnfield House, Westmorland Rd,
Maidenhead SL6 4HB ☎ (01628) 778856,
Mobile (07774) 257817
Small outfit run by a Norland Trained nanny
offering independent advice to new and
expectant mums. Not a stockist, but services
include assisted shopping and product
evaluation.
<u>Baby equipment</u> – **Stockists.**
<u>Nursery decor</u> – **General stockists.**

Nutshell Natural Paints ⌂

PO Box 72, South Brent, Devon TQ10 9YR
☎ (01364) 73801 ⊕ www.nutshellpaints.com
<u>Nursery decor</u> – **Paints:** mail order business
supplying paints made from natural raw
materials including milk derivatives; can be
used on all absorbent and clean surfaces and
gloss-painted woodwork which has been
sanded; fungicide and solvent-free wallpaper
paste, floor varnish etc. / *Hours: Mon-Fri 9.30am-
1pm, or answerphone; free catalogue/ hand-painted
colour chart £5; online ordering; no credit cards.*

NYA Plastic & Rubber Industry

92 North Road, Hertford, Herts SG14 2BU
⊕ www.biodegradable-products.com
<u>Nappies</u> – **Protective bedding:** rubber sheets
for babies in biodegradable, cold-cured (ie
without chemicals) latex rubber, in hand-sealed
double layer construction for greater durability
and with soft bubble surface to enhance air
circulation. Sheets are 90x60cm and are
recommended for use as mattress protectors,
also doubling up as an insulation sheet, and as
a soft surface for nappy changing.

Ocado

☎ (0845) 399 1122 ⊕ www.ocado.com
You get easy access to Waitrose in-store offers
on this, their home delivery service partners'
website. As well as groceries (see 2.02 Feeding)
they also supply a range of essentials for
changing, bathing and so on.
<u>Nappies</u> – **Suppliers-Eco friendly**
disposables.

Oilily ⌂

9 Sloane St, London SW1X 9LE ☎ (020)
7823 2505, HQ (01225) 469237
⊕ www.oilily-world.com
Top designer brand with one shop in London
but which is also widely stocked in other

tlets (call for nearest stockist).
by clothes – **Luxury:** wacky, colourful,
rable clothes from denims to pretty
ovençal prints. – **Funky.** / Hours: Mon-Sat
am-6pm (Wed 7pm); seasonal magazine; Delivery:
p extra.

llipops 🖰
Yarnhams Cottages, Upper Froyle, Alton,
mpshire GU34 4DB ☎ (0870) 121 3409
www.ollipops.com
n-line store.
by clothes – **Sun-protection clothing:**
osh sun protection gear.
oes – **Suppliers:** bobux (soft leather baby)
oes and Sole Mania slippers.
oys – **Traditional toys:** escor wooden toys,
ddly bears and Hopscotch dressing-up
ts. / Hours: daily 8am-11pm; Delivery: free
pping; same day; not wooden toys or paintings.; no
nex.

ne Fine Day 🖰
(01524) 263300 ᐧ᠊ www.onefineday.co.uk
ming gifts – **Naming gifts:** limited edition
me prints from three artists, an alphabet
ster; more designs in the pipeline.

ne Night Stand
Chelsea Manor Studios, Flood St, London
W3 5SR ☎ (020) 7352 4848
www.onenightstand.co.uk
aternity wear – **Hire:** the emphasis is on
odern designer dresses; £100-£150 for three
ghts' hire; no specific 'maternity' dresses,
t with over 400 dresses at any time, there
ould be something suitable. / Hours: by
pointment only; Mon-Fri 10am-6.30pm, Sat 10am-
m; Delivery: p&p extra (registered).

range Tree Toys 🖰
) Box 308, Cheltenham, Gloucestershire
L52 4GR ☎ (0870) 444 2643
www.orangetreetoys.co.uk
oys – **Traditional toys:** a nicely designed
line shop, offering a wide range of rag dolls,
d other soft, and wooden, toys.

rchard Toys 🖰
ebdale Lane, Keyworth, Notts NG12 5HN
(0115) 937 1620
www.orchardtoys.com
oys – **Brand:** manufacturer with over 25
ars experience of producing games, play
cks, jigsaws and other educational items
ing bright simple designs; mail order
usiness or phone for a list of stockists in your
ea. / Hours: Mon-Fri 8.45am-5pm; free catalogue;
livery: p&p extra.

regano UK 🖰
0 Holwell Road, Welwyn Garden City,
ertfordshire AL7 3RW ☎ (01707) 883 569
www.oreganouk.com
aby clothes – **Eco-friendly clothing:** baby
d children's clothes made on an Israeli
obutz in organic cotton, coloured using
tural materials and without chloride or
hitening chemicals. Garments include shorts,
ousers, leggings, vests, long and short-sleeved
shirts, sleepsuits, bodysuits, dresses, hats,
ots and underwear.

Oreka Kids 🖰
209 Lynchet Way, Enfield EN3 5XU ☎ (020)
8804 2045 ᐧ᠊ www.orekakids.com
<u>Nursery decor</u> – **Furniture:** designer children's
furniture – the range called Biscuit aims to be
multi-functional and playful, (it includes for
example a fun bench which can turn into a car,
a ship and lots more); more collections are
planned; buy direct or call for details of
stockists; prices start from £100 for Shortcake
(the bench). / Hours: Mon-Fri 9am-5pm; Delivery:
p&p £14.50 per item; no credit cards.

Ostermann & Scheiwe UK
Unit 2, Pembroke Rd, Stocklake Industrial
Estate, Aylesbury, Bucks HP20 1DB
☎ (01296) 481220 ᐧ᠊ www.osmouk.com
<u>Nursery decor</u> – **Paints:** a German make of
(among other things) OS Color – biocide and
preservative-free colour paints, and natural,
oil-based timber finishes; also hard wax,
stain-resistant finishes for wood or cork; call or
see the website for ingredients lists and
stockists. / Hours: Mon-Fri 9am-5.30pm.

Otterburn Mill 🖰
Otterburn, Northumberland NE19 1JT
☎ (01830) 520225
ᐧ᠊ www.otterburnmill.co.uk
<u>Nursery decor</u> – **Bedding:** there's quite
a history of making soft wool pram rugs
(which come in many colours, and plain or
checked – from £20) at this venerable mill,
now converted into a shop and museum; gift
wrapping available. / Hours: Mon-Sat 9am-5pm;
Delivery: p&p included; no Amex.

Over The Moon Babywear 🖰
19 Roe St, Macclesfield, Cheshire SK11 6UT
ᐧ᠊ www.overthemoon-babywear.co.uk
Web-based retailer.
Baby clothes – **Mid-range:** simply-designed
all-in-ones, sleepsuits, long-sleeved T-shirts,
sweatshirts and leggings; all garments made or
lined using natural fibres are listed separately;
gift wrap/card service.

Owl Bookshop 🖰
209 Kentish Town Rd, London NW5 2JU
☎ (020) 7485 7793
Books, music & videos – **Bookshops:** the
children's section is strong with a wide range of
picture books and titles for under-twos. The
play area is equipped with bean bags and
toys. / Hours: Mon-Sat 9.30am-6pm, Sun noon-
4.30pm.

Owls Educational Direct 🖰
3 High St, Eynsham, Oxford OX29 4HA
☎ (0845) 330 4050
<u>Toys</u> – **Educational:** mail order company set
up by an ex-teacher aiming to select top
quality, stimulating toys and activities. The
catalogue contains over 500 items including
thick-cut card and wooden puzzles, games,
books, and cassettes; also fun educational
resources for older kids, and craft materials
(paper, paints, pens and collage). / Hours: Mon-
Fri 9am-5pm, or answerphone; free catalogue;
Delivery: p&p £4.99 under £88.

Paddington Bear Shop
Main Concourse, Paddington Station, Praed St, London W1 ☎ (020) 7706 0268
<u>Toys</u> – **Character toys:** part of Peter Rabbit & Friends (see also), this (surprisingly nice) stall on Paddington station stocks mostly Paddington-branded goods. / *Hours: Mon-Fri 7.30am-7.30pm, Sat & Sun 9am-7pm.*

Maureen Palmer
Beaumaris, Colts Hill, Capel, Tonbridge, Kent TN12 6SJ ☎ (01892) 834109
<u>Toys</u> – **Repairs:** experienced toy repairer – can mend any stuffed toy from a soft animal or teddy bear to a rocking horse. / *no credit cards.*

Pares Footwear
24 Tranquil Vale, London SE3 0AX ☎ (020) 8297 0785
<u>Shoes</u> – **Suppliers:** brands stocked here include: Start-rite, Ricosta, Elefanten, Salamander, Clarks, Kickers; all shoes are fitted by trained fitters. / *Hours: Mon-Fri 9.30am-6pm, Sat 9am-6pm, Sun 11am-5pm.*

Patchwork Palace 🖼
Kenton House, 104 Harlestone Rd, Dallington, Northants NN5 7AQ ☎ (01604) 464 537 ᐟ www.patchworkpalace.co.uk
<u>Nursery decor</u> – **Bedding:** quilts in 100% cotton; commissions welcomed (indeed, preferred) with both hand and machine-quilting available. A machine-quilted cot quilt might be around £30.

Patricia
London W4 ☎ (020) 8747 3045
<u>Hairdressers</u> – **Hairdressers:** freelance, child-friendly hairdresser, who can cut hair in her home or yours; flat rate charge for children; lock of hair from first haircut given to parents. / *Hours: by appointment.*

Patrick's Toys & Models
107-111 Lillie Rd, London SW6 7SX ☎ (020) 7385 9864 ᐟ www.patrickstoys.co.uk
<u>Toys</u> – **General stockists:** established 1948 – a friendly and unusually well-stocked local toy shop with a wide ranging selection of pre-school toys covering all the best known brands – Brio, Tomy, Fisher-Price; also more specialist brands and outdoor items such as TP activity toys. / *Hours: Mon-Sat 9.15am-5.45pm; free catalogue.*

Paul Smith 🖼
Westbourne House, 122 Kensington Park Rd, London W11 2EP ☎ (020) 7727 3553 ᐟ www.paulsmith.co.uk
The Notting Hill branch is the main outlet for the designer's children-related items.
<u>Baby clothes</u> – **Luxury:** a wide selection of printed T-shirts for £20-£65; also a bought-in cashmere range.
<u>Toys</u> – **General stockists:** small selection of well chosen, often small items – finger puppets £3, wind-up robot £4. / *Hours: Mon-Thu 10.30am-6.30pm, Fri & Sat 10am-6.30pm.*

Pearlfisher
12 Addison Avenue, London W11 4QR ☎ (020) 7603 8666
<u>Baby clothes</u> – **Luxury:** designers of attractive clothes for newborns in plain cotton-looking fabrics with patterned trim using 'smart' textiles (as used in extreme sportswear to help control body temperature). The range includ hats, sleepsuits, bootees, vests, T-shirts, swea pants and pyjamas – priced from £20. The selection is due to be extended for older children and also to include outdoor clothing call for stockists.

Pearson Toymaster
171-175 High Rd, London N22 6BA ☎ (020) 8889 3111 ᐟ www.pearsons-enfield.co.uk
<u>Toys</u> – **General stockists:** located in a shopping centre; brands include Tomy, Fisher-Price, Play School, Tiger, VTech; "Toymaster price promise: you can't buy cheaper". / *Hours: Fri 10am-6.30pm, Sat 9.30-6.30pm, Sun 11am-5pm.*

Pelirocco 🖼
34 Yoakley Rd, London N16 0BA ☎ Office (020) 8802 2861, Mail Order (020) 8802 6497 ᐟ www.pelirocco.co.uk
(Note: contact details are set to change late in 2004.)
<u>Baby clothes</u> – **Luxury:** traditional clothing f children from 0-6 years in soft cottons, Libert prints, linen, and hand-knitted Scottish cashmere. Prices from £16-£80. / *Hours: Mon-F 10am-5.30pm, Sat 9.30am-1pm; free catalogue; Delivery: p&p £3.95; no Amex.*

Peony Records 🖼
Northmace House, Viaduct Rd, Cardiff CF15 9XF ☎ (029) 2081 5201
<u>Books, music & videos</u> – **Music tapes:** 'The Sang and Were Glad', £7.99 inc p&p, nursery rhymes, action and educational songs; all real instruments plus vocals with original arrangements; cheques payable to Julia Plaut; money back if not satisfied. Also God's Wonderful World.

People Tree 🖼
Studio 7, 8-13 New Inn St, London EC2A 3PY ☎ (0845) 450 4595, (020) 7739 0660 ᐟ www.peopletree.co.uk
A Fair Trade and eco-friendly mail order catalogue from a company working directly with farmers and artisans in Asia, Africa and Latin America, offering advance payments ar training in design and marketing.
<u>Baby clothes</u> – **Eco-friendly clothing:** from three months, colourful casual items with lot of organic cotton, stripes and prints. / *Hours: Mon-Fri 9am-6pm; free catalogue or online; Delivery p&p £3.50 on orders up to £75; over free.; no Amex.*

Peppermint
321-323 Walworth Rd, London SE17 2TG ☎ (020) 7703 9638
<u>Baby clothes</u> – **Luxury:** labels including Armani, Paul Smith, Versace, DKNY, Elle, Kenzo, Levi's, Ted Baker, D&G, Diesel, Oilil Cakewalk, Burberry and Moschino; party dresses from £20-£100. / *Hours: Mon-Sat 10am-6pm, Sun 11am-4pm; no Amex.*

Peter Rabbit & Friends 🖼
Unit 42 The Market, London WC2E 8RF ☎ (020) 7497 1777, Mail Order (01539) 822888 ᐟ www.charactergifts.com
This shop (and others around the UK, some called Paddington & Friends) and mail order

business is devoted not only to Beatrix Potter and Paddington, but also Pooh, Thomas the Tank Engine, Postman Pat et al.

Baby clothes – **Mid-range:** branded clothing range for babies up to 24 months old, and a children's range too; designs change regularly.

Toys – **Character toys:** large soft toy range, as well as games and accessories (aprons, wallets, rucksacks).

Books, music & videos – **Bookshops:** the full range of character-related books and videos.

Naming gifts – **Naming gifts:** china items, collectibles and Christening stationery. / Hours: Mon-Fri 10am-7pm, Sat 10am-8pm; free catalogue; Delivery: p&p £4.

Peter Topp Interiors

343 Fulham Palace Rd, London SW6 6TD
☎ (020) 7736 4821

Nursery decor – **Wallpaper & fabrics:** all the big name designer papers and fabrics, including their children's ranges; paints also stocked; can give decorating advice and can put customers in touch with interior decorators and muralists. / Hours: Mon-Fri 9.30am-5pm, Sat 10am-4pm; no Amex.

Petit Bateau

CENTRAL CONTACT DETAILS
☎ (020) 7838 0818 or (020) 7436 5336
⊕ www.petit-bateau.com
62 South Molton Street W1K 5SR
188 Chiswick High Road W4 1PP
106-108 King's Road SW3 4TZ
19 Hampstead High Street NW3 1PX
56-58 Hill Street TW9 1TW

Note that there's also a factory outlet shop in Bicester Factory Shopping Village (see also).

Baby clothes – **Luxury:** one of France's most popular childrenswear labels. Though not the cheapest, the attention to comfort seems to be appreciated by small wearers. Daywear, sleepwear, casual items and underwear are all available; Selfridges has a Petit Bateau concession and stocks the whole range, and Harrods also has a very large selection. / Hours: Mon-Sat 10am-6pm (Wed & Thu 7pm), Sun noon-6pm.

Petra Boase ⊞

Pinfold Cottage, Foulden, Nr Thetford, Norfolk IP26 5AQ ☎ (020) 7419 1061, Mobile (07956) 345 107, (01366) 328232
⊕ www.petraboase.com

Baby clothes – **Funky:** a range of white babygrows, with bright and modern Chinese-style images. Prices from £12.

Naming gifts – **Naming gifts:** fun but not kitsch albums and keepsake boxes, plus handmade cards and the like. View the items online and ring for prices (which generally range from £15 to £45). / Hours: Mon-Fri 10am-4pm, or answerphone; online catalogue; Delivery: p&p extra; no Amex.

Philips

⊕ www.philips.com/babycare

The electronics manaufacturer sells a number of baby items including a steriliser, bottle warmer, baby bath and room thermometer, baby thermometer set and a 'cradle player' which records a minute of the parents' voice to comfort a baby to sleep.

Baby equipment – **Monitors-brand:** the brand's monitors use DECT radio technology (digital enhanced cordless telecommunication) – an international standard to avoid interference with any nearby families with similar kit. As well as a monitor incorporating a thermometer, there is a baby cam so you can watch your child (it includes infra-red nightvision to overcome the issues of a darkened room).

PHP ⊞

Head Office: 37 Rothschild Rd, London W4 5HJ; Warehouse PO Box 333, Gateshead NE10 8YQ ☎ Catalogue requests (0870) 607 0545, Office (0870 122 0215)
⊕ www.thebabycatalogue.com, www.phpbaby.com

Perfectly Happy People Ltd – a catalogue company with its own range of Kooshies cloth nappies (see also) and where you can shop online at www.thebabycatalolgue.com.

Baby equipment – **Stockists:** miscellaneous range of useful items, for example: car safety products, bottle sterilisers, long-sleeved bibs and safety gates; UK distributor of Baby Bjorn products which include a clover-leaf design plate, bibs, booster seats and potties; see also Baby Bjorn entry for slings and change bags.

Baby clothes – **Sleepwear:** baby kimono and pyjamas.

Toys – **Educational:** good selection, including a good number of wooden and 'developmental' items. / Hours: Mon-Fri 10am-5pm; free catalogue; Delivery: p&p £2.95.

Picture Wear Originals ⊞

Lillyhorne Cottage, Bournes Green, Oakridge, Stroud, Gloucestershire GL6 7NN
☎ (01285) 760845

Baby clothes – **Mid-range:** clothes featuring animals in original designs, all in pure cotton: elasticated trousers, dungarees, shorts, hats, pinafores, reversible jackets and waistcoats; dungarees, £30; pinafores £25. / Hours: 24hr answerphone; free catalogue; Delivery: p&p £1+; no credit cards.

Pied Piper

234 Upper Richmond Rd, London SW15 6TG ☎ (020) 8788 1635

Established over 20 years ago, a children's shoe and dance clothes shop (with the emphasis on the former).

Baby clothes – **Traditional:** ballet and dance wear.

Shoes – **Suppliers:** brands stocked include Start-rite, Bobux and Ricosta. / Hours: Mon-Sat 9.30am-6pm.

Pieton Shoes

9 Westbourne Grove, London W2 4UA
☎ (020) 7792 0707

Shoes – **Suppliers:** brands include Start-rite, GBB and Clarks; all shoes fitted by trained fitters. / Hours: Mon-Sat 10am-8pm, Sun noon-6pm.

Pin Toys

8 Carousel Way, Riverside, North Hampton NN3 NHG ☎ UK distributors (01604) 774 949 ⊕ www.john-crane.co.uk

Toys – **Brand:** a Thai toy firm, producing excellent wooden toys in solid, eco-friendly rubberwood (from spent rubber trees). Call for stockists. / *Hours: Mon-Fri 9am-5pm; no credit cards.*

The Pitshanger Bookshop

141 Pitshanger Lane, Ealing W5 1RH ☎ (020) 8991 8131

<u>Books, music & videos</u> – **Bookshops:** reference and health-related books for mother and baby; children's book section with toys and puzzles. / *Hours: Mon-Sat 9.30am-5.30pm.*

Pixies ⌂ Q

14 Fauconberg Rd, Chiswick, London W4 3JY ☎ (020) 8995 1568

⌂ www.pixiesonline.co.uk

New and nearly-new stockist.

<u>Baby equipment</u> – **Second-hand:** equipment such as the Handysitts and Tripp Trapp chairs; also cots and high chairs; the website will eventually hold details of all nearly-new items. – **Buggy accessories:** stockists of the 'KiddyBoard', 'BuggyBoard', and Baby Beyond. – **Cots:** stockists of the Stokke Sleepi cot, which converts from a cradle, through to a cot, playpen and junior bed, to a sofa or two chairs; available in natural or cherry. – **High chairs:** stockists of the Handysitt and Tripp Trapp chairs.

<u>Baby clothes</u> – **Second-hand shops:** all the major high street names; also some new items and UV protection swimwear.

<u>Toys</u> – **Second-hand shops:** large range of nearly-new products. Parents can also sell through this shop (receiving about 50% of the sale price). / *Hours: Tue-Fri 10am-4.30pm, Sat 10am-3pm; Visa, Mastercard, Switch & Delta.*

David Plagerson ⌂

28 Bridgetown, Totnes, Devon TQ9 5AD ☎ (01803) 866786

⌂ www.toymakersguild.co.uk

<u>Toys</u> – **Traditional toys:** bespoke service of hand-crafted Noah's Arks (inspired by one in the Bethnal Green Museum of Childhood) painted or in beeswaxed mixed woods; farms, circus, nativity and chess sets; as all toys are made to order, can include representations of your own home, for example, of family pets; painted animals from £30. / *Hours: by appointment; free price list and photos; no credit cards.*

Plan Toys ⌂

Messenger Close, Loughborough, Leicestershire LE11 5SP ☎ UK distributors (01509) 231874 ⌂ www.plantoys.com, www.brio.co.uk

<u>Toys</u> – **Brand:** a Thai toy firm, producing excellent wooden toys in solid, eco-friendly rubberwood (from spent rubber trees). / *Hours: Mon-Fri 8.30am-5pm; free catalogue; UK; no credit cards.*

Planet Little Kids Furniture

80 Bushey Rd, Spaces, Unit 4001, Raynes Park, London SW20 0JH ☎ (020) 8946 3320

⌂ www.planetlittle.com

Quality, slightly unusual furniture makers – see the website for stockists.

<u>Nursery decor</u> – **Furniture:** good-looking cots in a range of (some quite lavish) styles, junior beds (wood and iron), changing tables, wardrobes and children's chairs (large and strong enough for adults to join the table), plus the odd fun item like sit-in rocking row boat.

Plate, Rattle & Bowl ⌂

38 Burwood Rd, Northampton NN3 2LS ☎ (01604) 406320

⌂ www.babies-rattles.co.uk

<u>Naming gifts</u> – **Naming gifts:** traditional hand-turned 'dovecote' rattles, in cherry or sycamore wood; they can be personalised (at extra cost, approximately £4) and are presented in a box with a gift tag and scroll and a brief history of baby rattles; £19 for plain cherry rattles; £55 for rattles with hallmarked silver bands. / *Hours: 9.30am-6pm, 24hr answerphone.*

Play Togs ⌂

Canada Hill, Isle of Bute PA20 9EN ☎ (01700) 504 588, (0800) 081 1870

⌂ www.togz.co.uk

<u>Baby clothes</u> – **Outdoorwear:** well-designed children's wind and waterproof jackets and dungarees in breathable, machine washable PU coated nylon with sealed seams, high visibility reflector bars and plenty of room for movement; peaks and volume adjusters on the hoods; microfleece hood lining; dungarees, from £18, waterproof jacket and all-in-one suits; also 'Safe & Seen' range of high visibility waistcoats, capes and accessories. / *Hours: Mon-Fri 8am-6pm; free catalogue or online; Delivery: p&p extra; no Amex.*

Playgear

3 Dennis Parade, Winchmore Hill Rd, London N14 6AA ☎ (020) 8882 1293

⌂ www.edutoy.co.uk

<u>Toys</u> – **Educational:** educational toys with a lot of play value, and books: range includes Little Tikes, Brio, Galt, Orchard, Step 2 and TP outdoor equipment; some soft toys also stocked. / *Hours: Mon-Sat 11am-5pm; Delivery: p&p included.*

Playmobil (UK) ⌂

6 Argent Court, Sylvan Way, Southfields Business Park, Basildon, Essex SS15 6TH ☎ (01268) 490184 ⌂ www.playmobil.com

<u>Toys</u> – **Brand:** the famous brand of little plastic characters and themed settings; call for details of your local stockist. / *Hours: Mon-Fri 9am-5pm; no Amex.*

Playsongs Publications ⌂

Wimbish Lower Green, Saffron Walden, Essex CB10 2XH ☎ (01799) 599 054

⌂ www.playsongs.co.uk

<u>Books, music & videos</u> – **Music tapes:** run by a music editor at A&C Black, one of the best selections of music for the very young; all are good but especially recommended titles are listed in the section on music.

Pleats Please

20 Brook St, London W1 5DE ☎ (020) 7495 2306 ⌂ www.pleatsplease.com

<u>Maternity wear</u> – **Luxury:** designer Issey Miyake's pleated garments are enormously comfortable to wear and the stretch encompasses a growing bump: the basic theme is varied each season, with different colours and cuts (dresses from £170). The wraps and shawls are good for special events. / *Hours: Mon-Sat 10am-6pm.*

Plush Pants 🖐

55 Newlands Avenue, Cheadle Hulme, Cheshire SK8 6NE ☎ (0161) 485 4430
🖥 www.plushpants.co.uk
Baby clothes – Mid-range: the bright and simple Tots Bots range including bodysuits, dungarees, trousers and more, for 0-24 months; a babygrow is £8.
Nappies – Reusable stockists - multiple brands: mail order supplies whose website offers a good deal of information on different types of nappy (and the opportunity to order the relevant supplies online); brands sold include Popolini, Bright Bots, Tots Bots, prefolds, organic knitted tie on, Imse Vimse, Nappy Nation, Fuzzibunz plus polyester, wool, cotton, fleece and secondhand wraps; also a nappy hire option. / *catalogue online; Delivery: &p extra; no Amex.*

Poco Ropa 🖐

PO Box 7881, Crowthorne, Berkshire RG45 6ZP ☎ (01344) 771 935
🖥 www.pocoropa.co.uk
Baby clothes – Mid-range: items imported from Spain by a mother who was depressed at the value offered in the UK. The range majors in smocked items and clothes for boys, both in fairly traditional styles. Options include a cross-over bodysuit for easy dressing and undressing, sheepskin hats and mittens and mock sheepskin jackets.
Shoes – Suppliers: imported sheepskin booties (from Spain) in sizes from six months–two years. Online ordering is an innovation for 2004. / *Hours: Mon-Fri 9.30am-3.30pm; free brochure.*

Pollock's Museum & Toy Shop

1 Scala St, London W1T 2HL ☎ (020) 7636 3452 🖥 www.pollocksweb.co.uk
Toys – Traditional toys: amongst a range that includes cardboard cut-out theatres for older children, the shop stocks an unusual selection of traditional toys and a fair selection of fluffy toys, wooden blocks, pull-along items and puppets. / *Hours: Mon-Sat 10am-5pm.*

Pollyanna

811 Fulham Rd, London SW6 5HG ☎ (020) 7731 0673
Baby clothes – Luxury: beautiful baby clothes and smart casual clothes for children from a mid to top-of-the-range supplier.
Shoes – Suppliers: shoe makes stocked here include Start-rite, GBB, Superga, buckle-my-shoe, and Naturino. / *Hours: Mon-Sat 9.30am-5.30pm; no Amex.*

Poppy 🖐

14 High St, Yarm, North Yorkshire TS15 9AE ☎ (01642) 790000
🖥 www.poppy-children.co.uk
"Classic with a zany modern twist" is how this company describes its products; all fabrics and furnishings are designed and manufactured in its British factory.
Nursery decor – Soft furnishings: everything is made to order; all items in the range co-ordinate: fabrics with borders, cushions, lampshades; patterns include ducks, mice, hedgehogs, moles, bears, clowns, stripes and elephants, and come in pastels, bold or primary colours.
Baby clothes – Mid-range: anything from jackets to party dresses in their own designs, which feature larger-than-life prints created by local artists. Cotton dresses, velvet coats and fleeces; prices from £20. / *Hours: Mon-Sat 9am-5.30pm; catalogue online; Delivery: p&p £2.99; no Amex.*

Potty People

316-318 Bethnal Green Rd, London E2 0AG ☎ (020) 7729 2217
Baby equipment – Stockists: cots, pushchairs, prams, and accessories; catalogue returns at half price; also repairs.
Nursery decor – Furniture: full range of Continental nursery furniture, from cots to change tables.
Baby clothes – Mid-range: small selection. / *Hours: Mon-Sat 9.30am-5.30pm.*

Pouch 🖐

Poplar House, Church Road, Gaydon, Warwickshire CV35 0EX ☎ (01455) 639 712
🖥 www.pouch.org.uk
Baby clothes – Mid-range: bright buggy-warmers, and co-ordinating children's fleece clothing.

Practical Pushchairs 🖐

Pump Cottage, Wheathold, Nr. Wolverton, Hampshire RG26 5SA ☎ (0118) 981 7372
🖥 www.practicalpushchairs.co.uk
Baby equipment – Buggy suppliers: mail order suppliers of 3-wheel single and double jogger/strollers chiefly of the imported US and New Zealand brand InSTEP and Phil and Ted's range from £170 onwards.

Prada

16-18 Old Bond St, London W1S 4PS ☎ Old Bond Street (020) 7647 5000
🖥 www.prada.com
Shoes – Brands: trainers for trendy non-walkers (£85 and up). / *Hours: Mon-Sun 10am-6pm.*

Prams Direct 🖐

☎ (0870) 4422 545
🖥 www.pramsdirect.co.uk
"Save time–money–hassle", is the mantra at this mail order business (attached to a shop near York); you can view some of the range online and call/email for a brochure.
Baby equipment – Buggy suppliers: brands include Graco, Maclaren, Cosatto and Britax. / *free brochure.*

Pramsonline 🖐

☎ (01254) 232235
🖥 www.pramsonline.com/
Baby equipment – Stockists: well-organised and detailed web business, with the deepest range amongst prams, but with some other items of baby equipment.

Premier Nametapes 🖐

1 Monks Dairy Workshops, Isle Brewers, Taunton, Somerset TA3 6QL ☎ (01460) 281 229 🖥 www.nametape.co.uk
Baby clothes – Nametapes: woven labels in seven colours and seven text colours (including gold lurex) and two ribbon widths (so you can

add more information), permitting different type styles and with optional fun and sporting figures. Prices start around £10 an order.

Preston Shoes

320 Preston Rd, Harrow HA3 0QH ☎ (020) 8904 2211

<u>Shoes</u> – **Suppliers:** brands stocked include Start-rite. / *Hours: Mon-Fri 9.30am-5.30pm, Sat 9.30am-5.15pm.*

Primark

[⌂] www.primark.co.uk

BRANCHES:

King's Mall, King St W6
☎ (020) 8748 7119
52a Kilburn High St NW6
☎ (020) 7624 4664
51 Rye Lane SE15
☎ (020) 7639 9655
11 Tooting High St SW17
☎ (020) 8672 1792
18 Hare St SE18
☎ (020) 8316 7988
51 High St North E6
☎ (020) 8472 2512
365 Mare St E8
☎ (020) 8985 2689
650 High Rd E11
☎ (020) 8539 3972

You'd never guess that these ultra-discount high street stores are backed by the same family who own Fortnum & Mason!
<u>Maternity wear</u> – **Cheap & cheerful:** the cost/style trade off may not be quite as attractive for adults as children, but the prices make sense for clothes you'll barely wear.
<u>Baby clothes</u> – **Cheap & cheerful:** it's tough to spend much more than a tenner on practically any item here, but given the ultra-budget prices (three babygrows £3, three sleep suits £6), quality and design are surprisingly good.

Prince Lionheart UK 🖃

Suite 252, 2 Lansdowne Row, London W1J 6HL ☎ (01189) 421 188, (020) 7286 3691 [⌂] www.princelionheart.co.uk
<u>Baby equipment</u> – **Stockists:** a wide range of products for parents and children including SPF 50 pushchair covers, seatsavers for car seats, baby wipes warmer, teats to fit to standard water bottles, and a mass of other ingenious ideas. Call for stockists, or you can order online.

Puffin Book Club 🖃

Penguin Books, Edinburgh Gate, Harlow, Essex CM20 2JE ☎ Head office (020) 7010 3000 [⌂] www.puffin.co.uk
<u>Books, music & videos</u> – **Book clubs:** this well-known book club operates solely through schools and playgroups, via volunteer co-ordinators. The 0-6 age group has a separate catalogue, sent out six times a year, from each of which the minimum amalgamated order must be 15 books. Free books and discounts are offered as incentives for bigger orders, and there's no fee to join; wide range of books, not just Puffins. / *Hours: Mon-Fri 8.30am-5pm; free catalogue; Delivery: p&p free (UK).*

Pumpkin Patch 🖃

PO Box 111, Tunbridge Wells North TN3 0FX ☎ (01892) 860606
[⌂] www.pumpkinpatch.co.uk
Claiming to be Australia's largest children's wear retailer, recently introduced to the UK. You can order online (there are also shops in Croydon, Uxbridge, Swindon, Southampton, Derby and Bromley).
<u>Baby clothes</u> – **Mid-range:** mid-range children's clothes (slightly stronger on girls), plus maternity wear. Embroidered jeans £12.

Purple Heart 🖃

College Parade, Salusbury Rd, London NW6 6RN ☎ (020) 7328 2830
[⌂] www.purple-heart.com
Shop and website: clothes, personalised gifts and balloons are available online.
<u>Baby clothes</u> – **Mid-range:** gifts and clothing, including a tie-dye babywear range (pyjamas, vests, shirts, trousers, bibs and T-shirts); tights and dresses; pyjamas £14.
<u>Naming gifts</u> – **Naming gifts:** a selection of unusual gifts, including helium balloons, handmade photo albums, Earth Friendly Baby products, hand-painted Claudia Meynell china (which can be personalised with names and dates), Daisy Roots and Starchild shoes. Free gift-wrapping; cards. / *Hours: Mon-Fri 2pm-7pm; Sat 10am-6pm; Sun 1pm-4pm; or by appointment; online catalogue; Delivery: p&p on order value of £2 and up; no Amex.*

QT Toys

90 Northcote Rd, London SW11 6QN ☎ (020) 7223 8637
<u>Toys</u> – **General stockists:** wide and varied range, from baby toys to board games, including lots of party toys; the full ranges of Lego, Brio and Playmobil are usually held in stock. / *Hours: Mon-Sat 9.30am-5.30pm; no credit cards.*

Quackers

155d Northcote Rd, London SW11 6QB ☎ (020) 7978 4235
<u>Baby clothes</u> – **Mid-range:** basics plus original items, from well-known English and Continental labels such as Osh Kosh, Petit Bateau, Balu and Alphabet, encompassing bright colourful modern and classic designs; winter babygrow from £15.
<u>Toys</u> – **Educational:** stockists of Sterntaler music toys. / *Hours: Mon-Sat 9.30am-5.30pm.*

Quality Children's Music 🖃

PO Box 2275, Rottingdean, Brighton BN2 7WE ☎ (01273) 309 452
[⌂] www.qualiychildrensmusic.co.uk
<u>Books, music & videos</u> – **Music tapes:** twinkle twinkle, Mozart, Brahms, Chopin, Schubert and the like, sung by a soprano. But that's not all: the lullabies come personalised with a range of some 300 girls' and 300 boys' names, so they are sung to your child personally. Other names may be ordered at no extra charge. Cost per album is £14.95.

Quickfit SBS

Safety Belt Service, Inertia House, Lowther Rd, Stanmore HA7 1EP ☎ (020) 8204 0200
[⌂] www.quickfitsbs.co.uk
<u>Baby equipment</u> – **Car seat fitting/seat belt**

djusting: supply and fit all children's car afety seats and harnesses, and also hire out nfant carriers for all ages and from all ranges; vill fit longer safety belts if required; all ranges, lso applications for children with special eeds. / *Hours: Mon-Sat 8.30am-5.30pm (Sat 4pm).*

Rabbitts ⌂
3 Wych Elms, Park Street, St Albans, Hertfordshire AL2 2AR ☎ (01727) 768 191
🖰 www.rabbitts.com
Nursery decor – Safety items: "At last: An rgonomic changing mat with an integral houlder/waist harness" – this (£25) British nvention is claimed to offer great advantages n the safety front. Visit the website for further nformation.

Rainbow Q
249 Archway Rd, London N6 5BS ☎ (020) 8340 8003
The shop specialises in good quality 'recycled' baby and children's clothes, toys and books and lots of bargains on good makes".
Baby clothes – Second-hand shops.
Toys – Second-hand shops. / *Hours: Mon-Sat 10.30am-5.30pm; no Amex.*

Rainbow Play Systems Inc ⌂
Hillier Garden Centre, London Rd, Windlesham, Surrey GU20 6LN ☎ For nearest store call (0845) 130 0335
🖰 www.rainbowplay.co.uk
Toys – Outdoor items & active toys: built on an American scale – large, impressively constructed wooden clubhouse/castle system with a large variety of accessories, such as cubes, slides, swings, tables and canopies. Packages' range from £1,200 upwards (not including delivery and assembly). Smaller climbing frames for smaller gardens also available. There are three stores in the UK, or a mail order 'deliver and build' service is available. / *Hours: Mon-Sat 10am-5pm, Sun 10am-4pm; free & DVDs; Delivery: p&p extra; no Amex.*

Rainbow Rooms
23 Sotherton Corner, Beccles, Suffolk NR34 8AP ☎ (07947) 199 416
🖰 www.rainbowrooms.biz
Nursery decor – Murals and other Decorating: hand-painted murals, furniture and themed rooms, available anywhere in the UK. A home visit is part of the planning service.

Rainbows End ⌂
246 Stonelaw Rd, Burnside, Glasgow G73 2SA ☎ (0141) 647 8106
Maternity wear – Bras and underwear: maternity support and nursing bras from brands including Emma-Jane (£14-£20); also the Reenie maternity support belt, tights and nightshirts. / *Hours: Mon-Sat 9.15am-5.15pm; free catalogue; Delivery: p&p £1.75 (maternity underwear only); no Amex.*

Raindrops ⌂
Berrington, Kings Drive, Midhurst, W Sussex GU29 0BH ☎ (01730) 810031
🖰 www.raindrops.co.uk
Baby clothes – Outdoorwear: a range of Scandinavian outdoor clothing for children; 100% waterproof jackets, dungarees and

Sou'Wester-style hats; splash-proof bootees (Polar Paws); dungarees from £19, all-in-one waterproof £32, bootees £8, fleece-lined mittens £10. / *Hours: 24hr answerphone; free catalogue or online; Delivery: p&p £3; no Amex.*

Ralph Lauren
143 New Bond St, London W1S 2TP ☎ (020) 7535 4888
This well-known American label now has a shop for infants, toddlers, boys and girls (the adult store having moved to new premises down the road).
Baby clothes – Luxury: traditional 'preppie', pared-down styles in pale colours; also shoes for toddlers, blankets, accessories and separates; babygrows around £25. / *Hours: Mon-Sat 10am-6pm (Thu 7pm), Sun 12pm-5pm.*

Red House Books ⌂
The Red House, Witney, Oxfordshire OX8 5YF ☎ (0870) 191 9980
🖰 www.redhouse.co.uk
Books, music & videos – Book clubs: general book club with an extensive range of children's books for all age groups, including educational titles. There's no minimum order from the monthly catalogues, and no membership fee to join. / *Hours: Mon-Fri 8am-8pm; free catalogue; Delivery: p&p £1.95 (£2.95 for express delivery).*

Red Studio
12A Spring Grove, London W4 3NH ☎ (020) 8994 7770
A design consultancy acts as sole UK agents for the Stybe range of children's furniture – some cool designs in solid wood – in a small showroom annexe to the consultancy offices.
Baby equipment – Cots: newborn and larger cots (some rocking), £400-£600; also bunk beds.
Nursery decor – Furniture: small tables and chairs; beds; a useful range of cupboards (some with roller blinds); items like foam animals which form a mattress; a small chest of drawers might be £350. / *Hours: Mon-Fri 9.30am-6pm; no credit cards.*

Redinap ⌂
PO Box 6632, Birmingham B37 6DD ☎ (0121) 788 0300 🖰 www.redinap.com
Nursery decor – Safety items: manufacturer of a wall-mounted baby changer, which is marketed as particularly suitable for the disabled; buy direct or call for a list of stockists. / *Hours: Mon-Fri 9am-5pm; free catalogue or online; Delivery: p&p included; no Amex.*

La Redoute ⌂
245-249 Harbury Rd, Wakefield WF2 8XZ ☎ Catalogue requests (0500) 350450, (0500) 777777 🖰 www.redoute.co.uk
French catalogue company, from the same stable as Cyrillus and Vertbaudet.
Maternity wear – Bras and underwear: maternity bras and lingerie.
Baby clothes – Mid-range: broad range of French fashion items and modern classics, including some familiar brands (Chipie, Kookai) – good detailing and embroidery, lots of natural fabrics, and reasonable prices; pack of three body suits for a newborn from £12; dress for a four year old £13; payment account scheme. / *Hours: Mon-Sun 8am-11pm; free catalogue; Delivery: p&p £2.45; no Amex.*

Regent Bookshop

73 Parkway, London NW1 7PP ☎ (020) 7485 9822

Books, music & videos – **Bookshops:** one-third of this general bookshop near Regent's Park is devoted to children's titles. / *Hours: Mon-Sat 9am-6pm, Sun noon-5pm.*

Rigby & Peller

CENTRAL CONTACT DETAILS

☎ (020) 7589 9293
🖰 www.rigbyandpeller.com
2 Hans Rd SW3 1RX
☎ (020) 7589 9293
22a Conduit St W1S 2TX
☎ (020) 7491 2200

Lingerie makers, most famous as suppliers of bras to HM the Queen; expert fitters.

Maternity wear – **Bras and underwear:** nursing range does not figure in their catalogue or on their website, as the store believe that professional fitting is essential; brands of nursing bras stocked include Royce and Anita from size 32 to 42 in A to L cups; also a US bra called Goddess with very soft cups that can be altered to make a feeding bra; buy and they offer 10% off your next non-maternity bra. / *Hours: W1 9.30am-7pm; SW3 Mon-Sat 9.30am-6pm, Wed 9.30am-7pm; Delivery: p&p £2.95.*

Rachel Riley 🖰

CENTRAL CONTACT DETAILS

☎ (020) 7935 7007
🖰 www.rachelriley.com
BRANCHES:
14 Pont St SW1X 9EN
☎ (020) 7259 5969
82 Marylebone High St W1
☎ (020) 7935 7007

Baby clothes – **Luxury.** – **Traditional:** upmarket ('50s inspired) clothes for kids; items include wool and cashmere dressing gowns, knitted bonnets with satin ruffled edges, cream flannelette pyjamas with tartan buttons, duffel coats and embroidered organza dresses; designed and made by an English mother of three living in France, so the styles reflect a combination of the styles of each country. The vast majority of items are machine washable; prices start at £6, and go up to around £100; cotton cardigan £42, smocked baby suit £49. The SW1 shop is also the base for the mail order company. – **Knitwear.**

Shoes – **Suppliers:** offers traditional Start-rite models that are only made for export, including styles with button and buckle straps plus handmade leather baby shoes; fitting by qualified staff. / *Hours: Mon-Sat 10am-6pm; free catalogue.*

The Rocking Horse Q

600 Kingston Rd, London SW20 8DN ☎ (020) 8542 4666

Second-hand shop where the emphasis is on clothes.

Baby equipment – **Second-hand:** prams, cots, high chairs and walkers.

Baby clothes – **Second-hand shops:** nearly-new clothing at "the good end of the market – items must be immaculate and fashionable".

Toys – **Second-hand shops:** good-quality second-hand books and toys. / *Hours: Mon-Fri 9.30am-4pm, Sat 10am-2pm (reduced hours in school holidays); no credit cards.*

Rocking Rhinos 🖰

The Old Corn Store, Station Road, Stalbridge, Dorset DT10 2RG ☎ (01963) 362 845 🖰 www.rockingrhinos.com

Toys – **Traditional toys:** rather amazing rocking African animals or special commissions, made by a specialist in fine furniture. The animals stand around 60cm high and weigh around 45kg. Included in the purchase is a Care for the Wild sponsorship to help protect endangered African wildlife. They're not particularly cheap – often over £1,000.

Roomers 🖰

1 Bishops Walk, Pinner, Middlesex HA5 5QQ ☎ (020) 8429 8000
🖰 www.roomergifts.com

Shop with online ordering promised soon.

Nursery decor – **Furniture:** hand-painted furniture for children, personalised by colour, design and with the child's name.

Naming gifts – **Naming gifts.** / *Hours: Mon-Fri 9.30am-5pm; online soon; Delivery: p&p extra; no Amex.*

Rosa

3 Stoke Newington Church St, London N16 0NX ☎ (020) 7254 3467

A business established in 1939.

Maternity wear – **Bras and underwear:** expert fitting in all kinds of bras, including maternity; brands include Emma-Jane and Royce; up to L cup. / *Hours: Mon-Sat 9.30am-5.30pm; Delivery: p&p depends (around £2.50).*

Rosa mundi 🖰

Mama Mia UK, Studio 24, Gilchrist Thomas Business Centre, Blaenavon, Torfaen NP4 9RL ☎ (01495) 790 660
🖰 www.rosa-mundi.com

Baby clothes – **Mid-range:** smart but practical clothes for 0-5 years including, for example, an all-in one with fleece inner and waxed outer, items in faux sheepskin, poncho suits, pyjamas and dressing gowns.

Rossi's

265 Chingford Mount Rd, London E4 8LP ☎ (020) 8529 1920 🖰 www.e4toys.co.uk

Twice winner of the London & South East 'Toy Shop of the Year' award.

Toys – **General stockists:** brands held in stock include Lego, Playmobil, Mattel and soft toys; lots of end-of-range branded toys at half-price. / *Hours: Mon-Sat 9am-6pm, Sun 10am-5pm.*

Route 73 Kids

92 Stoke Newington Church St, London N16 0AP ☎ (020) 7923 7873
🖰 www.route73kids.com

Toys – **Traditional toys:** toy shop specialising in hand-finished wooden toys (including dolls houses and furniture), train sets and cloth toys (rag dolls); no characterisation items; brands include Galt, Sevi, Brio and soft toys; play area. / *Hours: Tue-Sat 10am-5.30pm, Sun 12pm-5pm.*

Rowan ⌂
Green Lane Mill, Holmfirth HD9 2DX
☎ (01484) 681881 ⁂ www.knitrowan.com
Yarn pattern stockist information.
Baby clothes – Knitwear: the online
bookstore includes a good choice of knitting
books for baby and children's clothing. / Hours:
Mon-Fri 9am-5pm; can order patterns online; Delivery:
p&p extra; no Amex.

Roxy Baby ⌂
2 Fountains Way, Knaresborough, North
Yorkshire HG5 8HU ☎ (01423) 869 589
⁂ www.roxybaby.co.uk
Online retailer.
Nursery decor – Accessories: soft padded wall
hangings in bold and bright or soft pastels
using the firm's own 'Roxy Baby'
characters. / Hours: Internet sales only; Mon-Fri
9am-5.30pm; Delivery: p&p £2.95; no Amex.

Royce Lingerie ⌂
Beaumont Court, Beaumont Close, Banbury,
Oxfordshire OX16 1TG ☎ (01295) 265557
⁂ www.royce-lingerie.co.uk
Maternity wear – Bras and underwear:
manufacturers of nursing and support bras;
designs focus not just on fit, support, comfort
and ease of use, but also fashionable styling;
easy opening features, machine washable;
every bra has four different width adjustments;
buy from website or call for a list of local
stockists. / Hours: Mon-Thurs 8.45am-5pm; Fri until
1pm; free catalogue or online; Delivery: p&p £2; no
Amex.

Rrappers ⌂
44 Market Jew Street, Penzance, Cornwall
TR18 2HY ☎ (01736) 365 091
⁂ www.rrappers.com
Baby clothes – Outdoorwear: a website
offering 'creative headwear' with crown-like
points, tassels etc, in fleece, for adults as well as
children.

Rub a Dub Dub ⌂
15 Park Rd, London N8 8TE ☎ (020) 8342
9898
Second branch of shop in Finsbury Park.
Baby equipment – Stockists: nursery items
including prams, car seats, cots, and high chairs
from names like Maclaren, Maxi Cosi, Klippan,
Stokke, Mountain Buggy, Bugaboo and
Kingswood.
Nursery decor – Bedding: cot bedding from
Apple Pie and Zorbit.
Baby clothes – Mid-range: brands include
Coco (traditional babygrows, sleeping bags,
rompers etc).
Shoes – Suppliers: shoes from Daisy Roots,
Bobux, Shoo Shoo.
**Nappies – Reusable stockists - multiple
brands:** stockists of Bambino Mio and Tushies
(cotton and terry) nappies. – **Suppliers-Eco
friendly disposables:** biodegradable Tushies
and Moltex nappies. / Hours: Mon-Sat 10am-
5.30pm; free catalogue; no Amex.

Russell & Bromley (Feet First)
BRANCHES:
Unit 57 The Broadway W5
☎ (020) 8567 0365
Brent Cross Shopping Centre NW4 3FG
☎ (020) 8203 4161
98 High St, Bromley BR1
☎ (020) 8460 2478
Shoes – Suppliers: the children's shoe section
of this quality shoe chain has a stand-alone
store at Brent Cross and operates as
a department of selected other branches;
Start-rite, Clarks and own-brand shoes are the
biggest ranges, but there are a numerous
others. / Hours: mostly Mon-Sat 9.30am-6pm.

Safety Zone ⌂
Unit C7, Deal Enterprise Centre, Western
Rd, Deal, Kent CT14 6PJ ☎ (01304) 374777
⁂ www.safety-zone.co.uk/
Nursery decor – Safety items: a
comprehensive range of security equipment
(for children and otherwise) – from VCR locks,
wrist reins and oven locks to surveillance
cameras – which you can browse and order
online.

Salvatore Ferragamo
24 Old Bond St, London W1S 4AL ☎ (020)
7629 5007 ⁂ www.ferragamo.com,
www.salvatoreferragamo.it
Naming gifts – Naming gifts: the Ferragamo
silk-square teddy bear (£129) makes a present
to treasure. / Hours: Mon-Sat 10am-6pm.

Sam-I-Am ⌂
Besthorpe Rd, Nth Scarle, Lincolnshire
LN6 9EZ ☎ (01522) 778926
⁂ www.sam-i-am.co.uk
Online supplier (with mail order catalogue also
available), that also has a network of
consultants around the country demonstrating
the nappies; (call or visit the site to find your
nearest).
Maternity wear – Bras and underwear:
nursing bra from Bravado, £23; also breast pads
available in silk, cottons and organic wools.
**Nappies – Reusable stockists - brands
& singles:** a wide range of cloth nappies and
accessories, including organic and GM free
cotton nappies, funky wraps and covers; brands
include Sam-I-Am, Popolino, Snugglenaps and
Snazzystuffs pocket nappies. / Hours: by
appointment; free catalogue; Delivery: from £1.60.

Sandman Beds ⌂
☎ (01923) 283598
⁂ www.sandmanbeds.com
Nursery decor – Beds: beds made by parents
who started off designing custom beds for their
daughters, with themes like butterflies, the sea,
trains and flowers; clean lines and simple
colours; butterfly bed £385. / free catalogue.

Sangenic
Green Oak Works, 29 Hamilton Way,
Oakham Business Park, Mansfield NG18 5BU
☎ (01623) 635447
⁂ www.nappywrapper.com
Part of the Jackel International group (along
with Tommee Tippee and Maws).
Nappies – Disposable nappy accessories: the
Nappy Wrapper is a special bin enabling 24
used nappies (large version around 45 nappies)
to be sealed within the bin in a long
'sausage'-string of plastic sacks; particularly
useful if you don't have easy access to outdoor
bins; small version RRP £30. Ring for stockists

or purchase direct. You will also need to buy
the antibacterial wrap which stores the nappies
(one roll is about a month's supply; £3.49
online, more in shops). / *Hours: Mon-Fri 8.30am-
5pm (customer services 3.30pm); free leaflet; no Amex.*

Sara Copeland Interiors
32 Byfeld Gardens, Barnes, London
SW13 9HP ☎ (07889) 228477
⌁ www.saracopelandinteriors.com
<u>Nursery decor</u> – **Interior designers:** a
complete interior design service, including
themed bedrooms using the firm's own
carpenters, painters and muralists; work on
a nursery might start from £2500 but is more
usually £2,000 in total; there are pictures on the
website of previous jobs; call for further
information or to book an initial consultation
(£65, refundable against subsequent services).

Sasti 🖂
8 Portobello Green Arcade, 281 Portobello
Rd, London W10 5TZ ☎ (020) 8960 1125
⌁ www.sasti.co.uk
Shop (with children's play area) and mail order
business.
<u>Baby clothes</u> – **Mid-range:** jackets, pinafores,
trousers, waistcoats, fake fur coats, wacky hats
and dragon dressing gowns with spiky hoods;
almost all items are handmade in the UK by
the company or one of their three labels (Ten
Fingers Ten Toes, R Life); stripey hat, £4.
<u>Shoes</u> – **Suppliers:** boots, bootees, shoes and
trainers. / *Hours: Mon-Sat 10am-6pm; free brochure.*

SBS (Step by Step) 🖂
Lee Fold, Hyde, Cheshire SK14 4LL ☎ (0845)
300 1089 ⌁ www.sbs-educational.co.uk
<u>Toys</u> – **Nursery suppliers:** established over
a century ago, this division of Premier
Educational Suppliers is an under-8s specialist
mainly supplies nurseries (but has no
minimum order); large range – categories
include arts & crafts, sand & water, physical
play, soft play, role play, construction,
numeracy, language & literacy, music, puzzles,
games, special needs and furniture; Little Tikes
is among the brands stocked. / *Hours: Mon-Fri
8.30am-5pm; free catalogue; Delivery: 7-10 days.*

Schmidt Natural Clothing 🖂
Corbiere, Nursery Lane, Nutley, East Sussex
TN22 3NS ☎ (0845) 345 0498
⌁ www.naturalclothing.co.uk
A large and meticulous catalogue from
a well-run, eco-friendly firm (aimed at adults as
well as kids); not cheap, but good value.
<u>Nursery decor</u> – **Bedding:** organic cotton
sheets and pillowcases; organic wool blankets
and wool-filled duvets from cot to king size
(from £70). – **Sleeping Bags:** exclusive
all-cotton two-layer sleeping bags for babies
and children.
<u>Baby clothes</u> – **Eco-friendly clothing:** natural
fibre clothing, organically produced and free of
chemical finishes: including untreated wool,
silk and cotton; the range majors in underwear,
sleepwear, tights, and baby grows; simple
practical outerwear includes socks and woolen
slippers. Items suitable for use in children with
eczema.
<u>Toys</u> – **Cuddly toys:** fluffy toys made from
organic cotton and wool, from a baby lion (£7)
to a panda bear teddy (£30).

<u>Nappies</u> – **Reusable stockists - brands
& singles:** organic washable nappies: cotton
inners have a brushed cotton or muslin liner
for extra absorbency, £1.90 each. (A raw silk
liner can also be added to relieve nappy rash.)
Woollen overpants (from £9.45) can be made
to measure as well as the standard sizes. Other
products: wool for knitting, £3.90; trial nappy
pack, from £8.20; microfibre plastic pants,
£8.10. / *Hours: Mon-Fri 9am-6pm, 24hr
answerphone; free catalogues; Delivery: p&p included
on most items.*

Scrumptious Design 🖂
Embargo, 1 Shakespeare Street, Stratford-
upon-Avon, Warwick CU37 6RN ☎ (0870)
240 6672 ⌁ www.scrumptiousdesign.co.uk
<u>Naming gifts</u> – **Naming gifts:** contemporary,
customised handmade stationery, accessories
and fashion and home items, including
baby-specific items, such as photograph
albums. / *Hours: Mon-Fri 9am-5pm.*

Sea Horse Furniture
Sea Horse Centre, 70 Colindale Avenue,
London NW9 5ES ☎ (020) 8200 9088
⌁ www.seahorsefurniture.co.uk
<u>Nursery decor</u> – **Furniture:** "Children's safety
furniture." Shop selling children's armchairs,
sofas and sofabeds in PU foam covered in
a selection of fabrics, many of them novelty
designs. / *Hours: Mon-Fri 9.30am-6.30pm; Sat-Sun
11am-6.30pm; free catalogue; Delivery: p&p extra; no
Amex.*

Second Impressions
10 Montpelier Vale, London SE3 0TA
☎ (020) 8852 6192
<u>Toys</u> – **General stockists:** good range of
pre-school toys. / *Hours: Mon-Sat 9.30am-5.30pm.*

SeeSaw Children's Clothing 🖂
The Granary, Bentley Rd, Willesborough,
Ashford, Kent TN24 0LB ☎ (01233) 662700
⌁ www.seesaw.uk.com
<u>Baby clothes</u> – **Mid-range:** reversible clothing
in bright colours and practical styles, sold by
party plan reps throughout London, or
available by mail order; pinafores, dungarees
and trousers (£20); call to find your nearest rep
or to order a catalogue. / *Hours: Mon-Fri 9am-
3pm, or answerphone; free catalogue or online;
Delivery: p&p £2.95; no Amex.*

James Selby
384-400 Holloway Rd, London N7 6PR
☎ (020) 7607 2466
⌁ www.james-selby.co.uk
<u>Baby clothes</u> – **Mid-range:** a wide range of
clothes from Adams.
<u>Toys</u> – **General stockists:** names stocked
include Chicco, Tomy, Galt, Fisher-Price and
Mattel. / *Hours: Mon-Fri 9.30am-6pm, Sat 9am-
6pm.*

Selfridges
400 Oxford St, London W1A 1AB ☎ (08708)
377377 ⌁ www.selfridges.co.uk
The extensive clothing and shoe department is
the prime reason to visit this famous
department store. (It does not stock any baby
equipment – apart from the swanky buggy,
the Bugaboo Frog – or maternity wear,

and offers practically nothing in the way of nursery furniture.)

Baby clothes – Luxury: lots of Continental styles, including the UK's largest Petit Bateau concession; designer ranges include D&G, Ralph Lauren, DKNY, Christian Dior, Trusardi, Catamini, Simonetta and Pringle.
Shoes – Suppliers: staffed with trained fitters, the shoe section stocks Buckle My Shoe, Moschino, Diesel, Prada, Cavelli, Sketchers and Timberland.
Toys – General stockists: a reasonable-sized department.
Books, music & videos – Bookshops: the basement bookshop of this Oxford Street landmark stocks more 4,000 children's titles, with a wide range for pre-schoolers, plus a good selection of gift books. / *Hours: Mon-Fri 10am-7pm (Thu & Fri 8pm), Sat 9.30am-7pm, Sun noon-6pm.*

Seraphine 🏠
28a Kensington Church St, London W8
☎ (020) 7937 3156 🖱 www.seraphine.com
Maternity items from a former Armani designer, whose business supplies other stores and is looking to add a second of its own; also arrival/naming gifts and baby clothes.
Maternity wear – Luxury: a few designers at the luxury end.
Nursery decor – Furniture: classic cots and cot beds; changing units from Belgium. / *Hours: Mon-Sat 10.30am-6pm; Sun 1pm-6pm; online catalogue; Delivery: p&p £3; no Amex.*

7+7 Futons & Interiors 🏠
109 Balham High Rd, London SW12 9AP
☎ (020) 8675 6727, (0800) 781 3667
🖱 www.futonsonline.co.uk
Baby equipment – Specialist mattress suppliers: cot futons with cotton fillings, priced from £60 for standard sizes; can be made to measure.
Nursery decor – Accessories: good range of lighting and mobiles. / *Hours: Mon-Sat 10am-6pm; online catalogue; Delivery: p&p extra; no Amex.*

Sevi
🖱 www.sevi.com
Toys – Brand: established in 1831, this excellent Italian brand (Europe's oldest) makes predominantly wooden items: notably mobiles, figures and letters.

Sheepland 🏠
The Hollies, Peacocks Hill, Barton Saint David, Somerset TA11 6BN ☎ (01458) 850991 🖱 www.sheepskin.co.uk
Specialists in lambskin products; gift service.
Baby equipment – Lambskins: size approximately 22in x 33in, £46.50. / *online catalogue; Delivery: p&p £5; no Amex.*

Shelfstore 🏠
Frognal Parade, 158 Finchley Rd, London NW3 5HH ☎ (020) 7794 0313
🖱 www.shelfstore.co.uk
Nursery decor – Furniture: shop and mail order business providing an expandable wood kit system suitable for building a child's bedroom: half of their products are aimed at children, including cupboards, wardrobes, beds and desks; all units are in solid pine, with different possibilities for colouring with paint

and fabric – items can be customised to your specifications or left plain for you to decorate. / *Hours: Mon-Fri 10am-5.30pm, Sat 10am-5pm; free catalogue or online; Delivery: p&p extra; no Amex.*

Patricia Sherwood 🏠
7 Crown Yard, Bedgebury Estate, Bedgebury Rd, Goudhurst, Kent TN17 2QZ ☎ (01580) 212777
Primarily a mail order operation (though there is a small showroom); visits to clients' home by appointment.
Baby equipment – Cots: supplier of cradles, cribs and Moses baskets in natural materials, complete with draped lace veils, satin ribbons and flounced edges.
Nursery decor – Accessories: specialises in redressing customers' cradles and baskets; also supplies nappy stacks, padded hangers, brush sets, cushions and layette baskets in cotton or silk.
Baby clothes – Christening gowns: made-to-measure silk and lace Christening gowns, and accessories; hand-beading an option; gowns can be made up from a wedding dress; prices from £250, say, for smocked silk taffeta. / *Hours: Mon-Fri 9am-6pm by appointment only; Delivery: p&p £17.50 (next day); no Amex.*

Shetland Collection 🏠
Exnaboe, Virkie, Shetland ZE3 9JS ☎ (01950) 460340 🖱 www.shetlandknitwear.net
Comprehensive, well-designed catalogue.
Baby clothes – Mid-range. – Christening gowns: beautifully soft and fine shawls from £70; cobweb lace shawl in one-ply wool, specifically designed for Christenings, £300. / *Hours: Mon-Fri 9am-5pm, or answerphone; free catalogue or online; Delivery: p&p £3.50 per item (gift wrap); no Amex.*

Shoe & Fashion Boutique
28 Stamford Hill, London N16 6XZ ☎ (020) 8806 5581
Baby clothes – Mid-range.
Shoes – Suppliers: some Continental brands, as well as Start-rite and Clarks. / *Hours: Mon-Fri 10.30am-6pm.*

The Shoe Station
3 Station Approach, Richmond TW9 3QB
☎ (020) 8940 9905
🖱 www.theshoestation.co.uk
Shoes – Suppliers: brands include Start-rite, Buckle My Shoe, Daisy Roots, Elefanten, Bobux, Ricosta, and Salamander. / *Hours: Mon-Sat 10am-6pm; no Amex.*

Shoozies 🏠
☎ (01726) 851 755 🖱 www.shoozies.com
Shoes – Brands: trendy knitted baby shoes/slippers in two sizes, for the first and second halves of the baby's first year; £12 inc p&p.

Shop4Toys 🏠
Jubilee Estate, Foundry Lane, Horsham, W Sussex RH13 5UE ☎ (0845) 130 4708
🖱 www.shop4toys.co.uk
Toys – Character toys: extensive range of character items (Mr Men, Noddy, Thomas the Tank Engine, Tweenies, Barbie, Teletubbies, Bob the Builder…) including toys, books and

videos. / *Hours: Mon-Fri 8am-6pm; free catalogue or online; UK mainland; no Amex, no Diner's card.*

Silk Story 🏠
Long Barn, Marshfield Farm, Marsh Gibbon OX27 0AG ☎ (01869) 277181
🖰 www.silkstory.com
Mail order company – see website or call for details.

<u>Baby clothes</u> – **Luxury:** pure silk jersey baby and childrenswear – absorbent, soft and light, it allows skin to breathe and reduces rashes and irritation (and may be helpful for babies with eczema). The range consists of tops, short and long leggings, all-in-one bodysuits for babies; plain colours and a leopard-print range, all machine washable; prices from £6-£25; gift-wrapping available.

<u>Naming gifts</u> – **Naming gifts:** gift pack, enclosed in organza gift bags, including silk clothing (babygrow and hat) for newborns, £21 (or £22 with long sleeves). / *Hours: 24hr answerphone; free catalogue; Delivery: p&p included.*

Silver Cross
Otley Rd, Guiseley, Leeds, West Yorkshire LS20 8LP ☎ (01943) 876177
🖰 www.silvercross.co.uk
Over 120 years old, this 'Rolls Royce' brand famed for its large, traditional, 'Mary Poppins' prams – all the Queen's children had one – has had a troubled recent history. It's current owners have run it since 2003.

<u>Baby equipment</u> – **Wheeled Transport-brands:** know for its traditional pram styles (the 'heritage' range), but the company does also produce more contemporary models (the 'lifestyle' range). Call for details and local stockists (in London, including Lilliput, John Lewis and London Prams).

Silver Editions 🏠
Unitek House, Churchfield Rd, Chalfont St Peter, Bucks SL9 9EW ☎ (01753) 888810
🖰 www.silver-editions.co.uk
<u>Naming gifts</u> – **Naming gifts:** silver and silver-plated gifts: plated items suitable for children include a mug (£10); teddy knife and fork (£10); trinket box (£10); rattle (£12); alphabet money box (£10). Solid silver gifts include a child's comb (£25); bristle hairbrush (£70); tooth fairy mushroom (£30); and child's tankard (£80); engraving extra. / *Hours: Mon-Fri 8.30am-5.30pm, 24hr answerphone; free catalogue or online; no Amex.*

Simon Horn 🏠
117-121 Wandsworth Bridge Rd, London SW6 2TP ☎ (020) 7731 1279
🖰 www.simonhorn.com
An international chain selling top-quality furniture which also sells mail order.

<u>Baby equipment</u> – **Cots:** hand-built beds in two sizes, both of which start as a cot, then convert to a bed (suitable for a child of up to 8 years old), and finally convert to a sofa; built in Californian cherry wood, oak or sycamore with a brass nameplate – priced from about £1,795.

<u>Nursery decor</u> – **Furniture:** convertible furniture which grows with your child, such as a changing unit (which transforms into a bookshelf/chest of drawers), a bookcase (which changes into a work station), a mini wardrobe (which converts to a TV cabinet), all in matching wood – cherry, oak or sycamore. / *Hours: showroom & mail order Mon-Sat 9.30am-5.30pm; free catalogue or online.*

Simply Baby
Northwick Park Hospital, Maternity Unit, Watford Rd, Harrow HA1 3UJ ☎ (07736) 660781
<u>Baby equipment</u> – **Stockists:** a shop offering brands including Mamas & Papas, Chicco, Cosatto, Bebecar and Avent.

Simply Outgrown ♀
360 Lordship Lane, London N17 7QX ☎ (020) 8801 0568
<u>Baby equipment</u> – **Second-hand:** car seats, buggies, babywalkers, cots and high-chairs; new, second-hand, ex-display and sample equipment.

<u>Toys</u> – **Second-hand shops:** wide range of toys for all ages; items from 20p. / *Hours: Mon-Sat 10am-5pm; no credit cards.*

Simply Stuck 🏠
Little Holt, Barrow Hill Barnes, Goodworth Clatford, Hampshire SP11 7RG ☎ (01264) 350788 🖰 www.simplystuck.com
<u>Baby equipment</u> – **Name labels:** name labels: dishwasher and microwave-proof stickers, ideal for bottles and feeding equipment (50 for £8; 100 for £10; red, blue or green); iron-on labels (50 for £8; 100 for £10; blue); iron-on permanent transfers (50 for £8; 100 for £10; blue only); traditional woven labels (100 for £10; blue or red; iron or sew-on). Also available: stickers bearing invitations, changes of address or Christmas greetings. / *online catalogue; Delivery: p&p £1.*

Skipper Ltd 🏠
Unit 12, Thompson Drive, Bentwaters Park, Rendlesham, Woodbridge, Suffolk IP12 2RQ ☎ (01394) 420 320
<u>Toys</u> – **Traditional toys:** handcrafted wooden toys including some to sit on and some to ride, including a red London bus, and some large enough to seat two small children. Also castles, farm houses, dolls' houses and yachts. / *Hours: Mon-Fri 8am-5pm; free catalogue; Delivery: £5.*

Sleepy Bunnies 🏠
☎ (01865) 300 310
<u>Nursery decor</u> – **Sleeping Bags:** machine-washable, cotton sleeping bags with zip front, extendable so suitable for use from 3 months-3 years. / *leaflet; Delivery: £3.50 ; no Amex.*

Sling Easy 🏠
172 Victoria Rd, Wargrave, Reading RG10 8AJ ☎ (0118) 940 4942
🖰 www.slingeasy.co.uk
<u>Baby equipment</u> – **Slings:** an over-the-shoulder-sling £27-£37 depending on your choice from a very wide range of fabrics (all 100% cotton with thick padding); made in Britain under licence from the original US manufacturer; instruction video shows the six different positions of using the sling; also duffel bags (£6.50) and 'dolly slings' for your child to carry (£8.50). / *Hours: 24hr answerphone; online catalogue, or leaflet with fabric swatches; Delivery: p&p included; no Mastercard & no Amex.*

Small Acorn 🏠
6 Cauper Rd, London W3 6PZ ☎ (020) 8993
3559 🖰 www.smallacorn.com
Hand-knitted clothes for babies.
Baby clothes – Luxury. – Knitwear:
hand-made in the UK using British wool;
bootees and knitted shoes £17; scarves and
bobble hats £16-£18; chunky jerseys and
cardigans in wool and cotton, generally
£30-£40. / free brochure; Delivery: p&p £3 (free over
£50); no Amex.

Small Folk 🏠
☎ (020) 8204 1861 🖰 www.smallfolk.com
Parenting and e-commerce site enlivened by
content from Great Ormond Street Hospital,
which includes a 'bazaar' for buying and selling
second-hand items; 5% of the money raised by
the site is donated to the hospital. The main
focus is children under five.
Toys – General stockists: good selection of
toys, from outdoor playthings to bath toys;
brands include Brio, Chicco, Little Tikes and
Tomy. / online catalogue; no Amex.

Smilechild 🏠
PO Box 274, Cheltenham, Gloucestershire
GL53 7YP ☎ (01242) 269 635
🖰 www.smilechild.co.uk
An all-purpose website selling clothes, shoes,
eco-friendly nappies and some baby
equipment.
**Baby equipment – Stockists - slings
& backpacks:** kelty KIDS backpacks and
carriers from America.
Baby clothes – Outdoorwear: outdoor
clothing.
Shoes – Suppliers: soft leather shoes from
Starchild: the printed catalogue includes
a measuring chart to ensure you get the right
size or download one from the internet.
Toys – Traditional toys: wooden toys and
mobiles.
**Nappies – Reusable stockists - multiple
brands:** a good range of nappies is available
online from this general baby
website. / Delivery: p&p £3.95 under £75.

Patricia Smith 🏠
Higher Amalwhidden, Towednack, Nr St
Ives, Cornwall TR26 3AR ☎ (01736) 793188
🖰 www.patriciasmith.co.uk
Baby clothes – Mid-range: modern, classic
designs with a humorous twist; cotton dresses,
rompers, knickerbockers, and Bermudas in
twills, checks and stripes; also baby sunsuits
and sun dresses, and special wedding
commissions; romper suit from £35.
– Christening gowns: made to order, with
smocking a speciality; varied prices on
application. / Hours: Mon-Fri 9am-5pm, or
answerphone; free catalogue; Delivery: p&p £5 (UK),
£12 (Europe).

Fi Smith Fairisles 🏠
Balcombe House, Balcombe, West Sussex
RH17 6PB ☎ (01444) 811267
Baby clothes – Mid-range. – Knitwear:
hand-framed and hand-knitted items, from
Shetland; 100 percent wool jumpers, cardigans,
hats and mittens; can knit to order; prices start
around £20. / Hours: answerphone; no catalogue

(customers can request photographs of the products);
no credit cards.

Smiths Bros Tooting
103-133 Mitcham Rd, London SW17 9PE
☎ (020) 8672 6556
🖰 www.smithsbros-tooting.co.uk
Toys – General stockists: small general toy
department; wider range is stocked at
Christmas. / Hours: Mon-Fri 9.30am-5.30pm, Sat
9am-6pm.

The Smock Shop 🏠
Little Rosemorran, Gulval, Penzance
TR20 8YP ☎ (01736) 367989
🖰 www.thesmockshop.com
Baby clothes – Mid-range. – Traditional:
classic seaside clothes produced in Cornwall:
smocks, Breton long-sleeved T-shirts, nautical
fleeces; great line in pirate accessories –
headbands and caps (all under £5), Jolly Roger
flag (£15), pirate T-shirts from £7.75; 10%
discount on orders over £50. / Hours: 24hrs
answerphone; free catalogue; Delivery: p&p included;
no Amex.

Snap Dragon
56 Turnham Green Terrace, London
W4 1QP ☎ (020) 8995 6618
🖰 www.snapdragontoys.com
Toys – General stockists: high-quality toys
including a good selection for younger children
with brands such as Brio, Fisher-Price, Galt,
Lego, Duplo and Tomy; also books.
– Outdoor items & active toys: sandpits and
items from the Little Tikes and TP outdoor
ranges. / Hours: Mon-Sat 9.30am-6pm, Sunday
11.30-5pm.

Snazzy Pants 🏠
Besthorpe Road, North Scarle, Lincs
LN6 9EZ ☎ (01522-778440
🖰 www.snazzypants.co.uk
**Nappies – Reusable stockists - brands
& singles:** a range including Bumpy wool
wraps, Nature Babies fleece wraps (with leg
gusset), Imse Vimse and Under the Nile
organic nappies, Sam I Am, Tots Bots and
Whisper Wraps.

Snips Q
The Crypt, St John's Church, Broomfield
Place, London W13 9LA ☎ (020) 8840 0651
Nearly-new store located within a community
centre-style space, with a free play area and
a kitchen for lunches and snacks.
Baby clothes – Second-hand shops.
Toys – Second-hand shops: toys, books and
video games.
Hairdressers – Hairdressers: open Tuesdays
and Thursdays during term time, 10am-1pm;
£5. / Hours: Tue-Thu 10am-1pm; no credit cards.

Snow & Rock 🏠
CENTRAL CONTACT DETAILS
☎ (0845) 100 1000
🖰 www.snowandrock.com
BRANCHES:
4 Mercer St WC2H 9QA
☎ (0845) 100 1018
188 Kensington High St W8
☎ (020) 7937 0872
150 Holborn EC1

☎ (020) 7831 6900

Large chain of ski-wear and climbing specialists that also sells gear for taking baby with you on the slopies, and when rambling or doing other outdoor activities; clothes are stocked seasonally – don't expect ski clothes in summer.

Baby equipment – Stockists - slings & backpacks: baby carriers (fit on your back); and baby joggers (rough terrain pushchairs).
Baby clothes – Outdoorwear: ski clothing (aims to stock everything for skiing from toddler-age upwards; the warm clothing, of course, is also useful when there is no snow), waterproofs, jackets, fleeces and splashsuits. / *Hours: Mon-Fri 9am-6pm, Sat 9am-5pm, shop hours differ; free catalogue; Delivery: p&p £2.50 (orders up to £100).*

Snowdown ⌨
19 Tudor Court, Tudor Way, London W3 9AQ ☎ (020) 8992 2301
⁷ www.snowdown.co.uk
Call for stockists, or online ordering coming soon.
Baby clothes – Outdoorwear: a graduate of the London College of fashion aims to provide a complete 'outdoorwear Wardrobe' – plastic umbrellas (£9), bags and raincoats (£16) – for toddlers. / *Hours: 9.30am-5.30pm, 24 hr answerphone.*

Snug as a Bug ⌨
Tania Chamberlain, 72a Madeira St, Edinburgh EH6 4AU ☎ (0131) 553 4191
⁷ www.snugasabug.co.uk, www.idealcottons.com
Nursery decor – Sleeping Bags: made from cotton in tartan or gingham checks; machine-washable with detachable sleeves; flame retardant (BS5722); summer and winter weights; sizes from three months to three years; prices from £30. / *Hours: 10am-5pm or 24hr answerphone; free brochure; no Amex.*

Snugger ⌨
PO Box 570, Cheam, Sutton, Surrey SM2 7LE ☎ (020) 8224 8766
⁷ www.snuggeruk.com
Nursery decor – Sleeping Bags: standard bags (tog rating 2.2 and 2.5), plus summer bags (tog rating 0.5), in three sizes; fabric options from plain ginghams to jungle animals or Winnie the Pooh; prices from £17 for summer bags; suitable for children up to the age of three. / *Hours: Mon-Sat 9am-6pm; no Amex.*

Snuggle Naps ⌨
2 Daybrook St, Sherwood, Notts NG5 2HD ☎ (0115) 910 7220
⁷ www.snugglenaps.co.uk
Baby equipment – Stockists: a wide range of baby equipment is stocked, from cots to buggies and highchairs; almost everything except clothes and toys. – Bathing: hooded towel and mitts, £10.50.
Nappies – Reusable stockists - brands & singles: claiming to make the largest range of nappies and accessories in Britain, in a 'grow with your baby' design. Suitable for children up to 55lbs – with an all-in-one or two-part option – the nappies have double elasticated leg barriers and waistband, patterned outers and absorbent cotton inner pads. The firm also

stocks traditional terries, including a new shaped version, with waterproof breathable outer pants; the outer covers can also be used with disposable inner pads for holidays, long journeys etc (trial pack of one cover and one pad £12.50); the company also supply swim pants, trainer pants and products for children with special needs. – Change bags: change bag, nappy bag and change mat as set or individually. / *Hours: Mon-Fri 8.30am-4.30pm; free catatlogue.*

Snuglo ⌨
Studio 54, Pennybank Chambers, 33-35 St John's Square, London EC1M 4DS ☎ (020) 7608 3000 ⁷ www.snuglo.com
Baby clothes – Funky: hip bibs, T-shirts, and all-in-ones, in colourful graphic prints; bodysuit £14.

Soma Books
38 Kennington Lane, London SE11 4LS ☎ (020) 7735 2101
⁷ www.childrens-books.uk.com
Books, music & videos – Bookshops: a specialist in black literature, stocking books and information on Africa, the Caribbean, Asia and black America. There's a whole room devoted to cultural diversity, educational, anti-sexist and anti-racist books for children, and the range of books for under-twos, while small, is probably one of the best available. Largest stockist of dual language books. / *Hours: Mon-Fri 9.30am-5.30pm.*

Soup Dragon
CENTRAL CONTACT DETAILS
☎ Head office (020) 8348 9444
⁷ www.soup-dragon.co.uk
BRANCHES:
27 Topsfield Parade, Tottenham Lane N8 8PT
☎ (020) 8348 0224
106 Lordship Lane SE22 8HF
☎ (020) 8693 5575
Duo of shops supplying a good range items.
Baby equipment – Buggy & pram repairs: all makes including Mothercare, including discontinued models.
Nursery decor – Furniture: furniture painted/customised on the premises, including chairs, blackboards and mirrors.
Baby clothes – Mid-range: bright and unusual children's selection: larger ranges include Osh Kosh; babygrows from £6.
Toys – Traditional toys: good selection of traditional wooden and other toys, including a number of non-mainstream educational makes such as Skwish, Orchard and Hopscotch jigsaws.

Sovereign ⌨
40 Towerfield Road, Shoeburyness, Essex SS3 9QT ☎ (01702) 291 129
⁷ www.sovereignplayequipment.co.uk
Toys – Outdoor items & active toys: professional playground installers, offering plastic and wood ranges. These include models suitable for restricted spaces (from £2,195). / *Hours: Mon-Fri 8am-6pm; Free catalogue.*

Spirit of Nature 🖘
Burrhart House, Craddock Rd, Luton, Beds
LU4 OJF ☎ (0870) 725 9885
🖑 www.spiritofnature.co.uk
Online and mail order retailer of over 1,000
products with an organic/ environmentally
friendly emphasis; as well as those below,
the firm sells the Natural Mat range of
matresses.
__Maternity wear__ – **Bras and underwear:**
nursing Bra Lena: organic cotton 97% and 3%
Lycra (£23).
__Baby equipment__ – **Cots:** cot-bed in natural
oiled beech, £235.
__Nursery decor__ – **Bedding:** assortment of
bedding, including various sleeping bags in
organic cotton.
__Baby clothes__ – **Mid-range.** – **Eco-friendly
clothing:** natural cotton and natural wool
garments – from socks, hats, tights and mittens
to fleece tops through to outerwear.
__Nappies__ – **Reusable stockists - brands
& singles:** shaped nappies, a cotton knitted
nappy, woollen/felted overpants and
waterproof microfibre overpants; also one-way
nappy liners, twilled cotton squares, muslins
and silk liners for nappy rash prevention.
Environmentally-friendly washing powders
and household cleaners are also available.
– **Suppliers-Eco friendly disposables:**
suppliers of Moltex Oko, to fit 6-12lbs; also the
Bambo range. / *free catalogue; Delivery: p&p £2.95;
no Amex.*

Spottiswoode Trading 🖘
PO Box 3009, Littlehampton, West Sussex
BN17 5SJ ☎ (01903) 733123
🖑 www.spottiswoodetrading.com
__Nursery decor__ – **Storage:** nursery organisers;
bright fabric basket containing stuffed cotton
animals, £24.95; Catch All drawstring bag
£12.95.
__Toys__ – **General stockists:** catalogue business
selling brightly coloured, handmade toys, gifts
and nursery presents; lots of cute toys based on
animals; also bags, mobiles (from £14) and
school bags. / *Hours: Mon-Fri 9am-5.30pm; free
catalogue or online; Delivery: p&p £2.95 (free on
orders over £100).*

Squeakyfeet
PO Box 428, Staines, Middlesex TW18 1WG
☎ (01784) 640 005
🖑 www.squeakyfeet.co.uk
__Shoes__ – **Brands:** suppliers of slip-proof baby
and infant footwear (up to four years),
designed to squeak so as to encourage walking
and to ensure that the child can be heard when
out of sight.

St John's Wood Interiors
27 St John's Wood High St, London
NW8 7NH ☎ (020) 7722 9204
A range of hand-painted furniture with
a polished or colour wash finish, designed to
order (examples of themes include giraffes,
Humpty Dumpty or motorbikes) or in plain
pine; call for a brochure.
__Baby equipment__ – **Cots:** hand-painted cot bed.
__Nursery decor__ – **Beds:** hand-painted and
pine-finished children's beds. – **Furniture:**
range includes toy chests (£295), wardrobes,
chests of drawers. / *Hours: Mon-Sat 9am-6pm; no
Amex.*

Star Child 🖘
109 Paget St, Loughborough, Leics LE11 5DU
☎ (01509) 550714 🖑 www.star-child.co.uk
Mail order suppliers of their own products.
__Shoes__ – **Brands:** handmade shoes in soft
leather with suede grip soles, non-toxic dyes
and an elasticated ankle; fun, colourful designs
(including one commissioned by Liam
Gallagher for his son); £14 per pair for 0-2 year
olds, £16 for 2-4 year olds. / *free catalogue;
Delivery: p&p included.*

Start-rite
CENTRAL CONTACT DETAILS
☎ (0800) 783 2138
🖑 www.start-rite.co.uk
BRANCHES:
Crome Rd, Norwich NR3 4RD
☎ (0800) 783 2138
47 High St SW19
☎ (020) 8946 9735
A two hundred-year-old business – the classic
children's shoe-making firm; the freephone
number can provide this season's catalogue
and point you to your nearest stockist. The
nearest factory outlet shop (where stocks are
mostly end-of-lines) is 8 High Street, King's
Lynn, Norfolk PE30 1BX, (01553) 760786.
__Shoes__ – **Brands:** widely acclaimed as the
ultimate in properly-fitted shoes for children –
traditional styles as well as, of late, more
style-conscious items (including special
corrective shoes for various foot problems,
which are generally ordered with a doctor's
letter.) Six different width fittings are available.
– **Suppliers:** many of the concessions run by
the store have now been taken over by Instep,
but as well as its factory outlets, it still has
a few own-brand stores.

Startsmart 🖘
Woodgate Manor Farm, Woodgate,
Bromsgrove, Worcs B60 4HG ☎ (01527)
821766 🖑 www.startsmart.co.uk
__Baby clothes__ – **Traditional:** the company's
off-the-peg range is classical, both smart and
casual, with natural fibres predominant. It
includes lots of nightwear, items such as slogan
sweatshirts ("small but dangerous", £15),
sound-effect sweatshirts (£17.50), and unusual
items including a range of cord & moleskin
pinafores; appliqued country motifs. Baby
garments include crawlers, shirts, pinafores,
polos and cotton underwear; also knitwear,
nightwear, socks and accessories. Items can be
made to the customer's specifications. / *Hours:
Mon-Fri 9am-5pm, or answerphone; free catalogue or
online; Delivery: p&p £3.50 (UK), £6 (Europe), £12
(worldwide).*

The Stencil Library 🖘
Stocksfield Hall, Stocksfield, Northumberland
NE43 7TN ☎ (01661) 844844
🖑 www.stencil-library.com
__Nursery decor__ – **Stencils & stamps:** shop and
mail order business with 3000 designs, of
which a substantial number are suitable for
children's rooms; also stocks stencilling
equipment. The catalogue contains a £5
voucher redeemable against stencil
purchases. / *Hours: Mon-Sat 9.30am-5.30pm;*

catalogue £10/ can order online; Delivery: p&p free in UK.

Step 2 (UK) Ltd 🖃
Lowkber Lane, Ingleton, N. Yorkshire
LA6 3JD ☎ (0800) 393159
🖱 www.step2.com or activitytoysdirect.com
Ohio-based company producing a range of moulded plastic goods – not beautiful but practical and ingenious. Mail order or see www.activitytoysdirect.com for brochures and lists of local stockists; sold through large retailers like Toys 'R' Us.
__Nursery decor__ – __Storage:__ interesting options including play tables with built-in storage, fun shaped toy boxes; some nursery furniture too.
__Toys__ – __Brand:__ many different categories of toy – from plastic people to sit-in trucks; good selection of play kitchen units. – __Outdoor items & active toys:__ frog-shaped sandbox with lid; also pools, slides and swings. / *free catalogue; Delivery: £4.95.*

Stepping Out
106 Pitshanger Lane, London W5 1QX
☎ (020) 8810 6141
Though primarily a shoe shop, this store stocks a well selected range of toys and other items (including accessories such as hats, gloves and bags); play area.
__Shoes__ – __Suppliers:__ full range of shoes and width fittings; brands include: Start-rite, Buckle My Shoe and Babybotte.
__Toys__ – __General stockists:__ selection of educational and unusual toys, soft toys and books; brands include Brio. / *Hours: Mon-Sat 10am-5.30pm (Sat 9am); no Amex.*

Stork Express 🖃
PO Box 150 Amersham, Buckinghamshire
HP7 0TH ☎ (01494) 434294
🖱 www.storkexpress.co.uk
__Naming gifts__ – __Naming gifts:__ gifts for 0-24 months including toys, Christening gifts, china, clothing, footwear, towelling, rugs, photo frames, soft play and wooden toys; plus a gift wrapping service. Nationwide next day delivery (and worldwide within seven days). / *Hours: Mon-Fri 8am-6pm.*

Stork Talk 🖃
16a Birkdale Close, Manners Industrial Estate, Ilkeston, Derbyshire DE7 8YA
☎ (0115) 930 6700
🖱 www.storktalk.midlands.co.uk
Northern discount store which also operates a mail order business.
__Baby equipment__ – __Stockists:__ very wide range of prams (including all-terrain, three-in-one, and twin units), cots, highchairs, and car seats from practically all of the big names. The company is happy to quote on practically any nursery item, and says it can "obtain almost anything"; (authorised child safety centre for Britax). – __Buggy & pram repairs:__ deals with most manufacturers; can quote over the phone. / *Hours: Mon-Sat 9.30am-4.30pm; free catalogue; Delivery: p&p extra (max £10); no Amex.*

Storm Enterprises 🖃
Lowton Farm, Moretonhampstead, Devon
TQ13 8PN ☎ (01647) 440 570
🖱 www.stormenterprises.com
A good-looking range of baby equipment tested by the Storm team and their families and chosen as the best of their type. The company reports that because of its testing it is actively involved with product development.
__Baby equipment__ – __Cots:__ ezee Rocker cots in wood and cotton fabric, which will rock with the baby's movement. A free-standing model folds flat (to be used much as a Moses basket), or the bed section can simply be clipped to the sides of a standard cot; can be packed flat for travel or storage. – __Slings:__ stockists of the Dutch Premaxx Baby-Bag sling in cotton – apparently the largest-selling sling in Europe – suitable for babies to four months lying down in a 'carrier bag' position, and to around 16 months seated on the adult's hip. The length of the sling makes it most suitable for adults 160-200cm high. Also a frong sling from Elite from 12 months made of durable outer fibre plus Microfleece inner. – __Slings- Backpack:__ adjustable Elite backpacks from New Zealand suitable from 4 months-3 years (or 16kg) using breathable fabrics and microfleece linings; pouches; canopy and raincover.
__Nursery decor__ – __Sleeping Bags:__ the Little Company's Combi Sleeper is an all-seasons sleeping bag: 80cm for babies to 12 months and 110cm for up to age four. The baby model includes an opening for the belt of a car seat.
__Nappies__ – __Change bags:__ a selection of useful and good-looking bags (including one to attach to the back of a pram), backpacks, body belt bags and a big shoulder bag. / *free catalogue.*

Storysack 🖃
Resource House, Kay St, Bury BL9 6BU
☎ (0161) 763 6232 🖱 www.storysack.com
__Toys__ – __Educational:__ storysacks are a cloth bag full of items to illustrate a story told to children – a wide selection (from £30) includes Little Red Riding Hood, The Old Lady Who Swallowed a Fly, and more modern stories including The Rainbow Fish, The Very Hungry Caterpillar, Gruffalo, Teddy Takes a Tumble and Ring the Flamingo. / *Free catalogue or details on the web site.; Delivery: p&p £5; no Amex.*

Stuck On You 🖃
Mulberry Cottage, Upper Hayesden Lane, Tonbridge, Kenton TN11 9AX ☎ (020) 7619 0362 🖱 www.hutchesonhall.com
__Baby clothes__ – __Nametapes:__ coloured and transparent vinyl stickers which will stick in microwaves, dishwashers and swimming pools and therefore suitable for everything from beakers to swimming caps. Made in Australia and with the option of a jolly icon alongside, such as an animal, teddy or tractor. From around £10.50 an order.

Su Su Ma Ma World Wear 🖃
2 Brambletyne Avenue, Brighton BN2 8EJ
☎ (01273) 300606, mobile (07956) 545975
🖱 www.susumama.co.uk
__Baby clothes__ – __Funky:__ 'World wear for children' – Western styles (dresses, jumpsuits, trousers and tops) in ethnic (Indian, Indonesian, Tibetan, Peruvian) fabrics (patchwork, embroidery, batik and knitwear); trades at festivals and fairs; prices from £5 (bootees) to £30. / *Hours: 24hr answerphone; free catalogue or online; Delivery: p&p extra.*

Sui Generis ⌂
The Chandlers Centre, Hythe Quay, Colchester, Essex CO2 8JB ☎ (01206) 798 798 ⌂ www.suigeneris.co.uk
Nursery decor – **Safety items:** makers of soft but firm slip-resistant surfaces that cushion falls, for use in play areas and pool surrounds; call for a list of stockists. / *Hours: Mon-Fri 9am-5.30pm.*

Sun-Togs ⌂
Direct Offers Ltd, Litton House, Saville Road, Westwood, Peterborough, Cambridgeshire PE3 7PR ☎ (01733) 765 030 ⌂ www.sun-togs.co.uk
Baby clothes – **Sun-protection clothing:** a chlorine-resistant range offering Ultraviolet Protection Factor (UPF) of 50+, the highest rating applicable to fabric. It includes swimsuits, legionnaire hats (with back flap) and playsuits (£20). Also accessories such as swim nappies, sunglasses (including 0-5 years). / *Hours: Mon-Fri 9am-5pm, or answerphone; free catalogue; Delivery: p&p extra.*

Sunday Best ⌂
115 Adnitt Rd, Northampton NN1 4NQ ☎ (01604) 470 168 ⌂ www.sundaybest.com
Mostly gowns, but also a few gifts, and special bibs for the big day.
Baby clothes – **Christening gowns:** christening gowns in English and other traditional styles, plus rompers, dresses and special occasion wear; also accessories. / *Hours: Tues-Sat 10am-2pm; or by appointment; online catalogue; Delivery: p&p £5.88 in UK.*

Sunhatters ⌂
40 Victoria Rd, Abingdon, Oxfordshire OX14 1DQ ☎ (01235) 521783
Baby clothes – **Sun-protection clothing:** children's Legionnaire-style sun hats which offer protection from the sun for the face, neck and ears; range of solid and fluorescent colours; £4.50 (£5.50 for styles with elasticated backs). / *Hours: Mon-Fri 9am-5pm, or answerphone; free catalogue; Delivery: p&p included; no credit cards.*

Sunproof ⌂
Unit 1, Monks Dairy Workshops, Isle Brewers, Taunton, Somerset TA3 6QL ☎ (01460) 281 229 ⌂ www.esunproof.co.uk
Baby clothes – **Sun-protection clothing:** web retailer offering Australian-made UV protection for infants and children from 6 months-10 years; sunsuits from £15. / *Delivery: p&p £1.80; no Amex.*

Super Tramp Trampolines ⌂
Langlands Business Park, Uffculme, Cullompton, Devon EX15 3DA ☎ (0800) 197 1897 ⌂ www.supertramp.co.uk
Toys – **Outdoor items & active toys:** manufacturers and suppliers of a complete range of trampolines widely available through toy and sports shops (including Harrods, John Lewis, Lillywhites) but also sold direct. Primarily designed for outdoor use, they can also be used in gyms. Their smallest model, 'The Frog' (for under 10s) is £259. / *Hours: Mon-Fri 9am-5pm; free catalogue; Delivery: p&p included.*

SW4
41 Abbeville Rd, London SW4 9JX ☎ (020) 8673 2221
Hairdressers – **Hairdressers:** monday through Thursday haircuts for children (and adults); £13 for ages six and under. / *Hours: Mon-Fri 10am-8pm, Sat 9am-5pm, Sun 11am-5pm; no Amex.*

Swallows & Amazons Q
91 Nightingale Lane, London SW12 8NX ☎ (020) 8673 0275
Well-established general baby store with a wide range, stocks mostly second-hand items and seconds with the occasional new item.
Baby equipment – **Second-hand:** a good number of seconds: "you name it, we've got it".
Baby clothes – **Second-hand shops:** claims the "largest range of children's second-hand clothes in south London" with everything from Mothercare to Baby Dior. Now also new 'Starchild' baby shoes.
Toys – **Second-hand shops:** puzzles, videos, books and activity things, 99p-£25.
Hairdressers – **Hairdressers:** appointments available for most weekday afternoons, Friday mornings and Saturdays; £6.50 up to the age of three. / *Hours: Mon-Sat 10am-5.15pm; no credit cards.*

Swann's Way
55 Hollywood Rd, London SW10 9HX ☎ (020) 7351 7907
Baby clothes – **Traditional:** a Chelsea-fringe boutique specialising in Tyrolean clothing, including little loden jackets and 'town & country' wear. / *Hours: Mon-Fri 10.30am-6.30pm (Wed 7pm), Sat 11am-5pm.*

Swingolino
Mother-Knows-Best, 2a Primrose St, Lancaster LA1 3BN ☎ (01524) 321 73 ⌂ www.swingolino.co.uk
Toys – **Comforters:** in the form of a soft toy (donkey or duck), a battery operated attachment for a baby's sleeping or sitting area. Activated by the baby's cry, the battery-operated item rocks (at a speed which can be adjusted) until the crying stops. See website for stockists.

Tairua Limited ⌂
London N2 ☎ Marina (020) 8340 5747
Nappies – **Suppliers-Eco friendly disposables:** suppliers of Moltex Öko nappies; free delivery to Highgate, East Finchley and Muswell Hill.

Talbots ⌂
1 Talbots Drive, Hingham MA 02043, USA ☎ (0800) 960402 ⌂ www.talbots.com
Baby clothes – **Mid-range:** catalogue of classic US clothing, with decent selection for kids: unfussy items and pastels for babies. / *Hours: 24hr answerphone; free catalogue or online; Delivery: p&p and duty extra.*

Tales from the Earth ⌂
Studio 51, Warriner House, 140 Battersea Park Rd, London SW11 4NB ☎ (020) 7720 4990 ⌂ www.talesfromtheearth.com
Naming gifts – **Naming gifts:** a website offering a collection of predominantly silver

items from far-flung places, including Christening and children's gifts; silver rattle, £48.

Tartine et Chocolat 🎁
66 South Molton St, London W1Y 1HH
☎ (020) 7629 7233
Baby clothes – **Luxury:** chic store selling French designer clothes of excellent quality (and prices to match); babygrows around £25; summer dresses £65-£85; also a limited stock of accessories and toys.
Naming gifts – **Naming gifts:** some baby gift baskets. / *Hours: Mon-Sat 10am-6pm (Thu 7pm); catalogue (no prices, just for showing product); Delivery: p&p extra.*

Tati 🎁
The Coach House at the Old Rectory, Sherfield English, Hampshire SO51 6FL
☎ (01794) 323633 🖥 www.tati.co.uk
Baby clothes – **Traditional:** traditional clothes and accessories in comfortable natural fabrics; the unfussy styles can appeal even to those with more modern tastes; the range includes everyday clothes, party outfits and nightwear. / *Hours: Mon-Fri 9.30am-5.30pm, Sat 10am-12pm; free catalogue or online; Delivery: p&p £3.95; no Amex.*

Teacher Trading 🎁
80 High Street, Winchester, Hampshire SO23 9AT ☎ (01420) 588 055
🖥 www.thespanishbookshop.com
Books, music & videos – **Bookshops:** language books for children including picture books. Can recommend suitable titles for different ages.

Teaching Trends 🎁
160 High Rd, London N2 9AS ☎ (020) 8444 4473 🖥 www.teachingtrends.com
Toys – **Educational:** educational items and games; wide range of American products as well as more usual items; also supply schools. / *Hours: Tue-Sat 10am-5.30pm; online catalogue; Delivery: p&p extra.*

Cecilie Telle 🎁
London ☎ (020) 7272 1335
🖥 www.cecilietelle.com
Baby clothes – **Funky:** felted wool items drawing on Scandinavian tradition, including ponchos, mittens and hats for children. / *Hours: by appt.*

Tesco
CENTRAL CONTACT DETAILS
☎ General enquiries (0800) 505555, home shopping (08457) 225533
🖥 www.tesco.com
BRANCHES:
(Branches throughout London – call the enquiry line for your nearest outlet.)
The UK's largest retailer stocks a fair amount of baby-related items, especially in its larger, out-of-town stores which include the likes of clothes and bedding. The website doesn't sell baby goods, but the section devoted to the Tesco Baby & Toddler Club provides a fair amount of information (much of it provided by iVillage).
Maternity wear – **Cheap & cheerful:** small range of mix and match separates – good

modern basics (sometimes themed around a single colour), plus swimwear and underwear.
Baby clothes – **Cheap & cheerful:** bright basics and simple newborn gear; the majority are machine washable, lots are in cotton and at reasonable prices; cartoon characters feature frequently (Winnie the Pooh, Postman Pat etc.) but own designs can be better.
Toys – **Pre-school specialists:** well chosen basic range, including bath toys, mobiles, activity arches, wall hangings, and small outdoor items.

The Outdoor Toy Co. 🎁
Notcutts Garden Centre, 150-152 London Road (A30), Bagshot, Surrey GU19 5DG
☎ (01276) 451535
🖥 www.outdoortoycompany.co.uk
Toys – **Outdoor items & active toys:** a large range of unusual and exclusive outdoor toys; importers of the classic Radio Flyer wagons and wooden trikes – the traditional wagon, has a seamless steel body, no-scratch edges and extra long handle for easy pulling; suitable from the age of one and a half, (one from a range of ten wagons) with a number of accessories; also walker wagons, trikes, treehouses, climbing frames, swings and bikes. / *Hours: 24hr answerphone; free brochure.*

Thimbelina 🎁
7 Acremead Rd, Wheatley, Oxfordshire OX33 1NZ ☎ (01865) 872549
Dressmaker and designer for children, who specialises in Christening wear, but will make anything including page boy and bridesmaid outfits.
Baby clothes – **Luxury:** rompers from £150. – **Christening gowns:** handmade traditional gowns and rompers – from sample stock or to order – in pure silk or fine cotton in various colours, prints, and types of piping; smocked gowns from £300, with optional matching bonnet and Edwardian style handmade lined box. / *Hours: 24hr answerphone; Delivery: p&p extra (registered); no credit cards.*

Thoe Tho
55 Fortis Green Rd, Muswell Hill, London N10 3HP ☎ (020) 8442 0419
Baby clothes – **Luxury:** boutique of designer children's and baby clothing – mainly French and German labels; a fleece for a six-month-old might be £15-£30. / *Hours: Mon-Sat 9.30am-6pm; no Amex.*

David Thomas
8 Croxted Rd, London SE21 8SW ☎ (020) 8670 8100, (020) 8766 7400
Shoes – **Suppliers:** brands stocked include Start-rite and Dr Martins as well as trainers – all properly fitted in store. / *Hours: Mon-Sat 9.15am-5.30pm, closed Wed; no Amex.*

Tiddly Pomme 🎁
The Tallot Barn, St Mary's Close, Kempsford, Glos GL7 4NF ☎ (01285) 810 115
🖥 www.tiddlypomme.co.uk
Baby clothes – **Luxury:** co-ordinating clothing for girls and boys from 3 months-3 years, with brands including Lapin Bleu, Berlingot and Steiff.

Tiddlywinks
23 St John's Wood High St, London
NW8 7NH ☎ (020) 7722 3033
(No longer run by the same people as at 414
Roman Rd, E1.)
<u>Baby clothes</u> – Luxury: big name designer
gear for kids: smart and casual styles from
Armani, Cavalli, D&G, Diesel, Versace and
Moschino among others.

Tiffany & Co 🖼
25 Old Bond St, London W1S 4QB ☎ (020)
7409 2790 🖑 www.tiffany.com
<u>Naming gifts</u> – Naming gifts: items in sterling
silver start from £60 – for example a silver
double teething ring at £120; everything can be
engraved and all items come in that famous
Tiffany blue box. There is also a shop in Sloane
Square, and a concession in Harrods. / Hours:
Mon-Sat 10am-5.30pm.

Timberland
CENTRAL CONTACT DETAILS
☎ (01784) 496000
🖑 www.timberland.com
BRANCHES:
72 New Bond St W1Y 9DD
☎ (020) 7495 2133
125 Long Acre WC2E 9PE
☎ (020) 7240 4484
<u>Shoes</u> – Brands: you can start your child off
with this US rugged-wear brand from birth
with crib booties from £20, and toddler boots
and sports hikers from £40.

The Tintin Shop 🖼
34 Floral St, London WC2E 9DJ ☎ (020)
7836 1131 🖑 www.thetintinshop.uk.com
<u>Toys</u> – Character toys: branded puzzles,
videos and jigsaws. / Hours: Mon-Sat 10am-
5.30pm; online catalogue; Delivery: p&p extra
(Parcelforce).

Tiny Set Toys 🖼
47 St Helier Ave, Morden, Surrey SM4 6HY
☎ (020) 8640 1195 🖑 www.tsttoys.co.uk
<u>Toys</u> – Outdoor items & active toys:
specialists in outdoor play for the garden
(sandpits, slides, paddling and swimming pools,
trampolines, tree houses and a mini
rollercoaster); rubber safety tiles for
surrounding climbing frames are also available.
The company manufactures its own range of
wooden play frames and swings, and is an
agent for TP Activity Toys. An installation
service is offered – all installers are qualified
carpenters. / Hours: Mon-Sat 10am-4pm; free
catalogue; Delivery: free within M25.

Titan Forge 🖼
Unit 3, Shaftesbury Court, Shaftesbury Rd,
London E10 ☎ (020) 8558 9000
<u>Nursery decor</u> – Safety items: metalworkers,
who as well as commissions produce
a catalogue of standard cast iron grills.

Tom Thumb Fantasy Designs
227a High Rd, London E18 2PB ☎ (01992)
700996
<u>Nursery decor</u> – Furniture: hand-painted
fantasy furniture, murals, curtains and
accessories; Goldilocks single bed £345, Heart
chair £39, three panelled mirror £250.

Tommee Tippee 🖼
Jackel International, Dudley Lane,
Cramlington, Northumberland NE23 7RH
☎ Helpline (0500) 979899
Widely-stocked brand (which can also be
purchased direct via the helpline).
<u>Nursery decor</u> – Safety items: starter safety
set including socket covers, corner protectors,
cupboard and drawer locks, and a door jammer
(also sold separately); also available – a video
guard, a multi-purpose lock (for fridges and
dishwashers), and a wrist link and
harness. / Hours: Mon-Thu 9am-4.45pm, Fri 9am-
2pm.

Tomy
PO Box 20, Totton, Southampton SO40 3YF
☎ (023) 8066 2600 🖑 www.tomy.co.uk
As well as toys, this well-known brand also
does a variety of smaller nursery equipment
items, of which the biggest types are listed. A
flashy website includes an impressive online
catalogue.
<u>Baby equipment</u> – Monitors-brand: the
market leaders in baby monitors in the UK.
– Slings- Backpack: mid-priced range.
<u>Toys</u> – Brand: huge well-known brand of
plastic toys. / Hours: Mon-Fri 9am-5pm.

Tops
55 Turnham Green Terrace, London
W4 1RP ☎ (020) 8995 9106
<u>Hairdressers</u> – Hairdressers: child-friendly
hairdressers; first haircuts, £14; comics, toys
and lollipops provide distractions. / Hours: Mon-
Tues 9.30am-6pm; Weds-Fri 9.30am-7pm; Sat 9am-
5.30pm; sun 10am-4pm.

Torkidz 🖼
27 Gladmuir Rd, London N19 3JY ☎ (020)
7686 4057 🖑 www.torkidz.com
<u>Baby clothes</u> – Funky: fun and wacky clothes
in cotton or linen for 2-8 years; £10–£20 for
patterned trousers, skirts and shorts with fun
trims. The designer used to go on tour with
the Spice Girls and Ant & Dec and make their
clothes. For winter there are jerkins in funky
print fake furs with bright satin linings. Buy
direct or, on Sundays, at Spitalfield market.

Totland
4 Bruce Grove, London N17 ☎ (020) 8808
3466
<u>Baby equipment</u> – Stockists: cots, prams,
pushchairs and general baby goods. Brands
include Mamas and Papas and Chicco. / Hours:
Mon-Sat 9.30am-7pm.

Tots Bots 🖼
Unit 5, Green City, 23 Fleming St, Glasgow
G31 1PQ ☎ (0141) 550 1514
🖑 www.totsbots.com
<u>Nappies</u> – Reusable stockists - brands
& singles: terry towelling, shaped and
elasticated nappies, with or without Velcro
fastenings; an unbleached cotton option is
available; voted best UK-manufactured cloth
nappy in a survey by Mumsnet. / Hours: Mon-fri
9am-5pm.

Tots in the Terrace
39 Turnham Green Terrace, London
W4 1RG ☎ (020) 8995 0520
🖑 www.totschiswick.com

Baby clothes – **Luxury:** designer children's wear such as Oilily, Marese, Babymini, Quicksilver, Miniman, Kenzo, Kookai and Timberland; also accessories; will try to obtain any requested articles; prices from £2 for hair decorations to £100 for a designer coat. / *Hours: Mon-Sat 10am-6pm, Sun noon-5pm.*

Tots to Teens Furniture Co. ⌂

The Byre, Tewin Hill Farm, Tewin Hill, Tewin, Hertford AL6 0LL ☎ (01438) 717616
🖰 www.totstoteensfurniture.co.uk
Off J6 of the A1 – ring for location map/directions.
Nursery decor – **General stockists:** "Probably the most extensive selection of tots-to-teens bedroom and playroom furniture and accessories in the South East", is the claim of this farm showroom (which controls the manufacturing of its range); options include painted or colour-grained finishes on natural pine or hard woods; the price range for a cot is £150-£600. / *Hours: Tue-Fri 9.30am-2.30pm, Sat (and first Sun of month) 11am-4pm.*

"Tough Customer" ⌂

Farfield Clothing, The Old School, Joss Lane, Sedbergh, Cumbria LA10 5AS ☎ (015396) 210 169, (0800) 389 6301
🖰 www.toughcustomer.co.uk
Baby clothes – **Outdoorwear:** nearly 20 years in business, a company that's made quite a success of outdoor clothing for kids and, progressively, for adults. Top tot's choice is their fleecy romper suit (£23). / *Hours: Mon-Fri 9am-5pm; Sat 10am-4pm; free catalogue or online; Delivery: p&p £3.50; no Amex.*

Toy Wonderland

10-11 Northways Parade, Finchley Rd, London NW3 5EN ☎ (020) 7722 9821
Toys – **General stockists:** most major brands are stocked. / *Hours: Mon-Sat 10.30am-6pm.*

Toycentre ⌂

6 Maida Vale Business Centre, Mead Rd, Cheltenham, Gloucestershire GL53 7ER
☎ (01242) 521935 🖰 www.toycentre.com
Toys – **General stockists:** toys and games (with some at half price or less); limited quantities of some brands (Lego and Brio, for example); 'Early Age' brands include Tomy, Tweenies, Tomica, Play-Doh and Playskool. / *Hours: Mon-Fri 9am-5pm; online catalogue; Delivery: p&p £4.50; no diners card.*

Toys 'R' Us ⌂

CENTRAL CONTACT DETAILS
☎ (01628) 414141
🖰 www.toysrus.co.uk,
www.discounttoys.co.uk
BRANCHES:
(Only selected branches are listed – call the enquiry line for other outlets.)
Geoffrey House, Vanwall Rd Business Park SL6 4UB
☎ (01628) 414141
Tilling Rd, Brent Cross NW2 1LW
☎ (020) 8209 0019
760 Old Kent Rd SE15 1NJ
☎ (020) 7732 7322
The largest toy retailing company in the world

introduced Babies 'R' Us (see also) in 1998.
Nursery decor – **Furniture:** nursery furniture.
Toys – **General stockists:** warehouses full of toys with a wide range of well-known makes; all products are backed by an unconditional exchange or money back guarantee; service is not a forte; for extra-low prices see sister website Discount Toys. / *online catalogue; Delivery: p&p £3.50.*

Toys for Children ⌂

The Old Foundry, Steam Mills, Cinderford, Gloucestershire GL14 3JE ☎ (01594) 824007
🖰 www.woodentoysforchildren.co.uk
Toys – **Traditional toys:** original, sculpted wooden toys; the range includes complete farm sets with individual pieces in different woods; also tractors, trailers, trains and a Nativity set. Pieces can be bought separately, or as a whole, from £1.35; Noah's Ark building block set for £195.
Naming gifts – **Naming gifts:** wooden farm sets and wild animals sculpted from a variety of woods. / *Hours: Mon-Fri 9am-5pm; Delivery: free over £50; no Amex & no Switch.*

Toystop

BRANCHES:
377 Upper Richmond Rd West SW14 7NX
☎ (020) 8876 5229
75 St John's Rd SW11 1QX
☎ (020) 7228 9079
Putney Exchange SW15
☎ (020) 8785 9955
Toys – **General stockists:** all the mainstream names in a good generalist toy store – Mattel, Brio, Galt, Lego, Playmobil, Tomy, Jellycats, Orchard Games, Little Tikes, John Crane. Adjoining the Sheen branch is Bookstop with a respectable children's department including audio tapes and cards.

Toytime ⌂ Q

Meopham Bank Farm, Leigh Rd, Hildenborough, Kent TN11 9AQ ☎ (01732) 833695, (01732) 832416
Farm-based business (with TP Activity frames and swings for younger visitors).
Toys – **General stockists:** ranges stocked include Lego, Playmobil, Tomy, Galt and Brio, at around a 12% discount – there are two barns full of new and second hand items. – **Outdoor items & active toys:** outdoor toys stocked include TP Activity Frames (at a 10% discount), trampolines and sandpits.
– **Second-hand shops:** buys and sells second-hand toys, and operates a waiting list of wanted items. / *Hours: Tue 9am-noon then 7.30pm-8.30pm, Thu 9am-4pm, Sat 9am-4pm; free TP/Brio catalogues; TP items delivered locally.*

TP Activity Toys ⌂

Stourport On Severn, Worcs DY13 9EX
☎ (01299) 872800, Brochure request (0800) 068 1870 🖰 www.tptoys.com
Toys – **Brand:** high quality outdoor activity toys, including items aimed at young children; space restrictions in shops make it a good idea to get a brochure; the company can give details of local stockists which include some 57 Activity Toys Centres around the country where children can try the toys first.
– **Outdoor items & active toys:** on-site toy

shop at the head office (address listed). / *Hours: shop Mon-Fri 9am-5pm, Sat 10am-4pm; free catalogue; Delivery: starts £17; no Amex.*

TreeTops Play Equipment
78 London Rd, Canterbury, Kent CT2 8LS
☎ (01227) 761 899
🔗 www.treetopsdirect.co.uk
<u>Toys</u> – **Outdoor items & active toys:** modular designs, largely in wood, including swings, climbing frames, clamber nets, rockwalks, monkey bars, playhouses and treehouses. / *free catalogue; Delivery: £19.50 under £300.*

Trendy's
72 Chapel Market, London N1 9ER ☎ (020) 7837 9070
<u>Baby clothes</u> – **Mid-range:** children's (0-16 years) designer wear clothing such as French Connection and Diesel.
<u>Shoes</u> – **Suppliers:** shoes from Buckle My Shoe, Kickers, Oilily, Elle and many more. / *Hours: Mon-Sat 9.30am-6pm (Sun 10am-4pm).*

Triangles
96 New Road Side, Horsforth, Leeds
☎ (0113) 2590523
🔗 www.allterrainpushchairs.co.uk/
A specialist internet branch of Baby Direct in Leeds specialising in all-terrain pushchairs and accessories. It offers online ordering.
<u>Baby equipment</u> – **Buggy suppliers:** there's a choice of around 20 models, plus accessories, plus a guide leading purchasers through the relevant options; the site's well laid out, and affords an easy overview of the different models.

¡tridias!
CENTRAL CONTACT DETAILS
☎ Mail order (0870) 443 1300
🔗 www.tridias.co.uk
BRANCHES:
25 Bute St SW7 3EY
☎ (020) 7584 2330
6 Lichfield Terrace, Sheen Rd TW9 1AS
☎ (020) 8948 3459
Small national chain and mail order business.
<u>Toys</u> – **General stockists:** original, interesting and creative toys from pocket-money-size to educational items and outdoor gear (for example, trampolines and slides); prices are competitive. / *Hours: shops Mon-Fri 9am-6.30pm, Sat 10am-6pm, mail order Mon-Fri 9am-8.30pm, Sat 9am-1pm; free catalogue; Delivery: p&p £3.25; no Amex.*

Trotters
CENTRAL CONTACT DETAILS
☎ Trotters Online (020) 7371 5773
🔗 www.trotters.co.uk
BRANCHES:
34 Kings Rd SW3 4UD
☎ (020) 7259 9620
127 Kensington High St W8 6LE
☎ (020) 7937 9373
45v Brent Cross Shopping Centre NW4 3FP
☎ (020) 8202 1888
Successful, small chain majoring in clothes, where some of the pain of shopping is relieved by parents' rooms and juice bars. Trotters Online, the website, sells a more limited range than the shops.

<u>Baby clothes</u> – **Mid-range:** wide range of mainly branded clothes: a mixture of classic British styles (jersey stripes, gingham pinafores, Chelsea Clothing Company), sharp fashion separates (Elle, Kenzo, Paul Smith) and Continental items in the mid to upper price range; sundress £40, striped T-shirt, £8, trousers £20; good quality accessories (hats, bags, braces, jewellery) and swimwear.
<u>Shoes</u> – **Suppliers:** a good range including Start-rite, Clarks, Buckle My Shoe, GBB, and Kickers.
<u>Toys</u> – **General stockists:** small selection of toys (with particularly nice furry ones).
<u>Hairdressers</u> – **Hairdressers:** fish tanks provide distraction for juniors awaiting haircuts; under three years old, £9 (with certificate for first cut); over three years old, £10; appointment necessary. / *Hours: Mon-Sat 9am-6.30pm (Wed 7pm, Thu 9.30pm), Sun 10am-6pm; free catalogue; Delivery: p&p £3.50.*

Tushies
🔗 www.tushies.co.uk
<u>Nappies</u> – **Eco-friendly disposables brands:** an American range of gel-free disposable nappies, claimed more friendly to the skin than standard disposables though also less absorbent; the nappies are bleached and feature a relatively stiff core of natural blend cotton and wood pulp and fastenings which do not function if in contact with nappy cream; also produce alcohol-free wipes using Aloe Vera; website contains list of stockists.

Twinkleontheweb
Beggars Hill Rd, Lands End, Twyford, Berkshire RG10 0UB ☎ (0118) 934 2120
🔗 www.twinkleontheweb.co.uk
<u>Nappies</u> – **Reusable stockists - multiple brands:** "For independent advice and assistance on choosing cloth nappies" – online information on the wide range of washables; also supplies all the main brands, plus accessories (Mother-ease, Kooshies, Imse Vimse, Popolino, Bummis, Sam-I-Am, ElliePants and Fuzzi Bunz – a fleece wrap to help keep the baby dry). Starter packs include samples of each nappy, from £30. / *Delivery: p&p £1.20 (orders up to £15), £2.55 (order up to £50), free on orders over £50.*

Two Left Feet
13 Sunbeard Rd, Bedford, Beds MK40 7BY
☎ (01234) 857777 🔗 www.twoleftfeet.co.uk
What claims to be "the UK's largest baby goods website, with over 800 products": there is also a Bedford showroom. Most brands are stocked, and you can browse either by manufacturer or product category. The site claims that 80% of products are shipped next day.
<u>Baby equipment</u> – **Stockists:** brands include Britax, Tomy, Maclaren, Graco, Chicco, Avent, Cosatto, Hauck, Implast, Quinny, Klippan. / *Hours: Mon-Sat 9.30am-5pm; Delivery: p&p included; no Switch.*

Two Plus Two
49 B (rear) Cliffe High Street, Lewes, Sussex BW7 2AN ☎ (01273) 480479
🔗 www.twoplustwo.uk.com
<u>Baby equipment</u> – **Bicycle-related items:** claiming to stock the UK's widest range of

bicycle trailers for children, goods and dogs – trailers to carry children up to age 6 start at £199; some convert into 3-wheel baby-joggers. / *Hours: by appointment.*

Tyrrell Katz ⌂

2 Kimberley Rd, London NW6 7SG ☎ (020) 7372 6696 ⏍ www.tyrrellkatz.co.uk
<u>Nursery decor</u> – **Bedding:** bedding, hangers and lampshades in their trademark 'all-over' prints; duvet sets, from £40.
<u>Baby clothes</u> – **Funky:** entertaining, all-over-printed T-shirts in themes including football, ballerinas, fairies and dinosaurs (£12); also pyjamas, aprons, painting smocks, bath robes and bags. / *Hours: Mon-Fri 9am-6pm; free catalogue or online; Delivery: p&p £1.50 per item; no Amex.*

Uglows

28-30 Station Rd, Chingford, London E4 7BE ☎ (020) 8529 0011
<u>Nursery decor</u> – **General stockists:** wide and stylish range of soft furnishings across the board – linens, towels, duvet covers, nursery fabrics, wallpaper and even carpets, with names like Designer's Guild, Anna French and Jane Churchill; services include making-up curtains, and a full advisory service (initial home consultation free). / *Hours: Mon-Sat 9am-5.30pm, closed Thu; Delivery: p&p extra; no Amex.*

UK Parents

☎ (0191) 260 2616 ⏍ www.ukparents.co.uk
<u>Nappies</u> – **Reusable stockists - multiple brands:** an online community which includes a buy and sell forum for reusable nappies.

The Uncommon Touch

184 Northcote Rd, London SW11 6RE ☎ (020) 7228 1487
<u>Nursery decor</u> – **Interior designers:** full design service available – will co-ordinate furniture and furnishings from a range of different suppliers. – **Wallpaper & fabrics:** large range of nursery fabrics, and wallpaper with about 28 children's 'books' – all the major names and some minor ones; a good source of information. / *Hours: Mon-Sat 10am-5.30pm; Delivery: p&p extra; no credit cards.*

Unique Interiors

64 Wolverhampton Road, Kidderminster, Worcs DY10 2UU ☎ (01562) 634 326 ⏍ www.unique-interior.co.uk/
<u>Nursery decor</u> – **Interior designers:** specialists in all aspects of interior design and decoration for children's bedrooms, playrooms and nurseries. See the website for a full description of products and services. (If you don't go for a full service you can commission individual items).

Urchin ⌂

8-9 High Street, Marlborough, Wilts SN8 1EA ☎ (0870) 720 3040
⏍ www.urchin.co.uk
"Funky stuff for baby, nursery and small kids" – mail order supplier whose emphasis is on items with catchy-looking designs. Its range covers most bases, but has relatively few choices in any particular category; perhaps strongest on bedroom/sleep-related items.
<u>Baby equipment</u> – **Stockists:** a number of

3-wheeler buggies, car-seats, cots, and Moses baskets.
<u>Nursery decor</u> – **Beds:** wide assortment of children's beds. The range includes wooden beds, metal junior beds and bunk beds all £99-£400. – **Furniture:** as well as numerous accessories, items like a child arm chair.
<u>Baby clothes</u> – **Mid-range:** small ranges including baby sleep suits.
<u>Toys</u> – **General stockists.**
<u>Nappies</u> – **Potty training:** dalmatian spot and clear plastic potty £17. / *Hours: Customer service Mon-Fri 10am-4pm; 24 hour order line; free brochure; Delivery: £4.50; no Amex.*

Urchins Baby World ⌂

810 Bury Road, Breightmet, Bolton BL2 6PA ☎ (01204) 433399 ⏍ www.urchins.co.uk/
A Bolton-based family business (started in the '70s) which now has a sizeable, quite sophisticated website. It prides itself on offering unbiased advice about all kinds of baby goods and equipment at discount prices.
<u>Baby equipment</u> – **Stockists:** a comprehensive range of equipment is offered from a laundry-list of brands. In keeping with the stores aim to give independent advice, it produces a series of buyers guides (available online) to different product categories.

V&A Marketing ⌂

Charlesworth House, Andrews Rd, Llandaff North, Cardiff CF14 2JP ☎ (029) 2057 5600 ⏍ www.tuff-n-tumble.com
Manufacturers of Tuff 'N' Tumble and Anywayup products: can provide details of stockists (or will send goods p&p free to individuals without a local retailer).
<u>Baby clothes</u> – **Cheap & cheerful:** bodysuits which undo over each shoulder so they can be taken down over the child's body rather than up over the head.
<u>Nappies</u> – **Potty training:** the Posh Potty – an anti-spill design with a lid for use when travelling, £6; also 'Weeman' – a device that attaches to the toilet bowl to help with toilet training boys, £7. / *Hours: Mon-Fri 9am-5pm; free product lists; no credit cards.*

V-Tech Electronics

Napier Court, Abingdon Science Park, Abingdon, Oxfordshire OX14 3YT ☎ (01235) 546810 ⏍ www.vtechuk.com
<u>Toys</u> – **Brand:** brightly-coloured electronic toys, many of which make noises, play tunes and talk back; some are more entertaining than educational, but a number are recommended by learning specialists and there is a focus on letter/number recognition; the IQ Builders brand features English (not US) voices and is developed in line with the National Curriculum; a list of stockists is on the website. / *Hours: customer helpline Mon-Fri 9am-5.30pm; no Amex.*

Van Blanken ⌂

Unit 1 Fleetswood Court, 431/441 Wimborne Rd, Poole Dorset BH15 3EE ☎ (01202) 661 699
⏍ www.vanblanken.co.uk/
Poole showroom, that also operates an online store.
<u>Baby equipment</u> – **Buggies for twins and triplets:** a range of all-terrain doubles.

– **Buggy suppliers:** specialists in all-terrain pushchairs, which can be viewed on the website (through which purchases can also be made); there's also a good range of more standard pushchairs from big-name brands.
Nursery decor – **Interior designers:** bebecar, Bébé-Jou (a Dutch brand) and Lemberg ranges provide a wide selection of matchable items; there is an in-house design and installation team to help you achieve a complete 'look'.

Versace Jeans Couture
113-115 New Bond St, London W1 1DP
☎ (020) 7355 2700 ⁷⁸ www.versace.com
Young Versace is their brand for junior fashionistas.
Baby clothes – **Luxury:** t-shirts range from £25 up to £650; also trousers, shirts, fleeces and party dresses.

VertBaudet ⊞
18 Canal Rd, Bradford BD99 4XB ☎ Order line (0845) 270 0270
⁷⁸ www.vertbaudet.co.uk
Ideal for the Francophile – all items stocked are French. A personal account facility is available.
Maternity wear – **Mid-range:** the 'Colline' range: a small selection of basic French casual separates with some more elegant items in interesting fabrics – for example velvet or crepe – and cottons for summer: jeans, swimwear, bras, briefs, tights (tunic top £20; trousers £24; leggings £18, t-shirt £9.99).
Baby equipment – **Stockists:** cots and bedding; car seats and prams.
Baby clothes – **Mid-range:** all-French children's wear; many different ranges from high fashion through classic styles to basics, with good attention to detail and design; some items are perhaps a little quirky for the UK market; plenty of special occasion outfits with matching accessories; all-in-one romper suit from £10.
Toys – **Pre-school specialists:** 'Early learning' toys and baby playthings. / *Hours: 7 days a week 8am-11pm; free catalogue; Delivery: p&p £2.45.*

Vicky Smith Interior Design & Decoration
39 Vernon Road, London SW14 8NH
☎ (07958) 729 516
Nursery decor – **Interior designers:** a specialist in children's rooms which also focuses on family-friendly ideas for other parts of the house.

Victoria 2 Nursery Goods & Schoolwear
246 Hoe St, London E17 3AX ☎ (020) 8520 2176
Baby equipment – **Stockists:** from prams, cribs and high chairs (Cosatto and Mamas & Papas) to mobiles. / *Hours: Mon-Sat 9.30am-5.30pm; no Amex & no Switch.*

VIPonline.co.uk ⊞
20 Osborne Road, Crowborough, East Sussex TN6 2HN ☎ (01892) 669788
⁷⁸ www.viponline.co.uk/
Toys – **Educational:** toys and baby goods selected for their durability, safety and educational value. A good selection, albeit from a rather busily designed website.

Voice Alert ⊞
349 Brighton Road, South Croydon, Surrey CR2 6ER ☎ (020) 8680 4009
⁷⁸ www.voice-alert.co.uk
Baby equipment – **Monitors-brand:** a patented system combining movement sensors and speakers whereby you can record an alert to be played within your hearing when someone moves past a downstairs part of your choosing – for example an intruder, or – more prosaically – your toddler going somewhere they shouldn't in the house or garden. The units have a range of 300 metres in open space or 100 metres through buildings.

Susan Wainwright
31 South End Rd, London NW3 2PY ☎ (020) 7431 4337
Toys – **General stockists:** gift shop where the range includes soft toys, dressing-up costumes, jewellery, children's handbags, wooden toys and art equipment. / *Hours: Mon-Sat 9.30am-6pm, Sun noon-6pm; no Amex.*

Warner Brothers Studio Store ⊞
Units F1, Bentalls Shopping Centre, Kingston upon Thames KT1 1TR ☎ (020) 8974 8893
⁷⁸ www.warnerbrothers.com, www.wbstore.com
As well as the store listed, there are out-of-town outlets of this well-known brand in Thurrock, Bluewater and Gatwick. The websites listed are American – you can order from them, but shipping is expensive and customs charges will be added in the UK.
Baby clothes – **Cheap & cheerful:** decent quality T-shirts, and other merchandise, featuring all the Warner Bros characters – Bugs Bunny, Tom and Jerry, Tweety Pie and even Harry Potter.
Toys – **Character toys:** soft toys of all your favourite characters (not to mention mugs, lunch boxes, bags …). / *Hours: Mon-Fri 10am-6pm (Thu & Sat 8pm), Sun noon-6pm; online catalogue; Delivery: p&p extra.*

Waterstones ⊞
203-206 Piccadilly, London W1V 9LE
☎ (020) 7851 2400
⁷⁸ www.waterstones.co.uk
Books, music & videos – **Bookshops:** the flagship branch (listed) of this bookshop chain has a large children's section with thousands of titles for pre-schoolers; there's lift access for buggies and a juice café in the next department. A reading club, regular events and promotions encourage children to get involved. Other London branches with good children's sections include Kensington High St, Islington, Old Brompton Rd, Notting Hill and Hampstead. The online mail order service offers over 130,000 titles with various discounts. / *Hours: Mon-Sat 10am-11pm, Sun 12pm-6pm; Delivery: p&p £2.50 max.*

WCD (Walter Castellazzo Design)
84 Highgate High St, London N6 5HX
☎ (020) 8340 3001 ⁷⁸ www.castellazzo.co.uk
A small furniture group established in 1992 with the aim of providing indivual service to customers wanting designer furniture.

Nursery decor – Furniture: wCJunior is the children's range, including for example a cupboard designed to look like a tree trunk and silver shelves in the shape of a rocket. Everything is tailor-made to requirements, and made of painted MDF.

Wear & Cheer
160-162 Rye Lane, London SE15 4NB
☎ (020) 7635 9252
Good local store spanning equipment and nursery items.
Baby equipment – Stockists.
Nursery decor – General stockists.
Baby clothes – Mid-range. / Hours: Mon-Sat 9am-6pm; no Amex.

James Webster
462 Brixton Rd, London SW9 ☎ (020) 7274 3539
Shoes – Suppliers: all the children's shoes stocked are Clarks, and are fitted in the shop. / Hours: Mon-Sat 10am-6pm; no Amex.

Weeman 🖃
Peppercorn Trading, 368 Alexandra Park Rd, London N22 7BD ☎ (020) 8888 9692
🖰 www.peppercorntrading.com
Nappies – Potty training: a kind of clip on-potty to attach to the lavatory bowl for little boys to learn to wee standing up without having to wobble on a stool; made from and to be rinsed during the flush. The patented design aims to minimise splashes and drips; £13.

Weenees
CENTRAL CONTACT DETAILS
☎ (01736) 799512
🖰 www.teamlollipop.co.uk
Nappies – Eco-friendly disposables brands: australian disposable nappy system using non-chlorine bleached, compostable pads that are also flushable if torn in two; made from farmed trees, they include a biodegradable 'stay dry' cover and high-absorbency 'lock-away' cells; there are no gels or plastic content; pads are placed in waterproof, washable Weenees pants with rear fastenings to deter removal; despite the absence of gel the design is good enough to prevent leaks; a medium and a small pad can be combined for extra absorbency; the pants can also be used with fabric pads allowing alternation between washable and disposable systems; also sell biodegradable nappy sacks; average price for a pair of pants plus a pack of pads, £13.

Wellspring Bookshop
5 New Oxford St, London WC1A 1BA
☎ (020) 7405 6101
🖰 www.rudolfsteinerbooks.co.uk
The trading outlet for The Rudolf Steiner Book Trust (a charity promoting the works of the well-known educationalist) also stocks a small selection of toys.
Toys – Traditional toys: a small range primarily of wooden items: floppy duck £12; set of coloured blocks £17. / Hours: Mon-Fri 10.30am-5.30pm Sat 12pm-5.30pm.

Wesco 🖃
Burnham Way, Queen's Bridge Road, Nottingham NG2 1NB ☎ (0115) 986 2126
🖰 www.wesco-group.com
This international company produces catalogues aimed at nurseries and crèches (it supplies to over 50 countries); catalogue prices exclude VAT.
Nursery decor – General stockists: a range of seating designed for nurseries including fun giant animal floor cushions; also cots, beds, linen and decorative floormats.
Toys – Nursery suppliers: especially good for large, floor-standing pieces, but also accessories like balls (a vast selection), jigsaw puzzles, model trucks and animals; specialists in products which develop motor skills, and 'soft-play' equipment. / Hours: Mon-Fri 9am-5.30pm; free catalogue; Delivery: p&p £5 (free for orders over £50); no credit cards.

WH Smith
CENTRAL CONTACT DETAILS
☎ (01795) 616161
🖰 www.whsmith.co.uk
BRANCHES:
(Only selected branches are listed – call the enquiry line for other outlets.)
36 Sloane Square SW1W 8AP
☎ (020) 7730 0351
16 King's Mall, King St W6 0PZ
☎ (020) 8748 2218
92 Notting Hill Gate W11 3QB
☎ (020) 7727 9261
The UK's leading news and books chain has a selection of toys in most branches.
Toys – General stockists: toys, puzzles and a range of pre-school games – the bigger central stores have the widest selection.
Books, music & videos – Bookshops: books and games, as well as colouring books, activities, pens and paints; the online bookstore offers a vast number of titles, of which approximately 15,000 are for young children. / Hours: hours vary by store.

What Katy Did
49 Kensington Church St, London W8 4BA
☎ (020) 7937 6499
🖰 www.whatkatydid.co.uk
Baby clothes – Luxury: bohemian ranges of childrens' clothing stocked in small numbers, so your child isn't dressed the same as all the others at parties; eclectic mix, from luxurious classics to affordable fashions; steers clear of well known labels. – Funky.

The White Company 🖃
Unit 30 Perivale Industrial Park, Horsenden Lane South, Greenford, Middlesex UB6 7RJ
☎ (0870) 160 1610 🖰 www.thewhiteco.com
On the arrival of her own son, the owner of this linen-by-mail-order service extended the range to include baby items. (As well as the items listed below, the firm also offers a simple Moses basket and stand.)
Baby equipment – Bathing: bathrobes, £20; hooded towels £12.50.
Nursery decor – Bedding: well-chosen, quality goods like chequered lambswool blankets, from £46; cot sheets, from £15; cushion cover, £13. – Sleeping Bags: bags for 6-12 months £35, 12-24 months £45, 24-36 months £49.

Baby clothes – Sleepwear: gingham pyjamas £19 and sleepsuits. / *Hours: Mon-Fri 8am-8pm, Sat 10am-4pm; free catalogue; Delivery: p&p £3.95 (orders under £50), £4.95 (orders over £50).*

The White House ✏
102 Waterford Rd, London SW6 2HA
☎ (020) 7629 3521
⌂ www.the-white-house.com
Top-drawer store where the look is moving from the traditional to the more contemporary and stylish; top-quality products, with prices to match.

Nursery decor – General stockists: nursery items include bed linen, cot sets, towels and blankets in natural fibres; bespoke service available.

Baby clothes – Sleepwear: simple range of pyjamas, sleepsuits and robes in easy care fabrics, designed for generations of use. / *Hours: Mon-Sat 10am-5.30pm; free catalogue; Delivery: p&p extra.*

White Mischief Bed & Table Linen ✏
Beorth Park, Slugwash lane, Wivelsfield Green, West Sussex RH17 7RG ☎ (01444) 471769
Nursery decor – Bedding: white cotton and linen items made to measure and hand-embroidered in a variety of attractive designs including pandas, ladybirds, teddy bears, bees, and jungle animals; sizes for bed linen range from cot to super-king size (although any size can be made, for example for antique beds); cot duvet cover £85, cot pillowcase £22.50; also hand towels and table linen.

Baby clothes – Sleepwear: white cotton and linen sleepwear; plain or hand-embroidered. / *Hours: 24hr answerphone; free catalogue; Delivery: p&p £3.*

White Rabbit England ✏
Battery House, Battery Lane, Wilmslow, Cheshire SK9 5LT ☎ (01625) 251188
⌂ www.whiterabbitengland.com
Nursery decor – Accessories: decorated, pottery nursery lamps in quaint designs. See the website for stockists, or you can print an orderform from the net.

Wicken Toys Limited ✏
Whitt Lebury Rd, Wicken, Milton Keynes MK19 6BJ ☎ (01908) 571 233
⌂ www.wicken-toys.co.uk
Toys – Outdoor items & active toys: large outdoor display of swings, climbing frames and outdoor garden toys; brands include Houtland, Plum, Tee-pee, SuperTramp, Hunter Green Playsystems and Playland; it's about an hour's drive from London, but you can tell the kids there's lots of kit to try out when you get there. / *Hours: Fri-Tues (closed Wed & Thurs) 10am-5pm; free catalogue; no Amex.*

Wicksteed Leisure Ltd ✏
Digby Street, Kettering, Northamptonshire NN16 8YJ ☎ (01536) 517 028
⌂ www.wicksteed.co.uk;
www.wicksteedathome.com
Toys – Outdoor items & active toys: charles Wicksteed erected a swing for local children at the end of the Great War, and the company he founded is now one of the biggest suppliers of outdoor play equipment to nurseries and institutional customers. Safety standards and durability are therefore high and the company claims to offer the widest range of play equipment, safety surfacing and leisure furniture available from a single source. A single swing starts at £30.

Patrizia Wigan
19 Walton St, London SW3 2HX ☎ (020) 7823 7080 ⌂ www.patriziawigan.com
Baby clothes – Luxury. – Traditional: classic traditional English-style clothing of the Patrizia Wigan own label; smart casual, well designed garments in natural fibres (all machine-washable) at comparatively reasonable prices; romper suits from £35, party dress from £65. / *Hours: Mon-Fri 10am-6.30pm (Sat 6pm).*

Wigglets ✏
50 Stockwell Park Crescent, London SW9 0DG ☎ (020) 7738 5124
Baby clothes – Sleepwear: mail-order business supplying traditional children's nightwear (nightdresses, dressing gowns) in various fabrics; pyjamas, £26. / *Hours: Mon-Fri 9am-5pm, or answerphone; free catalogue; Delivery: p&p £2.50 (orders under £50), £3.50 (orders over £50); no Amex & no Switch.*

Wigwamkids ✏
Broomhills, 49 Frogston Road East, Edinburgh EH17 8RT ☎ (0870) 902 7500
⌂ www.wigwamkids.co.uk
Nursery decor – General stockists: catalogue and website business specialising in coolly themed rooms for children of all ages, providing both the furniture (cots, cot beds, changing tables, wardrobes) and matching accessories (linen, quilts, baby blankets, cushions etc) and toys. Storage is a strong point. The look eschews logos, cartoon characters and the like and focuses on a limited colour palette and muted tones. Ideas are tested on the children of the two mothers who own and run the business. / *Hours: Mon-Fri 9am-5.30pm; Sat 9am-1pm; free brochure; Delivery: p&p depends, £5 for small items; no Amex.*

Wilkinet Baby Carriers ✏
PO Box 20, Cardigan SA43 1JB ☎ (01239) 841844 ⌂ www.wilkinet.co.uk
Baby equipment – Slings: designed by a mother, recommended by paediatricians and osteopaths, the Wilkinet can be used on the front (with the baby facing out or in), on the back or the side. Although the long straps can seem daunting at first they are extremely comfortable and can be mastered in a few days. Straps prevent the baby from toppling sideways when asleep, designed so the position is more comfortable for the baby than other similar slings; fits children from newborns (5lbs) to around 30lb in weight (if you use it regularly and build up the stamina required); available in a dozen colours, £37; capes to use with the sling are £15. / *Hours: 24hr answerphone; free catalogue and fabric samples; Delivery: p&p included.*

Mark Wilkinson Furniture 🗔
Overton House, Bromham, Chippenham,
Wilts SN15 2HA ☎ (01380) 850004
🖰 www.mwf.com
Best known as a manufacturer of bespoke
kitchens, this UK designer has a number of
beautiful (but extremely expensive) kids'
furniture ranges in pine, ash or oak.
Baby equipment – Cots: traditionally-styled
cribs, cots and starter beds.
Nursery decor – Furniture: traditionally-styled
furniture, from hooks and shelves (both about
£100) to carved wall mirrors and tables (both
about £250) to wardrobes (about £1,000); Tom
Thumb and Goldilocks designs
available. / *Hours: Mon-Fri 9am-5pm, or
answerphone; appointments by arrangement; free
brochure; no Amex & no Switch.*

Willesden Bookshop 🗔
Willesden Green Library Centre, 95 High
Rd, London NW10 4QU ☎ (020) 8451 7000
🖰 www.willesdenbookshop.co.uk
Books, music & videos – Bookshops: part of
the library centre complex (which includes
a cinema), this local bookshop has a strong
children's section, with good choice for
pre-schoolers; books on multicultural issues are
a speciality. / *Hours: Mon-Fri 10am-6pm, Sat
9.30am-5.30pm; Delivery: p&p extra.*

Willey Winkle 🗔
Offa House, Offa St, Hereford HR1 2LH
☎ (01432) 268018
🖰 www.willeywinkle.co.uk
A firm of 40 years standing, with many items
made of organically-produced fibres.
**Baby equipment – Specialist mattress
suppliers:** pure organic wool cot mattresses
(with unbleached cotton ticking covers),
duvets and pillows; sizes available include cot,
maxi cot, junior bed, crib and Moses basket; all
wool is tested for excess amounts of chemicals;
£255 for traditional cot mattress, £299 for
organic.
Nursery decor – Bedding: organic cotton
bedding, sheets, towels and flannels. / *Hours:
Mon-Fri 9am-5.30pm; free catalogue; Delivery: p&p
extra.*

Willy Um-Yum 🗔
PO Box 39323, London SE8 5XE ☎ (020)
8297 1576 🖰 www.willyumyum.co.uk
Offers a gift wrapping service for £3 or £5.99
for every three items. As the child who inspired
it grows older it is planed to introduce items
for slightly older children.
Baby clothes – Mid-range: slogan sleepsuits
("I'm in charge", "Did I wake you?"),
bodysuits, T-shirts and sweatshirts; bodysuits
£9, discounts for multiples.
Nappies – Change bags: sells a large canvas
bag with the words 'Bag of baby stuff' on it,
£13. / *free catalogue with further items found on line;
Delivery: p&p £3.95; no Amex.*

Wilton Cycles & Radios
28 Upper Tachbrook St, London SW1V 1SW
☎ (020) 7834 1367
Specialist toy shop.
Toys – General stockists: there is a fair range
for younger children: Duplo, Lego, Primo and
soft toys. / *Hours: Mon-Wed & Fri 9.30am-6pm,
Thu 9.30am-1pm, Sat 9.30am-5pm; no Amex.*

Win Green 🗔
Reason Hill, Westerhill Road, Coxheath,
Kent ME17 4BT ☎ (01622) 746 516
🖰 www.wingreen.co.uk
Nursery decor – Bedding: a range of plain and
gingham cushions in bright colours, plus
simple but charming pillow and duvet covers.
Toys – Outdoor items & active toys: outside
play tents including castles, wigwams, wizard
and fairy tents, plus accessories including
rather charming children's director's chairs and
matching tables. A wizard tent costs
£145. / *Hours: Mon-Fri 9am-5pm; free catalogue; no
Amex.*

Cate Withacy
58 Regent Rd, London SE24 0EL ☎ Mobile
(07931) 978170, (020) 7326 3913
**Nursery decor – Murals and other
Decorating:** complete interior décor service by
artist (responsible for a number of public
murals and author of a book on painted
wooden furniture), who co-ordinates a team of
decorators; styles range from modern stripes to
fairytale pastels via standard childhood
images. / *Hours: 24hrs; no credit cards.*

Wonderwalls
☎ (020) 7978 9712, (07771) 792646
🖰 www.wonderwalls.fsnet.co.uk/
**Nursery decor – Murals and other
Decorating:** gentle (but not twee) murals for
children by a children's illustrator. Or she can
work on canvas, so her work can move house
with you.

Wonderworld 🗔
Thailand ☎ +66 2978 3300
🖰 www.wonderworldtoy.com
Toys – Brand: wooden toys for birth to
around 5 years made in Thailand from wood
from old rubberwood trees (and whose
production process is claimed to be
eco-friendly). Items include a variety of bead
games, musical instruments and some
charming role-play items.

The Woodland Trust 🗔
Autumn Park, Dysart Rd, Grantham, Lincs
NG31 6LL ☎ (08000) 269650
🖰 www.woodland-trust.org.uk
Naming gifts – Naming gifts: the UK's leading
woodland conservation charity
owning/managing over 1,000 woods with free
public access. For £10 you can plant and
dedicate the broadleaf tree of your choice, in
one of 20 woods nationwide; the recipient gets
a certificate, a card and details of the wood
(its flora and fauna and any related history).
For £25 you can plant three trees (with extra
trees at £5 each). Dedications are recorded
centrally. Alternatively, membership costs £30
per year, for which you receive a dedicated
tree and a bi-annual magazine. / *Hours: 9am-
5pm; no Amex.*

Woolgar's Wooden and
Traditional Toys 🗔
4-5 Hatton Shopping Village, Hatton Country
World, Warwick CV35 8XA ☎ (01926) 842
841 🖰 www.fun-shop.co.uk
Toys – Traditional toys: attached to a shop in
the midlands, this comprehensive and well

organised website sells the range of toys the name would suggest.

Woolworths

CENTRAL CONTACT DETAILS
☎ Customer information (01706) 862789
🖰 www.woolworths.co.uk
BRANCHES:
(Only selected branches are listed –
call the enquiry line for other outlets.)
168-176 Edgware Rd W2 2DX
☎ (020) 7723 2391
356 Chiswick High Rd W4
☎ (020) 8994 0773
263–277 High St TW3 1EG
☎ (020) 8570 8613
115 Camden High St NW1 7JS
☎ (020) 7485 3923
40–42 Chapel Market N1 9EN
☎ (020) 8570 5986
17-21 Mitcham Rd SW17
☎ (020) 8672 7010
Only the top branches are listed; all branches carry some children's clothes; outside of London larger 'Big W' stores are introducing a 'Babyshop' area, which includes equipment and nursery decor.
Baby equipment – Stockists: primarily in Big Ws and under the Ladybird brand – a number of buggies, a highchair, a travelcot and so on.
Nursery decor – Bedding: primarily in Big Ws – a range of bedding.
Baby clothes – Cheap & cheerful: the Ladybird range (in recent years exclusive to 'Woolies') of underwear and outerwear (plus babygrows and blankets) is excellent for basics, and often for more as well; high-quality, easy-care fabrics (lots of cotton at reasonable prices) and good, bright, stylish clothes live up to the well-established Ladybird name, especially if you avoid the 'media tie-ins' of the moment.
Toys – Own brand: their own well-priced brand (Chad Valley) plus big names like Fisher-Price and Tomy; good for film and TV tie-in items. / *Hours: mostly 9am-5.30pm; no Amex.*

Word Play

1 Broadway Parade, London N8 9TN
☎ (020) 8347 6700 🖰 www.whatson.com
Toys – Educational: the range emphasises stimulation and education with brands like Galt; some soft toys and videos.
Books, music & videos – Bookshops: range of children's books for all age groups. / *Hours: Mon-Sat 9am-5.30pm, Sun 11am-5pm; no Amex.*

Wotwu 🖰

Claverton, The High Street, Angmering Village, West Sussex BN16 4AH ☎ (01903) 783 152
Baby clothes – Funky: something of a cult label, apparently popular with celebrities, all made in the UK and all in natural fibres. Sell (mainly) through the trade – a list of outlets is available – but also at shows like the London Baby Show. / *leaflet; Delivery: from £3.95; no Amex.*

WOW Toys 🖰

Suite 5, Unit 23 Coda Centre, 189 Munster Rd, London SW6 6AW ☎ (020) 7381 2302
🖰 www.wowtoys.com
Toys – Brand: wide range of chunky, moulded plastic toys, designed in the UK; all battery-free; options include rattles, dumper trucks, activity farm items and mechanical bath toys. / *Hours: Mon-Fri 9am-5.30pm.*

XTS

36 Charles Street, Sileby, Leics LE12 7RJ
☎ (01509) 816444 🖰 www.babystyle.co.uk
Baby equipment – Wheeled Transport-brands: small range of very well-designed three-wheel buggies; their most popular model – originally called the 'Boogie' – is now known as the XTSport; also a double option; call or see the website for stockists.

Year Innovations 🖰

16 Felton Close, Turnford, Hertfordshire EN10 6BT ☎ (01992) 444 444
🖰 www.yearinnovations.com
Nursery decor – Safety items: a clip designed to keep doors safely ajar in a fixed position, preventing children from getting out of, or into, particular rooms, and from trapping their fingers in doors. Available in a range of colours and can be folded away when not in use.

Yorkshire Dales Millenium Trust 🖰

Old Post Office, Main St, Clapham LA2 8DP
☎ (01524) 251 002 🖰 www.ydmt.org
Naming gifts – Naming gifts: for £5 will plant a native tree for you in an area of the National Park in need of re-forestation. / *Hours: Mon-Fri 9am-5pm.*

Young Book Trust

Book House, 45 East Hill, London SW18 2QZ ☎ General (020) 8516 2977, Book Info Service (0906) 516 1193
🖰 www.booktrust.org.uk, www.booktrusted.com
Books, music & videos – Book clubs: an educational charity to promote books and reading for children; subscribers receive three magazines a year, and an annual edition of '100 Best Books'. The linked Booktrusted website is a comprehensive resource for childrens' books and reading material. The company is also responsible for National Children's Book Week, the Smarties Book Prize, Bookstart (which encourages the earliest possible introduction of books to babies) and CALL (Children and Literature in London), which aims to provide listings of all book events for children in the capital. / *Hours: Mon-Fri 9am-5pm.*

Young England 🖰

47 Elizabeth St, London SW1W 9PP ☎ (020) 7259 9003 🖰 www.youngengland.com
With a large space devoted to layette items, you can (if you're not counting the pennies) make this a one-stop shop for a new baby.
Baby clothes – Luxury. – Traditional: beautifully-made, traditional clothes (specialising in hand-smocked dresses); babygrows from £30. / *Hours: Mon-Sat 10am-5.30pm (Sat 3pm); Delivery: p&p depends on size and destination; also courier.*

Young Explorers 🖰

The Minories, Stratford upon Avon CV37 6NF ☎ (01789) 414791
🖰 www.youngexplorers.co.uk

Mail order company and shop devoted to childrens' outdoorwear and equipment.

Baby clothes – Outdoorwear: comprehensive range from baby thermals and fleecy rompers to waterproof trousers, jackets and fleeces for toddlers; also goggles, helmets, life jackets and ski wear; footwear with rubberised soles for extra grip; age range from 0-16.

– **Sun-protection clothing:** 'Sposh' range of UV-resistant swimwear: swimsuit, hat (round or 'legionnaire' styles). Matching accessories include a Kelty Kids carrier to put on back with child in. / *Hours: Mon-Sat; Mail order 9am-5.30pm; Retail 9.30am-5pm; free catalogue or online; Delivery: p&p £3.95.*

Young Ones 🖵

6 Rangifer Road, Fazeley, Tamworth, Staffs B78 3ST ☎ (01827) 288947

🖰 www.youngones.biz/

Baby equipment – Stockists: midlands-based online retailer with a clear site (and which hails its 2003 performance regionally in the British Association of Nursery and Pram Retailers awards). There's a good selection in each category – typical brands include Jané, Chicco and Brevi. A few clearance items are shown. / *online catalogue; Delivery: £10, over £100 free.*

Young Smarties

64 Edgware Rd, London W2 2EH ☎ (020) 7723 6519

Baby equipment – Stockists: cots, cribs, prams, pushchairs and baby walkers – brands include Maclaren, Cosatto and Mamas & Papas; also some toys and clothes. / *Hours: Mon-Sat 10am-7pm (Thu 8pm).*

Youth Sport Trust/Davies The Sports People 🖵

Novara House, Excelsior Rd, Ashby Park, Ashby de la Zouch, Leics LE65 1NG ☎ (0870) 600 0195 🖰 www.youthsport.net, www.novara.co.uk

A lottery-funded group that designs sporting items; many items bought by LEAs; order through Novara (the parent company of Davies) or the website.

Toys – General stockists: items include a Top Tots bag (£25), a rucksack containing sports equipment and a booklet of suggested activities; beach balls, floppy frisbees, flexible marker cones, bean bag turtles, first skills bat, a quoit and a soft mini rugby ball. / *Hours: Mon-*

Fri 8.30am-5pm; free catalogue or online; Delivery: in UK (£6.95 delivery charge); no Amex.

Yummies 🖵

15 Bond St, Brighton, East Sussex BN1 1RD ☎ (01273) 872632

🖰 www.yummiesnappies.co.uk

Nappies – Reusable stockists - brands & singles: "Natural products for happy, healthy babies": pre-fold cotton Yummies nappies, with breathable leak-proof covers, plus disposable (or silk) liners, nappy washbag and accessories. The company claims to be the cheapest of its kind in the UK.

Zaki-do-dah 🖵

18 Hans Place, London SW1X 0EP ☎ (07808) 159 211

You can visit by appointment, but this is primarily a mail order company.

Baby clothes – Luxury: interesting items for babies and children, including pram sets in hand-dyed wool, feather embroidered silk/pashmina blanket, Fairisle sweaters, cashmere knitwear and Bangladeshi hand-embroidered tunics and trousers. Pashmina blanket £59. / *Hours: by appointment only; free catalogue; Delivery: includes p&p.*

Zorbit Babycare 🖵

Trencherfield Mill, The Pier, Wigan, Lancashire WN3 4EF ☎ (01942) 497191, Showroom (Babybase Ltd) (01886) 888170 🖰 www.zorbit.co.uk

Mail order company with a showroom in Worcester.

Nursery decor – Accessories: a wide range of practical and colourful nursery accessories: Moses baskets, rugs, translucent 'jelly' baths and lamps. – **Bedding:** sheets, towels, robes and blankets in flannel, fleece and cotton, in trendy colours or patterns.

Nappies – Reusable stockists - brands & singles: stockists of "the famous terry nappies". / *Hours: Mon-Fri 8.30am-5pm; free catalogue.*

ZPM 🖵

29 St Stephens Gardens, St Margarets, Twickenham TW1 2LT ☎ (020) 8288 1091

Nappies – Change bags: retro fabric changing and travel mats (£20), some with 3-D patterns; also retro coloured bibs, £7.50. / *Hours: Mon-Fri 9am-6pm; free catalogue.*

Databank

CHAPTER 4.01

LONDON BOROUGHS

1. INTRODUCTION

Borough Councils are legally obliged to provide services for children from birth to eight years and to publicise these services. Some produce excellent booklets listing all the facilities in their area. Others don't even tell their own staff what is available, in which case the listings below should prove particularly helpful.

Education and Childcare are the two areas of council responsibility which are of most universal interest to parents. Nurseries, childminders and schools must submit to regular council inspections.

The Children's Act requires that all day care services for children are reviewed every three years and that the review should be part of an on-going process, taking into account the views of those involved in providing, developing or receiving day care services. Not all boroughs are as willing to involve parents as others, but some appear to make a special effort, such as Haringey, Hammersmith, Merton and Sutton.

Councils offer a variety of services and support groups to parents and carers of children with disabilities.

2. BARKING & DAGENHAM

Information Unit
Civic Centre, Dagenham, Essex RM10 7BN

☎ (020) 8592 4500 ⏚ www.lbbd.gov.uk

PUBLICATIONS

Child Choices: choosing day care, registration and inspection, crèches, day nurseries, childminding services (contact the number below for details of current vacancies) family centres, toy libraries, before and after school and holiday care, sports centres, leisure and community services and parks.

Childcare Policy document.

A-Z Barking & Dagenham Guide to Main Services.

Contact numbers:

Social Services (Children & Family), *(020) 8227 2338:* information on day care, playgroups, childminders, day nurseries, etc (listed by area) or see www.childcarelink.gov.uk

3. BARNET

Town Hall Information Centre
The Burroughs, NW4 4BG

☎ Council Services (020) 8359 4000
⏚ www.barnet.gov.uk

PUBLICATIONS

Information pack : *leaflets on clinics, day care, childminding, parent & toddler groups, playgroups, school nurseries, healthcare, libraries, recreation and leisure.*

Contact numbers:

Social Services, East *(020) 8359 6284;* West *(020) 8359 4079*

Children's information service, *(020) 8359 3191*

Health and social care infoLINK, *(020) 8359 2075:* Also contactable via terminals in libraries – details of children's.

Early Years centre, *(020) 8359 7679:* have some places for children & babies with special needs; services include assessment although parent will need to provide a referal.

Children with disabilities team, *(020) 8359 4246:* information and advice on activities and daily living, equipment and adaptations.

Occupational Health unit, *(020) 8371 9334:* provide equipment and help with living adaptations.

Road safety unit, *(020) 8359 6000*

Leisure services, *(020) 8359 7380:* details of at least 48 public playgrounds in the borough.

Recreation & parks, *(020) 8359 7380*

Parent Partnership in Barnet, *(020) 8359 7694:* advice and support to parents and carers of children who have special educational needs.

4. BEXLEY

Civic Offices
Broadway, Bexleyheath, Kent, DA6 7LB

☎ (020) 8303 7777
⏚ www.bexley.gov.uk

PUBLICATIONS

Lists of after-schools clubs, registered playgroups, day nurseries and childminders.

Contact numbers:

Social Services, *(020) 8303 7777.*
Children's information service: *(020) 8856 5398*
Parkwood: *(01322) 350287*

5. BRENT

Town Hall
Forty Lane, Wembley Park, HA9 9EZ

☎ (020) 8937 1234 ⏚ www.brent.gov.uk

PUBLICATIONS

Childcare, After School Facilities, Leisure Activities.

Contact numbers:

Social Services, *(020) 8937 4300*
General information line, *(020) 8937 1200*
Children's play service, *(020) 8810 9126*
Children's information service, *(020) 8937 3001*
Parks & open spaces, *(020) 8937 5619*
Education Department: *(020) 8937 3000*

6. BROMLEY

Civic Centre
Stockwell Close, BR1 3UH

☎ (020) 8464 3333
⏚ www.bromley.gov.uk

PUBLICATIONS

At Your Leisure: *facilities and programmes.*

Think Safety: *do you know how to make your home safer; from Environmental Services; Child home safety*

Services for Young Children

Parent & Toddler Group lists.

Contact numbers:

Social Services, *(020) 8464 3333*
Early Years team, *(020) 8313 4757*
Road safety, *(020) 8313 4546:* runs in-car seat restraint centre for public to try new child safety seats.
Childcare information service, *(020) 8464 0276*
Environmental health, *(020) 8464 3333*

7. CAMDEN

Town Hall
Judd St, WC1H 9JE
☎ (020) 7278 4444
⌐🖉 www.camden.gov.uk

PUBLICATIONS

Cindex computer database printouts
(and an online service) are available
in all Camden libraries; they offer a
comprehensive list of useful
organisations; activities for children
in Camden; day care centres; etc.

Contact numbers:

Social Services, (020) 7911 4444:
Early Years information holds lists of nurseries.

Early Years service, (020) 7974 1603
Childminders, (020) 7974 1679
Children's information service,
(020) 7974 1679

8. CITY OF LONDON

Corporation of London,
Guildhall, EC2P 2EJ
☎ (020) 7606 3030
⌐🖉 www.corpoflondon.gov.uk

PUBLICATIONS

None.

Contact numbers:

Social Services, (020) 7332 1224

Children's information service,
(020) 7332 3126

9. CROYDON

Taberner House,
Park Lane, Croydon, Surrey, CR9 3JS
☎ (020) 8686 4433
⌐🖉 www.croydon.gov.uk

PUBLICATIONS

Community information pack: details
organisations and societies in Croydon;
produced by the library service. Available
from Croydon central library (see below);
Childcare Information service provides a
variety of leaflets.

Contact numbers:

Children's information service,
(0845) 1111 1000
Croydon central library, (020) 8760
5400: holds up-to-date information on:
how to get a childminder; toy libraries;
playgroups; day nurseries; swimming
classes; support groups for children and
parents; lists of adventure playgrounds;
parks and play areas; gymnastics clubs;
crèches; swimming pools; carer and baby
rooms and baby-changing facilities.
Nursery provision & childminders,
(0845) 1111 1000

Road safety, (020) 8760 5484: information on any road safety problems
including child seats and restraints.

10. EALING

Perceval House,
14-16 Uxbridge Rd, W5 2HL
☎ (020) 8579 2424
⌐🖉 www.ealing.gov.uk/children

PUBLICATIONS

Provide a list of childminders, nurseries
and playgroups on request.

Parents' Guide to Choosing Childcare

Contact numbers:

Social Services, (020) 8579 2424
Children's Information Service,
(020) 8825 5588

11. ENFIELD

Civic Centre
Silver St, Enfield, EN1 3XA
☎ (020) 8366 6565
⌐🖉 www.enfield.gov.uk

PUBLICATIONS

Under 8s Directory (also available on
web): day care; education; things to do;
places to go; shops & services; children's
health.

Infopointers: information sheets covering
children's activities, arts, clubs sports etc.

Contact numbers:

**First Stop information office (Civic
centre),** (020) 8379 4006
Social Services, (020) 8379 3333
Road safety, (020) 8379 8546: advice
on which seats fit which car and the age
range they are suitable for; if necessary
will make home visits by appointment.
Childcare information line, (020)
8482 10661

12. GREENWICH

Town Hall
Wellington St, SE18 6PW
☎ (020) 8854 8888
⌐🖉 www.greenwich.gov.uk

PUBLICATIONS

Lists of registered day nurseries,
playgroups, after school clubs,
crèches and childminders, activities
and holiday provision tax credit
information and other leaflets.

Contact numbers:

Children's information service,
(020) 8921 6921

13. HACKNEY

1 Reading Lane, Hackney, E8 1GQ
☎ (020) 8356 5000
⌐🖉 www.hackney.gov.uk

PUBLICATIONS

Hackney Childcare and Playguide:
*published by the Early Years dept,
includes details of group day care; listings
of playgroups and day nurseries; how to
choose a playgroup or day nursery; play
centres; primary schools with nursery
classes; health centres; One o'Clock clubs;
and play facilities.*

Contact numbers:
**One Stop Shop (Nurseries, Under
8s & Early Years Information)**, *(020)
8356 3000*

Children's Information service,
(020) 8356 7590

14. HAMMERSMITH & FULHAM

Town Hall
King St, W6 9JU
☎ (020) 8748 3020 Ⓕ www.lbhf.gov.uk

PUBLICATIONS

Under 8s: information fact sheet; leaflets
on daycare, mother and baby,
childcare groups and minders are
available from information centre

Contact numbers:
Children's information service,
(020) 8735 5868

Children's Social Services, *North,
(020) 8749 3331, South, (020) 8753
5842:* details of nurseries and childminders; if you are unsuccessful getting your
child into a nursery class or school the
Education Department (see chapter *2.07
Education*) will provide information on
playgroups and day nurseries in the borough.

15. HARINGEY

Civic Centre
High Road, N22 8LE
☎ (020) 8489 0000
Ⓕ www.haringey.gov.uk

PUBLICATIONS

Under 8s in Haringey: directory listing a
wide variety of information including
drop in centres; parent and toddler
groups; libraries including toy
libraries; childminders; playgroups;
crèches; outings; shopping; and
children with disabilities.
Leaflets on Services for Children and
Young People with Disabilities and
Special Needs.

Contact numbers:
Childcare Information Service,
(020) 8801 1234
Social Services, *(020) 8489 0000*
Team for children with disabilities,
(020) 8489 1129
Early Years and Play Unit, *(020)
8862 3840:* information on self-help
groups and help for children with disabilities.

Leisure Line, *(020) 8489 5396:* booking and information helpline for sports
and leisure.
Road Safety Training Centre, *(020)
8862 1715:* offers local information on
avoiding accidents to children.

16. HARROW

Civic Centre
Harrow, HA1 2XF
☎ (020) 8863 5611
Ⓕ www.harrow.gov.uk

PUBLICATIONS

State Schools and Nurseries;
Childminder, play scheme, pre-
school, parent & toddler groups.

Contact numbers:
Council Information Desk, *(020)
8424 1102*
Children's Information Service,
(020) 8861 5609
People First, *(020) 8863 5544*
Play Schemes & Sports, *(020) 8424
1242*
Libraries, *(020) 8424 1059*

17. HERTSMERE

Civic Offices
Elstree Way, Borehamwood, Herts,
WD6 1WA
☎ (020) 8207 2277
Ⓕ www.hertsmere.gov.uk

PUBLICATIONS

'Young in Herts', (01438) 737502, deals
with pre-school children's
information service.

Contact numbers:
**Social Services Children & Families
dept**, *(01438) 7375000*

18. HOUNSLOW

Civic Centre
Lampton Rd, Hounslow, TW3 4DN
☎ (020) 8583 2000
Ⓕ www.hounslow.gov.uk

PUBLICATIONS

Lists and leaflets on variety of topics.

Contact numbers:
Social Services, *(020) 8583 2000:*
provide lists of registered childminders
and crèches and help with special needs.
Child information service, *(0800)
7831696*
Childcare, *(020) 8583 3470*
Child & Family Centre, *(020) 8583
6510*
Road Safety Centre, *(020) 8583
2000:* offer talks about child safety including in-car safety and correct fitting of child
restraints; open weekdays 10.00–16.00.
**Nursery Classes c/o Education
department**, *(020) 8583 2653*

19. ISLINGTON

Town Hall
222 Upper St, N1 1XR
☎ (020) 7527 2000
🖰 www.islington.gov.uk

PUBLICATIONS

Starting Out: day care and part day care
centres; groups for parents and
toddlers; services for those with
special needs; toy and book libraries.

Contact numbers:

Children's information service: 020
7527 5959
Early years support team (020)
7527 5625
Social Services, (020) 7527 6400
Sure Start, (020) 7527 5923

20. KENSINGTON & CHELSEA

Town Hall
Hornton St, W8 7NX
☎ (020) 7937 5464 🖰 www.rbkc.gov.uk

PUBLICATIONS

Directory of Services for the Under 8s:
information on day care; educational
facilities; arts, play and sports options;
health services; services for children
with a disability.

Contact numbers:

First Stop Information Service,
(020) 7361 2828
Children's information, (020) 7361
3302

21. KINGSTON UPON THAMES

Guildhall
High St, Kingston upon Thames, KT1
1EU
☎ (020) 8546 2121
🖰 www.kingston.gov.uk

PUBLICATIONS

Parents Guide to day care provision in
Kingston for children in their Early
Years 0-14.

Contact numbers:

Early Years Information Service,
(020) 8547 6582: Information officer
and computerised database to help
parents find childcare and improve
standards; free information and
advice on childcare in the borough;
resources for young children; setting
up a day care facility; lists of all registered childminders, playgroups, and
day nurseries.

22. LAMBETH

Town Hall
Brixton Hill, SW2 1RW

☎ (020) 7926 1000
🖰 www.lambeth.gov.uk

PUBLICATIONS

Guide to Lambeth's Parks & Open
Spaces: children's play areas, paddling
pools, etc.
Lists of information on nurseries,
nursery schools and One o'Clock
clubs.

Contact numbers:

Social Services, (020) 7926 1000
Children's Information Service,
(0845) 6015317
Childminding, (020) 7926 9550
Early Years Service, (020) 7926
9567
Children's Play Service, (020) 7926
9561
Special Educational Needs, (020)
7926 9468

23. LEWISHAM

Town Hall
Broadway, off Bromley Rd, SE6 4RU
☎ (020) 8695 6000
🖰 www.lewisham.gov.uk

PUBLICATIONS

Early Years – The Directory of Services
for Young Children in Lewisham:
obtainable from (020) 8314 7455 or
(0800) 085 0606.

Contact numbers:

Early Years information office,
(020) 8314 8556
Social Services, (020) 8695 6000
Childcare information line, (020)
8314 8556
*Nursery & Pre-School Learning
Alliance,* (020) 8695 5955

24. MERTON

Civic Centre
London Rd, Morden, Surrey, SM4 5DX
☎ (020) 8543 2222
🖰 www.merton.gov.uk

PUBLICATIONS

Choices for Children in Merton
Playcare Merton: *arguably the most
thorough of all local authority guides,
produced by Playcare Merton, a
voluntary charitable organisation, listing
pre-school childcare, activities, education,
special needs groups, health information,
activities for children, information for
ethnic groups, libraries, and other
support services.*
Wraparound Care

Contact numbers:

*Family and Children Social
Services,* (020) 8544 4201: *responsible
for day nurseries.*
Playcare, (020) 8648 5588: *a voluntary charitable organisation.*

Merton Wel-Care Association,
*(020) 8640 5506: for lone parent families
with a child under eight.*
Merton Toy Library, *(020) 8687
2007*

25. NEWHAM

Town Hall
Barking Rd, East Ham, E6 2RP
☎ (020) 8430 2000
🖰 www.newham.gov.uk

PUBLICATIONS

Information Leaflets obtainable from
Children's Information Service;
*information on selecting childcare, pre-
school playgroups, parent/carer and
toddler groups, nursery schools, health
services, and support services.*

Leaflets on Childcare Options, Choosing
a Day Nursery, Choosing a
Parent/Carer and Toddler Group,
Choosing a Childminder – all
available from Children's Information
Service.

Contact numbers:
Social services, *(020) 8430 2000*
Early Years, *(020) 8430 5031*
Children's information service,
(0800) 074 1017.
Newham Family Centre, *(020) 7511
7308*
Community Links, *(020) 7473 2270:*
information about play projects and play-
groups.

26. REDBRIDGE

Town Hall
128-142 High Rd, Ilford, Essex, IG1 1DD
☎ (020) 8478 3020
🖰 www.redbridge.gov.uk

PUBLICATIONS

Children & Families Summer Activities
brochure; *sports for children; provisions
for those with special needs.*

Lists of parent and toddler groups,
childminder vacancies, full-time
nurseries, and playgroups.

Contact numbers:
Children & Families Advice Centre,
(020) 8708 5353: The first port of call for
all enquiries relating to children and their
families; responsible for sending out all
daycare information
Children's Information service,
(0800) 587 7500
Family Centres, Albert Road, *(020)
8708 9132,* Thackerey Drive, *(020) 8708
7778;* Woodford, *(020) 8708 7646.*
Children with Disabilities, *(020)
8708 7529*
Road Safety, *(020) 8708 3577:* offers
information on child car seats, has a recognised garage in Ilford running a free
service to check that the car seat has been
correctly fitted.

27. RICHMOND

Civic Centre
44 York St, Twickenham, TW1 3BZ
☎ (020) 8891 1411
🖰 www.richmond.gov.uk

PUBLICATIONS

Childminder advice to parents:
information sheet and listings.

Contact numbers:
Social Services, *(020) 8891 7600:*
holds range of information on provision
for under 8s including parent and toddler
groups, clinics, libraries, parks and open
spaces, health and community services
and advice and information sources.
Early years, *(020) 8831 6298*
Children's information service,
(020) 8831 6298
Education Department, *(020) 8891
7500*
Leisure services information, *(020)
8940 8351*

28. SOUTHWARK

Town Hall
Peckham Rd, SE5 8UB
☎ (020) 7525 5000
🖰 www.southwark.gov.uk

PUBLICATIONS

Parent and Toddler Groups listings from
Early Years.

Information sheets on childminding,
nursery schools and starting school in
Southwark from Early Years.

Contact numbers:
Social Services, *(020) 7525 3838*
Early years information, *(020) 7525
5189*
Leisure Department, *(020) 7525
1993:* play areas etc.

29. SUTTON

Civic Offices
St Nicholas Way, Sutton, SM1 1EA
☎ (020) 8770 5000 🖰 www.sutton.gov.uk

PUBLICATIONS

What Can We Do Today: guide for
parents with pre-school children.

Contact numbers:
Childcare information centre, *(020)
8770 6000, Mon-Sat 10am-3pm:* free, up-
to-date information and advice centre in
the Times Square Shopping Centre.
Information about facilities and services
for children in Sutton and the surrounding area (including Merton); childminders,
day nurseries, nannies, playgroups, parent
and toddler groups, play schemes, nursery schools and occasional care; activities
and events for children, GPs and clinics,
and child-friendly businesses and shops.

Play Service, (020) 8770 6616, operates three play centres and three out of
school clubs.

30. TOWER HAMLETS

Town Hall
Mulberry Place, 5 Clove Crescent, E14
2BG

☎ (020) 7364 5000 ⏚ www.towerham-
lets.gov.uk

PUBLICATIONS

Early Years Directory of Services: social
   services and education; nurseries
   schools and classes; private and
   voluntary sector nurseries;
   playgroups; parent toddler groups;
   toy libraries; crèches; activities such
   as One o'Clock Clubs museums,
   adventure playgrounds, and
   supervised parks; services for special
   needs; useful contacts.

Contact numbers:
   Children's Information Service,
   (020) 7364 6495
   Early Years, (020) 7364 4293

31. WALTHAM FOREST

Town Hall
Forest Rd, E17 4JF

☎ (020) 8496 3000 ⏚ www.lbwf.gov.uk

PUBLICATIONS

None

Contact numbers:
   Early Years, (020) 8496 3000 ext
   4601

32. WANDSWORTH

Town Hall
Wandsworth High St, SW18 2PU

☎ (020) 8871 6000
⏚ www.wandsworth.gov.uk

PUBLICATIONS

The Leisure Guide: *details parks and open
   spaces, leisure centres, One o'Clock
   Clubs, play areas, and libraries.*

The Children's Information Service
   provides leaflets on: *childcare; minders;
   after school clubs; parent and toddler
   groups etc.*

Contact numbers:
   Social Services, (020) 8871 6622
   Education Department, (020) 8871
   8014
   Children's Information Service,
   (020) 8871 7899

33. WESTMINSTER

City Hall
64 Victoria St, SW1E 6QP

☎ (020) 7641 6000
⏚ www.westminster.gov.uk

PUBLICATIONS

Under 14s guide to Westminster: *topics
   include education, health, advice,
   information, holiday and after school
   activities, clubs and organisations, and
   sport and leisure.*

Contact numbers:
   Social Services, (020) 7641
   5470/5428/5344/7592
   Children's Information Service, (020)
   7641 7929
   Children with Disabilities, (020)
   7641 7476

CHAPTER 4.02

HEALTH PRACTITIONERS

Note: 1) Inclusion of a given practitioner in this chapter does not constitute a recommendation; 2) We have taken information from practitioners and health centres at face value – e.g. if a listing states that a place is child-friendly, it is almost invariably because the provider in question has told us that this is the case, rather than the result of independent assessment; 3) This chapter goes under the banner of 'complementary medicine', although some of the practitioners listed (physiotherapists, for example) take exception to such a term, regarding themselves as part of mainstream medicine; 4) Several of the practitioners listed practise at one or more clinics as well as independently.

1. INTRODUCTION

A GP's practice is, for many people, the first port of call with most types of ailment. However, for many of the conditions either associated with pregnancy or which afflict small children, there is little doctors can do to help. In these cases, many pregnant women and mothers turn to other kinds of practitioner, and some find alternative techniques and complementary therapies useful. Similarly, some women find alternative techniques such as acupuncture useful alternatives to the conventional forms of pain relief used in labour.

THE STATUS OF COMPLEMENTARY TREATMENTS

Mainstream and complementary medicines are, to some degree, converging. The NHS is now making increasing use of some complementary therapies (particularly homeopathy which has been available on the NHS since 1948), and *The Economist* has reported that, in recent years, around 40% of GPs have been using complementary treatments including homeopathy, acupuncture, osteopathy and chiropractic. Osteopathy is now entirely a graduate profession, and the high-profile Osteopathic Centre for Children would like to be seen as the first point of call in the treatment of a child with *any* illness.

To date, scientific studies have been unable to prove the effectiveness of most complementary techniques. However, few doctors doubt the importance of mental attitude amongst patients and even some sceptics of alternative medicine acknowledge that if people feel they are benefiting, this is not an advantage to be sniffed at. The British Medical Association no longer opposes complementary medicine, and is now pressing for compulsory registration of practitioners. To date this has only been arranged for osteopathy and chiropractic, but disciplines such as acupuncture are now also creating single governing bodies with appropriate codes of conduct.

Whether you choose to tell your GP and other carers if you decide to adopt a complementary approach is partly a matter of their attitude to such treatments and partly a question of how far you feel they need to know. The British Acupuncture Council advises you to inform your GP, and states that alternative practitioners should be happy to report to your GP or antenatal carers on your progress, should this be requested of them.

If you plan to use complementary techniques during labour, you should certainly discuss this with your midwives in advance. Some hospitals have honorary contracts that they require therapists to enter into before they are able to assist at the birth.

Safety

Most complementary disciplines have existed for many years – in some cases thousands – and when practised properly are neither toxic nor harmful.

Many complementary techniques are more 'natural' than medical ones, which is why they can be particularly useful in pregnancy and for babies. This is not always the case, however, and herbs in particular must be taken with caution. Most complementary techniques, however, have little downside, unlike many pharmaceutical products used in conventional medicine, where more 'concrete' benefits are bought at the risk of a given drug's potential side effects.

With some conditions, *if* the right complementary treatment is practised on the right individual, the results can be startlingly impressive.

Pointers to ensuring safe complementary care

➢ If there is a credible governing body for the relevant therapy, ensure that any practitioner you plan to use is registered with it, and check how long they have been registered. Membership means that there is an organisation to which you could take any complaint. Beware, though, of organisations with high-faluting names but have no statutory backing – many are little more than marketing organisations. If in doubt, check with the ICM (see below).

➤ Make sure that the practitioner is insured. Insurance is generally only available through central bodies, and only if they deem the practitioner to be competent.

➤ If you have any doubts, enquire what kind of training the practitioner has undergone. In some fields individuals are free to call themselves practitioners after a few weekends of study.

➤ Ensure that the practitioner has some experience of treating the kind of problem that you are presenting and query their success rate. Genuine practitioners are not interested in treating just for the sake of it and may be able to refer you to a more appropriate practitioner or form of treatment.

➤ Check fees and whether medication or treatments prescribed are included in the figure quoted (and, if relevant, whether concessions are offered). If someone will not quote a fee in advance, go elsewhere.

➤ Check how many visits will probably be required.

➤ If you are pregnant, it is wise to avoid all treatments in the first trimester. Thereafter, ensure that any practitioner you consult is competent in treating pregnant women and knows that you are pregnant.

➤ Consult your doctor, midwives or health visitors immediately if there is any chance that the condition might require conventional medical attention.

Finding a practitioner

The best way of finding a practitioner is by personal recommendation. Midwives or antenatal teachers may be a good source of information and contacts, and some may even have relevant skills and training. Alternatively – and especially where more conventional forms of treatment are concerned (e.g. physiotherapy) – your GP may be able to make a recommendation. Note, though, that the best practitioners are often booked months ahead, especially for new patients.

If you are not quite sure which treatment would suit you best, consider approaching one of the complementary health centres that offer a range of therapies – they may be able to suggest an appropriate course of action.

TERMINOLOGY: PRACTITIONER OR THERAPIST?

The Institute of Complementary Medicine defines a practitioner as "someone capable of making an individual diagnosis and offering a treatment which will vary according to the condition of the patient". A therapist is defined as "someone offering a standard treatment", for example, a massage to promote relaxation.

GOVERNING AND CENTRAL BODIES

The better-established therapies have governing bodies, which are the most reliable source of information on practitioners in their field. Membership is dependent on a significant level of study and practice. They will have a members' code of conduct and will probably offer insurance. In certain fields, such as osteopathy, membership of the central body is mandatory for those who wish to practice in this country.

For all the most important organisations, see the listings at the end of the chapter. For therapies with no legal governing body, the listings include details of the organisation that appears to be the most reliable source of information: note, though, the cautionary comments under Safety, above. In less organised disciplines training colleges sometimes set up their own registers, with varying degrees of usefulness.

UMBRELLA ORGANISATIONS

The Institute for Complementary Medicine's British Register of Complementary Practitioners (BRCP) (see below) aims to become the national register for the whole field of complementary medicine and is helping to establish national standards.

The Department for Education and Employment (DfEE) launched National Training Organisations (NTOs) in May 1998, bringing together industrial training and standards organisations for all sectors of employment. The Healthwork UK NTO covers most complementary medicines, and aims to outline national training and occupational standards.

USEFUL CONTACTS

British Complementary Medicine Association (BCMA),
☎ (0845) 345 5977 ⊕ www.bcma.co.uk
This organisation, formed in 1992 (evolved from the National Consultative Council for Complementary Medicine), aims to promote professional standards in complementary medicines throughout the UK, and to assist in the integration of alternative medicine into the healthcare system. Members (including 40 associations representing 11 therapy groups) are part of a voluntary self-regulation system which involves a code of conduct and disciplinary procedures.

Institute for Complementary Medicine (ICM), ☎ (020) 7237 5165 ⊕ www.icmedicine.co.uk
A registered charity, whose main function is to maintain the British Register of Complementary Practitioners (BRCP), which details fully qualified practitioners in 18 complementary disciplines, who are insured and who abide by a recognised code of conduct. Those on the register have to prove their competence to a registration panel, or through externally monitored exams and clinical tests. The Institute also monitors examination standards across all complementary disciplines, and may be able to give advice (to written queries) about obtaining complementary medicine. / PUBLICATIONS List of practitioners in your area (SAE + 2 first class stamps).

International Guild of Professional Practitioners (IGPP),
☎ (0118) 973 5757 ⊕ www.igpp.co.uk
A national membership organisation founded in 1995, covering the majority of complementary medicines and therapies. Recently merged with ITEC (International Therapists Education Council). All members (of which there over 5,500) must be insured (the IGPP has its own insurance scheme), and must adhere to the IGPP's codes of practice and disciplinary procedures. A register of professional members is available for the general public on their website.

International Therapy Education Council (ITEC),
☎ (020) 8994 4141 ⊕ www.itecworld.co.uk
One of the UK's leading awarding bodies for professional qualifications in complementary therapies (also beauty therapy and sports therapy); ITEC qualifications are recognised worldwide; ITEC Professionals has established a register of therapists with ITEC and other approved qualifications, available to search on their website.

Natural Medicines Society, ☎ (0870) 240 4784
⊕ www.the-nms.demon.org.uk
An independent charity which works to improve the status and availability of alternative and complementary systems of treatment.

What Doctors Don't Tell You, ☎ (0870) 444 9886
⊕ www.wddty.co.uk
A website offering little-disseminated information about the pros and cons of conventional and complementary treatments. It offers a 'Find a Practitioner' service, which includes an option to search for those who treat children.

World of Health, ☎ (020) 7357 9393 ⊕ www.worldofhealth.co.uk
Health, fitness and lifestyle video and DVD supplier, with titles looking at how complementary treatments can be used to treat problems ranging from asthma to ADHD, as well as birth trauma and the more day-to-day coughs and colds.

QUALIFICATIONS

Particularly in fields where there is no legal requirement for practitioners to pass exams, top people may – strangely enough – boast fewer qualifications than less skilled counterparts, because they do not see the point of attaining letters of dubious significance after their name. As ever, caution is the watchword in identifying a good therapist.

Qualifications you may encounter include:

RGN: Registered nurse.

RM: Registered midwife.

SCM: State certified midwife.

ITEC: International Therapy Examination Council.

BRCP: British Register of Complementary Practitioners, the register of the ICM.

AIPTI: Association of Independent Therapists; used by some therapists for their insurance.

MGCP: Member of the Guild of Complementary Practitioners.

CHARGES

Almost all complementary treatments have to be paid for by the patient, though there are some low-cost clinics and a few practitioners working within the NHS. However, access to these depends on your GP or antenatal carers. A few practitioners charge on an 'ability-to-pay' basis.

Because treatments and remedies work best if they are tailor-made, the complementary approach can work out expensive. Generally, charges range up to £60 for an initial consultation, which will involve taking a case history and a discussion of any ailments. Subsequent sessions are usually cheaper. There may be lower rates for children. Medication is often charged extra.

COMPLEMENTARY MEDICINE IN LABOUR

A practitioner willing to attend labour will generally charge £100 to £150. However, it does appear that the more people who are involved in a birth, the longer it takes. Therefore, it might be preferable for your birth partner to learn something about simple techniques that may help, for example useful acupressure points to help with contractions. Practitioners may be able to provide birth kits, and may be willing to be consulted by phone during labour to help choose the appropriate remedy.

Should you choose to use any complementary techniques make sure that you discuss these in advance with the staff and that they appear in your birth plan. You should also discuss their use in the case of an abnormal labour.

READING

What Really Works for Kids ★ – Susan Clark (The Insider's Guide to Natural Health for Mums and Dads; Bantam; 2002; £10.99; 0593049195) – *An excellent resource for parents wanting to use nutrition and complementary treatments to keep their children healthy. Specific issues addressed include vaccination and behavioural disorders. There is also an A-Z of possible treatments for specific problems from asthma and cradle cap to yeast infections.*

The Alternative Pregnancy Handbook – Dr Tanvir Jamil & Karen Evennett (Complementary remedies for a healthy and stress-free pregnancy; Piatkus; 2000; £10.99; 0-7499-2117-X) – *An information source on natural remedies suitable for conditions from morning sickness to labour. There is also outline information on different therapies and children.*

Alternative Therapies for Pregancy and Birth – Pat Thomas (Element; 2001; £9.99; 1843330075) – *Options to be used alongside conventional treatments.*

Complementary Therapies for Pregnancy and Childbirth – ed Denise Tiran & Sue Mack (WB Saunders; 2000; £19.95; 0702023280) – *A research-based textbook written originally for midwives facing increasing demand from mothers wanting to use complementary therapies in pregnancy and birth; covers massage, aromatherapy, reflexology, water birth, shiatsu, herbal medicine, homeopathy, acupuncture and osteopathy, plus dealing with stress; also covers applications for the newborn baby.*

Dr Foster Good Complementary Therapy Guide (Vermilion; 2002; £16.99; 0091883784) – *With details of over 5,000 complementary therapists in the UK, covering osteopaths, chiropractors, herbalists, acupuncturists and homeopaths; the theories behind the therapies, diagnosis and what to expect as treatment.*

Healing Your Child – Frances Darragh & Louise Darragh Law (An A-Z guide to safe natural remedies; Vermilion; 2000; £7.99; 0091856035)

Natural Medicine – Beth MacEoin (A practical guide to family health; Bloomsbury; 1999; £25; 0747530238) – *Written in association with The Natural Medicines Society; includes assessments of problems, treatment of over 120 conditions; covers the underlying principles of therapies, diagnostic techniques, methods of treatment and advice on finding a practitioner.*

[Tape] **Neal's Yard Natural Remedies** – Susan Curtis, Irene Kohler & Romy Fraser (Penguin; 1997; £8.99; 0-140195-43-2) – *The use at home of herbs, homoeopathy, aromatherapy and Bach Flower Remedies in an accessible A-Z of ailments; sensible and useful.*

[Magazine] **Proof!** (What Doctors Don't Tell You; £19.75 for a year's subscription.) – *Examination of specific conditions and complementary treatments for them, with information on whether the treatments are safe and whether they work, including running lab ests on different complementary mediciens and supplements to compare effectiveness between brands; coverage is not restricted to pregnancy- and baby-related concerns. / WDDTY (020) 8944 9555, www.wddty.co.uk.*

What Works, What Doesn't – Pat Thomas (The Guide to Alternative Healthcare; Newleaf; 2002; £12.99; 0717133648) – *Eighteen different therapies are considered, and the guide gives details of effectiveness studies, as well as suggesting which conditions are most likely to respond to which treatments. Also areas to exercise caution.*

2. ACUPUNCTURE (& TRADITIONAL CHINESE MEDICINE)

REPORTED BENEFITS

Acupuncture is used in pregnancy to treat a wide range of ailments: nausea; dizziness; oedema; high blood pressure; tiredness; and insomnia. It has also been used for: bleeding during pregnancy; turning breech babies (where moxibustion – see below – is also said to be highly effective); stimulating labour; co-ordinating irregular and ineffective contractions; pain relief in labour; haemorrhaging after birth; after pains; insufficient or blocked milk supplies; and in countering postnatal depression. When used for induction, some practitioners report that labour itself and recovery afterwards may be aided.

Acupuncture is not so commonly used for babies and children but practitioners who do use it report that it can be successful with recurrent coughs and colds, earache, sore throats and digestive problems including colic and broken sleep.

THE TREATMENT

Very fine needles are inserted into the skin at locations that are believed to lie on 12 channels of energy in the body, known as meridians. Each meridian is considered to be linked to one of the major organs. The needles should be taken straight from sterile, sealed packaging.

A related technique is moxibustion – the burning of specific herbs including moxa close to relevant acupuncture points.

Note that although acupuncture is thought to be perfectly safe for a mother (and baby) in pregnancy, certain body points should be avoided as they can potentially trigger a miscarriage.

CENTRAL BODIES

Acupuncture is used by a number of practitioners who primarily specialise in some other form of complementary therapy. These people are not usually members of the Acupuncture Council but may be accessed on the ICM's British Register of Complementary Practitioners – Chinese Medicine Division.

British Acupuncture Council (BAcC), ☎ (020) 8735 0400
🖰 www.acupuncture.org.uk
Once known as the Council for Acupuncture, this organisation represents the largest group of traditional acupuncturists (over 2,500 in the UK). Acupuncturists are not legally obliged to be registered, but the council are working towards statutory regulation with the government. Members – who have all completed a three-year full-time or equivalent part-time training course (at an approved college) – have MBAcC after their name and are bound by the council's codes of conduct. (Practitioners who are not members of the BAcC probably have more limited training in diagnosis and treatment.) Call for a free list of local accredited members and leaflets about acupuncture, or use the search facility and information on the website. / HOURS Mon-Fri 9am-5.30pm.

The British Medical Acupuncture Society (BMAS),
☎ (01925) 730727 🖰 www.medical-acupuncture.org.uk
This organisation is for GPs and fully qualified medical doctors (it has over 2,000 members), who have all undertaken full training (up to diploma level) in 'western medical acupuncture'. The society believes that acupuncture is useful alongside – but will never replace – conventional medical treatments. As a result, use by its members tends to be principally for pain relief, rather than the holistic style of 'eastern-trained' practitioners. Call or write for a local list of accredited members. A London clinic is held on a Tuesday at the Royal Homeopathic Hospital. / HOURS Mon-Fri 9am-5pm.

QUALIFICATIONS

Lic Ac: Licenciate acupuncture.

Dip Ac: Diploma acupuncture.

Dip Ac&H: Diploma of Acupuncture and Homeopathy.

BAc: Bachelor of Acupuncture.

MBAcC: Member of the British Acupuncture Council.

MAcAC: Member of the Acupunture Association of China.

MRTCM: Member of the Register of Traditional Chinese Medicine.

MRCHM: Member of Register of Chinese Herbal Medicine.

DipCHM: Diploma of Chinese Herbal Medicine.

PRACTITIONERS

CENTRAL

Maura Bright (MAR MBAcC)
The Progressive Health Clinic, 140 Harley St W1G 7LB ☎ (020) 7224 3387
🖰 www.brightpractice.com
Acupuncturist and reflexologist, treating women in pregnancy and postnatally, £50 per hour. Hours: Weds 8am-1pm, Fri 8am-7pm, Sat 9am-2pm. / HOURS Mon-Fri 9am-7pm.

Chi Centre
1 Lower Grosvenor Place SW1W 0EJ ☎ (020) 7233 5566
🖰 www.chihealthcentres.com
A centre founded by sufferers of skin conditions. Acupuncture, acupressure and tailor-made herbal treatments are used to relieve skin complaints such as eczema, and also other conditions including asthma, hay fever, loss of appetite, hyperactivity and introversion, as well as conditions which flare up during pregnancy. The phone line operates as a general health helpline. The cost of consultation and the first week's treatment is £85; herbs £20-£50 a week; children's play area. (Children and babies are treated in the Chi Centre for Children.) The centre is a member of the ICM. / HOURS Mon-Sat 9am-5.30pm; PUBLICATIONS Free information pack.

Ken Lloyd (MBAcC, RCHM)
Poly Clinic, Westminster University W1 ☎ *Mobile (07957) 197603, 020 7328 6830*
Experienced in acupuncture and Chinese herbal medicine for pregnancy (turning babies £40, induction £45) and in treating babies and children; £40, thereafter £25. / *HOURS vary.*

WEST

Clinic 251
251 Acton Lane W4 5DG ☎ *(020) 8747 4816*
Maureen Cromey (MBAcC, RCHM) acupuncturist and herbal practitioner with experience of pregnancy management, including labour and postnatally; also treats babies; first visit £45, thereafter £35. / *HOURS Mon 3pm-8pm, Tue 9.30am-8pm, Wed & Thu 9.30am-7pm.*

Linda Coviello (Lic Ac, MBAcC)
14 Jersey Rd W7 2JF ☎ *(020) 8566 4478*
Treatment for pregnancy; no experience of attending at the birth itself but would be willing to attend labour for an existing patient; can refer parents if they need someone with specialist paediatric knowledge.

Rosey Grandage (SRP, MCSP, MBAcC)
40 St Dunstan's Rd W6 8RB ☎ *(020) 8563 1330 home, Prospect Chinese Medicine and Physiotherapy Centre (020) 7381 5727* ☞ *www.prospect health.co.uk*
Physiotherapist specializing in acupuncture and Tui Na massage. / *SEE ALSO 1.04 Antenatal classes.*

Liu Clinic
13 Gunnersbury Ave W5 3XD ☎ *(020) 8993 2549* ☞ *www.liuclinic.co.uk*
Practitioner (BRCP, ICM) experienced in all branches of Chinese medicine including acupuncture and Chinese herbalism; treatments for eczema and problems in pregnancy (back pain, morning sickness); £25 initially, variable thereafter; Male and female fertility problems a speciality. / *HOURS Wed & Fri 10am-11.30am & 3.30pm-6pm, Sat & Sun 10am-11.30pm.*

NORTH

Meredith & Wainwright Churchill
49 Woodland Gardens N10 3UE ☎ *(020) 8444 1007*
Meredith (trained as a midwife, now practising acupuncture and osteopathy; DOBSc, SCM, LicAc, MBAcC) specialises in all aspects of the reproductive cycle, from pre-conception to postnatal (induction, positional problems with babies, common problems of pregnancy); Wainwright (BAc, MBAcC, DipCHM, MRCHM) is a Chinese medical herbalist and acupuncturist, who also specialises in the reproductive cycle, with an emphasis on fertility and recurrent miscarriage; £50 initial consultation and £45 after. / *HOURS Mon-Fri: 9am-5pm.*

Eve Rogans (BAc, MBAcC, MRCHM)
☎ *(020) 7813 3708*
Experienced treating pregnant women and children, with acupuncture and Chinese herbal medicine; £28, children £15 (herbs extra); Kentish Town and Highgate areas.

Anne Lewthwaite (Lic Ac, MBAcC)
Courthope Rd NW3 2LE ☎ *(020) 7267 9995*
Member of the British Acupuncture Council; practices antenatally and postnatally from home; experience with inductions and breaches; £50 per treatment. / *HOURS Mon-Fri 9am-5pm.*

Sarah Moon (MBAcC)
30 Linden Ave, Kensal Rise NW10 5RE ☎ *(020) 8969 1506*
Specialising in pregnancy, Sarah Moon is also experienced in Chinese medicine and herbalism; does not practise with babies or children, but is happy to recommend practitioners who will; payment on a sliding scale according to income £40-£50, thereafter £30-£40. Also experienced in sub-fertility issues.

S-Y Kyan Clark Hong Tao Acupuncture & Chinese Herbal Clinic (MBAcC, MRCHM MAcAC)
21 St Thomas Drive, Hatch End, Pinner Middlesex HA5 4SX ☎ *(020) 8421 2668*
Practitioner, Lily Shwe-yin Clark uses electro-crystal therapy to treat women and also babies; £40, thereafter £35.

Shai Golan (DipAc MBAcC MRCHM)
20 Ramsden Rd Friern Barnet N11 3JE ☎ (020) 8361 5522
Treatments for both pregnant women and babies using acupuncture, herbalism and
Tui Na massage; specialises in treating colic, digestive, upper respiratory tract, skin
and asthma problems. Able to help pregnant women suffering from morning
sickness, back pain and fatigue.

SOUTH

Southfields Clinic
41 Southfields Rd SW18 1QW ☎ (020) 8874 4125
Acupuncturist Adrian Stoddart (MBAcC) offers treatments to help with the
symptoms of pregnancy (fatigue, nausea, etc); help with turning babies and
induction; also alleviation of postnatal problems (such as insufficient milk, depression
and healing of wounds); treatments at 14 and 26 weeks of pregnancy can, they say,
reduce colic and sleeplessness in the baby. / HOURS *Mon-Thu 8am-6.30pm.*

The Traditional Acupuncture Centre
75 Roupell St SE1 8SS ☎ (020) 7928 8333 ⏚ www.acupuncturecentre.org.uk
Some of the centre's therapists may offer other therapies, but all are primarily
acupuncturists; recommendations can be made for specialists in pregnancy, postnatal
treatment and treating children; £65 initially, £44 thereafter (free initial 30 minute
discussion); some practitioners may be available to attend during labour.

Geraldine Worthington (MBAcC)
Echo Cottage, 192 Park Rd Kingston upon Thames KT2 5LS ☎ (020) 8546 5525
Traditional acupuncturist, experience in treating pregnant women and also children
and babies and clients with fertility issues. Free consultation and then £40 for 90
minutes.

OUTSIDE LONDON

Dianne Stewart (Dip Ac&H, MRCHM, MBAcC)
The Canterbury Clinic, 47 Castle St Canterbury CT1 2PY ☎ (01227) 454404
⏚ www.diannestewart.co.uk
Works with women, babies and children (including problems in pregnancy),
combining acupuncture and Chinese herbalism. / HOURS *Tue & Fri.*

Traditional Chinese Medicine

Acupuncture is sometimes practised in combination with the use of
Chinese herbs, or the herbs may be used alone in what is usually termed
Traditional Chinese Medicine.

REPORTED BENEFITS

Herbal treatments have claimed some well-publicised successes with childhood eczema and may be helpful with other chronic problems. Such
treatments may be combined with massage, which works along the same
network of energy channels used by acupuncturists (but as it is a gentler
process, is better suited to babies and children). Practitioners recommend
such treatment for virtually all chronic baby and childhood problems –
from hyperactivity to tonsillitis.

A combination of Traditional Chinese Medicine and acupuncture can
be used to treat many pregnancy-related problems: threatened miscarriage; cystitis; oedema; raised blood pressure; pre-eclampsia, and breech or
transverse presentation. Postpartum problems such as mastitis, excessive
discharge and postpartum weakness can also – it is said – be alleviated.
Traditional Chinese Medicine has also been used to treat inter-uterine
growth retardation (when the foetus is small for its age); headaches during
pregnancy; difficult delivery; and problems after birth like an unsettled
or colicky baby and insufficient milk in the mother.

Practitioners of Chinese medicine believe that the changes in a
mother's body during pregnancy and birth are so great that they offer an

opportunity to correct any previous health problems, enabling her to become even healthier than she was before her pregnancy.

THE TREATMENT

Of all complementary treatments, Traditional Chinese herbal medicine – with its use of potent drugs – is one where clients should exercise particular caution, and in 2001 the government's medicine control agency issued a warning that some products could be dangerous. Some outlets are run by untrained staff; forged certificates are a problem and there have been cases in which prescribed creams have been found to contain steroids, or even arsenic. It is therefore advisable to check the status of a practitioner with the Register of Chinese Herbal Medicine (RHCM), particularly if their training appears to have been exclusively in China or Taiwan.

Chinese Medicine traditionally includes some products from endangered animals and plants. The Metropolitan Police operate a scheme whereby practitioners can sign a certificate declaring that they will not deal in products from endangered species, and may display a window sticker indicating this. Members of the RCHM are governed by a code of conduct that forbids the use of products from endangered species and restricted drugs.

3. ALEXANDER TECHNIQUE

REPORTED BENEFITS

The Alexander Technique can be useful during pregnancy to help the mother cope with both changes in her posture and any compression of her internal organs as the baby grows. The technique is also used in preparation for labour, by helping the mother to adopt positions which will help facilitate a natural delivery.

THE TREATMENT

The teachers aim to improve your awareness of your posture and of habits which interfere with the natural functioning of your body, with a view to improving co-ordination and mind-body functioning.

Lessons (usually of 30–40 minutes) are often found to result in increased energy.

There are books available on the subject, but, especially for beginners, there is no substitute for a session with a qualified practitioner.

READING

Alexander Technique – Chris Stevens (An introductory guide to the technique and its benefits; Vintage/Ebury; 1996; £6.99; 0-091809-79-7)

Pregnancy and Birth: The Alexander Way – ed Ilana Machover (Robinson Publishing; 1995; £12.99; 1-854873-94-6) / Society of Teachers of the Alexander Technique.

CENTRAL BODIES

The Society of Teachers of the Alexander Technique,
☏ (0845) 230 7828, (020) 7284 3338 ⌖ www.stat.org.uk
Registered teachers (MSTAT) undergo three years of training, which includes working with pregnancy; call for a list of practitioners. / HOURS Mon-Fri 9.30am-5pm; PUBLICATIONS Books on pregnancy and childbirth.

PRACTITIONERS

CENTRAL

Alexander Studio
16 Balderton St W1Y 1TF ☎ (020) 7629 1808
Two practitioners (both MSTAT) offering one-to-one tuition in Alexander technique;
£30-£45 per session. / *HOURS vary for each practitioner.*

Bloomsbury Alexander Centre
Bristol House, 80a Southampton Row WC1 4BB ☎ (020) 7404 5348
⁀ www.alexandertechniquelondon.co.uk
Seventeen practitioners (all registered with Alexander Technique organisations)
offering both one-to-one and group tuition; happy to work with
pregnancy. / *HOURS Mon-Sat 8.30am-8pm.*

WEST

Jean & Harvey Goodliffe (BA Hons)
Flat 5, 19 Gledhow Gardens SW5 0AZ ☎ (020) 7373 7939
Husband (MSTAT, BA Hons) and wife (MSTAT, BA Hons) team who feel that the
Alexander Technique is particularly useful in dealing with the physical stresses of
pregnancy and the postnatal period, £35 (45 minutes); Harvey also practises as an
acupuncturist, and has experience of treating during pregnancy, £50 (one hour).

NORTH

Jane Gillie (MSTAT)
13 Mortimer Terrace NW5 1LH ☎ (020) 7284 1737
Teacher whose particular emphasis is advising partners and friends on how to
support a woman during birth.

Ilana Machover (MSTAT)
5 Milman Rd NW6 6EN ☎ (020) 8969 5356
⁀ http://homepage.ntlworld.com/ilana.m/
One of the biggest names in the teaching of the Alexander Technique in the capital
(and also a founder member of Doula UK), who has taught many other practitioners,
and written books on the subject; classes in small groups for pregnant women who
must have previous experience and understanding of the Alexander
Technique. / *HOURS Thu 11am-12.30pm.*

Rosalie Segal & Jonathan Dean
43 Pine Rd NW2 6SB ☎ (020) 8452 7010
Husband and wife (also parents), both MSTAT, whose teaching includes pregnancy
and handling the postnatal period.

SOUTH

Alison Harper (MSTAT)
☎ (020) 8673 3853
Teaches Alexander Technique on a one-to-one basis, both during pregnancy and
postnatally; £25 (negotiable according to ability to pay). / *HOURS Variable (most evenings).*

Karen Wentworth (MSTAT)
6 Ravenslea Rd SW12 8SB ☎ (020) 8673 3853
Alexander Technique teacher (and a mother of two) who has worked with NCT
teachers, some pregnant women and attended a number of births; price £10-£25
session.

EAST

Alexander Technique Centre
82 Great Eastern St EC2A 3JL ☎ (020) 7749 7246
A number of practitioners are based at this City teaching centre, including some who
are specialists in working with pregnancy.

4. AROMATHERAPY

REPORTED BENEFITS

In pregnancy, aromatherapy is recommended for a plethora of problems, from stretch marks to varicose veins: tiredness; nausea; mood swings; fluid retention; cramp and piles. Suitable oils massaged on the perineum may prevent tears at birth.

Aromatherapy may also help with pain relief during labour. There are claims that certain oils, by triggering parts of the central nervous system, help the release of endorphins. One study showed that 65% of mothers found the use of aromatherapy effective, while 12% said it was not. Aromatherapy may also help to increase milk supply and assist with postnatal depression.

For the baby, oils can be soothing or stimulating as a massage or in the bath.

THE TREATMENT

Essential oils – perfumed plant extracts – are believed by aromatherapists to have particular healing properties. They can be used in massage (diluted in almond, grape seed, olive or peach kernel oil), baths and compresses, and through inhalation. The oils are thought to work psychologically as well as physically, but are usually described in rather precise-sounding terms by aromatherapists as being anti-bacterial, anti-viral, fungicidal, anti-spasmodic or soothing. The range of properties may overlap in any given oil. Because oils appear to be anti-infective in both liquid and vapour form, they may be particularly useful after a hospital birth.

Opinion varies, but aromatherapy is not generally advised during the first 12 weeks of pregnancy – and a few practitioners recommend it only during the last three weeks. This is because some oils are believed to stimulate uterine contractions and could therefore cause miscarriage. As a precaution, it is suggested that all aromatherapy oils should be avoided in cases of vaginal bleeding, previous miscarriage and history of birth problems, although there are no recorded incidents of aromatherapy oils causing problems in pregnancy. Manufacturers Green People maintain that provided essential oils are diluted to 1 or 2% in the finished product, there is no risk at all from the oils they use in pregnancy. Whatever the condition, it is recommended that no oil be used without interruption for more than three weeks.

Lavender and chamomile in minute quantities, diluted in carrier oil, are the two most widely recommended oils for use with babies. Few others are considered suitable for use on a newborn.

Another factor in the effectiveness of aromatherapy is the pleasure of the perfumes involved. Some practitioners believe that the pleasure is shared by the baby while still in the womb, so – the argument goes – using the same oils before and after birth makes the environment feel more familiar to the newborn

Some therapists will actually attend labour (with a fee also for an initial consultation), while others will put together a tailor-made selection of oils for you to use during the birth. This usually costs up to £40. Alternatively some therapists offer phone consultations.

READING

Aromatherapy and Massage for Mother and Baby – Alison England (How essential oils can help you through pregnancy and early motherhood; Vermilion Arrow; 1993, revised 1999; £7.99; 0-091774-87-X)

Aromatherapy During Your Pregnancy – Frances P Clifford (CW Daniel; 1997; £3.99; 0-852073-12-7)

Aromatherapy for Babies and Children – Shirley Price & Penny Price Parr (Thorsons; 1996; £8.99; 0-722531-07-9)

Aromatherapy for Pregnancy and Childbirth – Margaret Fawcett (Element Books; 1993; £6.99; 1-852303-90-5) – *A specialist guide focusing almost exclusively on the mother (as the author does not recommend aromatherapy oils for small babies).*

Aromatherapy for the Family – Kusmirek (Wigmore Publications; 1993; £1.99; 0946982066) – *Includes pointers on use in pregnancy.*

Aromatherapy for Women – Maggie Tisserand (Beautifying and healing essences from flowers and herbs; Thorsons; 1990; £5.99; 0-722522-60-6) – *A small book with simple ideas.*

Aromatherapy for Women & Children – Jane Dye (Pregnancy and childbirth; CW Daniel; 1992; £7.95; 0-852072-26-0)

Aromatherapy for Your Child – Valerie Ann Worwood (Essential oil remedies for children of all ages; HarperCollins; 2001; £14.99; 0007109148) – *Covering over 100 childhood ailments and 'recipes' for the first aid kit and bathroom.*

Essential Health - The Complete Aromatherapy Guide – Kolinka Zinovieff (London Natural Health Press; 1996; £4.95; 0952-78250-2) – *A concise rundown of the physical, mental and spiritual conditions which may be treated with oils.*

Fragrant Pharmacy ★ – Valerie Ann Worwood (A complete guide to aromatherapy and essential oils; Bantam; 1991; £8.99; 0-553403-97-4) – *Coverage includes pregnancy and aromatherapy for babies and children.*

[Leaflet] **Understanding Aromatherapy** (Nelsons; free) / Nelsons (see Stockists).

CENTRAL BODIES

Aromatherapy Organisations Council (AOC), ☎ (0870) 774 3477 ⌂ www.aocuk.net

The Council represents the 13 aromatherapy associations in the UK. Its training standards have been adopted by the BCMA, NHS Trusts and the Chartered Society of Physiotherapists. As the lead unifying body for aromatherapy, it is campaigning to become the statutory body for the profession, and already runs what will become the required national register (currently voluntary). The Council is also developing the foundations of a BSc in Aromatherapy, and is the Complementary & Alternative Medicine (CAM) representative on the Health Care National Training Organisation (NTO). A list of accredited schools and practitioners is available by post (send an A5 SAE). / HOURS 10am-2pm; Mon-Fri.

International Federation of Aromatherapists, ☎ (020) 8742 2605 ⌂ www.ifaroma.org

The longest-established membership body for aromatherapists is in the process of applying for statutory status; practitioners trained at IFA accredited schools can use the letters MIFA, and will have knowledge of aromatherapy in pregnancy. / PUBLICATIONS Lists of accredited members (send A5 SAE + £2).

LETTERS YOU MAY ENCOUNTER INCLUDE:

AOC Reg: member of the national register of the Aromatherapy Organisations Council.

MIFA Reg: member of the International Federation of Aromatherapists.

ITEC: diploma in Aromatherapy (also Massage, Anatomy and Physiology).

MTI: Massage Training Institute.

AA Dip: Aromatherapy Associates diploma.

MRQA: member of the Register of Qualified Aromatherapists.

MISPA: member of the International Society of Practising Aromatherapists.

ITHMA: member of the Institute of Herbal Medicine & Aromatherapy

IHT: Institute of Holistic Therapists.

ICHT: International Council of Holistic Therapists.

HAF: Holistic Aromatherapy Foundation.

PRACTITIONERS

It is important if you use an aromatherapist when pregnant to ensure that the practitioner is properly trained. There is no legislation qualifying the use of the

term, and some training courses are very short: practitioners should have trained for at least a year.

CENTRAL

Portland Hospital, Physiotherapy Unit
234 Great Portland St (opposite main hospital) W1N 6AH ☎ *(020) 7390 8061*
🖰 *www.theportlandhospital.com*
Aromatherapy massage and yoga tailored for pregnancy (based in the physiotherapy department of the Portland Hospital); massage is £60 for an hour, yoga is £18 per class or 6 classes for £100. / *SEE ALSO 1.04 Antenatal classes; 2.01 Postnatal; 2.03 Baby health.*

WEST

Kathleen Pepper (MA, ITEC, MTI, IFPA, Cert ZB)
84 Swyncombe Ave W5 4DS ☎ *(020) 8560 7201*
Ex-primary school teacher; instructs mothers in the use of aromatherapy in the home; also relaxation and yoga; aromatherapy £50 for first two-hour consultation, £40 subsequently; £35 for an hour's individual yoga; only organic oils used.

NORTH

Ella Beech
N6 ☎ *(020) 7813 2322*
Practising in the Highgate area, Ella has a particular interest in eczema and allergies, and holds an Active Birth Centre diploma in baby massage; treatments for tired parents and counselling are other treatments offered.

Stuart Chambers
☎ *(020) 8733 4095*
Clinical aromatherapist and acupressurist; practices in Finchley.

Earth Mother
59 Muswell Ave N10 2EH ☎ *(020) 8442 1704*
A tailor-made blend of oils can be made up for you, with advice on the most effective method of application, after a telephone consultation with Alan Stuart (MRQA) or Juliette Preston (IMFA; an ex-Active Birth Centre aromatherapist). Both are specialists in the use of aromatherapy through pregnancy. Personal consultations and workshops also available.

Eileen Fairbane (MIFA, MHAF, CertEd, NLP Skills)
NW2 ☎ *(020) 8450 2470, mobile 07956 553924*
Hale Clinic integrated practitioner treating many mums-to-be, specialising in back problems using a range of techniques; combining aromatherapy, shiatsu, detox programmes, corrective exercise and dance in a holistic health maintenance programme which aims to help postural difficulties; also claims successful treatment of toddlers with problems like hips out of alignment; also toddler meditation; £75 per hour, £30 for half hour. / *HOURS Phone for details; SEE ALSO 2.02 Feeding.*

Hacketts
23 Princess Rd NW1 8JR ☎ *(020) 7586 0969*
Qualified beauty therapists (and hairdressing salon) who offer aromatherapy massage for pregnant women.

Sarah Montgomery
34 Oakfield Court, Haslemere Rd N8 9QY ☎ *(020) 8340 4512*
A generalist with experience of treatment in pregnancy, and working with children; treatments at home can be arranged.

Mala Morjaria (RGN, RM, MISPA, BRA)
65 Southfield Park North Harrow HA2 6HF ☎ *(020) 8427 2932*
Qualified midwife, nurse and aromatherapist offering treatments for pregnancy and postnatally in your own home; neonatally trained – able to offer help to parents whose babies are in intensive care; also focuses on treating childhood asthma and depression. / *HOURS flexible.*

SOUTH

Marguerite & Declan Bowers-Clarke (RDHA, ITEC)
32 Kenley Rd Kingston upon Thames KT1 3RS ☎ (020) 8336 1532
Holistic practitioners with 12 years experience, combining aromatherapy and
reflexology for pregnancy and postnatal treatments; baby massage is their speciality,
and the couple offer a variety of workshops in people's homes. / *HOURS flexible.*

Diana Phillips TIDHA, ISPA
☎ (020) 8542 2459
Tisserand-trained holistic aromatherapist with 12 years experience offering
aromatherapy massage and advice on self-treatments in pregnancy and postnatally in
Wimbledon, Southfields and Wandsworth.

OUTSIDE LONDON

Thilaka Perera (ICHT)
44 Chatham Ave Hayes BR2 7QD ☎ (020) 8462 2071
Qualified midwife practising aromatherapy from home and in West Wickham; will
visit your home if you live nearby; also offers Indian head massage; extremely
cautious about the use of aromatherapy during pregnancy until the last three weeks;
prices depend on location and therapy. / *HOURS Flexible daytime hours; SEE ALSO 2.06 Baby &*
toddler activities.

DIY aromatherapy

Vastly more people use aromatherapy products on themselves and their
family than ever visit an aromatherapist, aided by the burgeoning number
of products and books on the subject.

You should educate yourself a little about this area, however, before
you DIY. Note that seventy per cent of essential oils on sale are not pure.
Price is usually the best guide to quality, but another good sign is a supplier
who marks all products with identifying batch numbers and dates. Many
oils, including all the citrus-based ones, are short-lived with a shelf life of
up to 6 months. The perfume may remain thereafter, but almost certainly
not the effectiveness.

Always look for the botanical name of the plant. Cedarwood, for
example, can come from three different species, only one of which is recommended for aromatherapy. Oil degrades in sunlight, and is corrupted
by plastic bottles over time, so look for products sold in dark glass bottles.

STOCKISTS

CENTRAL

Micheline Arcier 🖼
7 William St SW1X 9HL ☎ (020) 7235 3545 🖰 www.michelinearcier.com
A wide range of aromatherapy products is sold in the shop and by mail order; face,
body and bath oils for babies and toddlers under two, to ward off infections;
and a preventative stretch mark treatment is also available. Special formulations can
also be made for individual problems. / *HOURS Mon-Sat 9am-6pm, (Tues 10.30-7pm, Sat*
5.30pm).

Neal's Yard Remedies
☎ (0845) 262 3145 🖰 www.nealsyardremedies.com
BRANCHES AT:
  15 Neals Yard WC2H 9DP ☎ (020) 7379 7222
A range of 50-plus essential oils, including organic ones, supplied with their botanical
names, countries of origin and methods of extraction. / *SEE ALSO 0 .*

A Nelson & Co 🖼
73 Duke St W1K 5BY ☎ (020) 7629 3118, Mail order (020) 7495 2404, Stockists
(020) 8780 4200 🖰 www.nelsonbach.com, www.nelsonandrussell.com
The Nelson & Russell aromatherapy range includes 30 pure and blended essential
oils, homeopathic remedies. / *HOURS Mon-Sat 9am-5.30pm (Sat 4pm); SEE ALSO 2.03 Baby health.*

WEST

Jurlique
The Naturopathic Health & Beauty Co Ltd, Willow Tree Marina, West Quay Drive, Yeading Middlesex UB4 9TB ☎ (0870) 770 0980 ⌁ www.jurlique.com.au
A range of 31 completely organic essential oils, also available as floral water sprays, body massage oils and bath concentrates. / HOURS Mon-Fri 9am-5pm; SEE ALSO 3.09 Lotions & potions.

Neal's Yard Remedies
☎ (0845) 262 3145 ⌁ www.nealsyardremedies.com
BRANCHES AT:
  Chelsea Farmers Market, Sydney St SW3 6NR ☎ (020) 7351 6380
⌁ www.nealsyardremedies.com
  9 Elgin Crescent W11 2JA ☎ (020) 7727 3998
See write-up in central.

NHR Organic Oils UK
5 College Terrace Brighton BN2 0EE ☎ (0845) 3108066 ⌁ www.nhr.kz
Aromatherapy products including organic essential oils (certified by Soil Association), floral waters, bodycare products, massage base oils and blended oils; oils are packed in clear glass bottles inside metal tubes for protection from sunlight; children's products and organic aromatherapy chocolate also available. / SEE ALSO 3.09 Lotions & potions.

NORTH

Blue Moon
153 Etchingham Park Rd N3 2EE ☎ (020) 8346 1400
Sells a range of ready-made products, including one for babies, children and pregnant mums, designed to promote calm and a good night's rest; custom-made blends are available for labour, stretch marks, aching muscles and so on.

Neal's Yard Remedies
☎ (0845) 262 3145 ⌁ www.nealsyardremedies.com
BRANCHES AT:
  68 Chalk Farm Rd NW1 8AN ☎ (020) 7284 2039
See write-up in central.

Verde
3 Princes Close, Old Town SW4 0LQ ☎ Mail order & advice line (020) 7720 1100, Office (020) 7720 1122 ⌁ www.verde.co.uk
BRANCHES AT:
  15 Flask Walk NW3 3HG ☎ (020) 7431 3314
Along with readymade products, approximately 50 essential oils. / SEE ALSO 0 .

SOUTH

G Baldwins & Co
171-173 Walworth Rd SE17 1RW ☎ (020) 7701 4892, Mail order (020) 7703 5550 ⌁ www.baldwins.co.uk
Sixty-plus essential oils available individually or in boxed sets; offers a wide range of carrier and massage oils (including a range of organic oils) and a specially developed children's range. / HOURS Mon-Sat 9am-5.30pm; SEE ALSO 2.02 Feeding.

Neal's Yard Remedies
☎ (0845) 262 3145 ⌁ www.nealsyardremedies.com
BRANCHES AT:
  6 Northcote Rd SW11 1NT ☎ (020) 7223 7141
  32 Blackheath Village SE3 9SY ☎ (020) 8318 6655
  15 King St Richmond TW9 1ND ☎ (020) 8948 9248
See write-up in central.

Verde
3 Princes Close, Old Town SW4 0LQ ☎ Mail order & advice line (020) 7720 1100, Office (020) 7720 1122 ⌁ www.verde.co.uk
BRANCHES AT:
  75 Northcote Rd SW11 6PJ ☎ (020) 7223 2095
See write-up in north.

OUTSIDE LONDON

Absolute Aromas ⌂
2 Grove Park, Mill Lane, Alton Hampshire GU34 2QG ☎ (01420) 549991
🖰 www.absolute-aromas.co.uk
Stockists of around 90 essential oils, 22 carrier oils and aromatherapy accessories; essential oils are batched and marked with sell-by dates, and all oils are checked for impurities.

Butterbur & Sage
7 Tessa Rd Reading RG1 8HH ☎ (0118) 950 5100 🖰 www.butterburandsage.com
Suppliers of essential oils, from a variety of countries; small range of organic oils, plus carrier oils. Aromatherapy Foundation is their range of fragrance-free cosmetics and toiletries (such as shampoo) designed for incorporating oils for aromatics. Also an Aroma Baby range.

Fleur Aromatherapy ⌂
Langston Priory Mews, Kingham Oxfordshire OX7 6UP ☎ (01608) 659909, Helpline (01772) 491074 🖰 www.fleur.co.uk
Essential oils, carrier oils and skincare products, including an organic range; essential oils are batched and marked with sell-by dates.

Kobashi ⌂
2 Fore St, Ide Devon EX2 9RQ ☎ (01392) 217628 🖰 www.kobashi.com
Around 60 aromatherapy oils, all pure and undiluted and from named botanical species – more than half of the range is from organic sources; blended oils, carrier oils, skin care, fragrance-free products (soap, shampoo and bath oil), baby lotion (with Roman chamomile and lavender) and organic Aloe Vera are all stocked; all products are independently tested. / HOURS Mon-Fri 8:30am-6pm; SEE ALSO 2.03 Baby health.

Living Nature ⌂
Gardeners Business Park Sherfield English Lane, Plaitford Hants SO51 6EJ ☎ (01794) 323 222 🖰 www.livingnature.com
A range of good-quality essential oil plus base oils; also suggestions for their uses. / SEE ALSO 3.09 Lotions & potions.

Napiers Direct ⌂
35 Hamilton Place Edinburgh EH3 5BA ☎ (0131) 343 6683, AdviceLine (0906) 802 0117 (60p per minute) 🖰 www.napiers.net
Comprehensive range of essential oils, some organic, for use in baths, massage and first aid. / HOURS Mon-Fri 10am-6pm, advice line 9am-1pm.

Shirley Price Aromatherapy ⌂
Essentia House, Upper Bond St, Hinckley Leics LE10 1RS ☎ (01455) 615466, Order line (01455) 615436 🖰 www.shirleyprice.co.uk
Offers a range of 50-plus essential oils plus bodycare products. / HOURS Mon-Fri 9am-5.15pm; PUBLICATIONS Aromatherapy for Babies & Children £11 (incl p&p).

5. CHIROPRACTIC

REPORTED BENEFITS
Chiropractic may be used to treat babies with colic, continual crying or sleeplessness. Spinal and especially neck problems caused by birth can, chiropractors believe, go on to trigger problems like hyperactivity and bed wetting as a child gets older.

THE TREATMENT
Chiropractic is not unlike osteopathy (and is similar in status in the US, to osteopathy in the UK), and similarly requires a five-year degree course of study. The technique uses more leverage and manipulation than osteopathy. It is therefore not generally suitable in pregnancy but using specially-designed gentle techniques (such as McTimoney) may be suitable from 13 weeks.

CENTRAL BODIES
Chiropractors are required by law to register with the General Chiropractic Council to practice in the UK.

The British Chiropractic Association, ☎ (0118) 950 5950

🖑 www.chiropractic-uk.co.uk
The BCA was established in 1925 and represents two-thirds of all chiropractors in the UK; all members must have trained at an internationally-recognised college (minimum of four years training), and will be registered with the General Chiropractic Council; all chiropractors train in the treatment of children; call for a free list of BCA registered members in your area. / *HOURS Mon-Fri 9am-5pm.*

General Chiropractic Council (GCC), ☎ (020) 7713 5155

🖑 www.gcc-uk.org
Since 1998, the GCC has been the UK governing body and statutory regulator of chiropractors; all chiropractors must be registered, and are obliged by law to fulfil the standards laid down by the GCC; members of the public consulting a chiropractor have the same safeguards as when consulting a doctor or dentist.

McTimoney Chiropractic Association, ☎ (01280) 705050

🖑 www.mctimoney-chiropractic.org
This specialist form of chiropractic was developed in the 1950s, and treats the whole body (not just the spine) with very gentle movements and pressure. It is very suitable for use in pregnancy; babies and older children are also said to benefit from realignment after birth trauma or accidents; local listings of practitioners can be supplied on request; the association worked with the General Chiropractic Council towards the establishment of the mandatory statutory status.

QUALIFICATIONS

> **DC:** Diploma in Chiropractic.
>
> **MMCA:** Member of the McTimoney Chiropractic Association.

PRACTITIONERS

NORTH

Richard Cook (DC)
Lowlands Chiropractic Clinic, 82 Lowlands Rd, Harrow Middlesex HA1 3AN ☎ *(020) 8864 6768*
Practitioner specialising in treatment of children.

George Rogerson
77 Hardinge Road, Kensal Rise NW10 3PN ☎ *(020) 8459 2903*
Practitioner of McTimoney chiropractic; has worked with women both during pregnancy and postnatally, and with children. Kensal Rise area; also practices at Hendon Natural Health Centre (8202 9747).

OUTSIDE LONDON

Chirocare
10 Sandbourne Rd, Alum Chine Bournemouth BH4 8JH ☎ *(01202) 768508*
Dr Louis Alicea (DC) offers chiropractic treatments using Neural Integration Technique, designed to help with dyslexia. (The technique is also used with children suffering autism, cerebral palsy, Downs Syndrome and attention deficit disorder.) The treatments are said to improve co-ordination, confidence and the ability to communicate, spell, read and write. Initial treatment is £76. Also have a clinic in Southampton. / *HOURS Mon-Sat (not Wed) 9am-2pm; PUBLICATIONS Leaflet available on this topic; SEE ALSO 2.03 Baby health.*

6. COUNSELLING & TALKING TREATMENTS (INCLUDING PSYCHOTHERAPY)

(For information on postnatal depression, related support groups, and social networks for new mothers, see chapter 2.01 Postnatal. For support after a miscarriage or stillbirth, see chapter 4.04 Miscarriage & still birth.)

REPORTED BENEFITS

Pregnancy and birth can bring to the surface all kinds of issues from your past as well as any issues related to your current relationship. It may be a good idea to tackle these subjects before the baby arrives to complicate matters further.

Reading can help (see below), as can talking to your partner or a good friend, or you might consider working with a specialist counsellor. Seeking help from professionals is by no means a 'quick fix' answer however – the idea is that you talk to them, and that they listen but offer no judgements, simply helping you find a new approach to issues.

Psychotherapy is a specific technique for dealing with practical problems by seeking deep-rooted motives in the subconscious. It does not suit everyone, nor do all practitioners have useful insights and suggestions. Given that postnatally you are likely to be in a particularly vulnerable state emotionally and, should your therapist offer inappropriate interpretations of your actions and motives, you may not be in the best position to take these observations with the necessary pinch of salt.

Psychotherapy is sometimes used in dealing with problems in children. In certain cases, psychotherapists diagnose the underlying problem as unresolved issues in one of the parents, such as grief over a miscarriage or memories from their own childhood. These are thought to affect a parent's relationship with their child and result in difficulties for the baby, such as sleeping problems. This can, in turn, then affect the parents, resulting perhaps in depression. Becoming aware of such potential issues may be a useful step towards tackling a problem.

Counselling is particularly recommended in the case of problems like miscarriage or stillbirth, or an antenatal test result indicating a potential problem with the baby. Such problems are specialised ones and your antenatal carers may be able to offer you an appropriate recommendation.

THE TREATMENT

Types of therapy recognised by the UK Council for Psychotherapy (UKCP) include Analytical Psychology; Behavioural and Cognitive Psychotherapy; Experiential Constructivist Therapies; Family Therapy; Couple Therapy; Sexual and Systemic Therapy; Humanistic and Integrative Psychotherapy; Hypnotherapy; Psychoanalytic; and Psychodynamic Psychotherapy.

Individual therapy usually involves a weekly one-to-one session with a therapist lasting approximately 50 minutes.

Group therapy works on similar principles, but is cheaper because individuals listen to each other under the guidance of a group therapist. Sessions are usually weekly for around 90 minutes. One of the benefits of group therapy is to make participants feel less isolated, as the sessions make it clear that others may be suffering similar problems.

Family therapy involves all the members of the family working with a therapist who observes the dynamics of the family and points to potential areas of difficulty.

READING

Family Therapy for Everyone – Dr Eia Asen (How to get the best out of living together; Parkwest Publications; 1997; £9.99; 0-563370-54-8)

Through the Night – Dilys Daws (Helping parents and sleepless infants; Free Association Books; 1993; £12.95; 1-853430-69-2) – *More on the theory that problems in the child can relate to unresolved issues in the parents which then result in further consequential problems.*

CENTRAL BODIES

If you want to try counselling it is wise, before you start, to go to a member of one of the recognised associations, to get an estimate of the time and costs involved. The UKCP emphasises that when selecting a psychotherapist or counsellor it is always worth trying to find out as much as you can about their training and professional background.

British Association for Counselling & Psychotherapy,

☎ *(0870) 443 5252 Information service* 🖰 *www.bacp.co.uk*
Since 1997, the organisation has maintained the United Kingdom Register of Counsellors, and has introduced a 'Framework for Good Practice' and a complaints procedure. Information on counselling services is available, together with details of practitioners in your area and a publications list, on the website or by post (SAE required). / *HOURS 8.45am -5pm.*

British Association of Psychotherapists, ☎ *(020) 8452 9823*

🖰 *www.bap-psychotherapy.org*
Offers an assessment consultation (£40); will try to find a suitable practitioner from among its members; call for details of the child psychotherapists.

The UK Council for Psychotherapy, ☎ *(020) 7436 3002*

🖰 *www.psychotherapy.org.uk*
A national register of qualified and accredited psychotherapists with details of the type of therapy offered. (All accredited UKCP training lasts a minimum of three years plus supervised work with clients; members must also abide by the council's guidelines, which has procedures in place for making a complaint.) / *HOURS Mon-Fri 9am-5.30pm.*

PRACTITIONERS

WEST

Marriage Care

Clitherow House, 1 Blythe Mews, Blythe Rd W14 0NW ☎ *(020) 7371 1341, Helpline (0845) 660 6000* 🖰 *www.marriagecare.org.uk*
Formerly the Catholic Marriage Advisory Council; marriage and relationship counselling. / *HOURS helpline 10am-4pm Mon-Fri.*

Westminster Pastoral Foundation

23 Kensington Square W8 5HN ☎ *(020) 7361 4800* 🖰 *www.wps.org.uk*
Individual and group counselling by referral from a GP or by self-referral. / *HOURS Mon-Fri 8am-8pm (Sat 8am-4pm).*

NORTH

Anna Freud Centre

21 Maresfield Gardens NW3 5SD ☎ *(020) 7794 2313* 🖰 *www.annafreudcentre.org*
A clinic funded on a charitable basis, which is primarily concerned with the mental health of children. Founded 50 years ago by the daughter of Sigmund Freud, the centre runs groups for parents who are concerned about either their relationship with their child, or their child's development or any psychological problems. Children may be referred to the centre for further diagnosis and assessment. Some services are funded by grants, or charges may be made according to a sliding scale. / *HOURS 9am-6pm; SEE ALSO 2.01 Postnatal.*

Institute of Family Therapy

24-32 Stephenson Way NW1 2HX ☎ *(020) 7391 9150*
🖰 *www.instituteoffamilytherapy.org.uk*
Counselling, mediation and family therapy services. / *HOURS Mon-Fri; 9am-5.30pm.*

Jewish Marriage Council

23 Ravenshurst Ave NW4 4EE ☎ *(020) 8203 6311* 🖰 *www.jmc-uk.org*
One-to-one counselling by volunteers for members of the Jewish community in north and south west London. Fees are based on a sliding scale. / *HOURS Mon-Thurs; 9.30am-5pm.*

NAFSIYAT

262 Holloway Rd N7 6NE ☎ *(020) 7686 8666*
Inter-cultural therapy centre. Short-term (up to 12 weeks) counselling and psychotherapy for non-Caucasians, minority ethnic groups or anyone for whom

issues of culture are creating tension (such as people in mixed-culture relationships). Referral is by letter from yourself, your doctor or the social services. / HOURS Mon-Thurs: 9.30am-5.30pm.

The Parent Infant Clinic
27b Frognal Rd, Hampstead NW3 6AR ☎ *(020) 7433 3112*
⌐ www.infantmentalhealth.com
The Parent Infant Centre (established 1990) is a non-profit-making organisation incorporating this clinic and also the School of Infant Mental Health. Staffed by children and adult psychotherapists, and others specialising in infant mental health, the clinic provides therapy for children under five where there are concerns that a child may have emotional problems. (It also runs courses for new parents, with videos and discussion on emotional development.) / SEE ALSO 2.01 Postnatal.

Parentline Plus
520 Highgate Studios, 53-79 Highgate Rd NW5 1TL ☎ *Freephone parent Helpline (0808) 800 2222, Textphone (0800) 783 6783* ⌐ *www.parentlineplus.org.uk*
The association can provide a list of private therapists who work with members of stepfamilies. / HOURS helpline Mon-Fri 2pm-5pm & 7pm-8pm; PUBLICATIONS Newsletter; booklets (on issues including grandparents, weddings, changing children's family names, and making a will; also downloadable from the website); A New Baby (£4) is for stepfamilies planning more children; SEE ALSO 2.01 Postnatal; 4.06 Support groups.

The Tavistock Clinic
120 Belsize Lane NW3 5BA ☎ *(020) 7435 7111* ⌐ *www.tavi-port.org*
NHS psychotherapeutic centre where treatment is available to those living in certain areas of London subject to a referral from a health professional; all ages are treated; the Child and Family Department is one of the larger departments and runs an under 5s counselling service reported as being particularly good at dealing with problems such as sleeplessness or difficulties with potty training. / HOURS Mon-Fri: 9-5.30pm for enquries, longer hours for appointments.; SEE ALSO 2.03 Baby health; 2.06 Baby & toddler activities; 4.04 Miscarriage & stillbirth.

Viveka
27a Queen's Terrace NW8 6EA ☎ *(020) 7483 3788*
Among the other complementary practitioners at this health centre are two specialist psychotherapists and counsellors, one of whom, Anne Herreboudt, is also a qualified midwife and expert psychologist. / SEE ALSO 1.04 Antenatal classes.

The Women's Therapy Centre
10 Manor Gardens N7 6JS ☎ *Advice & info line (020) 7263 6200, Admin (020) 7263 7860* ⌐ *www.womenstherapycentre.co.uk*
Established in 1976, the centre offers somewhere to talk through women's issues away from an orthodox medical setting. Although the centre is only able to deal with one in 12 of the women who make contact by means of individual and group psychotherapy, it does also operate a Community Workshops Project, and provides advice and information about therapy; fees are on a sliding scale. / HOURS advice line Mon-Fri 10am-noon, 2pm-4pm.

EAST

Family Welfare Association (FWA)
501-5 Kingsland Rd E8 4AU ☎ *(020) 7254 6251* ⌐ *www.fwa.org.uk*
– / HOURS Mon-Fri: 9-5pm; SEE ALSO 4.06 Support groups.

7. FLOWER REMEDIES

REPORTED BENEFITS

Countering negative emotions and any physiological symptoms they produce; success is reported in treating faintness in pregnancy and soothing toddlers after small accidents.

THE TREATMENT

Drops invented by a Harley Street doctor in the '30s, using floral products, in small quantities. They are intended primarily for self-help – the most popular option is the Bach Rescue Remedy, sold in most chemists. It is a pre-mixed blend of five herbs to be taken in any emergency, dropped on the tongue or taken in a drink. As well as the original Bach range, modern alternatives are now available, of which Australian Bush Flower Essences is the best known.

READING

A Guide to Bach Flower Remedies – Julian Barnard (CW Daniel; 2001; £3.99; 0852073496) – *From the maker of the Healing Herbs range of products, a concise, standard introduction to the remedies.*

Australian Bush Flower Essences – Ian White (Findhorn Press; 1993; £11.95; 0905249844) – *Information on the properties of the Australian range of essences. / (01309) 690 582.*

Bach Flower Remedies Step by Step – Judy Howard (A complete guide to selecting and using the remedies; CW Daniel; 1990; £3.99; 0852072236) – *A basic guide.*

Growing Up with Bach Flower Remedies – Judy Howard (A guide to the use of the remedies during childhood and adolescence; CW Daniel; 1994; £7.95; 0-852072-73-2) – *Written by a midwife and mother of twins.*

CENTRAL BODIES

Bach Centre, ☎ (01491) 833712 ⏚ www.bachcentre.com
The company's pharmacist can give information on the safety of taking remedies, selecting remedies and general advice; customer services can give details of stockists (of which there are over 4000 in the country). / *PUBLICATIONS How Bach Flower Remedies can help YOU – the believed effects of the different remedies; how to choose the right ones – free from customer services.*

Australian Bush Flower Essences
45 Booralie Road, Terrey Hills, NSW, 2084 ☎ + 61 2 9450 1388
⏚ *www.ausflowers.com.au/*
A range of 65 essences put together by an Australian fifth-generation herbalist, using indigenous plants. It includes Emergency essence to be used similarly to the Bach Rescue Remedy.

PRACTITIONERS

CENTRAL

A Nelson & Co ⏛
73 Duke St W1K 5BY ☎ (020) 7629 3118, Mail order (020) 7495 2404, Stockists (020) 8780 4200 ⏚ www.nelsonbach.com, www.nelsonandrussell.com
The full range of Bach remedies, including Rescue Remedy, is available and a leaflet includes suggested remedies in pregnancy, for labour and birth, and postnatally. Customer Enquiries are to a separate address, Broadheath House, 83 Parkside, Wimbledon, London SW19 5LP (020) 8780 4200, www.bachremedies.com. / *HOURS Mon-Sat 9am-5.30pm (Sat 4pm); SEE ALSO 2.03 Baby health.*

NORTH

Ancient Roots ⏛
23 Broadwalk Shopping Centre, Station Road, Edgware Middlesex HA8 7BD ☎ (020) 8905 6931 ⏚ www.ancient-roots.com
A company that aims to source products at the cutting edge of alternative remedies, ideally exclusively in the UK. On the website you can search for potential treatments for specific problems, although without any specific details on suitability for babies. It offers combination remedies from the Australian Bush Flower range. Individual remedies can be tailor-made, and a training programme is available. Branches at Edgware, Muswell Hill and Watford.

Anne Hellinger
56 Queens Grove NW8 6EN ☎ (020) 7483 1640
Homeopathic practitioner who specialises in pregnancy programmes and childhood vaccination programmes. Prices on application.

Kailash
Centre of Oriental Medicine, 7 Newcourt St NW8 7AA ☎ (020) 7722 3939, 020 4833476. ⏚ www.orientalhealing.co.uk
Karin Mittiga (ITEC, MAR, MGCP, Bach registered) treats with Bach flower remedies and runs workshops. Beginners course £150; remedies for children, £100 (must do beginners course first). Over 30 different practitioners work with Karin. / *HOURS Mon-Sat 9am-7pm; SEE ALSO 2.06 Baby & toddler activities.*

8. HERBALISM

(See also Acupuncture & Traditional Chinese Medicine.)

REPORTED BENEFITS

The right herbal remedies may be helpful with a number of pregnancy-related problems ranging from piles to heartburn. Raspberry leaf tea, for example, is believed to tone the uterus (though it is recommended only during the last three months of pregnancy). Herbalism has reportedly been found to help with bleeding in pregnancy; with the painful 'practice' contractions that may occur in late pregnancy; with mastitis and blocked nipples; and with a shortage of milk. Some herbal treatments are also said to help during birth, in speeding and easing delivery, in strengthening contractions and in relaxing tension. Benefits are further reported with respect to healing afterwards

Some herbs may be harmful or at least best avoided during pregnancy, although hard-and-fast information on this topic is difficult to come by. Sage, rhubarb, cinnamon and liquorice are commonly cited as potentially problematic (though most pregnant women ignore the risks, at least when it comes to the small quantities included in normal cooking).

For babies, calendula (marigold) is considered good for nappy rash, and chamomile tea for colic.

THE TREATMENT

Medical herbalists are trained in the same diagnostic skills as orthodox doctors but take a more holistic approach to illness, looking for an underlying cause to treat, not just symptoms. Practitioners treat patients using the naturally-occurring chemicals found in plants. Note that some herbs are every bit as powerful as synthetically-produced chemicals and should not be taken except under expert guidance.

READING

Herbal Remedies for Children's Health – Rosemary Gladstar (Storey Communications; 1999; £5.99; 1580171532)

Natural Medicine – Andrew Chevallier & Tony Weare (Herbal first aid; Amberwood; 1996; £3.50; 0-951772-35-X) / Napiers.

New Holistic Herbal – David Hoffman (Element Books; 1994; £9.99; 1-852301-93-7)

Wise Woman: Herbal Healing – Susan Weed (Ash Tree; 1989; £10.99; 0-961462-02-7)

CENTRAL BODIES

National Institute for Medical Herbalists, ☎ (01392) 426022
⌖ www.nimh.org.uk
Members of this body (founded in 1864) need to have studied for four years, and to have more than 500 hours of clinical experience. The institute can supply register of practitioners in your local area if you send an A5 SAE for 46p. The website answers FAQs and lists member practitioners. / *HOURS Mon & Fri 10am-4pm, Tue-Thu 9.30am-3.30pm, 24hr answerphone; PUBLICATIONS Information pack, with details of local practitioners (SAE + 44p stamp).*

QUALIFICATIONS

BSc in Herbal Medicine

ITHMA: member of the Institute of Herbal Medicine & Aromatherapy.

MNIMH or FNIMH: member or fellow of the Institute of Medical Herbalists.

USEFUL CONTACTS

Herbline UK, ☎ (020) 8534 7154

Before taking any herbs in pregnancy check with a qualified herbalist or this organisation, based at the London Clinic of Phytotherapy, which can also supply information on herbs advised for and contraindicated against for breast-feeding; the helpline can also refer you to a national register of medical herbalists. / *HOURS Mon-Sat 10-12pm/2-4pm.*

PRACTITIONERS

CENTRAL

Pure Health ⌨

3 Neal's Yard WC2H 9DP ☎ (0800) 092 8828 ⏁ www.eastwestherbshop.com
Herbal store and centre of excellence for Oriental medicine; diagnosis (using Chinese herbal medicine as treatment) is available on the shop floor (£10) or – for more serious conditions – in the adjoining clinic (from £25), where acupuncture (£40) is also available. All practitioners are members either of BAcC or the Register of Chinese Herbal Medicine. / *HOURS Mon-Fri 10am-7pm, Sat 10am-6pm.*

SEN

59 South Molton St W1 ☎ (020) 7629 2243 ⏁ www.senhealth.com
High-fashion Traditional Chinese Medicine centre where Chinese and Western diagnoses are combined. Items are available over-the-counter or on recommendation after 45-minute consultations. All consultants have studied for a minimum of four years at accredited UK TCM teaching institutions and have at least five years of clinical experience. Their formulations are also available through Boots Kensington and well-known chemists John, Bell & Croydon.

NORTH

Archway Clinic of Herbal Medicine

Clerkenwell Bldg, Archway Campus, Highgate Hill N19 5LW ☎ (020) 8411 4411
The National Institute of Medical Herbalists and the Middlesex University both use this centre for clinical training for students in their third year of the BSc in Herbal Medicine. Fees can therefore be kept low – consultations and case histories are completed by the students, overseen by a qualified medical herbalist. Those overseeing treatments will have experience in treating pregnant women and children. First consultation, adults £25 (one hour); subsequent sessions, £12.50 adults, £8 children; medicines charged extra (approx. £8 per week); concessions available, (£16 first hour for children, OAPs and those receiving benefits). / *HOURS Mon-Fri: 10am-4pm.*

EAST

London Clinic of Phytotherapy

180 The Grove E15 1NS ☎ (020) 8534 8050
A low-cost training clinic where third and fourth year students of the BSc in Herbal Medicine take consultations and case histories fully supervised by a qualified medical herbalist, with other students observing. First consultation, £18; subsequent sessions, £12; children £10, then £6; herbs charged extra (approx. £4-£5 per week).

DIY herbalism

If you choose to treat yourself and/or your baby, do not rely on anecdotal evidence, but carefully read a well-informed book on the subject. Useful home herbal treatments – with garlic, chamomile or mint, for example – are detailed in some of the general titles listed at the beginning of this chapter, but check first that whatever you plan to take is suitable for use in pregnancy. Especially if you are planning to use herbs not used in cooking (or in greater quantities than in cooking), it is best to take advice from a professional.

To obtain fresh and effective herbs you need to buy from a supplier with a good turnover. It is also best to use a supplier who can either offer advice, or point you to where to find it before selling you something which may be unsuitable. Licensing is currently under consideration for the retail sale of medicinal herbs, which may help improve standards. For the moment, it can be difficult to guarantee the quality of herbs, although batch numbers and sell-by dates are included on herbal pills and tinctures.

STOCKISTS

CENTRAL

Neal's Yard Remedies
☎ (0845) 262 3145 ⏱ www.nealsyardremedies.com
BRANCHES AT:
  15 Neals Yard WC2H 9DP ☎ (020) 7379 7222
Dried herbs, herbal tinctures and some Chinese herbal tinctures. / *SEE ALSO 0* .

Pure Health 🔲
3 Neal's Yard WC2H 9DP ☎ (0800) 092 8828 ⏱ www.eastwestherbshop.com
Chinese herbal dispensary and health centre (see above); stockists of Pure Health products and supplements. / *HOURS Mon-Fri 10am-7pm, Sat 10am-6pm.*

WEST

Neal's Yard Remedies
☎ (0845) 262 3145 ⏱ www.nealsyardremedies.com
BRANCHES AT:
  Chelsea Farmers Market, Sydney St SW3 6NR ☎ (020) 7351 6380
⏱ www.nealsyardremedies.com
  9 Elgin Crescent W11 2JA ☎ (020) 7727 3998
See write-up in central.

NORTH

Neal's Yard Remedies
☎ (0845) 262 3145 ⏱ www.nealsyardremedies.com
BRANCHES AT:
  68 Chalk Farm Rd NW1 8AN ☎ (020) 7284 2039
See write-up in central.

SOUTH

G Baldwins & Co
171-173 Walworth Rd SE17 1RW ☎ (020) 7701 4892, Mail order (020) 7703 5550
⏱ www.baldwins.co.uk
One of the widest ranges of herbs in the country, including Chinese herbs and powders, Chinese tinctures and herbal fluid extracts. Also a selection of related books. / *HOURS Mon-Sat 9am-5.30pm; SEE ALSO 2.02 Feeding.*

Neal's Yard Remedies
☎ (0845) 262 3145 ⏱ www.nealsyardremedies.com
BRANCHES AT:
  6 Northcote Rd SW11 1NT ☎ (020) 7223 7141
  32 Blackheath Village SE3 9SY ☎ (020) 8318 6655
  15 King St Richmond TW9 1ND ☎ (020) 8948 9248
See write-up in central.

EAST

The Jeyarani Centre 🔲
34 Cleveland Rd E18 2AL ☎ (020) 8530 1146 ⏱ www.jeyarani.com
A range of ayurvedic herbal products designed for use in pregnancy: herbs to ease digestion; a pregnancy oil reported to prevent stretch marks; an intravaginal oil (for use from week 36 of pregnancy) designed to shorten the second stage of labour by softening the ligaments, and making it easier to push the baby out. Postnatal products are also available, including one designed to improve breast milk, and another to restore the tone of pelvic and uterine ligaments. / *SEE ALSO 1.04 Antenatal classes.*

OUTSIDE LONDON

Bioforce (UK) 🖃
2 Brewster Place, Irvine Ayrshire KA11 5DD ☎ (01294) 277344 🖰 www.bioforce.co.uk
High-quality supplier of around 50 herbal products, largely in tincture and homeopathic form. Founded in Switzerland in the '60s, the company grows its own herbs and marks all products with batch numbers and sell-by dates. They do not recommend home diagnosis and treatment for pregnant women or under-twos, insisting that a practitioner should be consulted. / *HOURS Mon-Fri: 9am-5pm.*

Napiers Direct 🖃
35 Hamilton Place Edinburgh EH3 5BA ☎ (0131) 343 6683, AdviceLine (0906) 802 0117 (60p per minute) 🖰 www.napiers.net
Herb teas, tinctures, lotions, creams, vitamins, food supplements and skin care products made from fresh or dried plant material. / *HOURS Mon-Fri 10am-6pm, advice line 9am-1pm.*

The Organic Herb Company
Court Farm, Milverton Somerset TA4 1NF ☎ (01823) 401205
🖰 www.hambledonherbs.co.uk
A Soil Association-certified company, using the brand name Hambledon Herbs – they employ some staff with more than 20 years experience. The company produces a wide range of organic herbs and tinctures as well as Bach flower remedies, flower waters, herb teas and more; all batches inspected for freshness; outlets include the Active Birth Centre.

Specialist Herbal Supplies
Freepost 1396, Brighton East Sussex BN41 1ZZ ☎ (0800) 542 5212
🖰 www.specialist-herbal.com
This company deals purely with herbal products: advice and information are available free to customers. / *HOURS Mon-Fri: 9-5.30pm; PUBLICATIONS The Guide to Natural Healthcare, £2.25 (also available online).*

9. HOMEOPATHY

REPORTED BENEFITS
In addition to boosting overall health in pregnancy, homeopathic remedies can be used to help many specific conditions, including: nausea; respiratory and urinary problems; diarrhoea; heartburn; varicose veins; thrush; cramps; anaemia; bleeding; high blood pressure; and emotional distress. Homeopathy is also said to help with pregnancy-induced forgetfulness.

Homeopathy may even help turning a breech baby, and there are remedies recommended for use during labour, to stimulate contractions, relieve exhaustion and clean the baby's cord.

Homeopathic remedies can also be used to aid healing and recovery after the birth, including the alleviation of postnatal depression, assisting recovery from the effects of surgery or stitches and soothing sore nipples. There are also remedies for breast-feeding problems, such as mastitis and the stimulation of milk production.

For children, homeopathy is often used as an effective on-the-spot treatment for anything from teething or nappy rash to bruises, and is also used as a preventive form of medicine. It is thought to help build up over-all health and increase immunity (particularly to potential problems such as hereditary asthma). Homeopathic remedies are also sometimes used to counter the side-effects of vaccination, and there are reports of treatments proving effective in helping restless babies to sleep through the night.

THE TREATMENT
Homeopathy acts on the belief that symptoms of a problem are a sign that the body is trying to cure itself. To help the body with this process, doses are given of substances that, in the absence of illness, would pro-

voke those same symptoms. However, the amounts used are infinitesimal. For reasons which are not clear, it is thought that the greater the dilution, the greater the effectiveness of the medication.

Because doses are so minute, the remedies cannot cause addiction or create side effects. This makes them ideal for treatment in pregnancy and for babies.

It is not clear how the treatment works but whereas one homeopathic teething product may have an instant effect, another will not, suggesting that the process is not merely psychosomatic. For greatest effect the medication should take into account the personality as well as the physique of the patient (so rendering the idea of self-treatment rather problematic). A visit to an experienced practitioner should reveal a constitutional remedy which is the one recommended for the individual to rebuild good health.

Homeopathy can work out expensive, but was one of the first complementary therapies to be available on the NHS. In London the Royal London Homeopathic Hospital is the best known centre though you will require a referral by your GP (or a consultant) to be treated there. (As you will probably have to wait some months for an appointment this will not be suitable for pregnancy-related issues or acute problems in a child.)

READING

The Complete Homeopathy Handbook – Miranda Castro (A guide to everyday health care; Macmillan; 1991; £15.99; 0-333555-81-3)

The Family Guide to Homeopathy – Dr Andrew Lockie (Symptoms and natural solutions; Simon & Schuster; 1999; £10.99; 0671767712) – *One of the most serious titles for home use.*

Help Your Child with Homeopathy – Sheila Harrison (Using natural homeopathic remedies to relieve common childhood ailments; Avery; 1996; £3.99; 0-895297-40-X) – *A guide to basic principles, which aims to help you identify your child's 'constitutional type' and find remedies to match; also lists of remedies for common illnesses.*

Homeopathy for Children – Gabrielle Pinto and Murray Feldman (A Parents Guide to the Treatment of Common Childhood Illnesses; CW Daniel Company; 2000; £9.99; 0852073372) – *The guide includes information on how to make a constitutional diagnosis of a child.*

Homeopathy for Midwives – ed Barbara Geraghty, Denise Tiran, Ellen Philpot & Deanne Williams (Harcourt Publishers; 1997; £19.95; 0-443057-08-7) – *Includes remedies appropriate for pregnancy, labour, breast-feeding problems and treating newborns.*

Homeopathy for Midwives (and all Pregnant Women) – Dr Peter Webb (British Homeopathic Association; 1999; £4; 0-946717-70-2) – *Pregnancy, labour and postnatal period in brief.*

Homeopathy for Mother and Baby ★ – Miranda Castro (Homeopathy in pregnancy, childbirth and the postnatal year for mother and child; Pan; 1996; £9.99; 0-330349-25-2) – *Not an effortless read, but once mastered a useful and comprehensive title and one recommended by homeopaths.*

Homeopathy for the Family (£2.99) – *A 40-page booklet on using Nelson products for treatment at home. / Nelsons mail order; retail outlets stocking Nelsons products.*

Homeopathy- Neal's Yard Remedies – Rebecca Wells (Aurum Press; 2000; £9.99; 1854107097) – *Written by a one-time employee of Neal's Yard Remedies, the title covers mental, physical and emotional symptoms, dosages and principles.*

BOOKSHOPS
Minerva Books, ☎ *(020) 7385 1361*

/ *HOURS Mon-Fri 9.30am-5.30pm.*

CENTRAL BODIES
As yet there is no single governing body for homeopathy although discussions are taking place. Most teaching colleges operate their own registers. Any college offering at least three-year full-time (or four-year part-time courses) may be considered reliable though some homeopaths

train for as long as seven years. Those listed below currently all function as independent bodies. The ICM has a listing of homeopathic practitioners and it may be that it demands higher standards than those listed.

The British Homeopathic Association, ☎ *(0870) 4443950*

🕮 *www.trusthomeopathy.org*
This charity, founded in 1902, promotes education and research into homeopathy. It maintains lists of homeopaths who are also trained as conventional doctors, including GPs who provide homeopathy on the NHS, and homeopathic hospitals. All those listed have either MFHom or FFHom qualifications; connected professional bodies include the Faculty of Homeopathy (see also) and British Homeopathic Dental Association. / *HOURS Mon-Fri 9am-5pm, or information on answerphone; PUBLICATIONS Free information pack (send A5 SAE).*

Faculty of Homeopathy, ☎ *(0870) 444 3950* 🕮 *www.trusthomeopathy.org*

A professional body regulating the training and practice of homeopathy, for homeopaths who are also GPs. They can provide a list of medically-qualified homeopaths (whose training in homeopathy may be limited – see qualifications).

Lakeland College, ☎ *(01539) 447 666* 🕮 *www.thelakelandcollege.co.uk*

One of the largest homeopathic training colleges in the UK, runs student clinics (in changing locations annually) in London, Edinburgh and the Lakes, in which groups of students are supervised by a qualified homeopath. The clinics are always looking for patients. The college maintains a database of old students and their specialities, and can provide free referrals.

The Society of Homeopaths, ☎ *(01604) 621400*

🕮 *www.homeopathy-soh.org*
This is an association for homeopaths who are not GPs. The Society recognises and works directly with homeopathic colleges, where practitioners train for five years, after which they can become licensed members. Only after a minimum of one year's clinical supervision and rigorous testing can they become registered members, and use the letters RSHom. The Society publishes leaflets on homeopathy in pregnancy and childcare and general information leaflets (e.g. Homeopathy Simply Explained). A detailed list of suggested books on the subject is also available. Send a large SAE for a list of registered members in your area – indicate on the return envelope any leaflets you would like.

QUALIFICATIONS & OTHER LETTERS YOU MAY ENCOUNTER

LCH: London College of Homeopathy.

UKHMA or MHMA (UK): member of the UK Homeopathic Medical Association.

LF Hom: Licensed Associate of the Faculty of Homeopathy – introductory level training (a suffix after this indicates their profession e.g. 'Med' for doctors).

MF Hom, DF Hom: Member of the Faculty of Homeopathy – higher (diploma) level training than the LF Hom. DF indicates a dentist with FoH membership.

LCPHom licenciate: London College of Practical Homeopathy.

MCP Hom: member of the College of Practitioners of Homeopathy.

PCH Dip Hom: Practitioner of Classical Homeopathy (advanced level).

LCP Hom: Licentiate of the London College of Practical Homeopathy.

LLSCH: Licentiate of London School of Classical Homeopathy.

PRACTITIONERS & CLINICS

CENTRAL

Dr Alice Greene (MRCGP, MSHon, Dip Obst, DCH, Dip Cons)

86 Harley St W1G 7HP ☎ *(020) 7580 4188*
Treats pregnant women and babies using diet, homeopathic remedies and counselling. / *HOURS Tues: 8am-5pm, Weds: 8am-6pm, Thurs: 8-5pm.*

The Royal London Homoeopathic Hospital NHS Trust (RLHH)

Greenwell St W1W 5BP ☎ *(020) 7837 8833, (020) 7391 8833*
An NHS hospital since 1948 (private patients also seen), the RLHH takes referrals

from over 40 health authorities and 5000 GPs each year, runs the largest Integrated Medicine training centre in the UK and carries out medical homeopathy and clinical effectiveness research. All doctors are qualified in both conventional and complementary medicine – outpatients are treated with the best and most appropriate combination of homeopathy, acupuncture and manipulative medicine. For treatment, patients need a referral letter from their GP or another NHS hospital consultant. Autogenic Training classes are also taught.

WEST

The Bushmaster Natural Health Practice
204 Uxbridge Rd W12 7JD ☎ (020) 8749 3792 ⏚ www.bushmaster.co.uk
Four homeopaths (all RSHoms), experienced in treating pregnancy, babies and children; fees vary among practitioners from £35-£65 for adults, and £15-£45 for children; osteopathy is also offered, £35-£40. / HOURS *Mon-Fri 9am-6pm, fairly flexible.*

Children's Homeopathic Clinic (BSc LCH RSHon)
St John's Practice, 2 St John's Rd Isleworth TW7 6NN ☎ (020) 8560 7073
A low-cost homeopathy clinic for children to age 11; osteopathy and chiropody for children are also available at the practice; adult appointments also offered – call for further information. / HOURS *alternate Saturdays.*

Dr Max Deacon (MB, BS, MS Hom)
63 Rowan Rd W6 7DT ☎ (020) 7602 1006
Offers homeopathic medical treatment for general conditions especially relating to children and family; also preventive medicine and treatment of skin disorders including infantile eczema. / HOURS *Mon-Wed 9am-6.30pm.*

Fiona McKenzie (LCH, MHMA, LLB)
27 Chapel Side W2 4LL ☎ (020) 7229 6689
An ex-lawyer, experienced in treating babies, children and women in pregnancy and postnatally; birth kits, neuro-linguistic programme work, 'life coaching' and homeopathic courses available; bookings outside office hours available.

Annie Summers (LCH)
30 Warwick Rd W5 3XJ ☎ (020) 8840 2485
With over 10 years of experience, Annie also runs a children's clinic and introduction to homeopathy courses.

Kathryn Tomlinson (RSHom)
23 Waldemar Ave W13 9PZ ☎ (020) 8840 2468
Craniosacral Therapist and ex-Homeopath, from an osteopathy background. Treats traumatic effects of birth on babies and also colic, sleep problems, and crying; also women during and after pregnancy. Prices on application.

Veda Young
Bushmaster Natural Health Centre, 204 Uxbridge Rd W12 7JD ☎ (020) 8749 6523, (020) 8749 3792 ⏚ www.bushmaster.co.uk
Classical homeopath with over 15 years experience; adults, first consultation £65 (90 minutes), then £40, including medication; under twos £25 (one hour), then £18 (30 minutes). Also the author of a booklet on childhood diseases, £3.50.

NORTH

Cally Bruer lcph, miir itec
40 Beresford Rd ☎ (020) 8374 1998
A homeopath who also offers reflexology, relaxation massage and deep tissue massage. Adults £40/30; children £30/£20. Home visits can be arranged.

Centre for Homeopathic Education
The Healthy Living Centre, 282 St Paul's Rd N1 2LH ☎ (020) 7359 7424, (020) 7704 6900
A homeopathic training college offering low-cost student clinics with supervised students, £15.

Annie Freedman (MCH, LCH, RShom)
38 St Gabriels Rd NW2 4SA ☎ (020) 8452 2946
Homeopath with 13 years experience in treating pregnant women and children, also working at Neal's Yard in Covent Garden; adults £60, follow-up visits £45; children £60, then £40. / HOURS *Mon-Thurs: 9am-6pm.*

Anne Hellinger
56 Queens Grove NW8 6EN ☎ (020) 7483 1640
Homeopath able to treat both adults and children; homeopathic vaccination for children, including an information pack, £45; Pregnancy programme, Bach flower remedies and reflexology also available.

Homeopathy Allergy Clinic
15 Westbourne Rd N7 8AN ☎ (020) 7700 4234 ⌁ www.homeopathyallergyclinic.com
Three homeopaths practice here (all RSHom) – they are experienced in treating pregnancy and babies (£65, then £40), and also run Well Woman and Fertility clinics. / HOURS *Tues-Fri 8am-8pm.*

Jan Perivolas
246 Ferme Park Rd N8 9BN ☎ (020) 8348 1091
Specialises in treating families and children (preferring to see patients initially once a month, less frequently with time). A first adult appointment costs £45 and follow-ups are £35. Children are a little less. Remedies are included unless by special order. 'Follow-on' members of the same family unit are treated at half price.

Margaret Johnson (RSHom)
The Garden Flat, 24 Parliament Hill NW3 2TN ☎ (01773) 822078
Offering classical homeopathy, treating children and pregnant women; adults £60; children's prices lower. Home visits available.

Muswell Healing Arts
169 Avenue Mews N10 3NN ☎ (020) 8365 3545
Homeopathic drop-in clinic, £10 including medication; other treatments suitable for pregnancy, childbirth and child ailments include acupuncture, aromatherapy, cranial osteopathy and shiatsu.

Lindsay Nash (RSHom)
47 Goring Rd, Bounds Green N11 2BT ☎ (020) 8888 1252
Experienced (18 years) practitioner who treats all types of patient, and also offers nutrition advice; £40-£65 adults; £20-£30 children; prices include remedies.

Salli Rose
55 Trinity Rd N2 8JJ ☎ (07940) 470284
Treats mothers, babies and children using natural remedies, occasionally attending births; she has specialised in this field since the early '80s. / SEE ALSO *2.03 Baby health.*

Sally Ann Hutcheson BA RSHom
West Hill Way Clinic, 50, West Hill Way Totteridge N20 8QS ☎ (020) 8446 7935
Treatment of mothers before, during and after birth, and of babies. Rates are £65 for an adult's first appoint £50 (children), and significantly less thereafter. Also runs four or six-week introductory courses on Homeopathy for Beginners two or three times a year and weekend courses linked to Lakeland College in Regents Park every September, open to members of the public, and costing £65. Also runs courses or private sessions on pregnancy and childbirth for couples so the husband can administer appropriate remedies in labour.

Gordon Sambridge (MCH, RSHom)
86a St John's Wood High St NW8 7HS ☎ (020) 7483 1288
The principal of The Centre for Homeopathic Education, Gordon has practised for well over a decade, and is experienced in treating pregnant women and children, specialising in the treatment of eczema.

Caroline Schuck (LCH, RSHom)
2c Fellows Rd NW3 3LP ☎ (020) 7722 1924
Homeopath with 14 years experience in working with pregnant women, babies and small children. She has also contributed to books on homeopathy in pregnancy and for children. Treatments for adults: £75, £45; children £50, £35 (remedies extra). Caroline also works with women before and after birth, addressing emotional as well as physical aspects of pregnancy, and will provide tailored birth kits.

Sunrise Children's Clinic
1 Cazenove Rd N16 ☎ (020) 7704 6900
Low-cost Saturday morning clinic in Stoke Newington, run by volunteer homeopaths and students; students sit in on consultations, and run the crèche and the appointments, £10.

SOUTH

Tricia Allen (LCH, MARH)
172 Dunstans Rd, East Dulwich SE22 0ES ☎ (020) 8693 7701
Treats families, women (ante- and postnatally) and babies (from birth); adults £50 first session, then £35; children £40, then £25 (special rates for family groups); homeopathic and allergy testing, flower essence treatments and a low-cost clinic also available.

Marianne Atherton (LCP, MHMA)
☎ (020) 8766 6988
Working from home in The Vale Practice in East Dulwich (8299 9798), with extensive experience of treating children and pregnant women (particularly with skin complaints).

City Health Partnership
37 Oxford Rd SW15 2LH ☎ (020) 8789 0607 ⏚ www.cityhealth.biz
A homeopathic clinic with two qualified homeopaths, offering a 24-hour emergency service (for existing patients) an unvaccinated child support group and a low-cost clinic; £25 for two initial sessions, then £15; children's clinic approximately £45 first session, then £35 or £50 for two children and £40 for follow-ups. Main focus is pre-conception and family health. / *HOURS Mon-Fri 8am-8pm, Sat 8am-12pm; SEE ALSO 2.06 Baby & toddler activities.*

The Drakefield Homoeopathic Centre
239 Balham High Rd SW17 7BE ☎ (020) 8672 5253
Three qualified homeopaths all of whom treat women during pregnancy, and children. / *HOURS vary, closed Sun.*

Barbara Geraghty (Lic, LCCH, RSHom, BA)
77 Kenilworth Avenue SW19 7LP ☎ (020) 8946 4950 ⏚ www.barbarageraghty.co.uk
A specialist in homeopathy for those hoping to start a family, treating pregnancy, labour, post-partum and childhood health problems; fees vary, but approx prices are adults £55 (first visit), then £35; children and babies £35. / *HOURS By appointment.*

Sabine Grocholski (LCH)
St Margarets Clinic, 89 St Margarets Rd East Twickenham TW2 ☎ (020) 8898 1952 ⏚ www.mapleleafpharmacy.co.uk
Sabine Grocholski, and also Roger Sharpley treat both children and adults (including pregnant women) at two different clinics in Twickenham; adults £45, children £35 – including medication.

Lavender Hill Homeopathic Centre
33 Ilminster Gardens SW11 1PJ ☎ (020) 7978 4519
Practice of several registered homeopaths, known for being good with babies and children, and who also treat in pregnancy; the centre also has osteopaths and psychotherapists; prices vary by practitioner. / *HOURS Appointments until the evening.; PUBLICATIONS An Educated Decision (on vaccination and homeopathy), £9.99.*

Olga Lawrence Jones (RS Hom)
☎ Hans Place (020) 7584 1642, Balham (020) 8333 2010
Homeopath, working from practices in Balham and Hans Place (SW1X), experienced in treating families (especially children with asthma, eczema and acute problems) and pregnant women; she offers homeopathic birthing kits (on loan) and is willing to attend labour. Olga also runs regular homeopathic first aid, childhood disease vaccination and travel health courses.

The Richmond Homeopathic Clinic
St Matthias Centre, Church Rd Richmond TW10 6PN ☎ (020) 8940 9949
Karin Leljevahl (LCH MHMA) is experienced in treating pregnant women, which she believes is helpful to the baby antenatally; she also treats specific complaints in women and children; adults £43/£33, children £33/23; babies under one, half price.

Roger Sharpley
Twickenham Homeopathic Clinic, Maple Leaf Pharmacy, 20 The Green Twickenham TW2 5AB ☎ (020) 8898 1952 ⏚ www.mapleleafpharmacy.co.uk
Roger and his wife Sabine Grocholski (see also) are both homeopaths, and specialise in problems including eczema; adults £45, children £35 (including medication); happy to treat pregnant women. / *HOURS By appointment.*

Neil Slade (LCH)
21 Replingham Rd SW18 5LT ☎ *(020) 8543 7948* ⌁ *www.neilslade.co.uk*
Homeopathic clinic run by a practitioner with a background in orthodox medicine, experienced in treating children and women in pregnancy; adults, £50 first consultation, then £40; children £40, then £30, including remedies.

Fran Sinclair Taylor
The Drakefield Centre, 239 Balham High Rd SW17 7BE ☎ *(020) 8672 5253*
Treatments for health problems during pregnancy and childbirth, also for babies and children (including chronic recurrent conditions such as ear infections).

Tom Meeneghan (RS Hom)
Homeland, 13a St Margarets Grove, Plumstead SE18 7RL ☎ *(020) 8855 3071*
Homeopath and member of the Institute of Allergy Therapists who works with pregnant women and babies; £35 then £30, children £20 approx. / *HOURS Mon-Fri 9am-5pm.*

Sunita Venchard (Lic LCCH)
20 Wontner Rd SW17 7QT ☎ *(020) 8764 4562, (07050) 133896*
Homeopathic treatments and advice for children, pregnant women and families: adults £50/£30; children £35/£25; concessions available for lower income families. Also: childbirth classes for women and partners (birthing kits available for hire), and homeopathic first aid classes.

Jan Walker (LCH, MHMA UK)
Tuition House, 2737 St. George's Rd SW19 4EU ☎ *(020) 8296 0405*
⌁ *www.jancwalker.com*
A homeopath who feels it is important to treat pregnant women both before and after birth to ensure that both mother and baby flourish; £65 first consultation, then £45; children £40, then £35; babies under one year old are treated free when the mother is treated; treatment for fertility and issues like elder sibling rivalry also offered.

Liz Whitehead
2 Desensans Rd SE21 7DN ☎ *(020) 8488 2027*
Practitioner with a fair amount of experience treating pregnant women and a good deal of experience treating children.

OUTSIDE LONDON

Maureen Rose (RSHom)
72 High St West Wickham BR4 09H ☎ *(020) 8776 1525*
Homeopath and ex-NCT teacher, experienced at treating children and pregnant women; £50, then £28; children £35, then £22.

DIY homeopathy

Homeopathic remedies can be administered without consulting a practitioner, providing useful first aid treatments for cuts, bruises, burns, colds and the like – available in increasing numbers of pharmacies. However, given that you will probably require any medication at short notice, it is worth investing in a kit.

When buying medicines, soft tablets are the easier option as they can be squeezed on to a baby or young child's tongue for easy absorption. Any remedy over the 200th potency should not be taken without advice from a homeopath (but these usually have to be made up to order anyway).

Many of the practitioners listed above run courses in the use of homeopathy in first aid.

STOCKISTS

CENTRAL

Ainsworths
36 New Cavendish St W1G 8UF ☎ *(020) 7935 5330* ⌁ *www.ainsworths.com*
Can supply lists of local practitioners as well as advice and remedies by post.

Neal's Yard Remedies
☎ (0845) 262 3145 ⌁ www.nealsyardremedies.com
BRANCHES AT:
 15 Neals Yard WC2H 9DP ☎ (020) 7379 7222
Range of homeopathic remedies which include ointments and homeopathic and herbal tinctures. / *SEE ALSO 0* .

A Nelson & Co 🖴
73 Duke St W1K 5BY ☎ (020) 7629 3118, Mail order (020) 7495 2404, Stockists (020) 8780 4200 ⌁ www.nelsonbach.com, www.nelsonandrussell.com
A range of first aid creams made from ingredients such as tea tree oil (antiseptic), calendula (for healing), hypercal (for cuts and sores), arnica (for bruises) and pyrethrum spray (for bites and stings); homeopathic medicines can also be made to order. / *HOURS Mon-Sat 9am-5.30pm (Sat 4pm); SEE ALSO 2.03 Baby health.*

WEST

Food for Thought
154 High St Hounslow TW3 1LR ☎ (020) 8572 0310
Homeopathic remedies (including teething relief) and multi-vitamins. / *HOURS Mon-Sat 9am-5.30pm; SEE ALSO 2.02 Feeding.*

Neal's Yard Remedies
☎ (0845) 262 3145 ⌁ www.nealsyardremedies.com
BRANCHES AT:
 Chelsea Farmers Market, Sydney St SW3 6NR ☎ (020) 7351 6380
 ⌁ www.nealsyardremedies.com
 9 Elgin Crescent W11 2JA ☎ (020) 7727 3998
See write-up in central.

The Organic Pharmacy
396 Kings Rd SW10 0LN ☎ (020) 7351 2232 ⌁ www.TheOrganicPharmacy.com
Homeopathic remedies which can be tailor-made to specification, including kits of 10 remedies for pregnancy, children and first aid. / *SEE ALSO 3.09 Lotions & potions.*

NORTH

Goulds 🖴
14 Crowndale Rd NW1 1TT ☎ (020) 7388 4752 ⌁ www.alternativepharmacy.co.uk
Specialists who can make up boxes of homeopathic remedies for use at home or for while travelling, such as a first aid kit. Advice can be given over the phone or by e-mail (via the website). / *HOURS Mon-Fri 9am-5.30pm.*

Healthy Living Centre
282 St Paul's Rd N1 2LH ☎ (020) 7704 6900 ⌁ www.thehealthylivingcentre.co.uk
Runs a Homeopathic Home-Prescribers one-day Workshop (£50) covering basic principles, common illnesses and simple remedies, and how to start prescribing. / *HOURS Mon-Fri 8am-8pm, Sat 9am-6pm.*

Neal's Yard Remedies
☎ (0845) 262 3145 ⌁ www.nealsyardremedies.com
BRANCHES AT:
 68 Chalk Farm Rd NW1 8AN ☎ (020) 7284 2039
See write-up in central.

SOUTH

Maple Leaf Pharmacy
20 The Green Twickenham TW2 5AB ☎ (020) 8894 5034
⌁ www.mapleleafpharmacy.co.uk
Wide range of homeopathic remedies including Helios and Weleda products; also produces range of first aid kits and childbirth kits from £26.95; the Twickenham Homeopathic Centre is based above the pharmacy. / *HOURS Mon-Fri 9am-9pm (Sat 5.30pm; Sun 5pm).*

Neal's Yard Remedies
☎ (0845) 262 3145 ⌁ www.nealsyardremedies.com
BRANCHES AT:
 6 Northcote Rd SW11 1NT ☎ (020) 7223 7141
 32 Blackheath Village SE3 9SY ☎ (020) 8318 6655
 15 King St Richmond TW9 1ND ☎ (020) 8948 9248
See write-up in central.

OUTSIDE LONDON

Galen Homeopathics 🖂
Lewell Mill, West Stafford, Dorchester Dorset DT2 8AN ☎ Mail order (01305)
265759, Enquiries & advice (01305) 263996
Extensively-stocked West Country pharmacy specialising exclusively in homeopathic
remedies – all of which are the same price and include postage; tablets are
home-made, meaning they are soft and have a good shelf life; aim to despatch same
day if orders placed by 4pm. / *HOURS Mon-Fri 8.30am-4pm, 24hr answerphone.*

Helios Homeopathic Pharmacy 🖂
97 Camden Rd, Tunbridge Wells Kent TN1 2QR ☎ (01892) 537254, (01892)
536393 (24hr answerphone), (01892) 538 400 (24hr answerphone practitioners)
🖰 www.helios.co.uk
Range of high-quality homeopathic remedies produced by homeopaths; available
individually or in kits: 'Double Helix' (18 basic remedies, £26.95), 'Basic Plus' (36
remedies, £38.95), childbirth kit (£26.95), travel kit (£38.95) and an accident and
emergency kit (18 remedies £26.95); also stock herbal soap, toothpaste, mouthwash
and shampoo; also books. (Also shop at 5 New Row, Covent Garden WC2N 4LJ,
tel 020-7379 7434 .) / *HOURS Mon-Sat 10am-5.30pm (Sat 10-2pm), answerphone.*

Weleda 🖂
Heanor Rd, Ilkeston Derbyshire DE7 8DR ☎ (0115) 944 8200 🖰 www.weleda.co.uk
Brand of largely organic creams and homeopathic products – call for stockists or to
place a mail order; the range includes items specifically designed for baby care,
and a homeopathic first aid kit. / *HOURS Mon-Fri: 9am-5pm ; SEE ALSO 2.03 Baby health;*
3.09 Lotions & potions.

10. MASSAGE

REPORTED BENEFITS

This is often as much a feel-good experience as a treatment, although
some practitioners do specialise in using massage for healing and preparation for labour, when massage is a common form of pain relief.

Tui Na Chinese massage is particularly suitable for babies and young
children. Believed to offer all the benefits of acupuncture, without the
needles, Tui Na has been used to treat asthma, eczema, sleeplessness and
croup, and is believed to promote resistance to allergies and infection.

Baby massage classes are an increasingly popular mother (or father)
and baby activity and appear to have potential psychological if not physical benefits for both parent and baby (see chapter *2.06 Baby & toddler*
activities).

During pregnancy it is advisable to avoid any massage to the stomach area (other than the general tummy stroking that most pregnant
women indulge in). Proceed generally with caution as many complementary practitioners believe that pressure on certain points of the body
can trigger labour.

THE TREATMENT

The term holistic massage indicates a practitioner who individually assesses
the physical and psychological condition of each client rather than simply
following a series of set strokes.

For therapeutic massage, look for someone with at least nine months
of training. At least two years training is ideal for remedial massage.
Treatments such as Indian head massage, baby massage and lymphatic
drainage should have been learned specifically rather than as part of some
form of general basic training.

Tui Na massage makes use of the meridian lines which feature in the
Chinese system of the body (though children's meridians differ from those

of adults). It is in some ways similar to shiatsu but comes with more theory.

READING

Chinese Massage Manual – Sarah Pritchard (A comprehensive step-by-step guide to the healing art of Tui Na; Piatkus Books; Oct 1999; £12.99; 0-749920-53-X) – *An illustrated guide.*

Massage for Healthier Children – Marybetts Sinclair (Wingbow; 1993; £13.99; 0-914728-76-8)

Tui Na for a Healthier, Brighter Child – Maria Mercati (Gaia Books; 2000; £9.99; 1856751252) – *Pointers on how to use the massage system to promote a healthy immune system and to treat a range of childhood problems such as night crying, teething and colds. / www.gaiabooks.co.uk.*

CENTRAL BODIES

There are too many styles of massage to list all the organisations operating in this area. One internationally-recognised qualification is ITEC (International Therapy Exam Council).

PRACTITIONERS

CENTRAL

Fran Millward (ITEC, IPTI)
☎ *(020) 7379 7662, 0795 7551930*
Holistic massage (with reflexology) for women in preparation for labour, relieving fluid retention and soothing aches and pains using a massage table specifically designed for pregnant women; practices in Covent Garden.

WEST

Rosey Grandage (SRP, MCSP, MBAcC)
40 St Dunstan's Rd W6 8RB ☎ *(020) 8563 1330 home, Prospect Chinese Medicine and Physiotherapy Centre (020) 7381 5727* ✆ *www.prospecthealth.co.uk*
Tui Na (Chinese massage). / SEE ALSO *1.04 Antenatal classes.*

Justine Peroni (LCMDip, ITEC)
The Garden Flat, 1 Bothwell St W6 8DY ☎ *(020) 7381 9860*
Full body massage, back massage (with or without aromatherapy oils), reflexology and facials, incorporating Shiatsu if required; also qualified aromatherapist; works from home or will travel to most of London; from £17.50 to £35 plus travel; experienced in treating pregnant women, especially if the baby is overdue. / HOURS *Thu-Sun & some evenings.*

Urban Escape
Jo McCallum (RGN) ☎ *(07976) 701041* ✉ *urbanescape@msn.com*
Antenatal, in-labour and postnatal massage; postural advice, visualisation and breathing techniques used; APNT recognised. / SEE ALSO *2.06 Baby & toddler activities.*

NORTH

Amber White Dip Cot, ITEC, RZT
81 Pert Close N10 2RZ ☎ *(020) 8442 0992*
Suggests massage during pregnancy to assist with physical and psychological changes and also, possibly, bonding more deeply with the baby. (Also colour therapy and reflex zone therapy of the feet and personal development sessions). / SEE ALSO *2.06 Baby & toddler activities.*

Earth Mother
59 Muswell Ave N10 2EH ☎ *(020) 8442 1704*
Practical workshops for both partners designed to demonstrate simple and safe massage techniques, including acupressure and reflexology, for use throughout pregnancy and labour; group or individual tuition, £35-£40.

Kailash
Centre of Oriental Medicine, 7 Newcourt St NW8 7AA ☎ *(020) 7722 3939, 020 4833476.* ✆ *www.orientalhealing.co.uk*
A wide range of massage styles, including Tui Na, are offered at this health centre in St John's Wood; also runs a short course in massage for children, taught to small groups, £25-£40 for three hours tuition. / HOURS *Mon-Sat 9am-7pm;* SEE ALSO *2.06 Baby & toddler activities.*

London College of Massage

Correspondence – Diorama, 34 Osnaburgh Street, London NW1 3ND; Venue – D2 Diorama, 3-7 Euston Centre NW1 3JG ☎ *Enquiries (020) 7813 1980, Clinic 0870 990 5828* 🖰 *www.massagelondon.com*

Established in 1987, the college aims to make massage widely available to all and to improve the standard of training throughout the country. All forms of massage are available here, as well as osteopathy and reflexology. Workshops in massage in pregnancy, £60, for practitioners and members of the public. / *HOURS Mon-Fri 9am-9pm; SEE ALSO 2.06 Baby & toddler activities.*

Alan Stuart (MRQA)

59 Muswell Ave N10 2EH ☎ *(020) 8442 1704*

Treatments combine aromatherapy with acupressure massage, £35; home visits £40; treats babies and women in pregnancy and postnatally, also focuses on partners and their role in birth, and offers a range of products for pregnancy and labour; runs workshops for massage through pregnancy at the Active Birth Centre, £40 per couple; also through Earth Mother partnership (see also).

SOUTH

Penny Briers (ITEC, IPTI)

Tooting, Wandsworth, Putney & Wimbledon areas ☎ *(020) 8677 6203*

Swedish massage and aromatherapy including during pregnancy and postnatally in your own home; first session includes free half-hour consultation, £25; thereafter, £30 for 90 minutes (does not include baby massage). / *HOURS weekends and evenings, otherwise by negotiation.*

Gilly Colledge

15 Portal Close SE27 0BN ☎ *(020) 8670 3132*

Combined massage and reflexology for mothers, both pre- and postnatally; also craniosacral therapy for mothers and babies, to help with feeding and sleeping problems, and also with colic. Gilly also works from Balham Therapy Rooms. / *HOURS Mon-Fri.*

EAST

Penelope Lee

7 Albion Drive E8 4LX ☎ *(020) 7241 3331, (020) 7224 2393*

Massage to help with physical stresses as the baby grows (potentially causing muscle tension and pains in the neck and lower back), improving circulation and inducing a greater state of relaxation. Therapeutic massage and aromatherapy, also at 140 Harley Street, London W1N 1AH.

11. NATURAL FAMILY PLANNING

If you are planning to have more children, you might prefer to stick to a contraceptive system which will interfere with conception as little as possible as soon as you have decided to go for it. Natural Family Planning (NFP) is just such a method. It depends on accurate monitoring of a woman's fertility. Technological developments have made this easier and more effective than has traditionally been the case. With instruction by an experienced teacher, the Family Planning Association found that effectiveness in using NFP to avoid pregnancy was 98% – equivalent to barrier methods or the IUD. Note, however, that some health problems can affect the woman's hormonal cycle, and proper instruction in using the method is particularly important in such cases. Use of NFP does not involve any side effects which could affect the chances of conceiving a further child. The fertility awareness involved should actually make this easier.

PRACTITIONERS

WEST

The Fertility Awareness & Natural Family Planning Service

☎ (0845) 310 1334 ⏚ www.FertilityUK.org
Promoters of fertility awareness and natural family planning education, including for breast-feeding women. Information is mainly disseminated via the website. / PUBLICATIONS *Recommended title: Fertility – Fertility Awareness and Natural Family Planning (Dr Elizabeth Clubb, Jane Knight, David & Charles, 1996, £7.99).*

NORTH

Family Planning Association (FPA)

2-12 Pentonville Rd N1 9FP ☎ (0845) 310 1334 ⏚ www.fpa.org.uk
Now officially known as 'fpa', the Family Planning Association is the only registered charity working to improve sexual health and awareness and rights in the UK. Free impartial advice and information on all forms of family planning, pregnancy, contraception, and sexual health. / HOURS *Mon-Fri 9am-7pm;* PUBLICATIONS *Leaflets for parents and children; booklets: Planning a pregnancy.*

OUTSIDE LONDON

The Wholistic Research Company ⌨

1 Enterprise Park, Glaggy Road, Kimpton Herts SG4 8HP ☎ (01438) 833100
⏚ www.wholisticresearch.com
Stock a range of NFP products and reading matter. / HOURS *Mon-Fri 9am-5pm;* SEE ALSO *1.02 Looking after yourself; 2.03 Baby health.*

DIY Natural Family Planning

Ideally, NFP should be learned from an experienced professional, but there are products to help you DIY.

STOCKISTS

Boots, ☎ Customer services (08450) 708090 ⏚ www.boots.com;
www.wellbeing.com
Offers a device called Persona which tests early morning urine (to be used 8 times a month or 16 times in the first month) to monitor changes in hormone levels and identify fertile and non-fertile days.

12. NUTRITION

REPORTED BENEFITS

Interest in nutrition can relate to the desire to alleviate a specific problem such as anaemia, bleeding, or cramp in pregnancy, or the cure of allergies in babies and children. However, for many women, the interest stems from a 'prevention is better than cure' approach.

Good nutrition is very important during pregnancy and dietary supplements can be useful in treating associated conditions. Some supplements are considered essential for the proper development of the unborn child, and the issue of how much a woman's diet affects her unborn baby is the subject of much research. After the birth, good nutrition is particularly important for those who breast-feed.

It is also increasingly believed by some researchers that supplements may be helpful for babies and young children, particularly if under any physical stress. A study in the US for example found that children exposed to even low levels of passive smoking had significantly lower levels of vitamin C than normal, implying that supplementation might be helpful.

While the best way for a baby to get supplements is via her mother's milk – the mother taking an appropriate adult supplement – there is a limited information on supplement levels appropriate for young children. If you can't consult a specialist practitioner you should at least check with the manufacturer.

THE TREATMENT

There are two types of practitioners in this area: State Registered Dieticians, and Nutritional Therapists.

State Registered Dieticians study the theory and practice of nutrition and dietetics for four to five years. They aim to give practical advice on what patients should be eating – usually based on government recommendations for vitamins, minerals, calories, etc,. The focus is often on specific problems like diabetes.

Nutritional Therapists generally offer a more holistic approach, focusing more on what you should not be eating. The aim is to help patients rid their bodies of toxins and stressful substances, so helping with problems such as allergies or the side effects of antibiotics. They are more likely than State Registered Dieticians to suggest supplements, believing these are necessary for almost everyone living in the stressful and polluted environment of cities.

They also tend to subscribe to the growing concern about soil depletion of minerals and consequent nutritional deficiencies in food. (According to the Rio Earth Summit, 75% of crops worldwide may be affected with, for example, a fall in levels of iron in spinach in the US from 15.8mg/100 in 1948 to 2.2mg/100 in 1973.)

Recommended supplements are likely to include elements less used by mainstream medicine such as acidophilus (which is believed to help re-establish bacteria in the intestines, perhaps after a course of antibiotics).

There is precious little agreement about appropriate intakes of different minerals and vitamins, let alone foods, with new theories surfacing regularly. Advice on levels for babies and children is even harder to come by, though Susan Clark gives it a shot in *What Really Works for Kids* (see Reading page 689 in the Introduction to this chapter).

A really thorough nutritional assessment takes one to two hours and is best done with a diet diary the patient completes in advance. This leaves more time for advice and questions.

The Reference Nutrient Intake (RNI) is replacing the Recommended Daily Allowance (RDA – used, for example, on cornflake packets) as the yardstick for assessing recommended levels of consumption. However, nutritionists argue that while these measures are high enough to prevent deficiency-induced diseases that they are still too low to promote really good health. Consequently they generally refer to the higher Optimum Nutrition Intake (ONI).

READING

The Daily Telegraph Encyclopedia of Vitamins, Minerals & Herbal Supplements
– Dr Sarah Brewer (Robinson Publishing; 2002; £9.99; 1-84119-184-1) – *Especially as the products themselves are forbidden from making health claims, this is a useful starting point for those who feel supplementation would be useful. Supplements are listed A-Z, and there is a section on health problems including ADHD, eczema and cystitis. Pregnancy- or children-specific information, however, is thin on the ground.* / www.constablerobinson.com.

Nutritional Medicine – Drs Stephen Davies & Alan Stewart, ed Andrew Stanway (The drug-free guide to better family health; Macmillan; 1987; £9.99; 0-330288-33-4)

The Optimum Nutrition Bible – Patrick Holford (The book you have to read if you care about your health.; Piatkus; 1998; £12.99; 0-749917-48-2) – *The founder of the Institute for Optimum Nutrition highlights the fact that nutritional needs are entirely individual; illustrated by complex research.*

Optimum Nutrition for Babies and Young Children – Lucy Burney (Piatkus; 1999; £10.99; 0-749920-28-9) – *Written by a lecturer at the Institute for Optimum Nutrition: guidelines on breast-feeding and weaning and on how to avoid allergies. Includes more than 150 quick "nutrient-rich" recipes.*

The Oxford Book of Health Foods – JG Vaughan & PA Judd (Oxford University Press; 2003; £19.99; 0-19-850459-4) – *A guide detailing the claims and folklore relating to a wide range of products from arnica to witch hazel, and the evidence for their effectiveness. The guide is conservative in its approach, and includes no pointers on how-to-use. / www.oup.co.uk.*

CENTRAL BODIES

Nutritionists do not have a nationally recognised qualification although nutritional science and therapy is now being offered as part of a Complementary Therapies degree at the University of Westminster.

British Association of Nutritional Therapists (BANT),
☎ (08706) 061284 ⁐ www.bant.org.uk
This relatively newly formed organisation is the UK's registered governing body for Nutritional Therapists. All the therapists on the BANT register have completed a training course, which includes considerable practical experience with clients. BANT requires all therapists to be fully insured and to abide by professional guidelines of ethics and practice. / PUBLICATIONS *List of BANT-registered therapists (send large SAE alternatively see website).*

British Dietetic Association, ☎ (0121) 200 8080 ⁐ www.bda.uk.com
The professional organisation representing registered dieticians.

The British Institute for Allergy & Environmental Therapy, ☎ (01974) 241376 ⁐ www.allergy.org.uk
Previously called the Institute of Allergy Therapists (and known locally as Ffynnonwen Natural Therapy Centre) – this is a group of therapists and health professionals, both in orthodox and alternative medicine, who have undergone specialist training in the diagnosis and treatment of food, chemical and environmental allergy. The organisation offers members of the public brief advice and a referral list for more detailed consultation. (Therapists usually test for allergy with a system called muscle testing followed by desensitising remedies which are prepared using homeopathic techniques. A retest is usual after four weeks followed by further remedies as required.)

General Council & Register of Naturopaths, ☎ (01458) 840 072
⁐ www.naturopathy.org.uk
A service run by the British Naturopathic Association to put the public in touch with its members. Naturopathy is a holistic treatment, often using herbs and nutrition and looking at the subject's lifestyle; homeopathy may also be involved.

Institute of Optimum Nutrition, ☎ (020) 8877 9993
⁐ www.ion.ac.uk/
A charity, founded in 1984 by Patrick Holford, which aims to promote awareness in nutrition. It is the biggest training centre for nutritionists in the UK and can provide a list of graduates and their areas of specialisation.

QUALIFICATIONS

DNN: Diploma of Natural Nutrition (College of Natural nutrition, Bristol and London).

DNMed: Diploma of Nutritional Medicine and Therapeutic Dietetics

Dip ION: Diploma from the Institute of Optimum Nutrition.

PRACTITIONERS

CENTRAL

Biolab Medical Unit
The Stone House, 9 Weymouth St W1W 6DB ☎ (020) 7636 5959/5905
⁐ www.biolab.co.uk
Nutritional screening – only with a GP or doctor's referral. A nutritional status assessment is available. / HOURS *Mon-Fri 9am-5.30pm; SEE ALSO 1.02 Looking after yourself.*

Create Health Centre for Reproduction and Advanced Technology

21 Devonshire Place WIG 6HZ ☎ *(020) 7486 5566* ✆ *www.createhealth.org*
Dr John Briffa, a doctor who has specialised in issues of nutrition, offers nutritional advice, including for pregnancy. / SEE ALSO 1.03 Tests.

Marilyn Glenville (BEd, MA, PhD)

c/o The Hale Clinic, 7 Park Crescent WIA 2RA ☎ *(08705) 329244*
✆ *www.marilynglenville.com*
The former chair of BANT and Foresight – a nutritional therapist specialising in women's and children's health who aims to offer natural solutions to problems in pregnancy, and also deals with children's eating problems and possible nutritional deficiencies and allergies; also practices in St John's Wood with Mr Yehudi Gordon. The web site includes pointers for example on diet and conception.

Nightingale Allergy Clinic

Lister House, 11-12 Wimpole St WIG 9ST ☎ *(020) 7436 2135*
Clinical allergist (medical doctor specialising in allergies) who uses muscle testing for diagnosis, and who is experienced in treating pregnant women and newborn children, a consultation is £100; remedies involving a desensitising technique combining conventional and complementary techniques. / HOURS Mon-Fri: 10am-5pm.

WEST

The Food Doctor (Vicky Edgson)

76-78 Holland Park Avenue WII 3RB ☎ *(0800) 093 5877, (020) 7792 6700*
✆ *www.thefooddoctor.com*
A consultancy (and – given its publishing operations – increasingly a brand) with nutritionists generally qualified at the Institute of Optimum Nutrition. A consultation is £75: two are generally recommended.

Fiona McKenzie (LCH, MHMA, LLB)

27 Chapel Side W2 4LL ☎ *(020) 7229 6689*
Homeopathic practitioner also specialising in nutrition and detox advice; works often with children and mothers before and after pregnancy.

NORTH

Lucy Daniels

☎ *(020) 8207 4758, (07976) 299027*
Dietician experienced in working with mothers and babies, by referral from GP or consultant only; also works at St John & St Elizabeth Hospital. / HOURS Mon- Fri only.

OUTSIDE LONDON

Natural Health Advisory Service 📠

PO Box 268, Lewes East Sussex BN7 IQN ☎ *(01273) 487366*
✆ *www.naturalhealthas.com*
A company which offers a telephone advisory service (three months, £128); after completing a detailed diary of your lifestyle, medical history, diet and exercise, you are given an appointment for a telephone consultation (backed up by a cassette) or can attend London clinics. / HOURS Mon-Fri 9am-5.30pm, or answerphone; PUBLICATIONS Books on health through diet: Healthy Parents, Healthy Baby (Maryon Stewart, Headline, £10.99).

DIY nutrition

Taking supplements in pregnancy or while breast-feeding – and even in advance of conceiving – is now widely recommended, and there are a number of tailor-made products available.

If you want to take supplements for a particular problem it is wise to seek advice, both to ensure that you are not wasting your money and to make sure what you are taking is safe for you and your baby. Some 'detox-ifying' substances, notably vitamin A, are not considered safe to take during pregnancy.

All nutritionists recommend different brands of supplements. They are however united in agreement that own-brand supplements from large chains and supermarkets are almost universally of poor quality. Some health shops have good selections of products as do many complementary health centres.

For optimum absorption, the advice is to avoid metallic or inorganic forms of minerals and to look for citrates, fumarates, gluconates and amino acid chelates, which, it is said, can increase absorption by up to 40%. Apparently better yet are versions of these preferred forms which include the metallic or inorganic forms as well, as it is believed there are often useful synergies between the two, further increasing absorption.

If in doubt about which brand to plump for, go for packaging in brown glass which protects the contents from sunlight.

STOCKISTS

CENTRAL

British Nutrition Foundation (BNF)
High Holborn House, 52-54 High Holborn WC1V 6RQ ☎ *(020) 7404 6504*
🖰 *www.nutrition.org.uk*
An organisation working closely with DEFRA to promote knowledge of nutritional issues; its website contains background lots of semi-technical food chemistry (what is hydrogenation for instance). / *SEE ALSO 2.02 Feeding.*

The Nutri Centre 📖
7 Park Crescent W1B 1PF ☎ *(020) 7436 5122* 🖰 *www.nutricentre.com*
In the basement of the Hale Clinic – the shop stocks the widest range of nutritional supplements in London, possibly even Europe, together with a wide range of books on the subject, some not available elsewhere. One of their products is Klamath Lake Blue Green Algae which is claimed to contain all the nutrients needed by the human body. / *HOURS Mon-Fri 9am-7pm, Sat 10am-5pm.*

OUTSIDE LONDON

Biocare
180 Lifford Lane, Kings Norton Birmingham B30 3NU ☎ *(0121) 433 3727*
🖰 *www.biocare.co.uk*
A highly-regarded supplier which produces a prenatal multivitamin and mineral supplement and a growing range of supplements for children, including essential fatty acid supplements, a multivitamin and mineral recommended by the Hyperactive Children's Support Group. Also other vitamin options and combinations plus supplements for digestion, including Bifidobacterium infantis, reported the primary bacteria found in breast milk and most appropriate prior to weaning. Recommendations are given for the appropriate minimum age for all supplements, together with recommended dosage.

Goodness Direct
South March, Daventry Northants NN11 4PH ☎ *(0871) 871 6611*
🖰 *www.GoodnessDirect.co.uk*
A website offering a range of health products. Full details of ingredients are given, plus online access to nutritionists. / *SEE ALSO 2.02 Feeding.*

Higher Nature
Burwash Common East Sussex TN19 7LX ☎ *(01435) 883484, (01435) 882880*
🖰 *www.highernature.co.uk*
Own-brand products and some US imports – relevant products include Super Nutrition Plus, Essential Balance Junior, omega oils for children; also chewable children's vitamins. You can consult a nutritionist before you buy. The catalogue includes a section on pregnancy and children, and a good selection of books. / *HOURS Mon-Fri: 9am-5.30pm, Sat: 9-12.*

NS3UK
Bracknell ☎ *(01344) 360 033* 🖰 *www.ns3.co.uk*
Nutritional specialists reported particularly interested in issues of children's health, the MD with 15 years' experience in nursing and midwifery; will provide details of a local nutritionist for one to one consultations, or offers postal consultations directly with the centre.

Renahall Ltd
Unit 343, Silk House, Park Green Macclesfield SK11 7QT ☎ *(07901) 815 521*
Suppliers of vitamins and minerals, at better-than-high-street prices.

Sage Organic
Clench Lodge, Wootton Rivers, Marlborough Wiltshire SN8 4NT ☎ (01672) 811 777
⊕ www.sagenutritionals.com
A range including Sage Organic Pregnancy Multivitamin, for use before and during
pregnancy and when breast-feeding. The company proclaims the values of
supporting British organic agriculture, fair trade and sustainability.

Solgar
Aldbury, Tring Herts HP23 5PT ☎ (01442) 890355 ⊕ www.solgar.com
Prenatal nutrient supplements, folic acid tablets and Acidophilus powder, for
children under four years old, to help maintain healthy intestines, full range of
multi-vitamins for children; also supplies essential fatty acid supplements, shown by
some research to be important for the development of the baby's brain while still in
the womb.

Zita West Products Ltd ⊞
100c High Street, Brackley Northamptonshire NN13 7DR ☎ (0870) 166 8899
⊕ www.zitawest.com
Nutritional products designed for pregnancy.

13. OSTEOPATHY & CRANIAL OSTEOPATHY (INCLUDING CRANIOSACRAL THERAPY)

Osteopathy is the main manipulative therapy in the UK, and was the first
complementary discipline to receive statutory registration. The term
covers a wide variety of techniques. Though practitioners train in most
elements of the overall discipline, at least briefly, many move on to specialise – for example in structural, visceral or cranial osteopathy.

Osteopathy is increasingly an all-graduate profession with study covering anatomy, physiology, pathological processes and biomechanics. As
a result of the Osteopathic Act of 1993 a patient visiting an osteopath is
offered the same safeguards as when they consult doctors, dentists and
other statutorily-regulated health care professionals. All qualified practitioners wishing to call themselves osteopaths must now be registered
with the General Osteopathic Council. (However, a typical annual registration fee of £750 means that some do not register, and practice under
a title of something like manipulative therapist.)

REPORTED BENEFITS

According to a report by the British School of Osteopathy expectant
mother's clinic, the vast majority of women suffering back pain in pregnancy receive considerable benefit within two to three treatments.
Osteopathic techniques are also said to help with other pre-natal conditions – for example nausea, by treating and relaxing the soft tissues around
the digestive system. Using similar methods, problems like heartburn,
constipation, fluid retention, tiredness and the pain of varicose veins can
be treated.

An osteopath may also be able to provide pregnant women with
simple exercises to ease the discomfort of spreading, flattening feet caused
by hormonal changes in pregnancy, and suggestions on how to help your
body adjust to its increasing weight and changing posture. In later pregnancy an osteopath may be able to show a birth partner pain relief
methods to be used in labour, utilising massage and pressure point techniques. It is thought that ensuring that the appropriate muscles are
limbered up can make an easier birth more likely. Osteopathy may also be
able to help mothers who have been told their hips are too narrow for
their baby to prepare for the birth (hips are designed to open up to an

amazing degree at birth and treatment may be able to facilitate this process).

After the birth osteopathy can help sort out nagging back problems and help different parts of the body get back into shape, particularly after trauma, or an epidural.

In babies, osteopathy is reported to help with colic and hence excessive crying and/or sleeping difficulties. It is believed that the treatment can also achieve marked improvements in children diagnosed as spastic, those who have suffered knocks to the skull, and babies who suffered problems during birth.

The Osteopathic Centre for Children would like osteopaths to be seen as paediatric GPs, i.e. the first port of call for a child with *any* illness (though, in their case, the waiting list can be three months long).

It is not necessary for your baby to have any specific ailment before you contemplate osteopathic treatment – it is estimated by some that nine out of ten babies suffer a degree of post-birth mis-alignment of their skull which would be benefited by osteopathy. It is claimed that one treatment may simply help a baby sleep better and clear problems like mucous or earwax. Converted parents argue that all babies should have at least one such session soon after the birth as a preventive measure.

Cranial osteopathy is the form particularly recommended for pregnancy and babies, though some osteopaths see cranial techniques as just another branch of osteopathy – see below for further information.

THE TREATMENT

Although widely perceived as a treatment relating to bones, osteopathy can treat the whole body, including the soft tissues. Practitioners use their hands as the major tools for diagnosis, relying on a highly trained sense of touch. The hands are also used to carry out the treatment using a variety of manipulative techniques. On children and pregnant women such techniques are used in an extremely gentle manner, sometimes to the point of being barely perceptible.

Cranial osteopathy

For information on craniosacral therapy, see the end of this section, after the listings.

Cranial osteopathy is a specialisation within the field of osteopathy based on the theory that any ailment is a sign of imbalance in the body, and specifically in the small tolerances of movement in the human skull. There is a rhythmic flow of cerebro-spinal fluid throughout the body, from head to toe, 10 to 15 times a minute. This is the 'shock absorber' fluid that bathes the brain and spinal cord. The practitioner listens and feels for irregularities in the rhythm. He or she then tries gently to release any tensions by correcting disturbances and stiffness around the joints of the skull and throughout the body.

Stuart Korth, founder of the Osteopathic Centre for Children, claims that the 29 bones in a newborn's skull can be pushed out of alignment by the highly compressive forces of birth, particularly if birth is very fast, slow or involves forceps. This in turn, Korth believes, can lead to physical and nervous disorders in childhood.

Cranial osteopathy is said by some to be a miracle cure for treating incessantly crying babies. Successes are also claimed in overcoming difficulties with feeding, teething, sleeping, relieving colic and earache.

Cranial osteopathy is studied by all osteopaths, but to different degrees. It is best to look for a practitioner whose practice is almost exclusively in cranial work, or who has carried out extensive postgraduate study in the field. Treatment is best carried out before the child is 18 months old. Specialists recommend a session every three to four months.

CENTRAL BODIES – OSTEOPATHY
General Osteopathic Council (GOC), ☎ (020) 7357 6655

🖰 www.osteopathy.org.uk
From May 2000, it became illegal to call oneself an osteopath without being registered with this, the statutory governing body of osteopathy. The GOC effectively replaced pre-existing voluntary bodies, ensuring that all practitioners using the title osteopath meet council standards (meaning a degree in osteopathy and membership of a professional body).

CENTRAL BODIES – CRANIAL OSTEOPATHY
International Cranial Association, ☎ (020) 8367 5561

Formerly called the Cranial Osteopathic Association, this organisation can send you an information sheet and details of practitioners who have completed their training course (or equivalent – five days for postgraduate osteopaths, manipulative therapists and chiropractors); send an SAE with five stamps for the pack.

Sutherland Society, 🖰 www.cranial.org.uk
Members are fully qualified osteopaths with an interest in cranial osteopathy. The website offers information on the use of the treatment in pregnancy and childbirth, and for babies and children. Also a list of members.

QUALIFICATIONS

DO or BSc (Ost): Diploma or Bachelor of Osteopathy.
MLCOM: medical doctors who have trained in osteopathy at the London College of Osteopathic Medicine.
MCO: Member of the College of Osteopaths.
FCO: Fellow of the College of Osteopaths.
MGO: Member of Guild of Osteopaths.

PRACTITIONERS
CENTRAL
Stephen Humphreys (DO)
20 Churton St SW1V 2LL ☎ (020) 7834 3149
Osteopath treating mothers-to-be, babies and children with cranial or standard osteopathy as appropriate; all visits £45.

Stuart Korth (DO, DPO)
27 Bickenhall Mansions, Bickenhall St W1U 6BR ☎ (020) 7935 0844
Private practice of the director and founder for the Osteopathic Centre for Children.

Oldbury Place Osteopathic Practice
1 Oldbury Place W1U 5PA ☎ (020) 7486 2875
All practitioners are experienced in treating babies with cranial osteopathy; also willing to treat mothers during pregnancy.

WEST
Cristagalli
52 Porchester Rd W2 6ET ☎ (020) 7221 3557 🖰 www.cristagalli@mail.com
This Bayswater practice has five osteopaths, who all treat pregnant mothers and also babies with a variety of conditions – from colic and hyperactivity to mental and physical handicaps. / HOURS Mon-Fri: 9-6pm.

Fulham Osteopathic Practice
769 Fulham Rd Fulham SW6 5HA ☎ (020) 7384 1851 🖰 www.fop.co.uk
Eight registered osteopaths who treat babies, children and adults; pregnant women can be treated for backache, general health in pregnancy and after the birth; approximate prices: adults £45, then £40 for follow-up treatment; children £35, then £30; concessions sometimes available. This practice has disabled access.

Harry Gunn
18 Gloucester Walk W8 4HZ ☎ (020) 7937 6194 ⌨ www.hgunnosteopaths.co.uk
Treats back pain pre- and postnatally using osteopathy, naturopathy and
acupuncture; children treated too. / HOURS Mon-Fri: 10.15am-8.30pm, Sat: 10-2pm.

Alison Judah (BSc Ost, DO, MGO)
Ealing YMCA, 14 Bond St W5 5AA ☎ (07956) 287776, Enquiry line (0956) 287776
⌨ www.registeredosteopath.co.uk
Osteopath and paediatric osteopath offering structural, visceral and cranial
treatments, £42 first session, then £38 (45 minutes); concessions available; over half
of clients are children. / HOURS Wed & Fri 8.45am-12.30pm.

Christine Lister (DO, MRO)
66 Cawdor Crescent W7 2DD ☎ (020) 8567 4044
Treats newborn babies – mostly for colic – and older children, giving postural advice
and some exercises; also treats in pregnancy; £36/£30 (concessions available).

Rachel Martineau (ND, DO, MRO)
168 Carlyle Rd W5 4BJ ☎ (020) 8560 5738
Experienced in working with pregnancy as osteopath and naturopath (advising on
lifestyle matters such as diet, hydrotherapy and counselling); happy to help towards
a home birth; adults £30 for first consultation, then £25, concessions for children.

Notting Hill Osteopathy
15 Pembridge Rd W11 3HG ☎ (020) 7937 2298
Osteopath and cranial osteopath Andrew Ferguson (with several associate
practitioners) is happy to treat women in pregnancy and postnatally, together with
babies and children. / HOURS Mon-Fri: 9am-5pm.

Susan Turner (MA, DO, MRO)
Ground Floor Flat, 41 Leinster Square W2 4PU ☎ (020) 7229 8144
Treatments for pregnancy (£43) and for children (£38) using cranial osteopathy
where appropriate.

NORTH

The Active Birth Centre 🖼
25 Bickerton Rd N19 5JT ☎ (020) 7281 6760 ⌨ www.activebirthcentre.com
Two osteopaths operate i the centre's therapy rooms. / HOURS shop Mon-Fri 9.30am-6.30pm
(Fri 4pm), Sat 10am-4pm; SEE ALSO 1.01 Where to have the baby; 1.04 Antenatal classes; 1.06 Birth
equipment; 2.01 Postnatal; 2.02 Feeding; 2.03 Baby health; 2.06 Baby & toddler activities; 3.01 Maternity
wear; 3.02 Baby equipment; 4.05 Finding out more.

British College of Osteopathic Medicine
Frazer House, 6 Netherhall Gardens NW3 5RR ☎ (020) 7435 7830
⌨ www.bcom.ac.uk
Holistic or naturopathic osteopathy college treating the physical system in
conjunction with lifestyle, mental well-being and diet; expectant mothers clinic, £20
first session, £15 follow-up; free children's clinic (under 16s); concessions available.

Canonbury Clinic of Osteopathy
265 Upper St N1 2UQ ☎ (020) 7226 0011
This practice has two osteopaths, both experienced in treating children and pregnant
women, with cranial osteopathy where necessary. In addition to osteopathy,
the practitioners adopt a naturopathic, holistic approach by looking at the dietary
and nutritional aspects of health too; from £40. They also give talks to Mother
& Baby groups about posture during and after pregnancy. / HOURS Mon-Sat: 8am-3pm
(closed Weds).

College of Osteopaths
13 Furzehill Rd Borehamwood WD6 2DG ☎ (020) 8905 1395
Low-cost supervised student clinic; baby and child clinic on Wed, £20 for first
consultation, then £17.50; children, £20 then £12.50. They can provide a list of
registered members and information on other supervised student clinics. / HOURS Mon,
Tues, Thurs: 9am-9pm; Wed, Fri: 8.30am-6.30pm; every other Sat: 9am-3pm.

The College Practice
60 Highgate Rd NW5 1PA ☎ (020) 7267 6445
The two osteopaths at this practice Suzanne Tugwell (DO) and Frances Aylen (BA
Hons, OST) both specialise in pregnancy – especially back pain. / HOURS Mon-Fri: 8.30-
6.30, Sat: 9am-3pm.

Deborah Doole
N6 ☎ (07970) 824637
Practises in Highgate and Kent, with experience in treating women ante-and postnatally, and in working with babies and children. Also teaches visceral osteopathy.

Dianna Harvey-Kummer (DO Reg, MCO)
c/o Clock Tower Practice, 50 Park Rd N8 ☎ (020) 8348 5848, 07957 634919
Traditional and cranial osteopath, experienced in working with children and pregnant mums.

Nadine M Hobson
☎ Viveka (020) 7483 3788, or (020) 7485 3579
Registered osteopath working at Viveka (previously the TLC Centre). For appointments elsewhere call (020) 7485 3579. Nadine can offer flexible working hours. / HOURS *Flexible.*

Ernest Keeling (DO, Reg Ost.)
55 Belsize Lane NW3 5AU ☎ (020) 7435 1740
Cranial osteopath experienced in treating children and pregnancy, £28. / HOURS *Mon-Fri 8.15am-5.30pm, Sat 8.15am-noon.*

Martien Jonkers BSc(Ost) Hons, Dip OT
30 Fortis Green East, Finchley N2 9EL ☎ (07748) 938 299
Osteopath and cranial osteopath, with treatment for babies, children and adults.

Máire Mayne (DO, Reg Ost)
16 St Paul's St N1 7AB ☎ (020) 7485 3848
Treats newborn babies, pregnant women and women who have just given birth, £45. Price for babies on application. / HOURS *Flexible.*

The Osteopathic Practice
The Kriya Centre, Bickerton House, 25-27 Bickerton Rd N19 5JT ☎ (020) 7272 8507
⌂ www.gururamdasproject.co.uk
Offering sessions of 1 hour for mother and baby in the first year, and then 45-minutes sessions, thereafter.

Dr Ann Roden (CST, RPT)
31 Downs Ave, Pinner Middlesex HA5 5AQ ☎ (020) 8866 5944
Retired paediatrician specialising in special needs cases; trained in craniosacral therapy (including the treatment of birth trauma, polarity therapy), and teaching the Indian Ayurvedic system of medicine. / HOURS *flexible (no home visits).*

Susan Tyrrell RGN BSc (Ost)
8 Richmond Road, East Finchley N2 8JT ☎ (020) 8371 9636
A mother of young children, who has experience of treating babies, children and pregnancy.

Hedwig Ver Donk (DO, MRO)
Lower Ground Floor, 8 Dalmeny Rd N7 0HH ☎ (020) 7609 8973
Highly-regarded practitioner with experience working with pregnancy and children (and of working with other practitioners); home visits can be arranged, and she has attended births. / HOURS *Mon-Fri only.*

SOUTH

Battersea Osteopathic Practice
2b Ashness Rd (Webbs Rd entrance) SW11 6RY ☎ (020) 7738 9199
⌂ www.thebatterseaosteopathicpractices.co.uk
General osteopathic practice, running clinics for babies, children and expectant mothers; cranial osteopathy also offered; adults £45; children £35. / HOURS *Mon-Sat: 7am-6pm.*

Blackheath Osteopathy & Acupuncture
19 Tranquil Vale SE3 0BU ☎ (020) 8852 1706
Two osteopaths offer cranial osteopathy in pregnancy and for babies and children, £35, first visit, then £30; also acupuncture (£35), reflexology (£35) and sports massage (£35). Babies also treated at £30 then £25. / HOURS *Mon-Sat: 9am-7.30pm.*

British School of Osteopathy

275 Borough High St SE1 1JE ☎ Admin (020) 7407 0222 ⏏ www.bso.ac.uk
Teaching clinics offering low-cost treatment from supervised students; expectant
mothers' clinic (with a qualified osteopath and two students), £19, then £16;
children's clinic open all day on Mondays, £12 then £9; sports clinic £23. Concession
rates offered. / *HOURS Mon-Fri: 8am-6pm.*

Marcia M Harewood (ND, DO, MCO)

255a Lavender Hill SW11 1JD ☎ (020) 7498 9966
Osteopath and naturopath – treats ligament strain during pregnancy, and babies for
colic; also uses cranial osteopathy and iridology; will see pregnant women once
a month, and then continue treating mother and baby after birth. / *HOURS Mon-Sat 9am-
7pm (Mon, Wed & Thu 8pm).*

Samantha Hurst (BSc Ost, MRO)

20 The Green Twickenham TW2 5AB ☎ (020) 8893 3084
Osteopath who runs a child-friendly clinic, also treating women in pregnancy; £30.

London Bridge Osteopathic Practice

10 Borough High St SE1 9QQ ☎ (020) 7378 0850
Two osteopaths who work with local midwives; prices from £30
(concessions). / *HOURS Mon-Fri: 9am-5.30pm.*

Elizabeth MacDonald (RPT, CST, NLP–USA, Cl.Hyp/MA)

Wimbledon Village SW19 ☎ (07973) 169259 ⏏ www.babytherapy.com
Believes pelvic problems after birth may be related to postnatal depression, and treats
mothers accordingly; also treats for depression, migraine sinusitis, spinal and jaw
problems; babies can be treated for colic and problems with suckling, breathing and
eliminating; home visits can be arranged throughout Greater London – fees, from
£35, dependent on travel distance and costs. / *HOURS flexible, not after 7pm.*

Tideswell Road Clinic

7 Tideswell Rd SW15 6LJ ☎ (020) 8788 5761
Osteopathy and cranial osteopathy for children and adults, prices start at £50. The
founder Anne Mamok uses a combination of osteopathy and applied kinesiology to
treat children with dyspraxia and dyslexia. Homeopathy also available. / *HOURS Mon-
Fri: 9-5.30pm.*

Krystyna Zielinski & Associates (MSc Ost, DO (hons), MRO)

*South West London Osteopathic Clinic for Children, 18 Daybrook Rd, off Dorset Rd
SW19 3DH ☎ (020) 8542 8596*
Cranial osteopathy for expectant mothers, babies and toddlers: adults £48 first
session, £33 subsequent sessions; mother and newborn (up to three months old)
together £50; children £43, then £28.

EAST

Alison Brown Osteopaths

1 Ernald Avenue, East Ham E6 3AL ☎ (020) 8470 8678
As well as pregnant mothers, Alison Brown DO, treats babies and children. Adults
treatment £35 first treatment £28 thereafter; children £30/£25.

Osteopathic Centre for Children (OCC)

*The School House, 159 Woodbridge St EC1R 0ND ☎ (020) 7490 5510
⏏ www.occ.uk.com*
With 25,000 treatments per year and a patient list of 13,500, this charitable
organisation would like to be seen as the first port of call for treating ill children. Not
only graduates, but also many top practitioners put in their time gratis – a minimum
donation of £15 is requested, although no one is turned away. The centre treats
patients up to their 19th birthday as well as pregnant and post-partum women.

Stephen Sandler (DO, MRO)

26a Station Rd E4 7BE ☎ (020) 8529 0815
Osteopath who largely works at The Portland Hospital (214 Great Portland St, W1);
accepts self-referrals as well as those from consultants, midwifes and GPs; runs
expectant mums clinic and mother and baby workshops at School of Osteopathy and
teaches; £40/£30. / *HOURS Mon-Fri: 9-5pm.*

Joyce Vetterlein (DO, MSc Ost)

☎ (020) 7729 8525 ⏏ www.cityhealthcentre.nildram.co.uk
Osteopath who works with acupuncturists: £45 adults, £30 children.

Craniosacral therapy

Craniosacral therapists, as opposed to cranial osteopaths, will not usually have done the rigorous and lengthy training undergone by osteopaths, though they should have trained for up to two years. There are a variety of forms of training, but only three training organisations are recognised by the Craniosacral Therapy Association. Some practitioners will be more skilled in, for example, working with shock and trauma after birth, although there is no register for this specialisation.

The treatment and benefits are similar to cranial osteopathy.

CENTRAL BODIES

Craniosacral Therapy Association, ☎ (07000) 784735

⌂ www.craniosacral.co.uk
This association is for trained craniosacral therapists: membership requirements include ongoing training (further training is needed for working with pregnant women, babies and children, usually under supervision from an experienced practitioner). Members are entitled to use the letters RCST (Registered Craniosacral Therapist) after their names. The organisation is approved by the ICM, and can provide a register of members. / HOURS Mon-Fri: 9am-1pm.

Gideon Hajioff BA Sacu, DipAcu, DipCST, MBAcC,

☎ (020) 8205 2929 ⌂ www.acu.me.uk
Head of Chinese Medicine at the Hendon Therapies Clinic, North London, where he practises craniosacral therapy (as well as Japanese and traditional acupuncture, sports massage and nutrition).

PRACTITIONERS

WEST

Ruth Sparkes (RCST)

35 Park Drive W3 8ND ☎ (020) 8993 2871
Craniosacral therapy, treating adults and children, starting from £35; also offers spiritual healing and Indian head massage. / HOURS Flexible.

Paul Vick (RCST)

☎ (020) 8690 9933, ⌂ www.resonance.org.uk
Craniosacral therapist (and a founder of the Academy for Bio-Cranial Resonance, where he teaches), experienced in treating pregnant women and children; likes to see mothers and babies together and sometimes works with whole family (at a family rate); price around £35. / HOURS By arrangement.

NORTH

The Shiatsu Place (SEITAI)

97-99 Seven Sisters Rd N7 7QP ☎ (020) 7281 1412 ⌂ www.shiatsu-do.co.uk
This clinic also offers craniosacral therapy, £35. / HOURS Mon-Fri: 9.30-5.30pm.

SOUTH

Richmond Physiotherapy

16 King St Richmond TW9 1ND ☎ (020) 8332 1132 ⌂ www.richmondphysio.co.uk
A practice one of whose staff is also trained in craniosacral therapy, £45. / HOURS Mon 9.30am-8pm, Tues-Thurs 8am-8pm, Fri 8am-5pm, Sat 9am-2pm.

14. PHYSIOTHERAPY

REPORTED BENEFITS

Obstetric physiotherapists are specialists in pregnancy and gynaecological problems and can help with pelvis pain (both in pregnancy and after birth), with incontinence, and with a prolapse threatened or caused by a weak pelvic floor.

Physiotherapists with a speciality in back problems may be able to help with back pain in pregnancy and pain caused by incorrect lifting of a baby. Note that obstetric problems and back problems are separate specialities so the same physiotherapist may not be able to help with both complaints.

Physiotherapy can be helpful to babies with physical and developmental difficulties, by helping to stimulate muscle development. Babies learn through movement, so teaching correct movement is believed to promote healthy development and good posture.

THE TREATMENT

In preparation for pregnancy, individual tuition or classes can help guide you through gentle exercises and stretches to aid better control of your abdominal and pelvic floor muscles, and also control of your breathing patterns. Breathing awareness combined with teaching on positioning can help with relaxation for, and facilitation of, birth. An obstetric physiotherapist may also be able to advise on sport and exercise in pregnancy but will probably err on the side on caution.

Postnatally, obstetric physiotherapists can help with perineal discomfort, for example offering ultrasound treatment for scarring.

READING

Exercise for the Childbearing Year – Eileen Brayshaw & Pauline Wright (Butterworth-Heinemann Medical; 1996; £5.95; 1-898507-29-5) – *Written by two obstetric physiotherapists for use in pregnancy, in labour and after the birth.* / *Royal College of Midwives.*

CENTRAL BODIES

Association of Chartered Physiotherapists in Women's Health, ☎ *(020) 7242 1941* ⁂ *www.acpwh.org.uk*
Can advise on how and where to find a specialist physiotherapist either privately or on the NHS.

QUALIFICATIONS

SRP: State Registered Physiotherapist.

MCSP: member of the Chartered Society of Physiotherapy.

Grad DP: graduate diploma in physiotherapy. (This is an old qualification which is no longer available, but some older practitioners may have it.)

Pg Dipl: Postgraduate Diploma.

PRACTITIONERS

CENTRAL

Portland Hospital, Physiotherapy Unit
234 Great Portland St (opposite main hospital) W1N 6AH ☎ *(020) 7390 8061* ⁂ *www.theportlandhospital.com*
The hospital's specialist women's health physios accept self referrals for pregnancy-related problems and postnatal pelvic floor therapy. / SEE ALSO *1.04 Antenatal classes; 2.01 Postnatal; 2.03 Baby health.*

WEST

Rosey Grandage (SRP, MCSP, MBAcC)
40 St Dunstan's Rd W6 8RB ☎ *(020) 8563 1330 home, Prospect Chinese Medicine and Physiotherapy Centre (020) 7381 5727* ⁂ *www.prospect health.co.uk*
Physiotherapist who uses a range of complementary techniques (including Tui Na) to treat antenatal and postnatal problems (high blood pressure, migraine, nausea, back pain) and babies (eczema, colic and sleeping problems): £35. / SEE ALSO *1.04 Antenatal classes.*

NORTH

O&L Women's Health Physiotherapy Clinic
Fortis Green Health Clinic, 150 Fortis Green N10 3PA ☎ (020) 8920 9407
Specialists in antenatal and postnatal gynaecological problems, particularly prolapse, incontinence and back pain. / HOURS *Mon, Tues, Weds, Fri: 8am-6pm; SEE ALSO 1.04 Antenatal classes; 1.06 Birth equipment; 2.01 Postnatal.*

The Oakwood Physiotherapy Clinic Ltd
95 Green Rd N14 4AP ☎ (020) 8440 3629/6318 ⌁ www.oakwoodphysio.co.uk
Physiotherapy (and other) treatments at this clinic target pre- and postnatal back and neck pains, episiotomy scars and tears, stress incontinence, children's aches and pains, and individual postnatal exercise programmes; other treatments available include craniosacral therapy, baby massage, aromatherapy, reflexology and acupuncture; physiotherapy, initial visit; adults £35, children £30. / HOURS *Mon-Fri: 8.30am-7pm, Sat: 9am-5pm.*

The Physio + Plus Clinic
The Oakwood Physiotherapy Clinic, 95 Green Rd Southgate N14 4AP ☎ (020) 8440 3629 ⌁ www.oakwoodphysio.co.uk
Physiotherapy plus aromatherapy, reflexology, massage, osteopathy and cranial osteopathy (with an osteopath specialising in baby problems), homeopathy, and acupuncture (with experience of treating women in pregnancy and postnatally as well as babies and children).

SOUTH

The Battersea Practice (Physio For All)
40 Webbs Rd SW11 6SF ☎ (020) 7228 2141
Four practitioners offering ante-and postnatal exercise/advice classes and 'pelvic floor education' classes (maximum four people, individual sessions available). Also available: paediatric first-aid courses, craniosacral therapy, paediatric orthopaedic physiotherapy and child respiratory care. / HOURS *Mon-Fri: 9am-5pm, Sat: 9am-12pm; SEE ALSO 1.04 Antenatal classes; 2.01 Postnatal.*

CC (Kiki) von Eisenhart-Goodwin (BSc Phys, MCSP, SRP, Pg Dipl, CNAA)
Kiki's Children's Clinic,133 Thurleigh Rd SW12 8TX ☎ (020) 7207 4234 ⌁ www.kikisclinic.com
One of only a few paediatric physiotherapists in London who uses massage, therapeutic exercise, postural education and neuro-developmental therapy to help with prematurity, developmental delay, posture and foot problems, dyspraxia, and special needs; sessions in clinic or own home: £100 consultation and initial report, treatments £55 an hour. / HOURS *Mon-Fri 9am-5pm, Sat 9am-1pm; SEE ALSO 2.06 Baby & toddler activities.*

Sue Lewis Grad DB, MCSP, SRP
65 Vineyard Hill Rd SW19 7JL ☎ (020) 8946 8561
Obstetric and gynaecological physiotherapist, able to help with prolapse, incontinence, and problems with abdominal and pelvic floor muscles. Also antenatal care for back and pelvic problems, £40. / SEE ALSO *1.04 Antenatal classes; 2.01 Postnatal; 2.03 Baby health; 2.06 Baby & toddler activities.*

Richmond Physiotherapy
16 King St Richmond TW9 1ND ☎ (020) 8332 1132 ⌁ www.richmondphysio.co.uk
A team of chartered physiotherapists, experienced in treating spinal problems during pregnancy and postnatally, £45; they can give referrals to paediatric physiotherapists for developmental work with children. / HOURS *Mon 9.30am-8pm, Tues-Thurs 8am-8pm, Fri 8am-5pm, Sat 9am-2pm.*

Barbara Ryan (MCSP, Grad DP, SRP)
64 Streathbourne Rd SW17 8QY ☎ (020) 8682 4708
Chartered obstetric and manipulative physiotherapist (apparently an unusual combination); prices start at approx £40. / HOURS *Hours negotiable.*

Vanbrugh Physiotherapy Clinic
121 Trafalgar Rd SE10 9TY ☎ (020) 8293 5484 ⌁ www.vanbrughphysio.co.uk
One physiotherapist here deals specifically with women's health: help with postnatal problems (including back pain, episiotomy pain and incontinence), massage and acupuncture also offered; home visits can be arranged; rates from £38, home visits £60 (in Greenwich/Blackheath). / HOURS *Thurs 8am-8pm, Fri 8am-5pm, Sat 9am-1pm.*

15. REFLEXOLOGY

REPORTED BENEFITS
Prenatally, reflexology is said to be useful in alleviating nausea, constipation, haemorrhoids, indigestion and heartburn. During labour the treatment is used to stimulate contractions and to help handle pain. After birth, the therapy is said to help keep up energy and to maintain breast-milk supplies. Women treated by experienced practitioners on a regular basis during pregnancy report significantly shorter labours than average and reduced pain in labour.

THE TREATMENT
The massage of specific pressure points, usually in the feet, based on the idea that the body's organs can be influenced by their nerve connections to certain points of the body.

Reflexology is not advised if you are suffering a threatened miscarriage, placenta praevia, pre-eclampsia, or feverish infections. It is also not recommended in the first few months of pregnancy, unless by a practitioner who has already treated you a few times.

READING
The Family Guide to Reflexology – Ann Gillanders (Gaia Books; 1998; £11.99; 1-856750-49-3) – *Companion to the author's Reflexology Step by Step, treatments for a range of complaints including childhood colic, teething and hyperactivity, plus adult ailments and family first aid.* / www.gaiabooks.co.uk.

CENTRAL BODIES
Association of Reflexologists (AoR), ☎ (0870) 567 3320
⌂ www.aor.org.uk
The largest of the British associations of reflexologists. The website offers searchable (by name or by area) listings of members – contact information only. / HOURS Mon-Fri 9am-5pm; PUBLICATIONS Lists of local registered practitioners.

The British Reflexology Association, ☎ (01886) 821207
⌂ www.britreflex.co.uk
Founded in 1985 by the Bayly School of Reflexology. / HOURS Mon-Fri 9am-4.30pm; PUBLICATIONS List of registered members (£2).

The British School of Reflexology MIFR, ☎ (01279) 429060
⌂ www.footreflexology.com
Established in 1986, this organisation has about 800 members; to qualify for the MBSR requires study of about one year part time; the APNT is their examining body and the association to which members apply once qualified. / HOURS Mon-Fri 9am-5pm.

QUALIFICATIONS
MIFR: Member of the Association of Reflexologists.

MBRA: Member of the British Reflexology Association (similarly FBRA, fellow; AMBRA, associate member no longer in practice).

HAR: Holistic Association of Reflexology.

MBSR: Member of the British School of Reflexologists.

MIFR: International Federation of Reflexologists.

MGCP: Member of Guild of Complementary Therapists.

PRACTITIONERS
CENTRAL
Maura Bright (MAR MBAcC)
The Progressive Health Clinic, 140 Harley St W1G 7LB ☎ (020) 7224 3387
⌂ www.brightpractice.com
A combination of reflexology with yoga, which Maura believes helps to release the pelvis and balance hormones. / HOURS Mon-Fri 9am-7pm.

WEST

Heather Guerrini
30 Redesdale St SW3 4BJ ☎ (020) 7352 0245
Treatment ante- and postnatally (at home if preferred); treatment from 41 weeks can help to start labour; she can teach simple techniques to relieve and calm a colicky or restless baby (from 12-14 weeks); £40-50. / *SEE ALSO 1.04 Antenatal classes; 2.04 Childcare; 2.06 Baby & toddler activities.*

Val Southorn (Associate MAR)
35 Avenue Rd Brentford TW8 9NS ☎ (020) 8400 7699
Women and children treated either at her home or in the Ealing area, £40. / *HOURS Mon-Fri only.*

NORTH

Anne Hellinger
56 Queens Grove NW8 6EN ☎ (020) 7483 1640
First consultation, £35 (90 minutes); thereafter £25.

Kailash
Centre of Oriental Medicine, 7 Newcourt St NW8 7AA ☎ (020) 7722 3939, 020 4833476. ⁀ www.orientalhealing.co.uk
Reflexology treatments, £50 (£40 on home visits); said to be useful for diagnosing the root causes of problems; Karin Mittiga also teaches courses in reflexology, £195. / *HOURS Mon-Sat 9am-7pm; SEE ALSO 2.06 Baby & toddler activities.*

Karin Mittiga (ITEC, MAR, Bach Registered, MGCP)
Kailash Centre of Oriental Medicine, 7 Newcourt St NW8 7AA ☎ (020) 7483 3476 ⁀ www.karin@mittiga.fsnet.co.uk
Offers treatments which combine massage, Bach flower remedies and reflexology, reporting particular success with digestion, asthma and skin conditions. Also runs workshops: basic reflexology course, with optional two further sessions on use with children; healing food workshops, adapting diets for better health and the use of home remedies; Bach flower remedies for children and a course on behavioural problems. / *HOURS Flexible.*

Mala Morjaria (RGN, RM, MISPA, BRA)
65 Southfield Park North Harrow HA2 6HF ☎ (020) 8427 2932
May occasionally offer reflexology during birth. / *HOURS flexible.*

Tony Porter
28 Hollyfield Ave N11 3BY ☎ (020) 8368 0865 ⁀ www.artreflex.com
Founder of ART (Advanced Reflexology Training), a company that trains reflexologists in beating hormonal imbalances. The practitioners here aim to help women with infertility, conception, gynaecological problems, depression and lower back pain during pregnancy among other problems. / *HOURS Hours flexible.*

SOUTH

Mama-Rhythms
Wimbledon area ☎ (020) 8879 7081
Angela Yates runs antenatal classes of the above name, and works from home in Wimbledon Park; £32 per session or £15 for vertical reflex therapy – a quicker way of treating problems such as back pain. / *SEE ALSO 1.04 Antenatal classes.*

Richmond Physiotherapy
16 King St Richmond TW9 1ND ☎ (020) 8332 1132 ⁀ www.richmondphysio.co.uk
Reflexology also available. Sessions are generally £30. / *HOURS Mon 9.30am-8pm, Tues-Thurs 8am-8pm, Fri 8am-5pm, Sat 9am-2pm.*

Jo Turnbull (IFR, AIPTI)
73a Flaxman Rd SE5 9DN ☎ (020) 7274 9984
Practitioner with experience of pregnancy treatment, postnatal work and treating children, and who specialises in seeing families together.

EAST

The Jeyarani Centre 🖼
34 Cleveland Rd E18 2AL ☎ (020) 8530 1146 ⁀ www.jeyarani.com
Practitioners very experienced in treatment in pregnancy and postnatally. Dr Motha is running a research programme, some of the results from which have already been published. / *SEE ALSO 1.04 Antenatal classes.*

OUTSIDE LONDON

Thilaka Perera (ICHT)
44 Chatham Ave Hayes BR2 7QD ☎ *(020) 8462 2071*
Aromatherapist, qualified midwife and member of the International Council of
Holistic Therapists and Association of Reflexologists, who also practises
reflexology. / HOURS *Flexible daytime hours;* SEE ALSO *2.06 Baby & toddler activities.*

16. SHIATSU

REPORTED BENEFITS

Prenatally, shiatsu is said to help with stress and tension, backache, neck
and shoulder pain, migraine and headaches. It can be used in pregnancy,
including to help turn the baby. Some midwives are beginning to use the
treatment to help with labour pain relief and to stimulate contractions.
Shiatsu is said to stimulate circulation and the flow of the lymphatic fluid,
helping the release of toxins and tensions and stimulating the hormone
system. The relaxation offered may also help the body's natural healing
processes.

THE TREATMENT

Shiatsu is based on the same principles as acupuncture, of meridians of
energy flowing round the body. It relies on finger pressure through loose
clothing rather than the insertion of needles, and so is easier to carry out
on babies and small children. In pregnancy, treatment is usually given
with the client lying on her side to minimise strain.

CENTRAL BODIES

The Shiatsu Society, ☎ *(0845) 130 4560* ⌂ *www.shiatsu.org*
Founded in 1981, this non-profit umbrella organisation sets standards in shiatsu
training and maintains a register of qualified practitioners. In return for an A5 SAE,
they can supply lists of practitioners (also listed on the website) who have
undertaken a minimum 3 years of study, and who are recognised as competent and
reputable by the society. / HOURS *Mon-Fri 9am-5pm.*

QUALIFICATIONS

MRSS: Member of the Register of the Shiatsu Society.

PRACTITIONERS

WEST

Amanda Denison (MRSS)
94 Dale St W4 2BZ ☎ *(020) 8994 7599*
Experienced at treating pregnant women by promoting non-invasive wellbeing,
alleviating back (and pelvic) problems and aiding digestion. Also pre and post-natal
and breach birth problems treated; women are clothed during all treatments; prices
from £50. Home visits are available and Amanda has also attended births.

NORTH

Helen Goldward (MRSS)
63 Okehampton Rd NW10 3EN ☎ *(020) 8830 4540*
Specialises in treating babies as well as women during pregnancy and after the birth;
runs classes for mothers in baby shiatsu. / HOURS *flexible.*

The Shiatsu Place (SEITAI)
97-99 Seven Sisters Rd N7 7QP ☎ *(020) 7281 1412* ⌂ *www.shiatsu-do.co.uk*
Eight shiatsu practitioners work from this north London centre. Fees range from £40.
Craniosacral therapy, osteopathy, homeopathy, holistic massage and acupuncture
are also available. / HOURS *Mon-Fri: 9.30-5.30pm.*

DIY shiatsu

If you feel shiatsu might be useful, there are certain pressure points that you can use on yourself, though getting someone else to take charge is less effort, particularly in labour. Note that there are contraindicated pressure points on the body (below the knee) that are not advisable for use in pregnancy – consult a practitioner, the Shiatsu Society (see above) or attend a short course before going ahead with DIY treatment.

17. COMPLEMENTARY HEALTH CENTRES

These centres offer a range of complementary therapists in one place and may therefore be able to advise you on the most suitable treatment for a specific ailment. Some may have baby or child specialists.

CENTRAL BODIES

British Register of Complementary Practitioners,
☎ (020) 7237 5165 ⁀ www.icmedicine.co.uk
The register is maintained by the ICM (see also), who have also helped to compile a directory called the 'Medical Book', of complementary therapists, sent out to all NHS trusts, GPs and Health Authorities. / HOURS Mon-Fri 10am-3.30pm.

The Health Partnership, ☎ (020) 7589 6414
A centre where the private practices include that of cranial osteopath Matthew Schrock, highly experienced osteopath Renzo Molinari, and GP and paediatrician Dr O Raymond; also homeopath, Dr Charles Innes.

COMPLEMENTARY HEALTH CENTRES

CENTRAL

Acupuncture & Osteopathic Centre
34 Alderney St SW1V 4EU ☎ *(020) 7834 6229*
Acupuncture, osteopathy, shiatsu, Alexander Technique, psychotherapy, counselling. Price for first visit is £50 then £40. / HOURS Mon-Fri 9am-5pm.

Farmacia
169 Drury Lane WC2B 5QA ☎ *(020) 7404 8808* ⁀ *www.farmacia123.com*
The clinic attached to this central London pharmacy offers beauty treatments using organic products, as well as acupuncture, craniosacral therapy, herbal medicine, homeopathy, nutrition, osteopathy, reflexology, shiatsu and four kinds of massage; health screening, and tests for food tolerance, hormone imbalance and vitamin deficiencies are also available. Prices start at £30. / HOURS Mon-Fri 9am-7pm, Sat 10.30am-5.30pm; SEE ALSO 3.09 Lotions & potions.

The Hale Clinic
7 Park Crescent W1B 1PF ☎ *(020) 7631 0156, New patient enquiry line & booking 0870 676667.* ⁀ *www.haleclinic.com*
The clinic aims to integrate the principles of conventional and complementary medicine – with 100 practitioners, and 20 GPs it is the largest alternative health clinic in Europe. The list of treatments offered is extensive but includes acupressure, acupuncture, Alexander Technique, allergy testing, aromatherapy, auditory integration training (for patients with dyslexia), ayurveda (Indian medical system) Chinese herbalism, chiropractic, counselling, eczema clinic, flower remedies, general medical screening (combining conventional and complementary medical assessment) homeopathy, hypnotherapy, iridology, massage, medical herbalism, naturopathy, nutrition, osteopathy. You do not need a referral from your GP to make an appointment. / HOURS Mon-Fri 8am-9pm, Sat 9am-5pm.

Kamkus Healthcare Centre
97 Harley St W1N 1AF ☎ *(020) 7935 3533* ⁀ *www.kamkushealthcare.com*
'Multi-dimensional healthcare': acupuncture; aromatherapy; Ayurvedic medicine; Buteyko Method (for the treatment of chronic allergies and disorders); clinical psychology; chiropractic; dermatology; family therapy; floral essence therapy; homeopathy; hypnotherapy; nutrition; massage; psychiatry; osteopathy; ozone therapy; shiatsu; reiki; and reflexology. / HOURS Flexible.

Natureworks
16 Balderton St W1Y 1TF ☎ (020) 6292927
A 'holistic therapy centre', just off Oxford Street, with 30 qualified practitioners, offering acupuncture, aromatherapy, Chinese herbalism, counselling, psychotherapy, craniosacral therapy, healing, homeopathy, hypnotherapy, iridology, chiropractic, meditation, naturopathy, nutrition, osteopathy, physiotherapy, reflexology, rebirthing, reiki, shiatsu, stress management, hypnosis, therapeutic massage and yoga.

Neal's Yard Remedies
☎ (0845) 262 3145 ⏁ www.nealsyardremedies.com
BRANCHES AT:
   15 Neals Yard WC2H 9DP ☎ (020) 7379 7222
Nine therapy rooms offering a very wide range of treatments, including acupuncture, homeopathy, allergy elimination using the NAET system developed in California (particularly recommended for children), QXI (using a computer to test for allergies, vitamin deficiencies, infection, toxicity and so on), Tui Na, aromatherapy, massage, reflexology, osteopathy, acupuncture, craniosacral therapy (including for babies), naturopathy, Chinese and western herbal medicine plus Kanpo Japanese herbalism, shiatsu, Indian head massage, body stress release, polarity therapy and nutrition. / *SEE ALSO 0.*

Neal's Yard Therapy Rooms
2 Neal's Yard WC2H 9DP ☎ (020) 7379 7662 ⏁ www.nealsyardremedies.com
Established in 1982, one of London's best known complementary therapy centres has some 50 practitioners of acupuncture, Alexander Technique, aromatherapy, Bach Flower counselling, cranial osteopathy, healing, herbalism, homeopathy, naturopathy, nutrition, reflexology, reiki, shiatsu, and stress management. The centre offers detailed leaflets on the different therapies for those new to complementary treatments and has therapists experienced in treating pregnant women – so ask for one! / *HOURS Mon-Fri 9am-9pm, Sat 9.30am-6.30pm, Sun 11am-5pm.*

South Westminster Health Centre
82 Vincent Square SW1P 2PF ☎ (020) 8746 5757
Services include an osteopath who works a great deal with pregnant women. Also available: hypnotherapy and physiotherapy. / *HOURS Mon-Fri 8am-5pm .*

The Penninghame Clinic
19 Upper Berkeley St W1H 7PF ☎ (020) 7724 4004 ⏁ www.penninghame.com
Acupuncture (£80, then £50) and Chinese herbal medicine (£40, then £25) are offered, alongside other alternative health treatments including healing. Some practitioners are experienced in treating pregnancy. / *HOURS Mon-Fri 9am-6pm, Sat 10am-3pm.*

Westminster Natural Health Clinic
34-36a Warwick Way SW1V 1RY ☎ (020) 7834 0861
Osteopathy (including cranial osteopathy), with one osteopath who works specifically with mothers and babies; a homeopath runs a mother and baby clinic. / *HOURS Mon-Fri 8am-6pm (sometimes available on saturdays).*

WEST

Apotheke 20-20
300 (Spa) Or 296 (Clinic) Chiswick High Rd W4 1PA ☎ Clinic (020) 8995 2293, Product Sales (020) 8842 3956 or (020) 8654 5783 ⏁ www.apotheke20-20.co.uk
Formerly known as Blackmores Naturopathic Clinic – a natural pharmacy with its own herbal dispensary, offering advice on nutrition, diet and lifestyle, with homeopathic medication where relevant. Also pampering programme for mothers-to-be and childrens consultations. A few doors down, hands-on treatments such as spa and massage are available. Prices start at £12.95. / *HOURS Mon-Fri 10am-6pm, Sat 9.30am-6pm, Sun 11am-5pm.*

Brackenbury Natural Health Centre
30 Brackenbury Rd W6 0BA ☎ (020) 8741 9264 ⏁ www.brackenburyclinic.co.uk
22 practitioners, whose services include: acupuncture, aromatherapy, Alexander Technique, allergy testing, clinical nutrition and dietary therapy, healing, homeopathy, Chinese and Western herbalism, hypnotherapy, massage, reflexology, shiatsu and osteopathy (including cranial osteopathy). / *HOURS Mon-Sat 9am-6pm .*

The Broadway Natural Therapy Centre
52 The Broadway W5 5JN ☎ (020) 8579 4323
Child-friendly clinic with three mother and child specialists offering osteopathy (including cranial osteopathy for mums-to-be and newborns), acupuncture,

aromatherapy, herbalism with nutritional advice, homeopathy, naturopathy, osteomyology, stress diffusion, reflexology and medical herbalism. / HOURS Mon-Fri 9am-6pm.

The Bushmaster Natural Health Practice
204 Uxbridge Rd W12 7JD ☎ *(020) 8749 3792* ⌁ *www.bushmaster.co.uk*
Approximately ten practitioners offering homeopathy, osteopathy, reflexology, counselling, and psychotherapy. / HOURS Mon-Fri 9am-6pm, fairly flexible.

Chelsea Complementary Health Centre
281 Fulham Rd SW10 9PZ ☎ *(020) 7352 8519* ⌁ *www.chelseacomplementary.com*
Therapies available here include acupuncture, hypnotherapy, osteopathy (including cranial), reflexology, massage, naturopathy, reiki, stress management, Swedish massage and sports injury treatment. Fertility workshops and some pre-and postnatal classes are occasionally held. / HOURS Mon-Fri 9.30am-5.30pm & some evenings.

Eden Medical Centre
63a Kings Rd SW3 4NT ☎ *(020) 7881 5800* ⌁ *www.edenmedicalcentre.com*
Mother and baby clinics offer preparation for a healthy birth. Therapies include homeopathy, child educational psychology/psychiatry, psychotherapy, remedial exercise, Tibetan medicine and naturopathic medicine. On the orthodox medicine side, they have a GP (with further training in musculo-skeletal medicine and osteopathy), three podiatrists, physiotherapists and a chiropractic practitioner. / HOURS Mon-Fri 8am-8pm, Sat 8am-6pm.

The Ladbroke Rooms
8 Telford Road, Portobello Rd W10 5SH ☎ *(020) 8960 0846*
⌁ *www.theladbrokerooms.com*
A centre with more than 18 practitioners covering homeopathy, acupuncture, cranial osteopathy, classical osteopathy, reflexology, nutrition, chiropractic and food sensitivity testing. Also Indian barefoot massage (which is unsuitable in pregnancy or for children). / SEE ALSO 1.04 Antenatal classes.

The Life Centre
15 Edge St W8 7PN ☎ *(020) 7221 4602* ⌁ *www.thelifecentre.com*
Therapies offered include aromatherapy, acupuncture, cranial osteopathy (newborns welcome), Chinese medicine, homeopathy (adults and children), reflexology, healing, manual lymphatic drainage, McTimoney chiropractic, psychotherapy, reiki, shiatsu, and pregnancy massage. / HOURS Mon-Fri 8am-9pm, Sat & Sun 9.30am-6pm; SEE ALSO 1.04 Antenatal classes; 2.06 Baby & toddler activities.

Neal's Yard Remedies
☎ *(0845) 262 3145* ⌁ *www.nealsyardremedies.com*
BRANCHES AT:
  Chelsea Farmers Market, Sydney St SW3 6NR ☎ *(020) 7351 6380*
  9 Elgin Crescent W11 2JA ☎ *(020) 7727 3998*
See write-up in central.

Notting Hill Traditional Acupuncture Centre
21 Ladbroke Grove W11 3AY ☎ *(020) 7221 1326*
Acupuncture, Chinese herbalism, homeopathy, cranial osteopathy. Practitioner experienced in treating women during pregnancy £25 -£40. Information on immunisation and alternatives to vaccinations is available from some practitioners.

NW London Medical Centre
56 Maida Vale W9 1PP ☎ *(020) 7624 2804*
The GP here is an acupuncturist; fees vary. / HOURS Mon-Fri 9am-6.30pm.

The Penn Clinic
Hayes Cottage Hospital, Grange Rd Hayes UB3 2RR ☎ *(020) 8561 0819*
Primarily a centre for osteopathy; some of the eight practitioners also offer physiotherapy, acupuncture, homeopathy and nutritional advice. Also baby and children clinic. / HOURS Mon-Fri 8.30am-7.30pm.

Sloane Health Clinic ⌂
27 Kings Rd SW3 4RT ☎ *(020) 7730 7046*
The clinic below the health food store offers a wide range of therapies, including nutrition, osteopathy and reflexology. Specialising in problems conceiving, also offers food allergy testing and homeopathy. / HOURS Mon-Fri 8.30am-7pm, Sat 9am-7pm; SEE ALSO 2.02 Feeding.

Stockwells Pharmacy & Natural Health Clinic
Stockwells Pharmacy, 75 New Broadway, Ealing W5 5DA ☎ *(020) 8567 0678*
Reflexology, aromatherapy, reiki, homeopathy, nutrition, hypnotherapy, osteopathy, shiatsu, herbalism, chiropody. There is also a children's homeopathic clinic. / *SEE ALSO 2.02 Feeding.*

The Organic Pharmacy
396 Kings Rd SW10 0LN ☎ *(020) 7351 2232* ⊕ *www.TheOrganicPharmacy.com*
A practice offering aromatherapy, holistic consultation and massage, a health assessment, allergy testing, naturopathic consultation, reflexology, homeopathy, ayurvedic consultation and Indian head massage. / *SEE ALSO 3.09 Lotions & potions.*

NORTH

The Active Birth Centre ⌂
25 Bickerton Rd N19 5JT ☎ *(020) 7281 6760* ⊕ *www.activebirthcentre.com*
Various practitioners work out of the centre offering acupuncture, therapeutic massage, aromatherapy, counselling, self hypnosis, reflexology, homeopathy and osteopathy. / *HOURS shop Mon-Fri 9.30am-6.30pm (Fri 4pm), Sat 10am-4pm; SEE ALSO 1.01 Where to have the baby; 1.04 Antenatal classes; 1.06 Birth equipment; 2.01 Postnatal; 2.02 Feeding; 2.03 Baby health; 2.06 Baby & toddler activities; 3.01 Maternity wear; 3.02 Baby equipment; 4.05 Finding out more.*

Angel Chiropractic Clinic
18 St Alban's Place, Upper St N1 0NX ☎ *(020) 7288 2999*
Run by Victoria Robinson MGCP, and offering therapeutic massage, reflexology, ante and post-natal massage, labour massage instruction for partners and treatments for children. / *SEE ALSO 2.06 Baby & toddler activities.*

Belsize Health
16 England's Lane, Belsize Park NW3 4TG ☎ *(020) 7483 2345*
⊕ *www.belsizehealth.co.uk*
Complementary medicine, therapy and massage for the whole family, from a practice which opened in 2002.

Centre for the Study of Complementary & Integrated Medicine
14 Harley House, Brunswick Place (formerly Upper Harley St) NW1 4PR ☎ *(020) 7935 7848*
Three doctors who are also homeopaths run a clinic just off Harley Street four days a week – address at other times: 51 Bedford Place, Southampton SO15 2DT (023) 8033 4752. A number of complementary practitioners work with them, and treatments offered include acupuncture, homeopathy, environmental medicine, nutritional medicine, herbal medicine, manipulative medicine, autogenic training, hypnotherapy, psychological and psychotherapy services, and teaching of the Alexander Technique.

Chatsworth Centre
1 Loveridge Mews NW6 2DP ☎ *(020) 7372 0093* ⊕ *www.chatsworthcentre.co.uk*
Treatments available include homeopathy, Chinese and oriental medicine, osteopathy and cranial osteopathy, nutrition, healing, Bach flower remedies, hypnotherapy and psychotherapy. Homeopath and osteopath specialising in mother and baby. / *HOURS Mon-Fri 8am-10.30am booking essential.*

Complementary Health Clinic
87 Tower Gardens N17 ☎ *(020) 8808 6464*
Treatments in pregnancy, postnatally and for babies and children, including homeopathy, herbal remedies, flower essences, craniosacral therapy, therapeutic massage, spinal touch, journey work, allergy testing and treatments. Plus a handmade aromatherapy range.

Crouch End Natural Health Centre
24 Hermiston Avenue, Crouch End N8 8NL ☎ *(020) 8340 6832*
Alexander Technique, aromatherapy, a range of massage therapies, counselling, homeopathy, hypnotherapy (including for childbirth), nutrition, osteopathy including cranial osteopathy, reflexology, reiki, shiatsu, physiotherapy and yoga. (Also a sports injuries clinic.)

Crouch End Natural Health Clinic
170 Weston Park N8 9PN ☎ *(020) 8341 9800*
A clinic offering osteopathy, acupuncture, Chinese herbalism, aromatherapy, massage, counselling, hypnotherapy, shiatsu, nutrition and Neuro Linguistic Programming.

Forty Hill Natural Health Centre
478 Baker St Enfield EN1 3QS ☎ *(020) 8367 5561*
Acupuncture, osteopathy (including cranial osteopathy), apitherapy (for multiple
sclerosis sufferers) and manipulation. / HOURS Mon-Fri 9am-5pm.

The Haelan Clinic
41 The Broadway N8 8DT ☎ *(020) 8340 1518* ⏁ *www.haelan.co.uk*
Osteopathy, homeopathy, massage, acupuncture, herbalism. / HOURS Mon-Fri 9am-6pm
(Fri 6.30pm), Sun noon-4pm; SEE ALSO *2.02 Feeding.*

Healthy Living Centre
282 St Paul's Rd N1 2LH ☎ *(020) 7704 6900* ⏁ *www.thehealthylivingcentre.co.uk*
Runs special craniosacral, childbirth and breastfeeding clinics for mothers, babies and
children and low cost homeopathic and craniosacral clinics for those who canot pay
the full therapy fee, often with students in practice who are under supervsion; also
drop-in clinics for emergencies or conditions that have come on suddenly;
practitioners all belong to recognised professional registers and associations and the
centre runs practitioner development workshops; the aim is to provide a range of
treatments and these include aromatherapy, acupuncture, reflexology, massage,
medical herbalism, osteopathy (including cranial), homeopathy (daily clinic, £15) and
reiki. Mother and baby clinics in craniosacral therapy and homeopathy. / HOURS Mon-
Fri 8am-8pm, Sat 9am-6pm.

Highgate Health Centre
31a Highgate High St N6 5JT ☎ *(020) 8348 5553*
Osteopathy, shiatsu, homeopathy, iridology, massage, aromatherapy, counselling,
craniosacral therapy, herbalism (Chinese and western), reflexology, reiki and
podiatry; homeopathy and shiatsu clinics for babies and children.

Kailash
Centre of Oriental Medicine, 7 Newcourt St NW8 7AA ☎ *(020) 7722 3939, 020
4833476.* ⏁ *www.orientalhealing.co.uk*
Therapies available include: acupuncture (Japanese, Chinese, and Vietnamese);
herbalism (Chinese, Indian, Ayurveda, Japanese, Kampo, and Tibetan), prices initially
£45, subsequently £25; massage (Chinese, Tui Na, Indian Charvutti, Mongolian, Thai
and shiatsu), prices £40-£60; oriental healing (reiki and bio-energy healing); oriental
health care (lifestyle, diet and exercise advice); nutrition and Bach flower remedies.
Classes in Tai Chi, Qi-Gong and yoga and courses in many treatments (Bach
remedies, reflexology, massage for children) are offered. / HOURS Mon-Sat 9am-7pm; SEE
ALSO *2.06 Baby & toddler activities.*

Natural Health
339 Ballards Lane N12 8LJ ☎ *(020) 8445 4397* ⏁ *www.naturesalternative.co.uk*
Homeopathy, osteopathy, acupuncture, holistic massage, reflexology, aromatherapy,
hypnotherapy, nutrition and allergy testing; shop stocks range of baby and health
books. / HOURS Mon-Sat 9am-5.30pm; SEE ALSO *2.02 Feeding.*

Natural Remedies
35 Brecknock Rd N7 0BT ☎ *(020) 7267 3884*
Acupuncture, aromatherapy, chiropractic, craniosacral therapy, homeopathy,
massage, nutritional advice, and shiatsu. Shop (always staffed by qualified advisors)
sells natural baby & child products, aromatherapy oils, homeopathic remedies and
food supplements. / HOURS Mon-Sat 9.30am-6.30pm.

Neal's Yard Remedies
☎ *(0845) 262 3145* ⏁ *www.nealsyardremedies.com*
BRANCHES AT:
  68 Chalk Farm Rd NW1 8AN ☎ *(020) 7284 2039*
See write-up in central.

North End Practice
8a Burghley Rd NW5 1UE ☎ *(020) 7485 9362*
Homeopathy, osteopathy, acupuncture, shiatsu, massage, medical herbalism,
Alexander Technique and psychotherapy are all offered at this practice. The herbalist
is particularly experienced in working antenatally.

Northwood Road Practice
2 Northwood Rd N6 5TN ☎ *(020) 8348 3011*
Osteopathy, acupuncture and homeopathy.

The Oakwood Physiotherapy Clinic Ltd

95 Green Rd N14 4AP ☎ (020) 8440 3629/6318 ↺ www.oakwoodphysio.co.uk
Apart from physiotherapy, treatments available include aromatherapy, reflexology, massage, osteopathy (including cranial), homeopathy and acupuncture. / HOURS *Mon-Fri: 8.30am-7pm, Sat: 9am-5pm.*

Primrose Hill Natural Health Centre

9 St George's Mews NW1 8XE ☎ (020) 7586 0148 ↺ www.ccst.co.uk
Osteopathy, homeopathy, iridology, acupuncture, Alexander Technique, Chinese herbs, massage, aromatherapy, craniosacral therapy, reflexology, diet and nutrition, psychotherapy and naturopathy.

The Shine Holistic

52 Stoke Newington Church St N16 0NB ☎ (020) 7249 9671, (020) 7241 5033
↺ *www.alt-therapies.co.uk*
Formerly known as the Alternative Therapy Centre – acupuncture, Alexander Technique aromatherapy, Chinese herbalism, counselling, craniosacral osteopathy, herbalism, holistic massage, homeopathy, hypnotherapy and tuition in self hypnosis, naturopathy, osteopathy, reflexology, past life regression, and healing, reiki, shiatsu, shoulder and facial massage, spiritual healing; the shop sells natural products, including nappy rash cream.

Space Natural Health Clinic

76 Mill Lane, West Hampstead NW6 1NL ☎ (020) 7433 3060, Mobile (07971) 112 111
'Holistic treatment plans', as well as specialist clinics for mother and baby and a homeopathic children's clinic. Therapies include acupuncture and Chinese herbs, aromatherapy massage, craniosacral therapy, homeopathy, life coaching, osteopathy, reflexology and reiki, hypnotherapy and sports injury massage.

Spiral

2 Shelburne Road, Islington N7 6DL ☎ (020) 7607 4403
Centre founded in 1995 to offer emotional and physical support, with counselling and psychotherapy, acupuncture, Alexander Technique, body psychotherapy and biodynamic massage, homeopathy, hypnotherapy, intuitive massage for women, reflexology and shamanic healing.

Symbiosis Health Clinic

390a Seven Sisters Rd N4 2PQ ☎ (020) 7697 8982
Specialists in osteopathy (including cranial osteopathy); other treatments include acupuncture, aromatherapy, chiropody, herbalism, homeopathy, hypnotherapy, massage, naturopathy, nutrition, reflexology, psychotherapy, shiatsu, and yoga. Many of the practitioners are experienced with pregnant women and children. / HOURS *Mon-Fri 9am-7pm Sat 9am-6pm.*

Violet Hill Studios

6 Violet Hill NW8 9EB ☎ (020) 7624 6101
Acupuncture, aromatherapy, craniosacral therapy, psychotherapy (including couple counselling), Alexander Technique, holistic massage, homeopathy, hypnotherapy, nutrition, stress management and reiki.

Viveka

27a Queen's Terrace NW8 6EA ☎ (020) 7483 3788
Previously the TLC Centre, this practice centres on the work of obstetrician Yehudi Gordon. Other specialists include an ultrasonographer, a fertility and endocrine specialist, a consultant paediatrician, a consultant nutritionist (the chairman of Foresight), a counsellor and family therapist, a psychotherapist, osteopaths (including craniosacral specialists), allergy specialists, homeopaths and teachers of yoga and massage. / SEE ALSO *1.04 Antenatal classes.*

Women & Health

4 Carol St NW1 0HU ☎ (020) 7482 2786 ↺ www.women-and-health.org
A centre (for women residents or workers in Camden borough only) with outbound service that travels to your home. A crèche is available (£2 per child if waged, £1 unwaged) at the centre, which holds a well woman clinic and doctor's advice sessions. Also provided: acupuncture, aromatherapy, Alexander Technique, counselling, craniosacral therapy, feldenkrais, first-aid courses, herbal medicine, homeopathy, massage, osteopathy, reflexology, shiatsu, yoga and relaxation, naturopathy meditation and workshops (for example, homeopathic first aid, your rights as a patient, self healing); free doctor & well women clinic. counselling £5-£20 depending on income, all other therapies £7-£20.

SOUTH

Acupuncture & Chinese Medicine Clinic
55 Tweedy Rd Bromley BR1 3NH ☎ (020) 8313 1577
Six practitioners, experienced in the treatment of pregnancy, postnatal problems and children, with a range of therapies including acupuncture, Chinese herbalism, osteopathy, chiropractic, aromatherapy and applied kinesiology. / HOURS *Mon-Fri 9am-6pm, Sat 9am-3.30pm.*

Beverley Clinic
362 Coombe Lane SW20 0RJ ☎ (020) 8241 2515
Eight practitioners provide homeopathy, acupuncture, chiropractic, counselling, hypnotherapy and chiropody; also dentistry. / HOURS *Mon-Fri 8.30am-8pm, Sat 9am-1pm.*

Bexleyheath Natural Health Clinic
284 The Broadway Bexleyheath DA6 8AJ ☎ (020) 8303 6288
🖰 www.bexleyheathnaturalhealthclinic.co.uk
20 practitioners offer a wide range of therapies, including homeopathy, acupuncture, Chinese herbalism, cranial osteopathy, physiotherapy and reflexology. The therapists can also treat children with developmental learning difficulties – call for further details. / HOURS *Mon-Fri 9am-5.30pm (Mon & Thu 7pm).*

City Health Partnership
37 Oxford Rd SW15 2LH ☎ (020) 8789 0607 🖰 www.cityhealth.biz
Homeopathic clinic (14 practitioners) also offering osteopathy, McTimoney chiropractic, acupuncture, reflexology, aromatherapy, sports massage, baby massage, clinical hypnotherapy, psychotherapy, counselling and reiki. / HOURS *Mon-Fri 8am-8pm, Sat 8am-12pm; SEE ALSO 2.06 Baby & toddler activities.*

Clapham Common Clinic
151-153 Clapham High St SW4 7SS ☎ (020) 7627 8890
🖰 www.claphamcommonclininc.co.uk
Therapists at this clinic have particular experience in treating pregnancy (including turning babies and induction) with acupuncture, Alexander Technique, homeopathy, McTimoney chiropractic, reflexology and shiatsu. Massage therapist Annie O'Dell specialises in pregnancy massage. Other therapies include chiropody, hypnotherapy, naturopathy, counselling and osteopathy; personal trainers and a beautician also available. / HOURS *Mon-Sat 9am-8pm (Sat 6.30pm).*

Family Natural Health Centre
106 Lordship Lane SE22 8HF ☎ (020) 8693 5515, (020) 8299 9798
🖰 www.osteopathuk.com
Family-orientated, child-friendly clinic, adjacent to the baby shop Soup Dragon: all therapists are experienced in working with pregnant women and children; therapies offered include aromatherapy, acupuncture, herbalism, homeopathy, shiatsu, craniosacral therapy, osteopathy, nutrition, reflexology and remedial massage. Also offered: classes on pregnancy yoga and postnatal exercise, and talks on homeopathy in pregnancy, childbirth, and childhood vaccination.

Greenwich Natural Health Centre
Neptune House, 70 Royal Hill SE10 8RF ☎ (020) 8691 5408
🖰 www.greenwichnaturalhealth.co.uk
Acupuncture, Alexander Technique, aromatherapy, counselling, craniosacral therapy, homeopathy, hypnotherapy, nutrition, osteopathy, massage, chiropody, reflexology, shiatsu and reiki; also a low-cost children's homeopathy clinic.

The Health Zone
30 Wimbledon Hill Rd SW19 7PA ☎ (020) 8944 1133
Shop with a clinic attached, offering acupuncture, allergy testing, Alexander Technique, aromatherapy, beauty treatments, counselling, craniosacral therapy, herbal medicine, homeopathy, hypnotherapy, nutrition, massage, reiki, reflexology, shiatsu and Indian head massage; some therapists are experienced in working with pregnant women; fees vary.

Kingston Natural Healing Centre
40 Eastbury Rd Kingston upon Thames KT2 5AN ☎ (020) 8546 5793
🖰 www.surrey-online.co.uk/knhe
Osteopathy (including craniosacral osteopathy), massage, homeopathy, nutrition, naturopathy, Chinese herbalism, reiki, stress management, psychotherapy, counselling, spiritual healing, hypnotherapy, acupuncture, reflexology, Alexander Technique, aromatherapy, shiatsu and kinesiology. / HOURS *Mon-Fri 9am-5pm; SEE ALSO 2.03 Baby health.*

The Living Centre Clinic
32 Durham Rd, Raynes Park SW20 0TW ☎ (020) 8946 2331
⌁ www.livingcentreclinic.com
Clinic for Complementary Medicine; all practitioners are registered with appropriate bodies; mother and child service.

Neal's Yard Remedies
☎ (0845) 262 3145 ⌁ www.nealsyardremedies.com
BRANCHES AT:
6 Northcote Rd SW11 1NT ☎ (020) 7223 7141
32 Blackheath Village SE3 9SY ☎ (020) 8318 6655
15 King St Richmond TW9 1ND ☎ (020) 8948 9248
See write-up in central.

New Cross Natural Therapy Centre
394 New Cross Rd SE14 6TY ☎ (020) 8469 0858
About 20 practitioners provide: acupuncture, Chinese herbalism, Alexander Technique, allergy testing, aromatherapy, counselling and psychotherapy, women's therapy group, craniosacral therapy, dietary therapy, healing, herbalism, holistic massage, homeopathy, chiropractic, osteopathy, reflexology and shiatsu. Also operate a children's clinic offering herbs and acupuncture for children's ailments plus a children's low-cost homeopathic clinic for families on low incomes, from £10.

Putney Natural Therapy Clinic
11 Montserrat Rd SW15 2LD ☎ (020) 8789 2548
Clinic which works with many pregnant women and prides itself on a child-friendly approach. Treatments available include Alexander Technique, acupuncture (the practitioner was previously a midwife), aromatherapy, herbalism, chiropody, homeopathy, massage, reflexology and shiatsu, as well as hypnotherapy, psychotherapy and counselling. / *HOURS Mon-Sat 9am-8pm (Sat 1pm).*

The Replingham Clinic
95 Replingham Rd SW18 5LU ☎ (020) 8875 1101
Chinese doctors practise Chinese herbal medicine and acupuncture, and offer other therapies including aromatherapy, chiropody, reflexology, nutrition, homeopathy, counselling, psychotherapy and hypnotherapy for both adults and children. Both structural and cranial osteopathy are used where relevant.

South London Natural Health Centre
7a Clapham Common Southside SW4 7AA ☎ (020) 7720 8817, Low cost clinic (020) 7732 1417 ⌁ www.southlondonnaturalhealthcentre.com
Osteopathy (including cranial osteopathy), reflexology, aromatherapy, acupuncture, herbalism, chiropractic, counselling, reiki, massage and shiatsu; also low-cost homeopathy clinic, yoga and Qi Gong classes.

Wimbledon Clinic of Natural Medicine
1 Evelyn Rd SW19 8NU ☎ (020) 8540 3389, (020) 8543 5477
⌁ www.wimbledonclinic.co.uk
The clinic specialises in biological medicine (a diagnostic system), but other services available include acupuncture, Alexander Technique, allergy testing, cranial osteopathy, chiropractic, homeopathy, herbalism, osteopathy and hormonal testing (used in connection with postnatal depression). / *HOURS Mon-Fri 8am-7pm (some Sat clinics).*

EAST

Ashlins Natural Health
181 Hoe St E17 3AP ☎ (020) 8520 5268 ⌁ www.ashlins.co.uk
The aromatherapy and reflexology practitioners are both particularly experienced in working with pregnancy, from pre-conception to induction. Other therapies offered include acupuncture, Alexander Technique, applied kinesiology, McTimoney chiropractic, chiropody, counselling, homeopathy, Indian head massage, stress relief/sports/therapeutic massage and reiki. / *HOURS Tue-Fri 9am-8pm, Sat 10am-2pm.*

Bodywise
119 Roman Rd E2 0QN ☎ (020) 8981 6938 ⌁ www.bodywisehealth.org
Around 30 practitioners, offering homeopathy, acupuncture, Alexander Technique, aromatherapy, art therapy, Bach Flower remedies, counselling, cranial osteopathy, hypnotherapy, massage, movement psychotherapy, naturopathy, nutrition, osteopathy, polarity therapy, psychotherapy, reflexology, reiki, shiatsu, tai chi, pre- and postnatal yoga, children's yoga and baby massage. £20-£70. / *HOURS Mon-Fri 9am-8pm, Sat 8.45am-1pm.*

City Health Centre
62 Paul St EC2A 4NA ☎ *(020) 7729 8525* ⏻ *www.cityhealthcentre.nildram.co.uk*
A number of the practitioners at the centre are experienced in dealing with pregnant women and babies, including acupuncturist Ann Bradford, Emma Farrant (who practices with Chinese herbs, Tui Na massage), homeopath Jo Redmond and osteopaths Joyce Vetterlein and Holly Makin. Other areas covered include Alexander Technique teachers, Shiatsu massage and reflexology. / HOURS *Mon-Fri 9am-6pm.*

Complete Health Care Centre
Kemp House, 160 City Rd EC1V 2NP ☎ *(020) 7336 0466*
⏻ *www.completehealthcare.co.uk*
Acupuncture, aromatherapy massage, Alexander Technique, Chinese herbal medicine, craniosacral therapy, holistic/sports massage, homeopathy, meditation, osteopathy, shiatsu, reiki, reflexology, tai chi and yoga. (Also beauty treatments, lifestyle coaching, personal training, Pilates and feng shui.) / HOURS *Mon-Fri 8am-8pm.*

Forest Complementary Clinic
843 Forest Rd E17 4AT ☎ *(020) 8531 7188*
Alexander Technique, acupuncture, aromatherapy, chiropody, homeopathy (one practitioner is experienced in working with children), hypnotherapy, osteopathy (including cranial osteopathy), reflexology and sports injuries; average cost £28 per session. / HOURS *Mon-Fri 9am-6pm, Sat 9.30am-4pm.*

OUTSIDE LONDON

Napiers Direct 📖
35 Hamilton Place Edinburgh EH3 5BA ☎ *(0131) 343 6683, AdviceLine (0906) 802 0117 (60p per minute)* ⏻ *www.napiers.net*
Therapies including herbal medicine, aromatherapy, massage, counselling and psychotherapy, nutritional therapy, osteopathy, craniosacral therapy, food sensitivity testing, reiki, naturopathy, acpuncture, homeopathy, reflexology, sports massage, therapeutic and Thai yoga massage, Alexander Technique and stress management. (London venue for complementary therapy: 44 Goodge Street, W1T 2AD.) / HOURS *Mon-Fri 10am-6pm, advice line 9am-1pm.*

Wood Street Clinic
133 Wood Street, Barnet Herts EN5 4BX ☎ *(020) 8449 7656, (020) 8441 0231*
Offers homeopathy (with Sally Ann Hutcheson) and acupuncture, including for induction, in pregnancy, postnatally, for depression and for lack of sleep and energy, and for children. Homeopathy first visit £65, then £38 – child £50, £32; acupuncture £36.

CHAPTER 4.03

MEDICAL ISSUES AT BIRTH

1. **Introduction**
2. **'Managed' labours (induction & augmentation of labour)**
3. **Episiotomies & tears**
4. **Instrumental deliveries (forceps & ventouse /vacuum extractions)**
5. **Caesarean section**
6. **Breech births**
7. **'Physiological' vs 'managed' third stage of labour**
8. **Options for pain relief**
9. **Alternative forms of pain relief**
10. **Electronic foetal monitoring (EFM) & Routine continuous electronic foetal monitoring (RCEFM)**
11. **Birth positions**
12. **Other issues**
13. **How to make a complaint about your care**

(For information relating to home births see chapter 1.01, Where to have the baby. For information relating to water births, see chapter 1.06 Birth equipment.)

I. INTRODUCTION

All research shows that the births women feel happiest with are those where they feel in control. This chapter is for those women who feel the more information, the better. For others choosing to take the advice of their professional carers may be all the control they require.

It is in the nature of the subject that the focus is on the negative – risks, side-effects and concerns. Given that foreknowledge of everything which can go wrong can be unnerving, ignoring this chapter may suit some readers best.

In the 1900s, the risks of giving birth were greater than those of working in seafaring and coal mining *combined*. At the turn of this new century giving birth is safer than horse riding. The procedures listed below aren't perfect, but nor is natural childbirth, which has its own set of risks, side-effects and concerns.

Forewarned is forearmed

According to a report published in October 2001 by the Royal College of Obstetricians and Gynaecologists, approximately one baby in three in England is now delivered by either a Caesarean section or by means of an instrumental delivery. Moreover, of the remaining non-surgical births a significant proportion are induced, or aided by modern medical techniques for pain relief.

Why read this chapter?

➢ To reassure yourself that you are receiving up-to-date treatment, proved by research to be effective.

➢ Because it is possible that your carers will not have the time, or the inclination, to go through issues in the detail you might like.

➢ To feel in control. It is not necessarily whether labour was long or short, painful or pain-free, natural or medically managed that makes women feel happy about a birth. Notwithstanding the importance of having been treated kindly and respectfully, for many mothers the key to feeling satisfied is a sense of having been in charge.

➢ Because understanding the choices and issues which you may face will help alleviate tensions, and fear of unfamiliar or new situations (tension being linked to increased sensation of pain).

➢ Because if your labour becomes complicated you are likely to feel happier and more positive about the whole experience if you are able to take an active and informed part in decisions about your care. Loss of control and a sense of disempowerment (especially if combined with physical side effects) can create a deep-seated sense of disappointment after the birth – a cause of postnatal depression and, in some cases, bad memories that stay with women throughout their lives.

'HEALTH WARNING'

This book is not a birth manual. The summary of the key issues in this area is designed to enable you to arm yourself with a basic degree of knowledge for whatever decisions you may be faced with in labour – to form the basis for an informed discussion with your carers. If you wish to dig in to any of these topics in real depth, further research is essential...

READING

A Guide to Effective Care in Pregnancy & Childbirth – Murray Enkin, Marc JNC Keirse & Iain Chalmers (OUP; 2000; £14.99; 019263173X) – *Mainly aimed at professionals but also for expectant parents: exhaustive coverage in 50 chapters based on the assessment of 7,000-plus research studies with conclusions on techniques and practices in antenatal, birth and postnatal care.*

Birth Reborn – Michel Odent (What childbirth should be; Souvenir; 1994; £10.99; 0285631942) – *Birthing methods from this famous obstetrician.*

Birthrights – Sally Inch (A parents' guide to modern childbirth; Green Print; 1990; £8.99; 1854250329) – *Perhaps alarming, but providing excellent material to argue against unnecessary intervention.*

Every Woman's Birth Rights – Pat Thomas (HarperCollins; 1996; £7.99; 0-722532-81-4) – *A forcefully-argued case for the importance of weighing up all the choices in childbirth and choosing what is right for you. Unfortunately the catalogue of possible problems is depressing, but especially if read early on in pregnancy this can be a useful source for helping mothers get the kind of birth they feel is right. (You may now find it under Your Birth Rights, ISBN 0704347105).*

Practical Parenting: Pregnancy and Birth – Gill Thorn (Hamlyn; 2001; £9.99; 0600603296) – *A reference book by a psychologist expert in this field, backed by Practical Parenting.*

Your Guide to the NHS (Department of Health; free) / available from Health Centres or (0800) 555777.

USEFUL CONTACTS

Association for Improvement in Maternity Services (AIMS), ☎ (0870) 765 1433 ⏚ www.aims.org.uk

A campaigning group which has done much to change childbirth since the '60s. The organisation aims to represent parents' views on maternity services as well as to support midwives. An excellent source of advice and encouragement for mothers and mothers-to-be, with information on rights and choices – they can help with making complaints if required. / *HOURS* Mon-Fri 9.30am-5pm; *PUBLICATIONS* Ultrasound? Unsound (£5); Safety in Childbirth (findings that hospital is not safer for the majority of women, £2.50); Birthing Your Baby – The Second Stage (£2.50); Delivering Your Placenta – The Third Stage (£2.50); What are my rights? – for care in home or hospital; The Journal quarterly magazine (£3, free with £15 membership) includes relevant research & personal accounts; send SAE for publications list.

Childbirth, ⏚ www.childbirth.org

Good US portal site (produced by a group of midwives, nurses and doulas) with numerous links to relevant sites on all subjects from birth plans to fertility and bookshops; the underlying message is to reclaim birth as a natural process, not just a medical procedure; questions on topics including foetal monitoring, Caesareans and episiotomies are answered on the site.

The Midwives Information & Resource Service (MIDIRS), ☎ (0800) 581009 ⏚ www.midirs.org

Charitable organisation primarily focused on providing information for health professionals and midwives. It publishes a quarterly review relating to midwifery and a number of informed choice leaflets. These are available direct. Women with special problems or needs may wish to consider using the literature-search service where a search can be made on a wide array of academic journals relating to a particular issue. The bookshop provides a variety of books and videos (on breast-feeding, positions in childbirth etc) primarily aimed at (and priced for) professionals which could benefit interested mothers. / *HOURS* Mon-Fri 9am-5pm; *PUBLICATIONS* Directory of Maternity Organisations available free on website. Informed choice leaflets: Support in labour; Foetal heart rate monitoring in labour; Scans in early pregnancy; Alcohol and pregnancy; Positions in labour and delivery; Epidurals; Feeding your baby – breast or bottle; Looking for Down's syndrome and spina bifida in pregnancy; Breech birth – what are your choices?; Where will you have your baby?; Do you want a waterbirth? and When you baby's overdue.

Primal Health Research Centre, ☎ (020) 7485 0095

⏚ www.birthworks.org/primalhealth

Founded by water birth specialist Dr Michel Odent, the centre co-ordinates research into the development of the foetus and related implications for adult life. For example, there is a range of illnesses and conditions which appear to have a connection with drugs taken during labour. Membership (£12 a year) includes a newsletter.

Sheila Kitzinger, ⏚ www.sheilakitzinger.com

A website with information on home birth and water birth, plus a large number of articles by Sheila Kitzinger in favour of a more relaxed approach to birth and campaigning against undue medicalisation.

Unassisted Birth, ⏚ www.unassistedbirth.com

A website celebrating birth without medical intervention, founded by an American mother of four, and author on the subject.

A primer on the interventionist debate

The 'dream scenario' for your birth is that some time close to your EDD you enter labour spontaneously. Labour becomes strongly established, and – after several exhausting but (in retrospect) exhilarating hours – a baby is smoothly delivered.

However, for a significant proportion of women the dream remains just that. The EDD passes … and nothing happens … and still nothing happens. Or you rush to hospital just like you're supposed to in the movies, but after many exhausting hours it is clear that you are not getting anywhere. Or, the problem can be as simple as the fact that the baby gets stuck.

When labour fails to happen, or becomes prolonged and complications threaten, the question of what to do next arises – more specifically, whether to intervene medically.

The benefits, risks, and appropriate frequency-of-use of some commonly used medical interventions are hotly debated in obstetric and midwifery circles. This is news to many parents who – as newcomers to the process of childbirth – may never have had cause to consider such issues, and might assume that by now there would be some clearer truths about such a commonplace and important occurrence.

Many women take the view that medical decisions concerning birth are best left entirely to the experts (a view shared by many experts). At the opposite end of the spectrum, some natural childbirth lobbyists raise the spectre of scalpel-happy obstetricians intervening needlessly.

One common concern is the fact that any form of intervention makes further interventions more likely – the so-called 'cascade of intervention'.

The debate about the appropriate level of use of medical procedures during childbirth continues. There is room for disagreement and it is to be hoped that the current efforts to improve the auditing of maternity 'episodes' continue. Only in this way can best practice be proven, rather than merely depend upon the convictions of, on the one hand, campaigners or, on the other hand, consultants.

Nobody claims that medical intervention is never necessary. According to the Association of Radical Midwives, 15–20% of all labours are unavoidably complicated. However, with over 50% of births receiving some form of intervention, this leaves a not inconsiderable grey area of 30–35% for the various camps to haggle about.

It is by no means just extremist campaigners who question current intervention levels. The Audit Commission's 1997 report *First Class Maternity* noted "The high levels of some procedures suggest that they are being carried out on a routine basis and that it is local policies rather than professional judgement that explain the frequency of some interventions."

APPROPRIATE AND ACTUAL LEVELS OF INTERVENTION

Recommendations drawn up by the 1985 World Health Organisation (WHO) Inter-Regional Conference for Birth included:

➢ Induced labour (see below) should not be above 10% in any geographic region (current rate in the UK about 20% of births).

➢ Artificial Rupturing of the Membranes (ARM) (see below) is not scientifically justified (but still accounts for 40% of inductions in the UK).

➢ The systematic use of episiotomy – as opposed to its use in aiding deliveries using ventouse or forceps – (see below) is not justified (and yet still occurs in approaching 10% of UK births).

➢ There is no justification in any specific geographic region to have more than 10–15% Caesarean births. (Current rate in the UK is approximately 20%: up from 10% about 10 years ago, and quintuple the rate of 4% at the start of the '70s.)

➢ There is no evidence that a Caesarean is required after a previous transverse lower segment Caesarean (i.e. involving a horizontal cut along the bikini line). Vaginal deliveries after a Caesarean should normally be encouraged wherever emergency facilities are available in case of complication.

Your rights, and what you should expect:

➢ The Court of Appeal in March 1997 ruled that women have the right to refuse medical intervention such as a Caesarean delivery even if it means she or the baby dies. The judgement requires the woman to be "competent". However the presumption is that the woman is competent and that what doctors may judge irrational does not amount to incompetence. This is believed to relate to all elements of care from monitoring onwards.

➤ The government's 1993 *Changing Childbirth* report stated that "Whenever possible, the [normal] physiological processes should be supported for all births. The principle of justifying any tests and use of technology should apply in all situations."

So while hospital staff may habitually use words such as "allow", "let" and "permit" in discussing decisions relating to your birth, such words do not, in fact, reflect the general thrust of the law. Your carers should inform and advise, but the final decisions are rightfully yours (although obviously it's easier to invoke your rights to prevent an intervention rather than to procure it). If your carers are unhappy with the choices you make, you can have it written into your notes that you take full responsibility.

Keep your expectations realistic

Many pregnant women and their partners know in advance from their childbirth preparation classes and other sources what sort of birth they would ideally like to have. Increasingly women are forearmed for their labour with birth plans.

More than half the women surveyed for a 1997 Audit Commission report knew whether they did or did not want a particular medical procedure to be used in the birth. Although this greater degree of preparation is almost certainly a good thing, it brings with it the danger of creating expectations that unexpected events render unrealistic.

Women's labours are divided by their carers into two distinct groups: low risk and high risk. Low risk women are generally left to get on with their birth plan with a midwife.

Deliveries judged to be a higher risk – and this might occur at any point in pregnancy or labour – will, from that point, be managed by a midwife superintended by a doctor. In this situation, the safety of you and your child is a much higher priority for your carers than respecting the letter of your birth plan. It may be that they deem necessary procedures that you had hoped to avoid.

Advance planning can be a tool to help women feel more control in childbirth. But some women are apt to feel that they 'failed' if they do not 'achieve' the birth they had envisaged.

As one very experienced active birth teacher is fond of pointing out, "God likes to laugh at our plans". Birth plans must allow for the need to be flexible and respond to changing circumstances. Writing them in stone can lead to feelings of bitterness, failure, or depression if events do not turn out quite as hoped.

Pressures on obstetricians to intervene:

➤ No doctor wants to feel they are responsible for an unnecessarily brain-damaged baby, an injured mother, or a death.

➤ It is thought that over half the obstetricians in the UK face medical malpractice suits at any given time – complaints are almost invariably about failure to intervene, rather than too much intervention.

➤ Medical practitioners and carers are trained to act if labour is not 'going to plan'. Even though Caesarean section involves a significant period of recovery for the mother, it is a safe medical procedure (and generally takes under ten minutes). Thus, in a problematic delivery it can be an attractive option from the doctors' perspective (and from many women's perspective too).

2. 'MANAGED' LABOURS (INDUCTION & AUGMENTATION OF LABOUR)

As with so many areas of life, the media has a lot to answer for when it comes to people's preconceptions about birth.

The onset of labour is usually portrayed in films and on TV as a dramatic and irresistible process ("Oh my God! The baby's coming…"), complete with high-speed dash to the hospital. That may happen in a tiny handful of cases, but for most women the reality is much more prosaic. Rather than the stress of coping with fast-moving events, the stress is often that the due date is passed and that nothing appears to be happening. Or, that there has been a dash to hospital on account of contractions that ebb away. (For this latter reason, midwives often suggest especially with a first birth, that a woman only go into hospital once she feels that contractions are very well established).

Over the last half-century, obstetric medicine has developed a combination of drug-based and surgical procedures with a powerful ability to stimulate labour artificially, either for the purpose of starting labour off in the first place (induction), or boosting progress when labour seems to be stalling (augmentation).

These procedures are a one-way ticket, however: once embarked upon, the labour must be seen through to its conclusion. Sometimes, the initial procedures of induction or augmentation are sufficient to stimulate the mother's natural readiness for labour, and with only a little medical intervention the natural process will reassert itself and the baby be delivered. In a significant number of cases, however, this is not the case and the birth must be fully medically managed through to delivery, with all the increased risks this entails of an instrumental delivery, or delivery by Caesarean section.

Induction

About one in five births in the UK is induced. In some cases this is because some medical issue has arisen during pregnancy (high blood pressure is a classic example) and doctors feel that the sooner the birth occurs, the better. In other cases, the issue is that the EDD has passed, and birth is not occurring spontaneously.

Some hospitals wait longer than others before advising induction – usually between a week and a fortnight after the EDD. The possibility of needing an induction is good reason to give careful thought to how accurately your EDD has been calculated in the first place. For example, if your menstrual cycle is different from the average, was allowance made for this?

Though inductions for non-medical reasons ('social inductions') are generally not available on the NHS, they are still relatively common in private births. This may be because the birth must occur at a certain time, in order to fit in with the consultant's diary, or because some women like to plan an induction well before the EDD (around 38 weeks is common), in order to guarantee a smaller baby which may be born more easily. (A significant number of practitioners feel that this means losing an important growth phase for the baby.)

Induction is almost certainly wise:
➢ If the mother's health will suffer from continuing the pregnancy, for example if she suffers from kidney disease.

➤ In multiple pregnancies, if one baby is being compromised – for example, by receiving less nourishment than the other.

➤ If the uterus is not functioning properly (a Caesarean delivery may also be considered in this situation).

➤ If the baby has a congenital problem which would benefit from immediate treatment.

Other reasons which are less universally agreed on are:

➤ Because the EDD has passed – the argument being that the placenta will gradually cease to function. However, though some practitioners suggest evidence of an increased risk of the baby dying if it remains unborn, there are sources that suggest there is no increased risk for up to four weeks beyond the EDD (so long as the baby is regularly monitored for problems). Other research indicates that although going two weeks over the EDD does nothing to improve the outcome for the baby, neither does induction improve the baby's condition.

➤ If the mother is considered high risk – for example if she has high blood pressure, or is a heavy smoker.

➤ If the baby is growth-retarded. However, prior to delivery there is no reliable method to identify a growth-retarded baby. Further, it is debatable whether a special care baby unit is a better environment than the mother's womb for such a child.

➤ If the waters have broken – because of the risk of infection, labour should ideally start within 24 hours. However, if the baby would be born prematurely (before 33–34 weeks) some consultants will try to delay. Others will try to wait until 37 weeks but in all cases careful monitoring of the baby's well-being is essential.

Induction – risks, side effects and concerns:

➤ Spontaneous birth involves a complex interaction of hormones produced by both mother and baby. Medical induction by contrast is a relatively crude procedure applied only to the mother. In consequence, the ensuing labour can be longer, more painful and more tiring.

➤ The process is reported to bring greater likelihood of instrumental or Caesarean delivery (the 'cascade of intervention'), though this is now debated.

➤ Induction often means pain relief is needed (especially if a Syntocinon drip is used), as days of pre-labour may be packed into a few hours. Contractions are likely to be longer, more intense and more painful from the start, with shorter intervals than in a spontaneous labour.

➤ The very powerful contractions that may be provoked by induction (see above) may restrict the blood vessels carrying blood – and therefore oxygen – to the placenta and baby, potentially leading to foetal distress. (Adopting some sort of upright posture and leaning forward can help reduce this risk.)

➤ Some commentators believe that induction stresses the mother's system, 'driving' her uterus too hard. The uterus may be overstimulated which can result in it becoming unco-ordinated and the cervix failing to dilate. In the most extreme cases the muscle may go into spasm, causing foetal distress.

➤ Post-partum haemorrhage is more likely – the over-stimulated uterus becomes tired and hence reacts less effectively to natural oxytocin, or similar medical drugs administered in the third stage of labour, that stimulate the delivery of placenta and membranes.

➤ Should the birth turn out to be premature (if the calculation of the EDD was incorrect) the baby is at risk of damage caused by the strong contractions. (The same is true for all babies where the Syntocinon is not administered with the proper degree of care, and/or the baby's condition not properly monitored).

Augmentation (speeding up) of labour

Once a woman is admitted to the maternity unit in established labour, most hospitals impose a relatively strict timetable on how the birth should progress.

Opinions on the time that should be allowed for the three stages of labour vary from doctor to doctor, and from midwife to midwife. Relatively subjective judgements are made on what is considered a 'normal' duration, with the definition of prolonged labour shifting from 36 hours in the '60s to 24 in the '70s to as little as 12 in some cases today, though some professionals still allow much longer.

If the labour falls too far behind whatever schedule is in operation at your hospital (a 'failure to progress'), the policy will be to accelerate the process of childbirth using procedures similar to those used to manage an induced labour.

The expected time for the second stage is generally an hour for first-time mothers, and half an hour for second-time mothers. There is some evidence, however, that two hours and – if the mother is still willing and the baby is not distressed – three hours is quite feasible.

Helping and supporting the mother into more upright, gravity-effective positions may also help her to deliver the baby without the need for medical intervention.

(If there is failure to progress in the second stage, the issue is whether or not to perform an instrumental delivery – see below.)

Augmentation – risks, side effects and concerns:

➤ As above for induction, plus ...
➤ Duration is not a good measure of how well a labour is progressing. A short labour with powerful contractions close together can be more difficult to cope with than a longer one with less intense contractions that are well spaced.
➤ Assuming that foetal monitoring does not indicate any problem with the baby, whether a labour is going on too long is simply a question of how the mother is coping – which only she can judge. This depends in large part on good emotional support, having the individual attention of whoever is with her, being treated kindly and with respect, and feeling in control.

How labour is induced (or augmented)

Note: the first two procedures below relate only to the induction of labour (because a women is past this stage by the time anything called augmentation takes place). Of the four procedures listed, by far the most powerful is the last – the use of Syntocinon. Initial steps are sometimes dispensed with, and often take place largely as a pre-cursor to fitting a Syntocinon drip.

I. SWEEPING THE MEMBRANES
(USED FOR INDUCTION ONLY)

During a vaginal examination, a doctor will move the thin membrane that covers the cervix (this stretches apart as the cervix opens up). This will – in some cases – trigger contractions, in which case the birth may well be a natural one.

Sweeping the membranes – risks, side effects and concerns:
➤ There is an increased risk of infection for mother and for the baby.
➤ It is not very effective if the cervix is not already 'ripe'.
➤ The general effectiveness of the procedure is in doubt.
➤ It can be painful.
➤ The procedure runs the risk of simultaneously breaking the waters (and is said, by some cynics, to be used deliberately by some practitioners in order to do so).
➤ Anecdotal evidence from mothers raises the concern that this procedure may sometimes be performed by 'subterfuge', i.e. mothers are not consulted whether they wish to be induced in any way at all, nor is their consent sought in those terms, but the procedure is carried out during what has been presented as a simple internal examination.

2. APPLICATION OF PROSTAGLANDINS (USED FOR INDUCTION ONLY)

This is a relatively modern procedure. Prostaglandins (hormone-like substances) are applied to the cervix to encourage it to ripen and dilate. They are applied in the form of pessaries or a gel at about twelve hour intervals. Some units believe that two is the maximum number of such applications that is effective, although it is not unknown for more to be administered.

Part of the aim of using prostaglandins is the chance that they may trigger contractions, although the failure rate for induction using prostaglandins alone is around 60% (usually because the cervix is 'unripe' – i.e. not ready to open). However, another reason for using these drugs is that even if they do not succeed in inducing labour, they will make a woman's body more receptive to the subsequent inductive steps (and make such steps less of a shock to the system).

Should the prostaglandins succeed in inducing labour, then it may be that no further medical intervention is necessary.

Prostaglandins – risks, side effects and concerns:
➤ The drugs can irritate the bowels, causing vomiting, diarrhoea or migraine.
➤ They can cause vaginal irritation, pain or an allergic reaction.

3. ARTIFICIAL RUPTURING OF THE MEMBRANES – ARM, OR "BREAKING THE WATERS" (USED FOR AUGMENTATION AND INDUCTION)

In only 12% of cases does a woman's water break spontaneously at the beginning of labour – this usually occurs later, at about 7cm dilation of the cervix.

It has become commonplace to help spontaneous labour along by pre-empting the natural process with the use of ARM. Using a long thin plastic implement with a hook on the end, a doctor or midwife breaks the membranes at the neck of the cervix, allowing the amniotic fluid to escape. This is often carried out at between 2cm and 5cm dilation.

The idea is that by removing the cushion of amniotic fluid, the baby's head weighs down more heavily on the cervix, thus stimulating stronger contractions.

In the case of induction, the procedure does carry with it the possibility that it may trigger labour, and that no further intervention will be necessary. In many such cases, however, ARM is very much merely a precursive step towards the fitting of a Syntocinon drip (see below).

(Aside from ARM's use as a method of augmentation and induction, the procedure is necessary in unusual circumstances to check for traces of meconium (passed by the baby) in the amniotic fluid – a potential sign of distress.)

ARM – risks, side effects and concerns:

➢ This process can lead to much more intense contractions than would naturally be the case and most of the general concerns rehearsed at the start of this section regarding induction and augmentation apply here.

➢ The increased force of contractions often results in the need for pain relief.

➢ The cushion of water protecting the baby's head from the powerful contractions is removed.

➢ Some women find the procedure invasive and uncomfortable.

➢ The procedure may not be successful, but intervention cannot be halted because of the increased risk of infection to mother and baby.

➢ Babies born to mothers whose waters have been broken are more likely to suffer breathing difficulties.

➢ Some commentators claim that use of ARM as a means of augmenting labour has been shown to save only 40–50 minutes of labour, at the cost of increased pain.

➢ With regards to induction, surgical methods (i.e. sweeping the membranes and ARM) have come in for increasing criticism in recent years. A December 1997 report from the Department of Health showed a decrease in the use of ARM in inductions from 55% in 1989–90 to 40% in 1994–95.

4. SYNTOCINON
(USED FOR INDUCTION AND AUGMENTATION)

If all else has failed, the next course of action is to use Syntocinon – a synthetic hormone similar to the contraction-causing oxytocin produced by mother and baby during labour.

The most common way of administering the drug is in increasing strengths by means of an intravenous drip (though an infusion is used in some cases). If the contractions are too much to bear it is possible to ask for the speed of the drip to be adjusted. You may be able to request a mobile drip.

Syntocinon – risks, side effects and concerns:

➢ This is a powerful drug and all of the general concerns outlined at the start of this section regarding induction and augmentation apply, as do the concerns above regarding ARM (which is often performed prior to use of Syntocinon).

➢ Unless a mobile drip or infusion are used, the mother can't move easily.

➢ Syntocinon is associated with neonatal jaundice in babies.

➢ In large doses Syntocinon may cause oedema and high blood pressure.

➢ Use of the drug has been associated with death or brain damage where not administered with proper care.

Alternative forms of induction:

Walking: appears to work by encouraging the baby's head to press down against the cervix, triggering the release of oxytocin.

Sex: semen contains prostaglandins similar to those used in pessary form for artificial induction; you will need to remain lying down for around half an hour.

Nipple stimulation: which releases oxytocin – noticeable results could require keeping this up for as much as an hour three times a day.

Curry or other spicy food: loosening up the bowels is widely believed to trigger the onset of labour.

Castor oil and orange juice: similar effects to curry.

A bath or water pool: some, but by no means all, mothers crave immersion in water just before birth. The effect may be purely psychological.

Homeopathy and acupuncture: acupuncture in particular is reported particularly effective (see chapter *4.02 Complementary medicine & Health practitioners*).

3. EPISIOTOMIES & TEARS

While tears occur in an estimated quarter of births in the UK, an episiotomy – a surgical cut of the perineum designed to ease the passage of the baby – is used in about 20% of cases. Increasingly, small tears have been found to heal better and less painfully without stitches, but episiotomies always need to be stitched, usually with some form of pain relief).

Episiotomies are almost always required for instrumental (forceps or ventouse) births, to make room for the instruments to reach the baby's head (see below).

However, in cases other than those involving instrumental deliveries, there is some debate about the usefulness of episiotomies (a technique which only became widely practised in the 1950s). Such deliveries account for about 9% of all births, and yet, for example, independent midwives almost never find it necessary to carry them out.

Occasionally an episiotomy may be performed without the mother's consent. It is therefore wise if you don't want one to make this absolutely clear both in your birth plan and in person.

Non-instrumental episiotomies may help:

➢ With a baby in a difficult position.
➢ For delivery of a premature baby (whose head will be softer than that of an older one).
➢ With a baby whose head is particularly large.
➢ To end a long labour if mother and baby are over-tired.
➢ To limit damage when tearing has occurred, though the usefulness of this is debated (see below).

Episiotomies and tears – risks, side effects and concerns:

➢ It was thought In some quarters that tears created worse damage than a clean cut but this is now widely questioned – especially given that the cut can be more extensive than a natural tear. Tears are believed by many practitioners to heal as well or possibly better than cuts unless the tear has damaged the underlying muscles – rare in an unforced birth. If the mother is upright the extent of any tear should, in any case, be minimal.
➢ First-degree tears are sometimes left unstitched and seem to heal just as well, if not better, than those that were stitched.
➢ Episiotomies can create long lasting problems, particularly when it comes to sex, if the repair is not good. Causes include scar tissue, a trapped nerve and being sewn up too tightly.

Hints for avoiding the need for an episiotomy, and reducing susceptibility to tearing:

➤ Giving birth in an upright or near upright position means the baby's head is directed towards the vaginal opening rather than straight out at the perineum.

➤ Allowing the baby's head to emerge and retreat at its own pace helps to stretch the perineum gradually. This is easier if no-one is exhorting you to push. (This is an old-fashioned approach, much seen in films, and best avoided.) Progressing gradually is feasible as long as you have sensation in the relevant area to feel what is going on (i.e. if you do not have too much pain relief at this point).

➤ Yoga, stretching exercises, possibly water birth and possibly massaging the perineum from around seven months can help prevent tears. Aromatherapists sometimes recommend specific oils. Calendula is also sometimes suggested afterwards to soothe and aid healing.

➤ Ask not to be washed down with an antiseptic as this removes natural lubrication. A towel or pad soaked in water so hot it is barely touchable brings blood to the perineum and may help, using a fresh one for each contraction. However, some mothers feel this just gets in the way.

4. INSTRUMENTAL DELIVERIES (FORCEPS & VENTOUSE/VACUUM EXTRACTIONS)

If the second stage of labour becomes prolonged, the question begins to emerge whether the natural process alone will be sufficient to deliver the baby: at this stage, the cervix is fully dilated, but the mother's contractions and other efforts have not yet provided sufficient force to push the baby out. The mother may be becoming exhausted, may have lost all sensation (through use of pain relief), or the muscles of the uterus may no longer be functioning efficiently. In such circumstances the risk of foetal distress needs to be monitored with a view to speeding delivery.

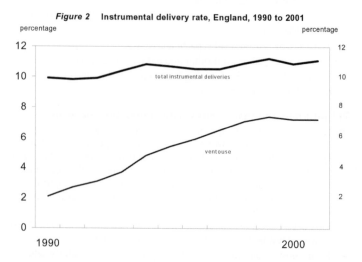

Figure 2 Instrumental delivery rate, England, 1990 to 2001

To aid the birth, forceps or ventouse can be inserted into the uterus, and used by a doctor to manoeuvre the baby into a better position and provide a dragging force to supplement the mothers pushing efforts.

Instrumental deliveries: risks, side effects and concerns:

➤ Both procedures can damage the mother's perineum (and, in rare cases, internal organs).

➤ Both procedures can distress and may hurt the baby; sometimes, the injury is serious.

➤ Of the two practices, ventouse is the less invasive; less likely to cause damage; and less likely to require an episiotomy or cause a tear (and its proportionate use has grown steadily). However, it is also the less likely to succeed, as it affords a less strong grip on the child.

5. CAESAREAN SECTION

About one in five women in the UK now have their baby delivered using this procedure. Of these roughly one third opt to do so well in advance of the birth ('elective' Caesareans), and for the other two thirds the need to do so emerges during labour (so-called 'emergency' Caesareans).

The process involves cutting through the mother's abdominal muscles, usually along the 'bikini line' (lower transverse), to take out the baby. A catheter (tube into the bladder) and glucose drip will probably be necessary, together with either an epidural, spinal, or general anaesthetic. In cases of maternal or foetal problems, the time between decision to go ahead and delivery of the baby should be no more than 30 minutes.

Afterwards there is a four to ten day hospital stay (four if no complications). The full physical recovery period is around six months and occasionally as much as a year. Mothers who undergo emergency Caesareans can take longer to recover psychologically as a result of shock and disappointment.

The frequency of the procedure's use draws regular media attention and concern. The NCT has, since 1998, campaigned against its increasingly widespread use. One survey of consultants found fear of litigation was the primary reason for performing a Caesarean. Recent reports on

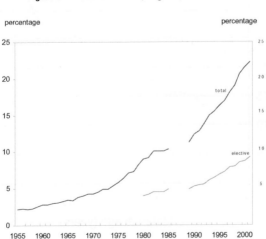

Figure 1   **Caesarean rate, England, 1955 to 2001**

shortages of midwives blame (at least in part) the consequent lower levels of midwife care. The author of a BMJ report of 2001 commented that complications in pregnancy can cause some doctors, especially junior ones, to opt for a Caesarean when alternatives would be safer.

This UK rate of approximately 20% is now comparable to that in the US and some other European countries (such as Italy). This rate compares poorly, though, with the WHO recommended level, and that achieved by the Nordic countries.

Some of the disparity is social. For example, part of the reason why the UK rate has risen is the increasing number of women who request an elective Caesarean. This in itself is controversial – some NHS consultants may refuse to provide a Caesarean unless there is some medical justification, (a Caesarean delivery being considerably more expensive than a normal one).

Another factor linked with the increase is the ageing of mothers. A 25-year old mother has a 15% chance of a Caesarean – at 35 this risk is over 25%.

The recent increase in Caesareans in the UK has not resulted in any demonstrably better outcomes for mothers or babies. Even amongst consultants, half in a survey for a major report published in 2001 thought the current rate to be too high.

There are very few incontrovertible indications for Caesarean Section:

➤ A baby in a transverse position.
➤ Placenta praevia.
➤ Placental abruption.
➤ Prolapsed umbilical cord.
➤ A serious heart condition in the mother.
➤ Kidney disease in the mother.
➤ Real cephalopelvic disproportion (mother's pelvis too small).
➤ Fibroids blocking the cervix.

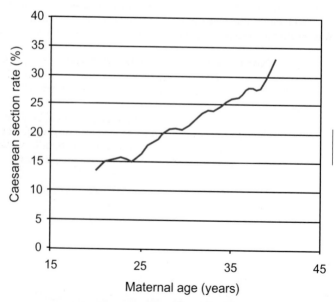

© *National Sentinel Caesarean Section Audit, October 2001*
by permission of the Royal College of Obstetricians & Gynaecologists

The most common reasons for a Caesarean are:
- A previous Caesarean birth (see Vaginal birth after Caesarean (VBAC) below).
- Failure to progress in labour (see Augmentation above).
- Foetal distress (the physical stresses of labour are proving difficult for the baby, indicated by a very rapid heartbeat, or a dramatic drop in foetal heart rate). Judgement of this is not always clear-cut, however, see Section 10, on monitoring, below).
- A breech baby (see Section 6, Breech births, below).

Less clear-cut reasons for a Caesarean section:
- Pre-eclampsia.
- Cephalopelvic disproportion (i.e. a baby's head that is too big for the mother's pelvis). However, the sacrum is actually designed to move out and back during labour, allowing more room for the head, but this can only happen if the mother's weight is supported (standing, squatting, etc). Some midwives believe that there is actually no such thing as CPD, and that it is the adverse effect of the mother lying on her back which is the culprit if a baby cannot get through the mother's pelvis. If you are keen to avoid a Caesarean, it may be possible to agree a trial period of labour with your doctors.
- A mother with herpes.
- To protect the pelvic floor and reduce the risk of prolapse in later life. The anti-Caesarean lobby argues that exercising the pelvic floor muscles both during pregnancy and after birth should improve muscle tone to survive the stretching.
- A mother with diabetes, which can mean the baby is very large.
- A situation where a previous Caesarean or other uterine surgery was carried out with a vertical cut rather than the current horizontal one, because a vertical cut results in weaker muscles and makes a rupture marginally more likely during contractions.

Risks

Caesarean section – possible side effects:
- Infection (of the urinary tract or the scar).
- Post-partum haemorrhaging caused by the uterus not contracting after the delivery. (This is more likely in an elective Caesarean, when the uterus has had no opportunity to contract spontaneously).
- Thrombosis (see below).
- Difficulty moving and therefore looking after a new baby because of problems lifting and finding positions to feed the baby which don't cause pain around the scar; the inability to drive for about six weeks.
- Increased risk of ectopic pregnancy in subsequent pregnancies.
- Greater difficulty conceiving another child.
- The possibility of respiratory distress in the baby who misses out on the squeezing stimulation of the birth canal.
- Backache.
- Depression.
- Flatulence.
- Thrush – to which the antibiotics that you may be prescribed make both you and the baby more vulnerable.
- Pain in subsequent pregnancies as pressure grows on the scar.
- The possibility after multiple Caesareans that the scar fails to heal properly.

THE TINY RISK OF FATAL COMPLICATIONS

The NCT points out that a Caesarean birth carries with it about five times the risk of death than a normal delivery. However, given the extremely high level of safety of a normal birth, it must be born in mind that this increased level of risk is still tiny (about 8 deaths per 100,000 Caesarean deliveries).

This five-times risk estimate includes both emergency and elective Caesareans – the risk of the former being quoted as about nine times that of a normal birth; the latter two to three times.

With emergency Caesareans, as they are by definition given in labours that have become high risk it is perhaps less surprising that such deliveries are more dangerous than a normal birth.

What these figures do emphasise is that where elective Caesareans are concerned, they should not be viewed as an entirely risk-free alternative to a normal delivery. (Five women died resulting from an elective Caesarean in the period 1997–1999).

One of the greatest risks resulting from a Caesarean section is thrombosis – the potentially fatal development of a blood clot. For this reason, it is also now recommended that there should be a strategy to prevent the condition for all women who have a Caesarean Section, and a 2001 study reported a significant fall in its occurrence as a result.

You are at moderate risk of thrombosis after a Caesarean Section if you have two of the following factors (and high risk with three or more):

➢ Aged over 35.
➢ Obese.
➢ Have had over four children.
➢ Have gross varicose veins.
➢ Current infection.
➢ Pre-eclampsia.
➢ More than four days immobility before surgery.
➢ Major current illness.
➢ Emergency Caesarean in labour.

Other high risk factors:

➢ Extended surgery.
➢ Lower-limb paralysis.
➢ Family or personal history of thromboembolic disease.

READING

Caesarean Birth – Deborah Derrick (Your questions answered; NCT Publishing; 1996; £3.50; 1870129873) – *A 64-page guide – research evidence, practical tips and parents' experiences.*

Caesarean Birth in Britain – National Childbirth Trust (A book for health professionals and parents; Middlesex University Press; 1993; £9.95; 1898253005) – *Recommended by the Caesarean Support Network for those who already know a little about the subject.*

Caesarean Experience – Sarah Clement (Pandora; 1992; £7.99; 0044407386) – *A recommended title, particularly for mothers who know they will have to have a Caesarean and will benefit from a bit of advance mental and practical preparation.*

Silent Knife – Nancy Wainer Cohen & Lois J Estner (Caesarean prevention and vaginal birth after Caesarean; Bergin & Garvey; 1983; $29.95; 0897890272) – *A US title recommended by the Caesarean Support Network; there is also a UK edition (£14.99 - 0318174995), but it doesn't seem as readily available.*

The Vaginal Birth After Caesarean (VBAC) Experience – Lynn Baptisti Richards & contributors (Bergin & Garvey; 1987; £15.95; 0897891198) – *A US title recommended by the Caesarean Support Network. Written by a mother who had a vaginal birth after a Caesarean and has compiled similar stories from other mothers.*

USEFUL CONTACTS

Caesarean Support Network, ☎ *(01624) 661269*

A network of contacts, and telephone information service giving practical, non-medical advice for women who have had or expect to have a Caesarean delivery. / *HOURS after 6pm and at weekends; PUBLICATIONS Birth the Caesarean Way (£1.50); Vaginal Birth After Caesarean; useful reading list.*

Vaginal birth after Caesarean (VBAC)

Up until the 1980s it was something of a given that if a woman had had a Caesarean section, then subsequent births should be by the same method. That position changed somewhat during the '80s for a number of factors, in particular the introduction of the 'bikini' cut (rather than the previous vertical cut), which is believed to heal better.

The perception of risk is now sufficiently low (about 0.5% of women suffer a uterine rupture) that most obstetricians are prepared to support women who wish to go for a normal birth having had a Caesarean (and some consider it a safer overall route). Approximately one third of mothers who have had a previous Caesarean have a VBAC, but the rate varies widely between units (from 6% to 64% according to a national audit published in October 2001.

That same audit suggests that a trial labour should be considered for all women who have had a previous Caesarean. However, a 2001 US study of 20,000 births indicated that the risks of a uterine rupture during a VBAC are considerably increased if birth is augmented using prostaglandins. This second study concluded, therefore, that if a VBAC birth is failing to progress for any reason a repeat Caesarean is by far the safest route.

INFORMATION

Vaginal Birth After Caesarean (VBAC), ⌂ *www.vbac.org.uk*

Website run by the home birth co-ordinator of the NCT with useful information (including for those wanting to plan on a repeat Caesarean) and links.

Spontaneous labour before a planned Caesarean

For Caesareans which are not carried out for a medical emergency (i.e. elective Caesareans or Caesareans for medical reasons which are known about well in advance), it is normal to book the operation for a specific time, irrespective of whether or not you have begun to feel any contractions.

There is evidence, however, to show that a period of spontaneous labour can be helpful, even in a Caesarean delivery. The onset of normal labour indicates that the baby is ready to be born and certain hormones are released which help the baby's lungs to start drying out, and stimulate the liver, kidneys and digestive system to start working independently. Allowing labour to progress to at least 4cm dilation also seems to help avoid slow subsequent labours.

6. BREECH BIRTHS

Up to a quarter of all babies are breech – i.e. head up – at 30 weeks, but there is still room for them to somersault. Only 3-4% of babies are still in the breech position at birth.

A first baby may change position at any time up to 32 weeks. A second or subsequent pregnancy may change position slightly later, as the uterus has already stretched a little and the baby has more room for manoeuvre.

Breech is a less safe position for birth than vertex (head down), because if the head is not delivered immediately after the body emerges, then brain damage may occur. Overall such births carry a higher risk to the baby of cerebral palsy or death.

Though a breech baby may be delivered vaginally, this is not always possible, nor are all hospitals happy to try (only 10–20% of breech births are delivered vaginally). Quite how much less safe a breech birth is than a normal birth has been the matter of some debate and whether the standard option of a Caesarean delivery is significantly safer than a vaginal birth is not entirely clear. According to a study published in the Lancet in 2000, a Caesarean delivery is safer for the baby (saving one in 29 of such deliveries from death), but slightly more risky for the mother.

The most common attempted solution to forestall a breech delivery is ECV (see below). This is dependent on your consultant (or a consultant at your hospital) having the 'knack' of turning the baby. Alternative ways of encouraging a breech baby to turn include complementary treatments such as acupuncture and moxibustion (a heat treatment, applied on acupuncture points, that involves burning a herb called moxa), homeopathy, and postural exercises for the mother which can encourage the baby to turn (though exercises are more effective if started fairly early on in pregnancy).

If you want to deliver a breech baby vaginally you may have to look for a consultant or an experienced NHS or independent midwife with relevant experience.

EXTERNAL CEPHALIC VERSION (ECV)

Some consultants will attempt to turn a breech baby by ECV. This involves the consultant (a few midwives also have this skill) persuading the baby to turn by manipulating the mother's abdomen. Various trials have indicated that two out of three babies can be turned in this way and will stay head down. The mother experiences a churning sensation – seldom considered pleasant. The process, however, offers the prospect of a safer birth, and one that is more likely to occur naturally.

There is thought to be a small chance of danger to the baby, though this is reduced with the skill of the practitioner. Clumsy manipulation can detach the placenta, or cause the umbilical cord to become looped around the baby's neck.

Sometimes drugs are used to relax the mother's abdomen, but some reports say this should not be necessary unless ECV has already been tried unsuccessfully. Some practitioners regard the mother's apparent comfort or discomfort as a useful indictor of how far it is safe to go with the procedure.

Success rates in one study were reported as 58%. However, it is thought that the point in the pregnancy at which the EVC happens may be key to the outcome and it is not clear when the best time is. Some practitioners act after 32 weeks. Some wait until after 37 weeks to give the baby more time to reposition itself of its own accord. (It also reduces the likelihood of the baby reverting to a breech presentation afterwards.) Other practitioners wait until labour itself when the baby can be more willing to move, and problems (for example with the placenta) can be handled on the spot.

7. 'PHYSIOLOGICAL' VS 'MANAGED' THIRD STAGE OF LABOUR

After the birth of the baby, in a natural ('physiological') birth, the umbilical cord joining baby and placenta gradually ceases pulsating as the baby becomes totally self-supporting. The placenta remains in the womb until after this has happened, and the continuing contractions of the uterus squeeze it from its place on the uterine wall, to be expelled some time after the baby is born.

This process may involve a loss of blood, particularly if drugs were given earlier in labour to stimulate the uterus (see above under *Managed labours*). In some cases this blood loss is sufficiently severe (post-partum haemorrhaging) that – if ignored – it threatens the mother's life. As a safeguard against this, it has become the norm to manage this final stage of labour with synthetic hormones which act as a prophylactic against any such rapid, excessive blood loss.

An injection of Syntocinon or Syntometrine (a combination of Syntocinon with ergometrine) is usually given in the mother's thigh as soon as the baby's first shoulder appears. This works immediately to separate the placenta from the uterus and shortly afterwards causes heavy contractions which cut off the blood vessels at the site where the placenta was attached. The placenta has to be removed swiftly or it will be trapped inside the mother as the uterus contracts and the cervix closes (a retained placenta) and the attending midwife usually pulls it out swiftly by the cord.

Increasingly it is being questioned whether the blanket-safeguard of always managing the third stage of labour is really justified, especially where no augmentation of labour has taken place. A routine hormone-injection is practically never used with home-births, nor at the small private hospitals with a midwife-led emphasis (including The Birth Centre and The St John & St Elizabeth).

It is argued that as long as a very careful eye is kept on the mother to see that she is not losing blood, there is time to react to any haemorrhaging, while the majority of births can derive the benefits of a natural (physiological) conclusion.

Possible contraindications for a physiological third stage:
➢ Anaemia in pregnancy, sometimes linked with…
➢ Antenatal bleeding.
➢ Blood clotting problems.
➢ Previous problems with this stage in labour.
➢ Multiple pregnancy.
➢ The cord wrapped around the baby's neck.
➢ A labour in which Syntocinon (or equivalent) has been given, as this is often associated with post-partum haemorrhage.

A managed third stage may also be necessary after a long and difficult labour (or a short, very intense 'precipitate' labour) when the mother's own hormones may not be functioning fully.

Advantages cited for a physiological third stage:
➢ The umbilical cord can be left to cease pulsating before it is cut. This preserves a 'lifeline' if the baby is slow to breathe independently for some reason.
➢ There is a reduced risk of a retained placenta.
➢ There appears to be less pain.

➤ The flood of spirit-raising endorphins (believed, by some, to be of great benefit) secreted immediately after even long births can flow into the baby via the uncut cord.

➤ A recent study has reported that, particularly for premature babies, waiting just one minute before clamping the cord improves the baby's chance of survival.

Managed third stage – risks, problems and side effects:

➤ Syntometrine causes blood to pump rapidly through the umbilical cord and, unless clamped, the baby can receive too much blood, which creates a stress on the baby's system. Jaundice may ensue as the baby's system tries to break down the excess red blood cells.

➤ If the cord is clamped too early there is the possibility of leaving the baby short of blood, thought to be a cause of breathing problems in newborns. This is a particularly important issue for premature or low birthweight babies.

➤ Syntometrine can cause side effects for the mother such as a rise in blood pressure or vomiting.

➤ If the Syntometrine does not have the desired effect, the natural mechanisms will no longer work and the placenta will probably have to be pulled out and may leave behind parts which will have to be removed manually, usually under a topped up epidural or general anaesthetic. This problem is rarer when the third stage occurs spontaneously.

Natural methods for aiding separation of the placenta:

➤ Babies who are put to the breast shortly after the delivery help stimulate the mother's natural oxytocin release which helps the placenta separate naturally.

➤ Kneeling or standing makes use of gravity to help expulsion of the placenta.

➤ Nipple stimulation or massage of the uterus.

READING

[Booklet] **The Third Stage of Labour** (NCT Publishing; 1993; 75p) – *A basic outline of the issues.*

8. OPTIONS FOR PAIN RELIEF

Although in the later stages of labour, pain may be caused by the stretching required to get the baby out, much of the pain in labour is caused by the contractions of the uterus, likened by some to extreme period pain. The resulting sensations are usually unbelievably intense, although this is not the case for everyone and even the location of the pain can vary enormously from woman to woman, and birth to birth.

Given that experts increasingly believe that pain is not an absolute experience but to a degree a subjective one, this is not surprising and highlights the role of beliefs, carers and surroundings in a mother's perception of what she his feeling.

Some community midwives reckon that if left to proceed naturally, in a relaxed environment almost three-quarters of women would not need pain relief. Whatever the validity of this claim, at present over 80% of women in the UK do, in fact, use some form of anaesthetic or analgesic in labour.

Rather than being prescribed a particular drug, it is standard practice for mothers to be offered a range of methods of pain relief from which to make their own choice. Each option carries with it its own pros and cons.

The breakdown of pain relief methods used in childbirth given by the Department of Health for the year 1994–95 was as follows: general anaesthetic 6% of deliveries; epidural 20%; other spinal anaesthetic 5%; and 'other' – mainly pethidine, or gas and air – 53%. (These figures relate to the *prime* form of pain relief used – it is, though, common to mix and match a combination of options).

Some people supplement these options with complementary therapies, and others again recommend mind-over-matter, putting in training prior to birth using methods such as self-hypnosis.

Oddly the effectiveness of different forms of pain relief may differ for the same woman in different labours, so predicting what will work in advance is almost impossible.

Medical pain relief can slow down labour, so if the cervix is close to fully dilated (7cm or more) the less pain relief the better. This is not only because it will lengthen the labour, but also because drugs used close to the delivery are more likely to remain in the baby's system after birth – a time when the newborn does not have the help of the placenta in excreting them.

In addition concerns have been voiced (for example by the famous obstetrician Michel Odent) about potential correlations between the use of painkilling drugs in labour and a risk of drug addiction in the baby once an adult. More research is clearly required into this.

Your perception of pain can be affected by:

➤ Whether you are being cared for by someone you know. A study by Queen Charlotte's Hospital found a decrease in the use of pain relief by those cared for by midwives known to them versus those cared for by midwives who were strangers to them.

➤ 'Macho' birth tales, from other mothers or in the media.

➤ Whether you understand what is happening.

➤ Your confidence in your ability to manage.

➤ Your ability to relax. Tension decreases endorphins – natural morphine-like substances – in the muscles. Heightened tension produces an adrenaline-like substance which is a pain transmitter.

➤ Your physical position.

➤ Whether the labour has been induced or accelerated.

➤ Whether your periods are painful or not. If they are not, you are less likely to find labour painful.

➤ Whether you use painkillers regularly. There is some evidence that the body adapts to this by increasing levels or functionality of pain transmitters.

The following methods of pain relief are covered below:

➤ Gas and air (brand name Entonox).

➤ Pethidine.

➤ Epidural.

➤ TENS.

➤ Water.

➤ Alternatives, including breathing.

READING

Childbirth Doesn't Have to Hurt – Nikki Bradford, Geoffrey Chamberlain (20 steps to an easier labour; Vega Books; 2002; £7.99; 1843336170) – *An assessment of the five key options, which the author categorises as: spinal injections, such as epidurals; a trained birth partner or doula which has been shown to make birth faster and to reduce the need for pain-relieving drugs; aromatherapy; acupuncture; and water injections in the base of the spine (common in Scandinavia).*

Labour and Birth in Water (NCT; £2.50) – *One of a series of NCT brochures, each of approximately 20 pages.* / NCT Maternity Sales (0870) 112 1120, www.nctms.co.uk.

Labour Pain – Nicky Wesson (A natural approach to easing delivery; Vermilion; 1999; £7.99; 0091817226) – *Real life stories, with an emphasis on how fear and psychology affect pain and pain relief options.*

Pain Relief in Childbirth – Nikki Bradford & Geoffrey Chamberlain (HarperCollins; 1995; £6.99; 0006383998) – *Lots of useful information exploring all forms of pain relief in detail; a sensible explanation of the physiology of birth, including the experience from the point of view of the baby; tips on dealing with any postnatal pain.*

[Tape] Relaxation for pregnancy and childbirth (NCT; £6.50) / NCT Maternity Sales, (0870) 112 1120, www.nctms.co.uk.

Gas and air (brand name Entonox)

Equal amounts of nitrous oxide (laughing gas) and oxygen, self-administered by inhaling deeply from a mouthpiece or mask at the beginning of a contraction. (The effect according to Nikki Bradford, author of *Pain Relief in Childbirth*, is a detachment equivalent to two or three large gins.) The effect lasts from around 20 seconds after inhalation for around 40 to 45 seconds. (It can be a good idea to try gas and air out antenatally to check that it doesn't make you nauseous.)

Pros:
➢ Few or no short or long-term side effects.
➢ Can be self-administered.
➢ Does not cross the placenta (being insoluble it is almost totally excreted by the lungs).
➢ Effective for most mothers.
➢ Works extremely quickly.
➢ Does not inhibit endorphin production.
➢ Can be combined with changing positions, movement and can be used in a variety of birth positions.

Cons:
➢ Rarely works for more than an hour-and-a-half to two hours and if used for a long period can cause sensations of nausea and dizziness.
➢ Is not helpful with great pain.
➢ Overuse can alter consciousness.
➢ If the mother starts to breathe rapidly and shallowly, this can reduce the oxygen supply for herself and the baby.
➢ Prolonged use in second-stage can be counter-productive.

Pethidine

A narcotic anti-spasmodic related to morphine, usually administered by injection, sometimes in conjunction with tranquillisers. It takes around 20 minutes to work once given. Pethidine is not technically a painkiller but may distance the mother from the sensation of pain, often by affecting the awareness of passing time. However, there is a debate about when it is most useful, with a suggestion that it is unhelpful if given very late in labour and that it is more effective and less potentially damaging if not combined with tranquillisers.

There is some argument about when pethidine affects the baby least. Usually it is thought best not given in the last two to four hours of labour, but there is evidence that giving it early in labour may be worse because then there is time for the drug to build up in the baby's system. Some commentators feel the antidotes that are sometimes given can also cause problems because the baby's system will be too immature to excrete these drugs. Doses have been much reduced since the '60s and early '70s and are seldom over 25mg.

Pros:
➤ Easily administered.
➤ A muscle relaxant, it helps the cervix dilate.
➤ Does not inhibit endorphin production.
➤ Can help women sleep during slow labours so they have more energy for later.

Cons:
➤ Crosses the placenta. Some babies (particularly premature ones), whose mothers have been given pethidine and/or an antidote drug need resuscitation because it can impair their ability to breathe and to feed.
➤ Babies whose mothers have been given pethidine may be more difficult to settle.
➤ It is only found effective by an estimated 25% of mothers.
➤ Nausea is a common side effect, affecting about one in three mothers, and the drug can trigger feelings of fear or paranoia.
➤ Because of the change in consciousness which the drug induces, it can interrupt the rhythm of labour and slow it down.
➤ If given with tranquillisers or drugs to combat nausea, the drug may make the mother particularly drowsy (it makes an estimated 80% of women drowsy anyway), and she may lose her sense of her role in the birth. Further intervention is then more likely.
➤ In high doses, pethidine may depress breathing.
➤ In less than 1% of women, the drug may cause hallucinations – these may or may not be pleasant.

Epidural

Nationwide, about one woman in four has an epidural in labour. Usage is higher for first deliveries.

A needle is inserted into the epidural space: i.e. in between the dura (the protective membranes surrounding the vertebrae). Anaesthetic is fed in via the needle – either continuously, or with top-ups every two hours or so – via a thin plastic tube inserted at the site.

The process takes a skilled anaesthetist 10–20 minutes to set up; it then takes another 10 minutes or so to take effect. An epidural can numb from the breasts down or just from the abdomen down.

Some hospitals offer 'mobile' or 'low-dose' epidurals which do not totally numb the legs (a 'high block') allowing the woman to retain a fair degree of mobility and avoid the need for a catheter (tube) into the bladder. However, judging the correct amount of anaesthetic can be tricky, and a mobile epidural must be given earlier than a standard epidural. and the procedure can make walking around difficult – the stand which moves with the mother may behave something like a supermarket trolley – hardly ideal, particularly when the driver is not in complete control of her legs.

Some epidurals are self-administered, allowing the woman to 'top them up' according to her own perception of how much pain relief she requires.

Later in labour a 'low block', affecting the vaginal area, can be given. Recovery takes around six hours.

Pros:

➤ The most effective form of pain relief available, epidurals were rated highly by 75% of users in one survey – some women saying they felt no pain at all.

➤ Useful in a long labour, allowing the mother to rest or even sleep (which may encourage dilation).

➤ Reduces the level of stress-related hormones in the mother that could cross to the baby.

➤ The mother can remain awake during Caesareans and hold and even feed the baby very soon after.

➤ If well-timed, an epidural can help with pain relief but be planned to wear off in time for the mother to help with pushing; then topped up again if required during any episiotomy repair.

➤ Epidurals can be useful when babies are breech or occipito posterior, when if the mother has full sensation there is likely to be an urge to push before the cervix is fully dilated.

➤ Helpful throughout labour if the mother has significantly raised blood pressure (epidurals reduce blood pressure).

Cons:

➤ May not be available on demand if the anaesthetists are otherwise engaged.

➤ The anaesthetic, a cocaine derivative, crosses the placenta. The drug can cause babies to be less alert and suffer breathing and sucking problems. Decreased muscle tone, strength and less responsiveness to human voices have also been noted. In the US, where different disclosure rules apply, other potential problems have been noted.

➤ Because the epidural paralyses the muscles of the pelvis it usually slows down contractions in the second stage of labour. As a result, labour tends to be longer and further drugs may be used to speed it up.

➤ Around 5% of mothers find epidurals do not work for them.

➤ Unless timed to wear off at just the right time, the procedure usually immobilises the mother and can affect the pelvic floor muscles to the extent that episiotomy and/or an instrumental delivery is required for the birth.

➤ The effect of the drug means an intravenous drip has to be placed in the mother's arm before the epidural is put in place. Because of the potential effect on the baby, constant foetal monitoring is required. Also, because sensation is removed from the bladder a catheter is usually fitted. The mother's ability to move around is thus significantly impaired.

➤ It reduces the mother's production of oxytocin which stimulates the uterus to contract, often resulting in the need for further drug use.

➤ The effect on the muscles appears to increase the likelihood of the baby failing to move into a suitable position by removing the natural stimulus for the baby's head to turn in the pelvic canal (an important process). It also reduces the mother's urge to push.

➤ If the dura is accidentally punctured, this reduces the amount of fluid in which the brain floats. Result: a crashing headache for three days to a fortnight. Some sources say that this occurs in one in 100 cases – others say that it is relatively unknown.

➤ Epidurals may result in a more irritable baby after birth for anything from 48 hours to six weeks.

➤ Epidurals that do not offer complete cover can focus pain in a particular patch of the body.

➤ Some research suggests that epidurals double the likelihood of Caesarean delivery, especially if given before 5cm dilation.
➤ The drug used may affect the flow of oxygen to the baby (perhaps why some epidural babies are born tinged slightly blue). On the other hand, other studies indicate that used correctly the supply of oxygen will actually be better than if the mother was in a lot of pain.

TENS (transcutaneous electrical nerve stimulation)

(For related information and suppliers of TENS machines see chapter 1.06 Birth equipment.)

Nobody knows exactly why TENS works.

The system consists of four electrodes attached to a tiny battery taped to the mother's back and connected to a push-button handset. The electrodes pass a small electric current in the area of the pain.

It seems the impulses stimulate the production of endorphins – natural painkillers. The effect seems to be cumulative, so TENS works best if used continuously from the onset of labour. It is also believed that by stimulating the nerve system which carries pain messages to the brain, it somehow jams the system and stops sensation.

Pros:
➤ It takes the edge off the pain.
➤ The mother controls the pain relief.

Cons:
➤ It doesn't work for everyone.
➤ It is only effective if used from early in labour.
➤ It does not remove pain completely.

Water

(For suppliers of birth pools and more information regarding water births, including videos, see chapter 1.06 Birth equipment.)

Pain relief with water can take the form of: a birthing pool for total immersion; a shower; an ordinary bath; or even just the sound of water.

This method of pain relief is said to work by relaxing the mother, who is then more likely to produce endorphins, the body's natural painkillers. There are also claims that it improves the blood supply to the uterus, and – by reducing the woman's gravity – helps head off fatigue.

Pros:
➤ No side effects for either mother or baby.
➤ Believed to offer a wide range of advantages primarily brought about by increased relaxation.
➤ Helpful in supporting the mother in an upright position.

Cons:
➤ Can slow down progress if used before 5cm dilation.
➤ Worries some midwives and doctors.
➤ Can be difficult to guarantee if hospital only has one birth pool and/or staff who prefer not to use water for birth – you really are much better off with a midwife with experience who feels capable of handling a water birth.

9. ALTERNATIVE FORMS OF PAIN RELIEF

In addition to the more conventional forms of pain relief, you may wish to consider the following.

The following alternative methods of pain relief are covered below:

➢ Support.
➢ Breathing.
➢ Massage.
➢ Hypnosis, self-hypnosis and autogenic training.
➢ Acupuncture.

Support of a sympathetic birth-attendant, family member or close friend

This has been shown in studies to reduce the need for pain relief. Some think it also can shorten labour and – as acknowledged by an influential October 2001 audit of maternity practice – continuous support reduces the likelihood of Caesarean Section.

Breathing

As taught in many antenatal classes, controlled breathing is a very effective method for reducing tension and increasing relaxation.

Pros:

➢ It can offer a sense of control during pain and reduce tension.
➢ With experienced birth attendants, it can be very effective.
➢ It can be combined with other forms of pain relief.

Cons:

➢ Effectiveness depends on the mental attitude of the individual mother and whether she has practised the technique before the birth.

Massage

(For more information on practitioners who can help with this see section 4.02, Health Practitioners). Rubbing the mother's back during labour can be soothing, help relax tense muscles, and induce a relaxed frame of mind.

Pros:

➢ Found in some research to be as effective as pethidine for pain relief.

Cons:

➢ Not all women like to be touched in labour.
➢ Requires a willing, and to a lesser extent skilled, practitioner.

Hypnosis, self-hypnosis and autogenic training

(For more information on practitioners. courses and tapes to learn self-hypnosis, see section 1.04, Antenatal Classes). An element of 'mind over matter' features in most antenatal preparation. Hypnosis and autogenic training are accepted by some but not all medical practitioners.

Pros:

➢ Some US research on autogenic training found more than 70% of users found the technique good or very good for pain relief.
➢ No known side effects.

➤ Controlled by the mother.

Cons:
➤ Depends on the mental attitude of the individual woman and how effectively she has been taught.
➤ For best results practice needs to be started at least two (and for some mothers up to six) months before the birth.

Acupuncture

(*For more information and practitioners see section 4.02, Health Practitioners*). Inserting fine needles into specified acupuncture points can – it is claimed – help the body act more effectively. The procedure can take up to an hour to take full effect and continue working for an hour with beneficial effects for up to 24 hours. The effect can be 'topped-up'.

Pros:
➤ Can help regulate irregular contractions.
➤ Takes the edge off pain – in some cases reducing it significantly.

Cons:
➤ Requires a skilled practitioner.
➤ Does not work for everyone.

10. ELECTRONIC FOETAL MONITORING (EFM) & ROUTINE CONTINUOUS ELECTRONIC FOETAL MONITORING (RCEFM)

The principal way of checking the wellbeing of babies in the womb is by monitoring their heartbeats. The methodology for doing so is called cardiotocographic monitoring (CTG), often referred to as electronic foetal monitoring (EFM).

A reading is generally taken over a period of 20–30 minutes. Carers are looking for a pattern whereby a steady 'base' reading (140 beats per minute would be typical) is punctuated by periods of 'accelerations' (up to around 160 beats per minute), usually coinciding with contractions. Such a pattern suggests that the foetus is in good condition, and has sufficient reserves to meet any difficulties the birth may present. Deviations from this norm may indicate a problem.

A period of monitoring using CTG (see below) has become practically mandatory on admission to hospital in labour. This provides carers with a baseline reading of the baby's heartbeat and of the uterine contractions.

Intermittent readings are then taken throughout most labours on an 'ad hoc' basis. If carers become concerned about how the baby is coping, however – or if an epidural has been administered – it is routine for monitoring to become continuous (RCEFM).

Those committed to the ability to remain mobile in birth dislike the restrictions on movement caused by most forms of monitoring. As a separate issue, the benefits of monitoring both when it is used routinely and on a continuous basis are debated.

Types of monitor:
Typical CTG monitors: two straps something like airline seat-belts (but larger and heavier) are placed over the mother's abdomen, effec-

tively immobilising her. One belt measures foetal heart rate and the other measures the intensity and frequency of uterine contractions.

Hand-held monitors: can also measure the foetal heart rate, but because their use is more labour intensive these monitors are generally only used for brief checks.

Scalp electrode monitoring: primarily used where there are significant concerns about the foetus – an electrode on the end of a spiral or s-shaped hook is screwed into the baby's scalp. Fitting the scalp electrodes will involve breaking the mother's waters using ARM (if they have not already broken). When used with foetal blood sampling this method is thought the most accurate way to assess the baby's wellbeing.

Monitoring – risks, side effects and concerns:

➤ Because the monitoring belts of the most commonly used monitors are relatively clumsy instruments that fall off easily, midwives like women to stay still and lie back so they can get a good reading. This can be very uncomfortable for any woman in labour (sympathetic midwives may agree that you sit upright or lie on your side), and for those keen on active birth imposes significant restrictions on mobility. Scalp monitoring is particularly problematic in this regard as the hook can easily fall out if the mother is mobile.

➤ One concern is that by requiring a mother to lie down for monitoring, pressure on the main blood vessels to the uterus could interfere with the blood supply to the placenta, so causing the very foetal distress such monitoring aims to detect.

Routine continuous monitoring – risks, side effects and concerns:

➤ Interpreting the results of foetal monitoring, (especially under stressful or complicated conditions) requires a fair degree of skill. On the principle that 'a little knowledge is a dangerous thing', the concern has been raised that the presence of a continuous, difficult-to-interpret stream of data tends to panic doctors (especially junior ones) into action where, in fact, none is justified. Intermittent monitoring is less likely than continuous monitoring to wrongly diagnose a healthy baby as being distressed.

➤ Monitoring can encourage attendants to concentrate on the machine, not the mother.

➤ Independently of other factors, routine monitoring has been found to increase the likelihood of an instrumental delivery. According to natural childbirth campaigner Sheila Kitzinger, continuous monitoring increases the rate of Caesareans by 160%.

➤ A major, oft-cited trial in the US showed that continuous foetal monitoring does not help and may actually hinder the outcome of labour for the baby. Notwithstanding this, the vast majority of labour units remain committed to its use.

11. BIRTH POSITIONS

Active birth is a term coined in the '70s to describe labour in which the mother is actively involved and gives birth in an upright position, with the option of changing position as desired – as opposed to the then 'orthodox' position of lying on one's back.

It is claimed that, historically, upright birth was only abandoned by women when doctors became involved with birth, obstetric forceps were invented and the practitioner needed to see what was going on. Lying on your back may still be urged if your midwife is not used to judging labour in any other position.

Giving birth on your back means:
➢ Interfering with the blood flow, including to the placenta.
➢ Working against the natural forward-tilting contractions of the uterus.
➢ Increasing pain because the baby's weight increases pressure on the sacral nerves.
➢ Pushing the baby out without the aid of gravity, upwards over the tailbone. This is much harder work and more likely to cause tearing and complications.

Giving birth in a sitting position means:
➢ Natural movement of the sacrum and coccyx are restricted.

Giving birth in an unrestricted upright position means:
➢ The force of gravity can help the baby down.
➢ In between contractions the baby's head will continue to press downwards, so continuing to stimulate the cervix to dilate.
➢ An upright or forward-leaning position demands less effort from the uterus as it contracts and seems to result in more regular and more powerful contractions. This means both more efficient dilation and more complete rest between contractions.
➢ The risk of tearing is reduced.
➢ Squatting is reported to open the pelvis, increasing its internal proportions by anything from 10% to 30% more than lying down.
➢ Some research suggests that babies born in an 'active' birth suffer less foetal distress and appear to be more alert.
➢ Mothers who take positive control over the birth, as happens in an upright birth, are reported to need less intervention and less pain relief.

Responding to a 1995 questionnaire most hospitals reported that active birth is accepted, though details varied. Your idea of an active birth and that of your hospital may differ. If this is an important issue for you, ask plenty of questions of your carers.

12. OTHER ISSUES

Antenatal monitoring

Screening creates the potential for worry and stress – an argument in favour of keeping it limited – and the usefulness of a number of routinely performed antenatal tests is questioned. It is now known, for example, that weight gain is not a significant indicator of problems in pregnancy, yet mothers continue to be weighed.

Furthermore, any test can miss some cases of abnormality and raise false alarms in others. The Audit Commission questioned in 1997 whether public money was being wasted by rather mindless antenatal testing.

Cervical stitches

A cervical stitch may be offered to a woman who has a damaged cervix. It is designed to help hold the foetus in place and to avoid a miscarriage.

Some observers, though, believe the risks of surgery and of actually stimulating early labour with the procedure outweigh the possible benefits for those who have not already had a miscarriage.

USEFUL CONTACTS

Miscarriage Association, ☎ *(01924) 200799*
🖰 *www.miscarriageassociation.org.uk*
The organisation provides a relevant leaflet, and can also offer non-expert advice to women who are considering whether such a measure is appropriate. / *HOURS Mon-Fri 9am-4pm, or answerphone; PUBLICATIONS The Cervical Stitch.*

Eating during labour

Some hospitals argue against mothers eating in labour on the grounds that if she eats, there is a risk of inhaling her own vomit should she need a general anaesthetic. This is a much-debated topic, with some commentators saying that eating is only a problem if the anaesthetic is not properly carried out. Moreover they assert that food is being denied at the very time of what is probably the hardest physical job of a woman's life, making it difficult for her muscles to work efficiently.

A dextrose drip is sometimes offered as a substitute for food, but the sugar can enter the baby's bloodstream, who will then experience a sharp drop in blood sugar levels after birth, giving cause for concern – see below.

Eating may also not be allowed if pethidine has been given.

If you do wish to eat in labour, complex carbohydrates like bread or plain biscuits are best, as they offer slow energy release, as do dried or cooked fruits. Plain water or herb tea is best to drink. Honey is also sometimes suggested for energy.

Vitamin K

Vitamin K prevents haemorrhaging and is administered to babies because they are born without it. It is considered particularly relevant for premature babies and those born by forceps or Caesarean section.

Some practitioners feel it is also important for breast-fed babies who would not otherwise reach the adult levels of the vitamin for a week (they may also be given extra doses at around a week old, and again at four to six weeks). Bottle-fed babies are in the opposite situation – formula milk is vitamin K fortified and the level of vitamin K in the blood of babies fed exclusively on formula can reach eight times those of an adult.

Though there is some debate (and little consensus) about whether the routine use of vitamin K is really justified, (and the usual element of dissent in intervening in the 'natural' course of things), the chief area of concern is the form in which it should be administered.

Oral versus injection:

➤ Some hospitals offer the vitamin orally which some people consider less of a shock for a newborn than an injection. The injection is considered more effective, however.

➤ The injection has been implicated in some research into child cancer, although this research did not cover the oral form.

Blood sugar (glucose) tests

Very low levels of glucose in a baby's blood can lead to loss of consciousness and then brain damage. A test for low blood sugar is considered particularly important for: premature babies; large babies; babies who did not breathe at birth; and babies whose mother has diabetes.

The test involves a heel-prick blood test which, though in no sense seriously harmful, causes real pain to babies and can be very distressing for their mothers.

There is a debate about the usefulness of this test in certain circumstances. NCT research highlights that babies – especially full-term babies – are not reliant on glucose alone for energy. The technology used for the test is often inaccurate, and there is little agreement on what constitutes a low glucose level.

If your hospital has a policy on how often your baby should feed, the test may be carried out without any specific indication of its need. If the glucose level is judged low, formula or dextrose solution will be given. Parents who consider that breast milk is the best bet for a newborn, and best given exclusively, may wish to query this process.

13. HOW TO MAKE A COMPLAINT ABOUT YOUR CARE

Complaining at the time

This section is primarily concerned with complaints after you have given birth.

Prevention is, of course, much better than cure and heading difficulties off before or as they arise – if possible – is clearly the best option. That said, complaining when you are pregnant can be more difficult than after the birth because you may still be dependent on the very system you feel is misfiring and you may feel that being branded as difficult will compromise your standing with carers you need to rely on.

In the situation where you feel the personal style of a particular midwife is particularly unsympathetic, consider taking one of her colleagues aside (or speaking to the supervisor, see below) and asking to be looked after by someone else. Most midwives are professionals who understand that personality clashes do occur from time to time and *should* have no problem with finding you a substitute, if one is available. The same is true of doctors, but – because doctors on a given maternity unit are thinner on the ground than midwives – it may be a case of Hobson's choice.

As with any disagreement, it's best to try and take your complaint to the top. If the issue is an obstetric one this is usually difficult: the consultant in charge of the unit will often be absent or hard to contact. When it comes to midwifery issues, though, the supervisor of midwives is comparatively more accessible and in all but the smallest units there should be one on duty, 24 hours a day.

Complaining in retrospect

If, on reflection, you feel let down by the care that you received during pregnancy or at the birth, consider making a formal complaint.

You may feel too tired immediately after the birth to be able to face making a fuss: there is a natural (and not necessarily unhealthy) tendency to let bygones be bygones. However, if you feel your situation really was handled badly, as your energy returns dissatisfaction may reassert itself. Making a complaint is not necessarily a negative activity – it can help in the process of coming to terms with whatever happened and an explanation and/or apology can do something towards making any painful memories easier to bear. If the problem was a serious one, making a complaint may also improve the situation for mothers coming after you.

Within the NHS, there is a three-month time limit for registering a complaint. The system for doing this is complicated so you may well need help.

You can begin either by contacting a CHC (see below) or the local health authority. However, some are more helpful than others and a better starting point is probably Action for Victims of Medical Accidents (AVMA – see listings) which publishes a useful booklet on what to do. One of the association's caseworkers may be able to explain to you what should have been explained to you at the time to help in phrasing your complaint.

The earlier you lodge a complaint the better. It is also a good idea to make a note as soon as possible of exactly what you remember happening, together with dates and times. Be prepared for quite a slog, though. It can take as long as three years to conclude a complaint, and during that time you may need outside help to advise you (possibly from the local Community Health Council, local and national NCT, or AIMS – see below for relevant organisations).

COMMUNITY HEALTH COUNCILS (CHCS)

These are the NHS users' watchdogs. Your local CHC should be able to offer help making a complaint about a hospital and obtaining an apology, a detailed answer to each part of your complaint, an offer of a meeting if appropriate, and details of any action taken to avoid the problem happening again.

COMPLAINT ABOUT AN NHS HOSPITAL

If your complaint is specifically about a hospital you should write to the chief executive of that hospital.

You might also like to send a copy to the hospital's Maternity Services Liaison Committee (MSLC), who are keen to hear comments from pregnant women and new mothers with a view to identifying areas of possible improvement. MSLCs are the forums where all those involved in planning and delivering maternity services in a particular area meet, co-ordinate and plan. There is often an NCT representative. If you have a complaint, informing the committee can be a way of encouraging change. Meetings are open to the public, or you can write to the chair of the committee. Details regarding contacting the committee should be available from your local hospital.

COMPLAINT ABOUT A PRIVATE HOSPITAL

If you need to take issue with your care at a private hospital or service you can contact the organisation itself, but there is also now a new regulatory body – the NCSC – who are the prime point of contact in such cases (see below).

COMPLAINT ABOUT A GP

Complaints about GP breaches of contract have to be made through the health authority complaints department. Those about professional misconduct of medical staff must be made to the General Medical Council.

It is a good idea to send copies of your complaint to your local Supervisor of Midwifery and anyone else you think it would be useful to inform. This helps prevent it getting lost. As with complaining about a hospital, it is also helpful to send a copy to your health district's Maternity Services Liaison Committee (MSLC).

YOUR NOTES

Practically all pregnant women in London having a birth with the NHS now hold their own medical notes. Should this not be offered to you automatically, you may ask to do so right from the start of pregnancy and at any stage thereafter up until 40 days after the last recorded entry. Later requests may mean you are charged for photocopying and postage and possibly an administration fee of about £10.

You don't have to offer any reason for asking for your notes although the consultant can refuse to let you see anything about you or the baby which he or she feels might upset you. This is of course open to wide interpretation. You might have to have your application signed by a third party, for example your employer, to confirm that you are who you say you are.

The ability to get hold of records from earlier pregnancies, for example to find out more about any potential problem next time round, is entirely dependent on the policy of each individual hospital.

USEFUL CONTACTS

Action Against Medical Accidents (AVMA), ☎ (0845) 123 2352
☝ www.avma.org.uk
A charity specialising in providing free independent advice and support to patients injured during the course of medical treatment: 25% of cases handled relate to obstetrics. The organisation offers advice about taking legal action with individual case workers assigned, and also provides a range of medico-legal services for lawyers, including recommending medical experts. / HOURS Mon-Fri 10am-12pm & 2pm-4pm.

Association for Improvement in Maternity Services (AIMS), ☎ (0870) 765 1433 ☝ www.aims.org.uk
This campaigning group can offer support and advice should you wish to make a complaint. / HOURS Mon-Fri 9.30am-5pm.

Birth Crisis Network, ☎ (01865) 300266 ☝ www.sheilakitzinger.com
Reflective, non-directive listening for women (and their partners), at any time after a bad or traumatic birth experience. The aim is to help callers gain confidence in their own ability to deal with the problem rather than simply refer them on to more experts; local contact numbers are listed on the website; birth crisis workshops are occasionally held in Oxford (call or see website for details).

General Medical Council (GMC), ☎ (020) 7580 7642
☝ www.gmc-uk.org
The much-criticised body which licences doctors to practise medicine in the UK, maintaining a register of 200,000 practitioners. "Protecting patients, guiding doctors" is how the organisation sums up its functions which includes acting as the disciplinary body for the profession. The council runs numerous enquiry lines, including (020) 7915 3603 – for enquiries or complaints about a doctor's fitness to practice.

Medical Litigation, ☎ (01494) 792621 ☝ www.medicalclaims.co.uk
Legal website: includes listings of solicitors and information on what is involved in making a claim for clinical negligence.

National Care Standards Commission (NCSC), ☎ Helpline (0191) 233 3556, HQ (0191) 233 3600 ☝ www.carestandards.org.uk
An independent public body which registers and inspects private care services in the UK. This includes (amongst other things) private doctors, hospitals and clinics and as such is an appropriate starting point for complaints against such providers (although all providers are themselves required to have a complaints procedure in place). The Commission will deal with most complaints by liaising with the service provider concerned (except where circumstances indicate that this would not be appropriate) - and by agreeing the best way to take forward a complaint. The Commission will assess any evidence that there has been a breach in the regulations or standards. Contact your local area offices, or by calling the NCSC customer services unit. / HOURS Mon-Fri 8.30am-5.30pm.

National Patient Safety Agency, ☎ (020) 7927 9500
☝ www.npsa.nhs.uk
An organisation designed to encourage the NHS to learn from 'patient safety incidents', encouraging the reporting of such incidents and of near-misses.

NHS Direct, ☎ (0845) 4647 ☝ www.nhsdirect.nhs.uk
Details of complaints procedures are available from the NHS's own helpline service. / PUBLICATIONS The Patient's Charter on Maternity Services.

Nursing & Midwifery Council, ☎ (020) 7637 7181 ⬟ www.nmc-uk.org

Previously known as the United Kingdom Central Council – as the statutory body responsible for regulating nursing, midwifery and health visiting in the UK, this is the place to make complaints about such carers. The body's ultimate sanction is to remove a carer from its register. The most frequently-cited reasons for which it does so include physical or verbal abuse, failure to keep accurate records or report an incident, and misadministration of drugs.

Patients' Association, ☎ (020) 8423 9111, Helpline (08456) 084455
⬟ www.patients-association.com

"Patients are the reason for the NHS, not interruptions to it" – this organisation campaigns on behalf of NHS patients and can advise by phone or letter on how to go about making a complaint.

CHAPTER 4.04

MISCARRIAGE & STILLBIRTH

1. How common is miscarriage or stillbirth?
2. Prevention & treatment

(For information on premature and special care babies, see chapter 4.06 Support groups.)

1. HOW COMMON IS MISCARRIAGE OR STILLBIRTH?

Estimates of the number of pregnancies that end in miscarriage vary widely – from one in eight to as many as one in two. Tommy's Campaign uses the figure of one in four, as does the Miscarriage Association.

In the vast majority of cases, this event does not, perhaps, deserve such a dramatic label, occurring in many cases before a woman even knows she is pregnant. Most miscarriages happen before 12 weeks, and often manifest themselves as what seems like a heavy and late period. Less than a quarter of miscarriages occur between 12 and 20 weeks.

After 24 weeks of pregnancy, the term stillbirth rather than miscarriage is used. This reflects the fact that, with intensive care, some babies do survive being born this early. An estimated 7%–10% of babies are born prematurely.

Just under 1% of mothers will – according to AIMS (see chapter *1.01 Where to have the baby*) – experience a stillbirth or the death of a baby less than a week old. Half of these fatalities are in cases of known risk. For the rest, explanations remain uncertain, though some of the potential hazards mentioned in chapter *1.02 Looking after yourself* probably play a part, as may some mentioned below.

THE SAD PRACTICALITIES SURROUNDING A LATE MISCARRIAGE OR STILLBIRTH

To lose a child at an advanced stage of pregnancy is the hardest blow some people face in their lifetime. Coping with such a tragedy can be made all the harder by the unexpected administrative responsibilities that fall on many bereaved parents.

The birth of any child over 24 weeks old – living or stillborn – must be registered. The medical certificate of stillbirth is issued by the midwife or doctor to give to the registrar. (If no doctor or midwife was present and none has examined the body, you must sign a form given to you by the registrar.) To make the registration the parents must agree on a name.

The child must also have a funeral. Questions need to be answered such as what kind of funeral (burial, cremation), what kind of coffin, what kind of headstone, and so on. Parents may be asked whether they wish to donate their child's organs.

A few hospitals have trusts to remove some of these burdens from the shoulders of grieving parents and may arrange a ceremony free of charge (sometimes even for home births within their catchment area). Many, though, do not and carrying out these necessary tasks can act as a focus for parents who would rather not dwell on what has happened. A number of organisations now exist to help parents by putting them in touch with others who have experienced such a loss.

Even if the miscarriage is too early for a funeral, some parents find that a ceremony of some kind is helpful. Some hospitals organise regular memorial or remembrance services for parents and may also hold a book of remembrance.

Alternatively you may organise a religious or other ceremony yourselves (see chapter 2.09 *Naming and Ceremonies*) .

HANDLING THE LOSS

Over the last couple of decades, thinking has changed considerably on how best parents should handle a late miscarriage or stillbirth. There has been a general move to encourage parents to grieve properly, rather than to pretend that their child never existed.

However, research in 2002, published in the Lancet, questioned this new accepted wisdom. It suggested that for some parents the old-fashioned 'pretend it never happened' attitude is in fact for the best.

The organisations listed below can help counsel you towards an approach that feels right for you. Even if you feel that you would just rather move on, a souvenir of some kind may still be a good idea in order to avoid potential regrets later (even if you just put it to one side indefinitely). If you have miscarried in hospital, and your child is large enough, consider whether you might like to ask to see and possibly hold the baby, as some parents find it can help with accepting their loss. If this is not possible, you might like to ask the baby's sex.

Professionals working in this area recommend that siblings be allowed to see the baby if possible. It seems that they are more relaxed about death than most adults, but if denied the chance to see with their own eyes will tend to find what happened harder to come to terms with.

Photographs and/or hand or foot prints or a lock of hair can also be helpful in offering a tangible memory of an existence which is likely to be unreal to anyone other than you and your partner. Other ideas include: a memory book of some kind; the sorts of items listed in chapter 3.10 *Naming Gifts*; tree planting; star naming; or a bench or plaque in a children's play area.

TIME OFF FROM WORK

Maternity Leave rights only apply to births, live or still, after 24 weeks. Before 24 weeks, any time off after a miscarriage would have to be taken as sick leave, or compassionate leave if agreed by the employer.

READING

Angels of the Heart – Paula Cruttenden Haines & Lesley Harris ed (Haines; 1992; £5; 0951935003) – *Anthology of poetry by parents, grandparents, brothers, sisters and friends affected by the loss of a child.* / 24 Rockcliffe Ave, Bath, BA2 6QP.

Brief Lives – ed Alison Wood (Parents' writings; NCT Publishing; 1998; £4.99; 1870129911) – *Thirty-two personal accounts of miscarriage and stillbirth.* / NCT Maternity Sales, (0870) 112 1120; www.nctms.co.uk.

Family – Susan Hill (Penguin; 1989; £6.99; 0-140108-86-6) – *A personal account.* / www.susan-hill.com.

How to Prevent Miscarriage and other Crises of Pregnancy – Stefan Semchyshya & Carol Colman (A leading high-risk-pregnancy doctor's prescription for carrying your baby to term; Collier MacMillan; 1990; £6.95; 0-020368-55-0)

Love, Labour and Loss – Jo Benson & Dawn Robinson-Walsh (Scarlet Press; 1996; £8.99; 1857270630) – *Personal accounts from those who have lost a baby; coverage of common medical conditions which may contribute to such a death; observations on coping with the situation, arranging funerals, and how to get help.*

Miscarriage – Margaret Leroy (Macdonald Optima in co-operation with the Miscarriage Association; 1988; £5.99; 0-356128-88-1) – *A soundly researched and sensible approach to this difficult subject. Now out of print – you may be able to find a copy in the library or via Amazon's 'zShop' service for out of print titles.*

Miscarriage ★ – Christine Moulder (Women's experience and needs; Routledge; 1995, revised 2001; £9.99; 0415254892) – *According to the Miscarriage Association, one of the two 'must reads' for women who have had this experience – this title's emphasis being on emotional issues.*

Miscarriage ★ – Prof Lesley Regan (What every woman needs to know; Orion; 2001; £7.99; 0752837575) – *One of the Miscarriage Association's two 'must reads' – a doctor at the world's largest miscarriage clinic outlines causes and treatments.*

Miscarriage (2003; 50p) – *A double-sided A4 sheet offering information on early signs of miscarriage, and explaining the terminology used by doctors and midwives.* / NCT Maternity Sales (0870) 112 1120, www.nctms.co.uk.

Miscarriage – Professor Lesley Regan (What Every Woman Needs to Know; Orion; 2001; £7.99; 0752837575) – *By one of the country's foremost experts in the field, a title which takes a sympathetic look at causes, prevention and handling.*

Miscarriage - the facts – Gillian Lachelin (Oxford Paperbacks; 1996; £7.99; 0192626132) – *Written by an authority on the subject for those who have suffered one or more miscarriages – a look at causes, effects on the family, and possible measures to prevent a recurrence.*

[Leaflet] Pregnancy Loss (WellBeing; £1.50) – *One of a series of women's health leaflets, available to download from the website.* / www.wellbeing.org.uk.

When a Baby Dies – Nancy Kohner & Alix Henley (The experience of late miscarriage, stillbirth and neonatal death; Routledge; 2001; £9.99; 0415252768) – *Advice for bereaved parents, families and professionals caring for them, based on parents' experiences and the causes of death, grieving, sexual difficulties and future pregnancies. Advice on hospital procedures and funeral arrangements.*

USEFUL CONTACTS

British Organ Donor Society (BODY), ☎ (01223) 893636

☞ www.argonet.co.uk/body

Run by parents of a donor, the society's members include families of donors and of recipients; bereavement counselling and handbooks for donor families; check website for more details.

Care for the Family, ☎ (029) 2081 0800 ☞ www.care-for-the-family.org.uk

A Christian charity aiming to bolster marriage and family life and also offering support to single parents. (Founder, Rob Parsons, has written a number of parenting titles including The Sixty Minute Father – see Finding Out More). The organisation operates a Bereaved Parents' Network, including a team of telephone befrienders who are themselves parents who have lost a child.

The Child Bereavement Trust, ☎ (01494) 446648

☞ www.childbereavement.org.uk

A national charity offering support and resources for grieving families as well as training for professionals working with them. / PUBLICATIONS *Many books and videos available to buy online including When Our Baby Died (£15 + £3 p&p).*

Child Death Helpline, ☎ (0800) 282986 ☞ www.childdeathhelpline.org.uk

Support for anyone affected by a child's death, including by miscarriage, is provided by this helpline run by Great Ormond Street Hospital and Alder Hey Hospital, Liverpool, which is staffed by volunteers who are bereaved parents and who have been given some medical training. / HOURS *Mon-Sun 7pm-8pm, Mon-Fri 10am-1pm, Weds 1pm-4pm.*

The Compassionate Friends, ☎ (0117) 966 5202, Helpline (0117) 953 9639 ☞ www.tcf.org.uk

National self-help organisation for parents whose child has died, which can refer you to one of 250 support groups around the country for comfort, support and encouragement. There are also groups for (and run by) siblings and grandparents. There is a postal library service for books on all aspects of bereavement. / HOURS *Mon-Fri 9.30am-8pm, Sat & Sun 9.30am-5pm; PUBLICATIONS Range of books, leaflets and booklets.*

CRUSE Bereavement Care, ☎ *(020) 8939 9530, Helpline (0870) 167 1677* ◌ *www.crusebereavementcare.org.uk*
A national association for helping the bereaved which refers individuals to local counselling and support groups and which can also advise on practical matters relating to bereavement, such as welfare. / HOURS *Mon-Fri 9.30am-5pm;* PUBLICATIONS *Various publications.*

Direct Marketing Association (DMA) UK,
◌ *www.mpsonline.org.uk*
A trade body which operates the Baby Mailing Preference Service. Parents who have suffered a miscarriage or whose baby was stillborn can register their wish not to receive baby-related mailings.

Jewish Bereavement Counselling Service, ☎ *(020) 8385 1874*
Bereavement counselling; send SAE or phone for leaflets about service.

Miscarriage Association, ☎ *(01924) 200799*
◌ *www.miscarriageassociation.org.uk*
National charity offering support and information for people affected by miscarriage or by ectopic or molar pregnancy. Staffed helpline; range of information leaflets (also downloadable from website); network of local telephone and group support. Annual membership £15. / HOURS *Mon-Fri 9am-4pm, or answerphone;* PUBLICATIONS *Leaflets: Why did it happen to us?; The hidden grief; Preparing for you next baby; We are sorry that you have had a miscarriage (all 20p).*

National Childbirth Trust (NCT), ☎ *Enquiry line (0870) 444 8707*
◌ *www.nctpregnancyandbabycare.co.uk; www.nctparentsconnect.co.uk*
Though generally the NCT refers bereaved parents to the Miscarriage Association, some NCT branches are also able to provide support for bereaved parents on a local basis. This can be particularly useful for parents whose miscarriage was not a first pregnancy, and who already have one or more children. / HOURS *Mon-Thurs 9am-5pm, Fri 9am-4pm; or answerphone.*

Stillbirth & Neonatal Death Society (SANDS), ☎ *Helpline (020) 7436 5881, Admin (020) 7436 7940* ◌ *www.uk-sands.org*
Support for parents (and their families) who have had a baby that has died before, during or shortly after birth. Support is provided by way of: a helpline; the sale of various books and informative literature; a newsletter; and a network of local self-help groups throughout the UK, run by people who have themselves lost a baby. / HOURS *Mon-Fri 9.30am-5pm, or answerphone;* PUBLICATIONS *After the Death or Stillbirth of Your Baby: What Has to Be Done?, 50p; Saying Goodbye to Your Baby, £1; A4 leaflets (10p each), subjects include telling other children, The next pregnancy, A leaflet for fathers, Sexual problems following a stillbirth, For grandparents and How family and friends can help; books include When Your Baby Dies and Miscarriage: Women's Experiences and Needs.*

The Tavistock Clinic, ☎ *(020) 7435 7111* ◌ *www.tavi-port.org*
NHS psychotherapeutic centre where treatment is available to those living in certain areas of London subject to a referral from a health professional. Through the Child and Family Department, parents who have suffered a perinatal bereavement can receive counselling. / HOURS *Mon-Fri: 9-5.30pm for enquries, longer hours for appointments.*

Tommy's, ☎ *(08707) 707070, Infoline (0870) 777 3060*
◌ *www.tommys-campaign.org*
Many people who have been through the experience of premature birth and miscarriage or stillbirth feel a desire to help others to avoid the experience, through fund-raising and so on. The campaign funds research into premature birth, miscarriage and stillbirth, with its own Professor of Foetal Health together with a dedicated research group. Its aim is to make pregnancy and childbirth safer for mothers and babies worldwide, and to inform mothers-to-be on how to reduce the risk of a complicated pregnancy.

2. PREVENTION & TREATMENT

Prevention

There is no general treatment to prevent miscarriage, apart from following the obvious pointers, avoiding stress and not exerting yourself too much (see chapter 1.02 *Looking After Yourself*). It is worth bearing in mind research at St Mary's Hospital where there is the world's largest miscarriage referral unit. This found that regular 'TLC' in the form of a weekly visit to the clinic for a chat, a scan, and plenty of reassurance, significantly increased the success rate of subsequent pregnancies in women who had suffered recurrent miscarriages.

Risk of miscarriage seems to increase with age. This is related to the fact that chromosomal abnormalities – the most common reason for miscarriage – do too and it may be that up to half of all miscarriages are for this reason.

In around 20 to 25% of cases a more easily defined cause may be found, generally in tests after the event. One known factor is incompatibility of tissue types between the parents. Another trigger is raised levels of a specific antibody called lupus anticoagulants, affecting blood vessels to the placenta and starving the foetus of oxygen. This can be treated with an anti-clotting agent, including Aspirin, after consultation with a specialist.

A hormone imbalance may also be a cause, treatable with artificial hormones. Uterine and vaginal infections are a known issue, particularly with late miscarriages, and may be treatable with antibiotics.

Another issue may be a weak cervix (sometimes called an 'incompetent' cervix). This may be treated with the insertion of a stitch to strengthen how the baby is held in the womb. This procedure itself carries with it some risk of miscarriage, however, and so you need to discuss with your doctor the balance of risks in your individual case.

Physical causes include fibroids or an irregularly shaped womb. There may also be immune system problems, while general infection, environment, allergies and stress can all contribute.

Nutrition is important (those who miscarry for example have been found to have low levels of selenium compared to those who go full term). High levels of lead or other toxins, including food additives, can increase the risk. If you both smoke and drink the chances of miscarriage increase by up to four times. Even if you do not smoke but your mother did the risk is increased.

What to do if you believe you are experiencing a miscarriage

First of take comfort from the fact that in half of all cases bleeding in early pregnancy does not result in miscarriage but a healthy, full-term pregnancy.

If you believe that you are starting to miscarry, hospital is the place to be if there is any possibility of saving the baby. A scan will reveal what is going on.

In the earlier stages of pregnancy, though, if you know that it is too late – and mothers often do – you could consider miscarrying at home, rather than putting yourself through the stresses of hospital. Although hospitals are supposed to provide separate facilities for those who have lost a baby away from those celebrating a successful birth, this may not always happen.

If you opt to stay at home however, make sure that you have somebody around in case you experience severe pain and need to be hospitalised.

WHAT TO DO AFTERWARDS

Ensure that you receive a full check-up as soon as possible. If you can bring yourself to do so, you should preserve the remains of the miscarriage, in order that it can be tested to provide information that may prove useful in the handling of future pregnancies.

Be prepared for the possibility of overwhelming depression for at least a couple of days as your hormones rearrange themselves.

Beware of subsequent heavy periods, which could indicate inflammation or infection.

If you want aftercare you will probably have to go looking for it as in four out of five cases it is not offered by the medical system.

INDUCED MISCARRIAGE

Sometimes antenatal checks may reveal that the baby has died, but remained in the uterus. In such a case, mothers are generally given some time to see if a miscarriage will occur spontaneously. If this does not take place, an induction will be advised using a procedure similar to that for a normal birth (see chapter *4.03 Medical issues at birth*).

CHAPTER 4.05

FINDING OUT MORE

1. INTRODUCTION

If you want to relax into quietude during pregnancy and birth you may not feel the need to do much background reading. On the other hand, many pregnant women, particularly with a first child, develop an insatiable appetite for information on anything and everything to do with pregnancy, birth and life thereafter. The following lists may help you to find appropriate titles.

As author Bruno Bettleheim (see Parenting titles, in Section 2, Books below) points out, parents generally gravitate to books that advocate the style of care they want anyway. If for any reason you find a book is making you feel inadequate or irritated, junk it. It's your life and your child. Enjoying both is more important than living in thrall to some pundit.

Note also that an overdose of information can create the conviction that your child is going to suffer from every problem under the sun, or that you are in some way a failure because you don't follow everyone's – contradictory – parenting suggestions. If you think this might be you, pick just a couple of key titles and forget the rest.

Recommended titles

Titles that have impressed and/or proved particularly helpful to the author are marked with a star (★).

Freebies

There is a range of free leaflets that you may or may not be given by your carers in pregnancy or your health visitor thereafter. Most are listed under the issuing body and are sometimes obtainable in exchange for an SAE. The range includes:

Birth to Five – Angela Philips (A complete guide to the first five years of being a parent; Health Promotion England; 1999; £6.99; 0752115510) – *After their baby is born, all mothers should be given a free copy of this book. It is a sensible and useful text, and often better than many of the childcare books you can buy.*

New Pregnancy Book – Nancy Kohler, Angela Phillips, Christine Roche & Virginia Beckett (A complete guide to pregnancy, childbirth and the first few weeks with a new baby; Health Promotion England; 1999; £6.99; 0752115499) – *All first-time mothers in England are entitled to a free copy of this guide which, like 'Birth to Five', is sensible, reassuring and informative but not designed to go into great detail. / Marston Book Services, PO Box 269, Abingdon, Oxon OXZ14 4YN – (01235) 465565.*

2. BOOKS

Although the best general titles have an enduring value, most books in this area go out of date fairly swiftly as new fashions and new research are taken on board. It is therefore a good idea to keep an eye out for new names, though there is an increasing sense of the same material being re-hashed and re-packaged.

LIBRARIES

If you want to read more than just a couple of titles it might be worth joining the NCT for access to their libraries, held in most areas (though not always as useful a resource as they could be). Should you want to buy any of the books you borrow, the NCT (see below) offers a very sensible range.

Alternatively, there is your local public library.

Relevant Dewey/library section classifications are:
➤ Baby/child care; 649.1
➤ Baby psychology; 136.7352
➤ Breast-feeding; 649.3
➤ Childbirth; 618.4
➤ Childcare: play; 649.5
➤ Childcare: sleep; 649.6
➤ Feeding; 649.3
➤ Food preparation and recipes; 641.562
➤ Miscarriage; 618.39
➤ Pregnancy (physiology); 612.63
➤ Pregnancy (obstetrics); 618.2
➤ Alternative/complementary treatments; 615.85

Reading list

Suggestions in this chapter cover the following sections
➤ Your unborn child.
➤ Pregnancy.
➤ Birth.
➤ Childcare.
➤ Parenting.
➤ Fatherhood.
➤ Older mothers
➤ Second (& subsequent children).
➤ Development.
➤ Emotions, psychology & the 'mind thing'.

In addition, chapters throughout the book contain extensive listings of reading suggestions.

Note that many organisations and support groups publish excellent brochures, and also run their own bookshops.

Your unborn child

These books give detailed information and pictures on the physical development of a foetus.

TITLES

From Conception to Birth – photos Alexander Tsiaras, text Barry Werth
(Vermilion; 2002; £25; 0091887682) – *From embryo to birth – a 300-page book of computer-enhanced 3-D images.* / *www.randomhouse.co.uk.*

The Miraculous World of Your Unborn Baby – Nikki Bradford (Salamander Books; 2001; £12.99; 1-840652-52-7) – *Tracks the development of your child in the womb on the basis of recent research; colour photography of the foetus at different stages of development; potentially useful for older siblings, though the text is less riveting.*

[CD-Rom] **Nine Months to Birth** – Montparnasse (£19.99; 2844600174) – *This software holds the equivalent of over 250 pages of scientific information and practical advice, as well as video clips, ultrasound images and 300 photos showing the development of the foetus and its organs.* / Computer Bookshop (0121) 778 6000; PC World.

The Secret Life of the Unborn Child – Drs Thomas Verney & John Kelly (Time Warner; 1988; £7.99; 0751510033) – *Probably best read only if you are sure that you would not in any event contemplate a termination; a look at what evidence there is of the baby's conscious life before birth.*

Pregnancy

As noted above, one typical symptom of pregnancy is a voracious appetite for books on the subject, allied with an insidious disregard of their cost.

TITLES

A Guide to Effective Care in Pregnancy & Childbirth – Murray Enkin, Marc JNC Keirse & Iain Chalmers (OUP; 2000; £14.99; 019263173X) – *Summarises scientific research results on most aspects of care in pregnancy and childbirth.*

Being pregnant, giving birth – Mary Nolan (NCT/Thorsons; 1996; £9.99; 0-7225-3636-4) – *A clear and well-informed book; one of the NCT's "core" titles.* / NCT Maternity Sales, (0870) 112 1120; www.nctms.co.uk.

The Best Friend's Guide to Pregnancy – Vicki Iovine (Bloomsbury; 1997; £9.99; 0-747533-25-3) – *Best-selling (especially in the US), love-it-or-hate-it title, dishing out opinion as much as tips – on bladder control, maternity underwear, post-partum dementia, sex ... in a friendly manner. Note however that despite some adaptation, there are details are not relevant in the UK - potentially confusing for the novice.*

Birth & Beyond – Yehudi Gordon (Your pregnancy, your baby, your family – from minus 9 months to plus 9 months; Vermilion; 2002; £17.99; 0091856949) – *By the chief obstetrician at the Hospital of St John & St Elizabeth; a holistic approach, looking not just at the medical aspects, but also emotional ones; information on complementary therapies; 160-page reference section.*

Complete Book of Pregnancy – Daphne Metland (Pregnancy, labour and birth; HarperCollins; June 2000; £14.99; 0-004140-99-0) – *Companion to Complete Book of Babycare; 192 pages; tests, birth options, labour, early days with new baby, women's birth stories; illustrated, with colour photographs; A-Z medical terms.*

Conception, Pregnancy and Birth – Dr Miriam Stoppard (The childcare bible for today's parents; Dorling Kindersley; 2001; £15.99; 0751336084)

Having a Baby ★ – Nancy Kohner & Penny Mares (BBC Books; 1996; £9.99; 0563370270) – *A sensible and well-informed title aimed at helping women take advantage of the Changing Childbirth policies. Not a long tome but individual comments bring the text to life.*

[Video] **Help I'm Having a Baby** (Nursery Cottage Productions; £17.50 + £2.50 p&p.) – *Step by step guide to pregnancy, birth and the first six weeks with a new baby; 150 minutes, presented by an antenatal teacher.* / Nursery Cottage Production Ltd, PO Box 370, Newquay TR8 5YZ tel:01637 831 001 or www.babiesdirect.com.

The NCT Complete Book of Pregnancy – Daphne Metland (Harper Collins; 2000; £14.99; 0004140990) – *Covers pregnancy, labour and birth with the NCT stamp of approval.* / NCT Maternity Sales, (0870) 112 1120; www.nctms.co.uk.

New Natural Pregnancy – Janet Balaskas (Practical wellbeing from conception to birth; Gaia Books; 1998; £8.99; 1-856750-74-4) – *A companion to the Encyclopaedia of Pregnancy and Birth – fitness, complementary therapies and healthy eating during pregnancy; includes details of gentle yoga, exercise and massage routines.* / www.gaiabooks.co.uk.

New Pregnancy and Birth Book – Dr Miriam Stoppard (The concise practical guide for all parents-to-be; Dorling Kindersley; 1999; £9.99; 0-751311-67-7) – *First published in 1985 – regularly revised and up-dated, with ever-more glossy photos and illustrations; from planning a family and conception to antenatal care and birth.*

New Pregnancy and Childbirth – Sheila Kitzinger (Dorling Kindersley; 2003; £20; 075136438X) – *By one of the original movers and shakers of the Natural Birth Movement who helped reshape the pregnancy and birth experience in this country and still devotes much energy to empowering mothers with both information and emotional support. Can be inspiring but the hippy '60s roots are visible.*

Pregnancy and Childbirth – Dr Kevan Thorley & Trish Rouse (A natural approach; Bloomsbury; 1997; £12.99; 0747530211) – *Written by the only GP to be named in the Changing Childbirth report, who has researched a new method of antenatal care over several years and comes up with some eminently sensible ideas.*

The Pregnancy Question and Answer Book – Christoph Lees, Dr Karina Reynolds & Grainne McCartan (Dorling Kindersley; 2002; £14.99; 075133975X) – *Ilustrated, easy to follow and arranged by subject. It offers snippets on almost any subject associated with the condition.*

Pregnancy: From Conception to Birth – June Thompson (Marshall Publishing; 1998; £9.99; 1-840280-39-5) – *Close to the format of magazines on the subject - easy to read with illustrative photographs in a wire-bound format; six sections cover conception, health and diet, exercise and relaxation, antenatal care, labour and birth, you and your baby, and your personal file.*

The Rough Guide to Pregnancy and Birth – Kaz Cooke (Rough Guides; 2001; £9.99; 1858287650) – *An Aussie title adapted for the UK market with the emphasis on a witty approach; a week-by-week account of the author's pregnancy, interspersed with information.*

What to Expect When You're Expecting – Arlene Eisenberg, Heide E Murkoff & Sandee E Hathaway (Simon & Schuster; 1996; £12.99; 068481787X) – *The ground is covered mostly in the form of questions and answers; good on medical issues and particularly on chronic ailments and illness in pregnancy, especially good for little tips. Although adapted for the UK market, the US origins are visible, especially in descriptions of what to expect and when, and also in terms of information that is absent (Listeria for example – not a big deal in the US – doesn't get a mention).*

Your Pregnancy Week By Week – Glade B Curtis & Judith Schuler (Fisher Books; 2000; £13.99; 1555612601) – *Week by week advice on all issues including diet and exercise though note that not entirely relevant to advice and treatment in the UK.*

Birth

(For information and reading more specifically aimed at: home birth see chapter 1.01 Where to have the baby; water birth, see chapter 1.06 Birth equipment; use of complementary therapies in birth, see chapter 4.02 Complementary medicine & Health practitioners; the medical issues surrounding childbirth, see chapter 4.03 Medical issues at birth.)

TITLES

Birth and Beyond ★ – Dr Yehudi Gordon (Pregnancy, birth, your baby and family - the definitive guide; Vermilion; 2002; £17.99; 0091856949) – *From the famed obstetrician who in his own practice champions parental choice and combining modern obstetrics with complementary techniques (including water birth). The book covers pregnancy and the nine months thereafter in enormous detail – including the baby's physical, cognitive and emotional development month by month, diet and exercise in pregnancy, how to understand your medical notes, what happens to mother and baby during labour, step by step baby care and the emotions of parenthood – without being prescriptive. It looks set to become the new baby 'bible'. / www.randomhouse.co.uk.*

Benefits of Gentle Childbirth – ed Douglas Crawford (Ecstatic Birth; £2) – *A booklet containing personal stories from parents who managed gentle births, and guidelines for achieving the same. / Connexions, No 4, 57 The Drive, Hove, East Sussex BN3 3PF (01273) 727 588.*

[Video] Birth - Eight Women's Stories (£35.25) – *With a gold medal from the New York Film Festival in 1993; birth in a range of ways including active birth at home and hospital, Caesarean, twins, multiple and water births. / B-Line Productions, 45 Muswell Road, London N10 2BS; (020) 8444 9574; www.b-lineproductions.co.uk.*

Birth Your Way – Sheila Kitzinger (Choosing Birth at Home or in a Birth Centre; Dorling Kindersley; 2002; £9.99; 0751307882) – *Another title from the well-known natural childbirth guru, including firsthand accounts of women's experiences.*

Every Birth is Different – Pat Thomas (Headline; 1997; £12.99; 0-747277-37-0) – *Compiled with the help of AIMS (the Association for Improvement in Maternity Services) to illustrate the wide variety of experiences in labour. / AIMS, www.aims.org.uk.*

Guide to Labour (A step-by-step guide for first-time parents; NCT; 2001; £2.50) – *A revised edition of the popular booklet giving practical advice and information on all stages of labour, common problems and issues, and the roles and needs of birth partners.*

Guide to Labour (NCT; 2001; £2.50) – *One of a series of NCT brochures, each of approximately 20 pages. / NCT Maternity Sales (0870) 112 1120; www.nctms.co.uk.*

Happy Birth Day – Robie Harris illus Michael Emberley (Walker Books; 1998; £5.99; 0744552648) – *A mother's story of a baby's birth. Suitable for reading with an older child, it starts from the moment the baby slides into the midwife's hands.*

Have the Birth You Want – Gill Thorn (Hodder & Stoughton; 2002; £6.99; 0340786124) – *A title for which helps you think through your options and pointers on how to achieve them. The author points out that women in the UK, being fitter than in previous generations, should be able to give birth more easily, but but that modern attitudes to risk and reliance on external expertise can obscure the fact that birth is controlled by the mother's brain. The guide includes a useful breakdown of the physiological process of birth and a final chapter of very different birth accounts.* / www.help-yourself.co.uk.

Labours of Love – Robinson-Walsh & Stewart (Aurora Publishing; 1993; £8.99; 1-859260-00-4) – *Written in association with the NCT – 40+ true stories of childbirth in the parent's own words.* / NCT Maternity Sales, (0870) 112 1120; www.nctms.co.uk.

New Active Birth – Janet Balaskas (Harper Collins; 1989; £9.99; 0722525664) – *From the woman behind the Active Birth Centre, with chapters on the history and physiology of labour and birth; the theory and advantages of an active birth; yoga-based exercise; posture; breathing and massage; and water birth. Also a recovery and postnatal section.*

Practical parenting - Pregnancy & Birth – Gill Thorn (Hamlyn; 2003; £9.99; 0600603296) – *Information on: pre-conception health and pregnancy planning; how the baby develops month by month; antenatal options; stages of labour; getting to know the new baby; dietary advice and postnatal exercises. The guide is spiced up with real life anecdotes and 'Q&As'.* / www.hamlyn.co.uk.

Rediscovering Birth – Sheila Kitzinger (Little Brown; 2000; £18.99; 0316853933) – *A guide looking at the importance of feelings and relationships in pregnancy and birth. This is a cross-cultural account, hoping to assist readers choose the care that's right for them.*

Childcare

(For information and reading regarding nannies, au pairs, etc, see chapter 2.04 Childcare.)

Plenty of parents manage without childcare texts. Unlike pregnancy, it is an area where people tend to have their own ideas, from convictions derived from their own experience of childhood.

However, not everyone knows what needs to be done to care for a small baby and childcare books can at least reassure you that you haven't missed anything grievous. They are also a source of useful ideas, even for those who already know the basics. General titles can also function as reference works, for example detailing symptoms of childhood ailments – something you won't want to be reading up on much in advance.

Like all experts, authors of baby manuals disagree with one another much of the time. Take, for example, issues such as whether you should sleep three in a bed, whether you should leave your baby to cry, or whether you should give your child sugar, or a dummy. You will find directly opposing views expressed amongst the books below.

Unless you find yourself in total agreement with the author, one broad rule of thumb is to take with a pinch of salt any proposition that is stated to apply wholesale to all babies.

TITLES

Babies – Dr Christopher Green (A parents' guide to enjoying baby's first year; Vermilion; 2002; £9.99; 0743220978) – *Wide-ranging title whose coverage includes: parents' worries at birth; feeding and dealing with crying; sleeping and bonding; postnatal depression; cot death; facing handicaps and what to do if you feel stressed to the point you may abuse your child.* / www.randomhouse.co.uk.

Baby and Child Care – Dr Benjamin Spock & Stephen J Parker (Simon & Schuster; 1998; £12.99; 0-684851-22-9) – *The famous childcare handbook by the late Dr Spock, updated and extended to reflect 21st Century issues, but no longer the unrivalled bible it once was.*

Baby and Child Health Care Handbook – Dr Miriam Stoppard (An authoratitive easy-reference A-Z guide to children's illnesses, their symptoms and their treatments; Dorling Kindersley; 1997; £9.99; 0-751305-01-4)

The Baby and Child Question and Answer Book – Dr Carol Cooper (Dorling Kindersley; 2000; £12.99; 0-751308-44-7) – *A quick reference Q&A text covering issues from birth to school age.*

The Baby Book – William Sears, Marta Sears with Robert Sears and James Sears (Everything You Need to Know About Your Baby from Birth to Age Two; Little Brown; 2003; £14.99; 0-316-77800-1) – *Written by a US baby guru, his wife and two of their many children who are paediatricians like their father. Some elements are irrelevant to the UK, but it's a good title for those interested in the Sears philosophy of bonding and understanding the baby, covering issues from nappy changing and nappy rash (diaper rash) to postnatal depression and potty training.*

[Video] **Baby Matters: A New Life** – Dr Mark Porter (NCT; 1994; £12.99) – *An NCT 'action pack' to help parents through the first few weeks with information, practical demonstrations and ideas on how to cope. / NCT Maternity Sales, (0870) 112 1120; www.nctms.co.uk.*

Baby Wisdom – Deborah Jackson (The world's best kept secrets for the first year of parenting; Hodder Mobius; 2002; £14.99; 0-340-79350-3) – *From the author of Three in a Bed, a fun read – very suitable postnatally – on the theory and practices of babycare in different cultures. Comparisons are made issue by issue with entertaining pointers on taboos (to ensure fathers avoid childcare...), as well as intriguing thoughts on alternatives to current conventions.*

Complete Baby and Childcare – Dr Miriam Stoppard (Dorling Kindersley; 2001; £10.99; 0789471515) – *Heavily-marketed expert (and the price of her books reflects this); comprehensive but perhaps they assume too little parental self-confidence.*

First Time Parents – Dr Miriam Stoppard (The essential guide for all new mothers and fathers; Dorling Kindersley; 1999; £9.99; 0-751319-58-9) – *From pre conception through pregnancy and birth to the end of the first year in the usual Stoppard style.*

The Great Ormond Street New Baby and Child Care Book – Tessa Hilton, Maire Messenger, and Philip Graham (The essential guide for aprents of children aged 0-5; Vermilion; 1991; £15.99; 0-09-185299-4) – *A guide which draws on the expertise of doctors, psychologists and other specialists at the Great Ormond Street and the Institute of Child Health (which is linked to the hospital and is the UK's biggest centre of research in children's health and illness). All books have their weak spots (the advice about disposable nappies reducing nappy rash is one here) but the pedigree of the source here is difficult to beat, and the style is accessible. / www.randomhouse.co.uk.*

How Not to Be a Perfect Mother ★ – Libby Purves (The crafty mother's guide to a quiet life; HarperCollins; 1994; £6.99; 000636988X) – *Amusing as well as useful – a sensible and well-researched title by this famous journalist who has no axes to grind (she even includes tips she says she personally doesn't agree with).*

The Magic Years – Selma H Fraiberg (Understanding and handling the problems of early childhood; Simon & Schuster; 1996; £8.99; 0-684825-50-3) – *Coverage of both the physical and psychological problems of early childhood.*

Natural Baby – Janet Balaskas (How to optimize your child's development in the first year of life; Gaia Books; 2001; £12.99; 1-85675-128-7) – *The Active Birth expert covers: the last weeks of pregnancy; greeting your baby; feeding and caring for the baby; development and play; sleeping; family life; and natural healthcare. The approach is holistic - for example, how to minimise the release of contaminants into breast milk. / www.gaiabooks.co.uk.*

NCT Complete Book of Babycare – ed Daphne Metland (HarperCollins; 1999; £16.99; 0004140532) – *Covering birth to three years with step by step guides, parents' comments, checklists, an A-Z of children's health, play, physical skills and language development. Including colour photographs as illustrations.*

New Babycare Book – Dr Miriam Stoppard (A Practical Guide to the First Three Years; Dorling Kindersley; 1990; £10.99; 0751336092) – *One of the 'classics' from one of the Big Names in this area which makes its points clearly and concisely. As with her other titles, some feel the book assumes too little confidence on behalf of the reader. / www.dk.com/uk.*

The Parentalk Guide to Surviving the First Six Weeks – Annette Briley and Tim Mungeam (Hodder & Stoughton; 2001; £5.99; 0340785446) – *By a midwife and a father of two, a simple-to-understand title which tackles some of the problems and challenges associated with childbirth. Subjects covered include lack of confidence, tiredness, lost sleep, feeding, crying, health worries, cot death, colic, wind, bathing your baby, juggling home and work, looking after yourself, maintaining your relationship and sex life, getting your body back, setting realistic goals, postnatal depression, grandparents and more.*

Practical Parenting - Your Baby from Birth to 18 Months – Nancy Stewart (Hamlyn; 2001; £9.99; 0600604322) – *Practical advice on feeding, bathing, changing nappies and getting the baby to sleep. Also covers basic health issues. / www.hamlyn.co.uk.*

Until They Are Five – Angela Phillips (A parent's guide; Rivers Oram Press; 1989; £4.99; 0044403615) – *Issues covered include alternative approaches to dealing with weaning, allergies, eating difficulties, and crying.*

What to Expect the First Year – Arlene Eisenberg, Heide E Murkoff & Sandee E Hathaway (Simon & Schuster; 1996; £12.99; 0684817888) – *See What to Expect When You're Expecting. Sensible advice, nothing too bossy and covers a vast amount of material.*

What to Expect the Toddler Years – Arlene Eisenberg, Heide E Murkoff & Sandee E Hathaway (Workman; 1998; £11.99; 0684816776) – *See What to Expect When You're Expecting.*

Your Baby and Child – Penelope Leach (From birth to age five; Dorling Kindersley; 2003; £16.99; 0-7513-4887-2) – *A new edition of a classic, densely written with everything from teething to the child coping with stress, plus a medical reference section. Some find the tone rather bossy, but she does take into account the child's point of view.*

Your Baby's First 18 Months – Anne Yelland (Marshall Publishing; 1998; £9.99; 1-840280-40-9) – *In an accessible quick reference format (part of the Factfile series) – looking after your baby; feeding your baby; how your baby grows; keeping your baby safe; parenting a sick baby; and baby first aid.*

Your New Baby – Christine & Peter Hill (How to survive the first months of parenthood; Vermilion Arrow; 1999; £8.99; 0091817129) – *Also known as 'You and Your New Baby' – a sensible book, which some consider rather old-fashioned on certain issues; particularly strong on the physical side of things as Christine Hill is an obstetric physiotherapist.*

Parenting

(See also parenting courses, listed in chapter 2.01 Postnatal.)

GENERAL

A Good Enough Parent ★ – Bruno Bettelheim (A guide to bringing up your child; Thames & Hudson; 1995; £12.95; 0500278334) – *A book by an extremely humane writer whose point is that there are no rules – you and your child react to each other as unique individuals on the basis of your individual experience; densely written.*

[Video] Baby Matters: Parentcraft – Dr Mark Porter with Penelope Leach (NCT; 1994; £12.99) – *How to be receptive and adaptable to the growing infant's needs; how to provide the new baby with the required physical and emotional care up to the age of one. / NCT Maternity Sales, (0870) 112 1120; www.nctms.co.uk.*

The Best Friend's Guide to Toddlers – Vicky Iovine (Bloomsbury; 2000; £9.99; 0747546053) – *Issues including discipline, eating, toilet talk and parental expectations of and reactions to toddlers in her trademark unjudgemental, if opinionated style.*

Confident Children – Gael Lindenfield (Help children feel good about themselves; Thorsons; 2000; £7.99; 0-722539-56-8) – *New edition of this very popular and deceptively simple tome that looks at how to develop children's self-esteem at all ages (including how to help parents rid themselves of guilt and themselves become confident in their parenting).*

The Continuum Concept – Jean Liedloff (Aarkna; 1989; £7.99; 014019245X) – *Based on the author's observations of South American Indian parenting – a polemic arguing that babies should not be separated from their mother until they are perfectly ready.*

Dorothy Einon's Complete Book of Childcare and Development – Dorothy Einon (Raising happy, healthy and confident children; Marshall Publishing; 2001; £20; 1-840282-45-2) – *From birth to six years, the book covers basic childcare, how children grow and develop, and how they influence parenting skills and family relationships; it includes some reassuring advice on coping with ups and downs.*

From Contended Baby to Confident Child – Gina Ford (Vermilion Paperback; 2000; £8.99; 0091875234) – *A follow-on title to The Contented Little Baby Book, this book tackles issues about babies and toddlers up to 3 years old in the uncompromising Ford style; feeding and sleeping; potty training (in a week); second babies; separation anxiety; discipline and manners are all topics covered.*

How Not be a Perfect Family ★ – Libby Purves (Coronet; 1999; £6.99; 034075138X) – *See How Not to be A Perfect Mother.*

How Not to Raise the Perfect Child ★ – Libby Purves (Coronet; 1999; £6.99; 0340751371) – *See How Not to be A Perfect Mother.*

How to Build Confidence in Your Child – James Dobson (Hodder & Stoughton; 2000; £6.99; 0340756489) – *An updated edition of a million-selling guide.*

The Parentalk Guide to Being a Mum – Janice Fixter (Hoder & Stoughton; 2000; £5.99; 0-340-75656-X) – *A short and easy read with tips and a can-do approach with a personal touch, covering how to survive the first months, how to deal with tantrums, how to stop worrying about your child, how to make time for yourself, and how to let them grow up. / Parentalk.*

The Parentalk Guide to the Toddler Years – Steve Chalke (Hodder & Stoughton; 1999; £4.99; 0-340-72167-7) – *Straightforward and unfussy, covering children from one to six years and the issues of making time; temper tantrums, preparing for school; making learning fun; and jealousy and sibling rivalry.* / Parentalk.

Sons and Mothers – ed Matthew & Victoria Glendenning (Virago; 1997; £7.99; 1-860493-55-6) – *Thoughts on this subject from 16 contributors.*

Wipe – Penny Wilson and Jane Cobb (Survival Tactics for Parents with Attitude; Hodder Mobius; 2002; £10; 0-340-73354-3) – *A kind of gung ho British version of the Best Friends books: a touch confrontational, but with humorous touches and very practical pointers. Topics include: the first few weeks; why your relationships will change; sex and the single parent; and what happens when your child has special needs.*

"STAYING IN CHARGE"

How to Talk so Kids Will Listen & Listen so Kids Will Talk – Adele Faber & Elaine Mazlish (Avon Books; 1998; £9.99; 0380811960) – *Not a 'How to' book, but one of exercises to help parents teach themselves parenting skills, with hundreds of examples and numerous cartoons; aimed at building family co-operation without nagging; includes alternatives to punishment.*

Kids & Co – Ros Jay (Winning Business Tactics for Every Family; White Ladder Press; 2003; £6.99; 0954391403) – *Applying business techniques to children in a title, like one on business management, and therefore designed for short attention spans. Issues include negotiating, win-win deals and encouraging teamwork, plus ideas like team briefings to let everyone know what's happening. The same author also plans a lighthearted title on fathers and babies.* / www.whiteladderpress.com.

Laying Down the Law – Dr Ruth Peters (25 laws of parenting to keep your kids on track, out of trouble and (pretty much) under control; Rodale; 2003; £8.99; 1405006714)

Love, Laughter and Parenting – Steve & Sharon Biddulph (Dorling Kindersley; 2000; £12.99; 0-751308-51-X) – *A full colour illustrated parenting book looking less at practicalities and more at issues of communication; written in a warm style, with non-prescriptive solutions to common problems and advice on understanding your child.*

More Secrets of Happy Children ★ – Steve Biddulph (A guide for parents; Harper Collins; 1999; £8.99; 0722536704) – *A follow-up title to The Secret of Happy Children, this book offers further practical advice on issues such as childcare, discipline and fatherhood.*

Mums on Babies – Rachel Foster, Carrie Longton and Justine Roberts (Cassell Illustrated; 2003; £9.99; 1844030717) – *Tips culled from the contributors to the Mumsnet website. They are punctuated by factboxes and summaries of what parents have to say.* / mumsnet.com.

NCT Toddler Tantrums – Penney Hames (Thorsons; 2002; £6.99; 0-00-713609-9) – *Written by an NCT counsellor and child psychologist – strategies for dealing with this phase of development to help both parents and the child.* / NCT Maternity Sales (0870) 112 1120; www.nctms.co.uk.

New Toddler Taming – Dr Christopher Green (A parents' guide to the first four years; Vermilion; 1984, revised 2001; £12.99; 0091875285) – *A reasonably entertaining book written by a consultant paediatrician – particularly good for those who have a difficult child (which the author estimates as slightly above 50% of parents), but the mellower second edition is potentially helpful to others as well.*

Parentalk's How to Succeed as a Parent – Steve Chalke (Survival tips for busy mums and dads; Hodder & Stoughton; 2003; £7.99; 0-340-86136-3) – *Written by the series editor, who writes punchily but intelligently, and covers all the key issues with reassuring warmth; these include a parent's job description; how to praise, not put down; and how to let go; a key point is that the later you leave it, the harder it is to get on track.* / www.madaboutbooks.co.uk.

Playful Parenting – Denise Chapman & Mark Weston (Turning the dilemma of discipline into fun and games; Little Brown; 1993; £12.99; 0-874777-34-8)

Practical Parenting - Tantrums – Eileen Hayes (Understanding and coping with your child's emotions; Hamlyn; 2003; £5.99; 0600605639) – *Practical tips on cutting down tantrums, or even avoiding them; includes case histories, parent stories, methods from child psychologists with tips, checklists, charts, case studies and question and answers.* / www.hamlyn.co.uk.

Raising Happy Children – Jan Stimpson, Jan Parker & Dorothy Rowe (What every child needs their parents to know – from 0 to 7 years; Hodder and Stoughton; 1999; £9.99; 0-340712-49-X) – *By the same authors as Sibling Rivalry, Sibling Love, options to help parents negotiate issues like sleep problems, food wars, divorce and more, including comments from parents.*

The Secret of Happy Children ★ – Steve Biddulph (A guide for parents; HarperCollins; 1999; £8.99; 0722536690) – *Advice on parent-child communication by the well known author and family therapist, covering babyhood to early teens; issues covered include tantrums, shyness, single parenthood, TV and food.*

Toddler Troubles – Jo Douglas (Coping with Your Under 5s; Wiley & Sons Ltd; 2002; £8.99; 0470846860) – *By a parent and psychologist, a guide covering coping with such potential problems areas as tantrums, toilet training, never-ending questions, eating and sleeping.*

[Magazine] **What Every Kid Wished Their Parents Knew... and vice versa** – Rob Parson & Lloyd Parson (Hodder and Stoughton; 1999; £4.99; 0-340735-56-2) – *A look at parent/child communication, written with insights from the author's now teenage son.*

BOYS/GIRLS

Bringing up Boys – Tim Kahn (A Parents' Guide; Piccadilly Press; 1998; £6.99; 1-85340-526-4) – *By an experienced parenting groups facilitator, this guide does not cover new ground but it does look at all the issues simply and succinctly. Specifically addressed are the pressures on boys and how to help sons overcome them, potential behavioural problems and solutions and how boys learn to become men.*

Raising Boys – Steve Biddulph (Why boys are different – and how to help them become happy and well-balanced men; HarperCollins; 1998; £7.99; 0722536860) – *This widely-praised book from an Australian parenting guru focuses on why boys need different parenting from girls, with advice for single mothers.*

There's A Good Girl – Marianne Grabrucker (Women's Press Ltd; 1990; £6.99; 0704340909) – *Written by a woman trying not to stereotype her daughter, but finding it almost impossible to avoid.*

Fatherhood

TITLES

Baby Alarm – Simon Brett (Thoughts from a neurotic father; Orion; 1998; £5.99; 0-575602-68-6) – *A humorous look at fatherhood for neurotics.*

Becoming a Father – Mike Lilley (How to make a success of your role as a parent; How to Books; 1997; £9.99; 1857033272)

[Video] **Dads** (B-Line Productions; 1995; £35.25) – *The experience of fatherhood through the eyes of ten different men. / B-Line Productions, 45 Muswell Road, London N10 2BS; (020) 8444 9574; www.b-lineproductions.co.uk.*

The Father's Book – David Cohen (Being a Good Dad in the 21st Century; Wiley & Sons Ltd; 2001; £8.99; 0470841338) – *Written by a father-psychologist, a light-hearted look at the issues faced by expectant and new dads (and including interviews with them). A questionnaire helps readers pin down their own views and to identify elements of fatherhood which are potentially problematic.*

The Father's Book – David Cohen (Being a good dad in the 21st century; Wiley & Sons Ltd; 2001; £8.99; 0470841338) – *Practical advice drawing on personal experience and academic research for men trying to fulfil their new role.*

Fatherhood – ed Peter Howarth (Victor Gollancz; 1998; £6.99; 0-575400-93-5) – *An anthology by men – everything from broodiness to IVF, an ill child, and parenting teenagers; writers include Tony Parsons, Robert Newman, James Hawes and John Hegley.*

How to be an Effective Father – Ian Grant (30 practical ideas to strengthen your family; Kingsway Communications; 2002; £7.99; 1842910485) – *An easy-to-read book with game plans designed to get immediate results. It covers sensible discipline, how to deal with unwanted behaviour, and being a hero to your children. There is also a section for fathers who don't live with their children.*

The Parentalk Guide to Being a Dad – Pete Meadows (Hodder & Stoughton; 2000; £5.99; 0-340-75655-1) – *One of the small and simple titles from the parenting charity, on making your child feel secure and special, working smart, keeping the glow with your partner, making it work as a distant dad, and top tips for getting the most out of fatherhood. / Parentalk.*

The Sixty Minute Father – Rob Parsons (Hodder & Stoughton; 1995; £5.99; 034063040X) – *Much-praised book helping fathers focus more on their children.*

The Thinking Man's Guide to Pregnancy, Childbirth and Fatherhood – Raymond Anthony & Ian Renshaw (ACE; 1996; £3.99; 0952628708)

You're Pregnant Too Mate! – Rodgers (The essential guide for expectant fathers; Robson Books; 1999; £8.99; 1861052774) – *Basic information for the period prior to birth in a humorous format.*

Older mothers

TITLES

Birth Begins at Forty – Corinne Sweet (Challenging the Myths About Late Motherhood; Hodder & Stoughton; 2001; £6.99; 0340756969) – *A positive look at the issues and misconceptions relating tolate motherhood, including interviews with numerous 40-plus mothers. She does not avoid the possible problems, including miscarriage, but notes that there are also upsides (not least a probability of more intelligent progeny). / www.madaboutbooks.com.*

Not Too Late - Having a Baby After Thirty-five – Gill Thorn (A Practical and Comprehensive Guide to Pregnancy and Birth; Bantam; 1998; £7.99; 0553505386) – *Featuring case studies, pregnancy and birth as it affects women having a baby after 35, the guide covers issues like tests for foetal abnormalities, the use of technology during labour, coping with work, tiredness and complex family relationships.*

Older Mothers – Julia Berryman, Karen Thorpe & Kate Windridge (Conception, pregnancy and birth after 35; Rivers Oram Press; 1999; £9.99; 0863584101) – *An alternative for those allergic to writers such as Sheila Kitzinger: written by three psychologists combining case histories and research; emphasises that risk in childbirth is more a function of health than age.*

Your Pregnancy Over 35 – Glade B Curtis, Judith Schuler MS (Perseus Publishing; 2001; £13.99; 1555613195) – *Caters to the growing ranks of older mothers (one in three mothers are now over 30) and relates to the specific needs of pregnancy for older women.*

Second (& subsequent) children

TITLES

Practical Parenting - Siblings – Dr Richard Woolfson (Encouraging your children to be friends; Hamlyn; 2003; £5.99; 0600606635) – *The book reminds parents to address the different needs of individual children, and includes recent research on sibling rivalry, and strategies for dealing with jealousy and bickering. Includes tips, checklists, charts, case studies and Q&As. / www.hamlyn.co.uk.*

Sibling Rivalry, Sibling Love – Jan Parker and Jan Stimpson (How to ease tension, conflict and develop healthy, happier relationships; Hodder Mobius; 2002; £10; 0-340-79346-5) – *By a parenting advisor and facilitator for Parentline Plus who also runs courses and workshops. This is an excellent book which recommends approaches which really work. It aims to boost parents' confidence, looking at the needs of both parents and children and the emotional relationship between parent and child. Covers all the bases, starting with the arrival of the sibling and looking at the many positives as well as potential areas of trouble.*

Siblings Without Rivalry ★ – Adele Faber & Elaine Mazlish (How to help your children live together so you can live too; Piccadilly Press; 1999; £8.99; 1853406309) – *An American title, as is evident from the style, but the ideas offered are excellent.*

Three Shoes, One Sock and No Hairbrush – Rebecca Abrams (Everything you need to know about having your second child; Cassell & Co.; 2001; £9.99; 0304354295) – *Why having two children is anything but a repeat of the first; some find it overly depressing – potentially a reassuring read, though, for those who thought they were on their own in finding coping with two a hard slog (she writes, for example, that siblings average four fights an hour).*

Development

(For information and reading on developmental concerns, see chapter 2.03 Baby health. For titles on play with your child, and its importance to development, see chapter 3.06 Toys.)

TITLES

A Child's World – Dr Sarah Brewer with Dr Alex Cutting (A unique insight into how children think; Headline; 2001; £20; 0-7472-4301-8) – *Tracing the development of babies into toddlers and children, the guide looks at the key six topics of understanding others: lying; gender; complex thinking; understanding of the human life cycle; and potential to become independent adults. Worth ordering from the library. / www.madaboutbooks.com.*

Baby It's You – Annette Karmiloff-Smith (Ebury; 1995; £9.99; 009180986x) – *TV tie-in with series looking at the experience of the child from tiny baby to separate person.*

Babyhood – Penelope Leach (Penguin; 1991; £10.99; 0-140130-61-6) – *Childcare guru's round-up of research from all over the world on how children develop and are affected by relationships and circumstances.*

[Video] **Babywatching** – Desmond Morris (Jonathan Cape; 1999; £8.99; 0224060112) – *Based on the book by Desmond Morris: why childbirth is difficult; why babies cry; how important is the presence of the mother? / Splashdown Water Birth Services – (020) 8422 9308.*

[Book & video] **Communication Between Babies in Their First Year** – Elinor Goldschmied & Dorothy Selleck (National Children's Bureau; 1996; £40; 1874579873) – *Shows babies taking pleasure in each other's company at a centre in Italy.*

Emotional Intelligence – Daniel Goleman (Why it can matter more than IQ; Bloomsbury; 1996; £7.99; 0-747528-30-6) – *The physical workings of the brain, the relationship between IQ and other personal characteristics, and the personality traits that are more important than IQ to success in life and becoming a happy individual; not targeted at parents but with a good section on babies' emotional needs and parents' sensitivity to them.*

From Birth to Five Years – Mary D Sheridan et al (Children's developmental progress; Routledge; 1997; 0-415164-58-3) – *Second edition of detailed title (not aimed at parents per se), with information on each stage of development, including details of hearing and sight tests, when referral to a specialist is appropriate, and on special needs support services.*

How Babies Think – Alison Gopnik, Andrew Meltzoff, Patricia K. Kuhl (Phoenix; 2001; £7.99; 075381417X) – *Drawing on evolutionary psychology, the title looks at pre-programmed skills and environmental influences that enable babies to learn, to perceive and to manipulate the world around them.*

How to Raise a Bright Child – Dr Joan Freeman (How to encourage your child's talents 0-5 years; Vermilion Arrow; 1996; £8.99; 0-091813-91-3) – *A book not just aimed at the top 10% (or gifted top 2%), but at all children who are better than average in something. The suggestions on stimulation from this expert in child psychology could benefit all parents.*

Illustrated Babywatching – Desmond Morris (Ebury; 1995; £15.99; 0-091806-82-8) – *Complete with glossy pictures, a summary of clinical observations of human babies.*

Introduction to Child Development – GC Davenport (Collins; 1994; £16.50; 0003223558)

Small Talk – Dr Richard C Woolfson (from the first gestures to simple sentences - understanding and encouraging your child's speech; Hamlyn; 2002; £14.99; 0600602885) – *A parent's guide to the psychology of speech development, and body language in babies and children of up to three years. / www.hamlyn.co.uk.*

The Social Baby – Lynne Murray and Liz Andrews (CP Publishing; £14.99; 1903275016) – *Packed with 'action photo' sequences of pictures of babies from the moment they are born to show their emergent social lives. The books complete with a "lollipop" printed with black and white geometric designs for your baby to react to. The book plus four books of similar stimulating graphics (plus greaseproof paper for sound, interesting holes and reflective mirrored paper), are available as a pack from NCT Maternity Sales. for £17. / www.socialbaby.com.*

The Social Toddler – Helen Dorman, Clive Dorman (Promoting Positive Behaviour; CP Publishing; 2002; £15.99; 1903275385) – *A guide including video stills from 12 months onwards, explaining how immature minds view the world and the frustrations of being without language. It looks at why behaviour patterns emerge and offering simple strategies to diffuse difficulties. / www.socialbaby.com.*

Understanding Your 1 Year Old – Deborah Steiner (Rosendale Press; 1992; £4.99; 1872803105) – *Popular and simple titles by professionals from north London's Tavistock Clinic, explaining the development of a child's personality.*

Understanding Your 2 Year Old – Susan Reid (Rosendale Press; 1992; £6.99; 1872803156)

Understanding Your Baby – Lisa Miller ed (Rosendale Press; 1997; £5.99; 1-872803-05-9) – *One of a range of popular and simple titles (Understanding your One-year-old, Four-year-old, etc) by professionals from the Tavistock Clinic to explain the development of a child's personality.*

Emotions, psychology & the 'mind thing'

Having a baby is now recognised as bringing to the surface all kinds of unresolved issues from a parents' own childhood. If you feel you might be facing serious issues in this regard you could contact a family therapist for help. A more low key approach is to read something on the subject.

The following are some more general titles. If you want greater depth or more specialisation, refer to the subsequent list of specialist booksellers.

TITLES

Baby Shock! – Elizabeth Martyn (Your Relationship Survival Guide; Vermilion; 2001; £7.99; 0091856590) – *Backed by Relate, this guide explores how to continue to function as a couple… even when you have children! Drawing on advice from the charity's counsellors, it covers such essential as creating time for yourselves, coping with rows, agreeing how to bring the children up and the work/home life balance.* / www.randomhouse.co.uk.

Becoming a Mother – Kate Mosse (A companion to pregnancy and birth; Virago; 1997; £9.99; 1860492916) – *A focus on the emotional rather than medical experience of 36 widely differing pregnancies and births, starting from the decision to have the child. Especially good for those who would like to attend an antenatal group and can't.*

Breaking Down the Wall of Silence – Alice Miller (To Join the Waiting Child; Virago; 2000; £7.99; 1-86049-347-5) – *By a leading psycho-analyst and researcher into the ill-treatment of children who eloquently pleads the case for listening to a child's emotional needs. It includes two case studies familiar to most readers – Hitler and Nicolae Ceausescu.*

Chicken Soup for the Mother's Soul – Jack Canfield et al (Health Communications; 1997; £8.99; 1-558744-60-6) – *One of the American compilation series. Terribly slushy - the printed equivalent of a weepie movie - with similar catharthic value for the postnatal mother.* / www.chickensoup.com.

The Childhood Roots of Adult Happiness – Dr Edward Hallowell (A five step plan to help children discover their strength and inspiration for life; Vermilion; 2002; £9.99; 0091884233) – *Drawing on both research and first hand experience as a parent, a Harvard psychiatrist argues for the practical importance of children developing a sense of connection with those around them and a sense of mastery over one or more aspects of their lives.*

The Drama of Being a Child – Alice Miller (The Search for the True Self; Virago; 2001; £7.99; 1-86049-101-4) – *The shortest and most overtly psycho-analytic title of those reviewed.*

Families & How to Survive Them ★ – Robin Skynner & John Cleese (Vermilion; 1993; £7.99; 0749314109) – *An intelligent look at the psychology of the family and with a title you can be caught reading without embarrassment.*

Family – Susan Hill (Penguin; 1989; £6.99; 0-140108-86-6) – *An autobiographical account by a novelist of her pregnancies and births, including the delivery – at just 25 weeks – of a baby who died. Not a medical book but a good read from which it is possible to absorb a fair amount of information.* / www.susan-hill.com.

For Your Own Good – Alice Miller (The Roots of Violence in Child-Rearing; Virago; 1987; £7.99; 0-86068-899-2) – *A powerful and empathetically argued case against harshness in childcare, arguing that the damage caused will simply surface in adulthood.*

Madonna and Child – Melissa Benn (Towards a new politics of motherhood; Vintage; 1999; £7.99; 0099272539) – *Argues that there has been a revolution in the rôle of women in their experience of motherhood.*

Paranoid Parenting – Frank Furedi (Abandon Your Anxieties and be a Good Parent; Allen Lane The Penguin Press; 2001; £9.99; 0713994886) – *Have experts exaggerated the problems of childcare, creating a sense of panic in parents who therefore mollycoddle their children? The author believes so, largley attributing the problem to the growth of the expert advice industry.*

They F* You Up** – Oliver James (Your Role in the Family Drama - Rewriting the Script of Your Adult Life; Bloomsbury; 2002; £16.99; 0747551561) – *A polemic arguing forcefully that nurture (especially in the first six years) as almost the only determinant of what we become. The author, a clinical psychologist, brings a lot of evidence to bear: if they didn't before, any new parent reading this book will feel impelled to do the the best they can, given the possibly far-reaching effects.*

What Our Children Teach Us – Piero Ferrucci (Lessons in Joy, Love and Awareness; Simon & Schuster; 2002; £10; 0743221087) – *By an Italian psychologist and father of two, a philosophical rather than practical look at family dynamics and what they reveal to parents.*

You and Your New Baby – Anna McGrail (NCT/Thorsons; 1997; £9.99; 0-722736-37-2) – *First published as Becoming a Family (British Medical Association); award winning comprehensive handbook for the first few months; one of the NCT's "core" titles.*

SPECIALIST BOOKSELLERS

Community Insight
Swindon SN2 ☎ (01793) 512612
Early years booksellers with books on care, play, education etc.

Growing Needs
11 Market Place Glastonbury BA6 9HH ☎ (01458) 833466
Specialist mail order supplier focussed on pregnancy, birth and childcare books. The company can also source relevant titles from the US. / *HOURS Mon 10am-5pm, Tue-Fri 9am-5.30pm; SEE ALSO 1.04 Antenatal classes.*

H Karnac
118 Finchley Rd London NW3 5HT ☎ (020) 7431 1075
Specialist bookseller covering psychoanalysis, psychotherapy and related subjects, including issues pertaining to children and families. / *HOURS Mon-Sat 9am-6pm.*

La Leche League of Great Britain
BM 3424 London WC1N 3XX ☎ Helpline (0845) 120 2918, (020) 7242 1278
⌂ www.laleche.org.uk
A wide range of specialist books on breast-feeding including special issues like twins, a diabetic mother, adopted babies, with breast implants and the like, as well as a number of titles on parenting. / *SEE ALSO 2.02 Feeding.*

National Childbirth Trust (NCT)
Alexandra House, Oldham Terrace London W3 6NH ☎ Enquiry line (0870) 444 8707
⌂ www.nctpregnancyandbabycare.co.uk; www.nctparentsconnect.co.uk
NCT Publishing produces a wide range of specialist books and leaflets. The website has the full catalogue and links to all the associated publishers, or you can mail order through NCT Maternity Sales, 0870 112 1120 or at www.nctms.co.uk. / *HOURS Mon-Thurs 9am-5pm, Fri 9am-4pm; or answerphone; SEE ALSO 1.01 Where to have the baby; 1.04 Antenatal classes; 2.01 Postnatal; 2.02 Feeding; 2.04 Childcare; 2.05 Travel; 2.06 Baby & toddler activities; 3.02 Baby equipment; 4.04 Miscarriage & stillbirth; 4.06 Support groups.*

Royal College of Obstetricians & Gynaecologists
27 Sussex Place London NW1 4RG ☎ Admin (020) 7772 6200, Bookshop (020) 7772 6275 ⌂ www.rcog.org.uk
Stocks a wide range of books on pregnancy, childbirth and breast-feeding; also a set of 18 patient information leaflets covering women's health (£1.50 each, £4.50 for the set, including p&p). Subjects covered include travelling in pregnancy, HIV screening in pregnancy, miscarriage in early pregnancy, birth at home, bleeding after childbirth and working and having a baby. Click through to the online bookshop from the home page of the RCOG. / *HOURS Mon-Fri 9am-5pm; SEE ALSO 1.01 Where to have the baby; 1.02 Looking after yourself.*

Words of Discovery
Freepost Words of Discovery LON 7858 Leics LE2 6ZY ☎ (0845) 458 1199, (0116) 262 2244 ⌂ www.wordsofdiscovery.com
"Books to nurture children's personal growth" – online and mail order bookseller with titles to help parents promote spirituality, creativity, self-esteem and environmental and social awareness in their kids – a number imported from the US; also parenting books on the same themes. / *HOURS Mon-Fri 9am-5pm or answerphone.*

3. MAGAZINES & PERIODICALS

It is arguable that the main role of the baby press is less to provide information, and more to give you a sense of belonging, plus a shop window for baby goods. Local publications, however, can be an excellent source of hard-to-find information included on childcare, nurseries, nannies and so on.

The sometimes sensationalist mainstream publications are, of course, financed by advertising from big name manufacturers. Perish the thought that product testing may on occasion be biased to manufacturers who support publications with their advertising spend.

TITLES

[Magazine] **Baby's Best Buys** (wViP; £2.95) – *Bi-annual specialising in equipment reviews.* / *(020) 7331 1000.*

Bumps and Babies (NCT) – *A free publication given out to new mothers at NHS antenatal checks at around 20 weeks.*

Food Facts – Hannah Hulme Hunter and Rosemary Dodds (For pregnancy and breastfeeding; National Childbirth Trust; 2003; £5.99; 0954301811) – *Information on the importance of nutrition before and after birth.*

FQ magazine (3 Dimensional Media; £2.99) – *From the publishers of GQ, "the first in a new genre of men's magazine" for men who've outgrown lads mags, "celebrating parenthood and lifestyle changes that come along with it". In other words, along with rather less sex there are several consumer oriented pieces on anything from facial products to cars, profiles of famous fathers, and some practical stuff for example on saving.* / http://www.fqmagazine.co.uk.

Hullabaloo! (it's about time - for parents; free) – *Distributed 10 months of the year to west London and parts of Surrey, a magazine containing information on family activities and services. It is found in town halls, playgroups, some doctor's surgeries, libraries, antenatal clinics and children's shops.* / (020) 8991 0008; hullaballooteam@hotmail.com; hullaballoopost@aol.com.

[Magazine] **Inspired Fatherhood** – ed R Harvey (Magazine for actively engaged fathers; £3.50 issue / £9 annual (3 issues)) – *A journal for fathers aiming to provide networking contacts, as well as interviews and personal stories.* / Send SAE for details to Richard Harvey, The Marles, Exmouth, Devon, EX8 4NE – 01364 73248.

[Magazine] **Junior** (Beach Magazines and Publising; monthly; £2.70) – *Newish publication aimed squarely at the fashion, badge-conscious parent of children aged up to eight, but with some decent information in between the pictures.*

[Magazine] **Junior Pregnancy & Baby** (Beach Magazines and Publising; £2.90) – *From the Junior stable, published every two months and including lots of fashion alongside the more serious articles. Big name columnists include Gina Ford, Vicky Lovine and Penelope Leach.*

[Magazine] **Mother & Baby Magazine** (Emap Elan; £1.80) – *The best-selling monthly glossy; aims to guide new mums with sound advice, no-nonsense consumer testing and readers' experiences.*

The Mother Magazine (The international magazne of fertility wareness, conscious conception, peaceful pregnancy, sacred birth, extended breastfeeding, natural immunity and more; £8 a year, sample issue £3.) – *'For the holistic mother and child', a UK-based international magazine on subjects like fertility awareness, conscious conception, peaceful pregnancy, sacred birth and extended breastfeeding.* / www.themothermagazine.co.uk The Cottage, Glassonby, nr Penrith, Cumbria CA10 1DU.

[Magazine] **Natural Parent Magazine** (What Doctors Don't Tell You; monthly; £24.95 annual sub) – *Monthly looking at prenatal care, birth, health, play, development and education: written by experts in their field rather than journalists. The angle is distinctly alternative but great if you like that sort of thing.* / WDDTY (020) 8944 9555, www.wddty.co.uk.

[Magazine] **New Baby** (wViP; £2.20) – *Monthly covering newborn care, product reviews and so on.* / (020) 7331 1000.

[Magazine] **Nursery Choices** – Sheila Lawlor (Centre for Policy Study; 1999; £5; 1897969295) – *Issues affecting every aspect of a child's development from pregnancy to pre-school. Unbiased and intelligent articles relating to the best in consumer products.* / 32 Sekforde Street, London EC1R 0HH – (020) 7306 0300.

[Magazine] **Practical Parenting** (IPC Magazines; £1.95) – *One of the biggest pregnancy and early childhood (birth-four) titles.*

[Magazine] **Right Start** (bimonthly; £11.70 for 6 issues) – *Aimed at ABC1 parents who care about their children's behaviour, development and health; special pullout play and learn activity section for one to seven year-olds.* / www.rightstartmagazine.co.uk, subscriptions (01732) 884023.

Twins & Supertwins (A publication for parents and families of multiples; Twincall Publications; Three months £9, six months £18, 12 months £36.) – *A low-tech publication which aims to put a more positive spin on the issue of multiple siblings than is found in many publications. It includes personal stories, practical pointers and tips and ideas.* / Twincall Publications, 28-30 Kings Avenue, Birchington, Kent CT7 9PP (01843) 845 885 www.tinsmag.com .

[Magazine] **Under Five Contact** – ed Ann Henderson (Pre School Learning Alliance; 10 issues per annum; £10 annually; 0-969948-1) – *As well as the pre-school movement, the magazine covers subjects like child development, nutrition, safety, play and learning.* / www.pre-school.org.uk.

Local London publications

TITLES

[Magazine] **Children's Ealing** (The Ealing 135 Group; £4) / www.ealing135.org.uk; local WH Smiths and libraries.

[Newsletter] **Families Magazines** (Free (postal delivery subscription £15.50 for 10 issues)) – *Particularly useful free newsletters produced several times a year with South west, South east, West, Thames and North London editions; information on all areas of child interest, particularly strong on education and childcare information; available in good toy and children's clothes shops, nurseries and libraries; recent back copies covering items of interest (for example nannies and au pairs) can be ordered at £2.99 for the first, £1 for each additional one thereafter; some features available on the website, www.familiesmagazine.co.uk. / PO Box 4302, London SW6 1EG, (020) 8986 9680, www.familiesonline.co.uk.*

[Periodical] **The Grapevine** (free) – *Editions covering Epsom & Ewell, and Sutton & Banstead, covering toddler groups and playgroups, childcare, education, leisure and advice on topics such as children's health. / PO Box 171, Reigate, Surrey RH2 7FW, (01737) 246153.*

Green Guide For London – ed Bel Jacobs (Green Guide Publishing; 1999; £5.99; 0952684160) – *Annually updated eco-friendly guide with sections on green parenting. An invaluable resource guide if having a child has made you think about doing your bit for the planet. / Central Books (020) 8986 4854.*

[Magazine] **The Parents' Guide** (£2.50; 13621327) – *Formerly the London Parents' Guide – a bi-monthly compilation of shops, companies and services as recommended by parents, largely from West London. / many bookshops and kids shops, or direct from 1 Stockwell Terrace SW9 0QD – (020) 7793 1990.*

South West & North West London Parents' Directories – *Free twice-yearly (May and November) listings guides of services in both areas, including extensive nursery school and nanny agency details. / (020) 8785 2430, (020) 8905 5480.*

[Booklet] **Toddlers Twickenham** (£2.75 + 25p p&p) – *Excellent booklet covering everything (in the borough of Richmond) from schools to pre-school playgroups, weekly story times at libraries, special needs groups, parks, playgrounds, outings and ideas for older children. / Richmond – (020) 8940 0981 and Twickenham – (020) 8892 8091 libraries.*

Toddlertime (The directory of activities and services for North and East London's under 3s; £1.50) / (01582) 620 960 www.toddlertime.co.uk.

West 4 Kids – A Hutchinson (NCT Publishing; £7.50; 0-952253-45-3) – *What used to be called Children's Chiswick is commonly known as the bible in the area and indeed is something of a tome (now in its 8th edition). Subjects covered include play activities for the under fives, sports and leisure, places of worship with details specific to children, parties, parks and green matters. / NCT Chiswick Branch.*

USEFUL CONTACTS

National Childbirth Trust (NCT)
Alexandra House, Oldham Terrace London W3 6NH ☎ *Enquiry line (0870) 444 8707* ⌂ *www.nct.org.uk; www.nctparentsconnect.co.uk*
Local NCT newsletters are sent to all members (membership £36 or £1 pa for those in receipt of means tested benefits) with useful advertisements about local services and activities. The quality varies depending on who is currently editing your local branch edition. / HOURS Mon-Thurs 9am-5pm, Fri 9am-4pm; or answerphone; SEE ALSO 1.01 Where to have the baby; 1.04 Antenatal classes; 2.01 Postnatal; 2.02 Feeding; 2.04 Childcare; 2.05 Travel; 2.06 Baby & toddler activities; 3.02 Baby equipment; 4.04 Miscarriage & stillbirth; 4.06 Support groups.

Parents Local
PO Box 38 Twickenham TW2 5YH ☎ *(020) 8755 4855*
Twice -yearly freebie local listings booklets, covering specific areas of London and the UK and with information relevant to children from newborn to 11 years.

4. VIDEOS

The following companies produce an interesting selection of videos relating to pregnancy and childcare issues.

USEFUL CONTACTS

B-line Productions
135 Sydney Rd London N10 2ND ☎ *(020) 8444 9574* ⌂ *www.b-lineproductions.co.uk*
Award-winning production company concentrating on family and health topics, which sells its videos direct: products include Dads (the experience of 10 different fathers); Birth (eight women's stories); Breast-feeding (if you want to you can); and Weaning Your Baby.

World of Health

PO Box 23103 London SE1 2GP ☎ *(020) 7357 9393* ⌂ *www.worldofhealth.co.uk*
A supplier of a wide range of health-related videos and DVDs, who sell a plethora of birth and pregnancy videos. / SEE ALSO *1.04 Antenatal classes; 2.01 Postnatal; 2.02 Feeding; 2.06 Baby & toddler activities; 4.02 Health practitioners.*

5. THE INTERNET

As with all areas of knowledge, for anyone with a plug into the "information superhighway", the World Wide Web is an increasingly valuable and reliable source of information on pregnancy, parenting and shopping for babies. (Especially in controversial areas, however, the validity of information offered needs to be treated with great caution.)

Websites for organisations and companies listed in this book are given wherever possible. Many offer online shopping or useful searchable databases of information and advice. It's certainly worth having a look. You can, of course, also search for information on a specific topic by using your favourite search engine.

The following are magazine-style sites which do not fit into listings elsewhere in the book.

GENERALIST SITES

The Active Birth Centre

25 Bickerton Rd London N19 5JT ☎ *(020) 7281 6760* ⌂ *www.activebirthcentre.com*
Register on the website for a free fortnightly e-mailed anenatal and baby diary sent until the baby is six months old. It offers a wide range of practical – and appropriately timed – advice. / HOURS *shop Mon-Fri 9.30am-6.30pm (Fri 4pm), Sat 10am-4pm;* SEE ALSO *1.01 Where to have the baby; 1.04 Antenatal classes; 1.06 Birth equipment; 2.01 Postnatal; 2.02 Feeding; 2.03 Baby health; 2.06 Baby & toddler activities; 3.01 Maternity wear; 3.02 Baby equipment; 4.02 Health practitioners.*

Ask Dr Sears

USA ☎ *US Online Sears Store +1 949 489 0020* ⌂ *www.askdrsears.com*
The website of a big name in US childcare theory, including information on his attachment parenting theories. FAQs cover a wide range of issues and concerns, often covering worries not featured in baby books. For example, what can you do if your baby goes on a feeding strike?

Association for Pre and Perinatal Psychology & Health

PO Box 1398, Forestville, CA USA 95436 ⌂ *www.birthpsychology.com*
Recommended by famed obstetrician Michel Odent, this site looks at the mental and emotional dimensions of pregnancy and birth, from both scholarly and personal perspectives.

The Baby Registry

11 Hillcrest Rd, Orgington Kent BR6 9AN ⌂ *www.thebabyregistry.co.uk*
Describing itself as an independent information service designed and maintained by a group of new parents; some sections are better than others, but all-in-all there's a very decent amount of information.

Baby Up

⌂ *www.babyup.com*
A small, friendly site "dedicated to all new and used parents around the world" – the content is slightly random, but there are, for example, numerous useful links to other sites.

Babycentre

⌂ *www.babycentre.co.uk*
Spin-off from the leading US site, adapted by British names in baby and child health and development; with the demise of former owner e-toys the focus these days seems to be more on community and less on commerce that it was.

Babyworld

Willowbank House, 84 Station Rd Marlow SL7 1NX ⌂ *www.babyworld.co.uk*
Originally part of Freeserve, now an independent – this site focuses on a wide range of issues from pre-conception to parenting; there are discussion groups, and if you dig deep quite a wide degree of content including some interesting product comparisons.

Bad Mothers Club
🖰 www.badmothersclub.co.uk
A site devoted to mothers who want to glory in what they don't do. The editorial is
less clichéd and more entertaining than most. Lively, opinionated forums are
a feature.

BBCi Parenting
🖰 www.bbc.co.uk/parenting
Part of the Beeb's apparently universal mission to explain and enlighten, the site
offers a wide range of information on pregnancy and childhood. You can also sign up
for a parenting newsletter.

Dads UK
85A Westbourne Street, Hove East Sussex BN3 5PF ☎ *(07092) 391489, (07092)
390210* 🖰 *www.dads-uk.co.uk*
For single (be it through separation or bereavement) and gay dads – advice from
those who have found themselves in similar situations, including tips on divorce,
custody and being without your children. It includes a forum. / HOURS Helpline Mon-Fri
11am-10pm; SEE ALSO 2.01 Postnatal.

Eparents
*NFPI (National Family And Parenting Institute), 430 Highgate Studios, 53-79 Highgate
Rd London NW5 ITL* ☎ *(020) 7424 3460* 🖰 *www.e-parents.org*
A site run by the National Family & Parenting Institute – an independent charity
which campaigns for a more family-friendly environment – it includes advice,
encouragement and a forum for parenting issues. / HOURS Mon-Fri 9.30am-5.30pm.

For Parents By Parents
Mossbank Road, Mossbank, St. Helen's Lancs 🖰 *www.forparentsbyparents.com*
Created and written entirely by parents, this site covers issues relating to babies and
children from birth to five years old, from postnatal depression to toilet training. It
aims to take a balanced view and not gloss over difficulties; separate sections for
mums and dads, shopping and information; links to support groups.

iVillage
☎ *(01992) 632222* 🖰 *www.ivillage.co.uk/pregnancyandbaby*
UK sibling to the extremely popular US community site, both of which feature
a Pregnancy & baby 'channel' amongst their array of woman-centred content;
hugely comprehensive, but at its best if you have a specific question in mind.

Mothering.com
🖰 www.mothering.com
The website of a leading US magazine, offering much useful free information, with
the emphasis on natural parenting and heath issues, but not neglecting practicalities
such as recipes.

Mothers35plus
🖰 www.mothers35plus.co.uk
A site for older mothers (an ever-more significant proportion of the total), including
a notice board and a forum, as well as a selection of practical information.

Mumsnet
🖰 www.mumsnet.com
'By parents for parents' – website with an emphasis on interactivity and chat, with
online discussions on regularly changing topics and the ability to 'ask the experts;
also noticeboard, parenting tips and a more static editorial section on parenting
issues.

National Childbirth Trust (NCT)
Alexandra House, Oldham Terrace London W3 6NH ☎ *Enquiry line (0870) 444 8707*
🖰 *www.nctpregnancyandbabycare.co.uk; www.nctparentsconnect.co.uk*
The organisation fields calls on pregnancy and birth related issues and is creating an
A-Z database covering 150 topices to provide callers with evidence-based and
up-to-date information. See the website for further information. / HOURS Mon-Thurs 9am-
5pm, Fri 9am-4pm; or answerphone; SEE ALSO 1.01 Where to have the baby; 1.04 Antenatal classes;
2.01 Postnatal; 2.02 Feeding; 2.04 Childcare; 2.05 Travel; 2.06 Baby & toddler activities; 3.02 Baby
equipment; 4.04 Miscarriage & stillbirth; 4.06 Support groups.

Netmums
🖰 www.netmums.com
A network of local websites with information about what's on, nurseries, schools and
local amenities (such as libraries and voluntary and community groups). There is also
a jobs corner, as well as notice boards for those with goods to buy or sell. Quality
varies somewhat by area, but the network appears to be growing.

Parent Soup
⌁ www.parentsoup.com
Part of the iVillage network; advertising-led US site with experts, resources, quizzes and so on; discussion 'communities' are broken up into areas for expectant parents, parents of newborns, toddlers and so on, up to teens.

Pregnancy Guide On-line
⌁ www.pregnancyguideonline.com
A US site with a week-by-week guide to pregnancy.

Pregnancy Today
PO Box 1780, Evanston, IL USA 60204 *⌁ www.pregnancytoday.com*
Highly-regarded US site, from the umbrella organisation iParenting; from pre-conception to teenagerhood, a regularly changing series of articles; regular e-mail newsletters.

UK Parents
☎ (0191) 260 2616 *⌁ www.ukparents.co.uk*
Interactive on-line magazine, one of the first British parenting sites, with a range of subject 'forums'; if you are looking for a place to chat online, or to post a question, this is an excellent place to start; also the 'Kid-online' shop, with 250 (generally smaller) products across a large range of categories. / SEE ALSO 3.08 *Nappies.*

6. SHOWS

The success in particular of the Baby Show sponsored by *Practical Parenting* has created a series of annual events around the country that make useful one-stop shops for parants and expectant parents.

USEFUL CONTACTS

Baby Show
Earls Court Exhibition Centre London SW5 9TA *☎ (0870) 122 1313*
⌁ www.thebabyshow.co.uk
Annually in London (and also now in Birmingham and Glasgow), a one-shop stop for new parents and parents-to-be where you can compare and buy everything from buggies and cots to baby clothes and shampoos. Tickets £10.50 (under 15s free).
/ HOURS *10am-5pm.*

Mother Baby and Toddler Show
Royal Bath and West Showground, Shepton Mallet Wiltshire *☎ (01749) 822222*
⌁ www.motherbabyandtoddlershow.co.uk/
"Everything for you, your baby and your child" – a series of retail fairs, in Bath and Bristol.

maternity worldwide
Saving lives in childbirth

The birth of your baby should be the happiest day of your life.....

▶ A woman dies in pregnancy or childbirth almost every minute. 99% of these deaths occur in developing countries. Most could be avoided with simple cheap measures. A million babies die soon after the death of their mothers.

▶ **maternity worldwide**, (registered charity no. 1093943) is developing an integrated programme of maternity care to help save these lives. Our project in Gimbie, Western Ethiopia, is providing trained professional staff for care in labour, as well as community education and health promotion.

body painting by Julia Laderman, photograph by Carolyn Cowan

A monthly donation of just £5 could save up to 5 mothers lives each year in Ethiopia

▶ **YES** I WANT TO HELP save lives in pregnancy and childbirth:

Web: www.maternityworldwide.org for information, secure online credit card donation and to print out a donation form for a new monthly standing order.
Email: info@maternityworldwide.org
Post: Send a donation (payable to 'Maternity Worldwide'), or a request for further information to: FREEPOST SEA14351, Brighton BN1 3ZZ
Phone: 01273 711464

CHAPTER 4.06

SUPPORT GROUPS

1. INTRODUCTION

Throughout the book there are a large number of support groups listed in individual chapters. This chapter covers groups whose area of concern does not fall neatly into any particular chapter. Local parent support groups, for example, can be found in chapter *2.01 Postnatal*.

For those facing special challenges of one kind or another, meeting or just corresponding with others in the same position can constitute a real lifeline. What's more, support groups can prove to be better sources of information than professionals working in the respective areas.

Note 1: here as elsewhere, the full postal address for these organisations is to be found in chapter *5.01 Index of organisations*.

Note 2: although support groups are useful sources of advice, especially in medical areas, it is generally advisable not to rely on them as a sole source of advice. Where support groups can be particularly useful is in directing you to sources where you can find the latest research.

Be aware of a trend in the US, which may well spread to the UK, for drug companies to offer funding to support groups. The practice generally results in some bias in the advice given by the group, in particular in favour of drug-based treatments. Particularly if you encounter any enthusiastic support for drugs to tackle a condition, look for details of how the organisation is funded.

FREEPHONE NUMBERS

0800 numbers (free calls) will not appear on itemised telephone bills.

USEFUL CONTACTS

Directory of UK Self Help & Support Organisations,
☎ *(01253) 402237* ☝ *www.UKselfhelp.info*
If you cannot find what you are looking for in this chapter or elsewhere in the book, you may be able to find it on this rather basic website which details more than 800 support organisations (mostly with website links) are available; more details are available in a book or on CD for £12.58.

OTHER INFORMATION SOURCES

Directory of UK Self Help Groups and Support Organisations (G-Text; £10) – *A book or CD of the contact names and numbers of 760 groups, including many relevant to pregnancy and for young children. Details are also available from the website.* / *G-Text, 259 Squires Gate Lane, Blackpool FY4 3RE (01253) 402 237 www.ukselfhelp.info.*

2. ADOPTION/ASSISTED CONCEPTION

USEFUL CONTACTS

Ace Babes, ☎ *(0115) 9879 266* ☝ *www.acebabes.co.uk*
Supporting parents of children born through assisted conception via a newsletter and get-togethers. The website includes news, articles, events listings, details of subgroups, information on a group for older children, a bulletin board, a for-sale board and useful links.

Adoption UK, ☎ *(0870) 770 0450* ☝ *www.adoptionuk.org*
Charity for adoptive families which maintains an 'experience resource bank' of families willing to share adoption experiences; formerly called 'Parent to Parent Information on Adoption Services'; some local groups. / PUBLICATIONS *Quarterly newsletter; leaflets: 'Adoption, Attachment & Development: Making the Connection' (considers the probable need for extra stimulation and nurturing to compensate the child for early losses, including pointers of behaviour patterns that may indicate a problem); 'Maintaining Links with Birth families' (£1). 'Adoption: The Inside Story' (a collection of articles from the newsletter, £7).*

After Adoption, ☎ *(0161) 839 4932, Helpline (0161) 839 4930*
☝ *www.afteradoption.org.uk*
Originally a face-to-face service for the Greater Manchester area (now also in the North East and Wales), but also a UK-wide helpline offering counselling and information to all family members affected by adoption. It claims to be the largest post-adoption service in the UK. / HOURS *helpline 10am-12pm, 2-4pm Mon-Thu (Tue 7pm);* PUBLICATIONS *Leaflets .*

Infertility Network UK, ☎ *(01424) 732361*
☝ *www.infertilitynetworkuk.com*
For couples suffering from infertility or whose children were born after assisted reproduction techniques (24-hour cover on number given). Annual membership (£20) gives access to confidential medical advice. / HOURS *Mon-Fri 9am-5pm ;* PUBLICATIONS *Various publications available.*

Overseas Adoption Service (Oasis), ☎ *(0870) 241 7069*
☝ *www.member.lycos.co.uk/adoption*
Support, information and advice for parents wishing to adopt children from orphanages overseas.

Post Adoption Centre, ☎ *Office (020) 7284 0555, Adviceline (0870) 777 2197* ☝ *www.postadoptioncentre.org.uk*
Advice for anyone who has been involved in adoption, offering support, counselling, family work and advice, individually or in group sessions, and also post-adoption parenting skills classes and family assessments. Around a quarter of people who use the centre are adoptive parents. The advice line is open Mon-Wed and Fri, 10am-1pm and Thu, 5.30pm-7.30pm. / HOURS *advice 10.30am-1pm;* PUBLICATIONS *Wide range of publications. Leaflets: Preparing People to Adopt Young Children and Babies (£3.50); Thoughts on Adoption for Adoptive Parents (£5); Adoption Comes of Age – Adoption in the 1990s (£3). Booklists on adoption (£1).*

READING

Parents for Children – Alice Fowler (Stories of Adoption; Profile Books; 2001; £8.99; 1861973438) – *A dozen families' adoption stories.* / *Published in association with the Parents for children adoption agency.*

3. ASIAN WOMEN

USEFUL CONTACTS

Asian Family Counselling Service, ☎ *(020) 8571 3933*
Family, marital and individual counselling. / *HOURS Mon-Thu 10am-4pm.*

Asian Women's Resource Centre, ☎ *(020) 8838 3462 Bilingual helpline*
A wide range of issues are targeted: from welfare and maternity rights, to dealing with sexual abuse. On Thursdays there are 'drop-in' sessions on different issues of interest; crèche, weekdays (not Tue).

Sangam, ☎ *(020) 8952 7062*
Association of Asian women which runs advice sessions – for example on legal, marital and welfare rights, housing issues and immigration problems. / *HOURS Mon-Fri 9.30am-5.30pm, Sat 10am-2pm.*

4. DIVORCE & SEPARATION

See also Relationships, above, for mediation services

USEFUL CONTACTS

Association of Shared Parenting, ⏃ *www.sharedparenting.org.uk*
A charity whose work involves giving support and advice to fathers and mothers who are worried about the welfare of their children after a separation or divorce. It encourages parents to recognise a child's right to nurture from both parents.

Both Parents Forever, ☎ *(01689) 854343*
An advice agency for parents who separate or divorce. It explains parental and children's rights under the Children's Act 1989, plus grandparents' rights to apply for orders to see the children. The organisation's recommendations, contrary to those of some solicitors, are based on the belief that children want to continue to see both parents, and both sets of grandparents, and resent being used as a pawn in the 'game' of reaching a settlement. Membership (£7) offers entitlement to second opinions on problems, and litigants are helped in the preparation of statements, affidavits and court cases. / *PUBLICATIONS A general information pack covers the rights of all parties relating to divorce, separation and care proceedings, £6.50; Grandparents' rights pack, £2; Child abduction pack, £4; newsletters cover relevant legal developments.*

Care for the Family, ☎ *(029) 2081 0800* ⏃ *www.care-for-the-family.org.uk*
This Christian charity organises events around the UK looking at marriage, parenting and family life, including the benefits of family-building breaks. For single parents it offers specialist resources, including a pen pal scheme. / *PUBLICATIONS Quarterly newsletter.*

Equal Parenting Council, ☎ *(0906) 550 1865* ⏃ *www.equalparenting.org/*
A not-for-profit company which is part of Family Law Training & Education Ltd – a fathers' lobby group which argues that children should not be asked which parent they want to live with or visit, because they need both parents. / *HOURS 24 hr helpline.*

Stepfamilies UK, ⏃ *www.stepfamilies.co.uk*
A website addressing all the relevant issues, and including a forum.

5. GAY PARENTS

USEFUL CONTACTS

Pink Parents UK, ☎ *(0117) 904 4500, (0870) 127 3274, Helpline (0117) 377 5794* ⏃ *www.pinkparents.org.uk*
A UK charity of, for and by lesbian, gay and bisexual parents, parents-to-be and their children. Their website is an invaluable starting-point for anyone contemplating pink parenthood. / *HOURS Helpline: Thurs 7pm-10pm; PUBLICATIONS PinkParents magazine, annual subscription £18, £10 concession; It's a Family Affair, the complete lesbian aprenting book, £12.50; Joint Residence Orders - a guide for same sex co-parenting couples, £1; plus books on lesbian motherhood, for gay men, about insemination, and about coming out to your children. .*

6. GRANDPARENTS

USEFUL CONTACTS

Grandparents' Federation, ☎ *(01279) 428040, Helpline (01279) 444964* ⏚ *www.grandparents-federation.org.uk*
A charity for grandparents; advice, information and support for grandparents of children affected by a divorce or separation; also offering advice for grandparents whose grandchildren are placed into care, and then adopted; also advice on applying for a Residence Order in respect of a grandchild living with them if they wish the child to continue living with them. / *HOURS Office 9am-5pm, Helpline Mon-Fri 10am-4pm some evenings and weekends. ; PUBLICATIONS The Children Act; What's in it for Grandparents? gives information for grandparents wanting to maintain contact plus information on how to obtain a Contact Order.*

7. LAW

(For support groups relating to employment law, see chapter 1.05 Rights.)

USEFUL CONTACTS

The Children's Legal Centre, ☎ *(01206) 873935* ⏚ *www.childrenslegalcentre.com*
A unique organisation concerned with law and policy affecting children; due to lack of funding their advice line is not currently running, but simple queries can be answered by e-mail via the website. The Education Advocacy Unit is for parents of children experiencing difficulties with their education, including disputes with local authorities. / *HOURS Mon-Fri 9am-5pm; PUBLICATIONS many publications, plus a monthly magazine 'childRIGHT'.*

Family Rights Group, ☎ *Helpline (0800) 7311696, (020) 7923 2628* ⏚ *www.frg.org.uk*
Established in 1974 to provide advice and support for families whose children are involved with social services, this organisation works to improve the services received, and to ensure that families can fully participate in decisions regarding their children. The group can advise on statutory rights, particularly those relating to child protection procedures; advice by phone or in answer to written correspondence; they can also provide intensive support and advocacy where it is needed. The organisation campaigns for support for parents in this area, and improvements in childcare policy and law. / *HOURS Mon - Fri 10am-noon, 1.30pm-3.30pm.*

Law Centres Federation, ☎ *(020) 7387 8570* ⏚ *www.lawcentres.org.uk*
Law centres are funded by local authorities (sometimes staffed by volunteers) and provide free legal services to people who live or work in their catchment area on housing, employment and childcare issues. Staff include solicitors and barristers who can offer appropriate legal representation. Priority is given to deserving cases. This, their HQ, can give contact details of their 22 centres in London. There are associate members of the federation such as the Disability Law Service.

Rights of Women, ☎ *Advice line (020) 7251 6577, Admin (020) 7251 657516* ⏚ *www.row.org.uk*
Funded by the London Borough Grants committee, this non-profit organisation provides free legal advice to women. It also promotes the interests of women in relation to the law. / *HOURS Tues, Weds, Thurs 2pm-4pm & 7pm-9pm, Fri 12pm-2pm.*

8. MULTIPLE BIRTHS (TWINS, TRIPLETS, ...)

(For suppliers of double buggies, see chapter 3.02 Baby equipment.)

Multiple births are somewhat on the increase in the UK – the result it seems of an aging maternal population and increasing use of fertility treatments (and, perhaps, according to some studies, because of the amount of folic acid now commonly eaten by women around conception).

Around 1.5% of pregnancies in the UK involve twins. Triplets used to occur no more than once in every 8,000 pregnancies and quadruplets just once in every 700,000. Fertility treatments especially have impacted on these figures, with, for example, some estimates of the rate of triplet births now approaching one in 300.

Despite such increases, the 'system' is still not particularly well equipped for multiple births, so some help can be important.

READING

Breast-feeding Twins, Triplets or More – Jane Middleton (TAMBA; 1994; £2) / www.tamba.org.uk, (0870) 770 3304.

[Video] **Coping with Twins** (Bounty Vision Production; 1991; £14.95) – *Available with Preparing for Twins (see also). / Multiple Births Foundation, www.multiplebirths.org.uk.*

Double Trouble – Emma Mahony (Twins and How to Survive Them; HarperCollins; 2003; £10.99; 0007153988) – *By a twin and mother of twins, a look at the practicalities in pregnancy and thereafter, with advice from experts.*

Mothering Multiples – Karen Gromada (Breastfeeding and caring for twins or more; La Leche League International; 1999; 0912500514) – *Given that the mainstream titles are not always encouraging on this subject, a title for mothers who know this is definitely what they want. / www.laleche.org.uk.*

Multiple Blessings – Betty Rothbart (Hearst Books; 1994; £7.99; 0-688116-42-6)

Preparing for Twins & Triplets – Elizabeth Bryan (Multiple Births Foundation; 1996; £2.50; 0951770985) / www.multiplebirths.org.uk.

Twins & Multiple Births – Dr Carol Cooper (The essential parenting guide from pregnancy to adulthood; Vermilion; 1997; £9.99; 0-091814-71-5) – *The reasons for multiple pregnancies, possible problems and practical suggestions for coping; a useful title in an area where professionals often lack experience, although there are regular looks at what could go wrong.*

Twins & The Family – Audrey Sandbank & John Acton (The essential guide to bringing up twins; TAMBA; 1992; £5.50; 0951870505) – *Needs of twins and their families from birth on, written by a family therapist and mother of twins.*

Twins and Supertwins – *A monthly publication for parents of multiple children. / Twincall Publications, Parkland House, 205-217 New Road, Chatham, Kent ME4 4QA (01843) 845 885 www.twins-supertwins.co.uk.*

The Twins Handbook – Elizabeth Friedrich & Cherry Rowland (From pre-birth to first schooldays - a parents' guide; Robson Books; 1984; £8.99; 0860512673) – *A book with a warm, relaxed style – everything from pregnancy onwards.*

Twins in the Family – Elizabeth M Bryan (Constable & Co; £5.95; 009465560X) – *History and mythology of twins, then pregnancy, and delivery are covered in some depth with discussion of special needs and complications, newborn twins, the first six months, identity, and pre-school years.*

USEFUL CONTACTS

Multiple Births Foundation, ☎ (020) 8383 3519

⌖ www.multiplebirths.org.uk
Based at Queen Charlotte's, the foundation offers specialist medical advice (including over the phone) to parents with, or expecting twins, triplets or more. Referrals may also be made to the medical or nursing director. Regular meetings, talks and clinics take place on development (particularly of language, and behaviour), 'supertwins' (i.e. triplets, quads, etc), growth and bereavement. Family members who also have twins are welcomed.

Twins & Multiple Births Association (TAMBA), ☎ (0870) 770 3305 ⌖ www.tamba.org.uk

National confidential listening, information and support service for parents with twins, triplets or more, which provides help individually, and through local Twins Clubs. Specialist sub-groups include: a Special Needs Group (to help families with illness or disability making it difficult to bring up twins); a Bereavement Support Group; an Infertility Group (for parents expecting twins as a result of fertility treatment); a Supertwins Group for families with triplets or more; and a One-Parent Families Group. / *HOURS Mon-Fri 9.30am-5pm; PUBLICATIONS Free information pack.*

9. ONE-PARENT FAMILIES

READING

Parentalk's How to Succeed as a Single Parent – Diane Louise Jordan (Hodder & Stoughton; 2003; £7.99; 0-340-86119-3) – *A one-time Blue Peter presenter uses her personal experience to discuss the issues, which include catering for your own needs as well as your child's, defining your role as a single parent and juggling time and money.* / www.madaboutbooks.co.uk.

Successful Single Parenting – Mike Lilley (How To Books; 1996; £9.99; 1857033027) – *A straightforward look at coping with a split or bereavement – handling stress, childcare and your social life, with practical advice on emotional, legal and financial issues.*

USEFUL CONTACTS

Gingerbread Association for One Parent Families,
☎ (020) 7488 9300, *Confidential advice line (0800) 018 4318*
✆ www.gingerbread.org.uk
Arguably the leading support charity for lone parents and children in England and Wales; local self-help groups meet weekly or fortnightly; there is also an online support group ('Virtual Gingerbread'); free helpline. / *HOURS Mon-Fri 9am-5pm; PUBLICATIONS Range of publications, including a lone parents handbook for members; quarterly newsletter.*

Holidays Endeavour for Lone Parents (HELP),
☎ (0114) 2882967
National volunteer organisation arranging quality, low-cost holidays in the UK and Spain for lone parents. Send SAE or call for further details.

National Council for One Parent Families (NCOPF),
☎ (020) 7428 5400, *Helpline (0800) 018 5026* ✆ www.oneparentfamilies.org.uk
Famously supported by 'Harry Potter' author JK Rowling, this charity campaigns for the rights of lone parents, aims to overcome the isolation and social exclusion of single parents, and runs a helpline offering advice, information and support. It maintains a database of national and local support groups of interest to lone parents and there is a quarterly newsletter for members. / *HOURS helpline Mon-Fri 9am-5pm; PUBLICATIONS Free leaflets: holidays; maintenance; splitting up; responsibilities for children; the CSA; being pregnant and single; coping with the death of a partner; housing; benefits; tax; legal rights; policy briefings; returning to work.*

10. PREMATURE/SPECIAL CARE BABIES

(For information about premature babies and cot death, see chapter 2.03 Baby health. For details of specialist manufacturers of clothes for premature babies, see chapter 3.04 Baby clothes. For information about Miscarriage and still-birth, see chapter 4.04 Miscarriage & still birth.)

Around 10% of UK babies, i.e. about 70,000 a year, spend time in a neonatal unit. It can be a very trying time, with much valuable support gained from talking to someone else who has been through a similar experience.

READING

Born Too Early – Peter Moore (Practical guide for parents of babies born too early; Thorsons; 1995; £5.99; 0722532296) – *Written in conjunction with Action Aid: a small book to help parents of babies who have been born prematurely; what is happening and why; what actions parents can take.*

Breastfeeding Special Care Babies – Sandra Lang (Bailliere Tindall; 2002; £16.99; 0702025445) – *The guide considers positioning and attachment, milk supply and the impact of common drugs, as well as breast conditions and problems and their resolution. Particular attention is paid to feeding the vulnerable baby and to alternative feeding methods.*

Your Premature Baby – Nikki Bradford (0-5 years; Frances Lincoln; 2000; £9.99; 0711216142) – *Aiming to explain medical procedures and terminology and offer advice on the help available and on emotional issues; backed up by personal case studies; royalties go to Tommy's Campaign which researches in this field.*

USEFUL CONTACTS

Baby Life Support Systems (BLISS), ☎ *(020) 7820 9471*

⌁ www.bliss.org.uk

Helpline and network groups for parents of sick newborn or premature babies.
Membership (£10 individuals, £15 families) includes a regular newsletter. / *HOURS Mon-Fri 10.30am-4.30pm; PUBLICATIONS Booklets: Taking Your Premature Baby Home; Guide to Neonatal Equipment (with pictures and explanations of all the equipment used in SCBUs); BPD (information on a lung problem occurring in premature babies, and how they are helped to breathe); send A4 SAE.*

National Childbirth Trust (NCT), ☎ *Enquiry line (0870) 444 8707*

⌁ www.nctpregnancyandbabycare.co.uk; www.nctparentsconnect.co.uk

Via the organisation's 'Experiences register' you can be put in touch with NCT
members who have themselves experienced being the parent of a premature
baby. / *HOURS Mon-Thurs 9am-5pm, Fri 9am-4pm; or answerphone.*

11. PROTECTING CHILDREN

(For support groups relating to child safety, see chapter 3.03 Nursery decor.)

USEFUL CONTACTS

ChildLine, ☎ *(020) 7650 3200, Helpline 24 hours (0800) 1111*

⌁ www.childline.org.uk

A free national helpline with counselling for children in trouble or danger, or adults
concerned about a child; over a million children have been helped since the helpline
opened in 1986; factsheets on a variety of topics are available (also on the
website). / *HOURS 24hr helpline; PUBLICATIONS Free factsheets on: bereavement; bullying; child abuse; suicide; HIV/AIDS; stepfamilies; eating problems; safe surfing.*

The Children's Society, ☎ *Switch (020) 7841 4400, Supportsline (0845) 3001128* *⌁ www.the-childrens-society.org.uk*

An organisation (originally founded and now supported by the Church of England)
concerned with the wellbeing of children in deprived areas: the focus covers a variety
of different areas – safety, the avoidance of crime, education and looking after
children with special needs. The organisation works to a large extent with local
authorities and schools in 90-plus projects around the country, but also provides
a general helpline for supporters– both children and adults. / *HOURS Mon-Fri 9am-5pm ; PUBLICATIONS Range of publications (especially on issues such as adoption & separation).*

Fair Play for Children, ☎ *(01243) 869922*

⌁ www.arunet.co.uk/fairplay/home.htm

An association of various interested groups which campaigns for children's right to
play (as stipulated in the UN Declaration and Convention on the Rights of the Child)
and publishes fact sheets to help those setting up a playgroup or play area. The
organisation holds training events on child protection all over the country (to give
people an idea of what they can do) as well as offering its members a 'police check'
service (to weed out those unsuited to work with kids). / *HOURS Tue-Fri 10am-4pm.*

Kidscape, ☎ *(020) 7730 3300, Helpline 0845 1205204* *⌁ www.kidscape.org.uk*

An organisation committed to keeping children safe from harm or abuse (including
bullying) – the only national children's charity which focuses upon preventative
policies. / *PUBLICATIONS Publication for children, parents and teachers; available to order off Web site; How to stop bullying, Kidscape training guide (£19); Free download of child safety pack and bully pack. .*

National Children's Bureau, ☎ *(020) 7843 6000* *⌁ www.ncb.org.uk*

Not a support group as such, but a research organisation largely for professionals,
providing a national centre for advice, consultancy and information on current
practice and thinking on early childhood. They will give parents contact numbers of
appropriate organisations from their database: Library service enquiry line (020) 7843
6008; Council for Disabled Children (020) 7843 6058.

National Society for the Prevention of Cruelty to Children (NSPCC), ☎ *Helpline (0800) 800500* *⌁ www.nspcc.org.uk*

This leading charity provides a number of leaflets to help parents stay cool when
dealing with their kids. The National Centre Child Protection Helpline offers
counselling and advice for anyone – including children themselves – concerned about
or at risk of child abuse. / *HOURS 24hr helpline; PUBLICATIONS Behave Yourself! A guide to Better Parenting; Handle with Care, a leaflet on handling babies; Putting Children First – a guide for parents of 0-5 year-olds; Leaving Kids on their Own, and Stress, a guide for parents.*

What About The Children? (WATCH), ☎ *(01892) 863245*

🖰 *www.whataboutthechildren.org.uk*
This national charity promotes parental responsibility and aims to raise awareness of
the emotional requirements of children under three. It advocates the need for stable,
continuous one-to-one care; information on separation anxiety and attachment is
available on request.

12. RELATIONSHIPS (INCLUDING MEDIATION & PARENT-ING)

USEFUL CONTACTS

African Caribbean Family Mediation Service, ☎ *(020) 7737 2366*
A member of National Family Mediation (see also): services include counselling for
men and child-focused mediation.

Asian Family Counselling Service, ☎ *(020) 8571 3933*
An organisation providing help with a range of difficult situations, including
problems with adapting to Western culture as well as aid in dealing with family and
marital conflicts. For the latter, there is a conciliation service – just call and make an
appointment. (The service also runs training courses for women who want to
become counsellors.) / HOURS Mon-Thu 10am-4pm.

Central Middlesex Family Mediation, ☎ *(020) 8427 2076*
A member of National Family Mediation; Mediation service and support for couples
making joint agreements on children, house and family items; Sliding scale
charge. / HOURS Mon-Fri 9am-5pm and by appointment.

Eye to Eye Mediation, ☎ *(020) 7701 1114, (020) 7703 2532*
🖰 *www.nch.org.uk*
A member of National Family Mediation (see also), managed by NCH (what used to
be National Children's Homes); mediators specialise in working with all ethnic
groups in the community, and work with extended family and grandparents. Also
a service for children, called Child's Eye, offering a place for children to discuss their
reaction to what is happening to their family. / HOURS Mon-Fri 9.30-5.

The Family Mediation Service, ☎ *(020) 7391 9150*
🖰 *www.instituteoffamilytherapy.org.uk*
'All issues' mediation, including specialist advice on complex children's issues and
high income financial issues. / HOURS 9.30am-5.30pm.

Mediation in Divorce, ☎ *(020) 8891 6860*
A member of National Family Mediation (see also), offering an out-of-court family
mediation and counselling service for adults and children: based in Twickenham,
it draws clients from south and west London. / HOURS Mon-Fri 9am-5pm.

National Family Mediation, ☎ *(0117) 904 2825* 🖰 *www.nfm.u-net.com*
A network of over 60 local family mediation services in England and Wales: all
members offer help to partners (married or unmarried) who have decided to
separate, enabling them to do so as amicably and peacefully as possible, especially if
children are involved. Referrals are from courts, GPs, Relate and other agencies as
well as from the parents themselves, either individually or jointly. Discussions cover
the decision to separate, ongoing arrangements for children, finance and property,
and other issues such as education and grandparents. The entire process is voluntary
(all centres are registered charities) and nothing is ever imposed; most services have
a small charge or use a sliding scale, although some make no charge. The nine
London centres are listed separately. / HOURS Mon-Fri 9.30am-3.30pm.

North London Family Mediation Service, ☎ *(020) 8343 9899*
🖰 *www.nfm.u-net.com*
A member of National Family Mediation (see also), covering north London's Barnet,
Haringey, Enfield and Highgate. / HOURS Mon-Fri 9am-5pm.

Parentline Plus, ☎ *Freephone parent Helpline (0808) 800 2222, Textphone (0800) 783 6783* 🖰 *www.parentlineplus.org.uk*
A membership organisation offering a range of information, support and advice to
parents, and especially members of stepfamilies; now also incorporating Parent

Network. / HOURS helpline Mon-Fri 2pm-5pm & 7pm-8pm; PUBLICATIONS Newsletter; booklets (on issues including grandparents, weddings, changing children's family names, and making a will; also downloadable from the website); A New Baby (£4) is for stepfamilies planning more children.

Psychotherapy for Couples, ☎ (0870) 902 4878

Aims to be more long-term than counselling; free matching service puts couples in touch with a local trained marital psychotherapist.

Relate, ☎ (01788) 573241 ⌁ www.relate.org.uk

The well-known support organisation provides confidential counselling on relationship problems. Weekly sessions are recommended – the first session will normally be within two weeks of booking. / HOURS Mon-Fri 9am-5pm; PUBLICATIONS Range of publications.

Relationship Counselling for London, ☎ (020) 7580 1087

⌁ www.counselling4london.com
The organisation provides details of relationship guidance counsellors; also offers counselling directly (not just for married couples). It has offices in the West End, SE London, and Battersea, and specialist expertise in postnatal depression and ethnic issues. Contributions are requested (the organisation is a charity), worked out on a sliding income scale.

South East London Family Mediation Bureau, ☎ (020) 8315 7460

A member of National Family Mediation (see also); offices in Croydon, Bromley and Bexley; separate children and parents counselling services. / HOURS Mon-Thurs 9.30am-5pm.

Women's Aid Federation England, ☎ Administration (0117) 944 4411, 24 hr Helpline (0808) 200 0247 ⌁ www.womensaid.org.uk

Support and information for women and children escaping domestic violence, or physical and mental cruelty, and those seeking to help people in such a situation. Telephone numbers of local refuges are available from the helpline and are listed on the website. / HOURS Mon-Fri 10am-1pm; 2pm-4pm.

13. SERIOUS CONGENITAL/MEDICAL CONDITIONS – CHILDREN

(See also chapter 4.01 London boroughs for details of services provided by local authorities. For support groups relating to problems that usually manifest themselves as developmental concerns – such as autism, dyslexia and ADD – see chapter 2.03 Baby health. Complementary health techniques, detailed in chapter 4.02 Complementary Medicine and Health Practitioners may also be helpful in treating a range of special needs conditions. Osteopathy and nutrition are reported to be particularly helpful.)

This section covers support groups for children affected by both physical and mental conditions, whether inherited or caused by accidents or birth defects.

Note that, as Suzanne Askham (author of Coping When Your Child has Special Needs) points out, misdiagnosis is relatively common in most areas and information provided through traditional medical channels can be limited, so independent investigations by parents can prove helpful. The web can be incredibly useful in this area, even if the bias is often to sites in the US (and even if usual caveats apply as to being extremely careful about relying on much of what is available online).

READING

The Autistic Spectrum – Lorna Wing (A guide for parents and professionals; Constable & Robinson; 2003; £9.99; 1841196746) – By a psychiatric consultant for the National Autistic Society and mother of an autistic daughter, a guide explaining how people with autism experience the world and their need for an organised and structured environment. It looks at ways of improving communication, developing abilities and enlarging social interaction, and also gives advice on coping with family stresses. / www.constablerobinson.com .

Can children and young people have mental health problems? (NHS; free) / (0800) 555777.

Children with Special Needs – Richard Woolfson (Faber & Faber; 1991; £6.99; 0571143571) – *Coverage includes the initial diagnosis, likely future, and integration and education of a special-needs child.*

Children's Consent to Surgery – Priscilla Alderson (Open University Press; 1993; £19.99; 0335157327) – *Drawing on research and interviews with children and their carers – the extent to which children can make their own decisions regarding their care.*

Coping When Your Child has Special Needs – Suzanne Askham (Sheldon Press; 2000; £6.99; 0-85969-825-4) – *An upbeat book by the mother of a special needs child with plenty of encouragement, as well as warnings about the relatively common issue of misdiagnosis, making it a good counter to the 'Dr Dooms' of the medical establishment. In addition to good coverage of all the issues, it includes a useful further reading list.*

Holding Time – Dr Martha Welch, Mary Ellen Mark (How to eliminate the conflict, temper tantrums, and sibling rivalry and raise happy, loving children; Simon & Schuster; 1989; £11; 0671688782) – *By a US child development psychiatrist, specialising in autism and mothering – a strategy based on the nurturing bond that forms when you hold your child physically. The author argues, with reference to her cases, that holding can help cure profound autism and achieve great results with whining, temper tantrums, sibling rivalry and more.*

To A Different Drumbeat – P Clarke, H Kofsky & J Lauruol (A practical guide to parenting children with special needs; Hawthorn Press; 1989; £7.99; 1869890094) – *By parents for parents with children with handicaps or special needs; practical suggestions and a look at the emotional needs and development of these children.*

USEFUL CONTACTS

Action for Leisure, ☎ (020) 8783 0173 ⏚ www.actionforleisure.org.uk
A small national charity (fka PLANET), promoting play and leisure with and for disabled children and adults. Provides information on all aspects of play and has started to establish a national database of local facilities. / HOURS Mon-Fri 9am-5pm.

Action for Sick Children, ☎ (020) 7843 6444
⏚ www.actionforsickchildren.org
Advice, information and listening service for parents and carers of sick children. Issues covered include hospitalisation, post-hospital care, education and play for sick children, family-centred care, pain management, and useful support groups. A Parent Adviser can answer queries about specific cases, but cannot give medical advice. ASC's library offers a unique collection of documents on the emotional and psychological needs of sick children and their families. The library is open to anyone with an interest in children's healthcare (open Wed & Thu only) – literature searches are available for a £5 fee. / HOURS Mon-Thu 9.30am-5pm; PUBLICATIONS Range of leaflets and books – phone or send SAE for list.

Addis (Attention Deficit Disorder Information Services),
☎ (020) 8906 9068 ⏚ www.addis.co.uk
Run by the mother of a child with ADHD, a support group handling 5,000 letters and 3,600 calls a year, most from parents seeking help with the right medical care or schooling. Visit the website or send a large SAE for information. / HOURS Helpline Mon-Fri 10am-5pm.

Association for Children with Hand or Arm Deficiency (REACH), ☎ (0845) 130 6225 ⏚ www.reach.org.uk
A charity which – as well as encouraging research into upper limb prosthetics and orthotics, causes of congenital upper limb deficiency and surgical techniques – can provide references to self-help local support groups. / HOURS Mon-Fri 9.30am-5.30pm; PUBLICATIONS Free information pack; quarterly newsletter.

Association for Children with Terminal & Life-threatening Conditions & their Families (ACT), ☎ (0800) 849 4545, (020) 7240 1275 ⏚ www.act.org.uk
This national organisation aims to provide information on support services available for families whose children have life-threatening or terminal conditions (regardless of the actual condition, which may stem from illness or a birth defect). The association is involved in consultation and contact between support providers, and campaigns for the development of children's palliative care services; free membership available to parents.

Association for Spina Bifida & Hydrocephalus (ASBAH),
☎ (020) 8441 9967, (020) 8449 0475 ⏚ www.asbah.org
The organisation provides advisory, advocacy and support services to people with spina bifida and/or hydrocephalus, their families and carers, through a network of

professional advisors plus specialists in mobility, continence management, education and medical matters. / HOURS Mon-Fri 9am-5pm; PUBLICATIONS factsheets on both conditions, antenatal screening, genetic counselling, vitamin supplementation for prevention, vaccinations – SAE.

BackCare (The National Organisation for Healthy Backs),
☎ (020) 8977 5474 ⏚ www.backcare.org.uk
The association (formerly known as the National Back Pain Association) has information aimed both at mothers and babies. / PUBLICATIONS Back Care, Pregnancy & Children, £2.

Bobath Centre for Children with Cerebral Palsy,
☎ (020) 8444 3355 ⏚ www.bobath.org.uk
A treatment centre (and postgraduate teaching unit) caring for children and adults with cerebral palsy. Having been referred by a consultant or GP, both NHS and private patients are treated. Patients are assessed and a treatment plan developed including specialised handling to give better co-ordinated movement. Outpatients are offered physiotherapy, speech language therapy and occupational therapy. / PUBLICATIONS Information pack; newsletter.

British Epilepsy Association, ☎ (0808) 800 5050
⏚ www.epilepsy.org.uk
The association offers general information on adult or child epilepsy (an estimated one in 200 births in the UK is to a sufferer, though the condition is rarely inherited). The organisation offers access to information, not least through its network of local support groups. Membership of £15 (£10 for unwaged) secures a quarterly magazine and personal accident insurance cover. / HOURS Mon-Thu 9am-4.30pm, Fri 9am-4pm; PUBLICATIONS epilepsy and children, 50p; women and epilepsy, 25p; various other factsheets – send SAE for printed material; sell many general books; videos (including relating to caring for kids) for sale.

British Heart Foundation, ☎ (020) 7487 7110, Heart information line
(08450) 70 80 70 ⏚ www.bhf.org.uk
Information service about all manner of heart conditions (congenital defects, hypertension, transplants) which can refer to local support groups. Advice on how to care for babies with heart conditions is also available. / HOURS Mon-Fri 9am-5pm; PUBLICATIONS Children with Heart Conditions: A guide for parents – SAE; videos.

The British Institute for Brain Injured Children (BIBIC),
☎ (01278) 684060 ⏚ www.bibic.org.uk
For children with Down's syndrome, autism, trauma injury, learning disability or developmental delay. The organisation (founded 1972) runs tailored programmes to encourage a child's neurological development: specialised exercises and nutritional advice. The programmes are reported to be effective in the vast majority of cases – the earlier a child starts, the better. Most costs are subsidised: families may pay around £1,600 a year although means-tested full bursaries are available. Family members are required to help with the programme (minimum one hour per day).

British Kidney Patients Association, ☎ (01420) 472021
⏚ www.britishkidney-pa.co.uk
A campaign and support group for sufferers. / PUBLICATIONS Three leaflets aimed at parents: Tests; Transplants; School & Sport.

Brittle Bone Society, ☎ (01382) 204446, (0800) 028 2459
⏚ www.brittlebone.org
Advice and practical assistance through a family network and newsletter for parents of children with osteogenesis imperfecta. / PUBLICATIONS Leaflets: Handling a brittle bone baby, also ideas for clothes which are easily put on and taken off.

Cancer & Leukaemia in Children (CLIC), ☎ Head office (0117) 311
2600, CLIC London (020) 7348 6019 ⏚ www.clic.uk.com
This organisation provides nurses (who contact families as soon as a child is diagnosed, offering practical help and routine treatments), play therapists (at clinical sessions) and homes-from-home for families with children receiving treatments. Grants may also be available. / HOURS Mon-Fri 8.30am-5pm.

Child Growth Foundation, ☎ (020) 8995 0257, (020) 8994 7625
⏚ www.heightmatters.org.uk
A support group for parents and children with growth disorders, this is actually an umbrella organisation for a number of conditions, for example Turner's Syndrome (which may be indicated at birth by puffy hands and feet); Interuterine Growth Retardation, IUGR (indicated by small-for-dates babies – a condition often missed); or achondroplasia (a bone and cartilage disorder which may result in a normal torso but short limbs and a heavy head). It also holds a large database of information on other growth disorders (including growth hormone deficiency).

Children Living with Inherited Metabolic Diseases (CLIMB), ☎ (0870) 770 0326, (0800) 652 3181 ⌁ www.climb.org.uk

Previously known as The Research Trust for Metabolic Diseases in Children – information for families, professionals and concerned members of the public: the organisation can provide a listening ear and contact with supportive groups and individuals. / HOURS Mon-Fri 10am-3pm.

Children's Heart Federation, ☎ (0808) 808 5000

⌁ www.childrens-heart-fed.org.uk

Nearly one child in 100 is born with a congenital heart condition, of which about half require surgery. This federation of groups across the UK provides a central point for information on such disorders, support for parents, and referral to appropriate local help. / HOURS 9.30am-9.30pm; PUBLICATIONS booklets from various organisations, including on disability living allowance, pre prenatal diagnosis (for parents before attending a screening test), bereavement (practical issues including arranging a funeral) and grief, help and support for heart children & their families, care standards – SAE; More publications are listed on Web site. Publications are free. .

The Children's Liver Disease Foundation, ☎ (0121) 212 3839

⌁ www.childliverdisease.org

Jaundice is very common in newborns – as many as 90% of all babies are estimated to be affected – because their liver is not yet properly developed. If the condition persists for more than 14 days, tests will need to be carried out, and any problem discovered needs tackling urgently. The foundation's Family Support Officer can provide telephone advice. / PUBLICATIONS Jaundice Protocol; also a range of medical factsheets – £10; SAE.

Congenital CMV (Cytomegalovirus) Association, ☎ (01743) 850055

Family contact network for parents of children with CMV – a virus (with flu-like symptoms) to which most people are immune, but which can cause the baby serious difficulties if the mother contracts it at any time during pregnancy. / PUBLICATIONS Leaflet (send SAE).

Contact a Family, ☎ Office (020) 7608 8700, Helpline (0808) 808 3555

⌁ www.cafamily.org.uk

Free help and advice to families caring for children any disability or special needs, especially those with rare conditions; information is provided on welfare benefits, respite care, special education and details of local resources. The organisation also tries to bring families sharing a similar problem together if no relevant network exists. / HOURS Helpline Mon-Fri 10am-4pm; PUBLICATIONS The CAF Directory of Specific Conditions and Rare Syndromes (information on 800+ conditions; directory for health professionals). Quarterly journal, Share an Idea (£10 per annum) contains information and thoughts from those caring for children with special needs.

Council for Disabled Children, ☎ (020) 7843 6000 (National Children's Bureau), (020) 7843 1900 (Council for Disabled Children) ⌁ www.ncb.org.uk/cdc

Though primarily a campaigning body, the organisation produces a useful guide for parents. / PUBLICATIONS Help Starts Here (32-page guide to the maze of support services available, and how to access the professionals working with them).

Diabetes UK, ☎ (020) 7424 1000, Careline (0845) 120 2960

⌁ www.diabetes.org.uk

Formerly called the British Diabetic Association, this organisation aims to offer support and advise parents of a newly-diagnosed baby or child. / HOURS Mon-Fri 9am-5pm; PUBLICATIONS From Tots to Teens magazine; A parent's guide to diabetes (available from (0800) 585088).

Dial UK (National Association of Disablement Information & Advice Lines), ☎ (01302) 310123

⌁ www.members.aol.com/dialuk

Help and information for disabled people and their families, through a network of disability advice centres.

Down's Syndrome Association, ☎ (020) 8682 4001

⌁ www.downs-syndrome.org.uk

A network of volunteer, parent-led groups supporting families of children with the condition (which affects approximately one in 1,000 babies). / PUBLICATIONS Publications list free: comprehensive guide to specific and general titles.

Down's Syndrome Research Foundation, ⌁ www.dsrf.co.uk

A good website for information on the syndrome.

Dystrophic Epidermolysis Bullosa Research Association (DEBRA), ☎ (01344) 771961 ⏰ www.debra.org.uk

A rare genetic condition affecting around 5,000 people in the UK: the condition causes skin to blister at the slightest friction. The association has nurses and a specialist healthcare team to which you can refer for advice and help, and produces leaflets and information. / HOURS Mon-Fri 9am-5pm.

Early Support Programme, ☎ (0870) 000 2288 ⏰ www.dfes.gov.uk

A new scheme to bring together inter-agency services and to help with the identification of disabilities in the under-twos (so they can be tackled as soon as possible). The scheme is being piloted in 15 areas before being rolled out across the country.

Ehlers-Danlos Support Group, ☎ (01252) 690940
⏰ www.ehlers-danlos.org

Self-help for a rare group of inherited disorders of the body's connective tissues, which can affect the skin, ligaments and internal organs; call for details of local support groups. / PUBLICATIONS booklet on pregnancy and childbirth, and general booklet with some information on pregnancy – both £1.50; factsheets 30p-31.

The Family Fund Trust, ☎ (0845) 130 4542
⏰ www.familyfundtrust.org.uk

A charity (funded by the Government) which aims to ease the stress on families caring for severely disabled children (under 16) by providing both information (see below) and grants (for items such as holidays, fridges and driving lessons); eligibility is means-tested. / HOURS Mon-Fri 9am-5pm; PUBLICATIONS Benefits checklist, grants for adapting housing, bedding and clothing, how to get living equipment, help with hearing impairment, holiday accommodation for families with disabled children, hyperactivity hints, help with transport; Taking Care, an 80-page book by and for parents including a resource directory.

The Genetic Interest Group (GIG), ☎ (020) 7704 3141
⏰ www.gig.org.uk

An alliance of charities and voluntary groups for those affected by genetic disorders. The organisation can put individuals in touch with other support groups and relevant services.

Goldenhar Syndrome Family Support Group, ☎ (01580) 714 042

A registered charity run by parents of a child with the syndrome, the group – which has around 85 members and organises information groups and family days. / PUBLICATIONS Monthly newsletter.

Group B Strep Support, ☎ (01444) 416176 (answerphone)
⏰ www.gbss.org.uk

Group B Streptococcus (GBS) is the commonest form of bacterial infection in newborns affecting around 500 babies a year and causing septicaemia, pneumonia and meningitis. Early-onset GBS infections are fatal in 15% of cases. This self-help group offers support to families whose babies have been affected by GBS as well as informing medical professionals how to prevent the infection developing. Infections are usually apparent at birth but may develop up to the age of three months. About a third of all men and women carry GBS in their intestines without symptoms. Further information can be downloaded from the website. / HOURS Mon-Fri 9am-1pm; PUBLICATIONS Leaflets: GBS & Pregnancy (for women who do not know if they are carriers).

Haemophilia Society, ☎ (020) 7380 0600, 0800 018 6068
⏰ www.haemophilia.org.uk

Information and advice for parents of children suffering from this hereditary blood disorder, with a network of local support groups. / HOURS 9am-5pm.

Heartline Association, ☎ (01276) 707636 ⏰ www.heartline.org.uk

A voluntary support group for families of children with heart problems (membership is free to all children with a heart defect and their families). / HOURS Mon-Fri 10am-4pm; PUBLICATIONS Factsheets on different disorders, education, exercise, feeling problems and preparation for surgery; Heart Children (£5) – a practical comprehensive handbook for parents of children with congenital heart problems.

Henry Spink Foundation Resource Center, ☎ (020) 7388 9843
⏰ www.henryspink.org

A charity set up by the parents of Henry Spink to assist families who, like them, have a child diagnosed with severe disabilities. It provides information on conventional and complementary/alternative medicine, therapies and research relating to a very wide range of physical and mental disorders.

The Institute for Advanced Neuromotor Rehabilitation (Advance), ☎ (01342) 311 137 ⌂ www.advancecentre.org.uk

The organisation teaches a painless therapy to aid children with cerebral palsy. ARN is reported to have been effective for a number of brain-damaged children previously diagnosed as incurable and the organisation claim its home-based exercises (centred on the trunk and respiratory system) "work 100% for every child".

Jennifer Trust for Spinal Muscular Atrophy, ☎ (0870) 774 3651, Support line (0800) 975 3100 ⌂ www.jtsma.org.uk

The charity offers support to those with this genetically inherited condition (which is carried by one in 40 people in the UK). This includes local support groups, a newsletter and advice on further education and independent living. They also offer an equipment loan service (for example special baby seats), and a library of specially selected toys. / HOURS Mon-Fri 9am-5pm; PUBLICATIONS A leaflet explains the different types of related conditions.

KIDS, ☎ National HQ (020) 7359 3635, London (020) 7520 0405 ⌂ www.kids-online.org.uk

A national organisation founded in 1970 to provide local services to families of children with special needs, particularly focusing on the need to enjoy childhood and overcoming basic inequalities in society and education. Services offered range from advice about education and development to information about respite care, befriending schemes and activity clubs.

Muscular Dystrophy Campaign, ☎ (020) 7720 8055 ⌂ www.muscular-dystrophy.org

A charity (formerly known as the Muscular Dystrophy Group) which funds medical research and provides an information service and redirection to local support groups for people with neuromuscular conditions. / HOURS Mon-Fri 9am-5pm; Infoline Mon-Thurs 10am-4pm; PUBLICATIONS General factsheets: Inheritance and the muscular dystrophies; Carrier detection tests and prenatal diagnosis (also individual ones on most neuromuscular conditions covering the relevant inheritance patterns); Target MD magazine; magazines cover research, support groups and management of conditions (all free).

The National Deaf Children's Society (NDCS), ☎ (0808) 800 8880 (voice and text) ⌂ www.ndcs.org.uk

A national charity exclusively for deaf children and their families. It gives advice on such things as audiology, technology, education and welfare benefits and also has a network of regional support workers, befrienders and local groups. / HOURS Mon-Fri 10am-5pm; PUBLICATIONS Family Information Pack, free to families with a newly-diagnosed deaf child; 'Talk' quarterly magazine; over 100 other publications, many of which are free.

National Society for Phenylketonuria (NSPKU), ☎ Helpline (0845) 603 9136, (020) 8364 3010, London & Home Counties (01279) 830162, Membership (0141) 954 6372 ⌂ www.nspuk.org

A voluntary parent support group which supports research in the area of this fully treatable inherited condition. The society provides an opportunity for parents of children with PKU to meet and share experiences, and disseminates information from medical professionals. A positive approach to diet is promoted, and food lists are available.

Neurofibromatosis Association, ☎ (020) 8439 1234 ⌂ www.nfauk.org

There are two types (Nf1 and Nf2) of this genetically inherited nerve tissue disorder which affects over 25,000 in the UK, and results in – amongst other symptoms – developmental difficulties. (There is a one in two chance of those with the condition passing in on to their children, though half of all cases are in families with no previous history.) The charity runs a network of advisors. There are two centres in London, one based at Guy's and St Thomas' (020 7955 5000 ext 5692) and one at Great Ormond Street Hospital (020 7242 9789 ext 0707). / HOURS Mon-Fri 9am-5pm; PUBLICATIONS Fact sheets – modest cost.

Our Kids, ⌂ www.our-kids.org

An online community of parents of special needs children, including tricks and technique suggestions for parents.

Parents for Inclusion, ☎ Admin (020) 7735 7735, Helpline (0800) 652 3145 ⌂ www.parentsforinclusion.org

Formerly known as Parents in Partnership: provides information, assistance and support to parents of children said to have special educational who would prefer their children to attend a normal school. / HOURS Tues, Weds, Thurs 10am-12pm & 1pm-3pm.

Parents of Ealing Self-help Training Scheme (PESTS),
☎ *(020) 8578 8794*
If you live in Ealing and have a pre-school child with special needs, PESTS runs
a term-time weekly parent and toddler group providing stimulating play for the
children (and there is also a special toy library which meets twice a month).
Door-to-door transport can be arranged for those within the Ealing
borough. / PUBLICATIONS *Leaflet on special needs services for children in the borough.*

Positive Parenting Publications, ☎ *(023) 9252 8787*
⌁ *www.parenting.org.uk*
Courses and information packs on parenting a child with special needs. / HOURS *Mon-Fri
9am-5pm.*

Positive Partners, Positively Children (PPC), ☎ *(020) 7738
7333* ⌁ *www.ppclondon.org.uk*
Support for families affected by HIV and AIDS (currently only provided by Lambeth,
Southwark and Lewisham Health Authority) that includes a free family support
service, crèche services, parenting groups and introductions to local groups for
parents and carers. / HOURS *Mon-Fri 9.30am-5.30pm.*

Potter's Syndrome Support Group, ☎ *(01938) 553755*
⌁ *www.geocities.com/potters_syndrome*
Support for parents whose unborn child has this condition, which involves the
absence of kidneys (this may be diagnosed by a foetal anomaly scan at 20 or so
weeks), also known as Renal Agenesis. This absence means that little or no amniotic
fluid will develop. Though the pregnancy is generally allowed to continue,
the chance of still birth is high and – even if the baby is born – the absence of kidneys
precludes survival. The group also provides some information about Potter's
Sequence – a serious condition, where the kidneys are present. / HOURS *early evening or
during school holidays;* PUBLICATIONS *factsheet – free; tape of radio interview with doctor, £3.*

Rainbow Centre for Children with Cancer & Life-Threatening Illnesses, ☎ *(0117) 985 3343* ⌁ *www.rainbow-centre.org*
This centre – the only one of its kind in the country – offers support, free counselling,
professional help and complementary therapies for children with cancer or
a life-threatening illness and their families; also bereavement counselling for
children. / HOURS *Mon-Fri 9.30am-4.30pm.*

Restricted Growth Association (RGA), ☎ *(0130) 889 8415*
⌁ *www.rgaonline.org.uk*
This self-help organisation promotes information, medical advice and support for
individuals and their families affected by restricted growth. Counselling is available,
together with practical help on sources of clothing (including a clothes exchange),
suitable children's toys, special furniture, and how to apply for benefits and
grants. / PUBLICATIONS *Booklets & publication lists (send SAE).*

Retinitis Pigmentosa Society, ☎ *Helpline (0845) 123 2354, Head office
(01280) 821334* ⌁ *www.brps.org.uk*
Retinitis Pigmentosa (RP) is the name given to a group of hereditary diseases
affecting the retina. There is no known treatment, but the society can offer
information, for example on the relationship between genetics and
RP. / PUBLICATIONS *Leaflet series (£2 each).*

Ricability, ☎ *(020) 7427 2460* ⌁ *www.ricability.org.uk*
An independent research charity which publishes practical guides for older and
disabled consumers based on professional research. Much of their research is also
appropriate for disabled parents (including, in 2004, a report on pushchairs and
highchairs).

Royal Association for Disability & Rehabilitation
(RADAR), ☎ *(020) 7250 3222* ⌁ *www.radar.org.uk*
National cross-disability charity (the UK affiliate to Rehabilitation International)
which provides advice and information on all aspects of living with a disability;
the organisation supports over 500 local and national disability organisations and
campaigns for improvements, independence and equality in disabled people's
lives. / PUBLICATIONS *Wide range of publications (available to buy on website); factsheets on mobility,
social security, housing, holidays and education; regular bulletin featuring equipment.*

Royal National Institute for the Blind (RNIB),
☎ *(08457) 669999, Customer services (08457) 456457, (020) 7388 1266*
⌁ *www.rnib.org.uk*
This leading UK charity for the blind provides a wide variety of services for visually
impaired parents and children. There is information on pregnancy and childcare in

Braille and on tape; a parent cassette magazine; a reference library; the Education information service; a catalogue of toys; factsheets on toy and play ideas; and a schools catalogue with educational resources and equipment. There are also centres which offer a multitude of services including: displays of education technology, training for parents, specialist assessments, advocacy and advice services, and vacation and weekend schemes. / HOURS *Mon-Fri 9am-5pm;* PUBLICATIONS *Getting started – SAE; You and Your Child braille magazine, 42p per month.*

Royal National Institute for the Deaf (RNID), ☎ (020) 7296 8000, Helpline (0808) 808 0123, Text helpline (0808) 808 9000 ⏁ www.rnid.org.uk

A national charity exclusively for deaf children and their families. It is dedicated to removing barriers to deaf children in the hearing world and ending prejudice through education; the helpline can direct parents towards local support groups and offers advocacy and information on benefits, education, technology and equipment. For specific problems they will re-direct people to more specialised organisations and/or local support groups (of which there is a listing relating to children on the website). / HOURS *Mon-Fri 9.30am-5pm;* PUBLICATIONS *comprehensive web site and list of leaflets/brochures including details of glue ear, and baby alarms for deaf parents.*

SCOPE, ☎ (0808) 800 3333 ⏁ www.scope.org.uk

A national disability organisation whose focus is people with cerebral palsy. Scope provides both national and local information and support services in four priority areas - early years, employment, education and daily living. / HOURS *Mon-Fri 9am-9pm, Sat & Sun 2pm-6pm;* PUBLICATIONS *Free leaflets.*

Sense, The National Deafblind & Rubella Association, ☎ (020) 7272 7774 ⏁ www.sense.org.uk

A provider of expertise and advice (with regional services) for the deaf or blind and their families – based on the premise that early diagnosis and intensive educational support are a key to development; it also runs a holiday programme. (Rubella is the prime cause of such handicaps: meningitis, birth trauma and Usher syndrome are others.) / PUBLICATIONS *Quarterly magazine (£10 per annum); range of publications and videos (including general special needs ones).*

Shared Care Network, ☎ (0117) 941 5361 ⏁ www.sharedcarenetwork.org.uk

Links families with disabled children to host families willing to offer occasional or regular short-term care 'breaks', to give parents time to themselves and time to devote to any other children; breaks can be anything from an evening to a weekend. / HOURS *Mon-Fri 9am-5pm;* PUBLICATIONS *Directory of family-based short-term care in the UK.*

The Society for Mucopolysaccharide Diseases, ☎ (01494) 434156 ⏁ www.mpssociety.co.uk

A charity which offers support through a nationwide advocacy support team to individuals and families with babies diagnosed with one of 21 related metabolic diseases (the most common being MPSI (Hurler Disease), MPSII (Hunter Disease), MPSIII (Sanfilippo), and MPSIIV (Marquio), which are inherited and progressive. The diseases can affect children in many ways, from behavioural and learning difficulties to severe disability; the organisation promotes awareness of the conditions, funds two centres for MPS care (one at Great Ormond Street) and helps to organise family weekend conferences, siblings activities and regional events. / HOURS *24hr helpline;* PUBLICATIONS *Range of booklets (£2 each) on specific types of this class of diseases; The Patterns of Inheritance; newsletter.*

STEPS, ☎ Admin (0871) 717 0045, Helpline (0871) 717 0044 ⏁ www.steps-charity.org.uk

A charity whose concerns are lower limb abnormalities: from congenital dislocation of the hip (which requires early treatment to avoid more serious and difficult treatment later), to talipes (club foot, which can be treated with gentle manipulation and splinting); to conditions as serious as missing limbs. There is a large library and resource centre. A contacts register enables families in a given area to meet parents who have a child with a similar condition, and provides referrals to local groups. / HOURS *Mon-Fri 9.30am-4pm;* PUBLICATIONS *Quarterly newsletter; booklets about the different abnormalities.*

Support Organisation for Trisomy (SOFT UK), ☎ Helpline (0121) 351 3122 ⏁ www.soft.org.uk

Organisation for parents of babies diagnosed (antenatally or after birth) with Trisomy 13 or 18 defects – the most common chromosomal defects after Down's syndrome. Regional offices cater to parents of the 400 or so babies born each year with such disorders, and offer prenatal advice and bereavement counselling; different offices have specialist knowledge about different types of trisomy. / PUBLICATIONS *Two books (free to parents, £5 to professionals): Your baby – aimed at parents with a baby born with Trisomy 13 or 18; Your Unborn Child – to help those faced with prenatal decisions. Free quarterly newsletter for members. .*

Twin to Twin Transfusion Syndrome Association, ☎ Correen Jackson (020) 8581 7359, Dionne Thompson (01895) 846688 ⏀ www.twin2twin.org

Twin to Twin Transfusion Syndrome (TTTS) or Feto-Fetal Transfusion Syndrome (FFTS) is a disease of identical twin foetuses caused by abnormal connecting blood vessels in the twins' placenta, leading to an imbalance in the blood flow between the twins. It is thought to affect up to one multiple birth in a thousand. Their website is an ideal starting point for research in the area.

UNIQUE, the Rare Chromosome Disorder Support Group, ☎ Helpline (01883) 330766 ⏀ www.rarechromo.org

An association of parents of children with very rare chromosomal abnormalities which links up families whose children have similar disabilities; two databases are managed by the association: one with clinical features relating to particular abnormalities – the other with historical information and developmental histories of sufferers of various chromosomal abnormalities; call for details of access. / PUBLICATIONS *Newsletter.*

Williams Syndrome Foundation, ☎ (01732) 365152 ⏀ www.williams-syndrome.org.uk

This condition is linked to a missing section of DNA, and results in varying degrees of brain, heart and kidney defects. (Early signs include very high calcium levels at birth, frequent vomiting, sometimes difficulty sucking, restless sleeping, slow growth, extremely emotional behaviour and a short attention span.) The foundation incorporates the charity Infantile Hypercalcaemia. / PUBLICATIONS *Various free leaflets & books.*

14. SERIOUS CONGENITAL/MEDICAL CONDITIONS – PARENTS

(Note: many of the organisations listed above (under Congenital/Medical conditions – children) also provide support to parents as well as affected children.)

READING

Disabled Parents – Michele Waters (Dispelling the myths; NCT Publishing in association with Radcliffe Medical Press; £16.95; 1-857752-57-0) – *A practical account of parenting for the disabled.*

USEFUL CONTACTS

Disability, Pregnancy & Parenthood International (DPPi), ☎ (0800) 018 4730, Textphone (0800) 018 9949 ⏀ www.dppi.org.uk

Information helpline for disabled parents, offering solutions for practical everyday parenting; information about baby and childcare equipment. / HOURS *by appointment only;* PUBLICATIONS *Quarterly journal.*

The Disabled Parents Network, ☎ (0870) 241 0450, Text (0800) 0189949 ⏀ www.disabledparentsnetwork.org.uk

Created from two organisations, ParentAbility and Parents Too! (and now no longer linked to the NCT): a peer support network for parents with disabilities. The organisation holds contact registers of other parents and of relevant health professionals; the helpline is run by Disability, Pregnancy and Parenthood International (DPPi, see also).

Kith & Kids, ☎ (020) 8801 7432 ⏀ www.kithandkids.org.uk

A charity and self-help organisation for families with a member who is physically disabled, or suffering a learning difficulty. / HOURS *noon-6pm;* PUBLICATIONS *Leaflets; Partners with Disability (training manual, £16).*

National Centre for Disabled Parents, ☎ (08000) 184730, Text (0800) 018 9949 ⏀ www.dppi.org.uk

Jointly funded by Disability, Pregnancy and Parenthood International and Disabled Parents Network (see also), the Centre provides an information service for disabled parents (or disabled people who want to become parents) and related professionals. / HOURS *Mon-Fri 9.30am-5pm;* PUBLICATIONS *Quarterly journal (£10) for disabled persons living in the UK (available on tape free for the visually impaired); also topic leaflets including Equipment: where to find and how to use it, and on specific disabilities; free to disabled people.*

NCT Maternity Sales, ☎ *(0870) 112 1120, Breatfeeding helpline (0870) 444 8708* ♁ *www.nctms.co.uk*
ParentAbility is an NCT network of disabled parents, offering support in pregnancy, childbirth and parenthood. A contact register puts parents and would-be parents in touch with each other. There is also a quarterly newsletter in print or on tape, a helpline to answer questions and gather information, a resource list and a professional contact register. / HOURS Mon-Fri 9am-5pm; Helpline 8am-10pm.

Oxford Centre Enablement, ☎ *(01865) 737200, (01865) 227600* ♁ *www.noc.org.uk*
NHS specialist disability service supporting parents with disabilities who may visit (on an out-patient basis) early in pregnancy to discuss any concerns they may have about how they will cope with parenthood, and to practice various parenting activities using a life-sized model (of a baby), in order to build experience and confidence. Advice may be given and suitable equipment recommended or customised as necessary. / HOURS Mon-Fri 9am-4.30pm.

15. SOCIAL (& FINANCIAL) SUPPORT

READING

Autism Us (Wilson Harris Publications; £15 a year For free trial copy send name and address.) – *A quarterly newsletter for the north London families of children with autism and Asperger's Syndrome. It draws on sources including parliamentary updates and information from north London schools on inclusion and education issues. Also book reviews, ideas for leisure activities, health issues, and reader comments. / Wilson Harris, PO Box 25687, London N17 6FW.*

Money for Families – Pat Nightingale ed (A guide for sources of financial and practical help for families; Family Welfare Association; 1996; £16.95; 0900954582) – *Details money available from statutory and voluntary bodies (including charitable trusts).*

Waterlow's Guide to the Social Services (£20.95) – *Explains social services provisions, welfare benefits, and other associated legislation together with practical advice. / Marketing Dept, Waterlow Information Services, Paulton House, 8 Shepherdess Walk, N1 7LB – (020) 7490 0049; www.waterlows.com.*

USEFUL CONTACTS

Family Service Units (FSU), ☎ *(020) 7402 5175* ♁ *www.cfsu.org.uk*
A voluntary organisation offering community-based services to families under pressure, who work together with the family, and any statutory and other agencies which have become involved in the situation. / HOURS Mon-Fri 9am-5.30pm.

Family Welfare Association (FWA), ☎ *(020) 7254 6251* ♁ *www.fwa.org.uk*
A charity supporting parents and other 'individuals in need' who are finding it difficult to cope for reasons of mental health, poverty, disability (in the parent or the child), and so on. Social support includes 'well family' and counselling services in GP practices and there are grants available for families in exceptional need. The Family Line aims to provide a listening and support service and, where appropriate, information on services and resources: for example on children's behaviour and development, or coping with ageing parents and children. / HOURS Mon-Fri: 9-5pm; PUBLICATIONS Money for Families (details grants available from various organisations, plus sources of help, £16.95).

Home-Start UK, ☎ *Head office (0116) 233 9955, London (020) 7831 7023* ♁ *www.home-start.org.uk*
A 25-year-old nationwide support scheme for families with a child or children five and under who are experiencing difficulties and stress in their family lives. Volunteers, who are themselves parents, pay home visits to provide practical help in preventing family breakdown. Of 280 schemes run nationally in co-ordination with local boroughs, there are about 25 in London. / HOURS Mon-Fri 9am-5pm.

Mother's Union, ☎ *(020) 7222 5533* ♁ *www.themothersunion.org*
Church-based organisation promoting the wellbeing of families worldwide.

National Family & Parenting Institute, ☎ *(020) 7424 3460* ♁ *www.nfpi.org*
A charity which aims to enhance the value and quality of family life, supporting parents in bringing up children and making society more family-friendly.

National NEWPIN, ☎ *(020) 7407 7255* ⏍ *www.newpin.org.uk*
A national charity which helps new parents under stress break the cycle of destructive behaviour, through a range of local centres (of which there are a dozen in London). Particular emphasis is placed on the prevention of emotional abuse of children by alleviating maternal depression, combating loneliness and lack of family support, and teaching parenting and life skills; most suitable for parents of children up to the age of five. / HOURS *Mon-Fri 9am-5pm.*

NCH, ☎ *(0845) 762 6579* ⏍ *www.nch.org.uk*
Help for children and their families, both through family centres and in the community; formerly called NCH Action for Children. / HOURS *Mon-Fri 9am-5pm.*

Parentline Plus, ☎ *Freephone parent Helpline (0808) 800 2222, Textphone (0800) 783 6783* ⏍ *www.parentlineplus.org.uk*
Parentline, the trading name of Family Lives, which incorporated the National Stepfamily Association and merged with Parentline and Parent Network parenting courses. As well as lobbying, the organisation offers a national network of telephone helplines (run largely by parents who have usually experienced problems themselves) for parents, grandparents and other carers requiring emotional support. Problems may include stepfamily issues, hard-to-handle behaviour, your feelings towards your children, racism or other discrimination, money worries, depression, living with a disability and your relationship with your partner. The organisation can help with looking for further professional advice, and can re-direct callers to more specific support groups and organisations. A correspondence service is also offered if preferred. The website offers information on parenting issues, allowing parents to try out reactions to scenarios such as a crying toddler; also a special area for fathers/stepfathers and leaflets to download. / HOURS *helpline Mon-Fri 2pm-5pm & 7pm-8pm;* PUBLICATIONS *Free leaflets available from the helpline, including educational and information material.*

reunite (International Child Abduction Centre), ☎ *(0116) 255 5345, Advice (0116) 255 6234* ⏍ *www.reunite.org*
A charity (part of a network of similar organisations in other countries) that specialises in the issue of child abduction (and the prevention thereof) and related problems; it offers a support network, advice line, useful contacts and publications. / HOURS *Mon-Fri 10.30am-5pm or call for details of 24hr cover numbers;* PUBLICATIONS *Lists of international lawyers specialising in this field; Child Abduction Prevention Packs (£3.50).*

CHAPTER 4.07

GLOSSARY OF MEDICAL & SPECIALIST TERMS

ADD/ADHD: attention deficit disorder/attention deficit hyperactivity disorder (see chapter *2.03 Baby health*).

AFP: alpha-fetoprotein. The antenatal test which uses this substance as a so-called 'protein marker' for abnormalities (such as spina bifida) is also known as AFP; other protein markers with names such as HCG and UE3 may also be measured (see chapter *1.03 Tests*).

Amniocentesis (amnio): withdrawal of cells from the fluid surrounding the baby (amniotic fluid), by means of a hollow needle inserted into the womb. Analysis of these cells checks for the existence of chromosomal abnormalities like Down's syndrome (see chapter *1.03 Tests*).

Amniotic sac (membranes): lines the inside of the womb and contains the baby. Inside is the amniotic fluid in which the baby floats.

Anaemia: a deficiency of iron in the red blood cells, the main effects of which are tiredness and shortage of breath (see chapter *1.03 Tests*).

Apgar score: a measure of a baby's well-being made at birth, and five minutes afterwards; a rating out of ten takes into account the newborn's pulse, breathing, movements, skin tone and reflexes.

ARM (artificial rupture of the membranes, amniotomy, 'breaking the waters'): the cervical membrane is broken by means of a hook-like implement for the purpose of inducing or augmenting labour (see chapter *4.03 Medical issues at birth*).

Augmentation (acceleration): the use of certain medical procedures to encourage a labour towards completion (see chapter *4.03 Medical issues at birth*).

Bear down: push out the baby. This becomes an irresistible urge once labour reaches a certain point, especially for an unsedated mother.

Bishop's score: a rating, based upon a vaginal examination, used to gauge a woman's readiness for induction.

Breech birth: birth after the baby's bottom, instead of the baby's head, has engaged in the mother's pelvis. Most babies turn head down before birth, at least in part because the head is the heaviest part of the body and tends to be pulled down by gravity. Head down is considered the easiest position for a baby to be born from. The mother's habitual posture during pregnancy, especially when seated, may have an effect on the baby's final position.

Caesarean (Caesarean section, C-Section, Section, C/S): a surgical procedure which involves cutting through the mother's abdomen and uterus to remove the baby. An emergency Caesarean (over half of all Caesareans) may be performed if the baby gets into an awkward position and seems unable to move, or is suffering foetal distress. Despite the term 'emergency', many are actually planned weeks in advance (Caesareans that really are decided upon in an emergency are sometimes called 'crash' Caesareans). Elective Caesareans are those performed on a normal mother on the basis of it being her preferred method of delivery (see chapter *4.03 Medical issues at birth*).

Cardiotocographic monitoring (CTG): technique for measuring an unborn baby's pulse using electrodes fitted to the mother's stomach (see chapter *4.03 Medical issues at birth*).

Colostrum: the first breast milk produced, made from before the birth until the first few days thereafter; particularly rich in vitamins, proteins and antibodies.

Congenital: denotes a condition or abnormality existing at birth; this might, but need not be, inherited.

Contractions: the tightening of the muscles of the uterus to open the cervix and push the baby out. As the sides of the uterus and cervix open they create the birth canal. See Labour.

Cord blood banking: collecting blood from the umbilical cord after birth for donation or private storage, because of its potential use in treating serious illnesses (see chapter *4.03 Medical issues at birth*).

DPT: diptheria, pertussis (whooping cough), tetanus vaccination (see chapter *2.03 Baby health*).

Dilation: gradual widening of the cervix to approximately 10cm for the baby to pass through. See Labour.

Double test: antenatal screening test (see chapter *1.03 Tests*).

Doula: from the Greek for handmaiden – woman experienced in childcare who helps mother during and after birth (see chapter *2.04 Childcare*).

Ectopic pregnancy: one in which the fertilised egg implants in the Fallopian tube instead of in the uterus. The internal bleeding caused can be life-threatening and is one reason why it is important to get vaginal bleeding in pregnancy checked; affects an estimated one in 200 pregnancies.

EDD: estimated date of delivery (see chapter *1.07 Timetable & What to pack*).

EFM: electronic foetal monitoring; see also RCEFM and Cardiotocographic monitoring.

EWC: expected week of childbirth – replacement term for EDD used for calculating maternity benefits (see chapter *1.05 Rights*).

Endorphins: the body's natural opiates (painkillers). They are powerful – similar to morphine in that they relieve pain and produce a sensation of wellbeing. Their production is aided by relaxation and diminished by tension or fear.

Engaged: a baby's head is considered to have engaged when it drops down into the mother's pelvis. In first pregnancies this usually happens in the last six weeks. In second and subsequent pregnancies, because there is less tension in the uterus muscles pushing down, the head may not engage at all. The degree of engagement is defined as how far down the head is into the pelvis – anything from 1/5 to 5/5 when fully engaged.

Engorgement: swollen breasts, common when breast milk is first produced ('comes in') but less so with 24-hour feeding on demand (see chapter *2.02 Feeding*).

Entonox (gas and air): 50% nitrous oxide and 50% oxygen, a potentially anaesthetic combination, self-administered using a face mask during labour (see chapter *4.03 Medical issues at birth*).

Epidural (epidural anaesthesia, lumbar epidural anaesthesia): a local anaesthetic injected into a space in the lower spine to block the nerves that transmit pain sensation from the uterus to the brain; a powerful form of pain relief (see chapter *4.03 Medical issues at birth*).

Episiotomy: a surgical cut from the back wall of the vagina through the perineum and underlying muscles, carried out to ease the passage of the baby's head at birth. In some hospitals episiotomies are very rarely carried out, except with forceps or ventouse deliveries (see chapter *4.03 Medical issues at birth*).

Ergometrine: a drug (derived from a fungus) that causes muscle contractions. An element of Syntometrine (see also).

External cephalic version (ECV): gentle manipulation of the mother's stomach in the last weeks of pregnancy (less often actually during labour) to try to persuade a breech baby to turn head down (see chapter *4.03 Medical issues at birth*).

Face or brow presentation: when the baby's head is tilted back so the first part to be born would be the face. Because the face is wider than the tip of the head which usually presents, this can make birth difficult. If the baby doesn't shift a Caesarean may be necessary.

Foetal distress: a baby is designed to cope with compression and blood flow reduction during labour. If oxygen supplies are low the baby can obtain energy from glucose (sugar) reserves for as long as 10 minutes. Foetal distress occurs if the flow of blood from the placenta is reduced for a relatively long time – in severe cases it can lead to brain damage and even death.

Foetal monitoring: checking for foetal distress by monitoring the baby's heart rate. This can be done with a variety of techniques, usually with mechanical aids. The 'ideal' trace shows a base reading of about 140 beats per minutes, with periodic 'accelerations' to 160 beats per minute (see chapter *4.03 Medical issues at birth*).

Foetus (hence foetal): the developing child before birth; technically speaking, the term should only be used from 12 weeks (before then, embryo), but it is also sometimes loosely used before that date. The American spelling fetus (fetal) is generally adopted in medicine.

First stage: see Labour.

Forceps: used to help deliver a child: arms, which look approximately like two salad servers, are placed on either side of the child's head (see chapter *4.03 Medical issues at birth*).

Gestation (hence gestational): duration of pregnancy.

Gestational diabetes: diabetes in the mother which starts and usually stops with pregnancy.

Hib: Haemophilus influenzae type b – a type of meningitis commonly vaccinated against (see chapter *2.03 Baby health*).

Hypertension: see Pre-eclampsia.

Induction: triggering labour artificially (see chapter *4.03 Medical issues at birth*).

Intervention: the term used for a medical procedure in pregnancy or labour. (see chapter *4.03 Medical issues at birth*)

Involution: the uterus returning to its pre-pregnant size, which may cause after-pains. The process is stimulated by breastfeeding.

Labour: the contractions of the uterus and opening (dilation) of the cervix that cause the baby and placenta to be born. The length and experience of labour vary widely between individuals (see table below).

1) First stage: what is generally the time-consuming part of childbirth, during which contractions of the uterus cause the cervix to dilate to about 10cm. This process occurs in phases, which are termed latent, active and transition.

2) Second stage: what everyone has been waiting for – delivery of the child, which involves pushing the baby through the cervix, pelvic canal and out through the vagina. This stage is much shorter than the first. Sometimes the contractions stop briefly for a 'rest'.

3) Third stage: delivery of the placenta after the umbilical cord ceases to pulsate and the placenta separates from the wall of the uterus. A Syntometrine injection may be given just as the baby is born to encourage this process (see chapter *4.03 Medical issues at birth*).

First birth:

1st stage:	four to 24 hours.
2nd stage:	30 minutes to two hours.
3rd stage:	ten to 90 minutes.

Subsequent births:

1st stage:	two to 12 hours.
2nd stage:	ten to 90 minutes.
3rd stage:	ten to 90 minutes.

Source for timings: Encyclopaedia of Pregnancy and Birth, by Janet Balaskas & Yehudi Gordon, Little Brown, 1992.

If labour appears to be significantly more protracted than is the norm, the usual obstetric procedure is to augment the labour (see chapter *4.03 Medical issues at birth*).

LMP: last menstrual period; pregnancy is calculated as the date this began plus 40 weeks.

Lochia: the blood from the place in the uterus where the placenta was attached. This is released for 2–6 weeks after birth (probably to flush out any bacteria that may have entered during birth).

MA: Maternity Allowance (see chapter *1.05 Rights*).

MMR: measles, mumps and rubella vaccination (see chapter *2.03 Baby health*).

Managed birth: one largely regulated by drugs and obstetric procedures (see chapter *4.03 Medical issues at birth*).

Mastitis: an acute and painful inflammation of the milk ducts and surrounding tissue which can turn into an abscess in the breast. This is usually caused by a blocked duct, often by the milk not being properly drained at a feed. It can also be caused by feeding to timetable rather than on demand. Combined with a fever, it indicates that an infection is present. Mastitis needs prompt treatment, but stopping feeding will make it worse (see chapter *2.02 Feeding*).

Meconium: greenish-black matter in the baby's bowels; if passed while still in the uterus it stains the amniotic fluid; this may be a sign of foetal distress, but can also simply mean that the baby is ready to be born. Foetal monitoring should provide clarification.

Membranes: the amniotic sac.

Miscarriage: a pregnancy that ends spontaneously before the 24th week (previously 28 weeks). The main symptom is vaginal bleeding. The medical term is spontaneous abortion (see chapter *4.04 Miscarriage & stillbirth*).

Mobile epidural: a refinement of the technique by which epidurals (see also) are administered, whereby a relatively low dose allows the woman to maintain a fair amount of mobility – the ability to walk, for instance (see chapter *4.03 Medical issues at birth*).

Monitoring: see Foetal monitoring.

Monovalent vaccination: see Single jab.

Multigravida (multiparious): woman in her second or subsequent pregnancy.

Neonatal: referring especially to the first week of life, but also up to the first month.

Neonatal (intensive) care unit (NNU, NCU, NICU): see SCBU.

Neural tube defect (NTD): when the nervous system does not develop normally; examples are spina bifida and anencephaly (see chapter *1.03 Tests*).

Nuchal fold test: ultrasound scan at about 12 weeks that can help to predict Down's Syndrome and neural tube defects (see chapter *1.03 Tests*).

Oblique: baby lying at an angle, head up under ribs, bottom on opposite hip bone.

Obstetrics: the branch of medicine concerned with pregnancy, childbirth and the care of women before and after birth.

Occipito anterior (OA): a head down baby facing approximately towards the mother's back – the desired position at the onset of labour.

Occipito posterior (OP): a baby with head down but facing the mother's navel. Kicks will be at the front. The position can result in back pain in labour and may prove somewhat more difficult than OA for the baby to move from.

Oedema: puffiness of feet, legs and fingers caused by increase in fluid in the mother's body.

Oxytocin: a natural hormone produced in the pituitary glands of mother and baby during labour which makes the womb contract. There are synthetic substitutes such as Syntocinon.

Partogram: a chart which helps carers monitor the progress of labour; the baby's heart rate, and mother's cervical dilation are plotted.

Perinatal: referring to anything happening from around three months before to up to one month after the birth.

Perineum: the area of skin between the vagina and anus which has to stretch to allow the baby out. (See Episiotomy.)

Pethidine: narcotic related to morphine which affects the perception of pain. Administered during labour by injection (see chapter *4.03 Medical issues at birth*).

Physiological: a description used relating to birth to describe what naturally occurs during a spontaneous labour without medical intervention, distinguishing it from one that is managed medically (see *4.03 Medical issues at birth*).

Placenta: a liver-like organ which develops attached to the uterine wall and connected to the baby via the umbilical cord. The placenta is the foetus's 'life support system', breathing, digesting and excreting for the baby before birth.

Placenta praevia: a placenta implanted in the lower, non contractile, part of the uterus, rather than in the upper half. This position may block the cervical opening, necessitating delivery by Caesarean.

Placental abruption: when the placenta comes away from the wall of the uterus prior to birth. This is dangerous for the baby, and necessitates an emergency Caesarean.

Posseting: baby vomiting due to the immature state of part of the digestive tract. It looks rather like the baby has simply overflowed and they rarely show distress.

Posterior: see occipito posterior.

Postmature: baby born more than two weeks after EDD.

Post-partum haemorrhage (PPH): loss of a large quantity of blood (over 500ml) from the uterus, usually caused at the end of the birth by placental tissue left in the uterus, preventing it from contracting to cut off the blood flow. Homeopathic remedies may help but medical practitioners will rarely give time to try them as the condition is potentially life-threatening.

Pre-eclampsia (pre-eclamptic toxaemia, PET, pregnancy induced hypertension, PIH, toxaemia, hypertensive disease of pregnancy, HDP, metabolic toxaemia of late pregnancy, MTLP): a condition combining high blood pressure, fluid retention and, protein in the urine. If left untreated it may progress to convulsions and damage the mother's heart, kidneys, liver and blood clotting. It may also cause risk to the baby. It is more usual in a first pregnancy, with only a 4% chance of recurrence in second or subsequent pregnancies (see chapter *1.03 Tests*).

Premature ('preemie'): a baby born before the EDD. Classification relies on dates (widely defined as under 36 weeks) and birthweight (widely defined as under 5lb 5oz). Very premature are 29 to 34 weeks, extremely premature 24 to 28 weeks. There are approximately 50,000 a year in the UK. Seriously premature babies lack subcutaneous fat, are usually still covered by a downy hair known as lanugo and may still have a thin, gelatinous skin. At 23 weeks around half will suffer brain damage though from 24 weeks the figure drops markedly. They will need to be looked after for some time in a SCBU (see also) and may at a later stage be offered physiotherapy. Reasons for premature birth include multiple birth, pre-eclampsia and haemorrhage but an estimated 40% occur for no known reason. Premature babies are generally ready to leave hospital at about the date they would normally have been born although sometimes sooner. A paediatrician usually attends the birth of a premature baby. Causes are not clear but may include smoking, multiple pregnancy or infection.

Primagravida (primiparous, nullipara): woman in her first pregnancy. A woman over 30 or over 35 is sometimes termed geriatric or elderly primagravida.

Progesterone: the hormone which increases in pregnancy, softening ligaments to allow space for the baby before and during birth.

Prolapsed cord: if there is not a close fit between the baby and the cervix as the baby descends, the umbilical cord can slip down past the baby and into the vagina when the waters break. The likelihood of this happening is one in 300 and is more likely with very small babies or those in an unusual position. This creates a dangerous situation, because as the baby emerges the cord is likely to be compressed, which endangers the supply of oxygen that it carries.

Prostaglandin: hormone used to induce labour.

Pudendal block: local anaesthetic used in episiotomies.

Puerperium: the six-week period after birth required for a woman's body to return to an approximation of its pre-pregnant state.

Qualifying week: a measure of when you must have been employed by to qualify for certain maternity benefits (see chapter *1.05 Rights*.

Retained placenta: occasionally part of the placenta may not be expelled by the uterus after labour (see also). If left, even in part, it will bleed and become infected so it has to be removed, usually under anaesthetic.

RCEFM: Routine Continuous Electronic Foetal Monitoring – a standard way of monitoring a baby during labour (see chapter *4.03 Medical issues at birth*).

Sacroiliac: relating to the joint between the sacrum (see below) and the ilium (the largest and widest of three hip bones), hence sacroiliac pain (see chapter *1.02 Looking after yourself*)

Sacrum: bone at the lower end of the spine.

SCBU: Special Care Baby Unit i.e. hospital unit for babies in need of special care. Also called NCU or NNU (neonatal care unit).

Second stage: see Labour.

Serum screening tests: blood tests which provide a quantification of the risk that a foetus may have Down's syndrome, or other abnormalities (see chapter *1.03 Tests*).

SGA: small for gestational age, i.e. a low birth-weight baby.

Show: the release from the cervix of a mucus plug, which may contain a small amount of blood. Labour may or may not be imminent.

Single jab: a vaccination against one disease only (see chapter *2.03 Baby health*).

SMP: Statutory Maternity Pay (see chapter *1.05 Rights*).

Spontaneous abortion: see Miscarriage.

Stillbirth: a baby born dead after 24 weeks of pregnancy (the definition used to be 28 weeks) – see chapter *4.04 Miscarriage & stillbirth*.

Syntocinon: a synthetic hormone similar to oxytocin used in almost a fifth of labours in the UK to induce or augment labour (see chapter *4.03 Medical issues at birth*).

Syntometrine: a drug combining syntocinon and ergometrine, used to manage the third stage of labour (see chapter *4.03 Medical issues at birth*).

Teratogen: things that could damage the baby's development such as X–rays, hazardous chemicals and certain infections.

TENS: a form of pain relief that avoids the use of drugs (see chapter *1.06 Birth equipment*).

Term: full length of pregnancy, generally taken as 40 weeks from the first day of the last menstrual period before conception (see chapter *1.07 Timetable & What to pack*).

Third stage: see Labour.

Transverse position (shoulder presentation): a baby lying with shoulder or upper back across the cervix; the baby will often move into a head down position before birth but if remaining in place cannot be born vaginally.

Trimester: period of three months – pregnancy is broken up into the first, second and third trimesters.

Triple jab: a vaccination against three diseases at once (see chapter *2.03 Baby health*).

Triple test: antenatal screening test (see chapter *1.03 Tests*).

Trivalent vaccine: see Triple jab.

Ultrasound: technique using high frequency sound and principles similar to those for sonar to create an image rather like a moving X-ray of the foetus (see chapter *1.03 Tests*).

Umbilical cord: the connection from the placenta to the baby for transferring all nutrients.

Urinary incontinence: stress incontinence may begin in pregnancy as hormones relax the muscles. As the baby grows its pressure on the bladder adds to the effect. It also occurs after birth once the pelvic floor has stretched in childbirth. Kegel pelvic floor exercises strengthen the appropriate muscles to help prevent this.

VBAC: vaginal birth after Caesarean (see chapter *4.03 Medical issues at birth*).

Ventouse (vacuum extraction): an alternative to forceps which involves attaching a suction cap to the baby's scalp, which operates on the same principle as a vacuum cleaner (see chapter *4.03 Medical issues at birth*).

Vertex (Vx): baby head down with chin tucked on chest.

Waters breaking (rupture of membranes): the sac holding the amniotic waters and baby almost always breaks at some stage during, or less often before, labour; the waters then gush or trickle out. This situation may be achieved artificially (see also ARM, and chapter *4.03 Medical issues at birth*).

SECTION FIVE

Indexes

Accelerated Learning Systems *50 Aylesbury Rd, Aston Clinton, Aylesbury, Bucks HP22 5AH* ☎ *(01296) 631177* ⏣ *www.acceleratedlearning.com / see 2.07 Education.*

Action Against Allergy *PO Box 278, Twickenham TW1 4QQ* ☎ *(020) 8892 2711 / see 2.03 Baby health.*

Action Against Medical Accidents (AVMA) *44 High St, Croydon, Surrey CR0 1YB* ☎ *(0845) 123 2352* ⏣ *www.avma.org.uk / see 4.03 Medical issues at birth.*

Action Asthma ⏣ *www.actionasthma.co.uk / see 2.03 Baby health.*

Action for Leisure *PO Box 9, West Molesey KT8 1WT* ☎ *(020) 8783 0173* ⏣ *www.actionforleisure.org.uk / see 4.06 Support groups.*

Action for ME *PO Box 1302, Wells, Somerset BA5 1YE* ☎ *(01749) 67099* ⏣ *www.afme.org.uk / see 1.02 Looking after yourself.*

Action for Sick Children *National Association for the Welfare of Children in Hospital (NAWCH), 300 Kingston Rd, Wimbledon, London SW20 8LX* ☎ *(020) 7843 6444* ⏣ *www.actionforsickchildren.org / see 4.06 Support groups.*

Action on Pre-Eclampsia (APEC) *84-88 Pinner Rd, Harrow HA1 4HZ* ☎ *Helpline (020) 8427 4217, Admin (020) 8863 3277* ⏣ *www.apec.org.uk / see 1.03 Tests.*

Action on Puerperal Psychosis *Department of Psychiatry, University of Birmingham, Queen Elizabeth Psychiatric Hospital, Mindelshon Way, Birmingham B15 2QZ* ☎ *Department of Psychiatry (0121) 678 2354 or (0121) 678 2361 / see 2.01 Postnatal.*

The Active Birth Centre *25 Bickerton Rd, London N19 5JT* ☎ *(020) 7281 6760* ⏣ *www.activebirthcentre.com / see 1.01 Where to have the baby; 1.04 Antenatal classes; 1.06 Birth equipment; 2.01 Postnatal; 2.02 Feeding; 2.03 Baby health; 2.06 Baby & toddler activities; 3.01 Maternity wear; 3.02 Baby equipment; 4.02 Health practitioners; 4.05 Finding out more.*

Addis (Attention Deficit Disorder Information Services) *10 Station Rd, Mill Hill, London NW7 2JU* ☎ *(020) 8906 9068* ⏣ *www.addis.co.uk / see 4.06 Support groups.*

ADHD National Alliance *209-211 City Road, London EC1V 1JN* ☎ *(020) 7608 8760* ⏣ *www.adhdalliance.org.uk / see 2.03 Baby health.*

Adoption UK *Manor Farm, Appletree Rd, Chipping Warden, Oxfordshire OX17 1LH* ☎ *(0870) 770 0450* ⏣ *www.adoptionuk.org / see 4.06 Support groups.*

Advisory Centre for Education Ltd (ACE) *Dept A, 1c Aberdeen Studios, 22 Highbury Grove, London N5 2DQ* ☎ *Freephone advice line (0808) 800 5793* ⏣ *www.ace-ed.org.uk / see 2.07 Education.*

Advisory, Conciliation & Arbitration Service (ACAS) *Brandon House (Head Office), 180 Borough High St, London SE1 1LW* ☎ *Helpline (0845) 747 4747* ⏣ *www.acas.org.uk / see 1.05 Rights.*

African Caribbean Family Mediation Service *2-4 St John's Crescent, London SW9 7LZ* ☎ *(020) 7737 2366 / see 4.06 Support groups.*

After Adoption *12-14 Chapel St, Manchester   M3   7NH* ☎ *(0161) 839 4932, Helpline (0161) 839 4930* ⏣ *www.afteradoption.org.uk / see 4.06 Support groups.*

Air Improvement Centre *23 Denbigh St., Victoria, London SW1 2HF* ☎ *(020) 7834 2834* ⏣ *www.air-improvement.co.uk / see 2.03 Baby health.*

Albany Midwifery Practice *Peckham Pulse, 10 Melon Rd, London SE15 5QN* ☎ *(020) 7525 4995, Peckham Pulse (020) 7525 4999* ⏣ *www.albanymidwives..org / see 1.04 Antenatal classes; 2.01 Postnatal.*

Alcohol Concern *Waterbridge House, 32-36 Loman St, London SE1 0EE* ☎ *(020) 7928 7377, Info Line 020 7922 8667* ⏣ *www.alcoholconcern.org.uk / see 1.02 Looking after yourself.*

Alcoholics Anonymous (AA) *AA General Service Office, PO Box 1, Stonebow House, Stonebow, York, North Yorkshire YO1 7NJ* ☎ *(01904) 644026, Helpline (0845) 767 7555* ⏣ *www.alcoholics-anonymous.org.uk / see 1.02 Looking after yourself.*

Allerbreathe *South Devon & Cornwall Institution for the Blind, Stonehouse Street, Plymouth, Devon PL1 3PE* ☎ *(01752) 662317 / see 2.03 Baby health.*

Allergy Induced Autism (AIA) *11 Larklands, Longthorpe, Peterborough PE3 6LL* ☎ *Helpline (01733) 331771* ⏣ *www.autismmedical.com / see 2.03 Baby health.*

Allergy UK *Deepdene House, 30 Bellgrove Rd, Welling DA16 3PY* ☎ *(020) 8303 8525, Allergy helpline (020) 8303 8583* ⏣ *www.allergyfoundation.com / see 2.03 Baby health.*

Alliance for Childhood *UK Partner, Kidbrook Park, Forest Row RH19 5JA* ☎ *(01342) 824 200* ⏣ *www.allianceforchildhood.org.uk / see 2.07 Education.*

Amateur Swimming Association (ASA) ☎ *(01509) 618 700 / see 1.04 Antenatal classes; 2.01 Postnatal; 2.06 Baby & toddler activities.*

America Hyperlexia Association ☎ +1 773 216 3333 ⏚ www.hyperlexia.org / see 2.03 Baby health.

The Anaphylaxis Campaign PO Box 275, Hampshire GU14 6SX ☎ (01252) 542029 ⏚ www.anaphylaxis.org.uk / see 2.03 Baby health.

The Angel Drug Services 332c Goswell Rd, London EC1V 7LQ ☎ (020) 7833 9899, (0800) 169 2679 ⏚ www.angeldrug.org.uk / see 1.02 Looking after yourself.

Anna Freud Centre 21 Maresfield Gardens, London NW3 5SD ☎ (020) 7794 2313 ⏚ www.annafreudcentre.org / see 2.01 Postnatal; 4.02 Health practitioners.

Antenatal Results & Choices (ARC) 73 Charlotte St, London W1T 4PN ☎ (020) 7631 0280, Helpline (020) 7631 0285 ⏚ www.arc-uk.org / see 1.03 Tests.

Antenatal Screening Service DEPM, Wolfson Institute, St Bartholomew's and The Royal London School of Medicine and Dentistry, Charterhouse Square, London EC1M 6BQ ☎ (020) 7882 6293 ⏚ www.smd.qmul.ac.uk/wolfson/epm/screening / see 1.03 Tests.

Aromatherapy Organisations Council (AOC) PO Box 6522, Desborough, Northants NN14 2YX ☎ (0870) 774 3477 ⏚ www.aocuk.net / see 4.02 Health practitioners.

Arthritis Care 18 Stephenson Way, London NW1 2HD ☎ (020) 7380 6500, Helpline (0808) 800 4050 ⏚ www.arthritiscare.org.uk / see 1.02 Looking after yourself.

Asian Family Counselling Service Suite 5 Windmill Place, 2-4 Windmill Lane, Southall UB2 4NJ ☎ (020) 8571 3933 / see 4.06 Support groups.

Asian Women's Resource Centre 108 Craven Park, London NW10 8QE ☎ (020) 8838 3462 Bilingual helpline / see 4.06 Support groups.

Association for All Speech-Impaired Children (AFASIC) 50-52a Great Sutton St, London EC1V 0DJ ☎ (020) 7490 9410, Helpline (0845) 355 5577 ⏚ www.afasic.org.uk / see 2.03 Baby health.

Association for Children with Hand or Arm Deficiency (REACH) PO Box 54, Helston, Cornwall TR13 8WD ☎ (0845) 130 6225 ⏚ www.reach.org.uk / see 4.06 Support groups.

Association for Children with Terminal & Life-threatening Conditions & their Families (ACT) 5 Goodwins Court, Off St. Martins Lane, London WC2N 4LL ☎ (0800) 849 4545, (020) 7240 1275 ⏚ www.act.org.uk / see 4.06 Support groups.

Association for Improvement in Maternity Services (AIMS) 5 Port Hall Rd, Brighton, East Sussex BN1 5PD ☎ (0870) 765 1433 ⏚ www.aims.org.uk / see 1.01 Where to have the baby; 4.03 Medical issues at birth.

Association for Postnatal Illness (APNI) 145 Dawes Rd, London SW6 7EB ☎ (020) 7386 0868 ⏚ www.apni.org / see 2.01 Postnatal.

Association for Spina Bifida & Hydrocephalus (ASBAH) South East Regional Office, 209 Crescent Rd, New Barnet EN4 8SB ☎ (020) 8441 9967, (020) 8449 0475 ⏚ www.asbah.org / see 1.02 Looking after yourself; 1.03 Tests; 4.06 Support groups.

Association for Spinal Injury Research, Rehabilitation & Reintegration (ASPIRE) ASPIRE National Training Centre, Wood Lane, Stanmore HA7 4AD ☎ (020) 8954 5759 ⏚ www.aspire.org.uk / see 2.03 Baby health.

Association of Breastfeeding Mothers (ABM) PO Box 207, Bridgewater TA6 7YT ☎ (020) 7813 1481 ⏚ www.abm.me.uk / see 2.02 Feeding.

Association of Chartered Physiotherapists in Women's Health Rachel Grubb, Byway, Chapel Lane, Box Corsham, Wiltshire SN13 8MJ ☎ (020) 7242 1941 ⏚ www.acpwh.org.uk / see 1.02 Looking after yourself; 4.02 Health practitioners.

Association of Parents of Vaccine-Damaged Children 78 Camden Rd, Shipston-on-Stour, Warwickshire CV36 4DH ☎ (01608) 661595 / see 2.03 Baby health.

Association of Radical Midwives 6 Springfield Road, Kings Heath , Birmingham B14 7DS ☎ (0121) 444 2257 ⏚ www.midwifery.org.uk / see 1.01 Where to have the baby.

Association of Reflexologists (AoR) 27 Old Gloucester St, London WC1N 3XX ☎ (0870) 567 3320 ⏚ www.aor.org.uk / see 4.02 Health practitioners.

Association of Shared Parenting PO Box 2000, Dudley, West Midlands DY1 1Y2 ⏚ www.sharedparenting.org.uk / see 4.06 Support groups.

AuPairs ⏚ www.aupairs.co.uk / see 2.04 Childcare.

The Avon Episiotomy Support Group 100 Holmesdale, Waltham Cross, Herts EN8 8RA ☎ (020) 8482 1453 / see 2.01 Postnatal.

Baby Basics 96 Erskine Hill, London NW11 6HR ☎ (020) 8455 8966 ⏚ www.babybasics.me.uk / see 2.01 Postnatal.

Baby Check PO Box 324, Wroxham, Norwich NR12 8EQ ☎ (01603) 784400 / see 2.03 Baby health.

Baby Echos (& Rad Pad) *Alison Brazendale, 349 Hungerford Road, Crewe, Cheshire CW1 5EZ* ☎ *(01270) 255 201* 🖰 *www.babyechos.co.uk / see 1.02 Looking after yourself; 2.03 Baby health; 3.02 Baby equipment; 3.03 Nursery decor.*

Baby Life Support Systems (BLISS) *68 South Lambeth Rd, London SW8 1RL* ☎ *(020) 7820 9471* 🖰 *www.bliss.org.uk / see 4.06 Support groups.*

Baby Milk Action *23 St Andrew's St, Cambridge CB2 3AX* ☎ *(01223) 464420* 🖰 *www.babymilkaction.org / see 2.02 Feeding.*

Baby Names 🖰 *www.babynames.com / see 2.09 Naming & ceremonies.*

Baby Naming Society *Yeomans Cottage, Kerswell Green, Kempsey, Worcs WR5 3PF* ☎ *(01905) 371070 / see 2.09 Naming & ceremonies.*

The Baby Products Association *The Coach House, Vicarage Rd, Pitstone, Leighton Buzzard LU7 9EY* 🖰 *Factfile requests (01296) 660990 / see 3.02 Baby equipment.*

Baby Sleep Guide ☎ *Orderlinen (0702) 092 2750* 🖰 *www.babysleepguide.co.uk / see 2.03 Baby health.*

Babybond Ultrasound *Head Office, High Street East, Uppingham, Rutland LE15 9PY* ☎ *Booking line (0845) 35 111 55 / see 1.03 Tests.*

Bach Centre *Mount Vernon, Sotwell, Wallingford, Oxfordshire OX10 0PZ* ☎ *(01491) 833712* 🖰 *www.bachcentre.com / see 4.02 Health practitioners.*

BackCare (The National Organisation for Healthy Backs) *16 Elmtree Rd, Teddington TW11 8ST* ☎ *(020) 8977 5474* 🖰 *www.backcare.org.uk / see 1.02 Looking after yourself; 4.06 Support groups.*

Best Bear *37 Warren St, London W1P 5PD* ☎ *(020) 7352 5852* 🖰 *www.bestbear.co.uk / see 2.03 Baby health; 2.04 Childcare.*

Better Business *Cribau Mill, Llanvair Discoed, Chepstow NP16 6LN* ☎ *(01291) 641222* 🖰 *www.better-business.co.uk / see 2.04 Childcare.*

Biolab Medical Unit *The Stone House, 9 Weymouth St, London W1W 6DB* ☎ *(020) 7636 5959/5905* 🖰 *www.biolab.co.uk / see 1.02 Looking after yourself; 4.02 Health practitioners.*

Birth & Beyond *8 Butts Close, Aynho, Oxfordshire OX17 3AE* ☎ *(01869) 811099, (0870) 905 7878* 🖰 *www.birthandbeyond.co.uk / see 2.03 Baby health; 3.02 Baby equipment.*

Birth Choice UK 🖰 *www.BirthChoiceUK.com / see 1.01 Where to have the baby.*

Birth Crisis Network ☎ *(01865) 300266* 🖰 *www.sheilakitzinger.com / see 4.03 Medical issues at birth.*

Birth Defects Foundation *BDF Centre, Hemlock Business Park, Hemlock Way, Cannock, Staffordshire WS11 2GF* ☎ *(01543) 468888, Here to Help Nurse Service (08700) 70 70 20* 🖰 *www.birthdefects.co.uk / see 1.03 Tests.*

Blooming Awful *29 Windermere Avenue, Basingstoke, Hampshire RG22 5JH* ☎ *(07020) 969728, Helpline (07050) 655094* 🖰 *www.hyperemesis.org.uk / see 1.02 Looking after yourself.*

BM - Cry-sis *BM - Cry-sis, London WC1N 3XX* ☎ *Helpline (020) 7404 5011* 🖰 *www.cry-sis.com / see 2.03 Baby health.*

Bobath Centre for Children with Cerebral Palsy *250 East End Rd, London N2 8AU* ☎ *(020) 8444 3355* 🖰 *www.bobath.org.uk / see 4.06 Support groups.*

Both Parents Forever *39 Cloonmore Ave, Orpington, Kent BR6 9LE* ☎ *(01689) 854343 / see 4.06 Support groups.*

Brain Injury Association (HEADWAY) *4 King Edward Court, King Edward St, Nottingham NG1 1EW* ☎ *(0115) 924 0800* 🖰 *www.headway.org.uk / see 2.03 Baby health.*

Braun *PO Box 21, 47 Aylesbury Road, Thame, Oxfordshire OX9 3LJ* ☎ *Consumer relations (0800) 783 7010* 🖰 *www.braun.com / see 2.03 Baby health.*

Breastfeeding Network *PO Box 11126, Paisley, Scotland PA2 8YB* ☎ *Helpline (0870) 900 8787* 🖰 *www.breastfeedingnetwork.org.uk / see 2.02 Feeding.*

The Bright Horizons Family Solutions *Morelands, 523 Old St, London EC1V 9HL* ☎ *(020) 7253 9620* 🖰 *www.bright-horizons.com / see 2.04 Childcare.*

British Acupuncture Council (BAcC) *63 Jeddo Rd, London W12 9HQ* ☎ *(020) 8735 0400* 🖰 *www.acupuncture.org.uk / see 4.02 Health practitioners.*

British Association for Counselling & Psychotherapy *BACP House, 35-37 Albert St, Rugby, Warwickshire CV21 2SG* ☎ *(0870) 443 5252 Information service* 🖰 *www.bacp.co.uk / see 4.02 Health practitioners.*

British Association for Early Childhood Education (BAECE) *136 Cavell St, London E1 2JA* ☎ *(020) 7539 5400* 🖰 *www.early-education.org.uk / see 2.07 Education.*

British Association of Nutritional Therapists (BANT) *27 Old Gloucester St, London WC1N 3XX* ☎ *(08706) 061284* 🖰 *www.bant.org.uk / see 4.02 Health practitioners.*

British Association of Psychotherapists *37 Mapesbury Rd, London NW2 4HJ*
☎ *(020) 8452 9823* ☝ *www.bap-psychotherapy.org / see 4.02 Health practitioners.*

British Association of Toy Retailers (BATR) *PO Box 13, Hampshire
SO23 0HG* ☎ *(01494) 474762* ☝ *www.batr.co.uk / see 3.06 Toys.*

The British Chiropractic Association *Blagrave House, 17 Blagrave St, Reading
RG1 1QB* ☎ *(0118) 950 5950* ☝ *www.chiropractic-uk.co.uk / see 4.02 Health practitioners.*

The British Coatings Federation *James House, Bridge St, Leatherhead, Surrey
KT22 7EP* ☎ *(01372) 360660* ☝ *www.coatings.org.uk / see 3.03 Nursery decor.*

British Complementary Medicine Association (BCMA) *PO Box 5122,
Bournemouth, Dorset BH8 0WG* ☎ *(0845) 345 5977* ☝ *www.bcma.co.uk / see 4.02 Health
practitioners.*

British Council *10 Spring Gardens, London SW1A 2BN*
☎ *Information centre (0161) 957 7755, (020) 7930 8466* ☝ *www.britishcouncil.org,
www.englishinbritain.co.uk (British schools site) / see 2.04 Childcare.*

British Dental Association *64 Wimpole St, London W1G 8YS* ☎ *(020) 7935 0875,
Patients' Helpline (0870) 333 1188* ☝ *www.bda-findadentist.org.uk / see 2.03 Baby health.*

British Dietetic Association *5th Floor Charles House, 148-149 Great Charles St,
Queensway, Birmingham, West Midlands B3 3HT* ☎ *(0121) 200 8080* ☝ *www.bda.uk.com
/ see 4.02 Health practitioners.*

British Dyslexia Association (BDA) *98 London Rd, Reading, Berks RG1 5AU*
☎ *Admin (0118) 966 2677, Helpline (0118) 966 8271* ☝ *www.BDA-dyslexia.org.uk
/ see 2.03 Baby health.*

British Epilepsy Association *New Anstey House, Gate Way Drive, Yeadon, Leeds
LS19 7XY* ☎ *(0808) 800 5050* ☝ *www.epilepsy.org.uk / see 1.02 Looking after yourself;
4.06 Support groups.*

British Gymnastics *Ford Hall, Lilleshall National Sports Centre, Newport TF10 9NB*
☎ *(01952) 822395* ☝ *www.british-gymnastics.org / see 2.06 Baby & toddler activities.*

British Heart Foundation *14 Fitzhardinge St, London W1H 6DH*
☎ *(020) 7487 7110, Heart information line (08450) 70 80 70* ☝ *www.bhf.org.uk
/ see 4.06 Support groups.*

The British Homeopathic Association *Hahnemann House, 29 Park Street
West, Luton LU1 3BE* ☎ *(0870) 4443950* ☝ *www.trusthomeopathy.org / see 4.02 Health
practitioners.*

The British Humanist Association *1 Gower St, London WC1E 6HD*
☎ *(020) 7079 3580* ☝ *www.humanism.org.uk / see 2.09 Naming & ceremonies.*

The British Institute for Allergy & Environmental Therapy
Llangwyryfon, Aberystwyth, Dyfed SY23 4EY ☎ *(01974) 241376* ☝ *www.allergy.org.uk
/ see 2.03 Baby health; 4.02 Health practitioners.*

The British Institute for Brain Injured Children (BIBIC) *Knowle Hall,
Bridgwater, Somerset TA7 8PJ* ☎ *(01278) 684060* ☝ *www.bibic.org.uk / see 4.06 Support
groups.*

British Institute of Learning Disabilities (BILD) *Campion House, Green St,
Kidderminster DY10 1JR* ☎ *(01562) 723010* ☝ *www.bild.org.uk / see 2.01 Postnatal.*

British Kidney Patients Association *Bordon, Hampshire GU35 9JZ*
☎ *(01420) 472021* ☝ *www.britishkidney-pa.co.uk / see 4.06 Support groups.*

The British Liver Trust *Central House, Central Ave, Ransomes Europark, Ipswich,
Suffolk IP3 9QG* ☎ *(01473) 276326* ☝ *www.britishlivertrust.org.uk / see 1.02 Looking after
yourself.*

The British Medical Acupuncture Society (BMAS) *12 Marbury House,
Bentley's Farm Lane, Whitley, Cheshire WA4 4QW* ☎ *(01925) 730727*
☝ *www.medical-acupuncture.org.uk / see 4.02 Health practitioners.*

British Nutrition Foundation (BNF) *High Holborn House, 52-54 High Holborn,
London WC1V 6RQ* ☎ *(020) 7404 6504* ☝ *www.nutrition.org.uk / see 2.02 Feeding;
4.02 Health practitioners.*

British Organ Donor Society (BODY) *Balsham, Cambridge CB1 6DL*
☎ *(01223) 893636* ☝ *www.argonet.co.uk/body / see 4.04 Miscarriage & stillbirth.*

The British Reflexology Association *Monks Orchard, Whitbourne, Worcester
WR6 5RB* ☎ *(01886) 821207* ☝ *www.britreflex.co.uk / see 4.02 Health practitioners.*

British Register of Complementary Practitioners *PO Box 194, London
SE16 7QZ* ☎ *(020) 7237 5165* ☝ *www.icmedicine.co.uk / see 4.02 Health practitioners.*

The British School of Reflexology *The Holistic Healing Centre, 92 Sheering Rd,
Old Harlow CM17 0JW* ☎ *(01279) 429060* ☝ *www.footreflexology.com / see 4.02 Health
practitioners.*

The British Society for Allergy & Clinical Immunology BSACI Secretariat, 66 Weston Park, Thames Ditton B3 3JY ☎ (020) 7637 9711 ✏ www.soton.ac.uk/~bsaci/ / see 2.03 Baby health.

British Society for Allergy, Environmental & Nutritional Medicine PO Box 7, Knighton, Southampton LD7 1WT ☎ Advice line (0906) 302 0010 ✏ www.bsaenm.org / see 2.03 Baby health.

British Stammering Association 15 Old Ford Rd, London E2 9PJ ☎ (020) 8983 1003, Helpline (0845) 603 2001 ✏ www.stammering.org / see 2.03 Baby health.

British Standards Institution 7th Floor East, 380 Chiswick High Rd, London W4 4AL ☎ (020) 8996 9000, Customer services (020) 8996 9001 ✏ www.bsi-global.com / see 3.02 Baby equipment.

British Toy & Hobby Association (BTHA) 80 Camberwell Rd, London SE5 0EG ☎ (020) 7701 7271 ✏ www.btha.co.uk / see 3.06 Toys.

British Toymakers Guild 124 Walcot St, Bath BA1 5BG ☎ (01225) 442440 ✏ www.toymakersguild.co.uk / see 3.06 Toys.

British Wheel of Yoga 25 Jermyn St, Sleaford, Lincs NG34 7RU ☎ (01529) 306851 ✏ www.bwy.org.uk / see 1.04 Antenatal classes.

Brittle Bone Society 30 Guthrie St, Dundee DD1 5BS ☎ (01382) 204446, (0800) 028 2459 ✏ www.brittlebone.org / see 4.06 Support groups.

Bug Buster Community Hygiene Concern, Mannor Gardens Centre, 6-9 Mannor Gardens, London N7 6LA ☎ (020) 7686 4321 ✏ www.nits.net / see 2.03 Baby health.

Caesarean Support Network 55 Cooil Drive, Douglas, Isle of Man IM2 2HF ☎ (01624) 661269 / see 2.01 Postnatal; 4.03 Medical issues at birth.

Campaign for State Education (CASE) 98 Erlanger Rd, London SE14 5TH ☎ (020) 8944 8206 ✏ www.casenet.org.uk / see 2.07 Education.

Cancer & Leukaemia in Children (CLIC) Abbey Wood, Bristol BS34 7JU ☎ Head office (0117) 311 2600, CLIC London (020) 7348 6019 ✏ www.clic.uk.com / see 4.06 Support groups.

Cancer BACUP 3 Bath Place, Rivington St, London EC2A 3JR ☎ Helpline (0808) 800 1234, (020) 7739 2280, Switchboard (020) 7696 2003 ✏ www.cancerbacup.org.uk / see 1.02 Looking after yourself.

Care for the Family PO Box 488, Cardiff CF15 7YY ☎ (029) 2081 0800 ✏ www.care-for-the-family.org.uk / see 2.01 Postnatal; 4.04 Miscarriage & stillbirth; 4.06 Support groups.

Careline PO Box 33439, London SW18 1XH ☎ (020) 8875 0500 ✏ www.careline.org.uk / see 2.01 Postnatal.

Cats Protection 17 Kings Rd, Horsham, West Sussex RH13 5PM ☎ Helpline (0870) 209 9099 ✏ www.cats.org.uk / see 2.01 Postnatal.

Central Middlesex Family Mediation Civic Centre Complex, Station Rd, Harrow, Middlesex HA1 2HX ☎ (020) 8427 2076 / see 4.06 Support groups.

Child & Family Consultation Centre Richmond Royal Hospital, Kew Foot Rd, Richmond TW9 2TE ☎ (020) 8355 1984 / see 2.03 Baby health.

Child Accident Prevention Trust (CAPT) 4th Floor, Clerk's Court, 18-20 Farringdon Lane, London EC1R 3HA ☎ (020) 7608 3828 ✏ www.capt.org.uk / see 2.03 Baby health; 3.03 Nursery decor.

Child Alert PO Box 29961, London SW6 6EZ ☎ (020) 7384 1311 ✏ www.childalert.co.uk / see 2.03 Baby health; 3.03 Nursery decor.

Child Benefit Centre (Washington) Inland Revenue, Child Benefit Office (GB), Washington, Newcastle Upon Tyne NE88 1ZB ☎ (0845) 302 1444 ✏ www.inlandrevenue.gov.uk/childbenefit / see 1.05 Rights.

The Child Bereavement Trust Aston House, High St, West Wycombe, Bucks HP14 3AG ☎ (01494) 446648 ✏ www.childbereavement.org.uk / see 4.04 Miscarriage & stillbirth.

Child Brain Injury Trust c/o The Radcliffe Infirmary, Woodstock Rd, Oxford OX2 6HE ☎ (01865) 552467, Helpline (0845) 601 4939 ✏ www.cbituk.org / see 2.03 Baby health.

Child Death Helpline ☎ (0800) 282986 ✏ www.childdeathhelpline.org.uk / see 4.04 Miscarriage & stillbirth.

Child Growth Foundation 2 Mayfield Ave, London W4 1PW ☎ (020) 8995 0257, (020) 8994 7625 ✏ www.heightmatters.org.uk / see 2.02 Feeding; 4.06 Support groups.

Child Poverty Action Group 94 White Lion St, London N1 9PF ☎ (020) 7837 7979 ✏ www.cpag.org.uk / see 1.05 Rights.

Child Support Agency (CSA) *Office of Chief Executive, Key House, c/o Pedmore House, The Waterfront, Brierley Hill, Dudley DY5 1XA*
☎ *National enquiry line (08457) 133133* ⏱ *www.csa.gov.uk* / *see 1.05 Rights.*

Childbirth ⏱ *www.childbirth.org* / *see 4.03 Medical issues at birth.*

Childcare Link *Opportunity Links, Trust Court, Vision Park, Histon, Cambridge CB4 9PW* ☎ *(08000) 960296* ⏱ *www.childcarelink.gov.uk* / *see 2.04 Childcare.*

ChildLine *45 Folgate St, London E1 6GL* ☎ *(020) 7650 3200, Helpline 24 hours (0800) 1111* ⏱ *www.childline.org.uk* / *see 4.06 Support groups.*

Childminders *6 Nottingham St, London W1U 5EJ* ☎ *(020) 7935 3000* ⏱ *www.babysitter.co.uk* / *see 2.04 Childcare.*

Children & Adults with Attention Deficit Hyperactivity Disorder (CHADD) ⏱ *www.chadd.org* / *see 2.03 Baby health.*

Children are Unbeatable *94 White Lion St, London N1 9PF* ☎ *(020) 7713 0569* ⏱ *www.childrenareunbeatable.org.uk* / *see 2.01 Postnatal.*

Children Living with Inherited Metabolic Diseases (CLIMB) *CLIMB Building, 176 Nantwich Rd, Crewe CW2 6BG* ☎ *(0870) 770 0326, (0800) 652 3181* ⏱ *www.climb.org.uk* / *see 4.06 Support groups.*

Children's Foot Health Register (CFHR) *Banbury Sq, Oxon W5 6EX* ☎ *(01295) 738726* ⏱ *www.shoe-shop.org.uk* / *see 3.05 Shoes.*

Children's Heart Federation *52 Kennington Oval, London SE11 5SW* ☎ *(0808) 808 5000* ⏱ *www.childrens-heart-fed.org.uk* / *see 4.06 Support groups.*

Children's Hours Trust *19 Devoil Close, Burpham, Guildford, Surrey GU14 7FG* ☎ *(01483) 578454* ⏱ *www.childrenshourstrust.org.uk* / *see 2.01 Postnatal.*

The Children's Legal Centre *University of Essex, Wivenhoe Park, Colchester, Essex CO4 3SQ* ☎ *(01206) 873935* ⏱ *www.childrenslegalcentre.com* / *see 4.06 Support groups.*

The Children's Liver Disease Foundation *38 Great Charles St, Birmingham B3 3JY* ☎ *(0121) 212 3839* ⏱ *www.childliverdisease.org* / *see 4.06 Support groups.*

The Children's Project *PO Box 2, Richmond TW10 7FL* ☎ *(020) 8546 8750* ⏱ *www.childrensproject.co.uk* / *see 2.01 Postnatal; 2.07 Education.*

The Children's Society *Edward Rudolf House, 69-85 Margery St, London WC1X 0JL* ☎ *Switch (020) 7841 4400, Supportsline (0845) 3001128* ⏱ *www.the-childrens-society.org.uk* / *see 4.06 Support groups.*

The Chiltern College *16 Peppard Rd, Caversham, Reading RG4 8JZ* ☎ *(0118) 947 1847* ⏱ *www.childcarelink.gov.uk* / *see 2.04 Childcare.*

Chirocare *10 Sandbourne Rd, Alum Chine, Bournemouth BH4 8JH* ☎ *(01202) 768508* / *see 2.03 Baby health; 4.02 Health practitioners.*

Choice in Education (CinE) *PO Box 20284, London NW1 3AA* ☎ *(020) 8969 0893* ⏱ *www.choiceineducation.org.uk* / *see 2.07 Education.*

Citizen's Advice Bureaux ⏱ *www.nacab.org.uk; www.adviceguide.org.uk* / *see 1.05 Rights.*

Cleft Lip & Palate Association (CLAPA) *235-237 Finchley Rd, London NW3 6LF* ☎ *(020) 7431 0033* ⏱ *www.clapa.com* / *see 2.03 Baby health.*

Clinical Diagnostic Services *27a Queens Terrace, London NW8 6EA* ☎ *(020) 7483 3611* / *see 1.03 Tests.*

The Coeliac Society *PO Box 220, High Wycombe, Bucks HP11 2HY* ☎ *Helpline (0804) 448804* ⏱ *www.coeliac.co.uk* / *see 2.03 Baby health.*

Coghill Research Laboratories *Lower Race, Pontypool, Gwent NP4 5UH* ☎ *(01495) 752 122* ⏱ *www.cogreslab.co.uk* / *see 1.02 Looking after yourself; 2.03 Baby health.*

Community Hygiene Concern *Manor Gardens Centre, 6-9 Manor Gardens, London N7 6LA* ☎ *Helpline (020) 7686 4321* ⏱ *www.chc.org* / *see 2.03 Baby health.*

The Compassionate Friends *53 North St, Bristol BS3 1EN* ☎ *(0117) 966 5202, Helpline (0117) 953 9639* ⏱ *www.tcf.org.uk* / *see 4.04 Miscarriage & stillbirth.*

Congenital CMV (Cytomegalovirus) Association *69 The Leasowes, Ford, Shrewsbury, Shropshire SY5 9LU* ☎ *(01743) 850055* / *see 1.02 Looking after yourself; 4.06 Support groups.*

Contact a Family *209-211 City Rd, London EC1V 1JN* ☎ *Office (020) 7608 8700, Helpline (0808) 808 3555* ⏱ *www.cafamily.org.uk* / *see 2.07 Education; 4.06 Support groups.*

Continence Foundation : The Helpline Nurse *307 Hatton Square, 16 Baldwins Gardens, London EC1N 7RJ* ☎ *(020) 7831 9831 helpline, (0845) 345 0165* ⏱ *www.continence-foundation.org.uk* / *see 2.01 Postnatal.*

Cool Baby Names ⏱ *www.cool-baby-names.com* / *see 2.09 Naming & ceremonies.*

Disability, Pregnancy & Parenthood International (DPPi) *Unit F9, 89-93 Fonthill Rd, London N4 3JH* ☎ *(0800) 018 4730, Textphone (0800) 018 9949* ✆ *www.dppi.org.uk / see 4.06 Support groups.*

The Disabled Parents Network *National Centre For Disabled Parents, Unit F9, 89/93 Fonthill Rd, London N4 3JH* ☎ *(0870) 241 0450, Text (0800) 0189949* ✆ *www.disabledparentsnetwork.org.uk / see 4.06 Support groups.*

Doctor's Laboratory *55 Wimpole St, London W1M 7DF* ☎ *(020) 7460 4800* ✆ *www.tdltlc.co.uk / see 1.03 Tests.*

Down's Syndrome Association *155 Mitcham Rd, London SW17 9PG* ☎ *(020) 8682 4001* ✆ *www.downs-syndrome.org.uk / see 1.03 Tests; 4.06 Support groups.*

Down's Syndrome Research Foundation ✆ *www.dsrf.co.uk / see 4.06 Support groups.*

Drinkline ☎ *(0800) 917 8282 / see 1.02 Looking after yourself.*

Dyslexia Institute *Park House, Wick Road, Egham, Surrey TW20 0HH* ☎ *(01784) 222 300* ✆ *www.dyslexia-inst.org.uk / see 2.03 Baby health.*

The Dyspraxia Foundation *8 West Alley, Hitchin, Herts SG5 1EG* ☎ *(01462) 454986 (Helpline)* ✆ *www.dyspraxiafoundation.org.uk / see 2.03 Baby health.*

Dystrophic Epidermolysis Bullosa Research Association (DEBRA) *DEBRA House, 13 Wellington Business Park, Dukes Ride, Crowthorne, Berks RG45 6LS* ☎ *(01344) 771961* ✆ *www.debra.org.uk / see 4.06 Support groups.*

E Sharp Minor *6 Earlswood St, London SE10 9ES* ☎ *(020) 8858 6648* ✆ *www.esharpminor.co.uk / see 2.03 Baby health; 3.04 Baby clothes.*

E-med *Brampton House, Hospital Of St. John & St. Elizabeth, 60 Grove End Rd., London NW8 9NH* ☎ *(020) 7806 4028* ✆ *www.e-med.co.uk / see 2.03 Baby health.*

Ealing 135 *Membership Secretary, PO Box 135, London W5 1FN* ☎ *(020) 8825 5588, Ealing Council's childrens infoservice / see 2.01 Postnatal.*

Ealing Education Centre *Mansell Road, Greenford, Middlesex UB6 9EG* ☎ *(020) 8578 6154* ✆ *www.ealing.gov.uk / see 2.07 Education.*

Early Support Programme ☎ *(0870) 000 2288* ✆ *www.dfes.gov.uk / see 4.06 Support groups.*

Eating Disorders Association *1st Floor, Wensum House, 103 Prince of Wales Rd, Norwich, Norfolk NR1 1DW* ☎ *Helpline (0845) 6341414, Under 18s Helpline (0845) 6347650, Admin (01603) 619090* ✆ *www.edauk.com / see 1.02 Looking after yourself.*

Ecozone *Birchwood House, Croydon, Surrey CR0 5AD* ☎ *(020) 8777 3121* ✆ *www.ecozone.co.uk / see 1.02 Looking after yourself; 2.03 Baby health.*

Eczemavoice ✆ *www.eczemavoice.com / see 2.03 Baby health.*

Education Advisory Service *97 Louisville Rd, London SW17 8RN* ☎ *(020) 8672 3185 / see 2.07 Education.*

Education Law Association (ELAS) *37d Grimston Ave, Folkestone, Kent CT20 2QD* ☎ *(01303) 211570* ✆ *www.educationlaw.org / see 2.07 Education.*

Education Now *113 Arundel Drive, Bramcote, Notts NG9 3FQ* ☎ *(0115) 925 7261* ✆ *www.educationnow.gn.apc.org / see 2.07 Education.*

Education Otherwise *PO Box 7420, London N9 9SG* ☎ *Recorded information line (0870) 730 0074* ✆ *www.education-otherwise.org / see 2.07 Education.*

Ehlers-Danlos Support Group *PO Box 335, Farnham, Surrey GU10 1XJ* ☎ *(01252) 690940* ✆ *www.ehlers-danlos.org / see 4.06 Support groups.*

Electromagnetic Hazard & Therapy Advice Line *9 Nine Acres, Midhurst, West Sussex GU29 9EP* ☎ *Premium rate advice line (0906) 4010237 £1.50 per minute* ✆ *www.em-hazard-therapy.com / see 1.02 Looking after yourself.*

Employers for Work-Life Balance *Peter Runge House, 3 Carlton House Terrace, London SW1Y 5DG* ☎ *(0870) 165 6700* ✆ *www.employersforwork-lifebalance.org.uk / see 1.05 Rights.*

Enfield *Schools Admissions Officer, Education Department, Civic Centre, Silver St, Enfield EN1 3XY* ☎ *(020) 8379 4453* ✆ *www.enfield.gov.uk / see 2.07 Education.*

Enuresis Resource & Information Centre (ERIC) *34 Old School house, Britannia Rd, Kingswood, Bristol BS15 8DB* ☎ *Helpline (0117) 960 3060* ✆ *www.eric.org.uk / see 2.03 Baby health.*

The Equal Opportunities Commission *Arndale House, Arndale Centre, Manchester M4 3EQ* ☎ *(0845) 601 5901* ✆ *www.eoc.org.uk / see 1.05 Rights.*

Equal Parenting Council ☎ *(0906) 550 1865* ✆ *www.equalparenting.org/ / see 4.06 Support groups.*

Cot Death Society *Maple House, Unit 6-8 Padgate Business Centre, Green Lane, Warrington, Cheshire WA1 4UN* ☎ *(01635) 38137, Monitor helpline (0845) 6010234* ⊕ *www.cotdeathsociety.org.uk* / *see 2.03 Baby health.*

Council for Awards in Children's Care & Education (CACHE) *8 Chequer St, St Albans, Herts AL1 3XZ* ☎ *(01727) 847636* ⊕ *www.cache.org.uk* / *see 2.04 Childcare.*

Council for Disabled Children *8 Wakeley St, London EC1V 7QE* ☎ *(020) 7843 6000 (National Children's Bureau),* *(020) 7843 1900 (Council for Disabled Children)* ⊕ *www.ncb.org.uk/cdc* / *4.06 Support groups.*

Coversure ☎ *(01706) 625559* / *see 1.02 Looking after yourself.*

Craniosacral Therapy Association *Monomark House, 27 Old Gloucester St, London WC1N 3XX* ☎ *(07000) 784735* ⊕ *www.craniosacral.co.uk* / *see 4.02 Health practitioners.*

Create Health Centre for Reproduction and Advanced Technology *21 Devonshire Place, London W1G 6HZ* ☎ *(020) 7486 5566* ⊕ *www.createhealth.org* / *see 1.03 Tests; 4.02 Health practitioners.*

CCRUSE Bereavement Care *Cruse House, 126 Sheen Rd, Richmond TW9 1UR* ☎ *(020) 8939 9530, Helpline (0870) 167 1677* ⊕ *www.crusebereavementcare.org.uk* / *see 4.04 Miscarriage & stillbirth.*

Culligan International (UK) Ltd *Bay Hall, Miln Rd, Huddersfield, W Yorks HD1 5EJ* ☎ *(01484) 512537* / *see 1.02 Looking after yourself.*

Cystic Fibrosis Trust *11 London Rd, Bromley BR1 1BY* ☎ *(020) 8464 7211* ⊕ *www.cftrust.org.uk* / *see 1.03 Tests.*

Cystitis Information Bureau *PO Box 2, Ellesmere Port, South Wirral L65 3BN* ⊕ *www.cystitis.org* / *see 1.02 Looking after yourself.*

Dads UK *85A Westbourne Street, Hove, East Sussex BN3 5PF* ☎ *(07092) 391489, (07092) 390210* ⊕ *www.dads-uk.co.uk* / *see 2.01 Postnatal; 4.05 Finding out more.*

Daval *Victoria House, 23 Winchester Rd, Andover, Hampshire SP10 2EQ* ☎ *(01264) 364474* ⊕ *www.travelwell.co.uk* / *see 1.02 Looking after yourself.*

Daycare Trust *21 St Georges Rd, London SE1 6ES* ☎ *(020) 7840 3350* ⊕ *www.daycaretrust.org.uk* / *see 2.04 Childcare.*

Dental Help Line *British Dental Health Foundation, Smile House, 2 East Union St, Rugby, Warks CV22 6AJ* ☎ *(0845) 063 1188* ⊕ *www.dentalhealth.org.uk* / *see 2.03 Baby health.*

Department for Education & Skills (DfES) *Sanctuary Buildings, Great Smith St, London SW1P 3BT* ☎ *(0870) 000 2288* ⊕ *www.dfes.gov.uk* / *see 2.04 Childcare; 2.07 Education.*

Department for Environment, Food & Rural Affairs (DEFRA) *Room G47, Nobel House, 17 Smith Square, London SW1P 3JR* ☎ *(020) 7238 5915* ⊕ *www.defra.gov.uk/farm/organic/* / *see 2.02 Feeding.*

Department for Work & Pensions (DWP) ☎ *(0800) 882200* ⊕ *www.dwp.gov.uk* / *see 1.05 Rights; 2.04 Childcare.*

Department of Health *Publications Unit, PO Box 777, London SE1 6XH* ☎ *(0800) 555777* ⊕ *www.doh.gov.uk* / *see 1.02 Looking after yourself; 2.03 Baby health.*

Department of Trade & Industry (DTI) *Employment Relations Directorate, 1 Victoria St, London SW1H 0ET* ☎ *(020) 7215 5000, Booklets (0870) 1502 500* ⊕ *www.dti.gov.uk* / *see 1.05 Rights.*

Depression Alliance *35 Westminster Bridge Rd, London SE1 7JB* ☎ *(020) 7633 0557, Postnatal depression helpline (0845) 120 3746* ⊕ *www.depressionalliance.org* / *see 2.01 Postnatal.*

Diabetes UK *10 Parkway, London NW1 7AA* ☎ *(020) 7424 1000, Careline (0845) 120 2960* ⊕ *www.diabetes.org.uk* / *see 1.02 Looking after yourself; 4.06 Support groups.*

Dial UK (National Association of Disablement Information & Advice Lines) *St Catherine's Hospital, Tickhill Rd, Balby, Doncaster, South Yorks DN4 8QN* ☎ *(01302) 310123* ⊕ *www.members.aol.com/dialuk* / *see 4.06 Support groups.*

Direct Health 2000 *6-7 Grove Market Place, Courtyard, Eltham, London SE9 5PU* ☎ *(0870) 200 0999* ⊕ *www.dh2.co.uk* / *see 2.03 Baby health.*

Direct Marketing Association (DMA) UK ⊕ *www.mpsonline.org.uk* / *see 4.04 Miscarriage & stillbirth.*

Directory of UK Self Help & Support Organisations *G-Text, 259 Squires Gate Lane, Blackpool FY4 3RE* ☎ *(01253) 402237* ⊕ *www.UKselfhelp.info* / *see 4.06 Support groups.*

Europ Assistance ☎ *(0870) 737 5720* 🖰 *www.europ-assistance.co.uk*
/ *see 1.02 Looking after yourself.*

Eye to Eye Mediation *231 Camberwell New Rd, London SE5 0TH*
☎ *(020) 7701 1114, (020) 7703 2532* 🖰 *www.nch.org.uk* / *see 4.06 Support groups.*

Faculty of Homeopathy *Hahnemann House, 29 Park Street West, Luton LU1 3BE*
☎ *(0870) 444 3950* 🖰 *www.trusthomeopathy.org* / *see 4.02 Health practitioners.*

Fair Play for Children *35 Lyon St, Bognor Regis, West Sussex PO21 1BW*
☎ *(01243) 869922* 🖰 *www.arunet.co.uk/fairplay/home.htm* / *see 4.06 Support groups.*

Families Anonymous *The Doddington & Rollo Community Association, Charlotte
Despard Ave, London SW11 5HD* ☎ *(020) 7498 4680, Helpline (0845) 1200 660*
🖰 *www.famanon.org.uk* / *see 1.02 Looking after yourself.*

Families Magazines *PO Box 4302, London SW16 1ZS* ☎ *(020) 8696 9680*
🖰 *www.familiesmagazine.co.uk* / *see 2.04 Childcare; 2.06 Baby & toddler activities;
2.07 Education.*

Families Need Fathers *134 Curtain Rd, London EC2A 3AR* ☎ *(020) 7613 5060*
🖰 *www.fnf.org.uk* / *see 2.01 Postnatal.*

The Family Caring Trust *8 Ashtree Enterprise Park, Newry, Co Down, Northern
Ireland BT34 1BY* ☎ *(028) 3026 4174* 🖰 *www.familycaring.co.uk* / *see 2.01 Postnatal.*

The Family Fund Trust *PO Box 50, York YO1 9ZX* ☎ *(0845) 130 4542*
🖰 *www.familyfundtrust.org.uk* / *see 4.06 Support groups.*

The Family Mediation Service *Institute of Family Therapy, 24-32 Stephenson Way,
London NW1 2HX* ☎ *(020) 7391 9150* 🖰 *www.instituteoffamilytherapy.org.uk*
/ *see 4.06 Support groups.*

Family Records Centre *1 Myddleton St, London EC1R 1UW* ☎ *(0151) 471 4800*
🖰 *www.statistics.gov.uk/registration* / *see 2.09 Naming & ceremonies.*

Family Rights Group *The Print House, 18 Ashwin St, London E8 3DL*
☎ *Helpline (0800) 7311696, (020) 7923 2628* 🖰 *www.frg.org.uk* / *see 4.06 Support groups.*

Family Service Units (FSU) *207 Old Marylebone Rd, London NW1 5QP*
☎ *(020) 7402 5175* 🖰 *www.cfsu.org.uk* / *see 4.06 Support groups.*

Family Welfare Association (FWA) *501-5 Kingsland Rd, London E8 4AU*
☎ *(020) 7254 6251* 🖰 *www.fwa.org.uk* / *see 4.02 Health practitioners; 4.06 Support groups.*

Fathers Direct 🖰 *www.fathersdirect.com* / *see 2.01 Postnatal.*

Federation of City Farms & Community Gardens *The Green House,
Hereford St, Bedminster, Bristol BS3 4NA* ☎ *(0117) 923 1800* 🖰 *www.farmgarden.org.uk*
/ *see 2.06 Baby & toddler activities.*

Feingold Association ☎ *+1 631 369 9340* 🖰 *www.feingold.org* / *see 2.03 Baby health.*

Fetal Medicine Centre *137 Harley St, London W1G 6BG* ☎ *(020) 7486 0476*
🖰 *www.fetalmedicine.com* / *see 1.03 Tests.*

Financial Services Authority *25 The North Colonnade, Canary Wharf, London
E14 5HS* ☎ *(020) 7066 1000* 🖰 *www.fsa.gov.uk* / *see 2.08 Finance.*

Flametree *Plumtree Court, London EC4A 4HT* ☎ *(020) 7804 8878*
🖰 *www.flametree.co.uk* / *see 2.04 Childcare.*

Food & Chemical Allergy Association *27 Ferringham Lane, Ferring-by-Sea,
Worthing, W Sussex BN12 5NB* / *see 2.03 Baby health.*

The Food Commission *94 White Lion St, London N1 9PF* ☎ *(020) 7837 2250*
🖰 *www.foodcomm.org.uk; www.parentsjury.org.uk* / *see 1.02 Looking after yourself;
2.02 Feeding.*

Food Intolerance Databank *Leatherhead Food International, Randalls Rd,
Leatherhead, Surrey KT22 7RY* ☎ *(01372) 376761* 🖰 *www.leatherheadfood.com*
/ *see 2.03 Baby health.*

The Food Standards Agency *PO Box 369, Hayes, Middlesex UB3 1UT*
☎ *(0845) 606 0667* 🖰 *www.foodstandards.gov.uk/* / *see 1.02 Looking after yourself;
2.02 Feeding.*

**Foresight, The Association for the Promotion of Pre-Conceptual
Care** *28 The Paddock, Godalming, Surrey GU7 1XD* ☎ *(01483) 427839*
🖰 *www.foresight-preconception.org.uk* / *see 1.02 Looking after yourself.*

Foundation for the Study of Infant Deaths (FSID) *Artillery House, 11-19
Artillery Row, London SW1P 1RT* ☎ *(0870) 7870885, Helpline (0870) 7870554*
🖰 *www.sids.org.uk/fsid* / *see 2.03 Baby health.*

Fragile X Society *Rood End House, 6 Stortford Road, Great Dunmow, Essex CM6 1DA*
☎ *(01371) 875100* 🖰 *www.fragilex.org.uk* / *see 2.03 Baby health.*

Free Range Education 🖰 *www.free-range-education.co.uk* / *see 2.07 Education.*

The Freshwater Company *Unit 8 Kentish Town Business Park, Regis Rd, London NW5 3EW* ☎ *(08457) 023998* ⏱ *www.freshwateruk.com* / *see 1.02 Looking after yourself.*

Friends of the Earth *26-28 Underwood St, London N1 7JQ* ☎ *Information service (0808) 800 1111, HQ (020) 7490 1555* ⏱ *www.foe.co.uk/safer_chemicals* / *see 1.02 Looking after yourself; 3.09 Lotions & potions.*

Full-time Mothers *PO Box 186, London SW3 5RF* ☎ *(020) 8670 2525* ⏱ *www.fulltimemothers.org* / *see 2.01 Postnatal; 2.04 Childcare.*

Gabbitas Educational Consultants *Carrington House, 126-130 Regent St, London W1B 5EE* ☎ *(020) 7734 0161* ⏱ *www.gabbitas.co.uk* / *see 2.07 Education.*

Galactosaemia Support Group *31 Cotysmore Rd, Sutton Colefield, West Midlands B75 6BJ* ☎ *(0121) 378 5143* ⏱ *www.gsgnews.tripod.com* / *see 2.03 Baby health.*

General Assembly of Unitarian & Free Christian Churches *Essex Hall, 1-6 Essex St, London WC2R 3HY* ☎ *(020) 7240 2384* ⏱ *www.unitarian.org.uk* / *see 2.09 Naming & ceremonies.*

General Chiropractic Council (GCC) *44 Wicklow St, London WC1X 9HL* ☎ *(020) 7713 5155* ⏱ *www.gcc-uk.org* / *see 4.02 Health practitioners.*

General Council & Register of Naturopaths *Goswell House, 2 Goswell Rd, Bath BA16 0JG* ☎ *(01458) 840 072* ⏱ *www.naturopathy.org.uk* / *see 4.02 Health practitioners.*

General Dental Council (GDC) *37 Wimpole St, London W1G 8DQ* ☎ *(020) 7887 3800* ⏱ *www.gdc-uk.org* / *see 2.03 Baby health.*

General Medical Council (GMC) *178 Great Portland St, London W1W 5JE* ☎ *(020) 7580 7642* ⏱ *www.gmc-uk.org* / *see 4.03 Medical issues at birth.*

General Osteopathic Council (GOC) *Osteopathy House, 176 Tower Bridge Rd, London SE1 3LU* ☎ *(020) 7357 6655* ⏱ *www.osteopathy.org.uk* / *see 4.02 Health practitioners.*

General Register Office *Smedley Hydro, Trafalgar Rd, Southport PR8 2HH* ☎ *(0151) 471 4800* ⏱ *www.statistics.gov.uk* / *see 2.09 Naming & ceremonies.*

The Genetic Interest Group (GIG) *Unit 4d Leroy House, 436 Essex Rd, London N1 3QP* ☎ *(020) 7704 3141* ⏱ *www.gig.org.uk* / *see 4.06 Support groups.*

Gifted Children Information Centre *Hampton Grange, 21 Hampton Lane, Solihull, West Midlands B91 2QJ* ☎ *(0121) 705 4547* ⏱ *www.ukindex.info/giftedchildren.co.uk* / *see 2.03 Baby health.*

Gingerbread Association for One Parent Families *7 Sovereign Close, Sovereign Court, London E1W 2HW* ☎ *(020) 7488 9300, Confidential advice line (0800) 018 4318* ⏱ *www.gingerbread.org.uk* / *see 4.06 Support groups.*

Goldenhar Syndrome Family Support Group *9 Hartley Court Gardens, Cranbrook, Kent TN17 3QY* ☎ *(01580) 714 042* / *see 4.06 Support groups.*

Grandparents' Federation *Moot House, The Stow, Harlow, Essex CM20 3AG* ☎ *(01279) 428040, Helpline (01279) 444964* ⏱ *www.grandparents-federation.org.uk* / *see 4.06 Support groups.*

Grobag *Fusion House, Union Rd, Kingsbridge, Devon TQ7 1EF* ☎ *(01548) 854 444* ⏱ *www.grobag.com* / *see 1.02 Looking after yourself; 2.02 Feeding; 3.01 Maternity wear; 3.02 Baby equipment; 3.03 Nursery decor; 3.08 Nappies.*

Group B Strep Support *PO Box 203 Haywards Heath, W Sussex RH16 1GF* ☎ *(01444) 416176 (answerphone)* ⏱ *www.gbss.org.uk* / *see 1.03 Tests; 4.06 Support groups.*

Guild of Infant and Child Massage *22 Elder Close, Uttoxeter, Staffordshire ST14 8UR* ☎ *(01889) 564 555* ⏱ *www.gicm.org.uk* / *see 2.06 Baby & toddler activities.*

Guy's Hospital (Poisons Unit) *St Thomas St, London SE1 9RT* ☎ *(020) 7955 5000* ⏱ *www.hospital.org.uk* / *see 2.03 Baby health.*

Haemophilia Society *Chesterfield House, 385 Euston Rd, London NW1 3AU* ☎ *(020) 7380 0600, 0800 018 6068* ⏱ *www.haemophilia.org.uk* / *see 4.06 Support groups.*

Gideon Hajioff *Hendon Therapies Clinic, 50 Colindeep Lane, London NW9 6HB* ☎ *(020) 8205 2929* ⏱ *www.acu.me.uk* / *see 4.02 Health practitioners.*

Haringey Parents *, London* / *see 2.01 Postnatal.*

The Harris Birthright Research Centre *King's College Hospital, London SE5 9RS* ☎ *(020) 7346 3040* ⏱ *www.kingshealth.com/clinical/women/harris-birthright* / *see 1.03 Tests.*

Head Lice Info ⏱ *www.HeadLiceInfo.com* / *see 2.03 Baby health.*

Health & Safety Executive *HSE Books, PO Box 1999, Sudbury, Suffolk CO10 2WA* ☎ *Infoline (08701) 545500, Publications (01787) 881165* ⏱ *www.hse.gov.uk* / *see 1.02 Looking after yourself; 1.05 Rights.*

Health Development Agency *PO Box 90, Wetherby, Yorkshire LS23 7EY*
☎ *(0870) 121 4194* ⚐ *www.hda-online.org.uk / see 1.02 Looking after yourself.*

The Health Partnership *12A Thurloe St, London SW7 2ST* ☎ *(020) 7589 6414*
/ see 4.02 Health practitioners.

Health Screening *1 Church Square, Taunton, Somerset TA1 1SA* ☎ *(01823) 325023*
⚐ *www.healthscreeningltd.com / see 2.03 Baby health.*

The Healthy House *The Old Co-Op, Lower Street, Ruscombe, Stroud, Gloucestershire
GL6 6BU* ☎ *(01453) 752216* ⚐ *www.healthy-house.co.uk / see 2.03 Baby health.*

The Healthy Start Clinic *65 Sancroft St, London SE11 5NG* ☎ *(020) 7411 5660,
(020) 7411 5686 / see 2.03 Baby health.*

Heart of Parenting *7 Endymion Rd, London N4 1EE* ☎ *(020) 8749 1964*
⚐ *www.spectrumtherapy.co.uk / see 2.01 Postnatal.*

Heartline Association *Community Link, Surrey Health House, Knoll Road, Camberley,
Surrey GU15 3HH* ☎ *(01276) 707636* ⚐ *www.heartline.org.uk / see 4.06 Support groups.*

Henry Doubleday Research Association (HDRA) *Natural Centre for Organic
Gardening, Ryton on Dunsmore, Coventry CV8 3LG* ☎ *(02476) 3035171*
⚐ *www.hdra.org.uk / see 2.02 Feeding.*

Henry Spink Foundation Resource Center *209-211 City Rd, London
EC1V 1JN* ☎ *(020) 7388 9843* ⚐ *www.henryspink.org / see 4.06 Support groups.*

Jayne Herbert *49 Mildenhall Rd, London E5 0RT* ☎ *(020) 8533 9925*
/ see 1.04 Antenatal classes; 2.01 Postnatal.

Herbline UK ☎ *(020) 8534 7154 / see 4.02 Health practitioners.*

Herpes Virus Association (HVA) *41 North Rd, London N7 9DP*
☎ *Helpline (020) 7609 9061* ⚐ *www.herpes.org.uk / see 1.03 Tests.*

Hertsmere Borough Council *Civic Offices, Elstree Way, Borehamwood, Herts
WD6 1WA* ☎ *(020) 8207 2277* ⚐ *www.hertsmere.gov.uk / see 2.07 Education.*

High/Scope UK *Copperfield House, 190-192 Maple Rd, Penge, London SE20 8HT*
☎ *(020) 8676 0220* ⚐ *www.high-scope.org.uk / see 2.07 Education.*

Holidays Endeavour for Lone Parents (HELP) *57 Owston Rd, Carcroft,
Doncaster DN6 8DA* ☎ *(0114) 2882967 / see 4.06 Support groups.*

Home Dad UK ☎ *(07752) 549 085* ⚐ *www.homedad.org.uk / see 2.01 Postnatal.*

Home Education Advisory Service *PO Box 98, Welwyn Garden City, Herts
AL8 6AN* ☎ *(01707) 371854* ⚐ *www.heas.org.uk / see 2.07 Education.*

Home Office *Lunar House, Wellesley Rd, Croydon CR9 2BY* ☎ *(08706) 067766,
Recorded information (020) 8649 7878* ⚐ *www.homeoffice.gov.uk / see 2.04 Childcare.*

Home-Dad Link *PO Box 636, Thornton Heath CR7 8TQ*
⚐ *www.slowlane.com/groups/homedadlink / see 2.01 Postnatal.*

Home-Start UK *London Regional – 3rd Floor, 9 Staple Inn, London, WC1V 7QH;
Headquarters – 2 Salisbury Rd, Leicester LE1 7QR* ☎ *Head office (0116) 233 9955,
London (020) 7831 7023* ⚐ *www.home-start.org.uk / see 2.01 Postnatal; 4.06 Support groups.*

homebirth ⚐ *www.homebirth.org.uk / see 1.01 Where to have the baby.*

Hopes & Dreams *339-341 City Rd, London EC1V 1LJ* ☎ *(020) 7833 9388*
⚐ *www.hopesanddreams.co.uk / see 2.04 Childcare.*

Hornsby International Dyslexia Centre *Wye St, London SW11 2HB*
☎ *(020) 7223 1144* ⚐ *www.hornsby.co.uk / see 2.07 Education.*

Hornsey Vale Community Centre *60 Mayfield Rd, London N8 9LP*
☎ *(020) 8348 4612 / see 2.01 Postnatal; 2.06 Baby & toddler activities.*

Hounslow Toy Library *Inwood Park, Inwood Rd, Hounslow TW3 1XA*
☎ *(020) 8569 5451 / see 3.06 Toys.*

Human Scale Education *Unit 8, Fairseat Farm, Chewstoke, Bristol BS40 8XF*
☎ *(01275) 332516* ⚐ *www.hse.org.uk / see 2.07 Education.*

Hyperactive Children's Support Group (HACSG) *Dept W, 71 Whyke Lane,
Chichester, West Sussex PO19 7PD* ☎ *(01243) 551313* ⚐ *www.hacsg.org.uk / see 2.03 Baby
health.*

I CAN *4 Dyers Buildings, London EC1N 2QP* ☎ *(0845) 225 4071* ⚐ *www.ican.org.uk
/ see 2.03 Baby health.*

Immunisation.org.uk ☎ *NHS Direct (0845) 4647* ⚐ *www.immunisation.org.uk
/ see 2.03 Baby health.*

Independent Midwives Association *1 The Great Quarry, Guildford, Surrey
GU1 3XN* ☎ *(01483) 821104 Answer phone* ⚐ *www.independentmidwives.org.uk
/ see 1.01 Where to have the baby.*

Susan Kennard ☎ *(020) 7690 6171 mobile (07966) 434 701*
⌁ *www.soul-purpose.org* / *see 2.01 Postnatal.*

Kensington & Chelsea *Hornton St, London W8 7NX* ☎ *(020) 7361 3334*
⌁ *www.rbkc.gov.uk* / *see 2.07 Education.*

KIDS *London Office, 49 Mecklenburgh Square, London WC1N 2NY*
☎ *National HQ (020) 7359 3635, London (020) 7520 0405* ⌁ *www.kids-online.org.uk*
/ *see 4.06 Support groups.*

Kids' Clubs Network *Bellerive House, 3 Muirfield Crescent, London E14 9SZ*
☎ *(020) 7512 2100* ⌁ *www.kidsclubs.co.uk* / *see 2.07 Education.*

Kidsaware *PO Box 115, Bedford MK44 2FA* ☎ *(01480) 869 244*
⌁ *www.kidsaware.co.uk* / *see 2.03 Baby health.*

Kidscape *2 Grosvenor Gardens, London SW1W ODH* ☎ *(020) 7730 3300,*
Helpline 0845 1205204 ⌁ *www.kidscape.org.uk* / *see 4.06 Support groups.*

Kingston Hospital Milk Bank *Galsworthy Rd, Kingston, Surrey KT2 7OB*
☎ *(020) 8974 5390* ⌁ *www.kingstonhospital.nhs.uk* / *see 2.02 Feeding.*

Kingston Natural Healing Centre *40 Eastbury Rd, Kingston upon Thames*
KT2 5AN ☎ *(020) 8546 5793* ⌁ *www.surrey-online.co.uk/knhe* / *see 2.03 Baby health;*
4.02 Health practitioners.

Kith & Kids *c/o Irish Centre, Pretoria Rd, London N17 8DX* ☎ *(020) 8801 7432*
⌁ *www.kithandkids.org.uk* / *see 4.06 Support groups.*

Lactation Consultants of Great Britain *16 The Gables, Fortis Green, London*
N10 3EA ⌁ *www.lcgb.org* / *see 2.02 Feeding.*

Lakeland College *The Postal Buildings, Ash Street, Bowness On Windermere, Cumbria*
LA23 3EB ☎ *(01539) 447 666* ⌁ *www.thelakelandcollege.co.uk* / *see 4.02 Health*
practitioners.

Lamburn & Turner *Nanny Payroll Service, Place Farm, Wheathampstead, Herts*
AL4 8SB ☎ *(01582) 834850* ⌁ *www.lamburnandturner.co.uk* / *see 2.04 Childcare.*

Law Centres Federation *Duchess House, 18-19 Warren St, London W1T 5LR*
☎ *(020) 7387 8570* ⌁ *www.lawcentres.org.uk* / *see 1.05 Rights; 4.06 Support groups.*

The Law Society *113 Chancery Lane, London WC2A 1PL* ☎ *(020) 7242 1222*
⌁ *www.lawsociety.org.uk* / *see 2.08 Finance.*

La Leche League of Great Britain *BM 3424, London WC1N 3XX*
☎ *Helpline (0845) 120 2918, (020) 7242 1278* ⌁ *www.laleche.org.uk* / *see 2.02 Feeding;*
4.05 Finding out more.

Leeds Antenatal Screening Service *3 Gemini Park, Sheepscar Way, Leeds*
LS7 3JB ☎ *(0113) 262 1675* ⌁ *www.leedsscreeningcentre.co.uk* / *see 1.03 Tests.*

Lesley Pavincich *Soup Dragon, Lordship Lane, London SE22* ☎ *(020) 8677 5776*
/ *see 1.01 Where to have the baby.*

Letts Educational *The Chiswick Centre, 414, Chiswick High Rd, London W4 5TF*
☎ *(020) 8996 3333* ⌁ *www.letts-education.com* / *see 2.07 Education.*

LGC *Queens Road, Teddington, Middlesex YW11 OLY* ☎ *(020) 8943 7000*
⌁ *www.lgc.co.uk* / *see 1.05 Rights.*

Liedloff Continuum Network ☎ *(01600) 861816* ⌁ *www.continuum-concept.org*
/ *see 2.01 Postnatal.*

Life (London office) *5 Goodwins Court, Off St. Martins Lane, London WC2N 4LL*
☎ *Hotline (0800) 849 4545, London Office 020 7240 1275* ⌁ *www.lifeuk.org*
/ *see 1.03 Tests.*

LifeRites *Gwndwn Mawr, Trelech, Carmarthenshire SA33 6SA* ☎ *(01994) 484527*
⌁ *www.liferites.org* / *see 2.09 Naming & ceremonies.*

Links Organic ☎ *(020) 7590 9272* ⌁ *www.linksorganic.com* / *see 2.02 Feeding.*

London Drug & Alcohol Network *Unit 14 Canonbury Yard, 190a New North Rd,*
London N1 7BJ ☎ *(020) 7704 0004, Drinkline 0800 917 8282,* ⌁ *www.idan.org.uk*
/ *see 1.02 Looking after yourself.*

London Hazards Centre *Hampstead Town Hall Centre, 213 Haverstock Hill, London*
NW3 4QP ☎ *(020) 7794 5999* ⌁ *www.lhc.org.uk* / *see 1.02 Looking after yourself;*
1.05 Rights.

London4kids ⌁ *www.london4kids.com* / *see 2.06 Baby & toddler activities.*

Look *49 Court Oak Rd, Harborne B17 9TG* ☎ *(0121) 428 5038* ⌁ *www.look-uk.org*
/ *see 2.03 Baby health.*

Lupus UK *St James House, Eastern Rd, Romford, Essex RM1 3NH* ☎ *(01708) 731251*
⌁ *www.lupusuk.com* / *see 1.02 Looking after yourself.*

The Marcé Society *PO Box 30853, London W12 OXG* ☎ *(01270) 752110*
⌁ *www.marcesociety.com* / *see 2.01 Postnatal.*

Nanny Payroll Services *Payday Services Ltd, The Studio, Benefield Rd, Brigstock, Kettering NN14 3ES* ☎ *(01536) 373111* ⏱ *www.nannypayroll.co.uk, www.paydayservices.co.uk / see 2.04 Childcare.*

nannyjob ⏱ *www.nannyjob.co.uk / see 2.04 Childcare.*

Nannytax *PO Box 988, Brighton BN2 1BY* ☎ *(0845) 226 2203* ⏱ *www.nannytax.co.uk / see 2.04 Childcare.*

Nappy Information Service *AHPMA, 46 Bridge Street, Godalming, Surrey GU7 1HL* ⏱ *www.nappyinformationservice.co.uk / see 3.08 Nappies.*

Nappy Nights *127A Twickenham Rd, Isleworth, Middlesex TW7 6AW* ☎ *(020) 8568 4913 / see 3.08 Nappies.*

Narcotics Anonymous *202 City Rd, London EC1V 2PH* ☎ *Helpline (020) 7730 0009, Office (020) 7251 4007* ⏱ *www.ukna.org / see 1.02 Looking after yourself.*

National Association for Gifted Children *Suite 14, Challenge House, Sherwood Drive, Bletchney, Bucks MK3 6DP* ☎ *(0870) 770 3217* ⏱ *www.nagcbritain.org.uk / see 2.07 Education.*

National Association for Mental Health (MIND) *Granta House, 15-19 Broadway, London E15 4BQ* ☎ *(020) 8519 2122* ⏱ *www.mind.org.uk / see 2.01 Postnatal; 2.03 Baby health.*

National Association for Primary Education (NAPE) *c/o University of Leicester, Moulton College, Moulton NN3 7RR* ☎ *(01604) 647660* ⏱ *www.nape.org.uk / see 2.07 Education.*

The National Association for Special Educational Needs (NASEN) *4-5 Amber Business Village, Amber Close, Amington, Tamworth B77 4RP* ☎ *(01827) 311500* ⏱ *www.nasen.org.uk / see 2.03 Baby health.*

National Association of Children's Information Services (NACIS) *33 Marylebone Lane, London W1U 2NJ* ☎ *(020) 7935 0088* ⏱ *www.nacis.org.uk / see 2.04 Childcare.*

National Association of Citizens' Advice Bureaux *115-123 Pentonville Rd, London N1 9LZ* ⏱ *www.nacab.org.uk / see 1.05 Rights.*

National Association of Early Years Professionals (NAEYP) ⏱ *www.nann.freeserve.co.uk / see 2.04 Childcare.*

National Association of Nappy Services (NANS) *Head Office, 271 Holdbrook South, Waltham Cross,, Harts EN8 7FL* ☎ *(0121) 693 4949* ⏱ *www.changeanappy.co.uk / see 3.08 Nappies.*

National Association of Toy & Leisure Libraries (Play Matters) *68 Churchway, London NW1 1LT* ☎ *(020) 7255 4600* ⏱ *www.natll.org.uk / see 3.06 Toys.*

National Asthma Campaign *Providence House, Providence Place, London N1 0NT* ☎ *Helpline (08457) 010203* ⏱ *www.asthma.org.uk / see 2.03 Baby health.*

National Autistic Society *393 City Rd, London EC1V 1NG* ☎ *Helpline (0870) 600 8585* ⏱ *www.nas.org.uk / see 2.03 Baby health.*

National Campaign for Real Nursery Education (NCNE) *BCM Box 6216, London WC1N 3XX* ⏱ *www.ncne.co.uk / see 2.07 Education.*

National Care Standards Commission (NCSC) *St Nicholas Building, St Nicholas St, Newcastle Upon Tyne NE1 1NB* ☎ *Helpline (0191) 233 3556, HQ (0191) 233 3600* ⏱ *www.carestandards.org.uk / see 1.01 Where to have the baby; 4.03 Medical issues at birth.*

National Centre for Disabled Parents *Unit F9, 89-93 Fonthill Rd, London N4 3JH* ☎ *(08000) 184730, Text (0800) 018 9949* ⏱ *www.dppi.org.uk / see 4.06 Support groups.*

National Childbirth Trust (NCT) *Alexandra House, Oldham Terrace, London W3 6NH* ☎ *Enquiry line (0870) 444 8707* ⏱ *www.nctpregnancyandbabycare.co.uk; www.nctparentsconnect.co.uk / see 1.01 Where to have the baby; 1.04 Antenatal classes; 2.01 Postnatal; 2.02 Feeding; 2.04 Childcare; 2.05 Travel; 2.06 Baby & toddler activities; 4.04 Miscarriage & stillbirth; 4.05 Finding out more; 4.06 Support groups.*

The National Childminding Association (NCMA) *8 Masons Hill, Bromley BR2 9EY* ☎ *(020) 8464 6164, (0800) 169 4486* ⏱ *www.ncma.org.uk / see 2.04 Childcare.*

National Children's Bureau *8 Wakeley St, London EC1V 7QE* ☎ *(020) 7843 6000* ⏱ *www.ncb.org.uk / see 4.06 Support groups.*

National Confederation of Parent Teacher Associations (NCPTA) *18 St Johns Hill, Sevenoaks, Kent TN13 3NP* ☎ *(01732) 748850* ⏱ *www.ncpta.org.uk / see 2.07 Education.*

National Council for One Parent Families (NCOPF) 255 Kentish Town Rd, London NW5 2LX ☎ (020) 7428 5400, Helpline (0800) 018 5026
🖰 www.oneparentfamilies.org.uk / see 1.05 Rights; 4.06 Support groups.

National Day Nurseries Association Oak House, Woodvale Road, Brighouse, West Yorks HD6 4AB ☎ (01484) 723 322 🖰 www.ndna.org.uk / see 2.04 Childcare.

The National Deaf Children's Society (NDCS) 15 Dufferin St, London EC1Y 8UR ☎ (0808) 800 8880 (voice and text) 🖰 www.ndcs.org.uk / see 4.06 Support groups.

National Drugs Helpline (aka "Talk to Frank") ☎ (0800) 776600
🖰 www.talktofrank.com / see 1.02 Looking after yourself.

National Eczema Society Hill House, Highgate Hill, London N19 5NA
☎ Infoline (0870) 241 3604 🖰 www.eczema.org / see 2.03 Baby health.

National Family & Parenting Institute 430 Highgate Studios, 53-79 Highgate Rd, London NW5 1TL ☎ (020) 7424 3460 🖰 www.nfpi.org / see 4.06 Support groups.

National Family Mediation Alexander House, Ave, Bristol BS1 4BS
☎ (0117) 904 2825 🖰 www.nfm.u-net.com / see 4.06 Support groups.

National Institute for Medical Herbalists 56 Longbrook St, Exeter, Devon EX4 6AH ☎ (01392) 426022 🖰 www.nimh.org.uk / see 4.02 Health practitioners.

National Meningitis Trust Fern House, Bath Rd, Stroud, Gloucestershire GL5 3TJ
☎ (0845) 6000 800 🖰 www.meningitis-trust.org.uk / see 2.03 Baby health.

National NEWPIN 35 Sutherland Square, London SE17 3EE ☎ (020) 7407 7255
🖰 www.newpin.org.uk / see 2.01 Postnatal; 4.06 Support groups.

National Osteoporosis Society Manor Farm, Skinners Hill, Camerton, Bath BA2 0PJ ☎ Helpline (0845) 450 0230, General enquiries (01761) 471771
🖰 www.nos.org.uk / see 1.02 Looking after yourself.

National Patient Safety Agency 4-8 Maple St, London W1T 5HD
☎ (020) 7927 9500 🖰 www.npsa.nhs.uk / see 4.03 Medical issues at birth.

National Playbus Association (NPA) Brunswick Court, Brunswick Square, Bristol BS2 8PE ☎ (0117) 916 6580 🖰 www.playbus.org.uk / see 2.07 Education.

National Portage Association 127 Monks Dale, Yeovil, Somerset BA21 3JE
☎ (01935) 471641 🖰 www.portage.org.uk / see 2.07 Education.

National Sexual Healthline ☎ (0800) 567123 / see 1.03 Tests.

National Society for Phenylketonuria (NSPKU) PO Box 26642, London N14 4ZF ☎ Helpline (0845) 603 9136, (020) 8364 3010,
London & Home Counties (01279) 830162, Membership (0141) 954 6372
🖰 www.nspuk.org / see 1.03 Tests; 4.06 Support groups.

National Society for Research into Allergy PO Box 45, Hinckley, Leics LE10 1JY ☎ (01455) 250715 🖰 www.all-allergy.co.uk / see 2.03 Baby health.

National Society for the Prevention of Cruelty to Children (NSPCC) 42 Curtain Rd, London EC2A 3NH ☎ Helpline (0800) 800500 🖰 www.nspcc.org.uk
/ see 2.03 Baby health; 4.06 Support groups.

The National Toy Council ☎ British Toy & Hobby Association (020) 7701 7271
🖰 www.btha.co.uk/toycouncil.html / see 3.06 Toys.

National Women's Register 3a Vulcan House, Vulcan Rd North, Norwich NR6 6AQ ☎ (0845) 450 0287 🖰 www.nwr.org / see 2.01 Postnatal.

Natural Medicines Society PO Box 134, Chessington, Kingston upon Thames KT1 1HP ☎ (0870) 240 4784 🖰 www.the-nms.demon.org.uk / see 4.02 Health practitioners.

Natural Nurturing Network Lower Hardwick House, Chepstow NP16 5PT
☎ (0116) 288 0844 / see 2.01 Postnatal.

NCH 85 Highbury Park, London N5 1UD ☎ (0845) 762 6579 🖰 www.nch.org.uk
/ see 4.06 Support groups.

NCT / Symphysis Pubis Disfunction National Childbirth Trust, Alexandra House, Oldham Terrace, Acton, London W3 6NH ☎ (0870) 770 3236 🖰 www.spd-uk.org
/ see 1.02 Looking after yourself.

NCT Maternity Sales 239 Shawbridge St, Glasgow G43 1QN ☎ (0870) 112 1120, Breatfeeding helpline (0870) 444 8708 🖰 www.nctms.co.uk / see 2.01 Postnatal; 2.02 Feeding; 3.01 Maternity wear; 3.02 Baby equipment; 3.04 Baby clothes; 3.06 Toys; 4.06 Support groups.

NetDoctor 🖰 www.NetDoctor.co.uk / see 2.03 Baby health.

Network 81 1-7 Woodfield Terraces, Stansted, Essex CH24 8AJ ☎ (0870) 770 3306
🖰 www.network81.co.uk / see 2.07 Education.

Network of Childbirth & Yoga Educators 🖰 www.maternitybras.co.uk
/ see 1.04 Antenatal classes.

Neurofibromatosis Association *Quay Side House, 38 High St, Kingston upon Thames KT1 1HL* ☎ *(020) 8439 1234* ⏚ *www.nfauk.org / see 4.06 Support groups.*

The New Baby Company *8 Souldern Road, London W14 0JE* ☎ *(020) 7751 1152* ⏚ *www.newbabycompany.com / see 1.04 Antenatal classes; 2.03 Baby health; 2.06 Baby & toddler activities.*

The New Learning Centre *211 Sumatra Rd, London NW6 1PF* ☎ *(020) 7794 0321* ⏚ *www.TNLC.info / see 2.01 Postnatal.*

NHS Direct ☎ *(0845) 4647* ⏚ *www.nhsdirect.nhs.uk / see 1.01 Where to have the baby; 1.02 Looking after yourself; 2.03 Baby health; 4.03 Medical issues at birth.*

Norland College *York Place, London Rd, Bath BA1 6AE* ☎ *(01225) 466 202* ⏚ *www.norland.co.uk / see 2.04 Childcare.*

NORM UK *PO Box 71, Stone, Staffs ST15 0SF* ☎ *National HQ (01785) 814044, London office (020) 7274 0086* ⏚ *www.norm-uk.org / see 2.03 Baby health.*

North London Family Mediation Service *267 Ballards Lane, Finchley, London N12 8NR* ☎ *(020) 8343 9899* ⏚ *www.nfm.u-net.com / see 4.06 Support groups.*

Nursing & Midwifery Council *23 Portland Place, London W1B 1PZ* ☎ *(020) 7637 7181* ⏚ *www.nmc-uk.org / see 1.01 Where to have the baby; 4.03 Medical issues at birth.*

Obstetric Cholestasis Support Group *4 Shenstone Close, Four Oaks, Sutton Coldfield B74 4XB* ☎ *(0121) 353 0699 / see 1.02 Looking after yourself.*

Office of Standards in Education (OFSTED) *Alexandra House, 29-33 Kingsway, London WC2B 6SE* ☎ *(020) 7421 6800* ⏚ *www.ofsted.gov.uk / see 2.04 Childcare; 2.07 Education.*

Omron Healthcare *Opal Drive, Fox Milne, Milton Keynes MK15 0DG* ☎ *(01273) 495033* ⏚ *www.omrom-healthcare.com / see 2.03 Baby health.*

Organisation of Chartered Physiotherapists in Private Practice (OCPPP) *Cedar House, Bell Plantation, Watling St, Towcester, Northants NN12 6HN* ☎ *(01327) 354441* ⏚ *www.physiofirst.org.uk / see 1.02 Looking after yourself.*

The Otherwise Club *1 Croxley Rd, London W9 3HH* ☎ *Admin (020) 7735 7735, Help Desk (0800) 652 3145* ⏚ *www.choiceineducation.co.uk/toc / see 2.07 Education.*

Our Kids ⏚ *www.our-kids.org / see 4.06 Support groups.*

Overseas Adoption Service (Oasis) *14 Ashdowne Avenue, Saltdean, East Sussex* ☎ *(0870) 241 7069* ⏚ *www.member.lycos.co.uk/adoption / see 4.06 Support groups.*

Paediatric Allergy & Immunology Clinic *St Mary's Hospital, Praed St, London W2 1NY* ☎ *(020) 7886 6384 / see 2.03 Baby health.*

The Parent Company *6 Jacob's Well Mews, London W1H 5PD* ☎ *(020) 7935 9365* ⏚ *www.theparentcompany.co.uk / see 2.01 Postnatal.*

The Parent Infant Clinic *27b Frognal Rd, Hampstead, London NW3 6AR* ☎ *(020) 7433 3112* ⏚ *www.infantmentalhealth.com / see 2.01 Postnatal; 4.02 Health practitioners.*

Parentalk *115 Southwark Bridge Rd, London SE1 0AX* ☎ *(020) 7450 9073* ⏚ *www.parentalk.co.uk / see 2.01 Postnatal.*

Parentline Plus *520 Highgate Studios, 53-79 Highgate Rd, London NW5 1TL* ☎ *Freephone parent Helpline (0808) 800 2222, Textphone (0800) 783 6783* ⏚ *www.parentlineplus.org.uk / see 2.01 Postnatal; 4.02 Health practitioners; 4.06 Support groups.*

Parents for Inclusion *Unit 2, 70 South Lambeth Rd, London SW8 1RL* ☎ *Admin (020) 7735 7735, Helpline (0800) 652 3145* ⏚ *www.parentsforinclusion.org / see 2.07 Education; 4.06 Support groups.*

Parents in Partnership – Parent Infant Network (PIPPIN) *Birch Centre Annex, Hill End Lane, St Albans, Herts AL4 0RB* ☎ *National office (01727) 899099* ⏚ *www.pippin.org.uk / see 2.01 Postnatal.*

Parents of Ealing Self-help Training Scheme (PESTS) *24 Beechmount Ave, Hanwell, London W7 3AG* ☎ *(020) 8578 8794 / see 4.06 Support groups.*

Patients' Association *PO Box 935, Harrow, Middlesex HA1 3YJ* ☎ *(020) 8423 9111, Helpline (08456) 084455* ⏚ *www.patients-association.com / see 4.03 Medical issues at birth.*

Penrhos Court *Kington, Herefordshire HR5 2LH* ☎ *(01544) 230720* ⏚ *www.greencuisine.org / see 1.02 Looking after yourself; 2.02 Feeding.*

Perspective Scientific *100 Baker St, London W1U 6WG* ☎ *(020) 7486 6837* ⏚ *www.perspective.co.uk / see 1.02 Looking after yourself.*

Pesticide Action Network UK (PEX Action on Pesticide Exposure) *Eurolink Centre, 49 Effra Road, London SW2 1BZ, London SW2 1BZ* ☎ *(020) 7274 8895, (020) 7274 6611* ⏚ *www.pan-uk.org / see 1.02 Looking after yourself; 2.02 Feeding.*

Red Cross *Westminster Tower, 10th Floor, 3 Albert Embankment, London SE1 7SX*
☎ *(020) 7933 3601* ✆ *www.redcross.org.uk / see 2.03 Baby health.*

Relate *Herbert Gray College, Little Church St, Rugby CV21 3AP* ☎ *(01788) 573241*
✆ *www.relate.org.uk / see 4.06 Support groups.*

Relationship Counselling for London *76a New Cavendish St, London W1G 9TE*
☎ *(020) 7580 1087* ✆ *www.counselling4london.com / see 4.06 Support groups.*

Release *National Legal and Drugs Service, 388 Old St, London EC1V 9LT*
☎ *(020) 7729 5255* ✆ *www.release.org.uk / see 1.02 Looking after yourself.*

Restricted Growth Association (RGA) *PO Box 4744, Dorchester, Leicester
DT2 9FA* ☎ *(0130) 889 8415* ✆ *www.rgaonline.org.uk / see 4.06 Support groups.*

Retinitis Pigmentosa Society *PO Box 350, Buckingham, Bucks MK18 1GZ*
☎ *Helpline (0845) 123 2354, Head office (01280) 821334* ✆ *www.brps.org.uk
/ see 4.06 Support groups.*

reunite (International Child Abduction Centre) *PO Box 7124, Leicester
LE1 7XX* ☎ *(0116) 255 5345, Advice (0116) 255 6234* ✆ *www.reunite.org
/ see 4.06 Support groups.*

Ricability *30 Angel Gate, 326 City Rd, London EC1V 2PT* ☎ *(020) 7427 2460*
✆ *www.ricability.org.uk / see 4.06 Support groups.*

Richmond Education Department *Regal House, London Rd, Twickenham
TW1 3QB* ☎ *(020) 8891 7500* ✆ *www.richmond.gov.uk / see 2.07 Education.*

Rights of Women *52-54 Featherstone St, London EC1Y 8RT*
☎ *Advice line (020) 7251 6577, Admin (020) 7251 6575/6* ✆ *www.row.org.uk
/ see 1.05 Rights; 4.06 Support groups.*

Salli Rose *55 Trinity Rd, London N2 8JJ* ☎ *(07940) 470284 / see 2.03 Baby health;
4.02 Health practitioners.*

Royal Association for Disability & Rehabilitation (RADAR) *Unit 12 City
Forum, 250 City Rd, London EC1V 8AF* ☎ *(020) 7250 3222* ✆ *www.radar.org.uk
/ see 4.06 Support groups.*

Royal College of Midwives (RCM) *15 Mansfield St, London W1MG 9NH*
☎ *(020) 7312 3535* ✆ *www.rcm.org.uk / see 1.01 Where to have the baby.*

Royal College of Obstetricians & Gynaecologists *27 Sussex Place, London
NW1 4RG* ☎ *Admin (020) 7772 6200, Bookshop (020) 7772 6275* ✆ *www.rcog.org.uk
/ see 1.01 Where to have the baby; 1.02 Looking after yourself; 4.05 Finding out more.*

Royal National Institute for the Blind (RNIB) *105 Judd St, London
WC1H 9NE* ☎ *(08457) 669999, Customer services (08457) 456457, (020) 7388 1266*
✆ *www.rnib.org.uk / see 4.06 Support groups.*

Royal National Institute for the Deaf (RNID) *19-23 Featherstone St, London
EC1Y 8SL* ☎ *(020) 7296 8000, Helpline (0808) 808 0123, Text helpline (0808) 808 9000*
✆ *www.rnid.org.uk / see 4.06 Support groups.*

Royal Society for the Prevention of Accidents (RoSPA) *Edgbaston Park,
353 Bristol Rd, Birmingham B5 7ST* ☎ *(0121) 248 2000* ✆ *www.rospa.co.uk
/ see 3.03 Nursery decor.*

Royal Society for the Prevention of Cruelty to Animals (RSPCA)
Wilberforce Way, Southwater, Horsham, West Sussex RH13 9RS ☎ *(0870) 333 5999*
✆ *www.rspca.org.uk / see 2.01 Postnatal.*

S-KD Educational Consultants *25 Tonsley Hill, London SW18 1BE*
☎ *(020) 8871 3057* ✆ *www.skd.co.uk / see 2.07 Education.*

Safe & Sound *60 Normandy Ave, Barnet EN5 2JA* ☎ *(020) 8449 8722*
✆ *www.safe-and-sound.org.uk / see 2.03 Baby health.*

St John Ambulance *London District HQ, 63 York St, London W1H 1PS*
☎ *(0870) 010 4850, Courses (020) 7324 4000* ✆ *www.sja.org.uk / see 2.03 Baby health.*

St Mary's Hospital *Praed St, London W2 1NY* ☎ *Helpline (0845) 4647*
✆ *www.st-marys.nhs.uk / see 2.03 Baby health.*

Salvation Army *101 Newington Causeway, London SE1 6BN* ☎ *(020) 7367 4856*
✆ *www.salvationarmy.org.uk / see 2.06 Baby & toddler activities.*

Samaritans *The Upper Mill, Kingstons Rd, Ewell, Surrey KT17 2AF*
☎ *Helpline (08457) 909090* ✆ *www.samaritans.org / see 2.01 Postnatal.*

Sangam *210 Burnt Oak Broadway, Edgware HA8 0AP* ☎ *(020) 8952 7062*
/ see 4.06 Support groups.

Schmidt Natural Clothing *Corbiere, Nursery Lane, Nutley, East Sussex TN22 3NS*
☎ *(0845) 345 0498* ✆ *www.naturalclothing.co.uk / see 2.03 Baby health; 3.03 Nursery decor;
3.04 Baby clothes; 3.06 Toys; 3.08 Nappies.*

School of Accelerated Learning 27 Hollingworth Close, Molesey KT8 2TW
☎ (020) 8979 3951 ⌁ www.acceleratedlearningschool.com / see 2.07 Education.

SchoolsNet ⌁ www.schoolsnet.com / see 2.07 Education.

SCOPE 6 Market Rd, London N7 9PW ☎ (0808) 800 3333 ⌁ www.scope.org.uk
/ see 4.06 Support groups.

Sense, The National Deafblind & Rubella Association 11-13 Clifton
Terrace, London N4 3SR ☎ (020) 7272 7774 ⌁ www.sense.org.uk / see 1.02 Looking after
yourself; 1.03 Tests; 4.06 Support groups.

Sensitif Products 386 Green Lane, Ilford, Essex IG3 9JU ☎ (0800) 074 8445
⌁ www.sensitif.co.uk / see 2.03 Baby health.

Shared Care Network 63-66 Easton Business Centre, Felix Rd, Easton, Bristol
BS5 0HE ☎ (0117) 941 5361 ⌁ www.sharedcarenetwork.org.uk / see 4.06 Support groups.

Sheila Kitzinger ⌁ www.sheilakitzinger.com / see 4.03 Medical issues at birth.

The Shiatsu Society Eastlands Court, St Peters Rd, Rugby CV21 3QP
☎ (0845) 130 4560 ⌁ www.shiatsu.org / see 4.02 Health practitioners.

Sickle Cell Society 54 Station Rd, London NW10 4UA ☎ (020) 8961 7795/4006
⌁ www.sicklecellsociety.org / see 1.03 Tests.

Sitters 126 Rickmansworth Rd, Watford WD18 7WS ☎ (0800) 389 0038
⌁ www.sitters.co.uk / see 2.04 Childcare.

The Society for Mucopolysaccharide Diseases 46 Woodside Rd, Amersham,
Bucks HP6 6AJ ☎ (01494) 434156 ⌁ www.mpssociety.co.uk / see 4.06 Support groups.

The Society of Chiropodists & Podiatrists 1 Fellmongers Path, Tower Bridge
Rd, London SE1 3LY ☎ (020) 7234 8620 ⌁ www.feetforlife.org / see 3.05 Shoes.

Society of Financial Advisers 20 Aldermanbury, London EC2V 7HY
☎ (020) 8989 8464 ⌁ www.sofa.org / see 2.08 Finance.

The Society of Homeopaths 4a Artizan Rd, Northampton NN1 4HU
☎ (01604) 621400 ⌁ www.homeopathy-soh.org / see 4.02 Health practitioners.

The Society of Teachers of the Alexander Technique 129 Camden Mews,
London NW1 9AH ☎ (0845) 230 7828, (020) 7284 3338 ⌁ www.stat.org.uk
/ see 4.02 Health practitioners.

The Soil Association Bristol House, 40-56 Victoria St, Bristol BS1 6BY
☎ (0117) 929 0661 ⌁ www.soilassociation.org / see 2.02 Feeding.

South East London Family Mediation Bureau The Stables, 1 North St, Kent
BR1 1SD ☎ (020) 8315 7460 / see 4.06 Support groups.

South East London Sickle Cell & Thalassaemia Centre Wooden Spoon
House, 5 The Guardway, (Off Refrew Rd), London SE11 4TH ☎ (020) 7414 1357
/ see 1.03 Tests.

Space Air Solutions Space Airconditioning, Willway Court, 1 Opus Park, Moorfield Rd,
Guildford GU1 1SZ ☎ (01483) 252 240/504 8883 ⌁ www.spaceairsolutions.com
/ see 2.03 Baby health.

Specialist Smoking Cessation Service ☎ (01524) 845 145 / see 1.02 Looking
after yourself.

Speech, Language & Hearing Centre 1-5 Christopher Place, Chalton St, London
NW1 1JF ☎ (020) 7383 3834 ⌁ www.speech-lang.org.uk / see 2.03 Baby health.

Squiggle Foundation 33 Amberley Rd, London N13 4BH ☎ (020) 8882 9744
⌁ www.squiggle-foundation.org.uk / see 2.01 Postnatal.

St George's Hospital Milk Bank Neonatal Unit, London ☎ (020) 8725 1937
/ see 2.02 Feeding.

Steiner Schools Fellowship Kidbrooke Park, Forest Row, East Sussex RH18 5JB
☎ (01342) 822115 ⌁ www.steinerwaldorf.org.uk / see 2.07 Education.

Stepfamilies UK ⌁ www.stepfamilies.co.uk / see 4.06 Support groups.

STEPS Lymm Court, 11 Eagle Brow, Lymm, Cheshire WA13 0LP
☎ Admin (0871) 717 0045, Helpline (0871) 717 0044 ⌁ www.steps-charity.org.uk
/ see 4.06 Support groups.

Stillbirth & Neonatal Death Society (SANDS) 28 Portland Place, London
W1B 1LY ☎ Helpline (020) 7436 5881, Admin (020) 7436 7940 ⌁ www.uk-sands.org
/ see 4.04 Miscarriage & stillbirth.

Support Organisation for Trisomy (SOFT UK) 48 Froggatts Rd, Walmley,
Sutton Coldfield B76 8TQ ☎ Helpline (0121) 351 3122 ⌁ www.soft.org.uk / see 4.06 Support
groups.

Support Society for Children of High Intelligence (CHI) PO Box 21461,
London N6 6WW ☎ (020) 8347 8927 ⌁ www.chi-charity.org.uk / see 2.07 Education.

Surgery Door *Preston Mill Barn, Siddington, Cirencester GL7 6ET*
⌁ *www.surgerydoor.co.uk / see 2.03 Baby health.*
SUSTAIN *94 White Lion St, London N1 9PF* ☎ *(020) 7837 1228*
⌁ *www.sustainweb.org / see 2.02 Feeding.*
Sutherland Society ⌁ *www.cranial.org.uk / see 4.02 Health practitioners.*
Sutton Childcare Information Centre *Times Square Shopping Centre, Sutton High St, Sutton SM1 1LF* ☎ *(020) 8770 6000* ⌁ *www.childcarelink.gov.uk / see 2.07 Education.*
SW London Nannyshare Register *17 Eardley Rd, London SW16 6DA* ☎ *(020) 8677 3015 / see 2.04 Childcare.*
Tailored Interactive Guidance on Employment Rights (TIGER) ⌁ *www.tiger.gov.uk / see 1.05 Rights.*
Talk Eczema ⌁ *www.talkeczema.com / see 2.03 Baby health.*
Talking Life *PO Box 1, Wirral CH47 3BS* ☎ *(0151) 632 0662* ⌁ *www.talkinglife.co.uk / see 2.01 Postnatal; 2.03 Baby health.*
The Tavistock Clinic *120 Belsize Lane, London NW3 5BA* ☎ *(020) 7435 7111*
⌁ *www.tavi-port.org / see 2.03 Baby health; 2.06 Baby & toddler activities; 4.02 Health practitioners; 4.04 Miscarriage & stillbirth.*
Taxing Nannies *28 Minchenden Crescent, London N14 7EL* ☎ *(020) 8882 6847*
⌁ *www.taxingnannies.co.uk / see 2.04 Childcare.*
The Tay Sachs Screening Programme *Dr S Simon, Booth Hall, Charlestown Rd, Blackley, Manchester M9 7AA* ☎ *(0161) 795 7000, ext 5094 / see 1.03 Tests.*
Teacher Trading *80 High Street, Winchester, Hampshire SO23 9AT*
☎ *(01420) 588 055* ⌁ *www.thespanishbookshop.com / see 2.07 Education; 3.07 Books, music & videos.*
Thames Water Utilities *Customer Centre, PO Box 436 Swindon, Wilts SN38 1TU*
☎ *(0845) 920 0800* ⌁ *www.thameswater.com / see 1.02 Looking after yourself.*
Thomas Cook ☎ *(01733) 417100 / see 1.02 Looking after yourself.*
Tommy's *Nicholas House, 3 Laurence Pountney Hill, London EC4R 0BB*
☎ *(08707) 707070, Infoline (0870) 777 3060* ⌁ *www.tommys-campaign.org / see 1.02 Looking after yourself; 1.03 Tests; 4.04 Miscarriage & stillbirth.*
Top Notch Nannies *Flat 2, 49 Harrington Gardens, London SW7 4JU*
☎ *(020) 7259 2626* ⌁ *www.topnotchnannies.com / see 2.04 Childcare.*
The Trades Union Congress (TUC) *Congress House, Great Russell St, London WC1B 3LS* ☎ *(020) 7636 4030* ⌁ *www.tuc.org.uk / see 1.05 Rights.*
Transport for London ☎ *(020) 7222 1234, Mobility information (020) 7941 4600*
⌁ *www.londontransport.com, www.thetube.com / see 2.06 Baby & toddler activities.*
Tufnell Park Parents Support Group (TPPSG) ☎ *(020) 7485 7625 / see 2.01 Postnatal.*
21st Century Health *2 Fitzhardinge St, London W1H 6EE* ☎ *(020) 7935 5440*
⌁ *www.21stcenturyhealth.co.uk / see 1.02 Looking after yourself.*
21st Century Learning Initiative *Business Centre West, Avenue One, Letchworth, Herts SG6 2HB* ☎ *(01225) 420290* ⌁ *www.21learn.org / see 2.07 Education.*
Twin to Twin Transfusion Syndrome Association
☎ *Correen Jackson (020) 8581 7359, Dionne Thompson (01895) 846688*
⌁ *www.twin2twin.org / see 4.06 Support groups.*
Twins & Multiple Births Association (TAMBA) *2 The Willows, Gardner Road, Guilford, Surrey GU1 4PG* ☎ *(0870) 770 3305* ⌁ *www.tamba.org.uk / see 4.06 Support groups.*
The UK Council for Psychotherapy *167-169 Great Portland St, London W1W 5PF* ☎ *(020) 7436 3002* ⌁ *www.psychotherapy.org.uk / see 4.02 Health practitioners.*
The UK Thalassaemia Society *19 The Broadway, London N14 6PH*
☎ *(020) 8882 0011* ⌁ *www.ukts.org / see 1.03 Tests.*
Ultrafarm *Centenary Business Park, Station Rd, Henley On Thames RG9 1DS*
☎ *(01491) 578016 / see 2.03 Baby health.*
Ultrasound Diagnostic Services *113 Harley St, London W1G 6AP*
☎ *(020) 7486 7991, (020) 7935 2243* ⌁ *www.uds.uk.com / see 1.03 Tests.*
Unassisted Birth ⌁ *www.unassistedbirth.com / see 4.03 Medical issues at birth.*
UNIQUE, the Rare Chromosome Disorder Support Group *PO Box 2189, Caterham, Surrey CR3 5GN* ☎ *Helpline (01883) 330766* ⌁ *www.rarechromo.org / see 4.06 Support groups.*